A History of
BRITISH MUSIC

A History of BRITISH MUSIC

PERCY M. YOUNG

ERNEST BENN LIMITED
LONDON

First Published 1967 by Ernest Benn Limited
Bouverie House · Fleet Street · London · EC4

Printed in Great Britain

Preface

NOW IS as good a time as any other to write a book on the subject of British music. So far as domestic affairs are concerned the support of the arts in general, and of music in particular, is an issue which seriously engages both national and local governmental consideration. As a result of such consideration funds which were not previously available have become so. In this case it is, perhaps, no bad thing that the structure of the indigenous musical traditions should be defined. From another point of view the task seems worth attempting, for in the world at large it is still noticeable that the British capacity for music—to some extent through inaccessibility of evidence—is in no immediate danger of being over-valued.

It is my submission that the British people have done much for the art of music, but not always in the most obvious way. That is, their contribution is not to be reckoned in terms of lists of great composers nor even of great executants. Rather should we note a certain respect for music itself (frequently expressed in hospitality to and acceptance of musicians bred in other traditions) and an appreciation of its fundamental purposes.

We are brought back to the conditions under which music may or may not flourish, and we are bound to recognise that its cultivation depends on general conditions. A history of music is, then, a particular kind of social history in that it is a record of one human activity in relationship to others.

Time was when our musical historians unwarrantably confined themselves to what they described as 'English' music. This really will not do. What has been achieved in this and other fields in England has been with the active collaboration of the sister nations. The English without the assistance of the Welsh, the Scots, the Irish, would in many cases be left in a state of imaginative nudity. By the same token it is to be emphasised that British music is not only music in London. What has been done, or even left undone or unfinished, in the provinces is not only of interest but also of significance. It need only further be remarked that the traditions described in this book have developed without the help of such facilities that European musicians received from regional rulers in time gone by.

Having considered the whole field we do, of course, realise what we already knew—or should have known. That among British composers there were (perhaps are) some with unique gifts of vision and expression. I am optimistic enough to believe that there are more than has often been allowed. At least there is certainly more British music that has some abiding value than is generally known. Even now it is not easy to persuade those in authority that this thesis should be submitted to practical test. I am, therefore, grateful to Messrs. Boosey & Hawkes and to Chappell & Co. Ltd. for their frequent encouragement in this respect.

This book places music in its general setting. At the same time the music itself is scrutinised in respect of its distinctive qualities. There are numerous music examples. Since major works are readily available for examination many of these have been taken from less familiar sources in the hope that a proper balance might be effected—even though I do not expect that all my enthusiasms will always be endorsed. There are also examples of what the 'man of taste' (if he were to exist) would dismiss as 'bad' music. These are of importance; partly because some of our noblest composers had distinctly liberal views on the subject of taste, partly because (as German music perfectly shows) the superior only emerges after dialectic with the inferior.

One is always a beneficiary of others. Thus I first acknowledge the great debt I owe to my own teachers of long ago. Like all my colleagues I am also grateful to the many musicologists who have done fundamental work in this field. The labours of the pioneers are detailed in the text, while those of more recent scholars are indicated in many bibliographical references. After due consideration it was decided that rather than add an inadequate bibliography to this book it would be preferable in due course to issue a separate but correlative bibliographical handbook. Questions of space also impose limitations on indexing. The two main indexes provide what is most frequently required by the reader. To have added lists of works and other often desirable subsidiary material would have meant sacrificing too many names which should be readily accessible. In view of the manner in which the chapters are subdivided it should not be difficult to locate particular works, while the disposition of the music examples (see pp. 609 ff.) is an additional help in this respect.

I must especially acknowledge the generous help of Mr. Oliver Benn, Dr. Chalmers Burns, Mr. Charles Cudworth, Mr. Owain Edwards, Mr. Geralt Evans, and Professor Ian Parrott, who have read this book in proof and have made numerous valuable suggestions. None of these friends, of course, are to be held responsible for any errors of fact or idiosyncracies of opinion, but without them there might well have been more of both. I would also record the kindness and frequent hospitality experienced in libraries both in Britain and elsewhere. In so doing I would draw attention to the many documents relating to British music which are still to be fully explored in municipal and county collections of local history. I am obliged to Fräulein Ursula Doege, of Hamburg, and to Dr. W. A. Richter of the State and University Library in the same city for kindly supplying me with certain information.

Music which is in copyright is quoted by permission of Boosey & Hawkes Ltd. (Stanford), Chappell & Co. Ltd. (Bax), J. Curwen & Sons Ltd. (Holst), Forsyth Bros. Ltd. (Smyth), Galliard Ltd. (Delius), Novello & Co. Ltd. (Parry, Stanford—*Irish Symphony*), Oxford University Press (Vaughan Williams and Warlock); and the Trustees of the Will of the late Sir Edward Elgar, and to Mrs. Burges Scott.

1 May 1967 P.M.Y.

Contents

pendently enshrined in Celtic legend. Diodorus[1] differentiated between songs of praise and songs of invective quality, noting that both were accompanied on instruments similar to lyres. The tradition of celebrating heroic deeds of the illustrious dead, continued in central Europe according to the same bardic principle until the sixteenth century,[2] was further remarked among the Celts by Ammianus Marcellinus in the fourth century of the Christian era; but by now the ritual use of music by the second main Celtic group, the Brythonic, had led to a form of organisation of some peculiar significance in the later development of local patriotisms within Britain.

The Goidelic Celts were displaced in the greater part of Britain by Iron Age invaders to be known as Brythons (or Cymri). In the twilight that lies between legend and history Geoffrey of Monmouth (1100?–54), in his *Historia Britonum*, claimed early musicality for this people by mentioning 'one Blegwryt, *A King of Britain*, about One hundred and ninety Years before Christ, who was a great Master of instrumental Music, and upon that Account called the God of Harmony'.[3] The Goidels were confined to the extreme west and north, and the Brythons occupied the main part of what is now England and Wales until, after having survived the Roman occupation, they in turn were driven west by the Jutes, the Saxons, and the Angles. The Brythons retreated to Wales, there, insofar as they were allowed, to preserve their language and vestiges of their first distinctive cultural organisation. The religious cult of the Brythonic Celts was Druidism, and the high priests—the Druids—were, according to Diodorus[4] and Ammianus, a learned class, and with a reputation for magic and soothsaying that also has been memorialised in legend. During the subjection of Britain by the Romans (who had been told by Cicero not to expect any musical or literary talent among the Britons[5]), the Druids were a particular target of attack and their power was greatly diminished after their

[1] 'Sunt etiam apud hos carminum Melicorum poetae, quos Bardas nominant. Hi ad instrumenta lyris non dissimilia, aliorum laudes, aliorum vituperationes decantant.' Diod. Siculi, *Bibliothecae* (Greek text with Latin translation), Hanoviae Typis Wechelianis, 1604. Lib. V, p. 308.

[2] Notably in Hungary, see Percy M. Young, *Zoltán Kodály*, London, 1964, p. 4.

[3] Quoted from Morris, op. cit.

[4] 'Philosophi apud eos sunt & Theologi (Druidas ipsi vocant) quos eximio honore dignatur.' ib.

Ammianus refers to the Celts of Gaul, who, however, practised the same language and habits as those in Britain: 'Meanwhile, as the men of this place were growne by little and little to civilitie, the studies of laudable sciences, begun by the Bards, Eubages, and Druides, mightily flourished here. And verily the Bards sung unto the sweet musick of the Harpe the valorous deedes of worthie men composed in heroick verse.' *The Roman Historie*, done into English by Philemon Holland of the Citie of Coventrie, Doctor of Physick, London, 1609, Lib. 15, Chap. IX, p. 47.

[5] '. . . In illa insula, neque ullam spem praedae, nisi ex mancipiis: ex quibus nullos puto te literis aut musicis eruditos expectare.' Cicero, *Ep. ad Atticum*, IV, 16.

I

Origins

‘THE ANTIENT Music of the People of *Britain* hath been so mixed with that of other Nations, who have from time to time made conquests, or otherwise inhabited in this Island, that, as well as in other Arts and Sciences among them, it is, at this day, a very difficult Matter to trace out the true *British Music* and its Revolution; . . .’ *A Brief Account of the British, or Cambrian Music*, Lewis Morris, 1746.

Celts, Britons, and Saxons

In the origins of the British people three main influences (each with its own subdivisions) appear; the Celtic, the Mediterranean, the Saxon. From the Celts came the first impulse to musical expression, from the Romans of the Caesarean invasion and of the later Augustinian mission a sense of uniformity and organisation, and from the Saxons the shape of the language that is the primary point of individual musical departure. Of the first Goidelic Celts, of central European extraction, communities were established in north-west Europe, Britain, and especially in Ireland, where the earliest musical instruments to have survived in the British Isles were in use during the Bronze Age. Horns of wood or of bronze, trumpets,[1] and rattles,[2] possessed magical properties useful for the repulse both of natural and supernatural adversaries. In due course Polybius (*c.* 204–122 B.C.) paid tribute to the efficacy of the martial music of the Celtic tribes. They were, however, allowed superior talent in more pacific forms of music. Of the chroniclers and travellers of the first century before Christ Poseidonius, Diodorus Siculus, and Strabo, all refer to bardic practices that are inde-

[1] Examples of these instruments are in National Museum of Ireland, Dublin, and detailed by Dr. John Coles in *Proc. Prehistoric Soc.*, Vol. 29, 1963, pp. 326–56.

[2] Horniman Museum, London.

pendently enshrined in Celtic legend. Diodorus[1] differentiated between songs of praise and songs of invective quality, noting that both were accompanied on instruments similar to lyres. The tradition of celebrating heroic deeds of the illustrious dead, continued in central Europe according to the same bardic principle until the sixteenth century,[2] was further remarked among the Celts by Ammianus Marcellinus in the fourth century of the Christian era; but by now the ritual use of music by the second main Celtic group, the Brythonic, had led to a form of organisation of some peculiar significance in the later development of local patriotisms within Britain.

The Goidelic Celts were displaced in the greater part of Britain by Iron Age invaders to be known as Brythons (or Cymri). In the twilight that lies between legend and history Geoffrey of Monmouth (1100?–54), in his *Historia Britonum*, claimed early musicality for this people by mentioning 'one Blegwryt, *A King of Britain*, about One hundred and ninety Years before Christ, who was a great Master of instrumental Music, and upon that Account called the God of Harmony'.[3] The Goidels were confined to the extreme west and north, and the Brythons occupied the main part of what is now England and Wales until, after having survived the Roman occupation, they in turn were driven west by the Jutes, the Saxons, and the Angles. The Brythons retreated to Wales, there, insofar as they were allowed, to preserve their language and vestiges of their first distinctive cultural organisation. The religious cult of the Brythonic Celts was Druidism, and the high priests—the Druids—were, according to Diodorus[4] and Ammianus, a learned class, and with a reputation for magic and soothsaying that also has been memorialised in legend. During the subjection of Britain by the Romans (who had been told by Cicero not to expect any musical or literary talent among the Britons[5]), the Druids were a particular target of attack and their power was greatly diminished after their

[1] 'Sunt etiam apud hos carminum Melicorum poetae, quos Bardas nominant. Hi ad instrumenta lyris non dissimilia, aliorum laudes, aliorum vituperationes decantant.' Diod. Siculi, *Bibliothecae* (Greek text with Latin translation), Hanoviae Typis Wechelianis, 1604. Lib. V, p. 308.

[2] Notably in Hungary, see Percy M. Young, *Zoltán Kodály*, London, 1964, p. 4.

[3] Quoted from Morris, op. cit.

[4] 'Philosophi apud eos sunt & Theologi (Druidas ipsi vocant) quos eximio honore dignatur.' ib.

Ammianus refers to the Celts of Gaul, who, however, practised the same language and habits as those in Britain: 'Meanwhile, as the men of this place were growne by little and little to civilitie, the studies of laudable sciences, begun by the Bards, Eubages, and Druides, mightily flourished here. And verily the Bards sung unto the sweet musick of the Harpe the valorous deedes of worthie men composed in heroick verse.' *The Roman Historie*, done into English by Philemon Holland of the Citie of Coventrie, Doctor of Physick, London, 1609, Lib. 15, Chap. IX, p. 47.

[5] '... In illa insula, neque ullam spem praedae, nisi ex mancipiis: ex quibus nullos puto te literis aut musicis eruditos expectare.' Cicero, *Ep. ad Atticum*, IV, 16.

defeat on the island of Mona (Anglesey) by Suetonius Paulinus in A.D. 59. Like the earlier fugitives they went north to Scotland and west to Ireland, 'the seat of Philosophy and Politeness for many Ages till Wars and Dissentions buried almost all in oblivion'. The Druid influence was eventually extinguished there, so it was said, by St. Patrick in the fifth century.

Since legend plays a strong part in the beliefs out of which traditions grow it is to be noted that it was from Druid origins that the institution of the Eisteddfod (with its Platonic association of music with literature and other branches of learning) was said to have grown. This, a consequence also of bardic energy, was in the first place a kind of vacation school for bards conducted (in due course in competitive manner) by the senior available practitioners of the art. In the sixth century the reputed Chief Bards were Aneirin and Taliesin,[1] the latter giving his name to the anthology of bardic poems collected into the so-called *Book of Taliesin* in the fourteenth century. Taliesin, as other bards, was dependent on princely protection, that of Urien, King of Rheged, for whom he fought against Ida of Northumbria, and—so the poems indicate—his prosperity was in ratio to the enthusiasm with which he extolled the virtues of his patron. Thus early were limits set to the absolute freedom of the artist. In A.D. 517 Taliesin superintended the reputed Eisteddfod held at Ystum Llwydiarth, in South Wales. The medieval scholar Giraldus Cambrensis (1146?–1223), a native of Manorbier, Pembrokeshire, reviewing the legendary past of his race picked up the allusions to bards and eisteddfodau and opined that the ancient Britons excelled in 'harmony' and in extemporisation. Certainly the bards were highly regarded, and among those of the post-Taliesin era Llywarch Hen (Llywarch the Old) took high place. A prince himself, and a putative cousin of the greater Urien, Llywarch was dispossessed by the Angles; whereupon, taking refuge with the chieftain Cynddylan at Pengwern, by Shrewsbury, he became a bard. His verbal picture of music at night in the princely household is to be found in his *Lament for Cynddylan*. The Legends of Llywarch (and others) were brought together in the *Red Book of Hergest* (col. 1026–49). In the meantime the Eisteddfod practice continued, a second such event in A.D. 540—at Deganwy, or Conway, in North Wales—ultimately finding a place in the records of the fourteenth-century poet Iorwerth Beli.[2] This

[1] Of whom the first documentary evidence is in the Anglo-Saxon Genealogies, forming Section d of the *Historia Brittonum* of Nennius (fl. *c.* 800): see *The Book of Taliesin*, J. G. Evans, London, 1910.

[2] The early Welsh historians advanced their cases with enthusiasm. Both Giraldus and Iorwerth were (in modern terminology) ardent Welsh nationalists. Giraldus found his nationality an impediment to ecclesiastical promotion. Iorwerth was disgusted when he found the Bishop of Bangor lauding English melodies ('earsplitting noises', as perpetrated by the Bishop's young English favourites) above the Welsh, and neglecting the bardic poet-musicians in favour of mere musicians.

Eisteddfod, held under the supervision of Maelgwn Gwynedd, was the last to be mentioned by the chroniclers until the twelfth century. But the antiquity of the institution has always exercised a proud fascination for the Welsh people, stimulating their faith in their own musical potential, their zeal for an independent cultural life, and their political aspirations, while in later years acting as something of a brake on musical development in the wider sphere. At the same time a respect for singing and for literature thus early built into the British consciousness has had a wider significance.

The occupation of Britain by the Romans apparently had little effect on the musical practices of the natives—which, in any case, were allied to the broader Celtic tradition—unless by the occasional introduction of unfamiliar instruments like the *tibiae*, or double-reed-pipes, which are sculpted on a legionary stone in Hadrian's Wall, at Bridgeness, and, possibly, by spasmodic demonstration of imported Christian songs from the eastern parts of the Empire when this new religion began to make its first appearance. The bardic tradition as established and maintained by Celts and Britons was readily taken over by the Saxons and the Angles, and scops and gleemen (the former ranking first in seniority) were in consistent employment so long as they obliged their masters. In the *Lament of Deor*, one of the Saxon poems of the sixth century Beowulf group, Deor explained what happened when a scop failed in his commission: he himself was put out of office by Heorrenda.

> I had, for many winters, a worthy office,
> A handsome Lord, until Heorrenda now,
> A man skilled in lays, the land-right has taken
> Which the Guardian of Earls of old had given me.[1]

Heorrenda has been identified with Hôrant of the High German poem *Kudrun*, who on his master's behalf, and 'shaming into silence the birds singing in the bushes', sang to win the hand of Hild, daughter of the Irish king, Hagen. In 'Finnsburgh' Widsith speaks with pleasure and pride of his duties as musician to Eadgil (who employed a second scop in the person of Skilling),

> When Skilling and I with sheer voices
> Before our royal Lord upraised the song,
> When loud to the harp the lilt made melody,
> Then many men whose minds were proud
> In words did say, who well had knowledge,
> That they never a sweeter song had heard.[2]

[1] *Beowulf, Widsith, Finnsburgh, Waldere, Deor*, trs. C. K. Scott Moncrieff, London, 1921, p. 110.

[2] ib. p. 4.

The Saxons, it will be seen, used the harp, which was popular in northern Europe. In the course of time, and with the multiplication of Saxons in Britain, it came to supplant the unbowed crwth (chrotta, rotte, or cruit) which had been noticed as peculiar to that people by Venantius Fortunatus, Bishop of Poictiers, at the beginning of the seventh century.[1] The crwth was also known in Ireland; Giraldus Cambrensis tells how that reputed to have been played by St. Kievan (d. 618), of Glendalough, was long venerated as a relic.

The monuments (to be discussed later) which illustrate harp and crwth, and other instruments, are among the few remaining pieces of musical evidence of the cultural expansion that accompanied the emergence as a separate ethnic entity of those commingled tribes inhabiting the British Isles between the time of the departure of the legions and that of the rise of the Carolingian Empire. At each point in the preceding history of these various peoples the relationship between Britain and continental Europe was strong, and a valid separate identity of groups only began to appear when frontiers of language, from which all later notions of national individuality ultimately derived, were established. The Roman Empire had developed one kind of international organisation and in the Anglo-Saxon period its successor, the Roman Church, created another.

Christian Influence

During the formative years of the Christian Church while melodies of different provenance were adventitiously assembled from many sources—Jewish, Oriental, ritual, and pagan—and their use was according to local taste and resource, a body of patristic dogmas on the subject of the effective purpose of music in association with religion was also being raised on the foundations of Platonic, Aristotelian, and Plotinian thought. Clement of Alexandria and St. John Chrysostom, of the third and fourth centuries respectively, inveighed against pagan music (its paganity being due to its artificiality on the one hand and its alleged lewdness of association on the other), and propagated the idea that plain, unadorned melody, uncontaminated by instrumental accompaniment, was the type of music most fitted 'for the glory of God and the propagation of the divine Word'.[2] The effective union of practice and theory, and the establishment of a central, authoritative, school of church song in Rome, came about under

[1] Romanusque Lyra, plaudat tibi Barbarus Harpa,
Graecus Archilliaca, CHROTTA Britanna canat.
Lib. VII, Car. 8.

[2] The general tenor of this philosophy of church music may be found at various points in the consideration of the subject by the British; see pp. 22 and 96.

the direction of Pope Gregory I at the end of the sixth century. It was he who dispatched the Benedictine Abbot Augustine to England in the year 596, and when Augustine, with forty religious companions and interpreters conscripted in France, landed on the Isle of Thanet and sang the antiphon *Deprecamur te, Domine* to Ethelbert, King of the English, and his retainers, the modern history of British music may be said to have begun.

At this time what is Britain was a divided land, with kingdoms in Wessex, Sussex, Essex, Kent, Northumbria, Mercia, and Wales. Ireland also had its kings, and its own form of Christianity established earlier than the Augustinian mission and nurtured by an independent monastic tradition. In turn these kingdoms, warring with each other, rose and fell in importance and after the decline of the power of Kent the most potent was Northumbria, whose preeminence endured for the greater part of the seventh century. Christianity had taken root in Northumbria from the exertions of Irish missionaries, before Augustine converted Ethelbert; for in the middle of the sixth century Columba had founded the monastery of Iona. Edwin, King of Northumbria between 617 and 633, having married Ethelburga, daughter of Ethelbert of Kent, officially embraced Christianity (being baptized at York in 627) and admitted the Roman preacher Paulinus to his realm. Under Edwin's successor, Oswald, Irish Christianity was spread throughout Northumbria by Aidan of Iona. In certain liturgical particulars Irish Christianity differed from Roman, but by the end of the seventh century, through the diplomacy of Theodore of Tarsus, Archbishop of Canterbury, the Roman method was generally accepted. Britain, if with occasional demonstrations of isolated distaste for the new theology, was nominally a Christian country. Each of the kingdoms was now organised into bishoprics and furnished with religious houses, which were to serve as conspicuous centres for the cultivation of the arts and sciences.

The Romanisation of English, or Anglo-Celtic, music is described in some detail by the Venerable Bede (673–735), pupil of Benedict Biscop, Abbot of Wearmouth (now in Sunderland), and monk of Jarrow, whose *Historia Ecclesiastica Gentis Anglorum* (completed in 731), is one of the fundamental documents of English historical literature. Bede illustrates the turning-point in Anglo-Saxon musical culture by his account of the career of Caedmon. Caedmon was a natural poet-musician who translated biblical narratives into his own language, whereby he beneficially affected the minds of those whose views on Christianity were otherwise sceptical, but who were casually attracted by Caedmon's gifts of exposition. At more ceremonial gatherings Caedmon was reluctant to practise, for he had 'never learned any thing of versifying; for which reason . . . when it was agreed for the sake of mirth that all present should sing in their turns, when he saw the instrument [the harp] come towards him, he rose up from table and returned home'.[1] One night after this had happened Caedmon was given an exhortation in a dream to have more confidence in his skills and to 'sing the beginning of created beings'. Relating his dream, and encouraged by the Abbess of Whitby, Caedmon proceeded to become a religious, to compose sacred verses, and thereby to ensure his place in the hagiology of verse and music. What the legend symbolises is the submission of the secular bardic tradition, outside of Wales, to the regulated art of the Church, and the official recognition of one kind of art as superior to another, on account of its technical efficiency on the one hand and (more importantly) its efficacy in imparting doctrine and improving morals on the other.

The bardic tradition had accustomed the British to the practice of music, and among the nobility—as the legend of Caedmon suggests—it engendered an enthusiasm which was matched by certain skills. The Welsh historians[2] claimed that important regulations in respect of the 'Keys of Music' used in the secular tradition were made in 'King Cadwaladr's [Caedwalla, d. 634?] Time'. If this were so (and it may well have been) one would presume, perhaps, a reform based on the modal system which by this time was beginning to assert itself in church music. In any case the claim may reasonably be seen as an indication of a considerable awareness of musical technique. There were then some at least who were, by acquired ability in the theory and practice of music, receptive to new music. This meant the music introduced from Rome, for the successors of Gregory I were studious in sending among their missionaries and administrators those who were qualified to teach this art. Enjoying the patronage of Paulinus, the priest, who baptized Edwin of Northumbria, James, sometime deacon and precentor at Canterbury was particularly expert. When Paulinus left York for Rochester James remained in the north in his stead. 'He was,' wrote Bede, 'extraordinarily skilled in singing, and when the province was afterwards restored to peace,[3] and the number of the faithful increased, he began to teach many of the church to sing, according to the custom of the Romans, or of the Cantuarians.'[4] In 664 Theodore became Archbishop of Canterbury and

[1] *Ecclesiastical History*, Everyman edn., 1910, Book IV, Chap. XXIV.

[2] Lewis Morris, *Brief Account*, 1746, and *Extracts from Dr. John David Rhys's Gramar* (B.M. Add. Ms. 14905), where there is reference to an 'account of what a Pencerdd or Master of Music (*c.* 700, supposedly) ought to understand'. Regarding this see Arnold Dolmetsch, 'An Analysis of the Harmonies and Forms of the Bardic Music', in *The Consort*, no. 3, June 1934, pp. 7–20.

[3] After the succession of Oswald to Edwin, who was killed in the battle of Hatfield, Doncaster, in 633.

[4] ib. Book II, Chap. XX.

he was accompianed to England by Hadrian, an African priest. Both commanded respect among the English, for their vision was wide; they brought not only sacred but also secular literature, and instructed their followers in Latin and Greek, in ecclesiastical poetry, astronomy, and arithmetic. 'From that time also they began in all the churches of the English to learn sacred music, which till then had been only known in Kent. And excepting James above-mentioned, the first singing master in the churches of the Northumbrians was Eddi[us], surnamed Stephen, invited from Kent by the most revered Wilfrid, who was the first of the bishops of the English nation that taught the churches of the English the Catholic mode of life.'[1] Eddi Stephen, to become Wilfrid's biographer, also much occupied in ecclesiastical administration, was assisted in his musical functions by Aeonan, an Anglo-Saxon, and general encouragement to their efforts was given by Wilfrid, sometime Archbishop of York and a firm champion of the Roman cause in matters of discipline and observance. It was Wilfrid who elevated the singing-teacher Putta to the bishopric of Rochester in 669; and Putta, Bede informs us, was particularly alive to the authentic tradition of church-chant, 'which he had learned from the disciples of the holy Pope Gregory'.[2] Wilfrid himself was responsible for some part of musical education, observing to Archbishop Bertwald, 'Was it not I who taught these monks to sing psalms, as did the primitive Church, in response and antiphon of twofold choir.'[3] The profundity of the Roman influence between the seventh and twelfth centuries, out of which developed the whole range of Romanesque arts and early medieval literature and philosophy, was nowhere more deeply felt than in the British Isles. When Bede wrote of his own master Benedict Biscop he was writing of one whom he knew intimately and Biscop's zest for *reres Romanae* is consistently evident. He made in all four journeys to Rome, and when he obtained land for his monastery at Wearmouth he went to France for masons who should 'build him a church in the Roman style, which he had always admired'. He sent also for glaziers to glaze his church and conventual buildings and to teach the English their craft. Books, pictures, vestments, and all other kinds of 'spiritual merchandise' unobtainable in England were imported. Needless to say, in respect of music, Biscop 'introduced the Roman mode of chanting, singing, and ministering in the church, by obtaining permission from Pope Agatho to take back with him John, the archchanter of the church of St. Peter, and abbot of the monastery of St. Martin, to teach the English. This John, when he arrived in England, not only communicated instruction by teaching personally, but left behind

[1] ib. Book IV, Chap. II.
[2] ib. Book IV, Chap. II.
[3] Eleanor S. Duckett, *Anglo-Saxon Saints and Scholars,* New York, 1947, p. 187.

him numerous writings, which are still preserved in the library of the same monastery'.[1] John remained in the north for two years, during which time many pupils came to him from all parts of the kingdom, and he was able to return to Rome with a satisfactory account of the state of ecclesiastical music in England. Wilfrid was succeeded at York by Acca, and he, a close companion of Wilfrid and sharing his views on the necessity for high standards in church music, again applied to Canterbury for a musical director. Thus the singer Maban was given a northern assignment. The nature and quality of music performed in the province of Canterbury was at this time attested by Aldhelm, who related how in the new church in Thanet founded by the Princess Eadburga (or Bugge)—who was a correspondent of St. Boniface—there were to be heard antiphons, psalms, responds, and hymns.

Aldhelm (d. 709), Bishop of Sherborne, Abbot of Malmesbury, and the founder of churches and religious houses in the west of England, was one of the leaders of the intellectual and artistic movement of the seventh century. A disciple of Theodore of Canterbury, he was distinguished in letters, by a zest for architectural innovation, and a conspicuous talent for music. While Roman influences were prevalent in the arts of the seventh century, these, especially architecture and sculpture, were generally assimilated with local styles. In church music, however, this did not happen to the same extent. The Roman style was intended to be exclusive. Aldhelm, nevertheless, demonstrated that there was some point in maintaining a secular interest. Thus, according to William of Malmesbury, the twelfth century chronicler, on occasions when the inhabitants of Malmesbury had left Mass without waiting for the sermon Aldhelm would intercept them at the town bridge, where he first captured their interest by singing in the guise of a gleeman, and then 'so blended words of scripture with his jesting that he brought health to their minds, when he could have done nothing if he had thought to manage them severely and by excommunication'.

Britain and the Carolingian Empire

During the eighth century the power of Northumbria waned, and after Mercia had established temporary supremacy among the English kingdoms Wessex next assumed pre-eminence. But the character of Europe was profoundly changed during this period by the establishment of the Carolingian Empire, the first strong, cohesive, and effective organisation

[1] Bede, *The Lives of the Holy Abbots etc.* with *Ecclesiastical History*, Everyman edn., 1910. p. 351–3.

of supranational authority since the Roman Empire. Britain was outside this Empire, and still rent with internecine dissensions, but nevertheless was greatly affected by social and artistic developments that took place under the aegis of Charlemagne. Carolingian motifs appeared in profusion in the decorations of Anglo-Saxon manuscripts—and in sculptures, while architectural method and style showed similar influence. Charlemagne, recognising the temporal value of a strong ecclesiastical government, furthered the unity of the Church and, by appreciation of papal authority and careful selection of superior ecclesiastical officials, endowed the Church with added power and dignity. By cultivation of the arts in association with religious practice he enhanced the dignity of the Church and thereby assisted its authoritarian development. Charlemagne was insistent on uniformity of musical practice and in 789 reminded the clergy that they should adhere to the Roman chant and forsake the Gallican variant that—although popular—had already been proscribed by his father Pepin. He also strengthened the division between sacred and secular music, by forbidding visits by minstrels (at whose morals he took a censorious glance) to religious houses, and any practice of minstrelsy by the clergy. Thirteen years later he enjoined on the clergy the obligation to submit themselves for examination in church music, and at the Synod of Aachen, of 803, further exhortations were issued, and the institution of choir-schools was advocated. In due course the song-schools of Metz and St. Gall came to occupy a particular place in the ordering and codification of the traditional music of the Roman Church, and in its further extension.

That uniformity in the music of the Church was achieved was in large measure due to Alcuin, of York, whom Offa, King of Mercia, and an admirer and acquaintance of Charlemagne, was persuaded to allow to go into Imperial service. In effect, Alcuin, librarian and teacher at York, associate of Irish scholars and strongly Francophile, became Charlemagne's Minister for education. Given several abbacies, the last being at Tours in 796, Alcuin brought to Europe the English tradition of singing—its authenticity achieved by much intercourse with Rome and protected by a series of direct injunctions, of which the latest had issued from the Council of Cloveshoe in 747.[1] Alcuin appointed assistants to research into church music at Aachen; he defined the theory of the four authentic and plagal modes proper to church music; he revised the Roman Sacramentary for Frankish use, and in order to safeguard the integrity of plainchant periodically sent to Rome for singers and for copies of the Gregorian antiphons. He selected and trained musicians and insisted on high technical efficiency. Thus, for instance, he wrote of Sulpicius, teacher at Aachen:

[1] This Council had also decreed against the practice of secular music by priests.

Candida Sulpicius post se trahit agmina lector;
Hos regat et doceat certis ne accentibus errent.
Instituit pueros Idithum modulamine sacro,
Utque sonos dulces decantent voce sonora,
Quos pedibus, numeris, rhythmo stat musica, discant,[1]

Sulpicius wrote an important treatise, *Musica Disciplina*: another treatise, *De Ordine Antiphonarii*, came from Amalarius, of Metz, who was also a pupil of Alcuin. Since Alcuin was in constant communication with his friends in York his influence was felt in his native land.[2]

If Europe was revivified by a scholar-prince, so England was brought nearer to unity by one cast in the Carolingian mould. This was Alfred the Great (849–901), under whom Wessex became a dominant power and recognised as such by the other English (and some Welsh) territories. Alfred fought against the Danish and Norse invaders, who added traditions of their own to the common stock, and made it possible in the course of time for them to become assimilated into the community of the nation. Legend, as so often, is the first index to Alfred's musicianship, for it was in the guise of a minstrel that on one occasion he gained admittance to a Danish camp, there to collect such useful military information as he could. But it is as scholar that Alfred chiefly merits attention. In the particular field of music it is to be noted that he too received his early education in Rome, and that he visited Paris and also Ireland. Although Alfred transformed separate Anglo-Saxon groups into something approaching a unified English nation, and established the Anglo-Saxon tongue as a language of literature by his translations from Boethius, Gregory the Great, and Bede, he laid stress on the European traditions that belonged to the common heritage. The Carolingian connection grew stronger by the immigration of artists and scholars, and so far as ecclesiastical music was concerned Alfred is said to have installed a Frankish musician, named John,[3] in the school at Oxford, and also to have entertained a colleague of John named Grimbald. In 919 a number of Breton monks came to England in consequence of the Norman invasion of Brittany and placed themselves under the protection of Aethelstan. Their influence is evident in the Breton notation which appears in the *Pontifical of Sherborne*.[4]

1 Poem 221, quoted by Peter Wagner, *History of Plain-Chant*, London, 1901, p. 208, f.n. 2.

2 In respect of the reorganisation of the Minster School at York into Grammar, Song, and Writing sections see R. B. Hepple, *Mediaeval Education in England*, Hist. Assoc. leaflet, no. 90, 1932, p. 7.

3 Possibly John Scotus Erigena, an Irishman employed at the Court of Charles the Bald, who wrote a number of philosophical treatises, in one of which, *Divisio Naturae*, he appears to be acquainted with the method of part-singing known as *organum*.

4 Paris B.N., Lab. 943; see Michel Hugo, 'La Domaine de la Notation Bretonne', in *Acta Musicologica*, XXXV, 1963, pp. 70–71.

Music in the Tenth Century

The commanding figure of the tenth century was Dunstan (*c.* 924–88). A pupil of the Irish community of monks at Glastonbury, Dunstan became the favourite of King Aethelstan, the policy maker of Aethelstan's successors Edred and Edgar, and the early adviser of Ethelred the Unready. Dunstan was the first in a long line of ecclesiastics who exercised near-dictatorial powers over many aspects of English medieval life. In the secular sphere he was invaluable in reorganising the administration and defences of the country after the ravages of the Danish invasion, and in helping to enlarge the prestige and power of the monarchy. In church affairs Dunstan—successively Abbot of Glastonbury, Bishop of Worcester and London, and Archbishop of Canterbury—was energetic and rigorous. He tightened the discipline of the monastic foundations, by insisting on adherence to the Benedictine rule[1] and the consequent expulsion of secular monks and insistence on clerical celibacy; he restored property that had been sequestrated to the monastic houses, and he exercised due supervision over the music of the Church.

According to tradition and his biographers,[2] Dunstan was a practising musician. He played the harp (he invented an Aeolian Harp, that, apparently playing by itself, added to his reputation as a miracle-worker), the psaltery, then defined as a *tymphanum*, the cymbals (or chime-bells struck with hammers), and the organ. He was, reputedly under direct divine inspiration, a composer. During the time of Dunstan the Abbot Ethelwold, Bishop of Winchester, Dean of Glastonbury, and organiser of a new House at Abingdon, brought into England a group of monks from Corbie (a celebrated song-school in Brittany) to ensure proper uniformity. The *Regularis Concordia*, by which King Edward proposed to order monastic life at Winchester, and elsewhere, laid down detailed instructions concerning the use of hymns.[3] By the end of the tenth century a considerable amount of reliable evidence regarding the cultivation of musical instruments in Britain and Ireland is beginning to accumulate. An illumination in the eighth-century Psalter of St. Augustine's Abbey,

[1] Oswald of Worcester, and Ethelwold, of Winchester, brought their establishments into line with Benedictine orthodoxy, but in the country at large there was much latitude and in some cathedral chapters the practice of communal living as developed by Chrodegany, at Metz, was preferred for a long time to come.

[2] An anonymous writer of the early eleventh century, and probably a Saxon priest at Canterbury known as Auctor B; Osbern, of Canterbury, who compiled a life of Dunstan at the instigation of Archbishop Lanfranc; and John Capgrave (1393–1464).

[3] Quoted in part by W. H. Frere, *Hymns, Ancient and Modern* (Historical edn., 1909), Introduction, p. xix, f.n. 1.

Canterbury,[1] shows David, the Psalmist, playing a psaltery, and surrounded by figures with shawms and percussion instruments, as well as dancers. Harps, or clarsachs, are shown in Scottish sculptures at Auldbar, Forfarshire (ninth century), Nigg, Ross-shire (tenth century), and Dupplin, Perthshire (eleventh century). On the High Crosses, of the eighth and ninth centuries, at Castledermot and Ullard, in Ireland, the persistence of the Celtic crwth is shown in sculptured examples of such instruments with five or seven strings, while on the Crosses of Monasterboice and Clonmacnoise the tymphanum (as played by Dunstan), as well as single- and double-pipes, are illustrated. In the supplement to *Aelfric's Saxon Vocabulary* (tenth-eleventh century) the Latin term *auloedus* is translated as 'reed pipere', while in the contemporary document described as Harleian 603 (British Museum) a cornet is shown. By the eleventh century the crwth was no longer only a plucked instrument, but also played with a bow.[2] By this time the rebec, or lyra, which had been developed in the east and had established itself in Germany during the eighth century, provided another type of bowed instrument, with rather more affinity with the later viol or violin.[2] But the most notable innovation was the organ, the introduction of which to the British Isles was due to the close cultural connection with the Carolingian territories.

The organ appeared in western Europe during the eighth century and in 757 certain Byzantine musicians presented Pepin with such an instrument, which was installed at Compiègne. A larger instrument of similar specification became one of the wonders of the Court of Charlemagne at Aachen, where it was erected in 812. During this period, Aldhelm of Malmesbury was acquainted with the organ, for he noted the Anglo-Saxon practice of gilding the front pipes; while it is reported that in 814 an organ in the church of Cloncraff, Roscommon, Ireland, was destroyed by fire. Dunstan, famous for his skill in metal-work, supervised the building of an organ at Malmesbury, of which the pipes were of brass;[3] and Count Elwin endowed the convent of Romsey with an instrument, with copper pipes which were reported to produce a fine and sweet tone.

[1] Brit. Mus. Cott. MS. Vesp. A 1, fol. 30 v.: for a discussion of the artistic significance of this important work, see Margaret Rickert, *Painting in Britain, The Middle Ages*, 1954, pp. 18–19. Dr. Rickert concludes her study thus: 'The Canterbury Psalter is an almost unique example of the well-balanced blending of the two antipodal styles, Hiberno-Saxon and Mediterranean, the success of which is a tribute to the ability of the artist.'

[2] Illustration in Anglo-Saxon Psalter in Cambridge University Library, in which a four-stringed crwth (or crowd), is bowed by St. Asaph. Three-stringed rebecs are shown in Bodl. 352 (Oxford), B.M. Tiberius C. vi, and, in the twelfth century, in a carving in the crypt of Canterbury Cathedral.

[3] Organo do sancto praesul Dunstanus Adelmo;
Perdat hic aeternum qui vult hinc tollere regnum:
William of Malmesbury, *De Gestibus Pontificum Anglorum*, ed. N. E. S. A. Hamilton, Rolls Series, LII, 1870.

But the most famous organ of the Anglo-Saxon period was that installed in Winchester Cathedral by order of Bishop Elphege. This was described in some detail by Wulstan, a deacon of Winchester, in a poem of which the romantic properties are more compelling than the precision of its definitions. 'Such organs as you have built are seen nowhere, built in two storeys. Twice six bellows above are ranged in a row, and fourteen lie below. These, by alternate blasts, supply an immense quantity of wind, and are worked by seventy strong men, labouring with their arms, covered with perspiration, each inciting his companions to drive the wind up with all his strength—the full-bosomed box may speak with its 400 pipes which the hand of the organist governs. Some when closed he opens, others when open he closes, as the individual nature of the varied sound requires. Two brethren of concordant spirit sit at the instrument, and each manages his own alphabet. There are, moreover, hidden holes in the forty tongues, and each has ten [pipes] in their due order. Some are conducted hither, others thither, each preserving the proper point [or situation] for its own note. They strike the seven differences of joyous sounds, adding the music of the lyric semitone. Like thunder the iron tones batter the ear, so that it may receive no sound but that alone. To such an amount does it reverberate, echoing in every direction, that everyone stops with his hand his gaping ears, being in nowise able to draw near and bear the sound, which so many combinations produce. The music is heard throughout the town, and the flying tone thereof is gone out over the whole country.'[1]

The Winchester organ according to this statement had forty sliders, each of which admitted the wind to or cut it from the pipes. These sliders, taking the place of the keys of later time, were labelled alphabetically (thus relating to the ultimate nomenclature of musical sounds) for the benefit of the performers. To each slider was a set of ten pipes so that when any one was withdrawn there was an inevitable complexity of sound. The scale was from G to C^2 and two additional sliders admitted the 'lyrical semitone' caused by the introduction of B flat. The sliders were divided into two sets of twenty each, over each of which one operator presided.[2]

This raises the question: what music did the two organists play? Remembering that the organ first gained admittance to the Christian Church on utilitarian grounds—as a teaching aid and to fortify the monastic plainsong—it was liturgical. With a large range of pipes and with two players, it was possible to pay a plainsong melody in octaves, or in fifths, in accordance with the principle of vocal organum. It was equally possible for the two players, for 'being of concordant spirit' admits of

[1] Translation of poem from Benedictine *Acta Sanctorum* in F. D. Wackerbarth, *Music and the Anglo-Saxons*, London, 1837, pp. 12–15.

[2] See F. W. Galpin, *Old English Instruments of Music*, 3rd edn., London, 1932, p. 217–19.

several valid interpretations, to play contrasting contrapuntal parts, of which the lower would be plainsong. The machinery inhibited any quick movement, but it is clear that the apparent enormity of the weight of sound was sufficient in itself to stimulate the listener. One may also deduce from the extravagant language of the original reporter that what was played came under the head of 'modern music'. To what extent two-part playing was cultivated at Winchester in the tenth century is not to be known.[1] The fact remains that two-part playing was not only possible but highly probable in that the music of the western Church had at this time reached a point of no return. In the past was monody: in the future polyphony.

In the almost 400 years that elapsed between the codifications assigned to Pope Gregory I and the death of Dunstan the monodic manner of composition allowed to be proper to music that was ancillary to doctrine and ritual had reached a climax in development. Within the prescriptions of the Modes[2] melodic impulse, enriched by inflections from Byzantium on the one hand and Ireland on the other, and by the melismatic expansion developed by trained singers interested in music for its own sake, had ridden away from its primary purpose of merely sustaining words, and through the Mass, and numerous antiphons, responds, proses, tropes, alleluias, hymns, and sequences, increasingly required for exceptional and sometimes extramural occasions, reached a point of maturity thereafter accepted as representing one ideal of perfection. For practical purposes the same music, certainly the same style, was universal within the *imperium* of the Church. As has been seen Roman or European musicians happily took on teaching assignments in Britain and the British and Irish, who between them evolved the early Benedictine hymn-cycle and Anglo-Irish cycle[3] that were generally adopted, were as readily accepted on the continent. In the eleventh century the standing of British musicians was still high, as is shown by the willingness of the monks of St. Martin, Cologne, to learn authentic Gregorian practices from their Scottish-born Abbot, Aaron. The integrity of the music was safeguarded by the song schools. These, being part of monastic establishments, were at early date given an academic bias and thus early writers on music devoted much attention to philosophical considerations. At the same time the labour of

[1] For a general discussion of the role of the organ in the ecclesiastical music of this period, see Walther Krüger, *Die authentische Klangform des primitiven Organum*, Kassel, 1958, pp. 15–29. The same author also discusses the use of other instruments, as detailed on p. 22, in connection with the Liturgy, see pp. 42–68.

[2] The eight modes regularised during this period, and mentioned as existing by Alcuin, were the Dorian, Hypodorian, Phrygian, Hypophrygian, Lydian, Hypolydian, Mixolydian and Hypomixolydian.

[3] See W. H. Frere, op. cit., pp. XV and XVII.

transmitting music from one place to another inevitably led to the desirability of some acceptable form of musical notation. The alphabetical system adopted from Greek practice by Boethius (*c.* 470–525) and applied to instrumental music (as in the case of the Winchester organ) and the neumatic system (to be defined by the addition of a stave by Guido d'Arezzo in the eleventh century) were in general, though not standardised, use. The Bosworth Psalter[1] thought to have been written at the instance of Dunstan, while Archbishop of Canterbury, shows the neumatic system employed in England towards the end of the tenth century.

Among the song schools prominent in the scientific development of early medieval music one of the most important was that at St. Gall, in Switzerland. Founded by Irish missionaries this house long retained connections with the Irish Church and it would appear that the musical tradition of St. Gall was much advanced towards the end of the ninth century by the Irish monk Marcellus. 'A fact', writes Peter Wagner, 'which more than anything else demonstrates the important influence of the Anglo-Irish musical customs over the practice of the rising German [*sic*] monastery, is the unmistakable similarity of the notation in the oldest German plainsong Mss. and the English. . . . The monks from the Island kingdom who christianized Germany certainly taught in the monasteries founded by them no other order of liturgy and chant than the one which was current among them. The foundation of St. Gall, in all that concerns Church chant, stands in close relation to the English and Irish Churches.'[2] If music was to be performed in parts a more or less accurate form of notation was, of course, a *sine qua non*. By the eleventh century the admissibility of two-part singing in Winchester, at least, was acknowledged by the compiler of the *Winchester Troper*,[3] who wrote into the manuscript examples of 'free organum'.[4] Since these are in neumatic notation they may not be interpreted exactly. Nevertheless they testify to the maintenance of professional standards in the practice of Anglo-Saxon church music and show a tradition at least hinted at a century and a half earlier by John Scotus Erigena.

[1] B.M. Add. Ms. 37517.

[2] Peter Wagner, op. cit., p. 221.

[3] Corpus Christi College, Cambridge, Ms. 473. A collection of monophonic music from the same source is in the Bodleian Library, Oxford, Ms. Bodl. 775.

[4] 'Strict organum' was part-singing, at the intervals of fourth, fifth or octave, in parallel motion. 'Free organum' showed some contrary motion.

2

Feudal Society

Norman Rule

ANGLO-SAXON and Anglo-Hibernian art, showing as the most familiar high points of development the *Lindisfarne Gospels*, the *Book of Kells*, and the *Benedictional of Aethelwold*, was a synthesis of ideas and techniques drawn from many sources. To any one of the anonymous scribes and craftsmen associated with these works the concept of a purely localised form of expression in art was unthinkable, even though regional characteristics may have shown themselves in details of execution, and in attitudes towards particular subjects. Moreover, however beautiful the end-product, the process of production had in the end to be justified on functional grounds. In the narrow sense the aim of transcribing and illustrating a liturgical book was to instruct the reader and the viewer. In a similar manner music too was functional, its principal purpose being to carry various verbal formulas. Plainsong melodies imprinted sacred dogmas on the mind; while minstrelsy concerned itself in large part with inspiriting tribal heroics and selected and topical news items. That there were 'lewd and lascivious' songs as well was indisputable, but on account of their demerits these were often presumed not to exist. One of the difficulties of drawing a picture of European musical life up to the dawn of the Renaissance is that it must inevitably appear unbalanced, secular music showing so few examples by which it may be appreciated. It is, of course, sad that the professional music scribes should have missed out on practically a whole world of music; but since one would hardly expect a twentieth-century musicologist to go to considerable trouble to see that the popular songs of his period were collected and codified one may hardly suggest that his medieval counterpart was guilty of any grave dereliction of duty to posterity. Before the end of the eleventh century it was, indeed, generally presumed that there would be no posterity; for the end of the world was expected either in A.D. 1000 or 1033. After such expectations had been unfulfilled the English had much to occupy their minds apart from the preservation of casual musical remains.

Anglo-Saxon England, formed from hitherto unaccommodating regional groups, existed as a political entity with some difficulty across the reigns of the Danish Canute—who saw his kingdom as a part of a Scandinavian confederation—and Edward the Confessor. The principles of the latter led directly towards French culture, as is shown by the installation of a Frenchman, Robert de Jumièges, as Archbishop of Canterbury, and the employment of techniques from the Cathedral of Jumièges in the construction of Westminster Abbey. The year of Edward's death was also that of the Norman invasion. The task of invasion was made easier for William of Normandy by the inability of the English, factionally disintegrated, to raise any coherent opposition.

England became a Norman province, but the occupying power exercised less cultural influence than has often been suggested. Their own Norman heritage was slender; that of the Anglo-Saxons rich and of long standing. Indeed the Anglo-Saxon arts were much respected by the invaders. The French and Latin languages became official instruments of communication, but Anglo-Saxon, touched by these alien tongues, was healthily maintained. This was inevitable. The Normans accompanying William numbered no more than 4,000 and intermarriage with English women ensured a continuity of the indigenous language which, gradually shaping itself into an eloquent instrument of expression, emerged in the fourteenth century, in the works of William Langland and Geoffrey Chaucer, as a powerful literary medium.[1]

Some part of the way poetry was accompanied by music. The music of the mid-thirteenth century (?) *Sumer is i-cumen in* has fortuitously survived; but that for most of the poetry, whether in Latin or English, of the medieval period has not. The examples contained in *Political Songs of England from the Reign of John to that of Edward II*[2] are of great social and political interest, showing at its foundation the popular and traditional English concept of freedom and liberty, and also nascent patriotism and even its reverse—xenophobia. In those poems bearing on ecclesiastical matters there was clearly room for parody music: as, for instance, in a poem from the reign of King John libelling the Bishops of Norwich, Bath, and Winchester. Otherwise the poem is interesting because of a specifically musical reference:

[1] See Elizabeth Salter, 'The English Vernacular I', *The Listener*, 24 October 1963, p. 652.

[2] ed. Thomas Wright, Camden Soc. No. 6, 1839.

Complange tui, Anglia
Melos suspendens organi;
Et maxima tu, Cantia
De mora tui Stephani.[1]

The English language became more significant when kings considered themselves as being English rather than French, a tendency which developed after the loss of Normandy at the beginning of the twelfth century. By this time the country was rich in monuments raised by Anglo-Norman builders. The style of architecture exemplified in the great churches of Ely, Gloucester, Durham, and many others, rose to a climax and then gave way to Gothic innovations at Worcester and Lincoln until the new style, now more distinctively national, burgeoned in the thirteenth-century felicities of Salisbury.

These buildings, with their invariably long periods of resonance, accommodated music as no previous buildings in England had done. Aided by ideal acoustics,[2] still to be appreciated in *a cappella* singing, both unison plainsong and *organum* in parts—the latter often accompanied by splashes of instrumental colour—must have held much of enchantment for the worshipper already conditioned by the liturgical patterns expressed through architecture, sculpture, painting, and ceremonial.

During this period the Cistercians came to England and by establishing themselves in the country, mostly in the north, brought architectural invention into a congenial relationship with the countryside, of which, by using scientific methods, they were otherwise able to improve the amenities. In the great churches belonging to other orders and in the secular churches the arts of stained glass and of mural painting were practised, while the ancillary art of embroidery was expertly so cultivated that by the fourteenth century, familiar by reason of countless banners and vestments, it was known throughout western Europe as the *opus anglicanum*.

Growth and expansion of this order is the result of stability. Between the eleventh and fourteenth centuries England—indeed Europe as a whole—enjoyed a stability unknown since that achieved by the Roman Empire. The Normans undertook the organisation of England as a whole, and the divisions hitherto created by the relative independence of Saxon aldermen and by differences of speech were obliterated by the rigours of the feudal system and the institution of a powerful and centralised system of government. Authority derived from the King, and this focal authority to which all paid homage increased in significance. At the same time the

[1] ib. p. 6.

[2] Acoustic properties of churches were sometimes artificially enhanced, as for example at Fountains Abbey, where earthenware jars were set into the masonry for this purpose.

spiritual dominance of the Church became absolute. Reforms in organisation and administration during the tenth and eleventh centuries led to a stronger Papacy, a more effective monastic system, and a doctrinal assurance that brooked no question from the laity. Being possessed of great wealth the Church was able to impose its views on the generality of medieval Europeans, and, at the same time, to ameliorate the human condition in many particulars. At the present time it is impossible not to be impressed in Britain by the ecclesiastical buildings that remain in all parts of the country to testify to this kingdom within a kingdom. The necessity for artistic enhancement of the secular and religious dignities gave scope to artists and craftsmen, not least of all to musicians. But insofar as the clergy held the monopoly of learning and teaching it was inevitable that official music of whatever kind should carry the mark of the cloister. Music in honour of the King, therefore, was of the same nature as that practised in the praises of God. For the general well-being of music it was as well that the common people kept a lively devotion for forms of musical expression which lacked ecclesiastical sanction. It is, in fact, to be noted that in medieval Britain secular practices exercised no little influence on the shaping of the official order of composition.

When the Normans arrived in England the ecclesiastical system, despite the reformist zeal of Dunstan, was inconsistent. As a first step towards improvement Stigand, Archbishop of Canterbury, who had relinquished his former allegiances and crowned William I, was deprived of his office, to which Lanfranc, then Abbot of Caen, was appointed. Under the forceful Lanfranc—scholar, administrator, and statesman—drastic reform of the whole of the affairs of the Church in England was undertaken. Recalcitrant monks and priests were compelled rigorously to observe the vows and way of life to which they had nominally subscribed, and many abuses were removed. Correct procedures for ritual and music were defined in the decrees issued by Lanfranc to the Benedictines in 1089. Insofar as cathedral government was concerned—sees now being removed from places of lesser importance and established in major centres of population where they had not previously been sited—Lanfranc imposed the Norman method, of administration by Chapter.

By the end of the century new constitutions were adopted at York, Lincoln, and Salisbury, in which the precise details of duty and ritual were prescribed. The order for Salisbury, a new and secular foundation, was drawn up by the founder of the Cathedral, Osmund, nephew of William I, under the title of *Institutio*. In 1210 the Sarum Customary, to become a model for general use in Britain,[1] was drawn up by Richard Poor as an expansion of Osmund's *Institutio*. This set of formularies differed from the

[1] Cf. Elgin, 1212 and 1236, and Aberdeen, 1256.

Roman in many details, and plainsong melodies—the foundation on which the first English polyphony was built—were also given in varied forms. The Sarum Use lasted until 1547.

Under the general direction of the Precentor of a cathedral vicars-choral and singing-boys performed the music of the Liturgy. The boys were housed in clergy residences and prepared for junior church appointments or for a higher education, leading to eventual promotion to the superior ranks of the clergy. The vicars-choral gradually formed themselves into separate corporations and throughout the Middle Ages occupied a position of some independence of and considerable importance in the development of church music. Subordinate to the vicars-choral there were in due course professional singing-men of lower ecclesiastical rank than that of deacon. These were the lay-clerks.

In monastic foundations the whole community formed the choir, which, as in a secular cathedral, was directed by the Precentor, to whom the Succentor acted as assistant. Instruction in plainsong was part of the education of every novice. That monks were sometimes inclined to protest against the imposition on them of a musical education is demonstrated by two monks, of the reign of Henry II, possibly from Norwich, who complained of the difficulties of learning church music in the poem 'Un-comly in Cloystre'.[1] It was not until the fourteenth century that singing-boys were employed in the performance of liturgical music in monastic foundations; and only then outside the monks' choir.[2] Until the fifteenth century larger groups of singers in church were concerned only with unison plainsong. Polyphony, as it developed, was for solo singers and players.

In order to achieve uniformity of practice drastic measures were sometimes necessary. When the Abbot Thurstan, transferred from Caen, tried to introduce the ritual practised at Fécamp to his new house at Glastonbury, the monks rebelled; to bring them into proper conformity the Abbot was obliged to call in the help of a company of soldiers. Two monks were reported to have been killed, eight wounded. At York, on the other hand, the first Archbishop of the Norman dispensation, Thomas of Bayeux, was more imaginative. No doubt he had need to be, for in the harrying of the north which the King had ordered, the Minster and its adjacent buildings were ruined and the new Archbishop, faced with a large-scale restoration, could not afford to alienate his subjects. So far as the music was concerned, according to William of Malmesbury, Thomas spent much time in 'making organs and in teaching his clergy to make them, and to set hymns both in prose and verse to music. . . . If he heard any of the secular minstrels sing a tune which pleased him, he adopted and

[1] B.M. Ar. Ms. 292.

[2] See F. Ll. Harrison, *Music in Medieval Britain*, 1958, p. 40.

formed it for the use of the Church, by some necessary variations'. By such means Thomas aimed at removing the taint of effeminacy from church music.[1]

Performing Practice

With the acceptance of polyphonic music, discipline was made more difficult, and Aelred of Rievaulx (1109?–66) was obliged to issue a commination in the middle of the twelfth century against the general character of musical performance in church. 'Whence hath the Church so many organs and musicall instruments? To what purpose, I pray you, is that terrible blowing of belloes, expressing rather the crashes of thunder than the sweetnesse of a voyce? To what purpose serves that contraction and inflection of the voyce? This man sings a base, that a small meane, another a treble, a fourth divides, and cuts asunder, as it were, certain middle notes: and while the voyce is strained, anon it is remitted, now it is dashed and then again it is enlarged with a lowder sound. Sometimes, which is a shame so to speake, it is enforced into a horse's neighing: sometimes the masculine vigour being laid aside it is sharpened with the shrillnesse of a woman's voyce: now and then it is writhed and retorted into a certaine artificial circumvolution. Sometimes thou may'st see a man with an open mouth, not to sing, but to breathe out his last gaspe by shutting in his breath, and by a certain ridiculous interception of his voyce as it were to threaten silence. . . . In the meantime the common people standing by, trembling and astonished, admire the sound of the organ, the noyse of the cymballs and musicall instruments, the harmony of the pipes and cornets.'[2] Testimony to the popularity of instruments in the twelfth and thirteenth centuries is afforded by many carvings of that time: for example, of a crwth at Worcester, of recorder and other wind instruments played by animals at Canterbury, of harps at St. Oran's Chapel and the Monastery of Iona, of bagpipes on St. Martin's Cross also in Iona. Sometimes the introduction of instruments into the service of the Church (according to Giraldus Cambrensis even to accompany dancing) was deplored; as by Nigellus, Precentor of Canterbury, and by John Cotton, who wrote that wind instruments sound 'indiscreetly . . . like the laughter or groaning of men, the barking of dogs, or the roaring of lions'.[3] Often, however, instrumental music was taken for granted, for high ecclesiastics

[1] M. Gerbert, *De Cantu*, I, p. 283; W. Nagel, *Geschichte der Musik in England I*, p. 15 *et seq.*

[2] *Speculum Charitatis*, 1123, trans. by Prynne. Aelred, or Ethelred, a historian, was in the service of Prince Henry of Scotland, was Abbot of Revesby and of Rievaulx, and in 1162 effected a meeting between Henry II of England, Louis VII of France, and Pope Alexander III.

[3] *Gemma ecclesiastica*, quoted by E. H. Meyer, *English Chamber Music*, London, 1947, p. 20.

tempered judgement according to personal predilection and there were those like Bishop de Swinfield, of Hereford, who employed secular musicians to entertain them during pastoral visitations.[1]

Aelred's account of church music also indicates the adoption of certain vocal techniques—such as 'nasal' tremolando and vibrato that characterised the method of singers of Notre Dame. It is also to be noted that he was accustomed to singing in four parts, which became commonplace at the beginning of the thirteenth century, as is shown by the reference thereto by the General Chapter of the Cistercian Order in 1217 in respect of Abbey Dor and Tintern. Clearly ornamentation was in vogue, while the reference to 'a certain ridiculous interception . . . as it were to threaten silence' denotes the hocket. This, which was increasingly used in polyphonic music until it ceased in the fourteenth century, entailed rests interjected (without relation to the sense of the words) into a line of melody, or the division of a melody between two voices.[2] All in all Aelred, a purist, was right in thinking that artistic ambition was moving too fast, if considerations of the inviolability of verbal sense and authentic melodic tradition were to be considered paramount in worship.

Another to fulminate against advanced practices in twelfth-century church music was John of Salisbury (d. 1180), who, after studying under Abelard in Paris, occupied many high posts in the Church and ended his career as Bishop of Chartres. John deplored both the increasingly decadent character of secular music and its effect on church music, and, in terms similar to those used by Aelred, the exhibitionism of ecclesiastical singers. His reference to the Phrygian Mode is used not in any technical sense but, as he later shows, as an indication of appeal to authority, the Greek philosophers having condemned melodies in their Phrygian Mode.

'. . . The Phrygian Mode', he writes 'and other corrupting types serve no purpose in wholesome training; [but] rather develop the evil inherent in its devotee. Legitimate musical instruction grieves and laments its disfigurement by a vice that is not inherent in it and by the fact that a harlot's appearance is given to that which was wont to inspire virile minds with manly ideals. The singing of love songs in the presence of men of eminence was once considered in bad taste, but now it is considered praiseworthy for men of greater eminence to sing and play love songs which they themselves with greater propriety call *stulticinia*.

'The very service of the Church is defiled, in that before the face of the Lord, in the very sanctuary of sanctuaries, they, showing off as it were, strive with the effeminate dalliance of wanton tones and musical phrasing

[1] Gerbert, *Scriptores*, II, p. 234.

[2] Cf. "Hocket=To hesitate and grow confused when speaking . . ." *The Dialect of Leeds and its Neighbourhood* (anon), 1863.

to astound, enervate, and dwarf simple souls. When one hears the excessively caressing melodies of voices beginning, chiming in, carrying the air, dying away, rising again, and dominating, he may well believe that it is the song of the Sirens and not the sound of men's voices; he may marvel at the flexibility of tone which neither the nightingale, the parrot, or any bird with greater range than these can rival. Such indeed is the ease of running up or down the scale, such the dividing or doubling of the notes and the repetitions of the phrases and their incorporation one by one; the high and the very high notes are so tempered with the low or somewhat low that one's very ears lose the ability to discriminate, and the mind, soothed by such sweetness, no longer has power to pass judgement upon what it hears. When this type of music is carried to the extreme it is more likely to stir lascivious sensations in the loins than devotion in the heart. But if it is kept within reasonable limits it frees the mind from care, banishes worry about things temporal, and by imparting joy and peace and by inspiring a deep love for God draws souls to association with the angels.'[1]

On the same side as Aelred and John of Salisbury stands Gilbert of Sempringham, who was concerned at the spread of improper music even in nunneries: 'We do not permit our nuns to sing. We absolutely forbid it, preferring with the blessed Virgin to hymn indirectly in a spirit of humility rather than with Herod's notorious daughter to pervert the minds of the weak with lascivious strains.'

While these chroniclers and theologians were neither more nor less precise in dealing with music than non-specialists at any time their information adds up to this: that in the twelfth century there was a considerable development of musical interest and expansion of technique. In short, however much in conflict with sacerdotal dogmas, musicians were not backward in attracting music to the increasing significance of the other arts ancillary to devotion. Taking a backward view one is too ready to assume music to have been a late developer. To the medieval listener the music of his age, full of surprises and modernities which have been oversimplified and rigorously codified by later theoreticians, offered as much as music can ever offer—a quickening of imagination and emotion and a concept of order, which derived from restatements and extensions of the familiar.

A Variety of Traditions

The developing music of the Middle Ages was in formal plan according to the principle of air and variations. The extent to which free extem-

[1] *Frivolities of Courtiers and Footprints of Philosophers, a translation of Policraticus* by John of Salisbury, trans. and ed. by Joseph B. Pike, 1938, p. 32.

porisation—the more likely to be free on account of the cult of the soloist—was practised cannot precisely ever be determined, but the previous citations give some general idea. The fact that the production of vocal tone in the Middle Ages was vastly different from modern method and possibly carrying something of an eastern quality, is emphasised by G. S. Bedbrook and Paul H. Lang.[1] That there were a distinctive English style and English songs is indicated by William Fitzstephen, who, in his *Vita Sancti Thomae*, describes Thomas Becket's mission to France in 1159 to negotiate the marriage of Prince Henry and the daughter of Louis VII. When the English party entered the French towns boy choristers in attendance 'sang English songs after the custom of their country'. During the campaign in Toulouse in the same year other national musical characteristics were evident, for the signal to the army to advance or retreat was given 'on one of those slender trumpets peculiar to [the army] but well known to all those taking part in the battle'.[2] Fitzstephen also gives a vivid musical picture when Becket returned from exile. 'The poor scholars and clergy of the London churches formed yet another procession and came to meet him about three miles from the city. At his approach they began to chant loud and clear the *Te Deum Laudamus* . . . [at Southwark] the procession of canons met him at the door of the church with great jubilation. Amid tears of joy they commenced singing the canticle "Blessed be the Lord God of Israel"; and the vast concourse of people, clergy and laity, of every age and rank, took up the strain of praise and thanksgiving with loud and united voice'.[3] In another place Fitzstephen refers to the 'holier plays, wherein are shown the miracles wrought by Holy Confessors or the sufferings which glorified the constancy of martyrs'.[4]

Fitzstephen overlaps Giraldus Cambrensis here and there, but the latter considers in more detail the capacity of the Welsh to sing contrapuntally and of the English of the north-east to exploit harmony. From what he writes it would appear that the musical education of children was not overlooked.

'The Welsh do not sing in unison like the inhabitants of other countries, but in many different parts; so that in a company of singers, which one very frequently meets with in Wales, you will hear as many different parts and voices as there are performers, who will at length unite with organic

[1] See G. S. Bedbrook, 'The Nature of Medieval Music', in *M. & L.*, 26, no. 2, p. 79, 1945, and Paul H. Lang, *Music in Western Civilisation*, 1942, pp. 46 *et seq.*

[2] *The Life and Death of Thomas Becket*, trans. and ed. by George Greenaway, Folio Soc., 1956, p. 48.

[3] ib. p. 144.

[4] *A Description of London*, trans. and ed. by H. E. Butler, in *Norman London*, Hist. Assoc. Leaflets, 93–4, 1934, p. 30.

melody, in one consonance and the soft sweetness of B flat [F or G modes presumed, with added B flat to avoid the tritone]. In the northern districts of Britain, beyond the Humber, and on the borders of Yorkshire, the inhabitants make use of the same kind of harmony, but with less variety; singing only in two parts, one murmuring in the bass, the other warbling in the acute or treble. Neither of the two nations has acquired the peculiarity by art, but by long habit, which has rendered it natural and familiar; and the practice is now so firmly rooted in them, that it is unusual to hear a simple and single melody well sung; and, what is still more wonderful, the children, even from their infancy, sing in the same manner. As the English in general do not adopt this mode of singing, but only those of the northern countries, I believe that it was from the Danes and Norwegians, by whom those parts of the island were more frequently invaded and held longer under their dominion, that the natives contracted their mode of singing as well as speaking.'[1]

The speculations of Giraldus regarding the northern manner of part-singing have often been somewhat cursorily dismissed. But in view of the long duration of Scandinavian influence in Yorkshire dialect (shown, for example, in the Wakefield Mysteries) and the consonances of the thirteenth century Orcadian Hymn to St. Magnus [Ex. 1] it may very well be seen deriving from a technique similar to that described above.

1.

The Cathedral of St. Magnus, in Orkney, was erected in 1137 under the protection of the Earl Rognald, himself a *skald* of some skill, who collaborated with Hall Thorarinson in compiling a famous key to the versification known as the *Hattalykil hinn forna*. The Sang Scule of St. Magnus, probably dependent on rents in the island of Eynhallow and

[1] *The Itinerary through Wales* and *Description of Wales*, Everyman edn., 1908, *Description*, XIII.

supported by Bishop Bjarni Kolbeinsson, had close associations with Scandinavia. In 1938 the Finnish scholar Dr. Otto Andersson attended service in St. Magnus Cathedral, and wrote, 'The congregation joined in to a fair degree. At times I noted the same heterophonie (a peculiar two-part singing) which I had heard in my childhood church in the Aland Islands—similar to some extent to the second part in the St. Magnus Hymn.'[1]

Theoreticians

Although church music in Britain during this period may be seen to have shown certain traits of independence, the main lines of progress, the same as in European music generally, were recorded by a succession of theorists, whose influence was international. In the tenth century *Musica Enchiriadis* (attributed to Hucbald or Otger) the nature of strict organum was first exposed. In the eleventh century Guido d'Arezzo, a prolific author, systematised the hexachordal system of computation, described the method of free organum, and, more importantly, introduced the principle of solmisation, and the necessary machinery of the stave. Also of the eleventh century were the anonymous *Ad Organum Faciendum*, which went still further in the direction of defining a fluid two-part counterpoint, and the treatise *Musica* written by Johannes Cotto. Cotto (otherwise John Cotton) is assumed to have been an Englishman according to the terms of the dedication of his treatise,[2] but his treatment of the processes of organum has no particular topical reference. In what he says regarding the permissible intervals to be used in organum, the nature of cadences, and the placing of organal groups of notes against single notes in the fundamental plainsong, Cotto is in general agreement with the author of *Ad Organum Faciendum*. A surviving example of twelfth-century (?) organum, part of the Respond *Sancte Dei pretiose*, for St. Stephen's Day, is contained as an interpolation within the manuscript Bodley 572.[3]

The main achievements in thirteenth-century music were accomplished in Paris, where at Notre Dame, a school of composers, led first by Léonin and then Pérotin, was established. Polyphony (mainly limited to the solo sections of responsorial plainsong and performed by a small, specially trained, group of soloists) expanded its range and in so doing made inevitable the ratification of a rhythmic system and a rhythmic notation.

[1] Communicated by the County Librarian, Kirkwall, Orkney.

[2] 'Domino et patri suo venerabili Anglorum antistiti Fulgentio.' In a contemporary anonymous work, *De script. eccles.*, reference is made to an English musician known as Joannes.

[3] Pub. in *The Musical Notation of the Middle Ages*, 1890; see also *O.H.M.*, I, 1929, pp. 50–52.

Thus there developed the new concept of *Musica mensurata*, of which the theoretical foundation lay in the quantitative organisation of poetic method, and the trinitarian dogma of theology. Léonin and Pérotin developed three-[1] and four-part counterpoint in which freely moving parts, coming to consonantal agreement only at end-points, were characteristic.

Of the theorists of the thirteenth century two or three of some importance were certainly of English extraction. John Garland, whose academic life was said to have commenced at Oxford, was mainly associated with educational and musical developments in Paris. Of his writings on music the most important was *De musica mensurabili positio*, in which the division of measured music was explained, as were the 'rhythmic modes' and the meaning of such terms as Discantus and Motetus.

In the late thirteenth-century treatise by an author—thought to have been a monk of Bury St. Edmunds—known as the 'Anonymous of the British Museum' reference is made to a predilection for intervals of the third (cf. the *Hymn to St. Magnus*), allowed as concordant, in west country practice in England.[2] At the same time, or at the beginning of the fourteenth century at latest, another English writer, Walter de Odington, a monk of Evesham and known for his work on astronomy at Oxford, produced his *De Speculatione musices*. Odington, also covering acoustics and musical instruments, gives a complete statement of the methods practised at the beginning of the fourteenth century and defines the forms by then in common use. While strongly scientific in his approach Odington was at least acquainted with another world of music, for he makes one tantalising reference to the folk-song practice of vineyard workers (in France?).[3]

Musical Forms

Organum has already been sufficiently defined. Discant was, for practical purposes, a form of organum; at first the discant (i.e. second part) was extemporaneously imposed on the written-out plainsong melody. The Conductus was a more extended form of composition, and emancipated from the control of plainsong to the extent that the lowest of two, three,

[1] In B.M. Add. Ms. 36929 there is part of a Psalter (written by an Irishman, Cormac) with notes for three voices. The Ms. is of the thirteenth century, but the music may be of later date.

[2] See Coussemaker, *Scriptores*, I, p. 358 (*O.H.M.*, I, 1929, p. 93): 'Ditonus et semiditonus apud aliquos non sic (i.e. pro concordantiis imperfectis) reputantur. Tamen apud organistras optimos, et prout in quibusdam terris, sicut in Anglia, in patria que dicitur Westcuntre, optime concordantie dicuntur, quoniam apud tales magis sunt in usu.'

[3] *De Speculatione*, IV, 1.

or four parts was independently composed. Some conductus items were punctuated by *caudae*, instrumental interludes sometimes of patently secular origin, which were useful accessories in processional usage.[1] The Conductus, as the name suggests, was itself functional to liturgical action. Motet referred to a type of work in which a plainsong theme is given in the tenor with free upper parts set to different texts. In all these works the textual situation was confusing, and vocal lines often dispensed with words altogether. In the Rondel the character of the music was similar to that of the Conductus, but the distinguishing feature of the form was the imitation practised by the voices, in this manner: [Ex. 2].

In *Sumer is icumen in* the two lowest voices are disposed in a rondel, which indeed was a favourite English form of composition, while the four upper parts are concerned with a rota (or canon), a term used for the first time, so far as is known, in the manuscript of *Sumer is icumen in.*

Of British compositions of this period too few have survived to give more than a partial glimpse of the polyphonic progress that was being made, with the result that the Reading Rota apparently stands at a greater distance from other contemporary works than, according to reason, it should. (Despite St. Dunstan's angelic visitation, masterpieces are not directly sent from heaven.) Nevertheless the general direction of polyphony as practised in Britain, strongly affected by what was happening in France, is charted in the three conductus pieces of the Cambridge University Ms. Ff. 1. 17,[2] the Lady-Mass music from the Priory of St. Andrew's Scotland,[3] and the pieces from the so-called Worcester collection,[4] of which this conductus-cum-rondellus comes within striking distance of the Reading piece. [Ex. 3.]

1 See Harrison, op. cit., pp. 128–9.

2 Facsimiles in *Early English Harmony*, pls. 25–30.

3 Wolfenbüttel, Herzog August Bibliothek, Ms. 677; facsimile in *An Old St. Andrew's Music Book*, ed. by J. H. Baxter, 1931.

4 *Worcester Medieval Harmony*, ed. by A. Hughes, 1928, and *The Worcester Fragments*, ed. by L. A. Dittmer, 1957.

The Chapel Royal

During the twelfth and thirteenth centuries the musical establishment of the English court was regularised according to the increasing demands and complexity of musical techniques and a growing appreciation of the value of such an organisation in projecting the personality and dignity of the monarch. In the past this had been done at Coronation ceremonies and it is said that the text of 'Zadok the Priest' was sung at the coronation of King Egbert.[1] Under the Normans the Chapel Royal, comprising a group of *servientes da capella*, accompanied the King wherever he went, and included a sufficiency of priests capable of singing Mass. In the reign of King John information regarding individual singers and what they sang was recorded, for in 1200 the Treasurer and the Chamberlain of the Royal Household were commanded to pay 25s. to Henry and Jacob, 'clerks of our chapel who have sung *Christus vincit* before us at Salisbury on the Day of Pentecost'. *Christus vincit*, the best known of the royal *Laudes Regiae*, being placed before the Epistle in the Coronation Service, was frequently sung during the progresses of King John, its performance at Westminster, Porchester, and Chelford being recalled.[2]

Under Henry III, a devout churchman, the establishment was further extended, and other musical clerks came in for commendation. Among them were Walter de Larch[es], who, 'with his fellows of the King's chapel sang at Westminster, Portsmouth, Reading, and Guildford; Peter de Bedyngton, "keeper of various abbeys", and Makeblite, who distinguished himself at Winchester together with one Blakesmit, also "in curia domini regis Henrici".' In 1226 one of the clerks, William de Blemes, was sent to study at Oxford, the first recorded case of such subsidisation of a clerk's education. By now the clerks comprised a 'fellowship'

[1] See Dom Anselm Hughes, 'Music of the Coronation over a thousand years', in *P.R.M.A.*, 79, 1952–3, pp. 82 ff.

[2] See Ian Bent, 'The English Chapel Royal before 1300', in *P.R.M.A.*, 90, pp. 77 ff.

and were subject to the discipline of a senior, who was the fore-runner of the later Master. In 1231 the principal clerk was Robert of Canterbury, a married man, who in that year was in charge of the arrangements for the royal progress to Worcester. His successor was William de Larches, above-mentioned, whose payments included 16s. to cover the cost of a new cope. At the end of the thirteenth century, during the reign of Edward I, the *Wardrobe Book* inventory of the property of the Chapel Royal listed two items of significance; 'unus liber de cantu organi qui incipit *Viderunt*', and 'Unus liber de cantu organi qui incipit *Alleluya*'.[1] The dynastic ambitions of Edward I in respect of France and the sequence of diplomatic and military interventions and consequent settlements that marked the later stages of his political career proved no impediment to exchanges of cultural information, as these acquisitions and a general influence of French ideas show. In the last years of the reign of Edward I the musical establishment of the Chapel Royal was brought into line with that of the cathedrals by the employment of choir-boys. In 1303 two of these, Richard of Nottingham and Thomas Duns, were sent to study at Oxford.

Poetry and Music

The twelfth century was the age of the Crusaders,[2] and the purpose of these expeditions to the Middle East helped to inspire those ideals of chivalry that furnished the basis of medieval poetry, especially in France. The office of minstrel—and minstrels were regularly maintained in royal and even conventual service[3]—was upgraded and the art of the troubadour and the trouvère was developed to the extent of providing for the ruling class a strong foundation for a cultured secular tradition of song. John of Salisbury had thus deplored the fashion: 'But our own age, descending to romances and similar folly, prostitutes not only the ear and heart to vanity but also delights its idleness with the pleasures of eye and ear. It inflames its own wantonness, seeking everywhere incentives to vice. Does not the shiftless man divert his idleness and court slumber in the sweet

[1] See Denis Stevens, *The Mulliner Book, A Commentary,* 1952, p. 12, no. 7 and Harrison, op. cit., p. 132.

[2] For a Crusader's song (B.M. Harl. Ms. 1717) see *O.H.M.*, II, 1929, p. 287.

[3] William I arrived at Hastings with Taillefer; in Doomsday Book lands were assigned to a King's Minstrel in Gloucestershire; Rahere, who founded the hospital of St. Bartholomew, in London, in 1102, was a royal minstrel. Edward I engaged minstrels in large numbers on the occasion of royal marriages and also when engaged in punitive excursions into Scotland (see Introduction to *Manners and Household Expenses of England in the 13th and 15th Centuries* . . . Printed for the Roxburghe Club, 1841, and pp. 140–45). Harpers were employed in religious houses, particularly by the Bishop of Durham and the Abbot of Abingdon. See also p. 44.

tones of instruments and vocal melody, with gaiety inspired by musicians and with the pleasures he finds in the narrator of tales or, and this is more disgraceful still, in drunken revels.'[1]

The troubadours, using the Provençal language practised in southern France, northern Italy and Spain, the trouvères for the most part in the central and northern parts of France. But the influence of both was widespread, and the cultivation of lyric poetry of a sentimental order—dealing with the praises of the Virgin Mary or of ladies more immediately accessible—on the one hand, and a heroic and militant temper on the other became general. In any case the words and the music conceived together were regarded as indissoluble. The art of the troubadour was practised in England by King Richard I, whose frequent absences from his kingdom, however, meant that his opportunities for popularising the art at home were limited. Taking an indirect route troubadour influence arrived at Romsey Abbey and took such effect that an extant manuscript dealing with the affairs of that house[2] contains two amorous French songs. Although there is no considerable corpus of such music in the English as in the French tradition its influence is vicariously evident in the pattern of English poetry which, passing through the chivalrous mysticism of Thomas de Hales's *Luve Ron*, the romantic fancy of Layamon's *Brut*, and the naturalism of the Dorsetshire *The Owl and the Nightingale*,[3] reached a climax in the poetry of Chaucer and the secular songs of the fourteenth century.

A few songs remain from the end of the thirteenth and the beginning of the fourteenth centuries, however, to show the musical treatment of two characteristic facets of English poetic thought as it was then beginning to emerge. In a collection of prayers and lives of the Saints, possibly at one time the property of Bishop Grosseteste, of Lincoln,[4] is a sacred song, *Stond wel moder under rode*, which is similar in style to a Latin sequence. Emphasising the close connection with France a semi-religious French song lies next to the English in this collection. Fragments of another song to the Virgin in English, *Seinte Marie, virgine moder*, the words attributed to Aelred of Rievaulx in a Life of St. Godric, also survive.[5] *Foweles in the Frith*[6] [Ex. 4] (*c.* 1270)

4.

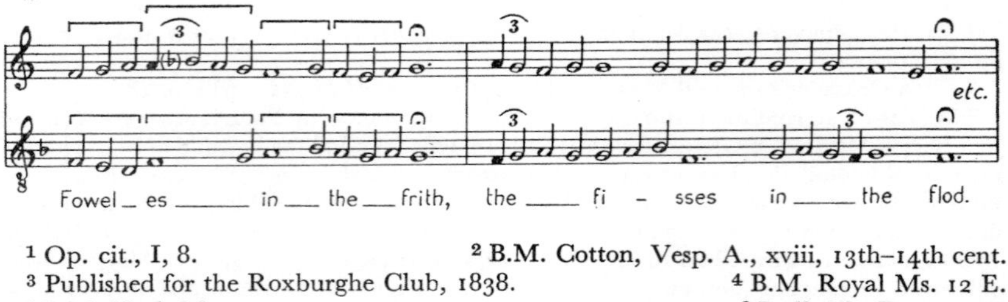
etc.
Fowel _ es ____ in ___ the ___ frith, the ____ fi - sses in ____ the flod.

[1] Op. cit., I, 8.
[2] B.M. Cotton, Vesp. A., xviii, 13th–14th cent.
[3] Published for the Roxburghe Club, 1838.
[4] B.M. Royal Ms. 12 E.
[5] B.M. Harl. Ms. 322.
[6] Bodl. Ms. Douce 139.

is a small landscape sketch associated with some introspection on the part of the poet. *Jesu Cristes Milde Moder* [Ex. 5],[1] a translation of the

5.

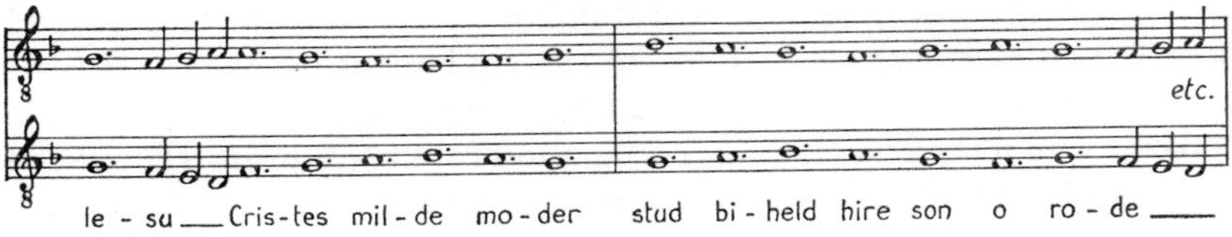
etc.
Ie - su __ Cris-tes mil - de mo - der stud bi - held hire son o ro - de __

sequence *Stabat juxta Christi crucem*, is tenderly sorrowful, a ballad on the theme of divine suffering couched in the language of an imaginative tutor of the unlearned. In the same manuscript are the Crucifixion song, *The Milde Lombe*, and *Worldes bliss*.[2]

Minstrels

If English poetry and music jointly aimed to match up with the more polished achievements of France a certain hang-over from the Anglo-Saxon tradition is evident: in poetry, where the practice of alliteration and the freer rhythmic accentuation of former times are maintained in Layamon; in music, in the popular appeal of the minstrel. Robert Grosseteste shows something of the fusion of courtly and popular tradition in his poem, *Manuel Peche*. This, composed in the Romance language, but intended for public performance with harp accompaniment, was translated into English in 1302 by Robert de Brunne (Robert Mannyng, of Bourne, in Lincolnshire). The continuity of the bardic or gleeman practice of declaimed, or intoned, narrative against harp is further instanced by the note of the visit of the Bishop of Winchester to St. Swithin's Priory in 1338: 'Et cantabur Joculator quidem nomine Herebertus Canticum Colbrondi, necnon Gestum Emme regine a judicio ignis liberate in aula prioris.'[3]

The Crusades not only affected attitudes to poetry and to music in indirect ways but also the constitution of the instrumental ensemble. The mandore was adopted by the Jongleurs of the twelfth and thirteenth centuries, quickly popularised in the Mediterranean countries, and employed in England in the course of the fourteenth century.[4] The trumpet

[1] B.M. Ar. Ms. 248.

[2] See p. 55.

[3] Quoted in E. Duncan, *The Story of Minstrelsy*, 1907, p. 77.

[4] The mandore is shown in the Missal of Abbot Nicholas de Litlington, Westminster Abbey.

(*Claro* or *Buzina*), with cylindrical tube, became popular in western Europe at this time, and was noted by William of Malmesbury in the twelfth century; and in the fourteenth century Edward III attached five trumpeters to his retinue. Together with the trumpet, percussion also came from the east, and timbrells (tambourines), tabretts (tabors), and nakers (kettle-drums) were added to the equipment necessary for ceremonial occasions. In 1304 Edward I's list of minstrels included Jamino le Nakerer, and forty years later, according to Froissart, Edward III entered Calais, 'à foison de trompettes, de tabours, de nacaires et de buccines'.

On the one side of British secular music then were the minstrels employed in the royal or aristocratic households. Keeping up with other royalties was a source of considerable and continual anxiety to monarchs, and a strong bodyguard of minstrels was increasingly desirable in order to boost morale. When Alexander III, of Scotland, was in London in 1278, paying homage to Edward I, he brought with him Elyas, his principal harper, two trumpeters, and six minstrels. (In 1296 Elyas le Harper having been dispossessed by Edward I was restored to his estates by John Balliol[1].) On the occasion of the marriage of Robert Bruce's son David to Johanna, sister of Edward III, in 1328, at Berwick, the Scottish minstrels supporting the bridegroom received the payment of £66. The bride was accompanied by English minstrels. Other famous northern harpers of the period were Robert of Ayrshire and Rogier of Berwick. Among the nobility the Warenne and Gloucester families employed minstrels towards the end of the thirteenth century, while in Newcastle upon Tyne a group of civic minstrels was in being in 1278.[2] The minstrels were treated with respect, enjoying reasonable emoluments and special liveries, and the senior among them were honorifically titled 'Kings'. They were in touch with continental development, sometimes incorporated in performances of church music, and pioneers in music for instrumental ensemble. Instrumental music, for which a rudimentary notation—the *simplicia puncta* of Anonymous IV—existed, was hardly yet independent and such examples as are extant gave the possibility of vocal intervention, even in the dance. The form most favoured between the twelfth and fourteenth centuries was that of the *Estampie*,[3] a dance formerly allied to the liturgical sequence and returned to the Church by way of the *Clausula*. [Ex. 6.]

[1] H. G. Farmer, *A History of Music in Scotland*, London, 1947, pp. 40–41.

[2] Madeleine Hope Dodds, 'Northern Minstrels and Folk Drama', in *Archaeologica Aeliana*, 4th series, Newcastle, 1925, I, p. 2, quoting from Account Rolls of Durham Priory.

[3] Three examples of this dance were copied into the so-called Robertsbridge Ms. (B.M. Add. Ms. 28550), the earliest extant collection of music for organ. It is doubtful, however, whether this Ms. was of English origin. Denis Stevens (*The Mulliner Book, A Commentary*, p. 12) suggests that it was left in England by a foreign visitor. For other

6.

In the centre of the secular scene were the peripatetic minstrels, descendants of the gleemen, who, dealing with the serfs and peasants on equal terms, were welcomed on arrival in town or village but likely to be condemned by the magistracy before they had been long in any one place. Always liable to ecclesiastical censure, as Aelred of Rievaulx and John of Salisbury indicated, their free and easy habits frequently brought them also within secular displeasure.

On one occasion, however, the lower order of minstrels were useful in another capacity, and being so gained certain privileges. When Randle Blundevil, Earl of Chester, was besieged by the Welsh in 1212 he retreated to Rhuddlan Castle, whence he sent a message to the Constable of Chester asking for relieving forces. It being the time of the city fair the Constable collected 'a tumultuous rout of fiddlers, players, cobblers, debauched persons, both men and women out of the city, [and] marched immediately towards the earl'. The Welsh seeing so large and noisy a company fled. Thereafter the Constable of Chester was allowed a charter of patronage and authority 'over the fiddlers and shoe-makers in Chestre'. Responsibility for the former he turned over to his steward, Dutton, but from this act of recognition, derived the beginnings of civic music in the city of Chester.[1]

In 1315 Edward II issued a decree regulating the profession of minstrelsy, drawing attention to the number of those who falsely claimed professional status.

'Foreasmuch as . . . many idle persons, under colour of Mynstrelsie, and going in messages, and other faigned business, have been and yet be receaved in other men's houses to meate and drynke, and be not therewith

dances of the period see B.M. Harl. Ms. 978, and Bodl. Douce Ms. 139, transcriptions of which appeared in Wooldridge, *Early English Harmony*. See also C. van den Borren, *The Sources of Keyboard Music in England*, London, 1913, pp. 8–12.

1 See 'Historical Antiquities', by Sir Peter Leycester, quoted in Ormerod's *History of Cheshire*, London, 2nd edn., 1882, I, p. 36.

contented yf they be not largely consydered with gyftes of the lordes of the houses etc. . . . We wyllyng to restrayne suche outrageous enterprises and idleness, etc. have ordeyned . . . that to the houses of prelates, earles, and barons, none resort to meate and drynke unless he be a Mynstrel, and of these Minstrels that there come none except it be three of four Minstrels of honour at the most in one day, unlesse he be desired of the Lord of the house. And to the houses of meaner men that none come unlesse he be desired, and that such as shall come so, holde themselves contented with meate and drynke, and with such curtesie as the maister of the house wyl shewe unto them of his own good wyll without their askyng of any thyng. And yf any one do agaynst this Ordinaunce, at the firste tyme he to lose *Minstrelsie*, and at the second tyme to forsweare his craft, and never to be receaved for a Minstrel in any house . . .'[1]

The Welsh Tradition

Meanwhile the bardic traditions were not only maintained but, under the shadow of Anglo-Norman attempts at suppression and plantation, renewed by the Cymric spirit that burned brightly in the twelfth century. Giraldus gives a charming sketch of Welsh entertainment from which it will be seen to what extent the traditional instrument was cherished; 'Those who arrive in the morning', he writes, 'are entertained till evening with the conversation of young women, and the music of the harp; for each house has its young women and harps allotted to this purpose . . . and in each family the art of playing on the harp is held preferable to any other learning.'[2] Regarding the manner of playing he adds this: 'Their musical instruments charm and delight the ear with their sweetness, are borne along by such celerity and delicacy of modulation, producing such a consonance from the rapidity of seemingly discordant touches, that I shall briefly repeat what is set forth in our Irish Topography on the subject of the musical instruments of the three nations. It is astonishing that in so complex and rapid a movement of the fingers, the musical proportions can be preserved, and that throughout the difficult modulations on their various instruments, the harmony is completed with such a sweet velocity, as if the chords sounded together fourths or fifths. They always begin from B flat, and return to the same, that the whole may be completed under the sweetness of a pleasing sound. They enter into a movement, and conclude it in so delicate a manner and play the little notes so sportively under the blunter sounds of the bass strings, enlivening with wanton levity, or communicat-

[1] *J. Lelandi . . . Britannicis Collectanea . . . ediditque T. Hearnius,* 1715, VI, p. 26.
[2] *The Itinerary through Wales,* Everyman edn., London, 1908, *Description,* X, p. 169.

ing a deeper internal sensation of pleasure, so that the perfection of their art appears in the concealment of it.'[1] There was clearly much opportunity for the harp—as well as the singing-teacher in Wales.

The organisation of Welsh music owed something to the statutes drawn up about 1065 by Bleddyn ap Cynfyn, Prince of Powys, but more to Gruffydd ap Cynan (1055–1137), Prince of North Wales, whose devotion to the arts showed itself in a positive patronage of music and literature. Gruffydd was said to have been born in Dublin. In later life he was obliged to take refuge in that city, and when he returned it was with Irish musicians, expert in the harp and the bagpipes.[2] Gruffydd attended an Eisteddfod at Caerwys, in or about 1100, and having shown the Welsh minstrels the best Irish practices proceeded to regulate their, too often disorderly, way of life by 'prescribing their Behaviour, Rewards, and Punishments'.[3] In 1107 according to the *Brut y Tywysogion* (*Chronicles of the Princes*) of Caradoc ap Llangarven, an Eisteddfod took place at Cardigan, and in 1135 there was another at Ysdrad Tywi, in Carmarthenshire. The principal champion of the Welsh cause in the last part of the twelfth century was Rhys ap Gruffydd, who fought against Henry II of England for many years before finally acknowledging him as overlord. Rhys, like Gruffydd, recognising the value of a national culture in support of a national independence, established something approaching the manner of a modern Eisteddfod in 1176:

'And the Lord Rhys made a great feast in the castle of Cardigan, where he instituted two species of contests—one between bards and poets, and another between harpists, pipers, and those who played upon the *crwth*. There were also vocal contrasts . . . the bards of north Wales got the prize for poetry, while those belonging to Rhys's own household were adjudged to have excelled in the powers of harmony.'[4] With the final subjugation of Wales by Edward I and the passing of the last of the great Llywelyns, the Eisteddfod went out of sight, until the fifteenth century.

The distinctive character of the earliest Welsh music may only be appreciated by inference, for, for patent reasons, authentic records are practically non-existent. In one particular, however, the very beginnings of music as it directly springs from speech are still evident. The *hwyl*, an

[1] ib. XII.

[2] Giraldus pays tribute to the skill of the Irish on the harp and observes that the priests and sacrists of that country accompanied their hymn-singing with this instrument.

[3] B.M. Add. Ms. 15003 f. 32b (late eighteenth-century copy). *Llyma Drefn ar wyr Gerdd Dafawd*—the ancient orders of Dehaubarth [S. Wales] relating to the minstrels, earlier than the so-called Statute of Griffith ap Cynan; B.M. Add. Ms. 15038, f. 94 (1575), copy of statute (twelfth century) attributed to Gruffydd ap Cynan. See also *A Brief Account of the British or Cambrian Music*; J. R. Roberts (Asaph), Chester, 1909, and *Hanes yr Eisteddfod* (*The Story of the Eisteddfod*), Thomas Parry, Liverpool [n.d.].

[4] Parry, op. cit.

emotive, even fearsome expression of words by means of an extempore chant of no clear definition but often carrying modal characteristics, is still practised in the chapels by old preachers, and imitated by the irreverent young in other places. It is surmised that the *hwyl* may carry back to a method used in the Celtic Church, and probably beyond. If the *hwyl* keeps antiquity alive in one respect so also does the art of *Penillion* singing in another. *Penillion*, though in a debased form, is still the subject of one contest in an Eisteddfod. *Penillion* represents a particular kind of descant. The harpist plays a well-known melody, and, maintaining the same rhythmic and harmonic patterns, extends it into variations, against which the singer delivers a poem—either traditional or composed *ad hoc*—in a separate rhythm to which he adds an original melody. In former days this melody was extemporised; latterly it has been prepared in advance in accordance with decorous formulas which rob the practice of its potential interest. An associated practice (and both may have been among the contests mentioned as taking place in the Eisteddfod of 1176) was the *canu ymryson*, in which two bards would answer each other with improvised stanzas. The earliest extant collection of Welsh harp music is the *Robert ap Huw Manuscript*, of the early seventeenth century, for whose authenticity and antiquity extravagant claims were at one time made.[1] When allowance for such claims has been made there is no doubt that in the retention of pentatonic patterns of melody, not otherwise characteristic of Welsh folk-song, and the equally unusual use of the drone bass, certain material in this collection is representative of early medieval influences from abroad on the native music of Wales.

Synthesis of Ideas

By the end of the thirteenth century a point of climax was reached in European affairs. 'The synthesis which had been gradually built up since the fall of Rome became as complete as it was capable of being.'[2] It was a period in which the supremacy of the Church was enhanced as a result of the statecraft of Pope Innocent III and the enforcement of its claims and powers by his successors. But if the determined lines of dogma were hardened by the upsurge of heresies born of a developing humanism, such as that of the Albigenses of northern Italy, the influence of the Church was made more gracious and grateful by the lyricism of St. Francis of Assisi

[1] B.M. Add. Ms. 14905 (see Chap. 1, p. 7). Some of the contents were from copies made by William Penllyn, an Elizabethan harpist. See A. Dolmetsch, 'Early Welsh Music', *Trans. Hon. Soc. Cymmrodorian, 1933–5*; P. Crossley-Holland, *Secular medieval music in Wales*, 1942, and *Music in Wales*, 1948.

[2] Bertrand Russell, *History of Western Philosophy*, 1946, p. 463.

and the honesty of St. Dominic. From among the discipleship of these two saints grew the Orders of Friars and a renewal of both pastoral and academic virtues. This was the age of the Gothic style, and the great thirteenth-century churches of France and Britain bear witness to freer impulses.

The synthesis, to which Bertrand Russell refers, came in Britain during the reign of Edward I. Firm government succeeded the chaos of the reign of Henry III and the Barons' War led by Simon de Montfort; but with firmness went a clearer dispensation of justice, and in the ordering of the judicial system and the recognition of the place of a Parliament in 1297 Edward brought the country towards more modern concepts of the organisation of society. The English by now were a nation with a national language. The Welsh were in submission and the Scots had been forcefully made aware of their future relationships with the English. In the thirteenth century the English language was virtually established as a literary medium. In architecture the flowing lines of the new style at Westminster, Lincoln, Salisbury, Wells, Exeter, York, and Southwell, and in other cathedrals and monastic churches, both reflected and inspired a new climate of aesthetic thought. Within this climate worked the sculptors, illuminators, painters, and embroiderers, whose expression of naturalistic, humanistic, even realistic, ideas, sprung from a new sense of joy in living. Of this the most notable instance is the explicit tabulation of English life in the margins of the Luttrell Psalter.

For a brief period it may seem that the sacred and secular elements in national life had achieved an unique fusion, in that within the national consciousness there was no marked line of division between the two. In music the fact is demonstrated by the close alliance, despite the teaching of John of Salisbury, between the ecclesiastical musicians and the minstrels. For voices were happily and often joined by instruments; there was juxtaposition of sacred and secular texts within the motet, and expansion of the dramatic, even entertaining, properties inherent within the liturgy. There was an apparent search for musical felicities, as exposed in colour and consonance, for their own sake. As has been seen, the British predilection for less astringent sonorities had for some time been accepted as a characteristic, and it is no accident that the symbol of the music of Britain of that age is *Sumer is icumen in*.

As to whether this work was composed in the mid-thirteenth or early fourteenth century is of no great consequence. If the earlier date, favoured by B. Schofield,[1] is correct, the work, combining the two forms of rota (upper voices) and rondellus (lower voices), is remarkable for its ease,

1 'The Provenance and Date of "Sumer is icumen in",' *Music Review*, 9, 1948, p. 81; see also J. B. Hurry, *Sumer is icumen in*, Novello, 1914.

elegance, and certainty. But if the later date, cogently argued by Bukofzer,[1] is accepted then it is still remarkable, for no other six-part polyphony earlier than the fifteenth century has survived, while *Sumer is icumen in* still remains unique in its combination of the two forms which, more than any others, dominated British music for a long time to come.[2] More than that, by its sheer musical quality it can compel the attention of a present-day audience as can no other piece of such antiquity. No special pleading is required to set *Sumer is icumen in* high on the list of musical pleasures of the twentieth century English schoolboy or schoolgirl. That, perhaps, is not unimportant.

Now the Rota is a complete synthesis. The English text, in Wessex dialect, carries a vernal quality already to have been perceived in the Latin lyrics of Alcuin, and reflects the pastoral scene with a naturalness also to be discovered in *The Owl and the Nightingale*. There is no reason for discounting the thesis of J. B. Hurry that the words sprang from the tradition and conventions of folk song. Beneath the English, however, a Latin text, *Perspice christicola*, in celebration of the Resurrection, is set. The supposition is that the sacred words, in red ink, were an afterthought, and added with a view to performance within the Abbey of Reading. The manuscript shows a further alteration, the significance of which is not really clear. The final state showed a consistent rhythmic pattern of long (1-beat note) followed by breve ($\frac{1}{2}$-beat note), a trochaic pattern suiting the metrical disposition of the poem. But where now appear square notes with stems followed by tail-less lozenge notes there were originally more of the latter, a fact as dismissed of no special consequence by Wooldridge, but discussed at greater length by Bukofzer in support of his dating theory.[3] The accepted version of the common melody after the final form of the manuscript is as follows:,

7a.

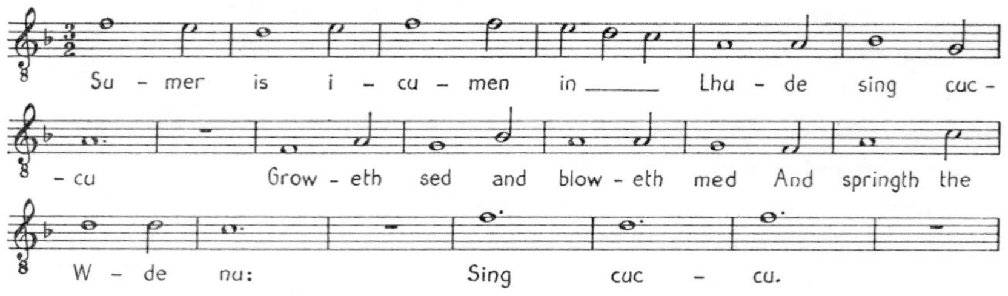
Su - mer is i - cu - men in Lhu - de sing cuc -
- cu Grow - eth sed and blow - eth med And springth the
W - de nu: Sing cuc - cu.

[1] 'Sumer is icumen in: A Revision', *University of California Publications in Music*, ii, 2, 1944.

[2] F. Ll. Harrison, *P.R.M.A.*, 86, 1959–60, pp. 98 *et seq.* 'Rota and Rondellus in English Medieval Music.'

[3] For further discussion of this, see Eric Blom's review of Bukofzer in *M. & L.*, 26, no. 2, 1945, pp. 113–16.

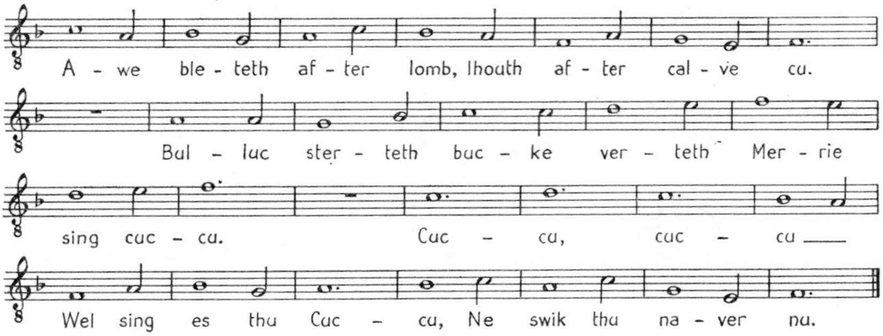
A - we ble - teth af - ter lomb, lhouth af - ter cal - ve cu.
Bul - luc ster - teth buc - ke ver - teth Mer - rie
sing cuc - cu. Cuc - cu, cuc - cu
Wel sing es thu Cuc - cu, Ne swik thu na - ver nu.

Beneath this the two-part pes[1] (which term appears to describe the tenor in the Worcester motets), thus forming the rondellus:

7b.

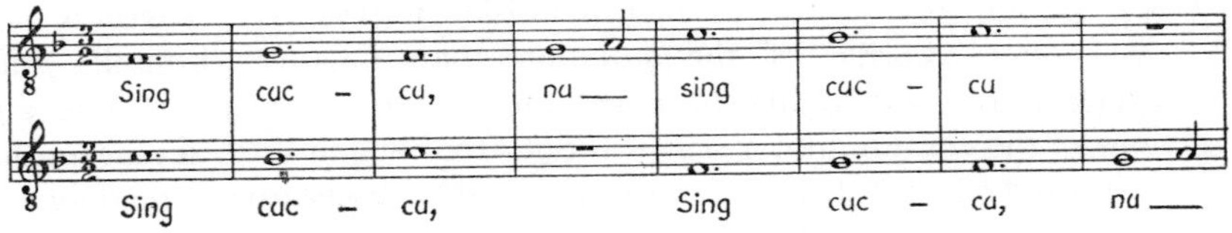
Sing cuc - cu, nu sing cuc - cu
Sing cuc - cu, Sing cuc - cu, nu

Thus two forms exclusive to ecclesiastical usage in the thirteenth century are conjoined to produce an end-product which can neither be called sacred nor profane; for the spirit of the age presided over a harmonious union of the two.

1 '. . . the lower part of the *pes* is the first five notes of *Regina Caeli*, the special May-antiphon of the Easter season . . .' F. Ll. Harrison, op. cit., p. 144.

3

Church and State

Social Advancement of Music

WHAT IS called the age of Chaucer appears as a somewhat paradoxical period in British music. It was—and there is no better recorder of the situation than Chaucer himself—one in which music was highly esteemed and widely practised among all sections of the community. Yet it was one from which little actual music survives (and of what there is, most is seemingly conservative in tendency), but at the end of which a School developed which was to play an important part in the musical tradition of Europe.

During this age, especially in respect of literature, a new national impulse became apparent: the language was modified and uplifted by Chaucer, while the subjects of literary observation increasingly became topical and personal. Chaucer, the experienced traveller, and the student of Dante, Boccaccio, and Petrarch, and of the French *Roman de la Rose* and the style of Guillaume de Machault, was able to integrate the technique and outlook of the leading Europeans with what he absorbed from the native folk tradition and from various English dialects[1] to develop an original style adaptable to a personal aim: to show the world as it appeared from his own standpoint—that of a courtier and civil servant of bourgeois origins with social ambitions. Chaucer was no theoretician, but effectively pragmatic, and it is this pragmatism as much as anything else which denotes a characteristic that sooner or later became recognised as national.

The *ars antiqua*, the tradition of Léonin and Pérotin that centred on organum and conductus and developed the clausula and motet, passed away in France under the impact of technical advance, as shown by the

[1] Cf. the shaping of fictional verse in such minstrel dialogues as the South Northumbrian *The Clerk and the Girl* (*temp.* Edward I); M. H. Dodds, op. cit., p. 5.

new rhythmic possibilities defined by the theorists Walter de Odington and Philippe de Vitry, by secular liaisons, and by the extension of instrumental practices. In its place came the *ars nova*—the term being adopted from a treatise of de Vitry written about the end of the first quarter of the fourteenth century—of which the principal exponent was de Machault, composer as well as poet. The *ars nova* embraced greater rhythmic variety, a new independence in the entry of voices in a contrapuntal texture, a more secure harmonic foundation, and a high degree of internal organisation culminating in the sometimes tortuous ingenuities of the isorhythmic motet. Secular polyphony, of a lighter kind, was advanced by the *ballade*, the *virelai*, and the *rondeau*, of which the musical pattern was based on the motet and for the popularisation of which de Machault was responsible. In Italy the *ars nova* led to more imaginative treatment of counterpoint than heretofore, and a wider range of instrumentation. The *ballade*, the *caccia*, and the *madrigale*, took music from the ecclesiastical environment to that of the private and aristocratic *accademia*. In this climate there thrived the art of Francesco Landini, the blind composer of Florence immortalised by Dante. For practical purposes the cultural revolution symbolised by the *ars nova* had little immediate effect in Britain—although Chaucer himself would appear to have been not aware of its implications—and official music for the first, but not last, time went into a phase of relative isolation.

There were substantial reasons for this. There were the Hundred Years War which began in 1337 and the Black Death of 1348–9—with further outbreaks in 1361 and 1369. There were momentous changes in agriculture, where alterations in the balance of the labour market gave some advantage to labourers seeking a greater degree of freedom from the claims of the landowners, and in the economic structure of the towns, where capitalism was providing a basis for the prosperous cloth industry and also for the collective attitudes of the Guilds. If there was conflict in social and labour relationships there was also a collateral religious conflict. The bishops, half of whom held high offices of state, delegated their diocesan responsibilities. The monasteries (containing about 5,000 monks) lived comfortably and at times away from reality. The peripatetic friars, now diminished in quality since the missionary days of the thirteenth century, warred with the established clergy, and the seculars feuded with the regulars. Both economic and religious discontent stirred the crusading John Wycliffe and the insurrectionary John Balle and Wat Tyler. Against this background, with diversionary disturbances in Scotland, Wales, and Ireland to be taken into account, were the reigns of Edward III (1327–77) and Richard II (1377–99).

During the fourteenth century, despite setbacks, the general standard of living rose. Castles were remodelled in less truculent form, and the art of living began to rank notably higher than the art of dying—this being the English, utilitarian interpretation of humanistic philosophy. There was more in the way of fun and games, and popular drama began efficiently to be organised in the streets of the larger cities. The starting-point for this was the Feast of Corpus Christi, instituted by Urban IV in 1264, and its culmination was the great sequence of communally produced sacred 'Pageants' and 'Dramatic Mysteries'. There was also a continual activity in public architecture and the emergence of a new, peculiarly English, variant on Gothic style in the characteristic and domesticated Perpendicular. Musical expansion was controlled by politics and economics. The English Court lacked the genial convictions deriving from the proposition that music was good in itself that prevailed in France, in the northern cities of Italy, and later in Burgundy, and for the most part gave only such support as was expedient. The Church maintained its official attitude, although deviations from the proper conventions were neither unknown nor unprofitable. The monks of St. Swithin in Winchester, and of the Abbeys of Abingdon and Bury St. Edmunds, for instance, enjoyed the secular music of the professional minstrelsy without inhibition.[1] The general run of citizens pursued musical entertainment with zest and practised with such skill as they possessed. There were, however, two kinds of music, and the gulf between the two—between the academic and ecclesiastical and the popular—was tending to widen. It is, perhaps, symptomatic that while Chaucer virtually ignored the former, scholastic writers, true to form, either by-passed or condemned the latter.

It was, of course, a principal purpose of official music that it should help to maintain prestige. To this end the creation of a royal chapel at Westminster had begun, under Edward I, in 1292, In 1347 this Chapel of St. Stephen, intended to rival the Sainte Chapelle of the French Court, was completed. Two years later Edward III instituted the Order of the Garter and to maintain its proper standing as the home of this department of chivalry St. George's Chapel, in Windsor Castle, was reconstituted, on the lines of the establishment at Westminster. The Chapel Royal, headed by a dean, now kept twelve secular canons, thirteen vicars, four clerks, six choirboys, two servitors, a verger, and a keeper, for whose maintenance endowments from land and property were assigned by the King. At Windsor, where one of the clerks was required to instruct the choristers in singing and grammar, a similar strength was maintained. In addition to these foundations the royal Household Chapel was kept in being for the purpose of providing the King's private devotions either at

[1] Richard of Eden, a monk of Jarrow, was reported as frequently attending the Prior of Durham's *Ludi* together with minstrels from Jarrow; M. H. Dodds, op. cit., p. 5.

home or abroad. It was this institution which—when opportunities to travel and to establish contact with foreign schools became more frequent in the fifteenth century—was to provide a centre for an effective and cohesive school of composers.

Of secular musicians Edward III kept '5 trompetters, 1 cyteler, 5 pypers, 1 tabrete, 1 nakerer, 2 clarions, 1 fedeler, and 3 wayghtes' in his retinue, while at Winchester where there was also a royal palace six minstrels and four harpers were jointly supported by the King and the Bishop.

On two particular occasions the citizens of London had opportunity to hear large companies of the best minstrels in the streets of the city. Stow in his *Survey of London* (1618) describes how, in 1377, there was a display in honour of Richard, son of the Black Prince, in which were 130 masked citizens on horseback, with trumpet, sackbut, cornet, and shawm players, and other instrumentalists, who paraded from Newgate to Kennington, there to present their homage. Fourteen years later Richard II, out of favour with the Corporation, sought to effect a public reconciliation with the City of London, and the musicians, according to Richard of Maidstone, were out in force:

> Fistula, cistula, tibia, timpana, cum monacordo,
> Organa, psalteria, cimbala, cumque lyra,
> Zambucu, citharae, situlaeque, tubaeque, viellae,
> Buccine cum nablis, simphonicisque choris.

One suspects some poetic licence in favour of scansion and assonance; but the catalogue serves to show what a full orchestra of that time could be, at least in theory.

In Scotland the continuing cult of minstrelsy is described in the fourteenth-century poem *Orfeo and Heurodis*—

> In the castel the steward sat atte mete
> And the man's lording was be him sate,
> Ther wer *trompours* and *tabourers*,
> *Harpours* fele and *crouders*,
> Miche melody thei maked alle, . . .

and in the *Buke of the Howlate* it is also recorded how

> At the myddis of the meit
> in come the menstralis.

Among the earliest Scottish ballads handed down through the minstrels were one, of which the words are preserved in Wyntoun's *Orygynale Cronykile of Scotland*, on the death of Alexander III, and another on the Battle of Bannockburn, said by Fabyan to have been sung by the 'maidens and mynstrelles of Scotland'. The minstrels of Robert II of Scotland, sometime regent for David II and his successor on his death, visited Spain and it is hazarded that they may have brought back to Scotland the dances detailed in the fifteenth-century *Cochalbie's Sow* as the *Portingall*, the *Naverne*, and the *Arragone*.[1]

In one way or another and at various levels the minstrels occupied a position of increasing importance, not least because they had connections with the two contrasted streams of social thought and musical practice. Their numbers multiplied. The Account Rolls of Durham Priory[2] show harpers in the households of the Horncliff, Neville, Scrope, and Dalton families, and minstrels employed by the Parrys, the Hiltons, and the Bishop of Durham himself through the fourteenth century. At this time too the towns (where the office of watchman was combined with that of wait) began to support the profession. In Leicester, for example (where civic minstrels or waits were maintained from 1338 to 1826), the Mayoral Accounts record payments to the municipal musicians and also to the royal minstrels, as well as those hired from the Earls of Leicester and Warwick, and the Duke of Lancaster, 'for the honour of the town'.[3]

Because they enjoyed a relative immunity from criticism in good times, when affairs were out of joint the minstrels were likely to come under suspicion. In 1402 edicts against harbouring them were issued both in Ireland and in Wales. In Ireland the Parliament of Lionel, Duke of Clarence, deemed it an offence to protect 'Irish minstrels, rhymers, and news tellers'.[4] In Wales it was decreed as follows: 'That no westours and rimers, minstrels or vagabonds, be maintained in Wales, to make kymosthas or qullages on the common people, who by their divinations, lies, and exhortations are partly cause of the insurrection and rebellion now in Wales'.[5] On the whole, however, the minstrels were treated as honourable professionals, popular as dispensers of both fact and fiction and entertainers. To a large extent their favour depended on the taste of their patron. John of Gaunt was a particular benefactor of the profession. He was also a promoter of popular entertainment.

In 1381 John of Gaunt set up a Court of Minstrels at Tutbury in Staffordshire, which, presided over by an elected King, was allowed to

[1] H. G. Farmer, op. cit., p. 43.
[2] M. H. Dodds, op. cit., p. 2.
[3] See *Records of the Borough of Leicester*, 1327–1688, 4 vols., London, 1889–1923: II, pp. 45–6, 148, 154, 170.
[4] Farmer, op. cit., p. 43.
[5] *Rolls of Parliament*, III, p. 508.

exercise authority over all of the craft in five of the midland counties.[1] Five years later John of Gaunt brought back from Spain a troupe of Moorish dancers, and the combination of their practices with those proper to the traditional English Fool's Dance is said to have provided the basis for the Morris Dance. It was in honour of John of Gaunt, therefore, that the Robin Hood and Morris Dancers continued to wear his emblem—of three ostrich feathers—and that the Red Lion on his shield after his marriage with Constance of Castile provided the name of inns—for example at Padstow and Kingston-on-Thames—which were for centuries the starting-point for ceremonial May Day dances. The enthusiasm of the fourteenth-century English for dancing is adequately shown by Chaucer, various types being noted in the 'Miller's Tale' (I. 142 ff.) and in the 'House of Fame' (I. 1235). The dances here described—'love-daunces, springes, reyes'—were of the type generically known as hays (heys).

If the *ars nova* made no immediate and direct impact on British musical thought it may at least be accepted that an indirect influence came by way of Chaucer, who catalogues such varied and specialised types of song as 'balades', 'complaints,' 'ditees', 'rondels', 'roundelets', and 'virelayes'—with *ars nova* implications—as well as referring frequently to the generic term 'song'. He also refers to the particular song-dance, the carol, in *The Romaunt of the Rose* on no fewer than four occasions. The development of the carol as a popular musical form in the fourteenth century owed much to the Franciscans, according to the *Red Book of Ossory* attributed to Richard de Ledrede, Bishop of Ossory between 1317 and 1360.[2]

The relative freedom of metre, the flow of humanistic imagination, the ear for nuance and syllabic timbre, which distinguish Chaucer, and which were partly derived from Franco-Italian models, are in themselves a parergon of musical experience. This was not the last time that English poetry was to reflect an alteration in the pattern of continental musical thought. Chaucer esteemed music, but less for its official than its private virtues. The extent to which he comes down on the side of popular music—and his references to church music are ever on the edge of that faculty—is symptomatic of the manner in which music was generally cultivated and of a conspicuous contempt for the pietistic admonitions that from time to time issued from the cloister. The corroboration of Chaucer's overall picture lies in the sculptured musicians of the Minstrel's Gallery and of the roof bosses of the Choir of Exeter Cathedral (one of which perpetuates St. Dunstan as musician), the angel harpers of Lincoln,

[1] See Burney, *History*, II, pp. 360 ff; also B.M. Add. Charters 42681 A, B. '. . . for the better ordering of the Tutbury Minstrels', and J. C. Cox, on the 'Tutbury horn', in *Journal of the Derbyshire Archaeological Society*, January 1886, Vol. VIII, pp. 7–14; cf. B.M. Lans. Ms. 896, ff. 153–7, *Orders of the Minstrels of Beverley*.

[2] See *New O.H.M.*, III, p. 118.

Carlisle, Worcester, and Chester, and the rather freer wooden carvings at Newport, in Essex, and at St. Luke's Church, Duston, in Northamptonshire. Of these the most exhilarating are the latter, especially the drummer who transfers easily into twentieth-century type, and the female bag-piper, a scandal—no doubt—to the neighbours and even more to the clergy.

Chaucer's literary use of musical imagery is revealing for its psychological implications. Instrument, type of voice, mode of performance, are all indicated as an extension of personality. In this Chaucer differs from the professional chroniclers. The Squire maintained the gallant troubadour tradition, being both adept at composition and performance; the Friar was accomplished as rote- and/or harp-player and singer; the Pardoner and the Summoner were expert in descant; the Prioress had a repertoire of sacred music which she delivered with a 'nasal tone' that may not have been then uncommon, but which displeased Chaucer. The 'Miller's Tale' abounds in instrumental references, Nicholas, Absalom, and the Carpenter's wife all being singers of one sort or another. In the 'Cook's Tale' the Apprentice, standing for all apprentices, was attached to his ribible and gittern. Direct allusions to titles are rare. But Nicholas, of the 'Miller's Tale', sings the *Angelus ad Virginem*, which exists in a thirteenth-century manuscript[1] and in three-part descant arrangement—the melody being in the middle voice—in a fourteenth-century setting.[2] The way in which children were taught in the monastic and cathedral schools is indicated in the 'Prioress's Tale', by the lengthy allusion to the *Alma redemptoris*. Citations from secular song appear in the Pardoner's 'Come hider, love, to me', in the 'Knight's Tale'—'May, with alle thy flours and thy grene', and elsewhere.

Chaucer not only particularises, but generalises. He, like Shakespeare, uses music, through verbal allusions, to heighten atmosphere. On the one hand, for instance, there are the

> Pypes, trompes, nakers, clariouns,
> That in the bataille blowen blody sounes

where, no doubt, he recalls his own military service which led to him being taken prisoner in France in 1359. On the other hand there is a long passage in the *Romaunt of the Rose* (lines 743–92) which is a complete illustration of a fourteenth-century *fête champêtre*, with singing, carolling (in the sense of singing and dancing), and dancing, to the accompaniment of minstrels and jongleurs. A side-glance at the music of France admits a lower standard of accomplishment in England:

[1] See *Early English Harmony*, pl. 34. Here are Latin words and an English text beginning 'Gabriel from evene king.'

[2] Trans. in E. Walker, *History of Music in England*, 2nd ed., 1924, p. 12.

Somme songe songes of Loreyne,
For in Loreyne hir notes be
Ful swetter than in this contree.

If, however, a condemnation of the follies of youth and the corrupting effects of music were required Chaucer could manage a homily with the best. Neither Aelred of Rievaulx nor John of Salisbury could outdo Chaucer's Pardoner whose heated outburst at the beginning of his Tale is uproarious comedy, and at the same time indicative of the wider scope of medieval music:

In Flaundres whylom was a companye
Of yonge folk, that haunteden folye,
As ryot, hasard, stewes, and tavernes,
Wher-as, with harpes, lutes and gitemes,
They daunce and pleye at dees bothe day and night,
And ete also and drinken over hir might . . .
And ech of hem at otheres sinne lough,
And right anon than comen tombesteres,
Fetys and smale, and yonge fruytesteres,
Singers with harpes, bandes, wafereres,
Which been the veray develes officeres
To kindle and blowe the fyr of lecherye . . .

The text here nearly enough parodies the didactic verse of an anonymous poet (monk?) of the same period, who put these words into the mouth of his allegorical Idleness:

I teche hem daunce,
And also, ffor ther lady sake,
Endyte lettyers, and songys make
Up-on the glade somerys dayes,
Balladys, Roundeleys, Vyrelayes,
I teche hem ek, (lyk ther ententys)
To playe on sondry Instrumentys.
On harpe, lut, and on gyterne,
And to revell at taverne,
Wych al merthe and mellodye,
On rebuke and on symphonye[1]

A further comment by an anonymous churchman at the end of the century dismisses the 'Roundelles, Balladas, Carollas, and Springas' of which Chaucer wrote, as 'fantastic and frivolous', and observes that 'no good

[1] Quoted in H. S. Bennett, *England from Chaucer to Caxton*, 1928, p. 91.

musical writer has ever thought it worth-while to explain their texture'.[1] Thus opposed by an ultra-conservative opinion that was frequently backed by the power of sanctions—indirect, at least—it is hardly surprising that the bulk of secular music of the age disappeared. What has survived is due to those clerks whose spirits were bold, or whose inclinations were towards compromise.

The Organ

In 1397 Bartholomaeus de Glanville proclaimed: 'And nowe holy Chyrche useth only this instrument of musyk [the organ], in proses, sequences, and ympnes: and forsakyth for man's use of minstralsye and other instruments of musyk.'[2]

The prevalence of organ music—illustrated in caricature in a miserere carving of *c.*1390 at Boston, where organist and blower are shown as bears—is also reflected in Chaucer,[3] and, in the larger churches, the office of organist is either directly or indirectly acknowledged. The use of organs at Westminster Abbey was first recorded in 1242. In 1304 an inventory showed one pair on the step of the Lady Chapel, and another, greater pair, on the wall. At Lincoln, Thomas de Ledenham, a vicar, received 20s. for taking care of, blowing, and cleaning the organs—for which, no doubt, he employed a deputy—in 1311. Eleven years later the function of blower at Lincoln was specialised; for his services on the occasion of the commemoration of Grosseteste the then officer received 6s. 8d. In the same year of 1322 the organist of the monastery of Glastonbury was named as 'William le Organistre'. At Norwich, 'Adam the Organist', for whom 13s. 4d. was invested in a suitable robe, was noted in 1333. The great Welsh poet Dafydd ap Gwilym, from Cardiganshire, commended Hywel, Dean of Bangor, from 1359–70, for the music of his cathedral, saying that the 'organ, and harmonious choir, are unrivalled in performance.' Organs were mentioned in the Fabric Rolls of the Minster at Ripon in 1399 and at the beginning of the fifteenth century Canterbury (1420), Wells (1428), Worcester (1415), Manchester (the Collegiate Church, 1421), Ely (1453), and Salisbury (1463) were all served by organists. The organist of Salisbury in 1463 was John Kegewyn, whose contract

[1] *De origine et Effectu Musicae*; see Hawkins, *History*, II, p. 218.
[2] *De proprietatibus rerum*, see Hawkins, ib., II, p. 281–2.
[3] 'His vois was merrier than the mery orgon,
On messe days that in the Chirche gon.'
'Nun's Priest's Tale,' l. 30–31.
'And whyl the organs maden melodye,
To god alone in herte thus sang she.'
'Second Nun's Tale' (of St. Cecilia), l. 134–5.

is still extant. He was required to instruct fourteen choristers 'in chant', to 'keep the Mass of the Blessed Mary with organs to the same, and other Antiphons at all seasons,' to remain 'loosed from a wife', and 'of good reputation, unblemished character and honest conversation'. Kegewyn found the conditions restrictive and at some unknown point in his career disappeared from the records. The instruments recorded in these various documents were positive organs, one of which is illustrated in the fourteenth-century *Peterborough Psalter*; handier portative organs were used for processional and out-of-doors use.

In 1428 the carriage of such an instrument, in the King's possession, was noted in respect of a payment: 'Et à Robert Atkysone pur carier les organes portatifs pur diverses foitz à Pre de Wyndessre jusques Eltham [where there was a royal palace]; et de Eltham jusques Hertford, vj s viii d.'[1]

At this time the names of organ-builders begin to appear with some frequency. In 1422–3 a pair of organs at Westminster Abbey was mended by Brother Thomas Gedney for 14s. On 29 June 1430 a Pardon was granted to Thomas Seyntjohn, of London, 'Orgon-maker'.[2] On 18 April 1436 letters of Denization were issued in respect of William Barbour, 'organ maker of Brussels, dwelling at Westminster', and for Lawrence 'organ maker of Nymmagen, dwelling at London'.[3] In 1442 a new pair of organs at Lincoln was made, at a cost of five marks, by 'Arnold Organer', who was perhaps identifiable with Arnold Mynhamber, an organ builder and Freeman of Norwich in 1446. Seven years later 'Will the Organ maker', possibly the same one noted at Westminster in 1465, attended to the instruments at Ripon.

Fourteenth-century Styles and Remains

The musical remains of the fourteenth century, few in number, give a picture of British musical life that is both inadequate and, necessarily, one-sided. At the same time they afford evidence of traits that were both in continuance of established method and predilection, and anticipatory of distinctive features which were to command wider attention in the next century. The major collection of polyphony from the beginning of the century (or the end of the thirteenth century) was that compiled for, or by, the community of the Augustinian Priory of Canons Regular of St. Andrew's in Fife, Scotland. This house founded by Robert, Bishop of

[1] Rymer, x, p. 387.

[2] *Cal. of Patent Rolls*, 1429–36, Henry VI, II, p. 20. On 8 July 1427 a similar Pardon had been given to John Ferlegh (Farley), 'late of London—organ-player'.

[3] *Cal. of Patent Rolls*, 1429–36, Henry VI, II, p. 549.

St. Andrew's, in 1144, was possessed of great wealth, and principal among the religious houses of Scotland: 'and the Prior, with the ring and mitre and symbols of Episcopacy, had rank and place in Parliament above abbots and all other prelates of the regular clergy.' The Song Schule[1] was of comparable dignity and the St. Andrew's Ms.[2] contained compositions in conductus form by Pérotin and Léonin as well as native contributions. There had been a strong French influence at St. Andrew's since the installation of French clergy in Scotland by David I. Among the compositions of local provenance, but written in the French style, are two responds for the Feast of St. Andrew, *Vir perfecte* and *Vir iste*, and various sections for the Lady Mass. These settings, in two parts, are the first examples of music for the Mass which appear to take account of the Mass as a whole. To this extent the musicians of St. Andrew's were ahead of their time.

It was characteristic of late medieval church music, now firmly centred on polyphonic principles and the constant subject of pedantic and quasi-philosophical scrutiny by scholars, that it existed for its own sake—subject to the convention that it was dedicated *ad majorem Dei gloriam*. It was highly professionalised, and to be understood by those who participated in its performance rather than by any audience. The argument that God appreciated the great anonymous works of art of the Middle Ages is by no means unattractive and insofar as music was concerned the opportunity for experiment within, and for the benefit of, a closed community encouraged stylistic perfection. In the early part of the fourteenth century two motets were composed at Bury St. Edmunds which illustrate the point. These, in honour of the patron saint, Edmund (the ninth-century King of Essex), were *Deus tuorum militum*, and *Ave miles*, the first for three, the second for four voices.[3]

Both pieces are based on the plainsong antiphon *Ave rex gentis Anglorum*. In the former, with different, but relevant, texts in each part, the beginning of the plainsong is set in the tenor, where it is treated in isorhythmic manner, thus reflecting current French practice and anticipating later formal developments. In the latter the English rondellus technique is evident, and the way in which melodic formulae pass from voice to voice within a fluent general pattern is a tribute to a quality of inventiveness that must presume a considerable amount of previous practice. Rhythmically *Ave miles* relies rather more than its companion on the strict patterns inherent in the medieval rhythmic-mode system that, under the influence

[1] Notable even so late as 1560, when Alexander Smyth, teacher of James Melville, was described as 'doctour of the Song Scole in the Abbay'.

[2] Acquired by Flacius Illyricus in 1553 and by the Duke of Brunswick in 1597. The Ms. is now in the Herzog August Bibliothek at Wolfenbüttel (Ms. 677).

[3] Bodl. Ms. e. Mus. 7.

of the *ars nova*, was breaking down. Harmonically it is notable for its richness, its suaveness, and its exploitation of the first inversion of the triad and the deployment of this effect in series. [Ex. 1, 2] Further examples of

1.

2.

this style and from this period occur in the sequences, antiphons, introits, and *Glorias* contained in a manuscript once in use at and now in the museum of Fountains Abbey.[1]

Works of this kind 'effectively counterbalance the aim of Gothic

[1] See H. K. Andrews and Thurston Dart, 'Fourteenth Century Polyphony in a Fountains Abbey Ms. Book', *M. & L.*, 39, pt. 1, 1958, pp. 1 *et seq.* and Denis Stevens, 'The Second Fountains Fragment: A Postscript', *M. & L.*, 39, no. 2, pp. 148 *et seq.*

music to differentiate and stratify the voices by means of register, colour, and especially rhythm, which prevailed in France more strongly than in England. English composers, with their sensibility to blending intervals and the spell of sheer sonority, followed only part of the way and preferred to adhere to what may be called chordal or 'harmonic' effects, although they did not entirely shut themselves off from the rhythmic innovations of the Petronian style.'[1] English composers were by now writing in score. Hitherto part-music, still within the range of vocal improvisation, had depended on the addition of one independent melody to another, subject only to concordance at terminal points. To compose in score was an acknowledgment of a relative parity between counterpoint and harmony.

In the later part of the fourteenth century the isorhythmic style practised in France by de Machault became more common in England, but the euphonious manner of descant, described by Richard Cotell (Cutell),[2] minor canon and 'cardinal' of St. Paul's Cathedral at the end of the century, was persistent. An example of this, in three parts, is the setting of the hymn *O lux beata Trinitas* in which the plainsong is given in the highest voice[3] [Ex. 3]. Plainsong melodies, by now consistently included within

3.

the texture of polyphony either as guiding motivs or points of departure for thematic interchange as in rondellus, were by now treated by English composers with a considerable freedom.

Of the music of the period which exists with vernacular texts similar tendencies are evident. In *Mirie it is while sumer ilast*[4] the trouvère tradition

[1] M. F. Bukofzer, *Studies in Medieval and Renaissance Music*, 1950, p. 20 (in 'Two Fourteenth-century Motets on St. Edmund'); . . . 'the so-called Petronian or "Fauvel" notation current in England about and after 1300, demonstrates the breakdown of a strict modal pattern in the upper voices and the turn to a more subtle and diversified rhythm which developed at the same pace as did the division of the breve into smaller units'. ib.

[2] In *Opinio Ricardi Cutell de London*, Bodl. Ms. 842; see Burney, *History II*, p. 434.

[3] B.M. Sloane Ms. 1210; see Harrison, op. cit., pp. 150–51.

[4] *Early Bodleian Music*, facsimile, pl. 3.

lingers. (This piece is, indeed, included with a set of trouvère songs.) In *Edi beo thu hevene quene* and *Worldes blisse have god day*[1] two-part descant with a frequency of thirds belongs to the manner which later was designated as *gymel*, an English peculiarity.[2] In the second of these items the English words are set over a tenor 'Dominus', a practice followed in the fragmentary motets of the Garrett Ms. 119 of Princeton University.[3]

Music at all times is a sequence of relationships, both internal and external. Of the latter the most important are with literature, and the dissolution of the rhythmic modes of the *ars antiqua* (in themselves a relic of a prosodic connection) helped music towards a form of expressionism which, in the next century and under pressure from drama, would go some way towards welding words and melody into a unity. In the fourteenth and most of the fifteenth century, however, words—confused in polylingual settings and by such devices as isorhythm and hocket—and music stood apart from each other except in ballads and other popular music. If music was subject to a good deal of intellectual formalism (which, however, contributed to a fuller development of techniques, and, in any case, was modified by English emotional responses) it was the internal relationships of techniques that were to be held responsible.

Scholars

In the universities music held a place of honour as a science, and together with Arithmetic, Geometry, and Astronomy formed the *Quadrivium*, the concomitant course with the *Trivium* (Grammar, Rhetoric, and Logic) for the qualification of *Magister Artium*. The musical theorists, and some of the composers—among whom the most notable example was John Dunstable, graduated through this discipline. In the fourteenth century those treatises which mark the academic limits of the music of the age were compiled by, or ascribed to, Simon Tunstede,[4] a Norfolk man who had become Master of the Minorites at Oxford, and was specified as expert in the seven liberal arts; Theinred[5] a Benedictine and precentor at

[1] See M. F. Bukofzer, 'The First Motet with English Words', *M. & L.*, 17, 1936, pp. 232–3.

[2] *Gymel*, or *gemellus*, was applied in later fifteenth-century English Mss., but not earlier, to a division of a part such as would now be annotated *divisi*. *Gymel* as a system of consecutive thirds or sixths maintained until resolution on the unison or octave from which the piece had started was described, as *modus Anglicorum*, by the Italian writer Gulielmus Monachus, *c.* 1475.

[3] For two other items of secular polyphony, see F. McD. Turner, 'Two Medieval Love-Songs set to music', *Antiquarian Journal*, XV, 1935.

[4] Possible author of *Quatuor Principalia Musicae*, 1351.

[5] *De Legitimis Ordinibus Pentachordorum et Tetrachordon*, 1371.

the Priory at Dover; John Wylde,[1] precentor at Waltham Abbey, in Essex; John Torkesey of the same house;[2] and Richard Cotell previously mentioned.

Starting with Boethius—the foundation author for medieval music students—and proceeding by way of mathematical and astronomical calculations and suppositions to a rehearsal of notational method, these writers eventually arrive at the contrapuntal practices of the generations before their own (this always being the case with musical theoreticians). Thus their contribution to knowledge of practical music is limited. At the same time they are all agreed on the general acceptance of imperfect concords in English polyphony, while in the *Quatuor Principalia* a prohibition, to become more familiar with the passage of time, forbade consecutive perfect intervals.

A School of Composers

If the age of Chaucer suggests primarily a coming to maturity of English literature, that which is spanned by the life of John Dunstable—who died in 1453—shows the first real effulgence of English music. The two phenomena were, of course, related, being parts of an enhanced awareness of nationhood. It was, indeed, the only time in history when English music was conceded primacy, when works by Englishmen were sought after by continental connoisseurs. Therein lies an enigma. For of the antecedents and the overseas activities of the majority of English composers of the first part of the fifteenth century virtually nothing is known; while they were barely known and recognised at home. What we are faced with during the reigns of Henry IV and V is a significant brain drain. At the same time there was a sufficiency of composers active in England to continue the traditions strengthened in the fourteenth century and now placed under a stronger patronage. The last Plantagenets to rule England were either especially aware of the public value of music, or convinced of its devotional efficacy, and sometimes, in private, expert in its practice. Henry IV, Henry V, and Henry VI, have all, at some time or other, been considered as candidates for identification with 'Roy Henry' of the Old Hall Ms.[3] The only safe conclusion is that, for stylistic reasons, Henry VI

[1] *Hunc librum vocitatum Musicam Guidonis*, belonging to the Waltham Holy Cross Ms., and the property of Thomas Tallis after the Dissolution of the Abbey, was consulted by Thomas Morley (see list of Authors quoted at the end of *A Plaine and Easie Introduction to Practicall Musicke*); B.M. Lans. Ms. 763.

[2] *Declaratio Trianguli*, also in the Waltham Holy Cross Ms.

[3] Barclay Squire considered Henry VI to be the composer thus denoted (see Harrison, op. cit., p. 220 f.n. 1); Bukofzer concluded that it was Henry V (see *Studies in Medieval and Renaissance Music*, pp. 78–80); Harrison prefers Henry IV (op. cit., p. 220). The Old Hall Ms. takes its name from the fact that in 1893 it was deposited in the collection of St. Edmund's College, Old Hall, Ware, Hertfordshire.

can no longer be considered as a possible contender, and must depend on his educational foundations, with their important music faculties, for the gratitude of the musical. All three monarchs, however, gave increased recognition to music and musicians with the result that the public place of the art was enhanced. Composers began to appear from behind the curtain of medieval anonymity, and in one instance at least something to be recognised as a personal style was seen.

It is not to be doubted that incentive and security had significance in the fifteenth century, and since both were somewhat expanded there was also an increase in production. The most favoured musicians were those who, as officers of the royal foundations, had the status of civil servants. In 1405 a 'Grant to John Tilbery, one of the boys in the king's chapel, of the Wardenship of the hospital of Ilford, in the diocese of London,' was recorded, while nine years later various clerks were thus pensioned: 'John Hunt given grant of land in Oxford, and four other clerks—John Prentys, Stephen Paynter, John Cook, Thomas Gyles, presented to ecclesiastical benefices.' Of these Cook, who joined the Chapel Royal at the time of the accession of Henry V in 1413, was a composer, as also were John Burell, Thomas Damett, and Nicholas Sturgeon, who became clerks at the same time as Cook. All are represented in the Old Hall Ms. During the nine exhilarating years of the reign of Henry V the music of the Chapel Royal[1] became famous, being thus lauded in a contemporary poem:

> Psallit plena Deo cantoribus ampla capella,
> Carmine sidereo laudabilis est ea cella.[2]

Henry V was not unmindful of the debt he owed to his clerks and they were remembered in his will. But the disbursement of his bequest was tardy, so that on 12 May 1432 there was noted: 'Grant to the executors of the will of Henry V the sum of £200 in gold for payments, according to his will, of said amount to the clerks of the Chapel of the household before they separate.' A year later the matter was still undecided. Nevertheless the posthumous approbation of the King made at least a pleasant recollection.

The French campaigns of Henry V, culminating in the conquest of Normandy and the Treaty of Troyes of 1420, provided background for many national legends and myths. The fortuitous survival of the *Agincourt Song*[3] ('descant' in two parts with a third voice added for the refrain),

[1] In 1423 the number of boys was reduced from sixteen to six (a usual number for such a choir) and the names of the choristers of that year are the first on record: Thomas Myldevale, John Brampton, John Maydeston, John Grymmesby, Nicholas Kyle, Stephanus Howell. Nicholas, *Proceedings and Ordinances of the Privy Council*, III, p. 104.

[2] *Memorials of Henry V*, 1858, p. 68.

[3] Bodl. Selden Ms. G. 26, also Pepysian Library, Magdalene College, Cambridge, Ms. 2505—which was consulted by Burney.

together with the heroic plays of Shakespeare, contributed a good deal to the euphoric nationalism of the English in later times. Hadow, therefore, could speak of the *Agincourt Song* as 'the climax and cynosure of them all, the superb song of thanksgiving for the victory at Agincourt. It is one of the finest popular tunes in the world, a noble Triumphlied in which the patriotism of a nation speaks out of a full heart. George Brandes once said that Shakespeare's *Henry V* was a national anthem in five acts. The *Agincourt Song* is its compendium and quintessence: a core of white heat that burns in the very soul of our people.'[1] Before dismissing the sentiment as a period curiosity it is to be noted that Henry's intentions relating to the potency of music were not dissimilar from Hadow's. The Chapel Royal was for some time stationed in Normandy and the choir was under the direction of John Pyamour, a clerk who acted as Master but without the title and also a composer represented in the Old Hall Ms. It is probable that Pyamour wrote the special music sung in the cathedral of Rouen after the capture of the city in 1419, and noted by the minstrel John Page in his description of the King's arrival:

Hys chapylle mette him at the doore,
And went by fore him in the floore,
And songe a responde gloryus,
That ys namyd *Quis est magnus ?*[2]

Although this piece has not survived, others that were similarly occasional have: for example, Cook's invocation of protection in time of war—*Alma prolea regins—Christe miles inclite*, and Damett's *Salvatoris mater pia—Sancte Georgi*. Cook's motet is founded on the tenor *Ab inimicis defende nos Christe*, while Damett's texts call on the assistance of the patron saint, 'gloriosa spes Anglorum', and also issue suitable prayers for the protection of the King.

On 14 January 1420 Pyamour was commissioned 'to take boys for the said chapel, and bring them to the King's presence in the Duchy of Normandy'. Recruitment of boys through impressment was no new thing—the names of those given on p. 57, f.n. 1 indicate a wide search for talent—and it continued for many years. The same practice obtained in respect of the minstrels, who also had their place in the expeditionary forces. When he was Earl of Derby Henry IV had his trumpeters, pipers, and a drummer with him in Prussia and the Holy Land, while Henry V took a company of fifteen to France under the control of the long-serving Walter Haliday.

During this phase of the Hundred Years War contact between English

[1] *English Music*, London, 1931, p. 19.
[2] *The Siege of Rouen, N.S. XVIII*: *The Historical Collection of a Citizen of London*, etc., ed. by J. Gairdner, Camden Soc., 1876, p. 45.

and continental musicians was close, as is evinced both by the constitution of the Old Hall Ms. (certain works appearing also in continental Mss.)[1] and by the activities of the group for convenience's sake headed by John Dunstable.

In the principal extant musical manuscripts of the first half of the fifteenth century lies the consummation of English musico-liturgical purpose and method, as well as the intention which would ultimately lead to a separate existence for music as an independent art-form. Liturgical music is described by Harrison as *Gebrauchsmusik*. Denis Stevens observes: 'The most powerful appeal . . . of any ceremony . . . was certainly visual—in church, silken copes, lighted tapers, jewelled crucifixes would fix attention. Next would come the dramatic quality of the scene—a ceremony is always an action, and a procession is not a meaningless walk. The music we may be sure was subordinate to the "sight" and the "plot", but it is not to be looked down upon on that account. On the contrary we must put resolutely aside our own ideas of the romantic self-sufficiency of art. To the medieval way of thinking even music had a function, and its function on these occasions was to adorn the ceremony'.[2] The lesser churches as well as the greater played their part in diffusing a knowledge of and skill in music. Thus in the royal Licence of Henry IV by which the Collegiate Church of Tong, in Shropshire, was instituted there was provision for five priests (including the Warden) and two clerks. The latter were to be responsible for farm-work as well as singing (a combination of musical skill with low-level employment that was to persist in English musical life). The whole of the music was subject to the governance of a properly qualified chaplain, learned in reading, singing, and Latin grammar, who should not only teach music to the two singing-clerks but also to other servants of the house and to poor children of Tong and neighbouring villages.[3]

The fifteenth century, partly on account of the operation of a national consciousness within the context of an international rivalry, partly because of an increase of investment by the wealthy in ecclesiastical art, and partly through the increased popular attraction of places and occasions of pilgrim devotion, saw a general enrichment of the embellishments to church services. The conspicuous features of the music are expansion of texture for larger choral bodies and a more comprehensive application of polyphony. The music of the Old Hall Ms., including antiphons, hymns, sequences, and sections of the Mass, covers all liturgical occasions for the Royal Chapel for which the collection was made. As an anthology this

[1] Bukofzer, op. cit., pp. 38–9.

[2] *Medieval Carols* (*Musica Britannica*, IV), Introduction, p. XIV.

[3] 'Documents relating to Tong College', in *Transactions of the Shropshire Archaeological Society*, 3rd series, VIII, 1908, pp. 169 ff.

collection runs over almost half a century of musical styles. The native practices of descant and conductus are continued and in the earliest part of the collection the relevant plainsong *cantus firmus* is set in the middle of the customary three voice scheme. It was characteristic of English composers, however, to treat *cantus firmus* with freedom, and in the Old Hall Ms. are frequent examples of a 'migrant' *cantus firmus*—the foundation melody being transferred from one voice to another. Of further interest was ornamental treatment of a plainsong motiv in the highest voice, this obviously anticipating later development of the musical form of air and variations, but also possibly relating to similar ornamentation within the field of folk-song. In the second group of the Old Hall Ms are evidences of close contact with continental music in that impulses from the French motet and, particularly the *chanson*, and the Italian *caccia*, with insistence on canonic expression, appear. The *chanson* gave opportunity for lively experimentation with cross-rhythms (now to be explained as 6/8 against 3/4 time) and for textural contrast in the employment of varying numbers of parts. So far as counterpoint was concerned the canonic virtuosity of some composers was considerable, Pycard, for instance, writing a *Gloria* in five parts as a double canon (involving four parts) against one free part. In the later sections of the Old Hall Ms. the isorhythmic motet in the French style was also included. The most noteworthy general feature, however, is the grouping together of the sections of the Ordinary of the Mass (each section based on a plainsong appropriate to the occasion). The earliest surviving example of a polyphonic Ordinary on a single tenor is Leonel Power's *Alma redemptoris mater* Mass of *c.* 1340. (In the fifteenth and sixteenth centuries it was customary in English polyphonic Masses not to set the 'Kyrie', which on Festivals was sung in unison to the melody prescribed in the Ordinal.) The 'cyclic' Mass, typified by Power and Dunstable, was a great step forward, and, says Bukofzer, 'the most influential achievement of the English school of Renaissance music.'[1]

The composers of the Old Hall Ms. included Excestre,[2] 'Roy Henry', Cook, Burell, Damett, Sturgeon, mentioned on p. 57, and Aleyn (Alanus, Canon of Windsor?), Byttering, Robert Chirbury, Jervays, Lambe, Olyver, Pennard, Leonel Power, Pycard, Queldryk, Rowland, Swynford, J. Tyes, W. Typp, while works by Dunstable were copied into the collection at some time after 1430.

Of this group, excepting Dunstable, the most important was Power who was the composer of two extant complete three-part Masses, various separate movements for the Mass, and seventeen motets.

[1] op. cit., p. 223.

[2] In 1394 a company of six clerks of the Chapel Royal went to Ireland. Among them was one William Excestre, possibly to be identified with the composer.

In the 'Fragment from Fountains Abbey'[1] tendencies apparent in the Old Hall are also seen; some of the composers indeed are represented in both collections. The Fountains collection contains probable examples by Rowland and Pennard; and by Queldryk and Fonteyns (i.e. Fountains), also in Old Hall, whose names are of Yorkshire origin. Altogether out of eighteen items in the Fountains Ms. seven are also in Old Hall.[2] A third important collection of fifteenth-century polyphonic music, which is also associated with Yorkshire, contains music for Holy Week and a series of carols. This music,[3] although claimed by Dr. Bertram Schofield for St. George's Chapel, Windsor,[4] would seem, on internal evidence,[5] more probably to have belonged to the Cistercian house at Meaux, near Hull. Apart from the carols, which will be separately considered, the most interesting feature of this collection is that it gives a complete polyphonic sequence for the ancient rites of Holy Week. Within it are the first known polyphonic settings—*secundum Matheum* and *secundum Lucam*—of the story of the Passion. For the dramatic representation of this story plainsong was retained for the words of Christ and the narrator, while three-part polyphony was assigned to the *turba* and to the words uttered by characters other than Christ and the narrator. The Meaux Passion is a fortuitous survival from a long series of such works from Anglo-Saxon times to the Tudor versions of Richard Davy and William Byrd (see p. 154), which in turn establish connection with similar works within the modern tradition.

The oldest surviving Passion drama is in an eleventh-century Ms. once the property of St. Augustine's Abbey, Canterbury.[6] This, in neumatic notation, shows dialogue between cantor and chorus dramatically conceived. Thus after the chorus-singers had asked why Christ should be hanged on a malefactor's cross and the cantor had answered, they broke into a hymn of praise, *Ave, rex noster*. From this it was a relatively short step to the first of the polyphonic settings of the Passion.

While the works of English composers of the late fourteenth and early fifteenth century are represented in manuscripts of native provenance there is a greater wealth of such works in continental, and especially Italian, collections of the period. From this fact others devolve. The first, indisputable, and supported by such observations as that of Martin le Franc, is that English musicians enjoyed high esteem abroad. The second, again already indicated, is that there had not yet arisen any limiting

[1] Add. Ms. 40011 B.
[2] Bukofzer, op. cit., pp. 86 *et seq.*
[3] B.M. Egerton Ms. 3307; ed. by G. S. McPeek, London, 1964.
[4] 'A Newly-Discovered 15th Century Manuscript of the English Chapel Royal', pt. i, *M.Q.*, October 1946, pp. 509–536.
[5] Bukofzer, op. cit., p. 114.
[6] B.M. Cotton Vespasian D. vi, f. 77 b.

concept of conscious musical nationalism, even though regional traits might be individually recognised. The third is that certain composers worked abroad rather than at home from preference. All three facts are to be linked with the long involvement of the English monarchy in continental affairs, and with the military and political successes derived therefrom. Since the Chapel Royal musicians were consistently at work in France and Burgundy during the visits and campaigns of Henry V and the Duke of Bedford, it is not surprising that works by Byttering, Jervays, Forest, Power, Aleyn, Pyamour, as well as anonymous pieces, which were within the repertoire of the Chapel Royal, should be copied into continental anthologies. That these appear mostly in Italian transcripts represents a movement of French and Burgundian singers to Rome, as members of the Papal Choir, after the election of Martin V and the return of the papacy from Avignon to Rome. Thus influential Burgundian musicians may be held particularly responsible for the transmission of English music to Italy, some of whose bishops had already admired the English style of composition and performance at the Council of Constance in 1416–17. No doubt they felt obliged to placate the English after the Council's insult to the memory of John Wycliffe.

The composers represented in Italian collections[1] include, in addition to those detailed in Old Hall and other English sources, Dunstable, John Hothby, the theorist, Leonel Power, and Walter Frye[2] (about each of whom, even though scanty, there is some biographical information), John Benet, John Bedingham, Hert, Forest, Richard Markham, Bloym, John Bodoil, Driffelde, and Sorbi, as well as others defined merely as Robertus de Anglia, Anglicus, or Anglicanus (all of these composers remain as yet but as names). Power (d. at Winchester, 1445), identified with a monk of Canterbury, and the author of a treatise in English[3] in the Waltham Holy Cross Ms., enjoyed a reputation second only to that of Dunstable, and the works of the two composers have been frequently confused. Hothby (d. 1487), a Carmelite friar and a graduate of Oxford, is the only composer of this group whose activities abroad are known. After travelling, it is said, in Spain, France, and Germany, he lived in Italy, principally at Lucca, whence, after seventeen or eighteen years of teaching, he was recalled to England in the last year of his life by command of Henry VII. In his

[1] Aosta, Faenza, Florence, Monte Cassino, Rome, Trent, etc.; see 'List of Manuscripts', *John Dunstable, Complete Works* (*Musica Britannica*, VIII), pp. 163–4; Brian Trowell, 'Some English Contemporaries of Dunstable', *P.R.M.A.*, 81, 1954–5, pp. 77–88; and Charles Harnon, 'A Group of Anonymous English Pieces in Trent 87', *M. & L.*, 41, no. 3, 1960, p. 211.

[2] See S. W. Kenney, *Walter Frye and the 'Countenance Angloise'*, Yale Univ. Press, 1946.

[3] '[A] Tretis contrivd upon ye Gamme for hem yt wil be syngers or makers [composers] or techers.'

Dialogus in arte musica Hothby named Dunstable, Power, Robert Morton, (whose sole surviving works are in the form of French *chansons*) and Frost as important musicians. The chief place, by Hothby as by others, was accorded to Dunstable.

John Dunstable's reputation stood so high that his claim to be regarded as the first great English composer has never been contested. The substantiation of this claim by reference to his works is now possible since the issue of all that are known (sixty-seven, including some that are incomplete, and others of doubtful ascription) in the quincentenary edition of Manfred Bukofzer in the series *Musica Britannica*. Biographical data are still, however, minimal. Brian Trowell's ingenious dialectic[1] which reduces John Benet (i.e. Benedictine) and John Dunstable to one composer permanently attached to St. Albans Abbey and rejects the idea of two contemporary English schools, the one home-based, the other peripatetic, is not sufficiently convincing. Had Dunstable remained in England, his reputation being such as it was both in his lifetime as well as posthumously, it is inconceivable that the chroniclers would have been as economical of information as they were.

The known facts concerning Dunstable are as follows. He died on Christmas Eve, 1453, and was buried in St. Stephen's, Walbrook, London, where an epitaph (in which his name, as it often was, was spelt as Dunstaple) recorded his skill in astronomy and his primacy as musician. In Weever's *Funeral Monuments* (1631) another epitaph by John Whethamstede (d. 1465, Abbot and founder of the Library of St. Albans) was recorded. Whethamstede described Dunstable as 'an astrologian, a mathematician, a musition and what not.' A possible product of Dunstable's mathematical skill (to have been expected of a graduate of those times) is a compilation of tables of latitude and longitude preserved in the Bodleian Library. In an astronomical treatise in the library of St. John's College, Cambridge,[2] Dunstable is described as 'musician to the Duke of Bedford.' In addition to references already detailed Dunstable's fame was also noted after his death by Tinctoris[3] (1477), Gatorius (1496), a writer in Seville (1480), and Eloy d'Amerval (1508). The first English theoretician to mention him, and then somewhat negatively on account of Dunstable's apparent disregard for the principles of word-setting, was Thomas Morley,

[1] 'Some English Contemporaries of Dunstable', see above.

[2] Ms. 162, f. 74 v.

[3] '. . . potentialities of our music have increased so remarkably that there seems to be a new art, of which . . . the *fons et origo* is held to be among the English at whose head was Dunstable and contemporary with whom were Dufay and Binchois in France'. Tinctoris goes on to contrast the freer (and/or rougher) English with the neater French mode of singing, and to comment on the conservative method of English composers at the time at which he was writing. See Harrison, op. cit., pp. 257–8.

in his *Plaine and Easie Introduction* (1597). Thomas Ravenscroft made allusion to a treatise by Dunstable (not otherwise recorded) in his *Briefe Discourse* (1614).

The name (Dunstable being a town in Bedfordshire), the fact of service with the Duke of Bedford and the memorial by Whethamstede make it tolerably certain that Dunstable was a native of the County of Bedford. In this connection reference may be made to a putative family association. On 10 February 1305 one John Dunstable, described as 'son of Roger Ivingho, chaplain,' was presented to the living of St. Peter, Sharnbrook, near Bedford, by the Abbot and convent of St. Mary, Leicester. In 1331 Roger Extildesham succeeded to the living on the 'profession of J[ohn] Dunstable as a friar minor'.[1] The composer Dunstable was musician to the Duke of Bedford, Regent in France from 1422 to 1435, and the only reference to him in his lifetime was in Martin le Franc's *Le Champion de Dames*. French composers, he said, followed the English—

> Et ont prins de la contenance
> Angloise, et ensuy Dunstable
> pour quoy merveilleuse plaisance
> rend leur chant joyeux et notable.

Dunstable's music comprises single movements and paired movements for the Ordinary of the Mass; movements in isorhythmic form; possibly one cyclic Mass—the *Missa Rex Seculorum* (sometimes ascribed to Power); motets for Saints' Days; isorhythmic motets, among which is *Albanus roseo rutilat*, in celebration of St. Alban; polyphonic settings of plainsong melodies; and a few secular items of which *O rosa bella* (of doubtful ascription) is the best known. In the sense that it was functional, ancillary to liturgical processes, Dunstable's music was existential, serving its purpose by merely being. This is true of most so-called 'sacred' music, which heightens an appropriate response by the fact of its timing. The word 'mystery' then held a dual meaning. Music was a mystery by reason of the hidden secret of its composition which was zealously maintained by the professionals, not least of all in their theoretical expositions. But to accomplish a complete polyphonic work for performance required mystery in its other significance, of mastery. The notion that sacred music (the case of quasi-popular music, such as belonged to dramatic representation, was rather different, being concerned with a freer process of personal emotional response) was in any way expressionistically communicative, that it had a descriptive capacity of its own, had no validity.

[1] *Reg. II*, 2586, and *Reg. IV*, 3046, quoted by A. Hamilton Thompson, *The Abbey of St. Mary of the Meadows, Leicester*, Leicester, 1949, p. 187.

If what is termed feeling is in any degree sensed, that is due to a particular responsiveness on the part of the present listener, who now, as not then, is generally released from the first discipline of liturgical observation. Dunstable was not concerned to clarify verbal sequences (which were, in any case, familiar enough). Thus he set one text against another, and paid scant attention, as Morley complained, to any niceties of musico-verbal enunciation. He was, however, concerned to prove his mastery. This was the first aim of the composer of that time (an aim followed often enough by Bach, whose 'Gothic' tendencies were unappreciated in his own day). In pursuing this aim the composer obeyed the medieval philosophy that allowed merit to labour undertaken as for divine offering and identified it with prayer. Therefore the art of Dunstable can only be appreciated some five centuries after its creation through an equivalent act of detachment. It is a form of music remote from the commonplace and (unless one accepts the appropriate theological and philosophical premises) apparently self-sufficient.

Being a synthesis, however, it is an aspiring form of art, looking towards an ideal: in this sense it would seem by Platonic standards to enshrine some kind of moral value. Dunstable's contemporaries and successors took his style to be somewhere near perfection. What he did to achieve this respect was to discriminate. While using the techniques then available, and which have been described, he brought melodic invention, contrapuntal construction, rhythmic diversity, and, above all, harmonic

4.

× Plainsong motiv outlines

syntax, into a state of interdependence, and in so doing gave to music a fluency and richness that it had hitherto lacked. As an example of this new-found plasticity there may be noted the end of the *Gloria* from the isorhythmic cyclic *Missa Rex Seculorum*, its relationship with the fundamental plainsong being outlined [Ex. 4].

At this point, both in place and time, English liturgy and drama may be seen in a new relationship; in the vernacular, without the walls of the church, and deriving also from the hitherto submerged folk tradition. In the fifteenth century the Mystery Play reached the peak of its popularity.

Passion and Mystery Plays

The chief origin of the medieval sacred drama was the Easter trope *Quem quaeritis?*, itself one of a number of dramatised extensions of the ritual (see p. 61). Established by the tenth century, its English form noted in the *Winchester Troper* (*c.* 980) and described by Bishop Ethelwold of Winchester in his *Regularis Concordia*, this traditional exhibition became widely popular, and fourteenth-century versions from Dublin and Barking, in Essex, are extant.[1] Collateral with the developed Easter Play was the Miracle Play. Matthew Paris recorded the performance of one such play on the subject of St. Katherine at Dunstable, in the year 1110, while more than two centuries later Chaucer's Wife of Bath was keen on 'playes of miracles'. In the Easter-Sepulchre drama 'dialogued chant and mimetic action have come together and the first liturgical drama is, in all its essentials, complete'.[2] In 1210 Pope Innocent III proscribed the performance of such drama within the churches, and then, from necessity, they were given out of doors. The institution of the Feast of Corpus Christi, however, gave opportunity for production in more clement weather than was likely to prevail at Easter, while extra-ecclesiastical organisation became general.

In Leicester, for example, initiative lay with the Guild of Corpus Christi, which had been founded in 1343, partly as a religious confraternity of influential laity (with a 'singing chaplain' to perform Masses for defunct worthies), but more particularly as a kind of mutual benefit society. At the Festival of Corpus Christi a great procession of Guild members, mayor and corporation, borough officers, chantry priests and other clergy, and persons dressed as saints, apostles, virgins, and other

[1] W. L. Smoldon, 'The Easter Sepulchre Music-Drama', *M. & L.*, 27, 1946, no. 1, pp. 1 *et seq.*

[2] E. K. Chambers, *The Medieval Stage* (1903), 1925, II, p. 15.

characters familiar from scripture, legend, and semi-sacred drama, marked the occasion.

Where there was an existing tradition, a lively municipality and enthusiasm on the part of the Guilds, the extension of the Easter Play to something more comprehensive became inevitable. In the fourteenth century, Beverley, Dublin, Newcastle, Shrewsbury, York, Wakefield, Lincoln, Norwich, Chester, and Coventry, took the lead in developing the communal plays that were to give distinction to the life of those towns for two centuries. There was also a series of plays performed in Cornwall.[1] The Chester cycle of twenty-four Pageants (eventually copied by James Miller in 1607)[2] was said to have started its long history in 1327, during the mayoralty of Sir John Armway. Stow, in his *Survey of London*, refers to the interludes played at Skinner's Well in 1390, and to the play, 'which lasted eight days, and was of matter from the creation of the world', of 1409, both being performed by the Parish Clerks of London.

The most complete text of a cycle of Mystery Plays or 'Pageants' is that of York, in a fair copy of the mid-fifteenth century,[3] based on drafts stretching back for a century. The York plays began at 4.30 a.m., for, in forty-eight sections, they spread over the whole day, and most of the city. Music was used either to add verisimilitude—as in *Mary's Magnificat* (plainsong) in the Pageant of the Spicers; to add a supernatural dimension—as in the Angel's Song of the Chaundelers' Play, or the music of the thirteen Angels in the Weavers' Play;[4] and to create diversion, as when the Shepherds, having heard the Angel sing, commented as follows:

Shepherd II: Haha, This was a mery note,
By the death that I shall die.
I have so croaked in my throat
That my lips are near dry.
Shepherd III: No boasting boys,
For what it was fain would I,
That has made this noble noise.[5]

1 *The Ancient Cornish Drama*, ed. by E. Norris, 1859.

2 B.M. Harl. Ms. 2124.

3 B.M. Ashburnham Ms. In the late sixteenth century this text was censored by the Protestant Archbishop Grindal in order to eradicate 'superstitious doctrines'. The characters of the York plays were given in Latin descriptions in the city's *Ordo Paginarium Ludi Corporis Christi*, 1415.

4 In a late fifteenth-century Ms.—B.M. Add. Ms. 35290—there is two-part music for this play in semi score:
(a) *Surge propera, Columba mea*, f. 235b.
(b) *Veni de libano, sponsa*, f. 238.
(c) *Veni, electa mea* with alternative settings of (1) and (2), ff. 241, 241b.

5 From the version of J. S. Purvis, prepared for Festival of Britain production of 1951 (the first since 1572).

In the first of the two Shepherds' Plays (*Prima Pastorum*) of the Wakefield Cycle the same episode is developed into comedy, that gains from a careful piece of measured miscalculation:

Shepherd I:	Godys, dere Dominus! What wa that song? It was wonder curiose, with small notys emang.
Shepherd II:	Now, by God that me boght, it was a merry song! I dar say that he broghte foure and twenty to a long.[1]

After which the comedy continues into the three-man song of the shepherds themselves.

The supposition is that the Wakefield Plays, rich in theological allusion as well as other details drawn from learned sources, were written (in their final form) by a clerk in lesser orders. In the second of the Shepherds' Plays (*Secunda Pastorum*) musical theory is thus worked into the dialogue:

Shepherd II:	Say what was his song? Hard ye not how he crakeyd it Thre brefes to a long.[2]
Shepherd III:	Yea, Mary, he hakt it: Was no crotchett[3] wrong, nor nothyng that lakt it.
Shepherd I:	For to syng us emong, right as he knakt it, I can.
Shepherd II:	Let se how ye croyne! Can ye bark at the mone?
Shepherd III:	Hold yore tonges! Have done!
Shepherd I:	Hark after, than (He sings and the others join in).

Christmas plays were also commonly performed and in 1378 the choristers of St. Paul's Cathedral petitioned the King to protect them against rival productions by 'ignorant and unexperienced persons'.[4] The connection between carol, of indigenous growth, and drama was close, and its development from Latin originals, through macaronic compositions to vernacular forms, may be seen on the one hand in the texts of the Mystery Plays and on the other in the collection of *Medieval Carols* (*Musica Britannica*, IV, 1952), edited by John Stevens. The well-known carols in the Coventry cycle—borrowed also for Wakefield—are later additions to the text, but nonetheless within the authentic tradition.[5]

[1] From the version of *The Wakefield Pageants*, ed. by A. C. Cawley, Manchester, 1958.
[2] Perfect time.
[3] The earliest mention of the crotchet in English literature.
[4] See Duncan, op. cit., p. 105.
[5] See *Oxford Book of Carols* (to which there is a useful Preface by Percy Dearmer), nos. 22 and 39.

Civic Music

This tradition was one of music of a functional nature placed within a particular social framework. The extent to which music impinged on the lives of the citizens of an important provincial city is well illustrated by the case of Coventry.

In the fifteenth and sixteenth centuries Coventry, regularly favoured by royal patronage, was well-placed to fuse the various traditions of Church, city, and country. It was central, the metropolis of a prosperous region, endowed with fine buildings, and fourth in eminence among all the cities of England. The confluence of the main traditions is implicit in this statement, made in 1416: 'The Pageants and *Hox* tuesday[1] invented, wherein the King [Henry V] and Nobles took great delight.'[2] Nearly thirty years later the participants in the festive procession were recorded: 'Pur le ridying on Corpus Xpi day and for watche on midsomer's even: The furst craft, fysshers and cokes; baxters and milners; bochers; whittawers and glovers; pynners, tylers and wrights; skynners, barkers; corvysers; smythes, wevers; wirdrawers; cardemakers, sadelers, peyntours, and masons; gurdelers; taylours, walkers, and sherman; drysters, drapers; mercers.'[3] The Pageants, eventually detached from the Procession, were organised by ten of the city's companies, others covering their obligations by subscription alone. The involvement of the secular musicians of Coventry in the Pageants is thus shown in the city records:

1451	It. payed to the mynstrells viij s.
	It. spend on mynstrells dinner and their soper on Corpus *Xpist* day, xx d
1471	It. paid to the waytes for mynstrelship vj s;
1477	It. payed to the waytes for pypyng v s;[4]

[1] Hock (hox) Tuesday, the second Tuesday after Easter, was a public holiday, characterised by the women, 'capturing the men and making them pay a fine or contribution to the church'. It was said to have originated in a Saxon victory over the Danes. See W. E. St. Lawrence Finny, 'Medieval Games and Gaderings at Kingston-upon-Thames', in *Surrey Archaeological Collections*, vol. 44, 1936, pp. 108–110. Hock Tuesday was abolished in Coventry in 1561.

[2] Thomas Sharp, *Dissertations on the Pageants or Dramatic Mysteries, Anciently Performed at Coventry, by the Trading Companies of that City*, 1828, p. 8.

[3] *Coventry Leet Book*, f. 122, 1445, quoted by Sharp.

[4] Sharp, op. cit., pp. 88–9. Later payments, to the later part of sixteenth century, specify the 'mending the trumpets' vij d (1538), the 'fechyng a pare of horgenes and the carrege of them whoume ij s (1557)', payment to one 'Thomas Nycles for settyng a song xjd (1556)', and fees of 'V s' for a trumpeter, and 'ijs vj d' for a flute player, for the new Pageant—*The Destruction of Jerusalem*—in 1584. There are similar references to such payments at York and Wakefield, while the constitution of the Chester 'waitmen' is referred to in petitions to the Mayor in 1485 contained in B.M. Harl. Ms. 2091.

The Mystery Plays contained many visual and dramatic possibilities, and while laying the essential foundations of later, purely secular, drama, assisted in the popularisation of musical values. In this setting music was welcomed not for its own sake, but for its histrionic and emotional relevance.

Liturgical music took on new life through the theatrical situation, as when souls delivered from Hell sang *Salvator Mundi*, angels signalled Christ's resurrection by *Christus resurgens*, or when, as stated at York, the procession into Jerusalem was led by choirboys. In the play of Noah in the *Ludus Coventriae* a chorus of sailors (*navi cantantes*) stands on the brink of a long operatic tradition. In *The Crucifixion* in the same cycle there is a stage-direction, which, again, anticipates a later, and apparently paradoxical convention: 'Here xule thei leve of and dawncyn a-bowte the cross shortly.'[1] In the *Massacre of the Innocents* a fanfare accompanies the bringing in of a banquet dish, and another when Herod, Juan-like, is taken into Hell: '*Hic dum buccinant mors interficiat Herodem et duos milites subito et diabolus recipiat eos.*'[2]

The place of music as an emotional stimulus and an aid to communication was apparent also in that used for royal occasions. Behind the honorific pageantry lay the *Ludi domini regis*, performed in the fourteenth century at Guildford, Oxford, and Merton;[3] the Coronation festivities; the experience of the *entremets* of the Courts of France, Italy, Spain, and Burgundy; and the musico-poetico-dramatical allegories such as greeted Henry VI on his return from France in 1431. What could be done in any other place could also be done in Coventry.

There were royal visits to Coventry in 1416, 1456, 1460, 1474, and 1498. On each occasion all the available musical resources were conscripted. So in 1474 there was 'mynstralcye of harpe and dowsemeris' at the Conduit, and 'mynstralcye of harpe and lute' at Broadgate. There were also 'Childer of Issarell syngyng', 'mynstralcy of small pypis' and 'mynstralcy of organ pleyinge', as well as such diversions as were provided by children casting down 'whete obles' [honey-cakes] and flowers, and the Conduit running wine.[4] When Prince Arthur arrived at the city Cross in

[1] See R. W. Ingram, 'The Use of Music in English Miracle Plays', *Anglia*, 75, 1957, pp. 64–5. The Dance of Death was a convention in ecclesiastical art, and there are remaining examples of wall-paintings of this subject in the Markham Chapel of Newark Church, and on a screen in Hexham Abbey.

[2] See Martial Rose, *The Wakefield Mystery Plays*, 1961, pp. 43–7. Rose's book is valuable for the producers of such plays, and is based on the revival of the Wakefield Cycle at Bretton Hall, Yorks, in 1958.

[3] Froissart, IV, xxxii.

[4] Sharp, *Illustrative Papers*, etc., p. 232. The entertainments dramatised episodes from the life of Edward the Confessor, and the legend of St. George. St. George (with dragon) was by now firmly set both in popular and royal presentations. In 1416 a St. George play had been given at Windsor before Henry V and the Emperor Sigismund. In 1511 'The Holy Martyr' St. George was played at the village of Bassingbourne in Cambs. for which 'a Mynstrell and three waits of Cambridge' were engaged to supply the music.

1498 a suitable ballad was sung of which the loyal, if trite, commencement was:

> Ryall Prince Arthur
> Welcome newe tresur } to this your city
> With all our hole cur [heart]

The enhanced status of the municipalities during the fifteenth century, and the ambition of the successful to perpetuate their names, led to an increase in the dignities of the greater parish churches of the country, and many were either enlarged or reconstructed. At Kingston-on-Thames, where once the Saxon kings had been crowned, for instance, a vigorous mid-fifteenth century expansion owed much to the new Fraternity of the Holy Trinity. Civic pride, however, showed no more striking demonstration of its vitality than in the completion of the crowning of the great tower of St. Botolph, in Boston, Lincolnshire, in 1460. The collegiate and parish churches increasingly came to play a larger role in the field of church music. Thus at Bablake Church, Coventry, the organ was mended in 1461, but sold in 1519 to the Priory to be replaced by a new instrument. At St. Michael's Church in 1505 the standing of the organ player, John Gylburd, was acknowledged by his admission to membership of the Guild of Corpus Christi. Competition led to the Church Wardens of Holy Trinity installing in 1526 'A Pair of Organs wt vij stopps, ov'r and besides the two Towers of Cases of the pitches of doble E f faut, wt xxvij pleyn keys, xix mastes, xlvj Cases of Tynn, and xiij Cases of Wood, wt two Sterres, and the Image of the Trinite on the Topp of the sayed Orgayn.'[1]

At the Collegiate Church of St. Mary de Castro, in Leicester, the fifteenth-century organist had a quarterly stipend of 3s. 4d. In 1505 the holder of this office was Roger Okley, but he was either frequently absent or merely unsatisfactory, for a year later the Accounts registered the engagement of deputies:

> 'Paid at several times to one for playing on the organ, 2d a day.'
>
> 'Paid to a friar-preacher for playing on the organs in die Assumpt. B. Mariae 6d.'

For another festival recourse was had to the Augustinians:

> 'For playing on the organs in die Omn. Sanctorum—to one of the abbey 4d.'

The organ-playing monk also charged the church for his supper, bed, and breakfast.

[1] Sharp, op. cit., pp. 103–4.

The musical establishments of many London[1] and some provincial parish churches[2] were, as now, often reliant on professional and free-lance singers, but at the same time were in a position to rival the cathedrals and collegiate churches in polyphonic efficiency. The extension of choral music through private schools of singing was sometimes frowned on by those with vested interests, as is indicated in letters containing injunctions against the setting up of such schools by the senior officials of the Abbey of Bury St. Edmunds.[3]

At the end of the fifteenth century the ancient tradition of the Passion story in musico-dramatic form, already alluded to on p. 61, was regularised in the parish churches. The nature of the Passion music of this period is shown by that composed by Richard Davy and incorporated in the Eton Choirbook. This is the earliest Passion setting composed by a known musician.

The Accounts of St. Margaret, Southwark, for 1456 show a payment for 'brede and wyne for the syngers on Palme sonday'[4]; at St Lawrence, Reading, in 1505, the Clerk was paid in kind, with a pennyworth of ale, for 'syngyng of the Passion on Palme Sunday', while four years later a quart of 'bastard' costing threepence was purchased for the singers of the Passion.[5] A later account, although violently partisan, gives this picture of the Passion performance: '. . . But, Lorde, what ape's playe made they of it in great cathedral churches and abbies! One comes forth in his albe and his long stole. . . . This solempne syre played Christes part, a God's name. Then another companye of singers, chyldren and al, song, in pricksong, the Jewe's part—and the deacon read the middel text. The prest at the Altar al this while, because it was tediouse to be unoccupyed, made crosses of Palme to set upon your doors, and to have in your purses to chase away the Divel.'[6]

[1] See Hugh Baillie, 'A London Church in Early Tudor Times', *M. & L.* 35, 1954, p. 55, and 'Some Biographical Notes on English Church musicians, chiefly working in London (1485–1569)' in *R.M.A. Research Chronicle*, no. 2, 1962, pp. 18 *et seq.*

[2] Bishop Lacey of Exeter was so impressed by the singing of the minstrels of Launceston, in Cornwall, in 1440, that he granted indulgences to all who were penitent and subscribers to the upkeep of the said minstrels. St. Mary's Launceston had an organ in 1461 and some forty years later the minstrels were set in sculpture on the East Wall. Another church in the diocese of Exeter with a strong musical tradition was St. Saviour's, Dartmouth (see Thurston Dart, 'The Dartmouth Magnificat', *M. & L.*, 39, no. 3, 1958, p. 209).

[3] B.M. Harl. Ms. 645, ff. 86, 86 b.

[4] J. Payne Collier, *Extracts from the Accounts of St. Margaret's, Southwark*, p. 45.

[5] C. Coates, *History and Antiquities of Reading*, Reading, 1862, p. 216.

[6] *A Dialogue or Familiar Talke, betweene two Neighbours, concernynge the Chyefest Ceremonyes that were, by the mighti Power of God's most holie pure worde, suppressed in Englande, and nowe for our unworthiness set up agayne by the Bishoppes, the Impes of Antichrist* etc., 1554; quoted in Brand, *Popular Antiquities*, 1841, I, p. 74.

Music in Educational Foundations

As the Old Hall Ms. serves as the most familiar guide to British music of the first part of the fifteenth century, so the *Eton Choirbook* may be taken as the main summary of that belonging to the end of the century. This collection moreover signalises the prestige of music in the newer educational foundations.

The recall of John Hothby from Italy in the first year of the reign of Henry VII was symptomatic of a heightened regard for the cultural properties of music. A previous gesture towards the art was the institution of degrees in music at Cambridge by command of Edward IV in 1464, the two first graduates being Henry Abyngdon, Master of the Children of the Chapel Royal,[1] as Bachelor, and Thomas Saintjust, to be elected Master of King's Hall (Trinity College), as Doctor. Thurston Dart advances the theory that this degree was thought up by Edward IV as an incentive to political loyalty (the King having come to the throne by conquest) and a reward for public service, both Abyngdon and Saintjust being administrators rather than creative musicians. Anxious to promote good relations with the intellectuals Edward, therefore, had chosen to confer degrees. 'In what branch of learning? In Music, which every prince in Europe was at pains to cherish. The more conspicuously the better.'[2] The Universities already housed a number of musical establishments, as well as opportunities for academic study in the science of the art, and choirs of some quality had existed in Queen's, Balliol, and New Colleges, Oxford, from the middle of the fourteenth and the beginning of the fifteenth centuries. There was also a musical foundation at William of Wykeham's College at Winchester. Henry VI founded King's College, Cambridge, in 1443, and Eton College a year later, and his zeal for learning and religious devotion led to other institutions, with similar scholastic and ecclesiastical aims. These included Magdalen College, Oxford, and the Grammar School of Rotherham, in Yorkshire.

The new educational, and charitable, institutions of the fifteenth century—which made provision for 'poor scholars'—were conveniently founded. They were to carry the best of the medieval traditions across the disruptive period of the Reformation, and unite these with the fresher impulses of the Renaissance. They brought a new energy into society when

[1] The first official Master was John Plummer who held office from 2 April 1441 to 1455, the year in which the Wars of the Roses broke out. It was during Plummer's period of office that the Dean of St. Paul's successfully protested against the impressment of any of his choristers for the Chapel Royal. Abyngdon's appointment took effect from 16 March 1456.

[2] Thurston Dart, 'The Origins of Music Degrees', *Mus.T.*, 1964, p. 190.

the ancient religious bodies were going into a decline, both caused and symbolised by complacency. At Whalley Abbey, in Lancashire, the proportion of monks to 'servants' was in the ratio of ten to thirty-eight, which, both in 1478 and 1521, was reflected in the relative disbursements to the minstrels on the one hand[1] and to the organists on the other. Tucked away in the fastness of northern Lancashire the community at Whalley caused little in the way of comment or censure. In the busy city of Leicester, however, it was otherwise. The fraternity of St. Mary's Abbey was reprimanded for its general laxity on the occasion of an episcopal visitation in 1440, while in 1518 Bishop Atwater was even more stringent in his strictures. There had clearly been no improvement since the last major inspection. Servants of the Abbey, who were paid four or five marks each to sing in the choir, either turned up when they felt so inclined, or neglected their musical duties entirely. As for the novices, they took no part in the singing of the offices, they had no knowledge of music nor any inclination to learn. The monks of Leicester passed much of their time in eating and drinking, in games of chance, and in making a nuisance of themselves in the town.[2] There was among this number, however, one who remembering former times preserved high ideals. This was William Charyte, who had entered the Monastery in 1439 and was still there at the beginning of the sixteenth century. Charyte was the librarian, and a benefactor to the Library. In 1493, in which year he made a catalogue of its contents, he was also Precentor. The choir and 'organ-books' [*sic*] numbered thirty-one. 'In . . . 5 Service-books [Charyte] ruled the lines and wrote the music "free of charge", and one of them he bound . . . [He] must have been skilled in music, for he wrote two of the organ-books, besides filling in the notation of processionals and antiphoners.' The admirable Charyte, true to form, was also expert in astronomy.[3]

Of the large number of the kind of service-books described in Charyte's inventory[4] the substantial survivors are a manuscript at Lambeth Palace, one at Caius College, Cambridge, the Scottish Carver manuscript, and the *Eton Choirbook*.

Prior to the Wars of the Roses the chapel at Eton was served by ten clerks and sixteen choristers. In 1476, after the foundation had been subjected to some diminution of its dignities and temporary submission to the Chapel Royal at Windsor, the choral constitution was regularised at

[1] £1 16s. 7d. in 1478, and £2 4s. od. in 1521, according to the Abbey *Compoti*.

[2] A. Hamilton Thompson, op. cit., pp. 76–80.

[3] M. R. James and A. Hamilton Thompson, 'Catalogue of the Library of Leicester Abbey' (Bodl. Laud. Misc. Ms. 623), *Transactions of the Leicestershire Archaeological Society*, xix, 1936–7, pp. 122–3.

[4] Cf. the '5 grete bokys coverde wyth rede lether conteynynge the most solemne antems off 5 partes' detailed in the King's College list of 1529 (*The Ecclesiologist*, XXIV, 1863, p. 100).

seven clerks and ten choristers. In the earliest period of polyphonic music the select singers required for its performance had been assembled round one manuscript copy. With the larger bodies of the fifteenth century the same uncomfortable practice was maintained, separate part-books not being in general use until the time of Henry VIII. The Eton Book, described in 1531 as 'a grete ledger of prick song', was compiled, it would appear, at the beginning of the last decade of the fifteenth century. Its unitary devotional theme, as in the most of English late medieval liturgical music, was the cult of the Virgin Mary. In connection with this candidates for degrees in music at Oxford and Cambridge were required to compose, as exercises, a Mass (Lady-Mass) and an Antiphon in honour of the Virgin. The intensity of the cult—underlining the ironic observation of G. K. Chesterton that in the Middle Ages people were thought to have caught Mariolatry like measles—explains the revulsion from it that set in when the Reformation reached its most acute phase.

The Lambeth Palace and Carver manuscripts preserve examples of Masses, Antiphons, and Magnificats; in Mass and Canticle settings of this period it was customary both in England and on the Continent to alternate choral with organ sections; thus the vocal polyphonic settings appear incomplete.[1] The Caius College manuscript has no antiphons, the Eton Book no Masses. The composers represented in the index of the latter, twenty-five in number, are not all identifiable with certainty, but include the principals in English music of that era and indicate a widespread talent.[2]

Composers of the Late Fifteenth and early Sixteenth Centuries

A five-part contribution from Dunstable, *Gaude flore virginali*, was indexed but the item was among those lost before the sixteenth-century re-constitution and re-binding of the manuscript. Of the senior composers Gilbert Banester is the author of an honorific antiphon *O Maria et Elizabeth*, thought to have been written for the marriage of Henry VII and Elizabeth of York in 1486. Banester, Abyngdon's successor as Master of the Children between 1478 and 1487[3] and previously a Gentleman of the Chapel Royal,

[1] See Hugh Baillie and P. Oboussier, 'The York Masses', *M. & L.*, 35, no. 1, pp. 19 *et seq.*, and Harrison, op. cit., pp. 216–17.

[2] The publication of *The Eton Choirbook*, I, II, III, ed. by F. Ll. Harrison as vols. X, XI, XII, (1956, 1958, 1961) of *Musica Britannica*, is a major musicological achievement and indispensable guide to a school of composers whose significance hitherto could hardly be appreciated.

[3] In 1484 a drive for new choirboys was initiated by Richard III, who commissioned John Melynek, a Gentleman, to raid cathedral chapels, and religious houses, for suitable boys. The one institution excepted was St. George's Chapel, Windsor (*Cal. Pat. Rolls*, Henry VI, IV, p. 90).

was a man of parts, illustrating by his works the wider aspects of human studies with which official musicians were expected to be acquainted. To Banester are ascribed the *Legend of Sigismund*, based on Chaucer's *Legend of Ladies*, and the *Miracle of St. Thomas*, both relating to the duty then imposed on the Master of the Chapel Royal to provide material for interludes to be performed at court by the choristers. In the so-called Fayrfax Ms. (B.M. Add. Ms. 5465) a secular three-part song, *My feerfull dreme*, also was connected with this part of his activities. Composers of the *Eton Choirbook* associated with the Chapel Royal, whose importance in the reign of Henry VIII was considerable, were William Cornyshe and Robert Fayrfax; Walter Lambe, a King's Scholar at Eton, who became Clerk and Master of the Choristers at Windsor; Robert Hacomplaynt, in due course Provost of King's College, Cambridge; and John Sutton, Fellow of Eton from 1477–*c.* 1479. Also directly associated with Eton was Robert Wylkynson, sometime parish clerk, and from 1500 Master of the Choristers. Richard Davy, otherwise remarkable as the composer of the *Passion* music (see p. 72), was organist at Magdalen College, Oxford, between 1490 and 1492, and was subsequently attached to the household staff of the Boleyn family. Richard Horwood[1] was appointed Master of the Choristers at Lincoln in 1477, in which task he was expected to teach his boys 'playnsong, pryksong, faburden, diskant [so is seen the perpetuation of conservative traditions in late fifteenth-century musical education], . . . playing the organ . . . and . . . the clavycordes'. The last part of this injunction of the Chapter Act of 1477 indicates a broadening of the curriculum and a recognition of the social value of music. Richard Hygons, a pupil of Henry Abyngdon, was organist of Wells Cathedral, and was commended by his Dean and Chapter 'for his diligent labour and good service to the honour of God and St. Andrew'. John Hampton was Master of the Choristers at the Benedictine Priory of Worcester. Of the other composers in the *Eton Choirbook*, biographical details are either speculative or non-existent.

The music of the Eton collection may be seen in relation to that which, at the same time, was exerting most influence on the Continent. The Flemish tradition which embraced Dufay and Binchois—inheritors of an earlier English technique,[2] Ockeghem, Josquin des Prés, and Obrecht, was pre-eminent. Each of these composers, by virtuosity of technique, by prolificacy as well as variety of output, was acknowledged as a master and a pioneer, and insofar as each ranged widely from a highly

[1] Presumed to be the 'Horwod' of the *York Masses*, which may have belonged to the cathedral at Lincoln (Baillie and Orboussier, op. cit., p. 24).

[2] Binchois had been sometime in the employment of William de la Pole, first Duke of Suffolk, and both he and Dufay exploited the euphonious method of the Dunstable school.

wrought and fluent scholastic counterpoint to the simpler, potentially more expressive *chanson*, it is not surprising that the more empirical English composers should have been denigrated as conservative by Tinctoris. It is, however, surprising that English composers were so apparently indifferent to the Flemish style in view of the close general connections between the two countries and the dominance of Flemish methods in the arts of illumination, wall-painting, and stained glass. Late fifteenth-century music in England omitted the intellectual canonic devices that absorbed half the interest of the Flemings, not necessarily because they were incompetent,[1] but because the claims of euphony appeared to rank higher. This is the compelling feature of British music from the twelfth to the sixteenth centuries.

The work of the *Eton Choirbook* composers is in direct line from those of the Old Hall anthology. But, aware of Dunstable and Power, it is melodically more spacious, and broader both in texture and rhythm. Unity was generally imposed by a fundamental plainsong theme varied according to the accepted principles of paraphrase and migration. But episodes of free material or others in which the *cantus firmus*, subject to considerable modification, could hardly be apparent to the ear, anticipated the eventual emancipation of vocal polyphony from its liturgical parentage.

5.

[1] See John E. Stevens, 'Rounds and Canons from an early Tudor Songbook (B.M. Add. Ms. 31922)', *M. & L.*, 32, no. 1, p. 29.

Greater freedom was otherwise enjoyed in the new respectability of imperfect, or duple, time, and in the opportunities afforded by larger choirs with adequately trained boys for the treble parts. The norm for polyphonic writing in the Eton Book is five voices, although there are also examples in six, seven, eight, and nine parts. Composers planned now on a grand scale. Richard Davy's *O Domine Caeli Terraeque Creator* is spread over 262 bars, with sections varied in rhythm, texture, and contrapuntal complexity, and marked off by cadences on differing finals. In Wylkynson's nine-part *Salve Regina* the voices, according to annotation, are symbolic of the nine choirs of angels. In this, as in one or two other instances, a new relationship with text may be seen in development. The age of multi-textual writing, being by now past the possibility of inspiring appreciation of a verbal concept through a musical formula, begins to be envisaged. Thus the final invocation 'O dulcis Maria', recapitulating the earlier invocations in general shape and density, represents a point of palpable repose [Ex. 5], while this interlude for the three lowest voices is at the other extreme, of energy, as indicated by the words [Ex. 6]. While the connection between music and words is not to be overlooked, the abiding impression left by these masterpieces of late fifteenth-century inventiveness is their suitability to the climate of doctrine and ritual.

6.

And here it is to be remembered that while these compositions were being created, so also were others in the field of architecture.

The age which spanned from Edward IV to Henry VIII was characterised by a demand for renewed splendour, of which the principal ecclesiastical architectural symbols are at Westminster Abbey, Magdalen College, Oxford, King's College, Cambridge, St. George's Chapel, Windsor, Bath Abbey, and Canterbury Cathedral. The felicities of the last phase of medieval Gothic in England, in that they had no relevance outside the country, were provincial. The same may be said of the music: but the genius for the handling of material resources that characterises the polyphony of—in this instance—Richard Davy [Ex. 7] may be felt as not less marked than that of William Orchard and Thomas Westell, the principal contractors and architects of Magdalen College, Canterbury Cathedral, and King's College.

7.

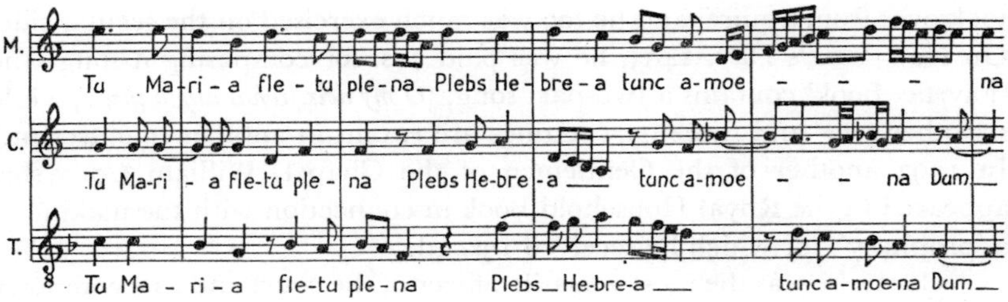

The latter part of the fifteenth century was marked by political and social changes that were to alter the significance, and means of diffusion, of music. The Wars of the Roses ended at Bosworth in 1485. Henry VII, the power of the feudal barons now destroyed, needed to secure his own position and also that of his country, of which the standing in European affairs had necessarily declined. The first of the Tudor monarchs, whose strong practical acumen was balanced by a mystical sense inherited from his Welsh ancestors,[1] Henry VII appreciated the possibilities inherent in music and drama in their various forms as useful aids to the establishment of an effective image of his Court. Henry VII and Henry VIII were more or less absolute monarchs. That they were, brought certain benefits to musicians, not least of all in the wider opportunities of expression that such absolutism, either directly or indirectly, encouraged. These benefits derived in large measure from a reduction of ecclesiastical influence, the power of which was finally destroyed in England by the Dissolution of the Monasteries and the Act of Supremacy of 1534. Tudor music was functionally affected by political operations. But its content also changed in response to the liberating motives of the humanism promulgated especially through Erasmus, More, and Colet, which were to make both aristocratic and bourgeois living conditions more civilised; to the manner of the works introduced by immigrant, and particularly Flemish musicians; and to a closer association between courtly and popular art-forms. Under the Tudors musicians were finally liberated from the confines of anonymity that had previously veiled their profession, and their activities, often profitable, show up in more recorded detail.

[1] The Welsh Eisteddfod once again assumed a national importance in the middle of the fifteenth century (see p. 109).

Banester's successor as Master of the Chapel Royal was Laurence Squire, a priest, whose appointment took effect from 8 November 1486 and whose duties were as much directed to drama as to music. In 1490 he was required to arrange a Christmas entertainment in which his choristers appeared as mermaids. In 1493 William Newark, a musician who served in the Chapel under five kings, from Edward IV to Henry VIII took over from Squire, and he too was much exercised on the secular side. On New Year's Day, 1493, he was paid 20s. for composing a song; the 'Fayrfax Book' contains a two-part song, '*O my deire what aileth thee ?*, while six other two- and three-part settings are extant in another manuscript.[1] In 1493 another of the Gentlemen of the Chapel, William Cornyshe, appeared in the Royal Household Book in connection with the making of a 'prophecy', for which he received 13s. 4d.

Cornyshe was the most versatile officer of the court and as a composer could be compared with his colleague, Robert Fayrfax. It is clear that Cornyshe, member of a family of musicians, had wider ambitions than Fayrfax, whose purposes as singer, organist, and composer, were more single-minded. Prior to his appointment as a Gentleman of the Chapel Royal, Cornyshe was Master of the Choristers at Westminster Abbey. The first holder of this office, he remained at the Abbey—within whose precincts both William Caxton, the printer, and John Skelton, the poet and tutor to Henry VIII, were busy at the same time—from 1479–80 to 1490–91. Cornyshe's association with Skelton is evident in his setting of that poet's rumbustious 'Provinciall Song, both quaint and gay,'[2] where the rough humour of the text is transferred to the music, which thus brought into prominence an earthy quality hitherto remote from the mainstream of English music.[3] Another composer friendly with Skelton was Robert Penne, Cornyshe's successor at the Abbey, for whom Skelton wrote his *Diodorus Siculus*. Cornyshe had strong literary talent, and as a Gentleman of the Chapel Royal he had opportunity to use it, although his propensity for satire—in particular at the expense of Sir Richard Empson,

[1] B.M. Add. Ms. 11583.

[2] See Edward Pine, 'The Westminster Singing Boys', *T.L.S.*, 12 December 1952, p. 828.

[3] *Hoyda, hoyda joly rutterkyn*, a supposed satire on the inebriate Flemings who attended the wedding of Henry VIII and Anne of Cleves, is one of three items by Cornyshe in the *Fayrfax Book*, B.M. Add. Ms. 5465. In this collection are songs in two and three parts by Davy, Fayrfax, Hamsher (Hampshire), Newark, Sheryngham, and Edmund Turges. *From stormy windis*, by the latter, is reputed to have been composed for the marriage of Prince Arthur and Katherine of Aragon in 1501. Other secular songs of this period are contained in B.M. Add. Ms. 31922 and Royal App. 58. See Hawkins, op. cit., III, p. 17, who quotes this and another song of Cornyshe: 'If the coarseness of the raillery, or the profaneness, or indelicacy of expression . . . should need an apology for inserting them, the most that can be made is, that they present to our view a true picture of the times.'

one of Henry VII's tax-collectors—was the cause of a term of imprisonment in the Fleet, in 1504. Cornyshe arranged the interludes presented in honour of the marriage of Prince Arthur and Katherine of Aragon in 1501 and on many occasions acted in the pageants at Court.

The development of formal pageantry into an artistic medium, from which grew the Stuart masque and the distinctive pattern of English seventeenth-century opera, was hastened by the enthusiasm of the early Tudors. To the stiff allegorical manner of Lydgate's official entertainments, Henry VII, influenced by the French *Sociétés Joyeux*, added the gaiety of French dances, the method of performance being demonstrated by visiting French players. From the field of folk-drama, and even from the miracle play,[1] came the 'revels' (for which the Tudors appointed a controller called the 'Lord of Misrule') and the 'disguisings', which, in turn, united with the style of the 'tournament' familiar at the Burgundian Court. The resulting entertainments, usually making a useful political point out of traditional allegorical symbols, were part professional, part amateur. None was keener in taking part than Henry VIII,[2] who encouraged the whole royal family so to do. Such performances took place either at stated seasons, on All Hallows Day, or Christmas, or on the occasion of visiting embassies. Cardinal Wolsey was also a patron of this early music-cum-drama.

Cornyshe was prominent in an administrative as well as an executant capacity and was acting Master of the Chapel Royal—Newark being in poor health—before succeeding to the office on Newark's death. In September 1513 Cornyshe travelled to Terouenne and Tournai with Henry VIII when the English captured those cities; seven years later he superintended the musical arrangements for the Field of Cloth of Gold, in which Fayrfax, and the next Master of the Chapel Royal, William Crane, also assisted. Cornyshe's capacity as choir-trainer was approved by the Venetian ambassador Sagudino, who, on 3 May 1515, wrote to Alvise Foscari, 'Mass was sung by H.M. Choir, whose voices were more divine than human; never heard such counter-basses.'[3]

Cornyshe wrote church music and secular vocal music. Three of his songs were among those first published in England, in 1530, in a *Book of XX Songs*, formerly thought to have been from Wynkyn de Worde. He was a favourite of Henry VIII, whose compositions are contained with

[1] God was introduced into a performance given in the spring of 1527 at Greenwich, for the French Ambassador. See J. Payne Collier, *The History of English Dramatic Poetry*, London, 1831, I, p. 99.

[2] See D. H. Traill, *Social England*, London, 1893–7, III, p. 163, quoting from Hall's *Chronicle*.

[3] Quoted by E. S. Roper, 'The Chapels Royal and Their Music', *P.R.M.A.*, 54, 1927, p. 24.

those of Cornyshe in important collections of part-songs,[1] which (by various composers) often show the same broad—if not bawdy—humour and directness of expression to be encountered in the later glee. In the foundation of a new tradition of freely lyrical song the influence of Sir Thomas Wyatt was strong. Although principally remembered for his adaptation of the Italian sonnet form (which also had consequences for musical development) Wyatt wrote much poetry before his visit to Italy in 1527, in which he had drawn on the common and popular stock of song and carol in order to create an individual style that should show how, as he said, he esteemed his own class less than 'the common sort'. Musical values stand out in Wyatt's work especially by his treatment of refrain. One of Wyatt's poems, *Ah Robin, jolly Robin*, was set by Cornyshe towards the end of his life.

Cornyshe died in 1523 and was succeeded by William Crane, who from 1526 presided over an enlarged choir, the number of boys being increased in that year from ten to twelve. It was during this period that the term 'anthem' according to its modern meaning was adopted. Fayrfax was paid for setting anthems on more than one occasion during the first two decades of the sixteenth century, and in 1526 it was ordained as follows: 'The Master, with six children and six gentlemen shall give their continual attendance in the King's Court and daily to hear a Mass of Our Lady before noon, and on Sundays and Holy Days, Mass of the Day, besides Our Lady Mass, and an Anthem (Antempe) in the afternoon.'[2]

Both Henry VII and Henry VIII introduced Flemish musicians to the royal establishment and English polyphonic method gradually, if belatedly, began to adapt itself to contemporary standards. The church music of Cornyshe, Hugh Aston (or Assheton), and Turges, represents the end of the freely decorative, quasi-improvisatory style of the English polyphonic tradition [Ex. 8], that of Fayrfax of its euphonious idiom

8.

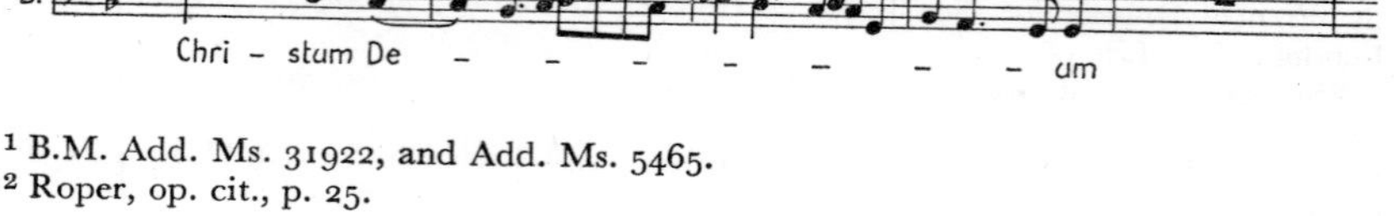

[1] B.M. Add. Ms. 31922, and Add. Ms. 5465.
[2] Roper, op. cit., p. 25.

[Ex. 9]. With the addition of Benedictis de Opitiis, of Antwerp, to the organ-playing staff of the Chapel Royal in 1514, the imitative counterpoint of the Netherlands school began to be adopted by English composers; who were otherwise assisted by a collection of Netherlands *chansons* and Mary-antiphons made for Prince Arthur, an anthology of continental motets assembled for Henry VIII,[1] and, presumably, many other importations.

9.

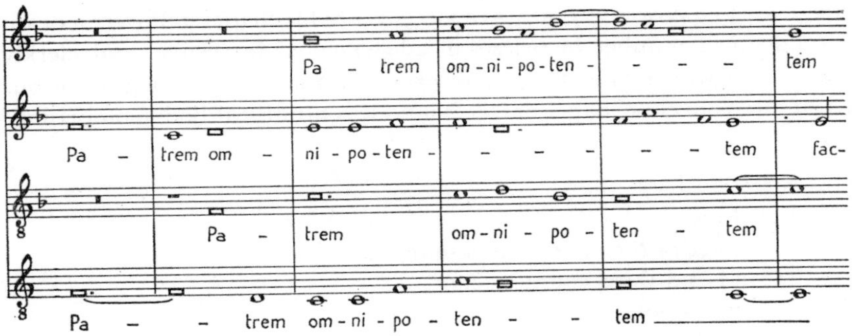

Patronage

If Henry VII and Henry VIII were ambitious to preside over a court of Renaissance splendour, there were those in high places who also measured their dignities by regal standards. Cardinal Wolsey rivalled his master insofar as he was enabled to do so by the appropriation of monastic endowments, and by generous contributions from clients seeking favours. The founder of Cardinal College (later Christ Church), Oxford, of a college in his native town of Ipswich, and the builder of Hampton Court Palace, Thomas Wolsey maintained his own ecclesiastical establishment. Richard Pygott was in charge of this from 1516 until the Cardinal's final downfall, taking up a place in the Royal Chapel in addition to that held under Wolsey, and was highly commended for his skill as choirmaster. Dean Richard Pace of St. Paul's suggested that Wolsey's choir was equal in competence to that of the King, and, exaggerating perhaps, since he was writing to Wolsey, even indicated that its members were more adept sight-readers. This was at that time when the King was persuading Wolsey to part with his best choirboy, which, after some demur, Wolsey eventually did, to the satisfaction of Cornyshe. He, said Pace, approved his acquisition

[1] B.M. Ms. Royal 8 G VII.

'not only for his sure and clearly singing, but also for his good and crafty discant'. He went on to observe that 'Cornysh doth in like manner extol Mr. Pygott for the teaching of him.'[1] Pygott, like Cornyshe, was a contributor to the *Book of XX Songs*, other composers represented being Robert Cowper,[2] Thomas Ashwell,[3] Fayrfax, Robert Jones,[4] and Taverner.

While Wolsey thus showed how a Prince-Cardinal, English style, could compete with his foreign compeers and his own sovereign, the fifth Earl of Northumberland, Henry Algernon Percy, member of the Council of the North, also lived in the state befitting one who, in the distant north-east, exercised power virtually as a viceroy. On his chapel staff were a dean, a subdean, a number of priests mostly engaged in secular and clerkly duties, one who was a 'maister of gramer', and one 'for singing of our Ladies mass in the Chapel daily'. There was a musical body comprising:

First bass
A second bass
Third bass
A maister of the childer, a counter-tenour
Second and third counter-tenor
A standing tenour
A second, third, and fourth standing tenour

———

Children of my Lorde's chappell
Three treble and three second trebles.

There were Rewards to the 'children of his chappell when they do sing the responde called Exaudivi at the mattyns time for xi M.Virgyns upon All Hallow Day, 6s. 8d.; on St. Nicholas Eve 6s. 8d. . . . to them of his Lordeshipe's Chappell if they doe play the play of the Nativitie upon Xmas Day in the mornynge in my Lorde's Chapell before his Lordship xx s.; . . . singing "Gloria in Excelsis" at the mattyns time upon Xmas Day in the mg 6s. 8d.; . . . to the Abbot [cf. 'Lord', p. 105] of Miserewle [Misrule] in Xmas xx s.; . . . to his Lordship's Chaplains and other servts. that play the Play before his Lordship on Shrofetewsday at night xx s. That play the Play of Resurrection upon Ester Daye in the mg. in my Lorde's Chapell before his Lordship xx s.' The singing-men took turns at playing the organ.[5] After the death of the Earl, in 1527, Wolsey obtained his Service Books for his own Chapel.

[1] Roper, op. cit., p. 26.
[2] Of King's College, Cambridge.
[3] Master of the Choristers, Lincoln Cathedral, 1508–18.
[4] Gentleman of the Chapel Royal.
[5] *Household Book of Henry Algernon, 5th Earl of Northumberland, Antiq. Repertory*, IV, 1809, pp. 242 ff.

The first Duke of Richmond had a like establishment but, since he was the illegitimate son of Henry VIII and Elizabeth Blount, he had some claim to such distinction. On a lower level of social eminence Sir Thomas Jermyn (d. 1552), of Rushbrooke Hall, Suffolk, was a competitor in the same field of endowment and patronage, being described as 'the best housekeper in the Contey of Suffoke, [who] kept a godly chapel of syngyng men'.[1]

Development of Keyboard Music

The prosperity enjoyed by those who were wise enough to keep their distance from political chicanery and military operations encouraged a new attitude towards music. It was, by the end of the fifteenth century, now possible to regard its practice as a proper, and polite, recreation. Thus keyboard music, other than that for organ, made a positive appearance on the domestic scene. A firm lead was given by the courts, both of England and Scotland. Items relating to the possession of clavichords are detailed in the Privy Purse Expenses of Henry VII and Elizabeth of York for the year 1502. A year later James IV married Margaret of England and during the festivities 'the kyng began before hyr to play of the *clarychordes*, and of the lute. And uppon the said *clarychordes* Sir Edward Stanley played a ballade, and sang therewith'. The Manor House at Leckingfield, in Yorkshire, one of the seats of the Earl of Northumberland, carried on its walls various verses relating to the practice of music, among which was this:

He that fingerithe well the keys of the *Claricordis* maketh a goode songe,
For in the meane is the melodye withe a reste longe;
If the tewnys be not pleasant to him that hath no skyll,
Yet no lac to the *claricorde* for he doith his goode will.

Cornyshe refers to the clavichords in a poem, printed by Wynkyn de Worde and composed while he was a prisoner in the Fleet, and Dean Pace bears testimony to the interest which Henry VIII had in the instrument.[2] Both the Leckingfield inscriptions and the inventories of Henry indicate also the popularity of the virginals, at which the King too was a master. Pasqualigo, Venetian Ambassador extraordinary, gave the King this testimonial:

'He speaks French, English, and Latin, and a little Italian, plays well

[1] *The Diary of Henry Machyn, Citizen of London*, ed. by George Nichols, Camden Society, 1848, p. 27.
[2] See E. F. Rimbault, *The Pianoforte*, 1860, pp. 42–3.

on the lute and virginals, sings from book at sight, draws the bow with greater strength than any man in England, and jousts marvellously. Believe me he is in every respect a most accomplished prince . . .'[1]

The earliest extant pieces for clavichord, or virginals, are in B.M. Ms. Roy. App. 58,[2] and only one carried the name of a composer. This is a *Hornpipe*, (f. 40b) attributed to Hugh Aston (Assheton), generally identified with the composer of church music of that name (see p. 82). Now this *Hornpipe*, as other pieces in the same manuscript, shows the manner in which popular music was being adapted to polite appreciation. Aston's piece is an effective essay in distinctively keyboard figuration and in motivic extension through repetition and variation.

10.

The hornpipe was particularly cultivated in Lancashire,[3] and in Derbyshire, in which counties it persisted in the popular repertoire after it had fallen into disuse elsewhere.[4] The details of Aston's career are obscure.

[1] See Rimbault, op. cit., p. 52.

[2] The pieces in this collection (ff. 40–49b) are:

1. La bell fyne.
2. [Without title].
3. Hornpipe 'Hugh Aston'.
4. My Lady Carey's dompe.
5. My Lady Wynkfyld's (Wingfield) rownde.
6. The emperorse pavyn.
7. Galliard.
8. King Harry the VIIIth pavyn.
9. The crocke.
10. The kyng's maske.
11. Galliard.

[3] Cf. *A Collection of Original Lancashire Hornpipes old and new . . . being the first of this kind published, collected by Thomas Marsden,* John Playford, 1705.

[4] Lancashire towns, when unable to support a team of waits, employed pipers; thus in 1425 John Couper was piper of Colne (*Clitheroe Court Rolls*, I, p. 217), in 1440 Lawrence, son of John of Burnley, was the piper at Burnley (*Publ Rec. Off. D/L. Min. Acc.*, 89, 1634), while on 11 July 1628 the Register of Burnley Parish Church recorded the death of Edmunde Jacksonn, piper.

He is assumed to be the Hugh Aston who graduated as Mus. B. at Oxford in 1510. Davey argued that he was the same Aston as the Archdeacon of York who died in 1522, while others, disputing this, have preferred to identify him as a sometime Canon of St. Stephen's, Westminster. Harrison puts him in the occupation of *magister choristarum* at Newarke College, Leicester. The Lancashire Asshetons, however, were a fertile race and apart from noting that they maintained a long musical connection, as patrons rather than practitioners, it is still open to question as to who composed Hugh Aston's Hornpipe.[1] The fact remains that the piece is not unjustly regarded as epochal, the progenitor of a splendid succession. A ground by Hugh Aston was used in the Hornpipe for a piece of that name by William Byrd in *My Ladye Nevells Booke*, and a four-part instrumental piece by William Whytbroke entitled *Hugh Aston's Maske*.[2]

The first keyboard pieces of the sixteenth century are less important for their actual musical value—which is slight—than for their referential significance. In them is acknowledged what had long been taken for granted in popular musical activity, the fact that music can function independently of theological, ideological, or academic warrant, as a stimulus to pleasant social intercourse. It has been represented that music of Church, and Court, and of the drama of the Middle Ages, was generally associated with, even subordinate to, visual display. This music necessarily had a public quality, for the good reason that private comfort, without which domestic music can hardly thrive, did not exist. The development of chamber music, the most remarkable feature of British music in the sixteenth and seventeenth centuries, can be attributed to a number of influences. Among these the one most likely to be overlooked, but by no means the least important, is the greater attention paid to household amenities.

During the fifteenth century the furniture even in palaces and manor houses was austere, ecclesiastical in detail of design, and narrowly functional. Chairs were reserved for royalty, and for the lords of great houses and their guests. During the reign of Henry VIII, and because of his employment of Flemish, French, Italian, and German artists and craftsmen who modified and lightened native styles in interior decoration by the

[1] Hugh Assheton, son of Sir William Assheton, for instance, is noted at various times from 1470 in the *Calendar of the Standish Deeds*, 1230–1575, ed. by T. C. Porteous, Wigan, 1933, and in February 1508 is named in an indenture as a clerk. *My Lady Carey's Dompe*, also in Ms. Reg. App. 58, has sometimes (erroneously?) been ascribed to Hugh Aston. Stafford Smith, who published these pieces in *Musica Antiqua* (1812), claimed one Edmund Spencer, otherwise unknown, as the composer of this piece. Before dismissing this as sheer invention it should be noted that at Hurstwood, Lancashire, was a large family of Spensers (Spencers), including several with the Christian name Edmund (the poet was of this family), and that this family was acquainted with the Asshetons.

[2] Christ Church Library, Oxford, Mss. 979–83.

introduction of Renaissance methods and motifs, the living quarters of the houses of the well-to-do changed in character. Not least of all by the installation of sets of upholstered chairs. The principal patrons of music and the arts in general could now begin to appreciate the offerings of their protégés with less discomfort. When the idea became general that this life was not less worthy of attention than the next the power of the theologian—even though he might continue to argue—was gravely diminished. The Middle Ages did not end, nor did the Renaissance ever begin in Britain; the conditions indicated by this accepted terminology being prepared from empiricism out of social organisation and not from theory or philosophy. Thus, in essentials, the Reformation affected British music much less than the refurnishing of town and country houses. Sixteenth-century composers, aware that the pattern of patronage was changing, increasingly turned their talents towards an environment where musical instruments were symbols of status, and Long Galleries a necessary show-case for the new cultural trappings of the wealthy.

4

The Reformation

Henry VIII and Edward VI

PROVIDED THAT he maintained discretion and kept his convictions to himself a musician in the employment of the Church in England during the Tudor period was generally able to keep his office, or, if that was affected by the reduction or abolition of the foundation to which he belonged, to find another that was equally congenial. In its first phase the Reformation in England was concerned more with politics and finance than with theology and forms of liturgy—except when extreme Protestants fired occasional salvoes—and the Monarchy remained constant in its accommodation of music.

Henry VIII was, of course, a considerable patron of music and, being a composer, was disposed to protect an art in which his countrymen were more likely to gain foreign approval than in any other. In his *Life of Henry VIII* (1649) Lord Herbert of Cherbury allowed that the King had composed two anthems, 'which were usually sung in his Chappels'. In Hall's *Chronicle* a more generous list is given, in the course of a highly coloured account of the cultural activities of the royal routine: 'From [Greenwich] the whole Courte removed to Wyndesore, than begynning his progresse, exercisyng hym self daily in shotyng, singing, dancyng, wrastelyng, casting of the barre, plaiying at the recorders, flute, virginals, and in setting of songes, makyng of balettes, and dyd set ii [two] goodly masses, every of them fyve partes, which were songe oftentimes in hys chapel, and afterwardes in diverse other places.'[1] Whatever the King's personal achievement there is no doubt that his servants did themselves

[1] Ed. 1809, p. 515, referring to the year 1520. Songs, Ballads and Instrumental Pieces reputedly composed by Henry VIII, and contained in B.M. Add. Ms. 31922, were arranged by Lady Mary Trefusis, a friend of Edward Elgar, and published for the Roxburghe Club in 1912. The same volume also prints the list of the royal musical instruments from B.M. Harl. Ms. 1419.

justice in their performance of sacred music. When the Italian plenipotentiaries Piero Pasqualigo and Sebastiano Giustiniani came to England in 1515 they were ecstatic in their praises of the Chapel Royal, whose 'voices . . . were in truth rather divine than human; they did not chaunt, but sang like angels'.[1]

The chief composer of this period was Robert Fayrfax, whose membership of the Chapel Royal was combined with the position of organist of St. Albans Abbey, where the organ—said to have been presented by Abbot John Whethamstede in 1462—was reputed to have been one of the best in England. In 1501 Fayrfax became a Bachelor of Music at Cambridge, proceeding to his doctor's degree three years later. His exercise was the Mass *O quam glorifica*. In 1514 Fayrfax became a 'Poor Knight of Windsor, and, although no record of his connection with the music of St. George's Chapel can be proved, it may be that he was, in some way, connected with the festivities previously described. Whether this be so or not, it is clear that any judgement of his music based on paper evidence, or without taking into account the resources over and above those of the singers, must be deficient. Even within the field of vocal music there were tonal innovations, of which the chief was the exploitation of the deep bass voice. Insofar as English composers had long enjoyed a reputation for euphony, for resonant and full harmonies, it is clear that in obedience to this tradition the purely sensuous effect of varied sonorities was given due consideration. In the light of such consideration the 'dignified' style of Fayrfax, enhanced by available instrumentation, takes on a significance hardly appreciated by some earlier writers such as Walker, who could write of 'smoothly massive sound . . . but (as a rule) decidedly heavy and inclined to be dull'.[2] The extant music of Fayrfax,[3] rather more restricted in purpose than that of the more versatile Cornyshe, includes six Masses, two Magnificats, a number of motets, nine part-songs, and two instrumental pieces. Church music was mostly in five parts—the full complement being used sparingly and in contrast with frequent two- and three-part groupings—and the secular songs in three. Except for that which was a 'parody-mass', based on his own motet '*O bone Jesu*', Fayrfax's Masses were each founded on a plainsong tenor motiv according to precedent. The *Albanus* Mass, for St. Albans Abbey, holds especial interest for two reasons. First, it used a theme previously employed by John Dunstable in his motet *Albanus roseo*; second, it was a highly scientific essay in academic counterpoint after the Flemish manner. Having thus

[1] Quoted in W. B. Rye, *England as seen by Foreigners in the days of Elizabeth and James I*, London, 1865, p. xlv.

[2] Op. cit., p. 27.

[3] Listed in Anselm Hughes, 'The Works of Robert Fairfax', *M. & L.*, 30, 1949, p. 118.

shown that he could compose in this manner Fayrfax thereafter relinquished the sterner disciplines of the style. Even so his retention of the general principle of imitative openings, as shown in the Mass *Tecum principium*—and the motet *Aeterne laudis lilium*, was a signpost to the future, when English method would formally become more closely associated with that of the Continent.

Of Fayrfax's contemporaries the Welshman, John Lloyd, a colleague in the Chapel Royal, and Nicholas Ludford, of the foundation of St. Stephen's, Westminster, were also engaged in the provision of liturgical music, of similar style to that of Fayrfax, for the royal devotions. The works of these composers, characteristic of their era, represent the consistent policy of Henry VIII in respect of the liturgy and the place of music within it. This policy was outlined by the King in an injunction to his household in January 1526: 'It is ordered for the better administration of divine service that the Master of the children of the King's Chapell with six of the same children and six men with some offices of the vestry shall give their contynuall attendance in the King's Court, and dailie to have a masse of Our Lady before Noone and on Sondaies and Holly Daies, masse of the day besides Our Lady Masse and an antempe in the afternoone.[1]

But by now events were in train which were radically to affect not only the direction of ecclesiastical music in Britain, but also the whole course of British life and thought. In Rome the rebuilding of St. Peter's led to Pope Leo X making additional demands on the faithful—and those who were less than faithful—which encouraged discontent in more than one country where papal pretensions were already under severe scrutiny. This discontent, set in a context of peasant dissatisfaction, of which the theological implications were developed by Thomas Müntzer, gave Luther the opportunity to assume leadership of Protestant thought in Germany. In 1517 his Ninety-Five Theses were affixed to the church door at Wittenberg. Three years later there followed his excommunication. In 1521 Melanchthon added his scholarly support to the principles of Lutheranism and among those who flocked to Melanchthon's lectures at the University of Wittenberg members of the University of Cambridge were to be found. In 1524 Wolsey, not unaware of the necessity for church reform, and for a process of rationalisation, instituted a Visitation of the religious houses, and at once suppressed some forty of the least effective, devoting the endowments either to his own needs or to those of his educational foundations. Dynastic requirements—Katherine of Aragon not having provided a male heir to the throne—and personal inclinations—Anne Boleyn exercising an irresistible attraction—led Henry VIII to

[1] H. C. de Lafontaine, *The King's Musick*, London, 1909, p. 5.

initiate proceedings for divorce. These, in due course brought to the consideration of legal and ecclesiastical authorities throughout Europe, were terminated by unilateral action on the part of the King, who in 1533 married Anne Boleyn—by now pregnant—and had her crowned as Queen. Events moved inexorably forward. In 1534 the King declared himself the Head of the Church. Two years later the Suppression of the Monasteries, during which more than a thousand houses were dissolved, began. The dislocation of the established order involved both peculation and speculation as properties and privileges were traded, in general favour of the royal revenues but with much personal gain, to innumerable agents. These formed a new élite. As this rough process of nationalisation went on, although without any particular intention of altering the substance of the Faith, division between Catholic and Protestant within the Church became apparent. Thus, on the one hand the Statute of Six Articles, of 1539, asserted Catholic doctrines, denial of which was discouraged by the probability of being burned at the stake, while on the other, Cranmer's 'Great Bible' in the vernacular based on Coverdale's authorised translation of 1535 was issued, also in 1539. The Catholics were led by the Duke of Norfolk and Stephen Gardiner, Bishop of Winchester, the Protestants by Cranmer, Hugh Latimer, and Thomas Cromwell.

In a situation in which prominent commitment to any political or religious principle was liable to result in incarceration or execution, most musicians chose the path of discretion rather than that of valour, and for the better part of a century accommodated conviction to whatever causes seemed least disastrous to their careers. Of the Henrican composers two stand out because, for various reasons, they were not content to temporise. One was Richard Sampson, sometime chaplain to Henry VIII, Dean of the Chapel Royal, and Bishop of Chichester and subsequently of Lichfield and Coventry; the other was John Taverner. Sampson, author of a motet in praise of the King—*Psallite felices*,[1] adopted the Flemish style not only on account of its aesthetic qualities but also because of its liturgical propriety. Additional encouragement to cultivate the Flemish style—the eventual influence of which is best indicated in the contents of the Petre Part Books (see p. 124)—came from Anne Boleyn, whose favourite composers were said to have been Josquin des Prés and his pupil Jean Mouton. Sampson, like Henry VIII, was vigorously Catholic in churchmanship, and as a supporter of Gardiner was arrested on Cromwell's orders in 1540, committed to the Tower of London, accused of treason, but released on the downfall of Cromwell later in the same year. At the time of his examination Sampson tried to exculpate himself by pleading that he had

[1] B.M. Royal Ms. 11 E. xi.

been under the influence of the more able and more political Tunstall, Bishop of Durham.

It is a perverse twist of fortune that has brought John Taverner down to the present time as one of the leading Catholic composers of his age. In all probability a native of Boston in Lincolnshire, Taverner was first employed at the Collegiate Church of Tattershall in the same county. In 1526 he became Informator (Master) of the Children in Wolsey's Cardinal College, in Oxford, which appointment he held until 1530. In 1528 Wolsey sent a commission to Oxford to investigate the orthodoxy of the members of his college, as a result of which Taverner, infected by the Lutheranism that caused the setting-up of the commission, was accused of heresy and imprisoned. He regained his freedom not through recantation but through Wolsey's contemptuous excusing of his misdemeanours on the grounds that he was 'but a musician'. In later life Taverner regretted that 'he had made Songes to Popish Ditties in the time of his blindness'. But those 'songes' represent the high point of Henrican music, and the effective terminal point of the English later medieval tradition. Taverner's surviving works included eight Masses, three settings of the Christe Eleison, a separate Kyrie entitled the 'Leroy' Kyrie, three Magnificats, a Te Deum, and twenty-eight motets, as well as three secular pieces. His music is comprehensive: it contains the background of experience of native style in a free flow of melody, in rhythmic diversity, and in occasional reference to such practices as rota and hocket. A distinctive feature of the melodic idiom is Taverner's frequent employment of sequence. His Masses adhere to the principles of *cantus firmus* and 'head-motive'—the 'head-motive' in Taverner sometimes being derived from the *cantus firmus*—but imitative points discipline the polyphony. In the Mass *O Michael* and in some of his antiphons Taverner practises the stricter canonic imitation characteristic of contemporary European style and to be familiarised in English music by the next generation of Tudor composers. In accordance with general convention Taverner gave more or less equal time to the four Mass movements customarily set by English composers,[1] but by skilled contrasts of groups of voices and by an evident feeling for the transmutation of verbal with musical symbols, he underwrote competence in technique with a sense of coherent design and semantic relevance [Ex. 1]. Of all Taverner's Masses the most celebrated is the *Westron Wynde*, in which the *cantus firmus* is a folk-melody, otherwise similarly and exceptionally used by John Shepherd and Christopher Tye.

[1] The Kyrie was not usually set in polyphony, exceptional cases being found, however, in Masses by Thomas Appleby, William Byrd's predecessor at Lincoln, William Mundy, vicar-choral of St. Paul's Cathedral and Gentleman of the Chapel Royal, and Byrd himself.

1.

Taverner's Protestant convictions, however, became so strong that he resigned his career as musician to join the company of Thomas Cromwell's agents, and in 1538–9, having returned to Boston, he took part in the suppression of four friaries. A member of the Corpus Christi Guild and in due course an alderman of the town, he destroyed the Rood in St. Botolph's Church and otherwise energetically assisted in the extirpation of Catholicism. In or about 1545 Taverner's Masses *Sine Nomine*[1] and *Small Devotion* were arranged with English words,[2] thus meeting a requirement on which the Protestant reformers became increasingly insistent.

While Sampson and Taverner stood on principle, or calculated their prospects with an unusual intrepidity, the majority of musicians watched

[1] The Mass *Sine Nomine* is described as a 'Meane Mass' in one of the Petre Part-Books; that is to say, a Mass in which the mean, or counter-tenor voice, is the highest part.

[2] Bodl. Mss. Mus. Sch. E. 420–22.

the processes of change with apparent unconcern. The surrender of the monasteries was virtually complete by 1540, and the resettlement of musicians in a society which was sympathetic to the art was easier to accomplish than that of some of the dispossessed religious. Thomas Tallis, formerly organist at Dover Priory and a singer at Waltham Holy Cross, for example, transferred to Canterbury Cathedral before being admitted a Gentleman of the Chapel Royal about 1542. John Byrchley, a schoolmaster in the monastery at Chester, became organist of the New Foundation of the Cathedral—and boarded the eight singing-boys at his house for 12d. a week per boy. In addition to the boys the establishment allowed for six Conducts (singing-men) and six Minor Canons.[1] The dispersal of organs from monastic institutions often meant their installation in manor houses, and with a general increase in opportunities for private tuition some formerly monastic musicians found new patrons among those who had appropriated the properties of the old. On occasion such employment was conditioned by religious sympathies, and later in the century sometimes served as a convenient cover for other and more hazardous activities.

Henry VIII re-organised the cathedrals in 1542 and in those of the New Foundation the office of organist (generally containing the Mastership of the Choristers) was recognised as one that was distinct, and not, as in the constitutions of the cathedrals of the Old Foundation, as a duty undertaken by a conveniently qualified lay clerk, vicar-choral, minor canon, or priest-vicar. The duties of an organist were much as they had always been, and are shown in the agreements made at Christ Church, Dublin, between the Dean and Chapter and Robert Hayward. The latter undertook to play the organ, 'to keep Our Lady's Mass and Anthem daily, Jesus' Mass every Friday, . . . and Matins when the organs play on the eight principal Feasts . . .; to procure, at the expense of the Church, suitable songs; . . . to instruct the choristers in Pricksong and Descant to "four minims", and to play Our Lady's Mass, all instruments being found for them during the time of their child's voice, and to present them to the Chauntor to be admitted . . .'[2] The choral foundations of the English Church, therefore, were on the whole unimpaired by the first phase of the Reformation, and smaller churches even improved their position. Thus in the Bablake Church in Coventry the post-Reformation constitution allowed for a Warden, eight priests, a Master for the Grammar

[1] The last Abbot became the first Dean of Chester. Of the six Canons of the new foundation four were ex-monks of St. Werburgh's and one ex-Warden of the Grey Friars. Most minor offices were carried on as before and so was the Order of Service until the time of Edward VI. See J. C. Bridge, 'The Organists of Chester Cathedral', in *Chester Archaeological Soc.*, XIX, I, pp. 63–81.

[2] See J. E. West, *Cathedral Organists*, London, 1921, p. 28.

School, two singing clerks, at the annual cost of £8, and two singing boys, who received £2 a year.[1]

But across the royal intention to preserve the ancient liturgy came the arguments of those who disputed the claims of music within religion and those who preferred a liturgy in the vernacular. In 1536 a set of *Seventy-eight Faults and Abuses of Religion* was presented to the King in which it was stated: 'Syngyng and saying of Mass, Matins or Evensong, is but rorying, howling, whistling, mummying, conjuryng, and jugelyng, and the playing of the organys a foolish vanitie'. Eight years later Cranmer wrote to the King proposing that church music should be 'not full of notes, [but] as near as may be for every syllable a note so that it may be sung distinctly and devoutly'.[2] It was, however, not until the reign of Edward VI—which gave the Protestant party under the leadership of Somerset an ascendancy—that the Reformation in the accepted sense of the word became effective. In 1548 it was enjoined that there should be allowed 'no Anthemes off our Lady or other saynts but onely of our Lord. And then not Latin but choseyng owte the best and moste soundyng to cristen religion they shall turne the same into Englishe settyng, thereunto a playn and distincte note, for every sillable one, they shall singe them and none other'[3] Two years later the first *Book of Common Prayer*, the principal work of Cranmer, was ratified by the Act of Uniformity. To ensure conformity in a divided society a strong heresy commission of twenty-five members was set up.

The arguments for simplification of church music were not unreasonable and, in different ways, were exposed not only in the Reformation but also in the Counter-Reformation. The consequences of debate were the model *Missa brevis* of Palestrina, the Calvinist Psalm, the Lutheran chorale, and the English Service, anthem, and psalm-tune. The English (but not Scottish) aptitude for compromise was fully tested in a period in which it was never clear which of the theological and political factions would gain the upper hand. Taverner, John Shepherd, of Magdalen College, Oxford, and Thomas Tallis, wrote Masses in similar homophonic style, with each syllable duly accommodated in accordance with the new injunctions: these were entitled 'Playn Song' masses. In the Wanley Part-Books[4] there are similar settings of the English Liturgy issued by Cranmer in 1544 with a plainsong melody, possibly supplied by John Merbecke. Anthems for the King had long occupied the attention of official composers. The first to an English text, a prayer for victory over his enemies (who may have

[1] Sharp, op. cit., p. 135.
[2] See E. H. Fellows, *English Cathedral Music*, London, 1941, p. 25.
[3] *Lincoln Statutes*, iii, pp. 592–3, quoted in Harrison, op. cit., p. 288 f.n. 1.
[4] Bodl. Mss. Mus. Sch. E. 420–22.

been Scots, French, or even riotous English), belongs to the opening years of the reign of Edward VI.[1] In 1550 John Merbecke produced the work for which he is remembered—the *Book of Common Praier noted*, in which the new liturgy, insofar as music was required, was set to a series of chants either adapted from those that were traditional or of Merbecke's invention in a mensural plainsong style.[2]

Merbecke, clerk and from 1541 organist of St. George's Chapel, Windsor, like Taverner was a convinced Protestant convert. In the early part of his career he wrote the Mass *Per arma justitiae*, and some motets. But, converted by Calvinism, he was arrested in 1542–3 after a search of his home had revealed incriminating literature and the manuscript of an English Concordance to the Bible of his own compilation. After interrogation by Gardiner he was returned to Windsor where, after being tried, he was condemned to death. Others arrested with him were executed, but Merbecke—being invidiously favoured as a musician—was reprieved. The changes in policy that took place after the death of Henry VIII gave Merbecke his opportunity to apply his Protestantism, and in the year in which he published the *Book of Common Praier noted*, he was made a Doctor of Music at Oxford. But the ideal of such plainness as was advocated by Merbecke made little headway against the Prayer Book revision of 1552, the reluctance of establishments to reduce their choirs to unison singing, and the Marian reversal of policy, Merbecke's melodies for the Litany and the versicles and responses were the foundation of the settings of this part of the liturgy by Tallis and Byrd. Among the earliest work for the English liturgy which conformed to the required Cranmer standards are Tallis's 'Short Service in the Dorian Mode', while his anthems *Hear the voice and prayer* and *If ye love me*[3] also belong to this period.

Among the innovations of the time none was more significant for the future of English church music than the adoption of the principle of the metrical psalter. After more or less academic experimentation by the poets Surrey and Wyatt, and the quasi-Lutheran *Goostly Psalmes and Spirituall songes* of Coverdale, which was indebted to contemporary German hymnbooks, Thomas Sternhold, Groom of the King's Robes, published a metrical psalter, without music, in 1549. In the same year Robert Crowley's *Psalter* appeared, with music anticipating the style of the Anglican chant of a century later. In 1550 William Hunnis, successor to Richard Edwards as Master of the Chapel Royal, also published a *Psalter*, but without music. Three years later Francis Seagar's *Psalter* was added to those already in use. In this book the music, in four parts, and in simple motet style, was

1 *O Lorde Christe Jesu, that art Kyng*, B.M. Ms. Royal Appendix, 74–6.

2 See 'John Merbecke' in *A Forgotten Psalter*, R. R. Terry, London, 1929, p. 56.

3 Both contained in Bodl. Mss. Mus. Sch. e. 420–22.

given. In the same year, the last of Edward VI's reign, Christopher Tye brought out his didactic, rhymed, *Actes of the Apostles*. These, like the Seagar collection in easy motet style, brought into the sphere of church music impulses evident in the secular part-songs of such earlier Henrican composers as Cornyshe and Fayrfax, which when subjected to still further modification resulted in the characteristic English psalm- and hymn-tune. But with the death of Edward VI and the accession of the Catholic Mary, further development of reformist ideals were halted. Those who entertained such ideals went overseas, to strengthen their convictions in the main centres of Lutheranism and Calvinism, and to await the next reversal of fortune.

Mary Tudor

Mary Tudor ruled for five years, during which a divided country was once again, after absolution, put under the spiritual dominion of the Pope. The 'old religion', at a cost of three hundred or so martyrs, was restored and the decencies of worship, that had been severely mauled during the previous reign, renewed. A few more years of the enthusiasm of Edward VI's anti-papist agents would have grievously reduced the capacity of the choral foundations. These, if associated with religious colleges or chantries, together with similarly supported schools, were to be abolished on the grounds that they propagated superstition. The Collegiate Church of Manchester, indeed, had its Charter of 1421 (Henry V) cancelled by Edward VI, but Mary immediately granted a new Charter, which was confirmed by both Elizabeth I in 1578, and Charles I in 1635. Organs, by now a severe cause of disputation between the extremists of religion, were in danger of indiscriminate destruction.

The intervention of the Marian period prevented further wholesale spoliation of churches and properties, but not before heaps of 'antiphones, missals, scrayles, processionals, manuals, legends, pyes, portvyses', and so on, had been offered up on the funeral pyres of Protestant zeal. Queen Mary (on the secular side, no less devoted to the maintenance of an adequate musical staff than her father) made it possible for the tradition of English church music to be maintained, and renewed under the protection of her successor. On the occasion of the marriage of Mary to Philip II of Spain in the summer of 1554 English musicians, if so disposed, were able to learn of the quality of the music of Spain. Under Antonio de Cabezón a company from the royal chapel in Madrid took part in the High Mass celebrated in Winchester Cathedral. At about the same time Orlando di Lasso is reported to have visited England. The incorporation of French and Italian church music of this era in addition to that from Flemish sources—within the anthologies and in Catholic establishments—is indicated by the contents of the Petre Part-Books.

Elizabeth I

With the accession of Elizabeth the Church reverted to its Henrican principles, and in 1559 another, modified, version of the Prayer Book in English became obligatory. The Queen became the 'Supreme Governor' of the Church, and conformity was enjoined by the Oath of Supremacy. Those in violent opposition emigrated,[1] and since the English people had developed a strong sense of nationalism under the Tudors a too overt show of Catholic belief could give rise to suspicions of treasonable behaviour. On the whole, however, the central affairs of Church and State were marked by a degree of tolerance. Sebastian Westcott, organist of St. Paul's from 1551 to 1582, was one who refused to subscribe to the Act of Uniformity in 1559 but was not penalised, while at the time of the rising in the north ten years later John Brimley, organist at Durham, came under the suspicion of disloyalty but managed to extricate himself without difficulty. Authority still remained, and was to continue to remain, generally indulgent, especially to musicians. The Church was so accommodating that the composer could set English words as given in the liturgy, or, by 1540, he could use Latin texts—a translation of the Second Prayer Book having been issued by Walter Haddon and approved for use in the Universities, the Colleges at Winchester and Eton, and the royal peculiars. The Elizabethan church musician thus had no lack of opportunity.

The Mulliner Book

At this juncture one particular collection stands out as symbolising the main trends of musical development in the middle years of the sixteenth century. This is the *Mulliner Book*,[2] once the property of the copyist Thomas Mulliner, a musician thought to have been associated with St. Paul's Cathedral, who became organist of Corpus Christi College, Oxford, in 1563. The *Mulliner Book* was made for an organist and is symptomatic not only of the reverence in which this instrument was held by English

[1] John Bolt of Exeter, and Nicholas Morgan and Thomas (or Richard) Morris, both of the Chapel Royal, were among those who took up church appointments in France or the Low Countries during Elizabeth's reign; while many English musicians were to be found in secular employment on the continent.

[2] B.M. Add. Ms. 30513. See *The Mulliner Book* (*Musica Britannica*, I, 1951), ed. by Denis Stevens and *A Commentary* thereon, 1952.

musicians, but also of the way in which keyboard music was progressing in its own right. Starting as a compendium of church music arranged for organ, the collection finished by including dance pieces for clavichord or virginals, and music for cittern. Within these broad limits the contents comprised Latin motets and English anthems, secular part-songs, arrangements of consort music, and fantasias for organ solo. Thus from the *Mulliner Book* alone an index of mid-sixteenth-century musical activity can be constructed.

In the first part of the collection (a number of pieces are anonymous) these composers are named: Richard Allwood, a priest;[1] (Richard?) Forrest, Gentleman of the Chapel Royal in 1552 and Master of the Children at Windsor in 1564; John Redford, successively chorister, vicar choral, and organist of St. Paul's Cathedral; William Shelbye, organist of Canterbury Cathedral from 1547 to 1553; and Taverner. In the second part, dating from Mulliner's taking up his appointment in Oxford, are: William Blitheman, organist of Christ Church, Oxford, in 1564, and of the Chapel Royal from 1585, and the teacher of John Bull; Nicholas Carleton, of whom no personal details are known, but whose 'Verse for two to play on one Virginall or Organ'[2] represents a departure in keyboard playing; Richard Edwards, Master of the Chapel Royal in 1563, and as such busily occupied not only in composing music but also occasional poetry, and dramatic interludes;[3] (John?) Heath; Robert Johnson, a Scotsman, who, facing a charge of heresy, fled to England to become a minor canon at Windsor during the reign of Henry VIII; William Mundy, a vicar choral of St. Paul's Cathedral, and member of the Chapel Royal in 1563; (?) Newman;[4] Tallis; Tye; and Robert White, Tye's son-in-law, organist at Ely and Chester Cathedrals, and, in 1570, Master of the Choristers at Westminster Abbey.

In the pieces based on plainsong the composers of *Mulliner* departed from the previous principle of maintaining the *cantus firmus* in the tenor part, and the varied treatments of given themes range from fluent but formal contrapuntal variation to pieces as imaginative in keyboard conception as those by Carleton and Blitheman, two composers who in feeling for virtuoso and decorative effects, and textural variety, anticipate the brilliance of the English school of keyboard composers of the next generation. A number of pieces bear the title *In Nomine*, and these have especial interest.

[1] Composer of the Mass, *Praise Him Praiseworthy* and of keyboard music in B.M. Add. Ms. 30485.

[2] B.M. Add. Ms. 29996, where there is also a similar piece by Thomas Tomkins.

[3] E.g. *Damon and Pythias*, 1565.

[4] Other musicians of this name practising during the sixteenth century were Thomas and John, both royal trumpeters.

A plainsong theme, for the antiphon *Gloria tibi Trinitas,* formed the basis of Taverner's six-part Mass of that title,[1] but only in one place does the complete melody appear in notes of equal length, in duple time, and accompanied by three other voices—at the section commencing with the words 'In Nomine'. This section of Taverner's Mass proved generally attractive. Taverner (or another) arranged it to English words as 'In trouble and adversitie'[2] and, again, as 'O give thanks unto the Lord',[3] and it appears in *Mulliner* as for keyboard. In *Mulliner* there are pieces on the *In Nomine* motiv by Allwood, Blitheman, Carleton, Johnson, and Robert White (formerly attributed to anon). Of these works by Johnson and White are indubitably for viols.[4] [Ex. 2] From this point the *In*

2.

× *"In Nomine" motiv in semibreves*

Nomine went forward into English chamber music to culminate in the fantasias of Henry Purcell.[5] While the consort of viols was in due course to provide music that must rank among the principal achievements of the English, it should not be overlooked that the foundations of viol technique were laid, in Tudor days, by players imported from the Netherlands and Italy.[6] The presence of French dance tunes in *Mulliner* is also an acknowledgment of the interest of Henry VIII in music of that kind, and probably represents the work of John Heywood, grandfather of John Donne, who, versatile as dramatist and musician, supervised the virginals studies both of Henry VIII and Mary Tudor. Although he received one payment from the then Princess Elizabeth, Heywood, a staunch champion of Catholicism, deemed it prudent to disappear to the Low Countries on her accession. Among the viol pieces in *Mulliner* there is one by Newman of some

1 *Tudor Church Music,* I, pp. 126 *et seq.*

2 John Day, *Certaine notes set forth in fowre and three parts to be sung at the morning, Communion and evening praier,* . . . 1560.

3 B.M. Add. Mss. 30480–84.

4 Cf. arrangements for viols in Bodl. Mss. Mus. Sch. D. 212–16, and B.M. Add. Ms. 31390.

5 See Meyer, op. cit., Stevens, op. cit., Robert Donnington and Thurston Dart, 'The Origin of the In Nomine', *M. & L.*, 30, no. 2, 1949, p. 101, and G. Reese, 'The Origin of the English In Nomine', *Journal of the American Musicological Society,* vol. II, no. 1, 1949.

6 See H. C. de Lafontaine, op. cit., pp. 6, 8, 13.

especial interest since it is entitled *A fansye*, the first extant item so to be named.

The most celebrated example of secular vocal music in *Mulliner* is Richard Edwards's *In going to my naked bed* which, referring back to the Tudor song as conditioned by Cornyshe and Fayrfax and across to the simplified motet-anthem, has been accepted as a precursor of the English madrigal. In fact this, and other part-songs of *Mulliner*, are more particularly affected by the dramatic and utilitarian considerations that lay behind most early Tudor secular choral music represented in this anonymous love song [Ex. 3] and this patriotic piece [Ex. 4] and do not go far

3.

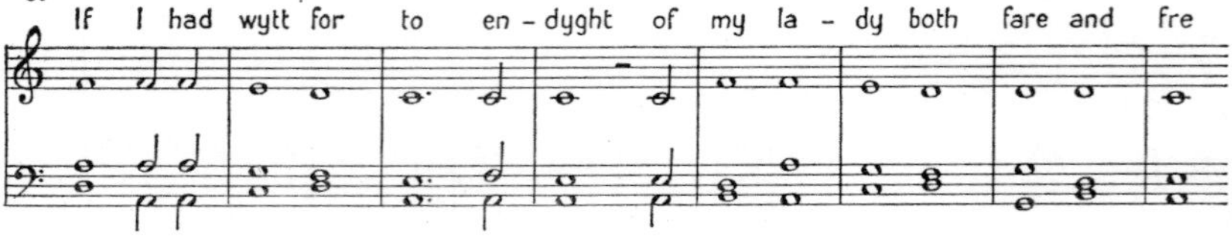

4.

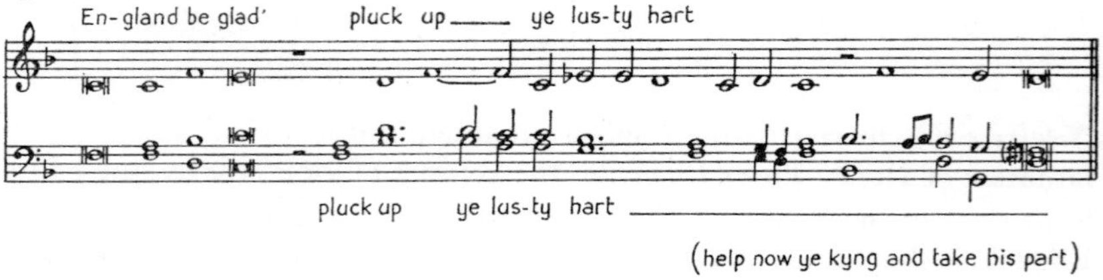

in the direction of intellectual and sensory stimulations as do the later madrigals. Nevertheless in their directness of utterance such works as those by Edwards and Tallis (*O ye tender babes* and *Like as the doleful dove* [Ex. 5]) have a persuasive quality, and their own individuality.

5.

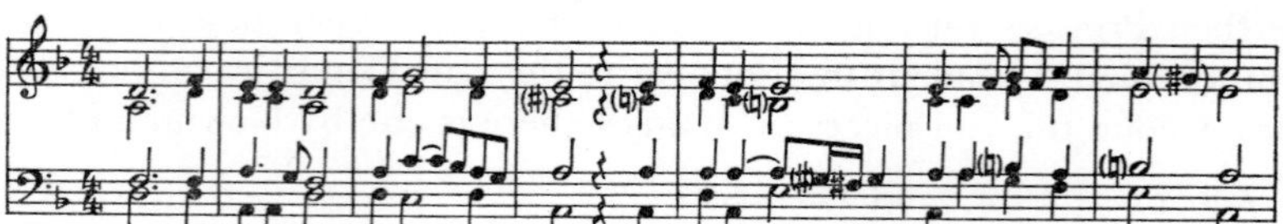

The *Mulliner Book* is a convenient summary of many aspects of British music during the initial stages of the Reformation and illustrates both developments in technique and the close relationship between secular and ecclesiastical practices. It represents, however, the official side of music—in so doing showing also the development of a professional musical status—and to be aware of the general richness of musical activity it is necessary to make an approach from another angle.

Popular Music and Drama

National unity may be imposed, as up to a point it was by the Tudors, with their talent for firm government and their method of putting policy into practice through the machinery of the Justices of the Peace. Equally, a condition of national solidarity may develop through the pressure of external events, as was demonstrated at the time of the Spanish Armada. But the permanent cohesion of a society depends on a community of interests and of feeling. That religious belief can contribute to stability may have been true at some point in the medieval history of Britain; by the sixteenth century it was palpably not true. On the other hand popular entertainment, holding the older values of pagan ritual and myth, did exercise a strong influence on the relationship between classes. Music and drama and their pageant progeny spread across town and country, embracing folk custom and court entertainment (by now restoring classical foundations in an earnest attempt to be contemporary insofar as European fashions were concerned) within a tradition of comprehensive expression. This embodied the elements of communal sentiments, sympathies, and antipathies. Folk art was rough and realistic, but it was also idealised. Its practice, involving many kinds of participant, both professional and non-professional, was some kind of democratic guarantee, and this in turn was assured by superior protection. Folk-art, however, contained all the qualities liable to prohibition by social dogmatists. It could be attacked on the grounds of irreligion, subversion, or immorality; it could also be put under restraint because it was said to encourage idleness. The kind of Puritanism that grew up in Britain during the Tudor period was so generously supported at the base that it could take exception to popular music and drama on every count. The philosophy engendered by the earliest Puritans is still to be observed in action in Britain.

The traditional scene showed an universal zest for Morris dances and jigs, for Robin Hood, St. George, and 'King' games, for mummery and minstrelsy in their various forms; for religious drama in all its vigour and variety; for the nonsensical, but socially critical, demonstrations of Licensed Fools and Lords of Misrule. Until 'the enforcement of the Elizabethan prayer-book', writes Margaret Dean-Smith, 'pagan and Christian rites could share the religious year, the same festival, the same building, and be witnessed by the same congregations.'[1]

[1] 'Folk-Play Origins of the English Masque', *Folk Lore*, LXV, September 1954, p. 77.

Among the Privy Purse expenses of Henry VII[1] there is ample evidence of royal support for the traditions. On 8 July 1492 there was payment of ten shillings 'to the may dancers of Lambeth for a May'; on 1 August the children [choristers] at Canterbury received 3s. 4d. 'for singing in the gardyn.' On 2 January 1494 two pounds was dispensed 'for playing of the Mourice Daunce'; on 30 September 1501 'theym that daunced the mer'[Morris] daunce' were recompensed with £1 6s. 8d., while on 4 February 1502 'one Lewes'[2] was paid £1 13s. 4d. for making arrangements for similar performance.

In the Churchwardens' Accounts of Kingston-on-Thames are many references to payments for players, dancers, pipers, and minstrels in respect of the Lord of Misrule and Hock Tide 'gaderyngs,' the Morris Dances, the May Day, Robin Hood and Kyngham Games,[3] which, under the patronage of the Vicar, brought in a steady flow of funds to the Parish Church. In the Churchwardens' Accounts of St. Helen's Church, Abingdon, items of expenditure selected from Nichols's abstract show how priorities changed with the strengthening of Puritan influence:

1559 For two doffin of Morres belles 1/0
1566 For setting up Robin Hoode's bower 1/6
1573 payde for a quire of paper to make
four bokes of Geneva salmes 4d.[4]

Games of one sort or another are also recorded, though less frequently, in other Churchwardens' Accounts, and the Kyngham Game appears in those of Croscombe and Yatton, in Somersetshire, and of St. Edmund's, Sarum. The Kingston performance, however, had more than a local reputation and at various times was transported to Croydon, and taken up and down the Thames by boat to be produced at convenient points between Walton and Richmond. In 1504–5 the part of the King in the Kyngham Game was undertaken by Robert Dengley, a member of the Butchers' Company, and, later, one of the two bailiffs of the town. In the May Day Game of the same year the King was played by William Kemp, thought to have been the grandfather of the celebrated dancer of

[1] Quoted by Chappell, *Old English Popular Music I*, 1893, pp. 33–4.

[2] Hakenett de Lewys, sometime minstrel of Henry VII?

[3] In 1489 Wynkyn de Worde published *Robyn Hode and Lytell Johan*, 'a newe playe for to be played in Maye games and very pleasaunte and full of pastyme'; there is a copy in the Bodleian Library.

[4] [John Nichols], *Illustrations of the Manners and Expenses of Antient Times in England*, London, 1797, pp. 142–3; Nichols writes: 'Upon my asking the late Mr. Handel, what he took to be the genuine and peculiar taste in music of the several nations in Europe; to the French, he gave the Minuet; to the Spaniard, the Saraband; to the Italian, the Arietta; and to the English, the Hornpipe, or Morris-dance'. This is attributed to T[homas] M[orell], p. 146.

Shakespeare's acquaintance. One by one financial records of these diversions disappear from the Kingston Accounts during the reign of Henry VIII, until only the Hock Tide ceremony remained in its pristine state. The final note of this occurs in 1578.[1] At the Gray's Inn Christmas Revels of 1594 the 'King-game' was performed, but described as a revival.

The Lord of Misrule was not only a parochial appointment in Tudor times, for such officers were to be found at Court, at the Inns of Court (a barrister of at least five years' standing, and of good birth), at the Colleges of Oxford and Cambridge (who must be a Master of Arts), and in larger private households. In 1551 George Ferrars was recognised, both ceremonially and administratively, as 'Lord of Misrule and Master of the Kinges pastimes' at the Court of Edward VI. The incorporation of popular drama-games in the royal entertainments resulted in a significant change of character in the more formal masques, which, in the time of Edward VI, became more burlesque, with 'drunken Maskes', masques of 'covetus men with longe noses', and masques of cats, all of which were to affect the ultimate shape of the Jacobean masque and, taking the long view, even of English opera. Some retrenchment during the Elizabethan period held further consequences for the future, for exotic elements were pruned and 'trade' masques—popular in Italy and France—with realistic dancing troupes of, for example, fishermen, fish-wives, market-wives and astronomers, were encouraged. Into these entertainments choristers, directed by their Masters, were introduced to provide the songs.[2] When Queen Elizabeth was on tour masques blending morality with pageantry were commonplace, notable provincial occasions being at Nottingham in 1562, at Kenilworth in 1575, in Norfolk in 1578,[3] and at Elvetham in 1591. When she was at Kenilworth certain citizens of Coventry, led by Captain Cox, a mason, came over to present their Hock-tide play in the hope that royal approval would save it from the Puritan preachers.

While the monarchy personally stood by popular entertainment and encouraged its fusion with advancing fashion, ministers of religion and other professional moralists continued a long campaign of disapproval.

[1] W. E. St. Lawrence Finny, 'Medieval Games and Gaderyngs at Kingston-upon-Thames', *Surrey Archaeological Collections*, 44, 1936, pp. 102 *et seq.*

[2] Sebastian Westcott of St. Paul's and Richard Edwards and William Hunnis of the Chapel Royal, and Richard Farrant, of St. George's, Windsor, were frequently required to train their choirboys both in singing and acting for interludes and other musico-dramatic entertainments. Richard Lee and John Taylor, Masters of the Choristers of St. Anthony's Hospital, were responsible for arranging music, performed by their choristers, for the Lord Mayoral Pageants of the mid-sixteenth century, for which the organisation was in the hands of the Merchant Taylors' Company.

[3] *A Discourse of the Queenes Maiesties entertainmente in Suffolk and Norfolk . . .*, Thomas Churchyard [n.d.].

In 1532 there was a proclamation against 'fond books, ballads, rhimes, and other lewd treatises in the English tongue', while four years later one John Hogon was arrested for furnishing words of impolite significance to the tune of *The Hunt is up*, a frequent vehicle for satire. In 1542 a Statute of Henry VIII forbade the ceremony of the boy-bishop, as being conducive to superstition. A purge of ballads was enjoined by the 'Act for the advancement of true religion' of 1543 on account of their generally deleterious effect on the youth of the realm.

In Coventry, where the city minstrels had long contributed to the entertainments managed by the municipality for St. John's Day, strong reaction set in before the middle of the century:

'And ye shall understond and know how the *Evyns* were furst found in old tyme. In the beginning of holi Chirche, it was so that the pepall cam to the Chirche with candellys brennyng, and wold *Wake* and come with light toward nyght to the Chirche to their devocions; and afterwards they fell to lecherie, and songs, daunces, harping, piping, and also to glotuny, and sinne, and so tourned the holiness to cursaydnesse; wherefore holi fathers ordained the pepall to leve that *waking*, and to fast the *Evyn*. But it is called *Vigilia*; that is *Waking* in English; and it is called the *Evyn*; for at evyn they were wont to come to Chirche.'[1]

By banning ballads and popular pastimes the authorities accomplished two things. First they rendered them more sectionally popular, for the greater the condemnation of popular songs by the upper the more enthusiastic was their cultivation by the lower classes; second, they encouraged a new edge of satire. This was particularly the case in Scotland, where after their abandonment by Statute in 1551, the Robin Hood entertainments described by Alexander Scott[2] were adapted for the purpose of ridiculing the Papists, while parody versions of ballads led to such stanzas as the following:

With huntis up, with huntis up,
It is now parfite day,
Jesus, our King, is gane hunting,
Quha lykis to speid they may.
The hunter is Christ, that huntis in haist,
The hundis ar Peter and Paull,
The Paip is the foxe, Rome is the rox
That rubbis us on the gall.[3]

[1] William Dugdale quoting from 'an old manuscript', in *History of Coventry*, p. 211.
[2] See 'Of May', *Poems of Alexander Scott*, in *Collection of George Bannatyne* (*Edinburgh*), *1568*, ed. by A. K. Donald, for Early English Text Society, 1902.
[3] Ibid.

Although some of the responsibility for the dispersal of established habits and conventions can be attributed to Puritans and politicians, they may be absolved from total censure. Ballads and folk-songs survived; so also did folk-plays, albeit in more modest forms, and as relics of the past rather than as living and spontaneous expressions of a communal purpose. The Mystery Plays were interdicted, but when Matthew Hutton and Edmund Grindal, Dean and Archbishop of York respectively, first lost the text of the Pater Noster play and then tried to eviscerate the Corpus Christi cycle the impetus of these plays was already spent. The reign of Mary could not restore the Mystery Plays to their former prosperity, although they were given due encouragement, and at Wakefield and Lincoln brief revivals took place. The Guilds of York, especially the Mercers, had continued to invest money in performances, but as early as 1527 neglect had set in so that the properties were in poor condition: the two great angels were each short of one wing; the little angel had disappeared altogether. So by 1575 had the York plays, the manuscripts having passed for the time being into the keeping of the Fairfax family. The Coventry plays also declined in popularity, the guilds increasingly trying to buy their way out of responsibility. The last authentic performance took place in 1579. With their conscience pricking somewhat after a five years gap, the authorities commissioned John Smythe, an Oxford scholar and formerly a pupil of the Free School, to write *The Destruction of Jerusalem*, taking due care to avoid all traces of popery. Although a good deal of money went into this the venture was not received with enthusiasm and the companies soon put their vehicles, pageant-houses, and properties on the second-hand market. The curtain came down in Coventry with an unwanted revival of John Smythe's play in 1591. The text of the Wakefield Plays was acquired by the Towneley family of Burnley, there, perhaps, to stimulate Edmund Spenser when writing his *Shepheardes Calendar*. After exactly two hundred years the civic authorities in Chester complained that the Plays were losing money (a modern point of view) and arraigned Sir John Savage, the Mayor, for extravagance. But there was an ominous lack of interest at a lower level, for in the same year Andrew Tailor, a dyer, went to prison rather than contribute 3s. 8d. towards the expenses of the Dyers' Company.[1] An attempt was made in 1600 to start the plays again, but to no avail: even the once popular wrestling-bout in the Play of the Shepherds had lost its attraction. The point was that by now dramatic interest was maintained by professional companies of which there were a number

[1] *A Brevary or some feue Collections of the Cittie of Chester* . . . compiled by David Rogers (*c.* 1609) from the papers of Robert Rogers, Archdeacon of Chester (d. 1595–6); copy in Chester City Archives, and B.M. Harl. Mss. 1944–8. In putting on 'Popish' plays Savage was also 'in contempt of an inhibition and the primate's letter from York'. Ormerod, *History of Cheshire*, I, p. 236.

attached to the greater households in the neighbourhood of Chester. In addition to teams of resident performers—usually supported by minstrels—there was opportunity to see touring troupes. In 1574 the Queen licensed Burbage, Perkyn, and Laneham to play in various counties. In 1584 the Earl of Essex's men performed in the High Street in Shrewsbury.[1] Six years later the Queen's players gave exhibitions of tumbling and rope-dancing in the same town. The Earl of Derby was a conspicuous patron of professional drama. In 1587 the Earl of Leicester's men visited Knowsley. A year later the Queen's players came. In 1589 the same players came again, followed later in the year by the Earl of Essex's company.[2] A nice balance was kept in those days: the Rector of Standish preached Puritanical sermons on Sunday mornings; the plays were put on in the afternoons. Against all this the old Mysteries stood no chance; but much of their tradition was absorbed into the drama of the Elizabethans, not least the tradition of music.

The Reformation affected taste directly, but its side-effects caused a major cultural revolution. For it was those to whom fortune and influence accrued as a result of the Reformation and collateral economic developments who were able to undertake fresh responsibilities in artistic patronage.

Since, however, special circumstances brought the music of Wales and Scotland into a new relationship with that of England during, and immediately after, the Reformation those countries may now be separately considered.

Music in Wales

The Tudor dynasty was not unmindful of its Cymric origins and when Owen, grandfather of Henry VII, was bringing the family name into prominence in the middle of the fifteenth century, a renascence of traditional Welsh music was taking place. In the first place this was due to Dafydd ap Gwilym (*c.* 1340–80), who developed the new metre of the *cywydd*.[3] Gwilym, whose poems were inspired both by the sentiments previously found in troubadour verse and by an endemic love of nature, renewed the bardic tradition in that he accompanied his declamation with harp. He also encouraged the separate development of music for the harp.

[1] The last Mystery Play to be performed in Shrewsbury was the *Passion of Christ*, produced in 1560 by Thomas Asheton, the drama-loving Headmaster of Shrewsbury School.

[2] *The Stanley Papers*, II, Chetham Society, Manchester, 1853, p. 65.

[3] The form of the *cywydd* centred on sequences of rhyming couplets, the lines ending with strong and weak accents alternately, and each being balanced in its distribution and repetition of consonants.

Such music, incorporating pentatonic elements borrowed from Ireland, but also including examples of chordal harmony in advance of such a convention elsewhere, passed through Eisteddfod usage into the keeping of William Penllyn.[1] Dafydd ap Gwilym, who was born in Cardiganshire, worked there, and was buried within the precincts of the Cistercian Abbey of Strata Florida (in the ruins of which is a memorial to him). This great church, founded by the Lord Rhys ap Gruffydd (a promoter of the Eisteddfod), in the twelfth century and staffed by Welshmen, was a powerful cultural centre and it is significant of the interfusion of church and bardic traditions that it was in this neighbourhood that the late medieval revival of music and poetry was most evident. This revival re-invigorated the institution of the Eisteddfod.

At a gathering of poets and musicians held at Carmarthen under the tutelage of Gruffudd ap Nicolas in 1451 the Eisteddfod arrangements approximated to those which are now familiar, with separate prizes for poetry, singing, and harp playing.[2] In 1523, the Eisteddfod now taking place at Caerwys, in Flintshire, the ancient Statute of Gruffydd ap Cynan was confirmed,[3] while in 1567 the successful candidates in the several competitions were respectively awarded silver models; of a bardic chair, of a tongue, of a harp and—since fiddling was now up-graded to competition status—of a *crwth*.[4] At this juncture the professional musicians of the Principality were concerned about the dilution of the profession by the unqualified, and in response to their supplication Queen Elizabeth signed a Proclamation of Chester, on 23 October 1567, with the intention of protecting their rights. Since '. . . Vagrants and Idle Persons naming themselves Minstrells, Rithmers and Barths, are lately grown into such an intolerable multitude within the principality of North Wales that not only gentlemen and others by their shameless disorders, are often times disquieted in their habitations, but also the expert Minstrels and Musicians in tonge and cunyng thereby much discouraged to Travail in the exercise and practice of their knowledge . . .'.[5] William Mostyn of Flintshire—whose ancestors held the privilege of bestowing the silver harp—was commissioned to form an examining body to license minstrels.

By this time, however, the musical culture of Wales—except that part of it represented in the one adequate cathedral establishment of St. David's —had passed its zenith, and the most gifted of its musical sons were to be

[1] See p. 38, fn. 1.

[2] This Eisteddfod is described in the Ms. of Paul Panton and Iolo Morganwg (B.M. Add. Ms. 15003, *c.* 1799).

[3] B.M. Add. Ms. 19711 (late sixteenth century).

[4] The details of this Eisteddfod, together with a list of the graduates, are recorded in B.M. Add. Ms. 14872.

[5] B.M. Add. Ms. 14905.

found in England. The Statute of the Union of England and Wales, effected in 1536, applied English laws to Wales and allowed to the Welsh the same rights enjoyed by the English. This enactment was a rational step necessitated not only by political and administrative requirements but also by the fact of the absorption of many Welshmen into English life over a period of years. The movement across the Marches at the end of the fifteenth and the beginning of the sixteenth centuries was similar to that across the Anglo-Scottish border which was to take place after the accession of James I. The Dissolution of the Monasteries was conducted in Wales with particular ruthlessness and liturgical music was almost entirely destroyed. But there had already been a considerable migration of trained personnel to England. The Welsh musician of greatest note practising in London at the beginning of the sixteenth century was the organist Philip ap Rhys, who was attached to St. Paul's Cathedral and was also organist of the Church of St. Mary-at-Hill in 1547.[1] Ap Rhys is the only British composer by whom an 'organ mass' is extant. This type of Mass, common in continental practice from the fifteenth to the seventeenth centuries, was organised antiphonally, with sections for organ alternating with those for celebrant or choir. The Mass by ap Rhys (denoting, possibly, foreign experience, or access to similar music in a Welsh acquisition since lost) is in two and three parts, fluently contrapuntal and rhythmically engaging, set over the relevant passages of plainsong.[2]

Other Welshmen known to have practised in the field of church music in London during the reign of Henry VIII included William Pasche, Clerk of St. Peter, West Cheap, organist and composer, and Richard ('Ryse') William, Master of the Choristers at St. Mary-at-Hill when ap Rhys was organist. Numerous other distinctively Welsh names may be found in the London church records of that era,[3] but Welshmen made their mark, as might have been expected, more conspicuously in secular vocations. The royal company of minstrels included Welsh players from 1485, and harpists found employment either at court or in private establishments, or both. Thus on 4 January 1548 the Petres of Ingatestone Hall, in Essex, were entertained by 'several Welsh harpers, three minstrels and Gilder the tumbler', all of whom earned their 'rewards'.[4] The most celebrated of the Welsh harpists was 'Blind More', who also visited

[1] Michael Tilmouth, *R.M.A. Research Chronicle No. 2*, 1962, p. 50.

[2] For discussion of this work see Denis Stevens, 'A Unique Tudor Organ Mass', in *Musica Disciplina*, vi, 1952. The Mass is contained in B.M. Add. Ms. 29996, which also has other settings by the same composer; of the antiphon *Miserere mihi Domine* (two-part), and of the offertory *Felix namque* (two/three-part).

[3] See Tilmouth, op. cit.

[4] F. G. Emmison, *Tudor Secretary*, London, 1961, p. 123.

Ingatestone, in 1550.[1] William Moore, who may have originated from near Shrewsbury,[2] was in the establishment of Henry VIII and was harpist both to Edward VI and Elizabeth. A composer of motets [Ex. 6][3] he was

6.

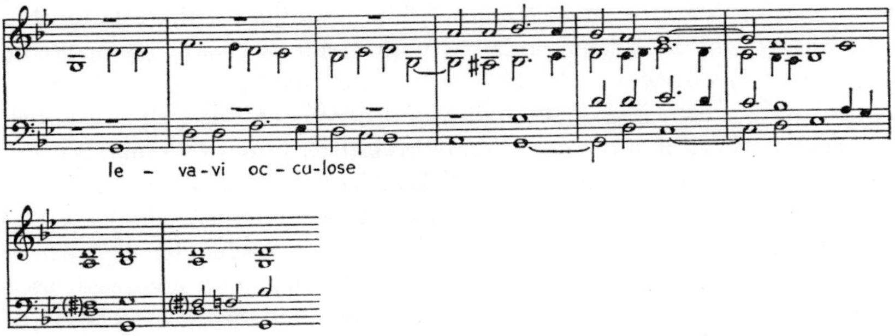

also otherwise involved in affairs and in 1539 was held in the Tower on a charge of treason, it being alleged that he had conveyed illicit messages from one abbey to another. Like other musicians he was quickly released. With the career of William Moore the place of the Welsh harpist in English society was established and the long line of his successors includes Powell, the acquaintance and colleague of Handel, and John and Thomas Thomas, who achieved world-wide recognition in the reign of Queen Victoria. But the diversion of Welsh talent to England in the sixteenth century struck Welsh music in its own right a damaging blow, from which it has never fully recovered.

Music in Scotland

The Scots, belonging to a separate kingdom, enjoyed a grander musical tradition than the Welsh[4] and the decline of this tradition during the sixteenth century appears, therefore, as more dramatic, though partial recovery at least was more quickly effected. The cultural independence of Scotland under the five James's, whose reigns stretched from the end of

[1] ib. p. 216.

[2] The records of Shrewsbury for 1520 show an entry 'In regardo dat' & vino expendito super Willum More, histrionem dni Reg' eo quod est cecus & principalis citherator Anglie 3/8'. H. Owen and J. B. Blakeway, *A History of Shrewsbury*, London, 1825, 2 vol., I, p. 326. The unusual term *histrionis,* covering also the profession of actor, is here used for the first time.

[3] *Levavi oculose* [*sic*], arranged for four viols, is in B.M. Add. Mss. 30480–84, and one single part of the five-part *Ad Dominum contribularer* in B.M. Harl. Ms. 7578.

[4] See, for instance, the splendour of the music for a royal occasion described by William Dunbar in *The Quenis Reception at Aberdein,* 1511.

the fourteenth to the middle of the sixteenth centuries, reached its peak during the sovereignties of James IV and James V. Both monarchs were skilled in music. James IV, under whose patronage the poetry of Henryson and Dunbar was written, maintained and extended the European connections of his country through the traditional association with France and a newly established mission to Venice, while he adjusted the relationship with England by his accommodation with Henry VII and his marriage with the Princess Margaret. His wider interests were reflected in his musical staff, which included English and continental as well as Scottish performers. Mindful of the intention of his father, James IV enhanced the royal dignities by refurbishing the royal palaces—his major work being at Holyrood—and renewing their ecclesiastical foundations. A major act of reconstitution was undertaken at Stirling, where James had been crowned, and in 1501 a Chapel Royal was there established, and endowed, as a collegiate foundation. Under Dean, Sub-dean, and Sacrist, its strength comprised 'sixteen canons sufficiently skilled in singing and other things, and six boys qualified also in singing and other things, or who may become so, for the celebration of the divine offices, as they are celebrated in the other collegiate churches of Scotland'. The church was furnished with three pairs of organs, and 'duo volumina in pergamino cum notis de ly faburdone'.[1] The Dean of the Chapel Royal at this time was Andrew Beaton, later to become Archbishop of St. Andrews, while the Sacristan was Alexander Paterson, author of a treatise *For Singing the Mass*.

The reverse suffered by the Scots at Flodden in 1513 supplied James V with incentive to strengthen the French alliance, which he underwrote with his marriages first to Madeleine, daughter of Francis I, and then, after her death, to Mary of Guise. From this connection sprang a new and lively impulse in Scottish secular music. James also continued the process of expansion of the greater royal and religious foundations, and in 1544 turned his attention to the ancient Cathedral of St. Magnus, at Kirkwall, a unique foundation in that it had come directly under the control of the Burgh of Kirkwall since the return of Orkney to the Scottish dominions in 1486. James V revised the Charter of James III and installed a Precentor to rule the singers in the Quire, 'in the elevation or depression of their Songs', a Chancellor, 'to look to the preserving and mending of the Books of the Quire', a Sub-Chancellor, 'who was also organist, thirteen Chaplains—the first acting as Master of the Grammar School, and the second as Head of the Song School, and six boys, who were to be Taper-bearers as well as choristers.'[2]

[1] J. G. Dalyell, *A Brief Analysis of the Chartularies of the Abbey of Cambuskenneth, Chapel Royal of Stirling, Preceptory of St. Anthony at Leith*, Edinburgh, 1828, pp. 52 and 69.
[2] James Wallace, *A Description of the Isles of Orkney*, Edinburgh, 1693.

The chief Scottish composers during the first part of the sixteenth century were Robert Carver, Canon of Scone; John Fethy, Master of the Song School of St. Nicholas in Aberdeen, a notable organist and poet; David Peebles, Canon of St. Andrews, described as 'one of the principall musitians in all this Land in his tyme', and also respected as a teacher; Andrew Kemp, master of Sang Scule of St. Andrews; Andrew Blackhall, Canon of the Abbey of Holyrood; and Robert Johnson. The latter, presumably coming under examination by the Ecclesiastical Commission for the Extirpation of Heresy, set up by James V in 1534, was found to be ideologically unreliable. To avoid the fate of David Straiton and Nicholas Gourlay, who were burned on Calton Hill, Johnson went to England.

The casualty rate in Scottish musical manuscripts was high when the Reformation eventually came to Scotland through John Knox, but among those that have survived are the *Carver Choirbook*, or *Scone Antiphonary*,[1] and the *Dunkeld Antiphonary*.[2] Of the works of Robert Carver in the first of these manuscripts, two compel particular attention. Although the secular melody *L'Homme Armé* was frequently used as the basis of Mass music on the Continent, the only British example extant is that by Carver [Ex. 7]. It is significant that the *Carver Choirbook* also contains the

7.

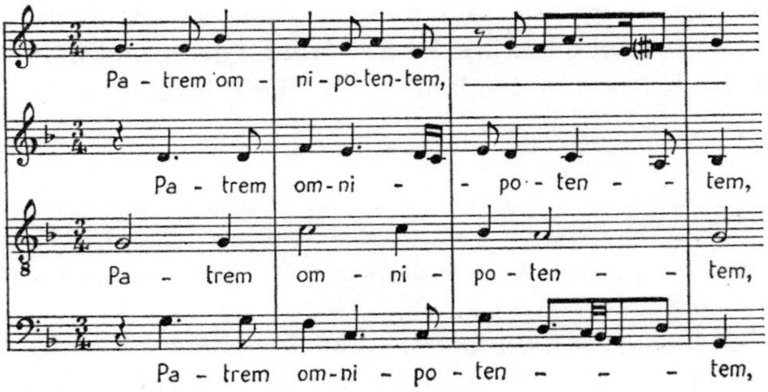

"L'homme armé" *motiv in tenor*

Mass *L'Homme Armé* by Dufay. The second outstanding work by Carver is the motet *O bone Jesu*, in which the composer, writing for nineteen (solo) voices, shows the same splendid feeling for new and varied sonorities that has previously been noted in the *Eton Choirbook*. The *Dunkeld Antiphonary*,

1 National Library of Scotland, Adv. Ms. 5.1.15.

2 Edinburgh University Library, Ms. 64. Other pre-Reformation music is contained in the Part-Books of Thomas Wode (1562–*c.*1590) preserved in Edinburgh and Dublin Universities and the British Museum. Wode, living in a turbulent period, cast his net as wide as possible, for he feared lest music 'sall perishe in this Land al utterlye'.

of which five of the six part-books are extant, gives strong evidence of the influence in Scotland of continental music, for the majority of its contents are derived from European printed sources. A finely fluent Mass, *Felix namque*,[1] shows, however, that native talent for polyphonic composition was widespread. The ability to undertake the performance of such music reflects creditably on the cathedral establishment of Dunkeld, in which, according to Alexander Miln, the outstanding members were Stephen Young, John Penecuick, John Stevenson, Thomas Bethoun, and William Martyn. Like the other Scottish cathedrals that at Dunkeld faithfully maintained its Sang Scule.

National characteristics are not so constant as is often thought, and the Scottish gentleman of the sixteenth century frequently had a strain of polished gaiety that could serve as a convincing passport when abroad. Thus the adventurer James Crichton, reputedly son of Lord Robert Crichton, could easily insinuate himself into the courts of Mantua and Venice because he was accepted as an expert in philosophy and music. That Crichton was a murderer was neither here nor there in the heated emotional climate of Italy. A Scottish aristocrat was amply prepared for the politer entertainments of the Renaissance by the civilised courtly exercises of his country. Mary of Guise and Mary, Queen of Scots, encouraged both secular vocal and instrumental music. Influenced by French *chanson*, the part-songs (or solo songs with accompaniment for viols) practised at Court were marked by a rhythmic definition induced by the dance. [Ex. 8]. If Mary of Scotland (who, like Elizabeth of England, was

8.

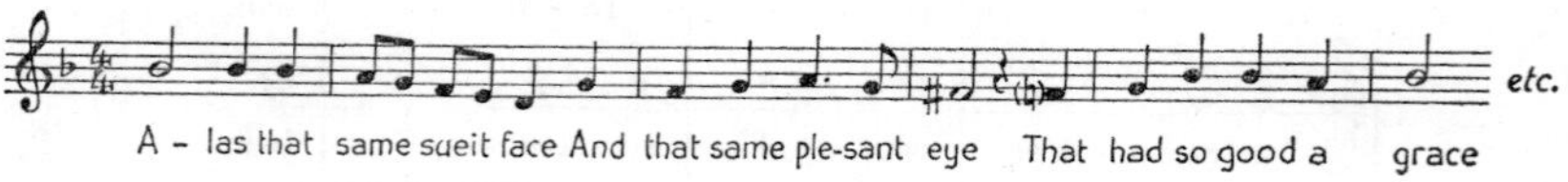
etc.
A - las that same sueit face And that same ple-sant eye That had so good a grace

proud of her talent as virginalist) thus benefited Scottish music her activities otherwise were less useful. On the political side, through a secret treaty which would deliver Scotland to France in the event of her dying without an heir, and the death of her French husband Francis II, in 1560, Scotland was put in pawn to her former ally and protector. Thus religious reform, sustained by Calvinist precepts, became accepted as a guarantee of national independence. By 1567 Mary was compelled to abdicate, and her infant son, by the Earl of Darnley, was enthroned at Stirling as James VI of Scotland.

During this period the principles of Calvinism, as preached by John Knox, were adopted with a fervour that owed as much to national pride

[1] Kenneth Elliott, *Music of Scotland 1500–1700* (*Musica Britannica*, XV), no. 4.

as to religious conviction. The old liturgical music underwent no such gradual metamorphosis as in England, but was simply discontinued. Church music, now intended for congregational use, was confined to metrical psalmody. This form of music had been introduced into Scotland in the 1540's, when the brothers Wedderburn of Dundee—one of whom had been a disciple of Luther at Wittenberg—issued a volume of *Gude and Godlie Ballatis*. This, confined to private use, became increasingly popular. It ran through many editions, in which parodies of court songs, convenient for the dissemination of new doctrines, were included, but they found no place in the canon of the Church of Scotland since the texts were non-biblical. The basis for orthodoxy in church music was established in the *Book of Common Order*, issued in Edinburgh in 1564, containing 'the whole of the Psalmes of David in English meter'.

Thus was an ancient musical tradition brought to an end. The musical corporations of cathedrals and collegiate churches were dispersed. The work of the Sang Scules was discontinued, though in 1579 it was found necessary to re-establish a number of them for the limited purpose of cultivating psalmody. Composers like Peebles, Blackhall, Kemp, and John Angus—formerly a monk at Dunfermline—adapted themselves to the new situation and wrote within the narrow limits permitted, or took advantage of courtly and private patronage. During the latter part of the sixteenth century the art of solo and part-song flourished as composers found inspiration in the lyrics of Alexander Scott and Alexander Montgomerie, and, writing French and English idioms with a native instinct for melody, promised to found a new school of distinctive quality. But the acceptance of England, a reformed country, as an ally against French Catholic ambitions began a disintegration of Scottish cultural values that was not to be effectively arrested until the eighteenth century.

The Scottish Chapel Royal, Thomas Hudsoun being its Master from 1586, preserved vestiges of the older ecclesiastical tradition and there was old-style polyphony at Stirling on the occasion of the baptism there of Prince Henry in 1594. But after the Union of the Crowns of England and Scotland and the departure of the King, and a large body of camp-followers and place-seekers to London in 1603, its glory passed.

5

The Elizabethans

Music Printing

DURING THE second part of the reign of Queen Elizabeth I and the whole of that of James I England became a demonstrably music-conscious country, and her composers, of whom there were many, prolific. Apart from the fact that there were firm foundations on which to build there were fresh reasons for this efflorescence. Few, however, were more important than the development of the technique of music printing. This was promoted under a system of granting monopolies and licences to selected subjects and/or royal favourites who would, in their own interest as well as that of the Crown, act as regulators of trade on the one hand and unofficial excise officers on the other. The practice of granting monopolies was greatly extended in Elizabethan times when, under the threat of insurrection, or war, or in the conditions that prevailed during times of pestilence or bad harvest, the national exchequer was otherwise severely strained.

One of the advantages of a place in the musical establishment of the Court was that it was possible to get in on this business of monopolies. On 13 March 1560, for example, William Treasorer, who had been instrument-maker to Philip and Mary, and who had 'devised and geven unto us a newe instrument musicall gevyng the sounde of . . . flutes and recorders and . . . promysed . . . to repair . . . our greate organ [at Greenwich] was given a licence to sell ashes and old shoes'.[1] On 4 September 1598 Arthur, Mark Anthony and Jeromino Bassano were privileged 'to export 6,000 dickers of calf-skins, paying 5/– a dicker customs, within seven years, after termination of a former privilege for seven years, ending 27 Aug. 1600; with a proviso not to transport any from Liverpool or Chester . . . ,'[2] while in the following reign—when monopolies multiplied

[1] B.M. Galba C. II, f. 255. [2] *Calendar of State Papers (Domestic)*, 1598–1601, p. 90.

still further—Alfonso Ferrabosco (II), Innocent Lanier, and Hugh Lydiard were, on 14 October 1609, licensed to 'cleanse the Thames of flats and shelves, with grant of the fines etc. incurred under Statutes 27 and 34 Henry VIII, for annoyances in the river, of permission to sell the sand and gravel they dig out, and of an allowance of 1d. per ton on strangers' goods imported and exported'.[1] This illustrates one side of the system of monopoly as then practised, and if minor members of the Royal Household were so privileged (though execution of the license in many cases led to subsequent acrimony and litigation) it is clear that those who were more influential enjoyed greater opportunities for exploitation. There was another side to the system, however, for the inventive were often protected in the development of genuinely productive enterprises.

Credit for the earliest printing of music from movable type—apart from those anonymous printers who issued liturgical books at about the same time—belongs to a German, Conrad Fyner, who issued Charlier de Gerson's *Collectorium super Magnificat* at Esslingen in 1473. In 1495 the first English example of music printing was a sequence of eight notes contrived from printer's quads and rules in an issue of Ranulf Higden's *Polychronicon* by Wynkyn de Worde, an Alsatian immigrant and successor to William Caxton. The general effect in Europe of Pierre Attaignant's publications of music in Paris, and of Ottaviano Petrucci's *Harmonice Musices* (1501) in Italy—in this there were almost a hundred pieces in three and four parts by such composers as Josquin des Prés, Antoine Brumel, and Alexander Agricola, disposed in separate part-books—was considerable; but the English were conservative. Before the book of *xx Songs*, 'imprynted in Londõ at the signe of the black Morẽs' in 1530, there were only some eight works containing liturgical music and a secular ballad,[2] composed by and from the press of William Rastell, produced in England. The book of *xx Songs* showed the influence both of Petrucci and of printers at Augsburg and Mainz and in the forty-five years following its issue some sixty works containing music were published. The early licensees in London were William Seres (1552) and John Day (1559), who became partners. Seres and Day, who deserved credit for enterprise, had experimented with various methods of music reproduction and by the time they became license holders had ensured a virtual monopoly by foresight in providing themselves with the requisite matrices and punches.[3] Day was responsible for the collection of English anthems and services entitled *Certaine Notes* (1560), *The Whole Booke of Psalms* (Sternhold and Hopkins, 1562), *The*

[1] ib.

[2] *Tyme to pas with goodly sport*, in *A New Interlude and a mery the nature of the iiii Elements*, c. 1525.

[3] The only other adequately equipped printer in Britain was Robert Leprevik, of Edinburgh.

Whole Psalms (1563), and *The Whole Psalter* (1567–8), to which Tallis was a contributor. Day published *Daman's Psalter* (1579), but a more interesting and less clearly utilitarian venture was his undertaking of Thomas Whythorne's *Songs for three, fower, and five voyces* in 1571.

Four years Later (22 January 1575) a licence for printing music was granted to Thomas Tallis and William Byrd for twenty-one years. Since the latter claimed not only exclusive rights in printing music books but also 'ruled paper', the trade as a whole was to become displeased. Byrd was not without a shrewd business acumen (he was able to aggregate offices and also to cultivate the right patrons) and two years after the establishment of the licence he drew the Queen's attention to the fact that the printing of music was less profitable than had been anticipated. Tallis, he said, was very old and he himself had given up a secure position at Lincoln to serve in the Chapel Royal. The upshot of this was the grant by the Crown of a lease in respect of the Manor of Longley, Gloucestershire.[1]

In 1575, however, Tallis and Byrd had issued one of the classics of Elizabethan music, the *Cantiones Sacrae*, dedicated to the Queen, to which each composer contributed seventeen Latin motets. In the next ten years some fifty musical works were printed, and in the last decade of the century approximately one hundred, which included many madrigals, as well as Thomas Morley's *Plaine and Easie Introduction* (1597). In the first twenty years of the seventeenth century about 160 works (sixty being *Psalters*) appeared, by which time the general emancipation of music had established a sellers' market.

On the death of Tallis the monopoly was vested in Byrd alone, and at the end of the appointed period of twenty-one years it passed to Morley and then to Thomas East (1566–1609), one of the most highly regarded printers of the age. Among other printers who undertook work for the principal licensees were Henry Denham (between 1560 and 1589), John Wolfe (1579–1601), John Windet (1584–1611), Edward Allde (1584–1628), Humfrey Lownes, the elder (1587–1629), Peter Short (1589–1603), William Barley (1591–1614), William Stansby (1597–1638), and Thomas Snodham (1602–24).

During the latter part of the sixteenth century a technique of music engraving, developed from that perfected in the useful service of geography in map-making, was practised in Italy and helped to extend knowledge of Italian music. The effect of a close relationship with Italy—shown in many ways—resulted in England being the first country outside Italy to engrave music, the first example, by William Hole, being the Byrd-Bull-Gibbons *Parthenia* of 1612–13. Ingenuity in the publishing house

[1] See E. H. Fellowes, *William Byrd*, 1936; pp. 7–11.

also led to the design of the 'table-book'—in which parts were set out facing the singers as they were seated opposite each other. This was the method employed by Peter Short in issuing Dowland's *First Booke of Songes or Aires* (1597).

Music and its Social Setting

By the time that printed music was widely available to music-lovers as well as to professional practitioners the character of native music had undergone a considerable change. Partly this was due to the increased accessibility of certain types of music and the consequent new relationship between composer and client, but mostly it derived from the circumstances that had indeed been responsible for both.

The effects of the Reformation were multiple. Old patterns of ritual were modified and simplified. Ecclesiastical supremacy within the parish although still considerable was reduced, because the minister was seen to fulfil his function on sufferance and in deference to civil authority, while the fact that the monarch was the Head of the Church, and not only in title, emphasised that the citizen's first allegiance was to Queen and to country. Above all, the ratification of the vernacular as the official language of the Church brought about a new conception of the function of music in worship other than that envisaged by theologians. If the politics of religion affected the English language, humanistic impulses from Italy and France exerted even stronger influence on its literary development; and since music and literature were inseparable companions in any Renaissance philosophy it was inevitable that music should be also strongly affected. This was rendered the more probable by the interdependence of art- and folk-music, -literature, and -drama. The cultivation of music by the Tudors and valuable regional developments—both within the Church and by skilled musical craftsmen working within the secular tradition—ensured the maintenance of such standards of technical competence as were alluded to in the previous chapter. The emancipatory effect of the Reformation together with that of the new Humanism in the upper and middle classes imbued music with a new vitality, which sprang from a new sense of purpose. In the Elizabethan era music was patently of social usefulness. It was also a support to and extension of the word. L. G. Salingar observes how 'as a consequence of the vitality of the spoken language . . . literature gained . . . a vastly sharper sense of the relative values of words and idioms, popular and learned, which was nowhere more active than in the theatre. The drama flourished as long as humanist-trained poets remained closely in touch with popular speech and popular tradition; and as popular influence grew weaker the drama declined'.[1] Broadly speaking this conclusion is also apt to music. The inspiration of language to the composer and the duty thereby laid upon him to accommodate his style are indicated in two celebrated passages. On the title page of his *Psalms, Songs, and Sonnets* (1611) William Byrd reverted to a thesis set out, in Latin, in the dedication of *Gradualia*, and wrote of vocal music that it should be 'framed to the life of the words'. In the *Plaine and Easie Introduction* Morley—repeating, no doubt, some part of his early lessons with Byrd—began his 'Rules to be observed in dittying' as follows:

'Now having discoursed unto you the composition of three, four, five, and six parts with these few ways of canons and catches, it followeth to show you how to dispose your music according to the nature of the words which you are therein to express, as whatsoever matter it be which you have in hand such a kind of music must you frame to it. You must therefore, if you have a grave matter, apply a grave kind of music to it; if a merry subject you must make your music also merry, for it will be a great absurdity to use a sad harmony to a merry matter or a merry harmony to a sad, lamentable, or tragical ditty.'[2]

The fertilisation of music by poetry and of poetry by music is indicated by practically every writer of importance of the period. Philip Sidney, who may have known Ronsard and was a guest of the *Académie de Musique et de Poésie* in Paris, and who noted with interest Tinódi's new songs when he undertook a mission to Hungary, was alive to the cultural, philosophical, and technical properties of music, and their relationship to the art of poetry was a close study. Sidney wrote poems to French and Italian melodies and also one to the popular ballad melody 'Greensleeves'. (The eighth song from Sidney's *Astrophel and Stella* was set to music by Charles Tessier, and published in Robert Dowland's *A Musical Banquet*, 1610. He was a French composer who visited England and published a set of part-songs with Thomas East in 1597 at the request of English friends, among whom was Sidney's 'Stella'—Penelope, Lady Riche.) Those who were acquainted with Sidney—Gabriel Harvey, Edmund Spenser, Samuel Daniel, Thomas Nash, and Thomas Watson—were also interested in and affected by the aesthetics of music. Watson, indeed, may be reckoned as an important pioneer within the field of music.[3] The way in which music as a social grace was upgraded by Castiglione, whose *Il Cortegiano* (1529) in the English version of Sir Thomas

[1] *The Age of Shakespeare* (*The Pelican Guide to English Literature*, 2), ed. by Boris Ford, 1955 edn., p. 54.
[2] Thos. Morley, *A Plaine and Easie Introduction* . . . , ed. by R. A. Harman, 1952, p. 290.
[3] See p. 165.

Hoby (1561) was a recognised manual of deportment for the new aristocracy of Elizabethan England, led to a general domestic extension of music-making, not only vocal but also instrumental. And while the instrumental music of the period, of which it became one of the chief ornaments, existed in its own right, it was never far from the ambit of literary expression, albeit often by allusion. During the Elizabethan age the gentleman sometimes turned professional musician—which only happened again in English music during the Hanoverian period when, however, the English gentleman was either a German or was affected by prevailing standards directly adopted through the German connections of the Court. Thomas Whythorne, Michael Cavendish, and Anthony Holborne, gentleman usher to the Queen, bear witness to the then respectability of the occupation. For professional musicians there were new opportunities, and the way in which composers of the age reacted to them was the reason for the climactic quality of the music of the age.

The operative word in respect of musical culture is patronage. Because of a condition of relative social homogeneity and because of the generous spread of patronage in different forms, the character of British music, as of musicians, retained independence. For the same reason changes in musical style were gradual, and revolution in this particular was generally unwelcome. That characteristic has remained.

When William Byrd complained of having left a well-paid post in Lincoln to enter Her Majesty's service he was being unnecessarily disingenuous. To be a royal musician (provincial organists were made Gentlemen of the Chapel Royal but only put in occasional attendances) was, as has been shown, profitable because it opened up a number of avenues. Such a musician, apart from business enterprises outside of his professional competence, was able to work himself into the graces of the influential. He could attach himself to the Companies and Corporation of London or to noble households whose pattern of hospitality gave much scope for free-lance activity. And he could teach. The spread of music encouraged composition—and the practising musician was expected to be a composer as a matter of course—and composition was required in various fields.

The personality cult, which was so successfully practised as to hand down the glamour of Elizabeth I to a distant posterity, called for numerous anthems—by Tallis, Byrd, Weelkes, Bull, and many other composers.[1] Byrd's *O Lord make thy servant Elizabeth* is a good example of a workaday offering of this kind, while John Bull's 'Anthem for the Garter', *How joyfull and how glad a thing*, was more spaciously conceived as a 'Verse' anthem, with solo sections, for '2 Children and a Meane' interpolated

[1] The words of such anthems from the Accession of Elizabeth to the Restoration of Charles II are contained in B.M. Harl. 6346.

between passages for full choir. Since the Queen made frequent progresses through the country the standards of cathedral music, prompted by the example of the Chapel Royal and the choirs of St. Paul's Cathedral and Westminster Abbey, were kept up. For instance when the Queen visited Worcester Cathedral in 1575 (John Colden then being organist) she 'entered into the Church with grett and solempne singing and musick, with cornets and sackbutts', while once inside there was 'a great and solem noyse of syngyng of service in the Quier, both by note and also plaing with cornetts and sackbutts'.[1] Instrumental enhancement of choral and ceremonial music continued to be commonplace, and so it continued. In the process English cornet players built for themselves an international reputation.[2]

Frederick, Duke of Würtemburg, was at Windsor in 1592: 'the music', he reported, 'especially the organ, was exquisitely played; for at times you could hear the sound of cornets, flutes, then fifes and other instruments; and there was likewise a little boy who sang so sweetly amongst it all, and threw such charm over the music with his little tongue, that it was really wonderful to listen to him.'[3]

Church music was one aspect of a court musician's activities and even those who were primarily concerned in this department spread their interests. The boys of St. Paul's Cathedral, the Chapel Royal, and St. George's Chapel, Windsor, were increasingly employed both for royal entertainments and after the opening of the first theatres—'The Theatre' and 'The Curtain' in Shoreditch—for public performances. The plays acted by the choristers of St. Paul's—sometimes in conjunction with those of the Chapel Royal—were Lyly's *Campaspe* (1584), *Sapho, Phao and Endimion* (1591) and *Gallathea* (1592 at Greenwich); the anonymous *The Wisdom of Dr. Dodypoll* (1600) and *Jacke Drum's Entertainment* (1601); Middleton's *Michaelmas Terme* (1607) and *A Tricke to catch the Old-one* (1608); and Wentworth (?)Smith's *The Puritaine* (1607). In 1579 Thomas Legge's *Ricardus Tertius* was performed at St. John's College, Cambridge

[1] *Chamber Order Book of Worcester.*

[2] Cornets, like recorders and viols, were used in consort. A correct consort comprised a treble, a tenor or common (fifth below treble in pitch), and a grand cornet (octave below treble). In 1604 the Duke of Lorraine sent his chief cornettist, Jean Presse, to enrol English players. John Adson, a composer of some importance, and William Burt accepted appointments. The cult of the cornet in church music lasted well into the seventeenth century, and William Lawes's setting of Psalm xc included 'verses for cornetts and sagbutts' (Harl. Ms. 6346).

[3] Jacob Rathgeb, *Kurtze und warhaffte Beschreibung der Badenfahrt* (Tübingen, 1602), quoted by Rye, op. cit., pp. 15–16. Further references to the part played by instrumentalists in Tudor church music (Canterbury, 1532, and Worcester, 1575) are given in W. L. Woodfill, *Musicians in English Society*, Princeton, 1953, p. 149, and (Queen Elizabeth's visit to Oxford, 1566) in Denis Stevens, *The Mulliner Book, A Commentary*, London, 1952, p. 49.

and in 1586 William Byrd set one of the songs from this play to music.[1] Commissions in respect of dramatic and other entertainment music brought the different groups of royal musicians together, and the resulting team represented a variety of national traditions.

The Tudors—and for that matter the Stuarts and the Hanoverians—practised no narrow protectionist policy in respect of their musicians, and their staffs were multinational. During the reign of Elizabeth several families who were to exercise a considerable and beneficial influence on the development of British music came into prominence. There were, for example, the Bassanos, the Ferraboscos, the Laniers, and the Lupos. The Bassanos[2] were chiefly known as instrumentalists, and Jeromino Bassano was an early composer of Fancies. The Ferraboscos originated in Bologna and the third of the branch that settled in England, Alfonso II, became a distinguished composer, both of ayres and instrumental pieces. The Lupos came from Milan during the reign of Henry VIII and the dynasty established by Ambrose, a viol player, was conspicuous in most branches of secular music. Of the Laniers, emigrants from Rouen who made their appearance about the middle of the sixteenth century, there were many engaged in the cultivation of instrumental music. The most distinguished member of this family was Nicholas II, whose contribution to English music and art during the Stuart period was outstanding.

Important as was the influence of the Court on Elizabethan music, that of domestic patronage in general was not less important. And this was widespread.

Private Patronage

The force of example is great. The Tudor monarchs not only approved music but were active participants—Elizabeth herself was reported as vain of her accomplishment as virginalist—and the Court circle—encouraged by the general principles of Italianate humanism—followed this lead. Nor were the new aristocracy of highly professional statesmen and civil servants—like the principal members of the Sidney, Cecil, Bacon,

[1] The surviving fragment of Byrd's music for this play is contained in B.M. Harl. Ms. 2412. St. John's College was famous for its annual play productions from 1530 to 1544 through Thomas Asheton, a Fellow of the College who became Headmaster of Shrewsbury School in 1561. The tradition was extended to Shrewsbury so that five Old Salopians were in the cast of *Ricardus Tertius* in 1579. The play was one which 'would move, I think, and terrify all tyrannous-minded men from following their foolish ambitious humours'. Sir John Harington, *Apologie of Poetrie*, 1591.

[2] They were a notorious family and in 1584 Arthur Bassano was committed to custody by the Recorder of London for his 'insolence and opprobrious language', while a year later Mark Anthony Bassano was nearly killed by soldiers on the point of departure for Flanders who mistook him for a Spaniard and took exception to his language.

Petre, and Devereux families—backward in establishing themselves as caretakers of culture. The Dedications of madrigals and the honorific titles of keyboard and lute music bear witness to high-class enthusiasm for music in general.

Robert Devereux, second Earl of Essex and sometime royal favourite, was spacious in his interests and lavish in his investments. Among his beneficiaries were Spenser and Ben Jonson and he was a chief promoter of musico-dramatic entertainments. The prestige value of such diversions was considerable and of the Duke of Würtemberg's reception at Reading in 1592 it was reported that the Earl 'entertained his Highness with such sweet and enchanting music, that he was highly astonished at it'.[1] Thomas Robinson, in the dedication of his *New Citharen lessons* (1609) to Sir William Cecil, indicates the generosity of the aristocrat to the musician when referring to 'Your Grandfather's beautifull . . . kindnesse towards my Father, who was (untill his dying day) his true and obedient servant. Duty bindeth me, for that I was my selfe sometimes servant unto the Right Hon. Thomas Earl of Exeter, Your Honours Uncle, and alwaies have tasted of the comfortable liberalitie of Your Honours Father.' A celebrated painting in the National Gallery shows the consort engaged to accompany the masquing at the marriage feast of Sir Henry Unton, who had travelled widely as a diplomat in France and Italy. Consort music thus illustrated represented new techniques.

On the other hand the Petre Part-Books,[2] belonging to a family of which the head—Sir William (later Lord) Petre—had impartially served four monarchs but retained the 'Old Faith', index the abiding strength of the high conventions of sacred music. In the first of the part-books, the *bassus* of a sequence of Latin motets, the composers represented are Philippe de Monte, Thomas Créquillon, Nicolas Gombert, and other lesser known members of the Flemish school, and Fayrfax, Robert Johnson, Taverner, Tallis, Osbert Parsley (a singer at Norwich Cathedral), John Shepherd, John Mundy, Byrd, Robert White, and Nicholas Strogers of the English school. The second book, with tenor and bassus, contains liturgical music for the most part—almost all by French and Netherlands composers—but also an *In Nomine* by White and French part-songs by Clemens non Papa, de Monte, Créquillon, Gombert, Andreas Pevernage and others. William Byrd, living at Stondon Place near the Petre home at Ingatestone Hall, was a frequent guest of the Petres,[3] his particular friend being John, the dedicatee of a Pavan and Galliard in *My Ladye Nevells Booke* and of the second book of *Gradualia*.

[1] W. B. Rye, op. cit., p. 11.
[2] Essex Record Office, Chelmsford, D/DP/Z6/1 and 2.
[3] See F. G. Emmison, op. cit., pp. 210 *et seq.*

The part-books which formerly belonged to Thomas Hamond, of Cressness, Hawkdon, near Bury St. Edmunds, Suffolk,[1] also indicate the strength of musical interest in East Anglia in Elizabethan times. Admirably comprehensive, these books contain English services and anthems, as well as Latin motets, madrigals, and arrangements for string consorts. There is also here to be found Byrd's Passion music, *Jesum Nazarenum* (ascribed to Tallis in Add. Ms. 31226, but published in Byrd's *Gradualia* I). The composers represented in this collection included Parsley, Mundy, Tye, Tallis, Taverner, White, Thomas Causton, Shepherd (a *Kyrie* and *Haec Dies* by whom is described as 'the best songe in England'), and Weelkes; and the unfamiliar Robert Adams, Philip de Wildroe (van Wilder, an immigrant Netherlander), 'Ferrying', John 'Fanctyne', and Sebastian Holland.

The Petres practised their devotions privately and the maintenance of adequate music was entrusted to the family organist John Bolt (also on the royal pay-roll as virginalist), but he, lacking the discretion of his superiors, proclaimed his Catholicism too publicly and was obliged to flee the country.

The Shrewsburys, with estates in the north, like other of the great families, were influential in keeping the provinces abreast of development in the south. The spectacular funeral of the fifth Earl, at Sheffield, on 21 October 1560, offered splendid opportunity to the church musicians of the city. It will be noted that the Funeral Service drew on both the old and the new traditions: 'After the said praise [by Charter Herald], the service began. That is to say a psalm was sung in English. After which the priest began the communion, and said the epistle and gospell. After the gospel the choir sang another psalm in prick-song. Which continued all the time of the offering . . . The offering done, the sermon began, made by Dr. Dod, whose anthem was, *Beati mortui qui in Domino moriuntur*.'[2] The sixth Earl had much occasion to promote both musical and dramatic entertainments, especially when he was the unwilling jailer of Mary, Queen of Scots who was kept at Sheffield between 1581 and 1584. The heir to the Earldom, Gilbert Talbot, assumed a place of importance in the history of English music when Nicholas Yonge[3] dedicated to him the first volume of *Musica Transalpina* in 1588.

The great families had their contacts with the world of power and

[1] B.M. Add. Mss. 30480–84, in Hamond's possession in 1615, and the property of J. Stafford Smith in 1776.

[2] Quoted by Joseph Hunter, *Hallamshire*, 1819, ed. by A. Gatty, 1886, pp. 76–7.

[3] Nicholas Yonge was of Yorkshire stock, although born in Sussex (see *Visitations of Sussex*, Harl. Soc. LIII, 1905, p. 185), and it is likely that Talbot made contact with him on this account. In this connection the Sheffield Municipal Records show a 'Mr. Younge' as schoolmaster in the city in 1567–8. On 2 August 1568 the *Sheffield Parish Register*, vol. I, p. 183, recorded the marriage of Nicholas Yonge and Isabella Hurste. See J. R. Wigfull, 'An early Sheffield School', in *Transactions of the Hunter Archaeological Society*, vol. III, Sheffield, 1929, pp. 336–43.

fashion and through their dependents (often indigent relatives) and wide family connections they circulated items of cultural novelty. The more modest families, vicariously in touch with affairs of Court and State and of local eminence and authority, did their best to keep abreast of the times, but they also had close association with drama and music of a more popular order. A feature of Elizabethan music is the contribution made by provincial composers. That this was so was due to those local worthies who lent their aid to the art—by active participation and also by way of subsidy.

Prominent families in Tudor and Jacobean Lancashire and Cheshire were the Nowells, the Towneleys, the Hesketh s, the Houghtons, the Shuttleworths, the Ashtons, and the Stanleys; the latter being the most powerful. Most of these families were inter-related and all united in the maintenance of a sturdy local tradition that was, however, in touch with what was happening elsewhere. Contact was often kept through the vacational homecomings of those who made good in London. There was, for instance, the case of Robert Nowell (*c.* 1517/20–69), a brother of Alexander Nowell, Dean of St. Paul's. Robert, a former pupil of Middleton Grammar School and a graduate of Oxford and Gray's Inn, cultivated the favour of Lord Burghley and obtained the Stewardship of St. Paul's. With chambers in Gray's Inn, an estate at Hendon, and five manservants, he showed how ability and assiduity, combined with a modicum of fortune, could lead to a modest affluence in the Elizabethan era. When he visited Lancashire it was necessary that he should be entertained as befitted his station. The Towneleys, of Towneley Hall (who then possessed the Ms. of the Wakefield Cycle of Mysteries), were often his hosts and, having no resident musician of their own, were, as in 1569, obliged to hire a minstrel from Sir Thomas Hesketh.[1]

Sir Thomas Hesketh (who was knighted by Queen Mary and confirmed as a 'disaffected Papist' in 1581 and whose son Richard incited Ferdinando Stanley to claim the throne in 1593) was widely known for his maintenance of a group of players at Rufford (his other house was at Martholme) to which, according to tradition and some circumstantial evidence, Shakespeare sometime belonged.[2] In 1581 Alexander Houghton, of Lea Hall,[3] decreed in his will (proved at Chester), that his brother

[1] 'To James Shr Thoms hesketh minstrell xijd', *The Spending of the Money of Robert Nowell, of Reade Hall, Lancashire,* 1568–80, from *The Towneley Hall Ms.,* A. B. Grosart, Manchester, 1877, p. 398.

[2] See A. Keen and R. Lubbock, *The Annotator,* London, 1954.

[3] Houghton's widow was aware of the educational value of music but her choice of tutor was dictated by other considerations. In 1592 she was 'reported to the Government for keeping at Lea Hall Richard Blundell, of Crosby, gent., who was an obstinate Papist and he was teaching the children to "singe and play upon the virginalls" '. Henry Fishwick *History of the Parish of Preston* . . . , 1900, Rochdale, p. 264 and *Cal. State Papers, Dom. Ser. Elizabeth,* vol. ccxliii, no. 52.

Thomas should have 'all my instruments belonging to mewsyckes and all manner of play clothes yf he be mynded to keppe and doe keppe players; and yf he wyll not keppe and mantayne players there yt ys my wyll that Sr Thomas Heskethe Knyghte shall have the same instruments and play-clothes'.[1] Whether or not Sir Thomas acquired this stock, Robert Hesketh, who inherited Rufford, was more than adequately supplied, an inventory of 16 November 1620, showing that the household possessed 'vyolls, vyolentes, virginalls, sagbutts, howboies and cornetts, cithrun, flute and tabor pypes'.[2]

Thomas Hesketh's brother, Cuthbert, had houses at Whitehill, Lancs., and Heskington, near York, and his acquaintance with the Shuttleworths was responsible for his engaging and making payment to 'the vicars chorall at Lychfeild', who seem to have taken part in a family festival at the Shuttleworth home at Smithhills, near Bolton, for 'fower minstrelles viij d' were engaged at the same time.[3] The then head of the Shuttleworth household was Sir Richard (1541–99), an alumnus of the Grammar School in Burnley, who became Serjeant at Law and Judge in Chester. He lived in his wife's family home at Smithhills, but when the estate passed to his brother Thomas he built Gawthorpe Hall. On his death in 1608 this was inherited by Colonel Richard Shuttleworth.

The Shuttleworths employed musicians frequently. At the New Year of 1584 'the musicions of Sir Piter Lyghe [Legh][4] were engaged; two years later, in October 1586, those of another neighbour, 'Mr. Trafforthe' [Edmund Trafford], came to Smithhills. Other local gentry with musicians to let out on hire, to whom the Shuttleworths were obliged in 1587, were William Tatton of Cuppal and Atherton, an attorney of Lostock, by Bolton. In December 1594, 8d. was expended on 'a minstrell and one with an eppe [ape]'. Richard Shuttleworth was not infrequently put to some expense by his wife (her activities representing a further stage in the emancipation and education of women) who would engage three or four musicians at Gawthorpe on her own initiative. When the Shuttleworths travelled there was additional expense in respect of music. In December 1609, for example, they went to London and made overnight stops at Birmingham and Aylesbury, where freelance minstrels entertained them: thus the Account Book recorded 'for musicke at Birmingham ijs', and in

[1] *Lancs. Wills*, Chetham Soc. II, p. 38.

[2] Inventory in County Record Office, Preston. Sackbuts were not infrequent in Lancashire houses, for in May 1612, the Shuttleworths of Gawthorpe bought one in Clitheroe for 8s.

[3] *The House and Farm Accounts of the Shuttleworths of Gawthorpe Hall in the County of Lancaster*, 1582–1621, ed. by J. Harland, Chetham Soc., 1857.

[4] Sir Peter Legh (1563–1636), Sheriff and M.P. for Chester, who kept his 'pyper' fitted out 'with jerkin and hose and a hatte', was a friend of Henry Lawes and Francis Pilkington. The latter dedicated to Legh his second set of Madrigals in 1624. (See Lady Newton, *The House of Lyme*, Heinemann, 1917, p. 70).

respect of Aylesbury (there would seem only to have been a soloist) ijd. On 18 April 1610 Richard's sister Eleanor married Ralph Ashton,[1] of Whalley Abbey, and there was 'given to the musitians at the marriage xjs viiid', which represents a large ensemble of about a dozen performers.

Three times a year as a rule—in January, March, and October—the Shuttleworths—who may be taken as a representative middle-class provincial family—indulged in the extravagance of concerts by visiting virtuosi. Town waits provided the programmes and they came relatively long distances. In 1586 the waits of Pontefract were engaged; in 1591 those of Eland, York ('Huete, the wyethe of York' was paid 2s.), and Halifax, all played for the Shuttleworths. The Halifax players were special favourites, appearing in the family records for many years.[2] In 1596 the waits of Chester played, in 1611 those of Carlisle, in 1612 of Manchester, in 1613 of Wakefield, in 1618 of Durham. The north of England was well supplied with waits, there being other notable companies at Alnwick, Darlington, Gateshead, and Newcastle.

Civic Musicians

The organisation of civic musicians in Elizabethan times was efficient and the larger towns were hardly less aware of their responsibilities in this respect than those, at that period, of Germany. It is possible that the British authorities today are unaware of the ancient subsidies levied on account of local culture. In 1562, for instance, the citizens of Chelmsford engaged the City Waits of Bristol for an occasion and since they were too few for festival performance engaged also forty other musicians.

In their liveries—scarlet gowns edged with silver, later gold, lace—which were granted in 1524, the waits of Leicester made a fine sight as well as sound when they played in the gallery of the Guildhall, or at the Easter Monday or May Day Fairs.[3] There were three regular waits,[4] with

[1] A member of a long-established family that acquired great wealth from confiscated properties at the time of the Reformation, Ralph (1579–1644) was related to another Ralph Ashton (d. 1617), to whom John Bennet had dedicated his *Madrigals to Four Voyces* (1599).

[2] Mrs. Shuttleworth took over the formalities of engagement of players: thus in 1610 12d. was 'given to the Hallifax fidlers by my Mrs. appointment'.

[3] When, in 1670, the local musicians were in dispute with their employers and, to all intents and purposes, out on strike, the municipality brought in the Nottingham waits.

[4] The establishment comprised three waits from 1524 until 1645, when, after the Siege of Leicester, their office was abolished until the Restoration. In 1668 there were five waits, which were later increased to six. The waits continued in this city until 1836 (see also p. 220 fn. 4). Cf. the number of Cambridge Waits, instituted as a civic body in 1425: in 1499 there were three; in 1511, four; in 1567, five; and in 1727, twelve. They were dispersed finally in 1790.

a boy apprentice to learn the craft, and in 1582 their emoluments were raised and their duties re-defined. They were, it will be seen, paid out of local taxation:

'*Waytes*. Item: it is agreed yat everye inhabiter or housekeeper in Leicester (being of reasonable abyllytee) shall be taxed (att the discretion of Mr. Mayor) what they shall quarterlye geve the waytes towards the amendinge of these lyvinge. In consyderacion whereof the said waytes shall kepe the towne, and to playe everye night and morninge orderlye, boethe wynter and somer, and not to go forth of the town to play except to fayres or weddings then by the license of Mr. Mayor.

Musicians. Item: that no estrangers, viz. waytes, mynstrells or other muzicions whatsoever, be suffered to playe within this towne, neyther at weddings, or fayr tymes, or any other tymes whatsoever.'[1]

In Doncaster the four waits, who were required to 'play about the towne every night between eight and nine of the clock as they do in other places,' were paid by the Corporation and kept under constant surveillance. They were not to receive 'at any wedding for this wage above 2s. 8d. and to divide the same indifferently amongst them.'[2] A closed shop principle was preserved as in other towns and unofficial waits were strongly discouraged. Since from time to time the town band was hired to Belvoir Castle, deportment was an important consideration. One day in 1589 Francis Copley, an Alderman of the town, was admonished since he had 'bound in his home in contempt of the Mayor's commandments a minstrel whom the Mayor had lately punished for his "roguish behaviour" and ordered to depart the town to the place of his dwelling . . .'.[3]

Among the best municipal musicians of the period were the versatile Waits of Norwich, whose office dated at least from 1288 when the rank of 'William de Devenschyre le Wayte' was confirmed. The collars and badges of the Norwich Waits of 1535 are still preserved in the city. Until 1570 the players took part regularly in the Mystery Plays.[4] But they were also engaged to give out-of-doors concerts, unless prevented by epidemic or by unruly behaviour on the part of the audience. Thus on 6 May 1552 it was 'agreed by this House [i.e. Corporation], that the Waytes of this Citie shall have liberty and licence every Sunday at nights, and other holly dayes at night, betweixt this and Michaelmas nextcomyng, to come to the Guyldhall, and upon the nether leads of the same Hall next the Consail House, shall, betwixte the hours of six and eight of the clok at night, blowe

1 *Records of the Borough of Leicester*, III, 'Minutes of Common Hall', pp. 191–2, for 17 November 1582.

2 *Extracts from the Calendar to the Records of the Borough of Doncaster*, vol. 4, 1902; 10 December 1585.

3 ib. 1589.

4 See *Norwich Pageants*, etc., R. Fitch, Norwich, 1856.

and playe upon their instruments the space of half an houre, to the rejoycing and comfort of the hearers thereof'[1]. Twenty years later the waits were in their heyday, their composition 'beeying a whoall noyse', comprising 'ij Trompettes, iiij Saquebuttes, iij hautboyes and v Recorders'. In 1589 Sir Francis Drake (who had taken musicians on his circumnavigation some ten years previously) requested that waits from Norwich should accompany him to Lisbon. Equipped with 'cloakes of stamell cloath', with 'three new howboyes and one treble Recorder and a Saquebutt Case', five or six of the city's strength were seconded. But after a disastrous expedition only two survived. The full complement, however, was quickly restored and in 1599 Will Kemp, greeted by the musicians at the end of his famous London–Norwich Morris Dance, was able to write: 'Such waytes (under Benedicite be it spoken) few citties in our Realme have the like, none better. Who, besides their excellency in wind instruments, their rare cunning on the Vyoll, and Violin: theyr voices be admirable, everie one of them able to serve in any Cathedrall Church in Christendoome for Quiristers.'[2]

In Manchester where the waits were first recorded in 1563, their administration was not in the hands of the Burgesses as at Westminster and Sheffield but was a responsibility of the Court Leet, and their salaries came from private benefaction. In 1577 a public appeal was made, 'the jury (requesting) that all those who have withdrawn their good wills or such stipend money as they have been accustomed to give the waites, that they would the rather at our request extend their good wills to further their stipend and not to hinder it.'[3] The Manchester musicians seem to have suffered more than most from unauthorised competition and in 1603, after a succession of infringements across the years, the jury ordered 'that in regard the waits of this town have lately received a man skilful in music into their society and company, and also that they have been secluded by foreign and other musicians at wedding dinners in this town from the favourable and friendly contribution which the inhabitants of this town, their loving friends, would willingly and liberally have imparted and bestowed upon them, in remedy whereof this jury doth now order that the said waits shall hereafter be received to play music at all and every wedding dinner in this town as aforesaid, and the foreign

[1] *Notices and Illustrations of the Costumes, Processions, Pageantry,* etc. (of) *the Corporation o*, *Norwich*, Norwich, 1850.

[2] *Kemps nine daies wonder*, 1600, p. 24. See G. M. Stephens, 'The Waits of the City of Norwich', in *The Proceedings of the Norfolk and Norwich Archaeological Society*, Norwich, 1933, pp. 9 *et seq.*

[3] Quoted from *Manchester Court Leet Records*, vol. I, by J. D. Leader, in *The Records of the Burgesses of Sheffield, commonly called the Town Trust*, London and Sheffield, 1897, pp. xxxiii, xxxiv.

musicians and all others be henceforth rejected, and that no inn-keeper or alehouse keeper do admit any in contempt hereof subpene to every such innkeeper and alehouse keeper so offending 3/4.'[1]

The place of the waits in Elizabethan music, especially in the provinces, was important. Their talent was often considerable, and, when they had the authority of the municipality, their standing (according to the Manchester records they had servants) and tenure of office secure. As the Gibbons brothers, Edward, Ellis, and Orlando, were the sons of a Cambridge wait, so in the succeeding centuries other composers—John Banister, Thomas Farmer, William Howes, and probably the Valentines of Leicester—emerged from the same background. By not being at the top of the profession—ecclesiastical and official court musicians being accorded primacy—the wait, like the medieval minstrel, was well placed to act as a co-ordinating agent. He was invited to the great house but also to the tavern (for which reason the tavern in later times became a cultural centre), and he played at fairs.[2] At the same time he was expected to be available for performances of church music and also for dramatic entertainments. In London secular musicians of the Court took over some of the functions exercised elsewhere by civic musicians but even in the capital the role of those on the pay-rolls of London and Westminster was important, and sometimes conjoined with that of the court musicians. The result of such professional versatility, and mobility, was reflected in a general spread of musical interest. As has been seen, part-books compiled at the request of particular patrons showed a wide range of interest, and collections of virginals, lute, and cither music displayed another, and complementary, side of appreciation. Here are to be discovered many of the popular songs and dances of the day, as well as pieces owing their origin to dramatic invention. Drama, long established both at Court and in the streets of the town and on the village green,[3] increasingly affected the intrinsic nature of music.

Popular Drama

On 20 August 1553, at Kilkenny, in Ireland, 'the yonge Men, in the Forenone, played a Tragedye of Gods Promyses in the Old Lawe, at the *Market Crosse*, with Organ, Plainges, and Songes very aptly. In the After-

[1] ib.

[2] The Chester minstrels, for instance, played at the Midsummer Fair, and the Cambridge Waits at the Stourbridge Fair.

[3] Village plays were especially popular and frequent in the eastern counties, as, for example, at Bassingbourne (Cambs.), and Lavenham and Mildenhall (Suffolk), at all of which waits were employed.

none agayne they played a commedie of Sanct *Johan Baptistes* Preachinges, of Christes Baptisynge, and of his Temptacion in the Wildernesse to the small Contentacion of the Prestes and other Papistes there'.[1] In *Jocasta*, presented at Gray's Inn in 1566, the authors (George Gascoigne and Francis Kinwelmarsh) give instructions regarding suitable music—or rather, suitable tone-colours—before each act. Thus before the first 'did sounde a dolefull and straunge noyse of violles, Cythren, Bandorion, and suche like, during the which, there came in upon the Stage a king . . .'. Later this music ceased and 'Jocasta the Queene issued out of hir house . . . At hir entrance the Trumpettes sounded . . .'.[2] The entry of two coffins before Act II called for flutes,[3] while when a great gulf opened up at the beginning of the next Act cornets played.[4] A military procession in Act IV anticipated later extravagances in scoring: 'the Trumpets sounded, the drummes and fifes, and a great peale of ordinaunce was shot of . . .' Finally, when a 'woman clothed in a white garment' showed up for Act V 'the still pipes[5] sounded a very mournfull melodye . . .' The use of interval music—with or without action—was a feature of Elizabethan drama, and after each Act of Anthony Munday's *The Two Italian Gentlemen* (*c.* 1584) 'a pleasant galliard', 'a solemn dump', or 'a pleasant Allemayne' was played. Munday, who had been an apprentice of John Allde, the printer, was a vigorous Protestant and polemicist, an actor who toured in Europe with the Earl of Pembroke's players, and writer and director of most of the pageants of the City of London. Since Munday was also a ballad-writer it is clear that he had a considerable influence on secular music.

A considerable credit for the development and popularisation of Elizabethan drama was due to the choirboy companies, especially those of the Chapel Royal and St. Paul's, as already noticed. The latter, under the membership of Thomas Giles and Edward Pearce, were much occupied in performances in theatre and court during the last quarter of the sixteenth century. They ceased activity in this sphere in 1607, by which time they had taken part in first performances of works by Ben Jonson. The Duke of Stettin-Pomerania paid tribute to the music of the Chapel Royal boys in 1602: 'For a whole hour before the play begins', he wrote, 'one listens to charming instrumental music played on organs, lutes, pandorions, mandolins, violins, and flutes; as, indeed, on this occasion, a boy sang *cum voce tremula* to the accompaniment of a bass viol, so delight-

[1] *The Vocacyon of Johan Bale to the Bishoprick of Ossorie*, etc., Harl. Misc., VI, 1745, p. 415.

[2] *Jocasta*, in *Four Old Plays*, Cambridge, George Nichols, 1848, pp. 133–4.

[3] ib. p. 154.

[4] ib. p. 191.

[5] ib. p. 213 and p. 231. Still = soft, see also quotation from Marston, O.E.D.

fully that, if the Nuns at Milan did not excel him, we had not heard his equal in our travels.'[1] The possibility of cutting the music regarded as ornamental[2] to drama was envisaged by William Percy, son of the eighth Earl of Northumberland, who attached to a collection of plays he was submitting to Pearce for reading the following '*A note to the Master of Children of Powles*:

'Memorandum, that if any of the five and formost of these Pastorals and Cumoedyes contayned in this volume shall but overeach in length (the children not to begin before foure, after prayeres, and the gates of Powles shutting at six) the tyme of supper, that then in tyme and place convenient, You do let passe some of the songs, and make the consort the shorter; for I suppose these plaies be somewhat too long for that place. Howsoever, on your own experience, and at your best direction, be it. Farewell to you all.'[3]

Adult companies, permitted to practise only under noble patronage, engaged musicians as and when required. Since the companies toured, in England and sometimes in Europe, dramatic music was either provided by such groups of performers who might be locally available [4] or produced by a peripatetic performer. Either way popular and country-house dramatic entertainment benefited; and choice pieces found their way into anthologies. A favourite form lying between drama and music was the Jig. This, much favoured at Court, was not merely a dance, but an extension of a dance into an interludial play or farce. Jigs were extemporised and interspersed with part-songs and other dances.[5] Music for jigs appeared in numerous collections. In one book of lute music[6] there are to be found a 'Scottish Jigge', 'Allins (Alleyn's?) Jigg,' 'Susanna Jigg,' as well as various unspecified jigs and one engagingly entitled 'Jiggy Jaggy.' In another collection—of bass viol, recorder, and lute music[7]—are a 'Northern Jigge,' and 'Tarletons Jigge.' In both collections there are numerous other dances and ballad arrangements. The following melody *High for*

[1] See E. K. Chambers, *The Elizabethan Stage*, 1923, II, pp. 46–7.

[2] Thomas Godwin, Master of Abingdon School: 'The *partes circumstantes*, or accidental ornaments were four, common to [tragedy and comedy], Titulus, Cantus, Saltatio, Apparatus, i. the title of the play, Music, Dancing and the beautifying of the scene.' Quoted in *The Age of Shakespeare*, 1955, p. 158.

[3] E. K. Chambers, ib. p. 21.

[4] E.g. at Shrewsbury in 1591: 'To my Lord of Derby's musysyons, and to the erle of Woster's players, 22/8.' Owen and Blakeway, op. cit.

[5] Cf. Books of Stationers' Company, 21 October 1595: 'Tho. Gosson entered for his copie under thande of the Wardens, a ballad called Kempe's new Jygge betwixt a souldier, and a miser, and Sym the clown.'

[6] Cambridge University Library Ms. Dd. 9.33.

[7] C.U.L. Ms. Dd. 5, 20–21.

Wiggin Town is a sixteenth-century jig preserved in a collection which was the property of the Earls of Crawford.[1]

1.

Music and Education

The nature and quality of a society is reflected in its attitude to education, and the school curriculum of any period is a convenient sign-post to its social philosophy. The upheavals of the sixteenth century led to a re-assessment of the content of education and, often on the ruins of the old, new establishments were set up. Music, anciently part of the university syllabus, was (for the only time in British education) incorporated within the general scheme on terms of equality. The reason was three-fold: music, as Richard Mulcaster, Headmaster of Merchant Taylors' School, observed in *Positions*, helped to ensure both good health and a sound moral sense; its practice was necessary to maintain belief in the eternal verities—thus the Song-schools survived on the understanding that the words of hymns and anthems should 'be distinguishable';[2] it served a utilitarian purpose. Instruction in music was given in many Elizabethan grammar schools both in the provinces and the capital. At Shrewsbury music and pageantry were closely associated and when Sir Henry Sidney left the town by river in 1581, he was sent off by 'scollars of the free scoole beinge apparelyd all in greene and greene wyllows upon their heads . . . and because the orac'ons of the sayd nymphes are somewhat tedious to put them down I thought it beast [*sic*] to place the fynyshinge of the later staffe of the last nymphe that spacke wth sange the hole songe wth mus'es playeing and fynyshynge in this man'

[1] Copy in the Borough Library, Wigan.

[2] Queen's Injunctions, 1559, quoted by Bruce Pattison, *Music and Poetry of the English Renaissance*, 1948, p. 9.

And wyll yor honor needs depart
and most it needs be soe
Wold God wee could lyck fyshes swyme
that we might wth the goe . . .'[1]

Merchant Taylors', Westminster, Dulwich, and Christ's Hospital of the London Schools were conspicuous by the attention paid to music, and emphasis was laid on practical musicianship based on a solid foundation in sight-singing; 'musical appreciation' was to be thought of by a later generation. When Christ's Hospital, primarily a charitable institution, was founded in 1552 the first appointments included a part-time 'schoole-Maister for Musicke', whose duties not only included the teaching of prick-song but also the superintendence of tuition in trumpet, cornet, recorder or flute, sackbut, and—in the words of John Howes, author of the *Contemporaneous Account*[2]—'all other instruments that are to be plaid uppon, either with winde or finger.' The early music-masters of Christ's Hospital remain anonymous, but in 1606 William Meacocke, singing-man of Christ Church, Greyfriars, was appointed, to be succeeded on his preferment to the choir of St. Paul's Cathedral by John Farrant, who was then organist of Christ Church. Farrant, required to have children ready to sing at city funerals, was industrious and 'pricked divers services very fit for the Quire at Christ Church into eight several books together with an Organ Book.' Such energy commanded Farrant to a benefactor, Robert Dow, who more than doubled Farrant's stipend and gave money to the Foundation for the purchase of musical equipment. In 1611 Dow gave further gifts so that three or four of the dozen children selected as the most likely to profit from intensive musical education should learn 'to play upon an instrument, as upon the Virginalls or Violl, but especially upon the Virginalls, thereby to adorne their voice and make them worthy members both for the Church and the Common Weale.'[3] Farrant, who was a tiresome employee wherever he worked, lasted longer at Christ's Hospital than in most places, but his unruly temper and spendthrift habits led to his dismissal in 1616. Among other early masters of music at Christ's Hospital were Thomas Ravenscroft, composer and editor, and Thomas Peirce, of the Chapel Royal. Thomas Brewer, music-master during the reign of Charles I and a leading viol player, had also been a 'child of the foundation.'

[1] *Early Chronicles of Shrewsbury 1372–1603*, Trans., *Shropshire Arch. Soc.*, III, 1880, p. 286. The poem was probably by Thomas Churchyard.

[2] Ms. 1582, reproduced privately (ed. by W. Lempriere), London, 1904.

[3] Dow's deed of endowment, quoted by E. H. Pearce, *Annals of Christ's Hospital*, 2nd edn., London, 1908, p. 138.

The Place of the Composer

Music thus being so generally diffused and approved, there was ample opportunity for composers. The wonder is not that there were so many composers during the Elizabethan (and Jacobean) period, but that there were so many who were so good. The excellence of British composers of this period has been acknowledged, somewhat wistfully by later generations of their fellow-countrymen, not only at home but abroad, and Thomas Morley had the satisfaction of seeing his music published and his teaching manual adopted in Germany during his lifetime.

The sixteenth-century composer was both realist and idealist. This combination, of course, is a mark of almost any musician or other creative artist accepted as 'great'; but in Elizabethan times it was, so far as we may judge, a national characteristic. That this was so was due to the challenging facts of international life, to the liveliness engendered by the need for an expanding economy and a higher standard of living, to a response to tradition, and to a Virgin Queen, whose chief officers were not unmindful of the virtues of positive leadership in all aspects of social organisation.

If nationalism was developing it was not yet exclusive. The British musician accepted the past and present achievements of music on their merits, irrespective of origin, and without the inspiration of Flemish, French, and Italian composers the fluency with which the Elizabethans wrote would have been impossible. A growing tendency on the part of voguish patrons at the end of the century to over-praise the exotic did meet with Morley's displeasure,[1] but his complaint derived not from xenophobia but from an instinct for proper discrimination. The composer who allowed his idealism into words acknowledged the claims of God, and the change of religion did not discourage acceptance of the function of composer as one invested with some degree of divine authority. Composers could have got away with pure utilitarianism: they did not and in their greater conceptions in the forms of Mass, Motet, Service, and Anthem, presented hazards to their singers which may still challenge the full skill of those of the present day. But the same condition applies to the masterpieces of secular music, within the field of madrigal, and if humanism was an inspiration so also was the implanted veneration of craftsmanship. Above all the Elizabethan composer was a craftsman, brought to a high level of competence through the rigours of a strict, vocational, apprentice-

[1] He speaks of 'the new-fangled opinions of our countrymen who will highly esteem whatsoever cometh from beyond the seas (and specially from Italy) be it never so simple, condemning that which is done at home though it be never so excellent'. Op. cit., p. 293.

ship, and encouraged to develop his skills in a sympathetic environment.[1] Realism provided the spur to experiment. The composer was ready to dedicate his talents to whatever might prove profitable. The idea that money is beneath contempt formed no part of the Elizabethan musician's attitude either to life or to art. There was no more hard-headed man of business than the frequently litigious, and eminently prosperous, William Byrd.

Composers of the period fall into four main classes: those who were principally attached to religious foundations (which included many who were also schoolmasters); those who practised abroad, either because of obstinacy in religious conviction or the favours of patronage; those who were attached to private households; and those who were court functionaries. The names of very many composers are known, but not all have biographies to fit them; and of those that have, details are often minimal. But, almost for the first time in the history of British music, the works of particular composers, either because of verbal content or stylistic individuality, serve as some kind of index to personality.

By virtue of office and the power of tradition the senior composers were those of the Church. The organist and choirmaster—well on his way to becoming the dominant figure in British musical affairs—is conspicuous among them, but the singing-man and sometimes the clerk in holy orders are to be found among the elect of the period. Christopher Tye fulfilled all those ecclesiastical functions, being a lay-clerk, at Cambridge, in youth; an organist, at Ely, in his middle years; and Rector of the Parish of Doddington, in the Diocese of Ely, in old age. During this progress he also served as music tutor to the royal family. A not uncharacteristic nepotism prevailed in respect of ecclesiastical appointments, and when Tye relinquished his cathedral post at Ely he arranged for his son-in-law Robert White (d. 1574) to succeed him. White left Ely for Chester and Chester for Westminster where he ended his career as *Magister Choristarum*. The frustrations and ambitions which led such musicians to move from one place to another (the lure of London was, however, already a potentially

[1] The power of family tradition was great. Take, for example, the Jewetts of Chester. Originally from Bradford, in Yorkshire, this family provided musicians for three generations. William Jewett gained a place in the Chapel Royal and then became a minor canon and merchant in Chester, of which he became a Freeman in 1546, and—taking the offices of Alderman and J.P. *en route*—Mayor in 1578. He was, said Thomas Chalenor, 'one of the Queenes Ma^tes^ Chappel, reputed for an excellent syngyng man in his youthe, a martchant of great adventures, and a lover of gentlemanye disportes and exercises'. (*A Fragment of the Visitation of the City of Chester* . . . 1591, B.M. Harl. Ms. 2163). His eldest son, Randle (Randolph), a King's Scholar, in Chester, also became a singer in the Chapel Royal. So too did his son, also Randle (1603–73), who was a pupil of Orlando Gibbons, then of Bateson, the Chester organist, whom he succeeded in Dublin. Jewett later became organist at Chester and, finally, Winchester.

disruptive force in the body of English music) were helpful in that they encouraged the circulation of ideas, and the stress laid on teaching as a part of an organist's duties also ensured a vital succession of competent, and sometimes more than competent, composers in different parts of the country. The profession had, however, another side: thus—'Jan. 1, 1591—Rondall Phaventon, a poore old man, sometime orgon player to the p'sh church of Ercall, and through wilfulness of himselfe tooke his end in the Chapell in the Church yard, and was bur. the first day of January.'[1]

It has been shown that East Anglia—where the requirements of the University of Cambridge helped to promote high standards in the craft of composition—was an especially fruitful region, and John Farrant commenced his career as cathedral organist at Ely. Afterwards he (or another, or others, of the same name and similarly disreputable characters) served as organist also at Bristol, Hereford, Christ Church, Newgate Street (see p. 135 above), and Salisbury. Elway Bevin—of Welsh descent, organist of Bristol Cathedral between 1589 and 1637—had been previously a vicar-choral at Wells, and in 1605 he became a (part-time) Gentleman of the Chapel Royal. In 1637 he was removed from office both in Bristol and London on the grounds that he was a Roman Catholic—a fact with which many people had contentedly lived for a long time. Chester claimed two composers of note among its organists of this period: Robert White, who took part in the musical arrangements for the Mystery Plays still held in the city,[2] and Thomas Bateson (*c.* 1570–1630). Bateson spent nine years at Chester (1599–1608), during which time he distinguished himself as a composer of madrigals—these being particularly cultivated in this area. He then transferred to Dublin (for which Chester was the port) and spent the rest of his life as organist of Christ Church Cathedral. In 1613 he became the first Mus.B. of Trinity College. While Bateson was organist at Chester another madrigalist, John Farmer, was successively organist at Christ Church (from which his unauthorised absences in England caused his dismissal) and St. Patrick's Cathedrals in Dublin.

Among other organists remembered as much for their secular as their sacred works are William Cobbold (1560–1639), sometime organist and singing-man in Norwich Cathedral, John Hilton I (1594–1612), lay-clerk at Ely and organist of Trinity College, Cambridge, John Holme (d. 1638), of Winchester and Salisbury Cathedrals, and Thomas Tomkins (1572—1656), of Worcester Cathedral and the Chapel Royal, all of whom were contributors to *The Triumphs of Oriana*.

The Tomkins family is one of the most distinguished in English and

[1] High Ercall (Salop); *Shropshire Parish Registers*, Lichfield Dioc., xx, 1939.

[2] He received 4s. in 1567 and 1568 for singing in the plays; see J. C. Bridge, 'The Organists of Chester Cathedral', *Journal of the Chester Arch. Soc.*, xlx, 1, 1912, pp. 63–81.

Welsh musical history. The first to be recorded, also Thomas (*c.* 1545–*c.* 1627), was vicar-choral and organist at St. David's Cathedral—where, on his complaining of an insufficient stipend, one of his sons (also Thomas) was given a vicar's place to help the family budget. The younger Thomas, however, was dismissed for disorderly behaviour, whereupon he ran away to sea and went down with Grenville's *Revenge*. Meanwhile Thomas I had become Precentor at Gloucester. A John Tomkins was briefly organist at Worcester in 1590. His successor was Nathaniel Patrick, who died in 1595 leaving a widow Anne who became the wife of Thomas Tomkins II. He, a pupil of Byrd, became organist at Worcester in 1596 and also of the Chapel Royal in 1621. By a second marriage Thomas Tomkins I had three other musician sons of some distinction: John (*c.* 1586–1683), who became organist of St. Paul's Cathedral, Giles (d. 1668), organist of Salisbury, and Robert, who, like John and Giles, was a court musician. Giles's son, also Giles, was at Worcester in 1661, but was dismissed on account of non-attendance in the course of the next year. The list of Elizabethan organist-composers includes the names of Richard Farrant (*c.* 1530–80), John Mundy (d. 1630), and Nathaniel Giles (d. 1633), of St. George's Chapel, Windsor, John Mudd (d. *c.* 1628), of Peterborough—each of whom belonged to a family musically prominent through other representatives—and Edmund Hooper (*c.* 1553–1621), a former choirboy of Exeter Cathedral, who was a singer in and then organist of Westminster Abbey from 1604.

The greatest of the Elizabethan school of church musicians were Byrd, Morley, Gibbons, Weelkes, and Bull, whose careers, however, were so various that their lives must be separately considered.

In general the temper of the age was accommodating to those whose inherited orthodoxy in matters of religion became the new unorthodoxy, which was a gain to British music. There were those, however, whose convictions were so strong that, rightly or wrongly, they came or were in danger of coming under suspicion of disloyalty. Accordingly they transferred their careers to a more congenial climate. Two considerable composers thus emigrated during the reign of Elizabeth: Peter Philips (*c.* 1560–?1634), who after travelling in Italy and the Low Countries became organist to the Archduke of the Netherlands; and Richard Deering (Dering), illegitimate son of a Kentish gentleman, who studied in Italy before settling in Brussels. Philips and Deering were versatile composers, strongly influenced by their foreign environment, but the works of both were well-known and esteemed in England. On the accession of Charles I and Henrietta Maria, when the official attitude became more permissive, Deering returned to England to become organist to the Queen. Deering is reputed to be the first Englishman to use the new method of figured bass.

In 1617 he published *Cantiones Sacrae vocum cum Basso Continuo ad Organum*, though a similarly titled volume (whether for five or six voices is uncertain) was said to have been issued in 1597. The names of Philips and Deering as they appeared in continental manuscripts were sometimes qualified by *Inglese*, a term found necessary for the purposes of definition more frequently than may be supposed for a period of two hundred years.

Church musicians, to some extent anchored by liturgical and stylistic precedent, moved towards the demands of new social obligations. They were, however, primarily conditioned by the dictates of polyphony. Secular musicians, on the other hand, especially those who were more or less free of other duties, often proceeded from another aesthetic starting-point. Monody did not suddenly burst on an astonished world at the end of the sixteenth century, for it is, of course, fundamental to musical expression. Its form, however, changes, and what led to a reassessment of the possibilities of monodic association with lyric poetry was the enthusiasm with which the lute was cultivated in England; particularly after editions of Adrien Le Roy's treatise on the instrument and the tablature form of notation appeared in English translation by John Alford in 1568 and 1574.[1] Hereafter no self-respecting household failed to acquire one or more lutes, and lutenist teachers were in demand. Students at the Universities and Inns of Court were especially bitten by the craze, and many manuscript collections—like that acquired by John Weld—passed from client to client through dealers' hands. The duties of lute teachers were prescribed by the recreational aspect of music. Thus they developed a style of composition that owed more to popular song and dance, and to the allusive conceits and metaphors of contemporary poetry, than to the avowedly more instructional forms of music derived from the Church. One might say that through the lutenists (their instrument being less trammelled by associations than keyboard instruments) popular music became high-brow.

Anthony Holborne, as has already been seen, was a gentleman-composer, and friend of Morley, Farnaby, and John Dowland. So too was Michael Cavendish. Thomas Bartlet was a pensioner of Sir Edward Seymour, Thomas Greaves of Sir Henry Pierrepoint, of Thoresby, in Nottinghamshire, William Corkine, Robert Jones, and Philip Rosseter were at the disposal of private patrons, even though precise details of employment are lacking. The number of lutenists attached to, or occasionally employed by, the Court was large, and included Daniel Bachelor, Francis Cutting, John Daniel, brother of the poet, John and Robert Johnson, and Edward Collard. Cutting, like Robinson and John Dowland, was

[1] Subsequent printed works of the period under review included: William Barley, *New Booke of Tabliture*, 1596; Thomas Robinson, *Schoole of Musicke*, 1603; Robert Dowland, *Varietie of Lute-lessons*, 1610.

for some time employed at the Danish Court. Dowland himself, a Catholic and apparently compromised on account of his faith, practised in Italy and Germany as well as in Denmark and finally came home to live under the patronage of Lord Howard de Walden. The lutenists were of international significance, and just as foreign works appeared in English manuscripts so also did pieces by English composers find places in continental collections. The lute was immensely popular throughout the reigns of Elizabeth I and James I, but in the reign of Charles I its influence declined as the independent character of English lute music gave way before the fashionable new tunings and the artificial style of the French. Nor could the lute (often used as a continuo instrument) stand up to the competition of violin and harpsichord. There are about forty principal sources of the remaining examples of English lute music, and some 2,000 pieces in all: song arrangements (including songs which do not otherwise survive),[1] dances of all sorts, preludes and fantasias predominating.[2]

Lute music—including that for such cognate instruments as cittern, pandora, and orpheoreon—and viol da gamba music stood at one end of the musical spectrum. The virginals, also a valuable aid to gracious living and social status, had its own repertoire, which overlapped that of the lute, but also those of instrumental consort and vocal ensemble. The madrigal, to the left of ecclesiastical polyphony (and homophony), was the consequence of the collision of many traditions; its sudden florescence was due to public fashion and private initiative. The domestic musician, *par excellence*, was John Wilbye, whose life in the household of the Kytsons of Hengrave Hall, near Diss, Suffolk, is amply documented.

The Elizabethan age is built into the English tradition as an effective point of departure for national self-esteem. After the passage of three and a half centuries its achievements are recollected with some nostalgia and often hopefully rehearsed by national leaders of one sect or another as incentive to further collective effort. It was, above all, an age of personal achievement and therefore of individual figures who have passed into the mythology of the national character which they helped to fashion. Sidney, Drake, Raleigh, Burghley, Donne, Bacon, Marlowe, Shakespeare, are indispensable to moralists and mythologists alike. English musicians have been grateful for the support given to the national cause of music by Tallis and Byrd, Morley and Bull, Wilbye and Weelkes, and Orlando Gibbons. Each of these masters could rightly be claimed—in a more or

1 The Weld Lute Book (Willey Park, Shropshire), formerly the property of John Weld, Town Clerk of London (1613–66) and owner of Willey Park, contains a number of songs mentioned by Shakespeare. See Robert Spencer, 'The Weld Lute Book', *Lute Society Journal*, vol. I, no. 6, 1960.

2 See the analysis of one of the most important collections, Lord Herbert of Cherbury's Lute-Book, by Thurston Dart, in *M. & L.*, 38, no. 2, April 1957, pp. 136ff.

less absolute sense—as a great composer without putting a too great strain on general credulity.

Just as—according to a familiar legend—it takes centuries to produce the perfect lawn, so the emergence of outstanding composers is the consequence of hundreds of years of preparation. The course of this preparation has been shown. So too has the climate of feeling and appreciation, derived from the increased interdependence of traditions engendered by favourable changes in the social and intellectual climate. During the reign of Elizabeth, musicians, as musicians, had the opportunity to operate with an enviable degree of freedom within a coherent cultural structure, and the rate of productivity was high. There were many composers—so many that some were bound to be destined for immortality by the law of averages that operates in the creative field—and many compositions. Those which rank indisputably as among the classics of English music are for voices, for which medium native composers had long had a predilection. In the field of instrumental music, however, there was a burst of energy and enthusiasm and a good deal of pioneering.

In this productive period of varied activity the personality of the individual composer began to show more positively and to be recognised as an entity. The essence of Byrd is markedly different from that of Bull or of Morley, while Weelkes may be readily distinguished from Wilbye. The personality of the composer, however, needs to be seen in relation to function and environment and then the role of the acknowledged master is recognised as the sum of the endeavours of his colleagues. While one applauds, therefore, the individuality of the major Elizabethan composers, one also accepts the collectivism that made such creative independence possible. There is one other reason for the larger impression made on history by the composers of this period. They can, up to a point, be accepted as persons, in that biographical minutiae begin to accumulate. It is not possible to write a convincing biographical study of, say, Fayrfax. It was possible to write a biography of Byrd.

William Byrd

Byrd rides into history on the affectionate recommendation of his pupil Thomas Morley, who dedicated to him *A Plaine and Easie Introduction* and in which he also extolled Byrd as one 'never without reverence to be named of the musicians';[1] on the dedication to him of another pupil, Thomas Tomkins, who inscribed his *Too much I once lamented* (1622) to his 'ancient and reverenced master'; and to the considered applause of Henry

[1] Op. cit., p. 202.

Peacham in *The Compleat Gentleman*.[1] The music of William Byrd, wrote Peacham, was of 'pietie and devotion', which qualities were in tune with the 'Gravitie and Pietie' characteristic of the man.

Byrd, like Bach, was nourished by long tradition but living keenly in the present was able effectively to alter the course of musical thought. So effectively did he do this—working empirically on evolutionary rather than revolutionary principles—that the magnitude of what he had done was not discovered until that point in time—within living memory—which found English musicians using his inspiration entirely to renew the quality and purposes of English music.

The antecedents of Byrd are in doubt.[2] It is possible that he was born in Lincolnshire, that he was a chorister of the Chapel Royal and that there he first came under the influence of Tallis. That he was 'bred up under Tallis' was a statement made by Anthony à Wood and not otherwise directly and reliably endorsed; but that a special relationship existed is indicated by facets of musical style on the one hand and the business partnership undertaken in 1575 on the other. At the age of twenty Byrd became organist of Lincoln Cathedral in succession to Thomas Appleby, incumbent of that office for more than twenty years. After six years at Lincoln Byrd became one of the Gentlemen of the Chapel Royal in place of Robert Parsons, who was drowned at Newark, but he retained his cathedral appointment until, in 1573, he was promoted to share the organist's duties at the Chapel Royal with Tallis. The closeness of the Tallis-Byrd association is further shown by the fact that the latter became godfather to Byrd's second son, Thomas,[3] who took his godfather's Christian name. In 1577 Byrd was living at Harlington, in Middlesex, where the recusancy of his first wife, Juliana, was industriously and frequently marked in the Sessions Rolls. In 1593 Byrd, now married for a second time, took possession of a handsome property of 200 acres at Stondon Place, in Essex. Byrd already had an interest in this county, in which was situated the manor of Battylshall, the subject of the first of Byrd's many cases at law. A stubborn man when it came to rights of the individual (thus he made no attempt to disguise his Catholicism), he fought numerous battles for the protection of the leases he acquired or sought to acquire.

Of Byrd's ability none were in doubt. His professional standing was matched by his comfortable style of living in a then fashionable commuter belt. Through attendance at Court—then sited at Greenwich or Whitehall—he established useful social connections. In 1579 the Earl

[1] p. 100.

[2] He was possibly a son of Thomas Byrd (d. 1561), a Gentleman of the Chapel Royal mentioned as among those attending at the Coronation of Edward VI.

[3] Who also became a musician, standing in for John Bull as Gresham Professor (see p. 148).

of Northumberland (later imprisoned for plotting on behalf of Mary of Scotland) wrote a testimonial on Byrd's behalf to Lord Burghley, in which he deposed that Byrd was 'my friend and chiefly that he is schoolmaster to my daughter in his art'.[1] A few years later Byrd became a frequent guest of the Petres, who would as often as not send a servant to London to conduct the musician to Thorndon or Ingatestone when he was entertained in those houses. In 1589 Byrd spent most of his Christmas vacation at Ingatestone, where on 8 January 1590 there was a concert by 'five musicians of London', who played 'upon the violins [viols]'. In token of his friendship with his family Byrd dedicated his second book of *Gradualia* to Sir John Petre in 1607.[2]

At the end of his life Byrd was living in rooms in London put at his disposal by Edward Somerset, Lord Worcester, patron also of one of the companies of actors. All such associations—and others are implied in the titles of pieces for virginals—were valuable. The authorities in London, Middlesex, and Essex, kept Byrd, as a Catholic, under fairly constant surveillance; but he went unmolested. This was a tribute to one who, rejecting prudence and compromise, kept faith with conscience, and protested in his Will that he hoped to 'live and dye a true and p[er]fect member of his holy Catholycke Church w^th^out wch I beeleve theire is noe Salvation . . .'.

Byrd was at the centre of English music for more than half a century. His direct responsibilities were in respect of church music and he was in official attendance at the funeral of Queen Elizabeth, the Coronation of James I, and the funeral of Queen Anne, King James's Danish consort. On this occasion, in 1619, the aged Byrd was no longer at the organ, but watching his distinguished pupil Orlando Gibbons, who now held the office of organist jointly with Edmund Hooper. Byrd was a notable teacher and his influence through this faculty was, as Morley acknowledges, very great. Some of his pupils, like Morley and Gibbons, were musicians of the highest order; but in general it is not unreasonable to suggest that what later became the English 'cathedral style'—thereafter a constant factor in English music—emerged as a result of his methodical instruction.

Professional musicians got on well enough with Byrd and he was especially intimate with Alfonso Ferrabosco I. Ferrabosco—whose nostalgia for Italy led him to break his court contract in London in 1587, in which year he published two sets of madrigals in Venice—was highly regarded for his scholarship. Thus it was that Byrd and Ferrabosco matched

[1] See Fellowes, *William Byrd*, 1936 edn., p. 6.

[2] The first book of *Gradualia* (1605) was inscribed to Henry, Lord Northampton, conspicuous as a prominent Catholic and also as a patron of the arts. Out of favour in Elizabeth's reign, Northampton was given high office by James I.

their respective skills in counterpoint in a series of canons in two parts based on the plain-song *Miserere*. They strove, said Morley, 'to surmount one another without malice, envie, or backbiting'.

Byrd was a teacher on the professional level; but he also devoted time to his amateur pupils, like Northumberland's daughter. This contact encouraged him to compose keyboard music, and not only to do this but to explore means whereby the skill and aspirations of the composer might be assimilated to the taste and inclinations of his patrons. Because he was no recluse his music—although his temperament led him naturally towards the intellectual and the austere—touched life at many points. There is an engaging picture of a Feast of the Merchant Taylor's Company, at which King James was a guest on 16 July 1607. The choristers of the Chapel Royal had a night out, and in the room in which the King dined 'were placed a very rich pair of organs, whereupon Mr. John Bull, Doctor of Music, and a Brother of this Company, did play all the dinner time; and Mr. Nathanyel Gyles,[1] Master of the Children of the King's Chapel, together with Dr. Montague, Bishop of Bath and Wells, and Dean of his Majesty's Chapel; Lenard Davis, sub-dean; and divers syngingmen, Robert Stone, William Byrde, Richard Canwell, Drüe Sharpe, Edmund Browne, Tho. Woodson,[2] Henry Eveseede,[3] Robert Allison, Jo. Hewlett, Richard Plumley, Thos. Goold, William Lawes, Elway Bevin, and Orlando Gibbons, Gen. extraordinary, and the Children of the said Chapel, did sing melodious songs at the said dinner . . .'[4]

Byrd was the first great English composer whose works were at all adequately published during his lifetime. The reason for this has been shown. Even so, only a small part of his output was issued in permanent form. After the joint *Cantiones Sacrae* of 1575 it was thirteen years before the *Psalmes, Sonets, and Songs of Sadnes and Pietie*, dedicated to Sir Christopher Hatton, and prefaced by the famous 'Reasons . . . to perswade everyone to learn to sing', appeared. In that same year two of Byrd's madrigals were included in Yonge's *Musica Transalpina*. In 1589 there were *Songs of Sundrie Natures* (2nd edition, 1610) and the *Liber Primus Sacrarum Cantionum*

[1] *c.* 1560–1634; sometime organist of Worcester Cathedral and Master of the Children in St. George's, Windsor, and the Chapel Royal. For his choirs he was permitted to 'press' suitable boys into service. At Windsor (1595) it was specified that he should teach his boys singing, composition, and instrumental music where suitable. This was the normal practice in the choral foundations.

[2] Chorister at St. Paul's Cathedral before receiving a Chapel Royal appointment in 1581. Among his few surviving works (Ms.) is a half-completed 'Forty wayes of two parts in one on the *Miserere*' for organ. Woodson was thereby indulging in an academic exercise much in favour at that time.

[3] His insobriety was notorious. On one occasion, according to the Cheque Book of the Chapel Royal, he made a violent physical attack on Orlando Gibbons.

[4] J. Nichols, *King James' Progresses*, 2 vols., London, 1828, II, pp. 138 ff.

quinque vocum. A *Liber Secundus* followed in 1591, by which time Byrd's skill as madrigalist was noted by Thomas Watson who included a six-part *This sweet and merry month of May* in his *First Sett of Italian Madrigalls Englished.* The canons of Byrd and Ferrabosco should have been published in 1603, but probably were withdrawn. About this time the three Masses, without date on the title page, were probably issued. In 1607 came two books of *Gradualia*, and in 1611 *Psalms, Songs, and Sonnets.* Four anthems by Byrd appeared in Sir William Leighton's *Tears or Lamentacions*, of 1614. These were the last works of Byrd published before his death.

Byrd was a comprehensive composer who, like all great artists, summarised accepted techniques and traditions while, at the same time, opening paths for fuller exploration by others. Of those conspicuous by their perception of fresh values Thomas Morley and John Bull were outstanding, both on account of the intrinsic quality of their work and their general influence. Both were pupils of Byrd. And both, being Elizabethan, lived more or less dangerously.

Thomas Morley

Morley,[1] became organist of St. Paul's in 1591, then being in his mid-thirties and having previously served as parish church organist in the City. He had otherwise acted as a political agent in the Low Countries and wrought some havoc among the ranks of the recusants.[2] Byrd's influence, it is clear, was confined to matters of music only. In 1592 Morley—a pavane by whom was successfully played on the occasion of Queen Elizabeth's visit to Elvetham in 1591—joined the Chapel Royal. On taking up this appointment he resigned that at the cathedral. He served ten years as a royal musician, but after his resignation, caused no doubt by the ill-health to which he referred in his *Plaine and Easie Introduction*, he lived only one more year.

During the last years of Elizabeth's reign Morley more than any other composer established the character and the status of the English madrigal. A resident of the City of London (between 1596 and 1601 he lived in Shakespeare's parish of St. Helen, Bishopsgate, and the two men appealed in 1598 against their respective assessments for subsidies) he adopted the social-aesthetic convictions of Nicholas Yonge—a colleague

[1] Possibly born *c.* 1557 in Norwich, and chorister and sometime organist of the Cathedral. See Watkins Shaw, 'Thomas Morley of Norwich', *Mus. T.*, September 1965, pp. 669 ff.

[2] See letter of [C.] Paget from the Low Countries, and reply; *State Papers*, Dom. Eliz., CCXL, no. 19, quoted in *Grove*, 5th edn., V, p. 895. See also David Brown, 'The Styles and Chronology of Thomas Morley's Motets', *M. & L.*, 41, no. 3, July 1960, p. 216.

at St. Paul's—and his enthusiastic group of madrigal-lovers, and showed how to incorporate English interests within Italian techniques. Morley, an impeccable and often gravely impressive composer of church music, was highly sophisticated and could not only emulate but possibly exceed his models Gastoldi and Anerio in execution. In 1593 he issued his *Canzonets* in three parts. *Madrigalls* for four, *Ballets* for five, and *Canzonets* for two voices appeared in the two years following. In 1597 and 1598 he edited volumes of Italian madrigals, while in the former year he also published a set of six-part Canzonets 'or little short Aers' of his own, and his monumental text-book—the *Plaine and Easie Introduction.* In 1599 he put out an anthology of Consort lessons, by 'divers exquisite Authors', and in 1600 his *First Booke of Ayres or Little Short Songs*, 'to sing and play to the lute with the Base Viole'.[1] The last, and one of his most notable, services to English music was his editorship of *The Triumphes of Oriana*, which included two of his own madrigals. Although dated 1601 this honorific collection, modelled on the Italian *Trionfi di Dori*,[2] was not published until 1603, by which time the Queen to whom the work was dedicated was dead. Morley, 'who did shine as the *Sunne* in the *Firmament* of our *Art*, and did first give Light to our understanding with his *Praecepts*',[3] also died in that year.

Morley came to terms with Italian music without relinquishing a sense of purpose inherited from native sources, and both his music and his teaching method, as exemplified in his treatise, demonstrate the width of his interests and the extent of his knowledge. Either through their appreciation by a visitor to England or the mediation of a well-placed acquaintance various of Morley's works were published abroad. The *Canzonets* in three parts were issued with German texts, in Kassel in 1612 and Rostock in 1624. The five-part *Ballets* were translated into Italian and issued in London in 1595 and, into German, in Nürnberg in 1609.[4] *The Plaine and Easie Introduction*, used extensively by Thomas Ravenscroft (*Brief Discourse*, 1614), was also known in Germany, being quoted by Michael Praetorius, of Wolfenbüttel, in his *Syntagma Musicum* (1618), and translated (but not published) by Gaspar Trost, of Jena[5]. In 1635 the

[1] In this was published his setting of Shakespeare's 'It was a lover and his lass', *Twelfth Night*.

[2] Published at Venice by Gardano, with dedicatory letter to Leonardo Sanudo (1592).

[3] Thomas Ravenscroft, *A Briefe Discourse*, 1614.

[4] The German translator and editor was Valentin Hausmann who, strongly Italophile, composed in the Italian manner and also edited works by Marenzio, Vecchi, and Gastoldi. His Morley edition appears as

Liebliche fröhliche Ballette mit 5 Stimmen, welche zuuor von Thoma Morley unter Italienische Texte gesezt, jezt aber mit deutschen Texte aufs neue in Druck gegeben. Durch V.-Gerbipol [*Gerbstädt*]. Nürnberg, 1609. [*Bassus* in Kassel Landesbibliothek, 4.138.c.]

[5] A copy of the 1608 edition is in the Wolfenbüttel Library (Vogel Hds. 673)—'Ex libris Johann Caspar. Trost, Jenensis Thür. ao 1649.'

Italian theoretician Giovanni Battista Doni described Morley, in his *Discorso*, as 'il erudito musico inglese'. Erudition he may have possessed: but as a composer he wore it lightly.

John Bull

So too did John Bull, who, once described somewhat extravagantly as 'the Liszt of his age',[1] did as much as anyone for the development of keyboard music. Reference to his flair for public performance has already been made (see p. 145). As a chorister at the Chapel Royal (he originated from the west of England) Bull was tutored by Blitheman[2] with whom he was joint-organist from 1588 to 1591. Bull retained his court position until 1613. A Doctor of Music both of Cambridge and Oxford Bull was high in favour during Elizabeth's reign and became the first lecturer in music at Gresham's College in 1596. Since he was no Latin scholar a usual condition of appointment was waived and he was permitted to deliver his lectures in English; to the satisfaction of his audience no doubt. In 1611 Bull was music tutor to Prince Henry (eldest son of James I) and in 1613 he composed an anthem, *God the Father, God the Son*, in honour of the marriage of Princess Elizabeth and the Elector Palatine.

In 1613, in order, so it was said, 'to escape the punishment . . . designed to have been inflicted on him by the hand of justice, for his incontinence, fornication, adultery, and other grievous crimes',[3] Bull emigrated. For three years he was organist in the archducal chapel in Brussels and then organist of Antwerp Cathedral. In the last period of his life he became friendly with Sweelinck, of Amsterdam, who included a canon by Bull in his *Rules for Composition*. Bull for his part composed a fantasia on a fugue by Sweelinck.[4] Sweelinck had a wider interest in English music, symbolised by his variations on a Pavan by Peter Philips and the popular song *Fortune*.[5] There are four pieces by him in the *Fitzwilliam Virginal Book*, a token of his connection with emigrant English musicians and also of the refugee background to this collection.

[1] M. Seiffert, *Geschichte der Klaviermusik*, Leipzig, 1899, I, p. 87.

[2] '[Blitheman's] passing skill in musicke's art
A scholar left behind,
John Bull by name, his master's veine
Expressing in each kinde.
from the Epitaph to Blitheman formerly preserved in St. Nicholas Olave Church.

[3] Letter from William Trumbull, Ambassador in Brussels, 30 May 1614, quoted in *Grove*, 5th edn., I, p. 1011.

[4] *Fantasia op de fuga van Sweelinck*. Complete works of Sweelinck, ed. by Seiffert, Leipzig, 1896–1901, 10 vols., I, p. 125.

[5] ib. I, p. 127.

Thomas Weelkes and John Wilbye

Byrd, Morley, and Bull impressed their mark on this age in a big way. The independence of their personalities comes through the mists of time. Thomas Weelkes and John Wilbye would appear to have been of more complacent disposition, and easily accepted the conventions of patronage as then understood. Weelkes became organist at Chichester Cathedral in 1602, prior to which he had occupied a similar post at Winchester College (where his salary was 13/4d. a quarter, with board and lodging). While he was at Winchester Weelkes had cultivated the acquaintance of George Philpot, of Thruxton near Andover, to whom his first *Book of Madrigals* was dedicated. Further books were published in 1598—the patron of this set being Edward Darcye, a minor court official—and in 1600. In this year two sets in fact were issued. These, under the generic title *Madrigals of 5. and 6. parts apt for the viols and voices*, gave patent recognition to the general practice of mixing voices and instruments (or of substituting the latter for the former when so desired) for the first time. In the dedication of the first set—to Lord Winsor—Weelkes protested his single-mindedness and, in that he is reckoned among the most notable of madrigalists, his determination to be a specialist justified itself. 'I confess,' he wrote, 'my conscience is untoucht with any other arts . . . this small faculty of mine is alone in me, and without the assistance of other more confident sciences.' Weelkes's last set of madrigals (he contributed *As Vesta was from Latmos Hill descending* to *The Triumphes of Oriana*) was entitled *Ayeres or Phantastick Spirites for three voices* and dedicated to Edward Denny (later Earl of Norwich). Weelkes's claim to fame depends principally on his forward-looking treatment of the madrigal, but he was also a considerable composer of church music, there remaining numerous anthems and services—of interest because of his development of the organ accompaniment and his exploitation of antiphony.

It was a quiet life in Chichester, but with modest resources in the Cathedral—as the *Statutes of the Dean and Chapter* (1616) show: 'the organist', it was stated, 'shall remain in the choir until the last psalm be sung and then go up to the organ, and then having done his duty, return with the Choir again to bear his part all along, under the amercement of iij. toties quoties. This is thought a meet matter in all double choirs, much more is it necessary in all half-choirs, as ours is.'[1] But there was opportunity to write, and London was accessible. Weelkes was friendly with Morley, to whose memory he devoted the remarkable *Death hath deprived*

[1] See also Thurston Dart, 'Music and Musicians at Chichester Cathedral, 1545–1642', *M. & L.*, 42, no. 3, July 1951, p. 221.

me (published in 1608); and he had other familiar acquaintances in town. It was at the house of one of them, Henry Drinkwater, that he died in 1623. He was buried in the Churchyard of St. Bride's, Fleet Street.

There is always the possibility that the enlightened patron will achieve immortality on the reputations of those to whom he extends his patronage. There are but few such patrons, outside of the Court, in the annals of British art; and Sir Thomas Kytson, to whom John Wilbye was appointed as domestic musician in 1595, Wilbye then being twenty-one, is among the most meritorious. Kytson, who like many Elizabethans of the second generation, owed his fortune and his social status to his father's industry,[1] lived in comfort and style at Hengrave Hall, in Suffolk, and in a town house in Austin Friars. The younger Kytson entertained Queen Elizabeth in 1578. At Hengrave 'the fare and banquet did so exceede a number of places, that it is worthy the mention. A show representing the fayries, as well as might be, was there seene; in the which showe a rich jewell was presented to the Queen's Highness'.[2]

Wilbye, son of a tanner and himself heir at least to a modest competence, spent his whole life in the employment of the family with which his own had long connections.[3] After the death of Lady Kytson in 1628 Wilbye retired to Colchester, where he was given a room in the house of Lady Rivers, younger daughter of the Hengrave Kytsons, and where, in 1638, he was buried in the Church of Holy Trinity. Wilbye, who contributed to Sir William Leighton's *Teares or Lamentacions* but otherwise wrote no church music that has survived, is the madrigalist *par excellence*. Sixty-five madrigals are extant—thirty in the First Set of 1598, thirty-four in the Second Set of 1609, and one, *The Lady of Oriana* in *The Triumphs of Oriana*. On these, for there are otherwise extant only fragments of viol music, his high reputation rests.

These brief biographies of five of the chief musicians of the Elizabethan age (Orlando Gibbons belongs to the Jacobean period, in which, in any case, the above-mentioned were all also active) serve to show first, how these musicians were employed; second, the way in which they were able to exercise their preferences within a musical culture that had a variety of commissions for the industrious and new opportunities for those with special interests; third, the corporate solidarity of composers, so many of whom were under the eye of Byrd, or other Chapel Royal

[1] Sir Thomas Kytson I (1485–1540) made a fortune out of trading in wool, and became Sheriff of London in 1533.

[2] Thomas Churchyard, *A discourse of the Queen's Majesties entertainment in Suffolk and Norfolk*.

[3] During the reign of Henry V a John Wilby (*sic*) was one of the trustees for the Manor of Hengrave. John Gage, *The History and Antiquities of Hengrave in Suffolk*, London, 1822, p. 90.

musicians, and otherwise brought into contact with the main stream through the co-ordinating activities of Morley. At the end of the reign of Elizabeth composers were increasingly able to see some at least of their works in print. But of major works it was, for the most part, those of a secular nature that were published. This emphasises the final point, that church music *per se* was in decline. It was an age of expanding humanism.

The Character of Elizabethan Music

It was one of the features of the age that the arts escaped from the direction of a Church now uncertain of its own doctrines and therefore of its purpose and gained the support of the worldly. The climax of the Elizabethan age came at its end, for which fact politics and a general stabilisation of social issues were responsible. And the energy released carried on into the next reign. Drama, once a court entertainment or a popular and peripatetic ritual, became a public responsibility, and in the period which saw the adoption of the madrigal the plays of Lyly, Greene, Kyd, Marlowe, and Dekker, and the first plays of Shakespeare—all requiring music of one sort or another—gave shape to national culture. Like the musicians the players also exported their wares, and those who performed *Dr. Faustus* in Germany gave a particular impetus to German literature and drama. The manner in which drama and music fused together is a matter for consideration in the next chapter.

While the art of the theatre affected music so also did that of architecture. The Elizabethan era was one of architectural extravagance. The prosperous fell over themselves to provide monuments to their name. Innumerable smaller houses were built in town and country, but there was a vigorous, ostentatious, development in the grand manner in the last two decades of the Queen's reign. During this period Longleat, Wollaton, Worksop, Hardwick, Kirby, and Burghley were built. Each was exuberant, complex with idioms picked up from continental textbooks and applied with more enthusiasm than aesthetic judgement. These and other houses were built in honour of the head of the house but also of the Queen for whose anticipated reception they were invariably furnished. If the great house reflected loyalty in this manner it also reflected it in the fulsome and rather repetitive entertainments that might be proffered. The musicians had at all times to be ready. They were.

While the movement away from purely liturgical music gained momentum during the second half of the sixteenth century, the necessarily varied nature of religious observances within contrasting doctrinal schemes made for a comprehensive character in the output of church musicians. Ecclesiastical music of the Elizabethan period extends from the great Catholic works of Tallis, White, Byrd, and Morley to the functional psalm-tunes contained in the collections of Cosyn (1585), Daman (1591), East (1592),[1] and Barley (1599).[2] Within these limits ecclesiastical music was sustained by a high technical competence and by an increasing awareness of the importance of verbal values. At the same time the general sixteenth-century process of rationalisation of compositional method—by the pruning of rhythmic and melismatic extravagances, and by adjustment of contrapuntal progress to the demands of harmonic logic and the consequent potency of the cadence—gave a welcome directness to a style that was still fundamentally polyphonic in conception. In the earlier part of the century the *cantus firmus* had been obligatory in most Latin church music. From the time of Tallis the practice of basing works on a given theme was either dispensed with (as in the three Masses of Byrd) or modified (as in the fluent hymn settings of White and Byrd that, related to instrumental method, developed imitatively in the manner of the later chorale prelude.) Freedom from such restriction combined with other changes in outlook encouraged, or seemed to encourage, opportunity for a composer to establish a personal style. The Elizabethan period is the first in which stylistic differences between composers may often be clearly recognised by the ear. At the same time, despite acquiescence in principles adopted from Flemish and Italian schools, a comprehensively English style is also recognisable. The main feature of this is the obstinate use of discord. It was paradoxical that when the English had maintained their earlier reputation for euphony for a long time they were arraigned for conservatism, they now were liable to the same criticism on account of their often ruthless exploitation of discord.

For obvious reasons the composition of Masses was a less frequent occupation during Elizabethan times than formerly, but those of Byrd are not only among the finest of his works but also outstanding in the whole range of English music. Unlike his immediate predecessors—Tallis, Tye, and Robert White—Byrd sets the text of the *Kyrie* in each of his Masses. While he uses no *cantus firmus* he does, as also does Tallis in his four-part Mass, employ 'head-motives' both as germs for contrapuntal growth and as unifying agents. In these works Byrd is succinct, containing the separate sections of each movement by carefully planned or effectively disposed cadential points and illuminating the details of the words by

[1] Containing settings by John Farmer, George Kirbye, Richard Allison, Giles Farnaby, Edward Blancks, John Dowland, William Cobbold, Edmund Hooper, Edward Johnson, and Michael Cavendish.

[2] For which the melodies were arranged—with accompaniment for lute, and other instruments—by Allison.

economic melodic patterns. His *melismata* are suggestive but not tedious. Byrd, conscious of the visual element inherent in Catholic worship but also of those dramatic musical gestures apt to popular and courtly drama, is ever quick to define action programmatically. But contours which have their origin in actuality serve the deeper purpose of enriching counterpoint, which is already inviolate on account of the interplay of rhythmic figuration. Byrd's sense of the interdependence of liturgical thought, verbal meaning and rhythm and overtone, and musical techniques is evident throughout the Masses. An instance of such interfusion is the beginning of the *Gloria* of the four-part Mass: [Ex. 2]. If on the other

2.

hand contrapuntal efficacy *per se* is sought, there is the conclusion of the *Credo* of the five-part Mass [Ex. 3].

Apart from settings of the Mass Tallis and White contributed noble settings of the *Lamentations of Jeremiah* to the classic repertoire of the Holy

3.

Week rites.[1] Where and how such works were performed is not known, but Tallis's *Lamentations*, in five-part free polyphony for the most part, are movingly evocative. Tallis adheres to the traditions of the Henrican period. So, to a point, does Byrd in his Passion music associated with the narrative as in St. John's Gospel. But his dramatic inclination encouraged a lucidity of exposition, typified by

4a.

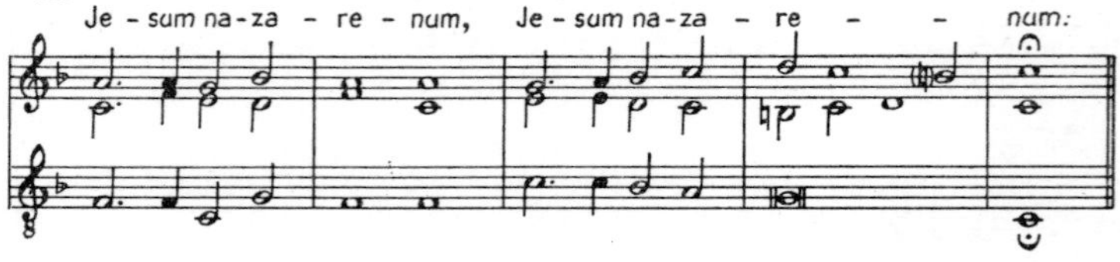

4b.

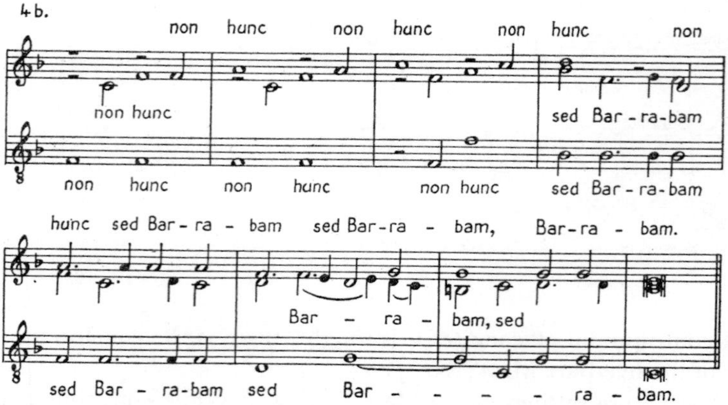

[1] Other settings of the *Lamentations* were by Parsley, John Mundy, Ferrabosco I, and Byrd.

Among the more attractive Latin works of this generation of composers are various settings of hymns. The process of progressive simplification of texture in church music generally may be noted by comparing John Shepherd's *Haec Dies*, a spacious piece for Easter, with Robert White's more clearly organised *Christe, qui lux es et dies*, and both with Byrd's familiar treatment of the latter hymn. In the pre-Reformation Church the motet was integral to liturgical exposition. In post-Reformation times the motet was freed from precise liturgical and ceremonial connection and, while Tallis and Byrd kept an eye on the seasons of the Church's year, texts were chosen, it would seem, according to the inclination of the composer. In *Cantiones Sacrae*, and in the *Gradualia*, first Tallis and Byrd, and then Byrd alone, showed that music derived from the Church could exist in its own right and yet at the same time contribute to the nourishment of the believer while also compelling the attention of the secular imagination.[1] Mastery of musical technique and constant consideration of the text, to the importance of which Byrd alluded in his Dedication of the first set of *Gradualia* to Lord Northampton, place the motets of Tallis and Byrd in the first rank. The introspective quality that sometimes characterises the reflective parts of Tallis's music is well illustrated by [Ex. 5] from *In Jejuno et Fletu* (1575). The contemplative character of Tallis's music is also reflected in Byrd (as also in the Latin music

5.

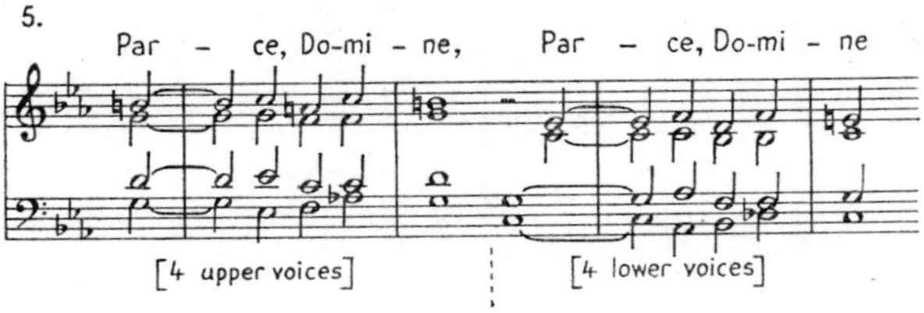
Par - ce, Do-mi - ne,
Par - ce, Do-mi - ne
[4 upper voices]
[4 lower voices]

of Byrd's pupil, Morley); but Byrd also had an exuberance that paradoxically appears rather more patently in his sacred than in his secular

[1] Since the sixteenth century attitudes to music founded on religious doctrines have been often ambiguous; and high respect for such works as Byrd's Masses (or, for that matter, Bach's *Passions*) would seem to derive from the need to fill a lacuna, from a sense of guilt, or from spiritual isolation, as well as from the music itself. One may in the end see the music occupying the place of what it was intended to symbolise. The progress of English church music as a whole lies along a line of religious devaluation and indicates, therefore, changes in social behaviour.

music. Hence the tintinnabulations of *Laudibus in Sancts i*(1591) [Ex. 6].

6.

With this may be compared Alfonso Ferrabosco's choral orchestration of a similar theme.

7a.

7b.

The motet type of work thus approached the independent position held by the fully developed and often derivative anthem of the English Church, each ultimately being self-sufficient and of no more than the most general liturgical significance. The finest of the motets and the anthems represent, in fact, a personal point of view. When one speaks of faith in this connection it is of the faith of the composers in their own powers and vision, for performing conditions—as shown by frequent references to deterioration in cathedral choral establishments—were progressively discouraging.[1] It is small wonder that organists sought opportunities in secular fields. The fact that they did so often encouraged a secularisation of the least essential if most prominent part of the church service—the

[1] Cf. Denis Stevens, *Tudor Church Music*, pp. 58 and 59: 'The fact was that retrenchments of one kind or another—not only in the "yearly allowance"—had been taking place steadily through the troubled reigns of Edward and Mary, and the damage done to the structure of Cathedral music was serious enough to create a continuing weakness in what should have been a strong national tradition. One method of making ends meet involved the reduction of numbers in the choir, so that the fixed amount of money available could be divided among fewer people.' This happened, for example, at Chichester where Weelkes had only a 'half-choir' to deal with.

anthem. The outcome of this was paradoxical, for the anthem developed in all ways and the whole corpus of Elizabethan work in this genre constitutes a powerful asset to the Church of England and to English music.

Of Tallis's anthems some were motets of which the Latin texts had either been translated, or replaced by new English texts. Both Tallis and Byrd carried forward into the penitential manner the gravity of the old-established Catholic style. Byrd, however, reacting to the challenge of the vernacular, infused texts of contrary quality with a vitality that is

8.

helped rather than hindered by the disciplined complexity of his rhythmic structures and contrapuntal involutions. The vigour and mobility of Byrd's treatment of words, his use of antiphony and his development of the anthem with instrumental accompaniment all encouraged his colleagues and successors to accomplish works of high merit. It is significant that many of Byrd's anthem-type works were published in the miscellaneous *Psalms, Sonnets and Songs* and *Songs of sundrie natures*, collections which were intended for general and not restricted use. The traditions of

English polyphony were long maintained, across the achievements of Weelkes (whose fifty anthems are now seen as a major part of his output) and Gibbons, and splendours that were inherent in the sonorous techniques of the *Eton Choirbook*—and Tallis's famous *tour de force* in forty parts, *Spem in alium non habui*—are magnificently maintained well into the seventeenth century, almost within earshot of Purcell, especially by Thomas Tomkins [Ex. 8]. The best-known anthems of the Elizabethan-Jacobean era are, within the conservative limits accepted, refreshingly free from overt piety: but the rigours of Puritanism sometimes also left their mark.

9.

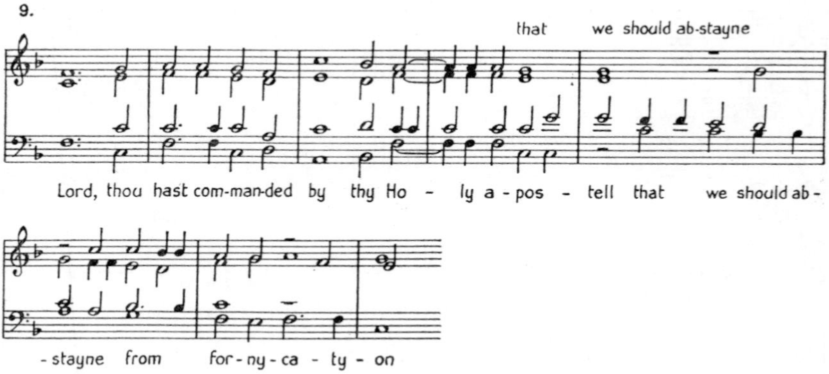

'The Pious Reformers of our Church,' wrote Thomas Tudway, 'from ye Errors of Popery having settled ye Doctrines thereof, thought it very necessary and advisable also, to appoint a standard of Church musick which might adorn ye dayly Service of God, by such a Solemn performance, as might best stir up devotion, and bridle in men's hearts, a warmth for divine worship.'[1] The requirement that church music of a directly liturgical order should conform to standards of simplicity led to the compendium of the 'Service' (Morning and Evening), of which the outstanding examples are by Byrd ('Great' and 'Short' Services), Weelkes (Evening Canticles in seven parts), and Gibbons. In these works the composers have their own interpretation of what constitutes simplicity. The provision of liturgical music according to the precepts of dogmatists and moralists was, however, generous, and the close connection between psalm- and service-setting (relieved in performance by the antiphonal division of works for *Cantoris* and *Decani*) established a useful precedent

[1] B.M. Harley Ms. 7337. Tudway's Collection of Services and Anthems; (Harley 7377–42), made for Edward Harley, later second Earl of Oxford, between 1714 and 1720, contains historical and critical observations on the trends of English church music from the Reformation to the Restoration.

for future composers of the Church of England. The solid foundations of the Church Service were laid by Tye, Parsley, Robert Adams, John Mundy, Thomas Caustun,[1] and others, whose works were contained in the part-books copied in the cathedral churches up and down the country. The utilitarian style, pointed as in the psalters by inner stresses, had dignity and even nobility. Morley's *Funeral Music* is justly famed for these qualities:

10a.

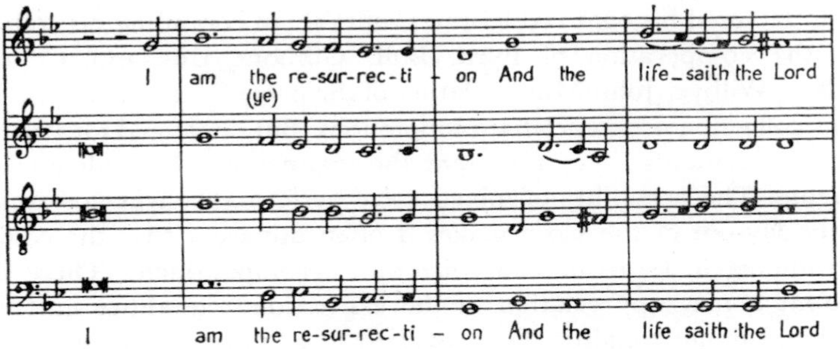

10b.

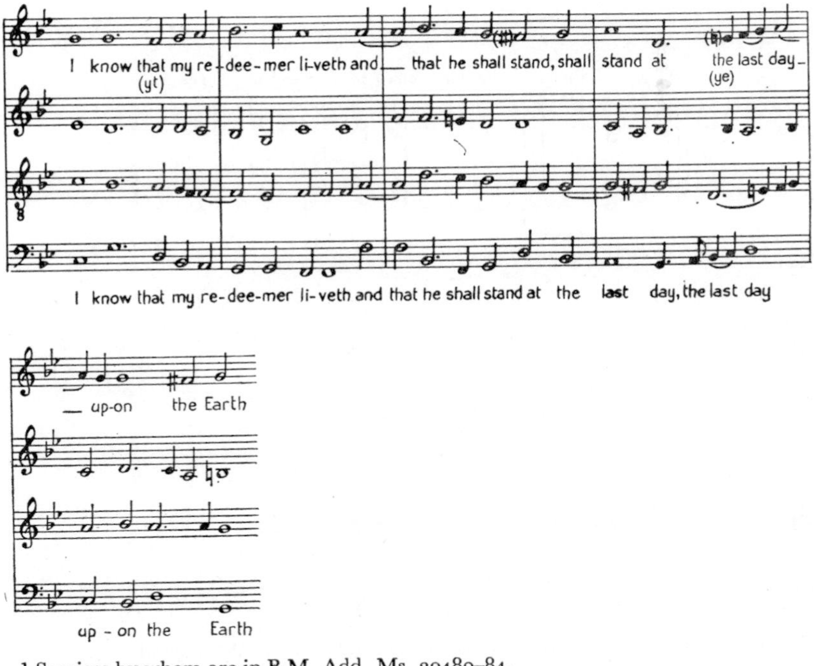

[1] Services by whom are in B.M. Add. Ms. 30480–84.

A certain show of melancholia was not unfashionable in Tudor England: it helped to advertise aesthetic progressiveness and the 'complaints' of poetry transferred to the part-song on the one hand[1] and merged with the breast-beating laments of pietistic Puritans on the other. A congenial compromise was arrived at in numerous collections compiled for private devotions. Of these that made by Sir William Leighton (*Teares and Lamentacions* etc.) and published in 1614 was the most important. Leighton, who belonged to a Shropshire family, was a courtier and a minor poet who was compelled to spend some time in a debtor's prison. He used his enforced leisure profitably in compiling his collection, with the co-operation of Byrd, Bull, Gibbons, Dowland, Coperario, Weelkes, Wilbye, John Milton (father of the poet), and others. The pieces in this collection are somewhat monotonous. But, arranged for voices and 'divers instruments', they represent the manner in which all music was changing. The possibility of mixed voice performance was not excluded, but the lay-out of the score makes it often apparent that the composer was thinking in terms of solo voice and accompaniment. There is also apparent a new appreciation of the expressionist qualities inherent in major and minor tonality. Two constant ideas in religious verse are thus shown by Giovanni Coperario and John Milton.

11.

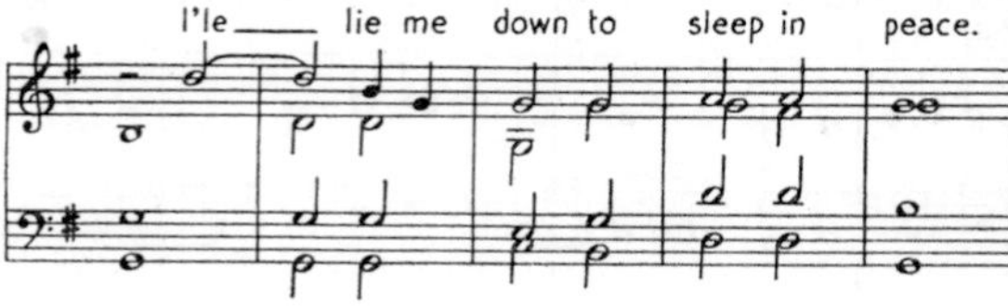

12.

[1] E.g. [R.] Johnson's 'Com, palefaced death' and Tallis's 'When shall my sorrowfull syghinge slake' (B.M. Add. Ms. 30480–84).

There was a homogeneity about Elizabethan music that was a perpetual source of strength. This homogeneity lay on the one hand in a sound and general excellence in technical accomplishment on the part of composers and, on the other, in an eager and perceptive appreciation of musical values on the part of a largely participant public. Patronage was widespread, and therefore the more accommodating, and both the patron and the musician were realists. Music touched life at most points and if its virtues were often idealised by the poets it was not allowed to turn in on itself. The peak of achievement was the madrigal; the *ne plus ultra* of English choral music, that burst on the world in all its maturity half-a-dozen or so years before the death of Queen Elizabeth; remained in a state of consistent excellence across most of the reign of King James and; departed, full of grace, in Tomkins's *Songs of 3, 4, 5 and 6 parts* of 1622. Except that the unexpected genius will make nonsense of any generalisation it may be urged that a community gets the music it deserves. The madrigal certainly exemplifies the basic viability of this thesis, for it was created conjointly, by poets and musicians, by amateurs and professionals; and it was intended for general household use. The elements out of which the madrigal was made were various. There was the existing English tradition of ensemble singing. The madrigal inherited the three-part song method as ratified in the Henrican period, the solo song with viol accompaniment—itself susceptible of revision for part-singing as in the case of Byrd's publications of 1588 and 1589[1], and the motet or anthem. If these correlative traditions seemed more interesting from a musical than from a musico-literary point of view, being considerably disciplined by the principles of Netherlands polyphony, they at least took notice of contrasts of mood, emotional situations, and verbal semantics: musical competence thus was assured. But at that point in history at which this was apparent there was also an emancipation of lyrical verse—by way of Petrarch and Ronsard and through Sidney, the members of the Areopagus, and Spenser. A madrigal, wrote Morley, 'is a kind of music made upon songs and sonnets such as Petrarch and many poets of our time have excelled in'.[2] Poets were for the most part musical and musicians literary, and both appreciated the definitive effect of the one art on the other evinced by the increasingly familiar Italian madrigal, canzonet, villanella, ballet, and frottola. So far as music was concerned works in this order, of Italian provenance, showed how style could be refined (as by a more allusive use of counterpoint than the Flemings normally practised), how point could be given to words by economy in melodic melismatic

[1] 'Heere', wrote Byrd by way of Preface to the 1588 volume, 'are divers songs, which being originally made for Instruments to expresse the harmonie, and voyce to pronounce the dittie, are now framed in all parts for voyces to sing the same.'

[2] Op. cit., p. 294.

and rhythmic design, and how passions and fancies could be exposed by a thorough exploitation of the increased resources of harmony. The madrigal was programmatic (so too was much keyboard music) and English composers kept in view the extravagances of Jannequin's *Verger de Musique* (1559), Striggio's *Il Cicalamento delle Donne al Bucato* (1567), Croce's *Mascarate Piacevoli et Ridicolose per il Carnevale* (1590), and moved towards the full exhibition of those moods contained by Vecchi in *Le Veglie di Siena overo i Varii humori della Musica moderna* (1604). Programming did as much for English music in the late sixteenth and early seventeenth centuries as it did for German music in the nineteenth century. The poets—among those whose verses were set were Sidney, Spenser, Carew, Marlowe, Drayton, Donne, Dyer, Raleigh, and Breton—covered most territories, and—since *The Shepheards Calendar* was a particularly strong inspiration—gave especial attention to the pastoral. The reciprocity existing between poets and musicians is shown in many ways. Poets were indeed eventually composing verses and entitling them Madrigals in the hope that they would attract some composer short of a text. Among them were William Alexander, Earl of Stirling (a courtier of James I and tutor to Prince Henry), and his friend and fellow-Scot, Drummond of Hawthornden; while the charming honorifics of the acrostical *Hymns of Astraea* (1599) by Sir John Davies[1] were another sign-post to the complimentary conceits of *The Triumphes of Oriana*. Davies like the madrigalists took delight in landscape which he pictured with clear charm.

The fusion of the basic elements of the madrigal was accomplished by two diligent middlemen, Nicholas Yonge and Thomas Watson, both of whom cashed in on the zest for Italian culture that came to a climax in the last years of the sixteenth century. Italian or Italianate music had been collected by connoisseurs for some time. A volume, dated 1564, containing madrigals by Arcadelt, Willaert, and di Lasso is now in the Fellows' Library of Winchester College. A set of madrigals[2] (*c.* 1568) by Innocentius Albertus de Tarvisius, musician to the Duke of Ferrara, passed to John, Baron Lumley, and then to his daughter's husband Henry Fitzalan, 18th Earl of Arundel. This volume included a setting of Ariosto's *La Virginella*, also to be set by Byrd. The Earl of Arundel also owned a collection of Neapolitan songs, or madrigals.[3] Later collections[4] show that the works of Marenzio, Mosto, Anerio, Palavicino, Spontone, Claude le Jeune, and Vecchi—as well as of 'Pietro Philippi Anglise', (who, said

[1] Cf. Corkine's complimentary 'Each lovely grace', a setting of an acrostic (*Second Booke of Ayres*, 1612), and Henry Youll's Canzonets to texts by Davies (*Canzonets to Three Voyces*, 1608); on the general subject of 'Music in Honour of Queen Elizabeth I', see article by Denis Stevens, *Mus. T.*, November 1960, pp. 698–9.

[2] B.M. Roy. App. Ms. 36–40.

[3] Roy. App. Ms. 59–62.

[4] Add. Mss. 18936–9 and 11608.

Peacham, 'affecteth altogether the Italian veine'), were assets in the private music-library; while Morley writes enthusiastically and knowledgeably about Marenzio ('for good air and fine invention'), Vecchi, Venturi, Giovanella, and Croce. The set of part-books[1] belonging to Thomas Hamond, of Hawkdon (see p. 125), is of particular interest in that they reflected the zeal of a local musician. In these books were 'Italian songs . . . collected out of Master Geo. Kirbies[2] 'blacke bookes,' and the composers represented were Vecchi, Bona, Gastoldi, Pevernage, Victoria, Croce, del Mel, and de Monte, as well as Peter Philips, Thomas Lupo, and the elder Ferrabosco. Alfonso Ferrabosco I, of course, was a useful linkman, not only able to appear as a thoroughly traditional English composer,[3] but also as an exemplar of current Italian style.

In the Dedication of *Musica Transalpina* Yonge explained how translations of madrigals by Ferrabosco, Marenzio, Palestrina, Donato, Lasso, and others—to which Byrd added *The Fair young virgin*, translated from *La Virginella* (Ariosti, *Orlando Furioso*, I, v. 42)—were made by a 'Counsellor of State' for the benefit of the 'great number of gentlemen and merchants of good account (as well of this realm as of foreign nations)' who gathered at his house. Yonge had been in the habit of having Italian madrigal books sent to him from Italy each year. Two years after the issue of the first volume of *Musica Transalpina* Thomas Watson, friend of Sidney, a classical scholar and Fellow and Dean of St. John's College, Cambridge (1577–86), and a member of the Areopagites, issued *The First Sett of Italian Madrigalls Englished*—with the translations sensibly done 'more after the affection of the note than the dittie.' Watson was abreast of the times and his volume, in which there were twenty-three works by Marenzio, drew on Italian collections published only three years earlier. Watson also asked for a contribution from Byrd and was given the six-part setting of *This sweet and merry month of May*. Since both Yonge's and Watson's collections were printed under Byrd's license, being the first volumes published that were not by Tallis and/or Byrd, it is clear that Byrd's responsibility for thus extending musical opportunities was considerable at all points.

The madrigal is the one branch of music in which the English may (and do) lay claim to some sort of supremacy.[4] Its final accomplishment

[1] Bodl. Ms. Mus. ff. 1–6; see Introduction to G. E. P. Arkwright, *Old English Edition*, no. XXI, 'Anthems and Motets by Robert White, George Kirbye, John Wilbye, and William Daman', London, 1898.

[2] Kirbye.

[3] E.g. in the four-part song *Susanna Fayer* (B.M. Add. Mss. 30480–84).

[4] See Peacham, *The Compleat Gentleman*, p. 103, where Dowland, Morley, Alfonso [Ferrabosco], Wilbye, Kirby, East, Bateson, and Deering, 'with sundry others [are reckoned] inferior to none in the world (how much soever the Italian attributes to himselfe) for depth of skil and richnesse of conceipt'.

was the work not of one or two composers but of an entire school of which the members, highly competent within the purely technical field and well acquainted with one another, were alive to the relationship then existing between words and music, and to the intellectual and social value set on both. Spenserian verse was 'artificial' and marked by the play of 'conceits', which were part of the everyday badinage of the polite: at the same time it was evocative and, in rusticity, even realistic. The madrigalist, by the inferences of figuration and subtlety of imitation, could also stimulate the wit by musical analogues to the literary conceit. But by extension and intensification of rhythmic formulas [Ex. 13], by affiliation both of rhythm and melody to popular idiom [Ex. 14*a* and *b*], by resolution in harmonic enterprise [Ex. 15] and masterly manipulation of vocal (and

13.

14a.

14b.

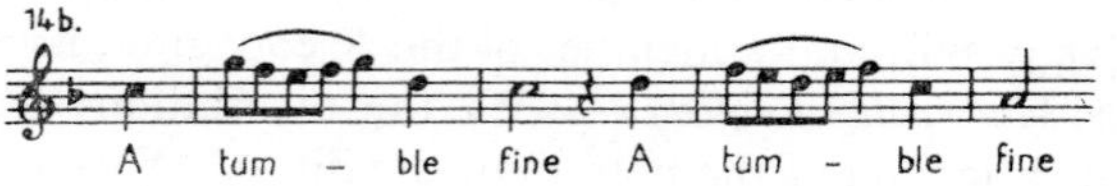

15.

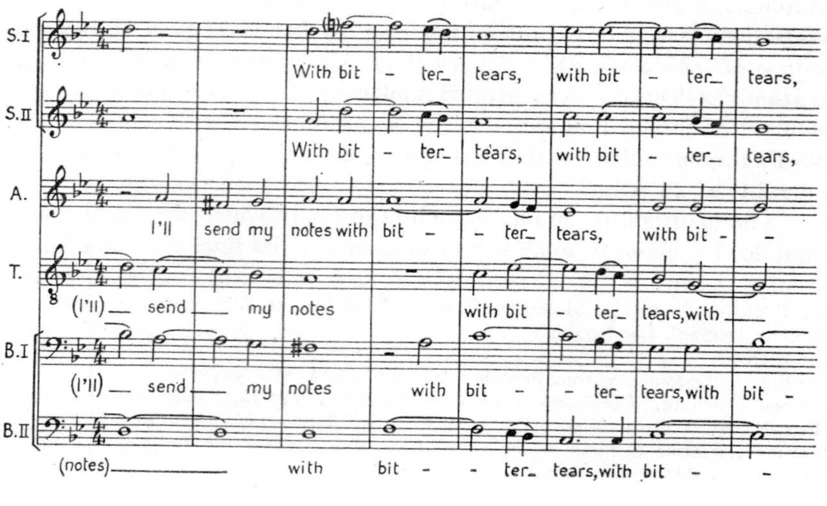

instrumental) ensemble he could give to music a new dimension. The madrigal had relevance to the way in which the Elizabethans lived, and felt.

English music was thus emotionally enriched, and this vitality—both the sum and the symbol of sixteenth-century humanism—was imparted not only to the partially derivative ayre but also to the anthem and to chamber music. The madrigal flourished only briefly. Morley's first book was published in 1594, in which year the first two books of Gesualdo's madrigals were issued. Tomkins's *Songs of* 3, 4, 5, *and* 6 *parts*, published in 1622—although probably written over a period of years—marked the end of the madrigal. Indeed it may be said that Tomkins brought the form back to its starting-point, for the noble, biblical, *David's Lament for Absalom* returns to the austerities of Byrd, but with an added degree of passion.

To say that the madrigal was effectively confined to a period of thirty years is true in one sense; but not in another. Madrigalian habits invaded a wider field during the reign of King James I and influenced the increasingly popular catches and glees that were cultivated by a larger circle of music-lovers than that which had practised the classical madrigal. During the later seventeenth, eighteenth, and nineteenth[1] centuries (as will be shown) the madrigal maintained some place in the common musical life of the nation. To speak of a twentieth-century revival is not in fact quite doing justice to countless enthusiasts who promoted the cause of Morley, Wilbye, Weelkes, Gibbons, and so on, among previous generations.

The Elizabethan composer was an empiricist. The part-song had an honourable history, but foreign travel and the enterprise of Yonge and Watson, and the requirements of royal and civic pageantry showed the necessity for re-thinking music of this kind. Morley, with a keen eye for the felicities of Croce and the delicate pointing of the more vivacious Gastoldi, showed the way.[2] He borrowed from both, *Hard by a crystal fountain* being a parody of Croce's *Ove tra l'herb'e i fivri* which had appeared in *Musica Transalpina* and *Sing we and chant it* lifting phrases direct from Gastoldi's Ballet *A lieta vita.* Two years after Morley's use of this piece in 1595 it was transposed into a German hymn-tune by Johann Lindemann and in due course found a place in Bach's *Orgelbüchlein.* It was maybe from *Ove tra l'herb'e i fivri* that Morley also borrowed the idea on which the famous last couplet of the Oriana madrigal was based so that

[1] The way in which madrigals could be built into the English tradition is represented by the singing of Wilbye's *Flora gave me fairest flowers* at a Sussex Harvest-home, *c.* 1830; see Luke Berrington, *From my boyhood*, London, 1887, p. 45.

[2] See Joseph Kernan, 'Morley and the Triumphs of Oriana', *M. & L.*, 34, no. 3, 1953, p. 185.

Poi concordi seguir Ninfe e Pastori,
Viva la bella Dori.

became

Then sang the shepherds and nymphs of Diana:
Long live fair Oriana.

If Morley favoured Croce and Gastoldi, Thomas Weelkes drew inspiration from Marenzio.[1] Marenzio's insight into the emotional properties of words and his capacity for defining these properties through expressive exploitation of harmony often (and for its own sake and without reference to its contrapuntal function) made a deep impression on Weelkes, whose works are particularly rich in analogous treatment of English words. If Morley, Weelkes, and their contemporaries were alive to the merits of the Italian school they were not overawed, and the manner in which integration of style took place is a further mark of the confidence of English composers. To effect such an alliance between disparate traditions is not common practice in English music, but when it is achieved, as in the sixteenth, century and afterwards by Purcell, Arne, Elgar, and Britten, the results are seen as regenerating. The '*Forraine Artist*', quoted by Ravenscroft, who said that 'an *Englishman* is an excellent *Imitator*, but a very bad Inventor',[2] missed the point.

When Morley treated the Italian madrigal as a basis for operations he did so expansively, replacing, as it were, Italian by English idiom. By extending the length of the madrigal he was able to accommodate his talent for word-painting. The English composers as a whole were loth to omit such details as

16

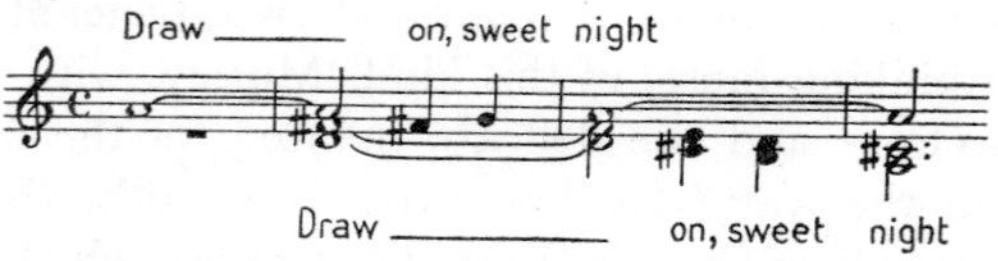

17.

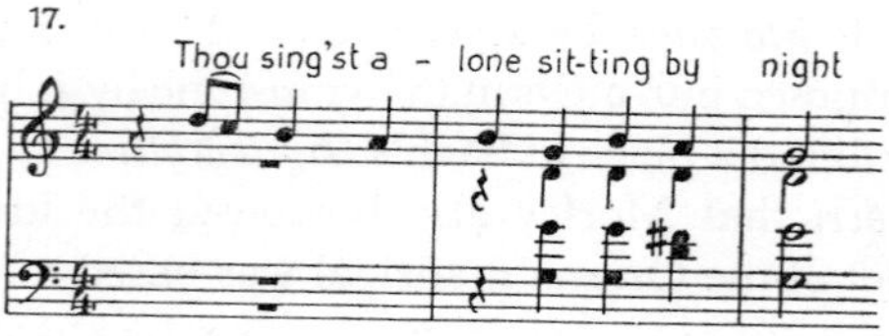

[1] See Denis M. Arnold, 'Thomas Weelkes and the Madrigal', *M. & L.*, 31, no. 1, 1950, p. 1.
[2] *A Briefe Discourse.*

18.

Birds o-ver her do ho – – – ver
Birds o-ver her do ho – – ver

These features, through imitation, became convenient points for sectional musical development. This development, however, had the effect, through allusion, of amplifying the whole line of verse. The extended, contrapuntal, madrigals were worked section by section, each new verbal clause being marked by a fresh musical 'point'. At the same time rhythmic flexibility and textural contrasts, finely and entertainingly exemplified in Weelkes's *As Vesta was from Latmos hill descending*, gave both variety and unity, the unity being one of mood rather than of material.

This ability to establish mood was a striking feature of the madrigalists, and it was rare that a composer failed to appreciate the overall effect of his text. Sometimes uniformity was imposed by skill in timing, as by Weelkes in the image-laden *Thule, the period of cosmography*. Sometimes it was introduced from without as when Morley went to the morris-dance for the inspiration of *Ho! who comes here* and John Mundy to folk-music for the melody of *Heigh ho! 'chill go to plough no more*. Sometimes it was caused by a genius for transmuting visual impressions; as patently as by Richard Nicholson [Ex. 19] in one of a series of naturalistic essays, or as subtly as by Wilbye in *Draw on sweet night*. In such a work as the last-named a personal emotion is indicated and a sense of involvement can lead to

19.

Cuc - koo, Cuc - koo, Cuc - koo

passages of such intensity as [Ex. 20]. This is taken from Weelkes's *Death hath deprived me,* the memorial to his friend, Thomas Morley.

20.

Such a passage is immediately impressive, but too much concentration on the harmonic vocabulary of the period leads to undervaluation of composers like Bennet and Wilbye who were able to make the most felicitous use of simple diction. Wilbye, who generally shares the top place among the madrigalists with Weelkes, was the classic of the school. He indeed looked to the future, but anticipated the eighteenth century (in which he enjoyed considerable esteem) rather than the twentieth. Wilbye exploited pedal points, sequential passages and alternations of plain dominant and tonic chords (as in the coda of *Flora gave me fairest flowers,* 1598), and even showed the value of the recapitulatory process (*O wretched man,* 1609).[1]

The madrigal evolved from English, Flemish, and Italian antecedents. The minuscule of the madrigal was the canzonet; its collateral the ballet. But terminology was imprecise. Pilkington's two sets of madrigals were also described as *Pastorals* while *Songs* was often found convenient as a generic term. The madrigal was replaced in esteem by the ayre; but the dividing line between madrigal and ayre was thin. Morley, for instance, entitled his fifth set *Canzonets or little short aers,* and made arrange-

[1] For a fuller treatment of Wilbye's style see: Robert Collet, 'Some aspects of his music', in *The Score,* no. 4, January 1951, p. 57; also Hugo Henrich, *John Wilbye in Seinen Madrigalen: Studien zu einem Bilde seinen Personlichkeit,* Prague, 1921.

ments of some of his five-part pieces for solo voice and lute, while Dowland's *First Book of Songs or Ayres* (1597) could as well be sung by four voices unaccompanied as solo—to the support of 'Lute, Orpherian, or Viol de gambo.' The madrigal suited one generation, but not the next. The dedications show to what extent it could gratify the vanity of peers of the realm, the new men who were beginning to establish the supremacy of the House of Commons, and provincial worthies of merely local renown. But the more practicable ayre could serve this purpose too. The masters of the madrigal form were by no means confined to London, but increasing centralisation of government and culture was already beginning to work to the disadvantage of regional composers. Most of all the pressure on music from drama told against the continuation of the polyphonic style. The madrigal had on occasion occupied a place in the outskirts, at least, of drama. Edward Johnson, a contributor to *The Triumphes of Oriana*, for instance contributed madrigals in settings of *Eliza is the fairest Queen* and *Come again* to the diversions provided for Queen Elizabeth at Elvetham in 1591; and Martin Peerson set *See, oh, see who is here come a-maying* for an Entertainment, at the Highgate house of Sir Richard Cornwallis, for James I and Queen Anne in 1604. But the complexities of counterpoint were no more fitting for such purposes than for the new style of *dramma per musica* in Italy. Instead of revolution, however, the English preferred evolution. The madrigal persisted throughout the reign of King James but was moved to the side-lines.

6

The New Music

Orlando Gibbons

THE KEY figures in music of the Elizabethan period were Tallis, who had directly carried over into that age traditions from earlier time, Byrd, and Morley. Byrd and Morley, as well as other notable composers generally accepted as Elizabethans, worked on well into the reign of James I but without evident awareness of the social changes that were altering the general character of music. When on the other hand the career of Orlando Gibbons is considered and the nature of his works examined it is clear that he was subject to fresh influences. Gibbons, who did not come to London until after the Queen's death, is often thrown in with the Elizabethans and, as ecclesiastical polyphonist and madrigalist, shown superficially as an orthodox and paid-up member of the 'school'. He inherited certain orthodoxies and—and this is part of the English custom—consulted tradition, but moved forward pragmatically. Gibbons was no revolutionary; neither was he a reactionary.

Changes in music took place in Britain when they were in conformity with new phases in social behaviour. They resulted from the musician's ability to move with the times, but not too far ahead of them. Thus the tradition shows no stylistic changes that came from theory, only those that were evolved through practice. What happened in Italy in respect of the initiation of the *nuove musiche* had no real counterpart in England, even though some English composers were well acquainted with what was going on beyond the Alps. During the reign of James I the future of British music was settled: it would remain independent, idiosyncratic, and, by reference to external standards, conservative.

Orlando Gibbons is one of the greater names in English music. This is partly because of the intrinsic quality of his creative skills but partly because of his *locus standi* as an official composer. He occupied the highest places in the musical hierarchy and having reached the summit of public ambition died at an early age. He also belonged to a dynasty of musicians which exerted an influence on musical affairs for more than a century. Gibbons's father knew the miracle plays and, as a wait, was associated with them; his second son Christopher became a prominent figure in Restoration music and, as a pioneer of English opera, a direct precursor of Henry Purcell.

William Gibbons (*c.* 1540–1595) was an Oxford town musician who in 1564 accompanied the Proctors of the University to Cambridge for the occasion of Queen Elizabeth's visit.[1] Gibbons remained in Cambridge, married a Cambridge woman, and came to occupy a leading position among the musicians of the town.[2] In 1567, however, he fell foul of the Proctors and was fined 40/– because he did 'upholde maintain, and kepe or cause to be kept a dansing schole within the Town of Cambridge.'[3] In the following year Gibbons's second son Edward was born. (The first son Richard died in infancy in 1566.) Edward in due course became a lay-clerk and master of the choristers at King's College and later, although a layman, a priest-vicar of Exeter Cathedral. He died in 1658. After Edward came Ellis (1573–1603) whose promise was acknowledged by Morley by the inclusion of two contributions in the *Oriana* set of madrigals.[4] Ferdinando,[5] the fourth son, would appear to have been named after the son of Orlando di Lasso[6] whose own Christian name was given to the fifth Gibbons son, born in 1583.

In about 1581 William Gibbons returned to Oxford and it was there that Orlando was born[7]. After practising as a wait in Oxford William went back to Cambridge in about 1590 and five years later he died. Orlando became a chorister at King's College in 1596, under the tutorship of his brother Edward, and two years later matriculated in the College as a Sizar. Maintaining his connection with King's Orlando appears in the College records in 1602 and 1603 as an occasional composer. In 1605, aged twenty-one, he was appointed Gentleman and Organist of the Chapel

1 Three plays were given in King's College Chapel: these included Nicholas Udall's *Ezechias* and E. Haliwell's *The Tragedy of Dido*.

2 'Mr. Maior did delyver to William Gibbons musitian fyve sylver cullers called the waites cullers, ponderinge xxvij oz. 1^{d}. And the said William Gibbons hathe found sureties for the delyverye of the same cullers agayne when they be required'; *Corporation Common Day Book*, 25 November 1567.

3 F. A. Keynes, *By-Ways of Cambridge History*, 1947, p. 53.

4 *Long live fair Oriana à* 5.
Round about her charret à 6.
Only Morley otherwise had two works in the *Oriana* set.

5 Ferdinando followed his father's profession and became one of the waits of Lincoln.

6 It is possible that di Lasso visited England in 1554 in the company of the Neapolitan nobleman, Cesare Brancaccio: in any case his music was well known in England.

7 He was christened in St. Martin's Church on Christmas Day, 1583.

Royal, which appointment he held for the rest of his life. In 1619, already rewarded by additional grants from the King and Queen in 1611 and 1615, he succeeded Walter Earle as a 'musician for the virginalles' and in 1623 on the death of John Parsons added the organistship of Westminster Abbey to his existing commitments. A Bachelor of Music of Cambridge (1606) and also, by incorporation, of Oxford, Gibbons became Mus.D. at Oxford in 1622 at the suggestion of William Camden, founder of the Chair of History. At this time the Chair of Music at Oxford was instituted by William Heyther, who, wishing to qualify himself as Mus.D., borrowed Gibbon's *O clap your hands together* to present as his 'Exercise'.

During his period of office as a royal musician Gibbons was commis-

1a.

1b.

Our gracious sovereign head unto the place
Where all our bliss was bred.

sioned to compose music for the visit of King James I to his Scottish dominions in May 1617. As has already been seen the Scottish Chapel Royal had been allowed to run down and although the revenues were entrusted to one of James's favourites—John Gib—the establishment had neither the equipment nor the personnel to rise to an occasion. Thus Thomas Dallam,[1] who had built organs for King's College, Cambridge, and Worcester Cathedral, was required to build one to be shipped to Leith in time for the royal visit (the ornamental but papistical angels proposed by Inigo Jones had to be left in England after Scottish protests); and the singers of the English Chapel Royal made to follow. This gave affront to the Scots. Whether Orlando Gibbons went to Scotland is uncertain, though probable; but he wrote the anthem *Great King of Gods* with a splendid, spacious opening, nicely, if fortuitously, attuned to the psalmodic preferences of the Scots [Ex. 1] and the welcome-song, *Do not repine, fair sun*[2]—a cross between a verse-anthem and a May-day madrigal—to celebrate the occasion. The latter work has some importance as the first recognisable work of the order of ode, which, half-a-century later, was to become a feature of English music until the nineteenth century.

Association with the Court enabled Gibbons to cultivate the acquaintance of potential patrons. The nine fantasies for strings, in three parts, which were published probably about 1612[3] were dedicated to Edmund Wray, who held office at Court, while the *First Set of Madrigals and Motets* 1612 were inscribed to Sir Christopher Hatton, son of Edmund Spenser's patron. From the dedication of this work it is clear that Gibbons lived with Hatton, and that the latter selected the texts.[4] Out of twenty pieces eight authors are to be identified, and they include Joshuah Sylvester, Spenser, Raleigh, and Donne. If the generally severe tone of the texts reflects Hatton's taste it is not unreasonable to suppose that Gibbons's own literary predilections lay along similar lines; for a degree of austerity marks his musical style and (since there is supporting evidence in his choice of function) this would seem to have been a personal trait.

[1] Thomas Dallam was one of a famous family of organ-builders. In 1599–1600 he took a mechanical clock-organ of his invention to Constantinople for the Grand Turk. His Diary was printed by the Hakluyt Society in 1893.

[2] Ed. by P. Brett, from New York Public Library, Drexel Mss. 480–85 (pub. Stainer and Bell).

[3] Reprinted in Paulus Matthysz, *T'uitnement Cabinet*, Amsterdam, 1646.

[4] The madrigals, wrote Gibbons, 'were most of them composed in your owne house, and doe therefore properly belong unto you, as Lord of the Soile; the language they speake you provided them, I onely furnished them with Tongues to utter the same'. The interest of well-known patrons in having their favourite poem set to music is also indicated by Robert Jones, the lutenist, in the address *To the Reader* in his *First Booke of Songs and Ayres*, 1600. For Lady Hatton Gibbons wrote a Galliard, see p. 180.

However this may have been Gibbons was a virtuoso performer on the virginals and the organ. Testimony to the reputation he enjoyed lies in John Hackett's account of the reception of the French mission which came to London to negotiate the marriage between Prince Charles (later Charles I) and Henrietta Maria. As the Ambassadors entered the Choir of Westminster Abbey for a service 'the organ was touched by the best Finger of that age, Mr. Orlando Gibbons'. This opinion was otherwise repeated by John Chamberlain, writing after Gibbons's death to Sir Dudley Carleton.

Gibbons took part in the funeral service for James I and shortly afterwards was required to travel to Canterbury with the rest of the Chapel Royal to attend the new King on his progress to meet the Queen whom he had already married by proxy in Paris. Before the royal pair came back to Canterbury from Dover Gibbons was taken ill and died: he was buried in Canterbury Cathedral.

The posthumous reputation of Gibbons depended for a long time on his ecclesiastical works—possibly for the wrong reason—and on one not entirely characteristic madrigal, *The Silver Swan*, which is more nearly an 'ayre.' Gibbons was conservative in holding to the general principles of Byrd, but he showed his appreciation of Byrd more by his extension of the dramatic insights of that master than by his derivative treatment of contrapuntal techniques. Gibbons was a splendid contrapuntist, and in this respect he maintained the *status quo*, but he recognised that times were changing and that new opportunities were inherent in the altered conditions of the seventeenth century. A dedicated church musician in a period in which the Church of England was concerned with other aspects of church life rather more than with its music, he saw the spiritual excellences which could be extrapolated from the humanistic essays of contemporary composers engaged in secular avocations.

It has already been observed that Gibbons set English texts exclusively. This puts him in the position of the first of our composers to be regarded as *pur sang* Church of England. He occupies a place of importance in the history of hymnody through his collaboration with George Wither, who, with the King's approval, sought to amplify the by now familiar but restricted repertoire of metrical psalms by the addition of more lyrical, and more metrically diversified, hymns. In 1623 he issued, therefore, his *Hymnes and Songs of the Church*, for which Gibbons composed some sixteen melodies.[1] By the side of these should be set his two contributions to Leighton's *Tears or Lamentacions*. In works of this calibre, as in *The Silver Swan*, Gibbons skirts round the 'ayre', a province in which he is

[1] The best of these are available in *The English Hymnal*, and 'Song 13' was used as the basis of a Hymn-Tune Prelude for piano by Vaughan Williams.

not otherwise represented. If hymn-tunes are of minor musical importance it must be observed that it is at all times difficult to compose good hymn-tunes. One or two by Gibbons, especially Songs 13 and 34, remained in the repertoire of hymnody and thus helped to keep his name actively alive.

2.

Above all Gibbons was distinguished as a composer of anthems. Of those that he wrote (and the two 'Services' may be included) eighty per cent were 'verse anthems', in which passages were laid out for solo voices in contrast with those for the 'full' vocal ensemble, and also had independent accompaniments for strings and/or organ. These anthems were undoubtedly for the Chapel Royal, where the instrumental resources were regularly to hand. The two specifically 'royal' anthems—*O all true* [*these*] *faithful hearts*, 'A thanksgiving for the king's recovery from sickness', and *Great King of Gods*—typify the Gibbons manner. In expanding the scope of the anthem and by introducing a strong dramatic declamatory element, Gibbons was experimenting along modern lines but within the limits of English music. The ultimate of these limits and of Gibbons's 'new music' is represented by the extract from the superb, *See, see the Word is Incarnate*, a miniature oratorio on the life of Christ [Ex. 2].

Of the great continental masters of his time Gibbons most resembled Heinrich Schütz in combining strength of statement with a controlled passion and a sense of human values. But Gibbons knew not Giovanni Gabrieli, nor Monteverdi; nor did he live on through the vicissitudes of war and political upheaval into a new epoch as did Schütz or, for that matter, his own son Christopher.

Although the madrigals match the anthems with their general dignity—*What is our life?* is typical—Gibbons was one of those composers (Weelkes and Deering being the others) who went out into the common life of London to pick up the cries of the street-vendors and to incorporate them within quasi-fantasia arrangements,[1] at a time when the madrigal itself was undergoing change. This, perhaps, is an acknowledgment of the wider activities of William and Ellis Gibbons of which there are other hints of permanent sympathy in the string fantasias, works which are among the most important of their time.

The fantasia, off-shoot of motet, developed in the later years of Elizabeth's reign into the pre-eminent type of abstract music as then conceivable. The composer, as Morley stated, taking 'a point at his pleasure, . . . wresteth and turneth it as he list, making either much or little of it according as shall seeme best in his own conceit'.[2] The general practice then was to deal with one main theme in a sequence of contrapuntal diversions, with the sections overlapping each other. Towards the end of the century, as Morley himself exemplifies, the sections began to separate out from one another. With the introduction of contrasted time-signatures each section virtually became an independent movement. In the fantasias of Thomas Lupo, Giovanni Coperario (a particularly prolific and inventive writer in this field), and the younger Ferrabosco the previous emotional neutrality of the form is abandoned, while the division into self-contained movements begins to be rationalised. (The progress was not dissimilar from that of the symphony in the eighteenth century.) Orlando

[1] B.M. Add. Mss. 29372–7, contains O. Gibbons's, *God give you good morrow* and *A good sausage, and let it be roasted*; and Deering's *God give you good morrow Sir Rice* [Rees ap Thomas ap William ap Johnes; cf. Add. Mss. 18936–9] '*Country Cries*'; Weelkes's *The Crie of London* is in B.M. Add. Mss. 37402–6.

[2] Op. cit., p. 296.

Gibbons, whose appreciation of the proportional properties inherent in and necessary to musical design was, like that of Byrd, classical in character,[1] wrote the most comprehensive and balanced examples of fantasia during the springtime of the form—that is, during the Jacobean period. In all there remain twenty-seven fantasias, including four *In Nomines*, by him. The seven three-part and one four-part fantasias in Marsh's Library, Dublin, are written to include 'the greate double base', or old violone. The most important of Gibbons's Fantasies are the set published as *Fantasies of III parts* at about the same time as *Parthenia*. In these a significant change of style is to be noticed. The first four of the series are according to the Elizabethan convention, with interlinked sections forming a homogeneous whole. In the final five, however, there is a clear division into movements, each terminated by a perfect cadence. It is argued by Thurston Dart[2] that these fantasias were not composed for viols, but, like similarly designed works by Coperario and Thomas Lupo, for two violins and bass viol, with chamber organ accompaniment, and to be played at Court. For this there is the supporting evidence of a seventeenth-century manuscript described by Dart, which includes 'Fancyes/of 2 and 3 parts to ye organ/of Mr. Gibbons, & Mr. Coperario/with ye violl and violin to ye organ.'[3] (Coperario was tutor to the children of James I and in his *Introduction to the Skill of Music* (1697 ed.) John Playford wrote that Prince Charles played 'his part exactly well in the Bass-Viol, especially of those incomparable Fancies of Mr. Coperario to the Organ'.) These prototypical trio-sonatas of Gibbons, Coperario, and Thomas Lupo were published in 1648 in Amsterdam.[4] In his four-part fantasias Gibbons moved further away from the traditional structure, incorporated fugato movements, with others in galliard and even morris dance style. [Ex. 3.]

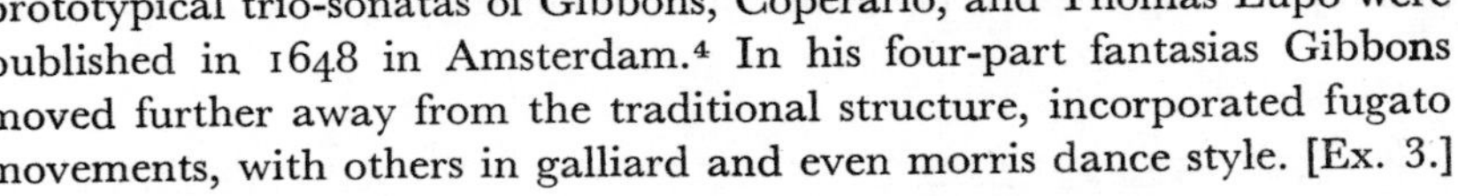

The final department in which Gibbons was especially distinguished was that of keyboard music. The seal of dignity was set on this order of music by the issue of *Parthenia, or The Maydenhead of the first musicke that ever*

1 In the address which prefaced his *First Set of Madrigals* he wrote: 'It is proportion that beautifies everything.'

2 Thurston Dart, 'The Printed Fantasias of Orlando Gibbons', *M. & L.*, 37, no. 4, 1956, p. 342.

3 'Purcell and Bull', *Mus. T.*, 1963, p. 31.

4 *xx Koninckiycke Fantasien, om op 3 Fioolen de Gamba en ander Speel-tuigh te gebruycken. Gestelt door de Konstige Engelse Speel-meesters, T. Lupo, J. Coprario, W. Daman. En noch ix Fantasien, om met 3 Fioolen de Gamba . . . door Orlando Gibbons, Organist en Zang-meester van de Koninck van Engeland. Eerste Deel. t' Amsterdam, by Paulus Matthysz, 1648.*

was printed for the Virginalls, at the end of 1612 or the beginning of 1613.[1] This volume of twenty-one pieces (a number favoured in other musical publications) by Byrd, Bull, and Gibbons, beautifully engraved by William Hole and published for Dorothy Evans (possibly a Lady of the Court) by George Lowe, was inscribed to Frederic, the Elector Palatine, and Princess Elizabeth (subsequently known as the 'Winter-Queen' of Bohemia), daughter of James I, who were betrothed on 27 December 1612. The volume contains gratulatory poems by Hugh Holland[2] and George Chapman.[3] Of Gibbons Holland not very elegantly observed:

> Yet this ORLANDO parallels di Lasso:
> Whose triple praise would tire a very Tasso.

Of Gibbons's keyboard pieces none remains in the composer's autograph and the ascription of some must be less than certain. However the range is wide, illustrating the general co-ordinating function of this class of music. Gibbons arranged, and composed, pavans, galliards, sarabands, almains and corantos; folk-songs—including the celebrated *Hunt's up*; *In Nomines*, fancies (fantasias), and voluntaries—some specifically for organ; 'grounds'; and airs and instrumental pieces contributed to the court masques. In general Gibbons's keyboard writing is marked by a strong feeling for the character of the keyboard, while his frequent adaptation of vocal figuration is characteristic of his capacity to see music as a whole and to make progress without letting go what was familiar. [Ex. 4a and b.] Although he had no distaste for brilliance (note the ornamentation

of his *Lincolns Inn Masque*[4]) he kept it within bounds—which the more volatile Bull sometimes failed to do—and he had a delicate appreciation of the value of varied textures, and of rests. In this respect his corantos[5]

[1] *Parthenia* was reissued in 1646, 1651, and 1655 (see O. E. Deutsch, 'Cecilia and Parthenia', *Mus. T.*, 1959, pp. 591–2).

[2] d. 1633, a member of the Mermaid Club, author of a sonnet prefixed to the first folio Shakespeare, and friend of John Dowland.

[3] 1559?–1634, playwright, masque-writer, famous for his translation of Homer's *Iliad* (1611) and *Odyssey* (1624).

[4] Contained in B.M. Add. Ms. 10444 and entitled 'The First of the Prince his.'

[5] See *Orlando Gibbons, Keyboard Works*, ed. by M. H. Glyn, Stainer and Bell, 5 vols., I, pp. 6–7, and p. 13.

are especially charming. The string fantasies show Gibbons's architectonic quality. This is apparent in his keyboard music in his lay-out of large-scale variations, of which those on the folk-song *The Woode so Wilde* (treated also by Byrd and Bull) are outstanding. In these nine variations Gibbons shows the virtue of early exercise in treatment of *cantus firmus*, but here he allows academic ingenuity to be supplemented by an imaginative perception of the effectiveness of thematic fragmentation, and contrasted and surprising placing of segments of melody: '. . . the variations have a fine romantic colouring, and show clearly how a musician of Gibbons's scope was able to make himself independent of a predecessor of the strength of Byrd when treating the same subject'.[1]

Declining Standards of Church Music

The position of Orlando Gibbons in English music is unassailable but in spite of his recognition of new values he was in general terms rather more at the end of a tradition than at the beginning of a new one. To this extent the frequent classification of him as an Elizabethan is not entirely unwarrantable. Two major developments he virtually ignored. These were in the art of solo song, or ayre, and in the collateral one of music and drama. When the enormous vogue for chamber music is also taken into account it is clear that the importance of the main tradition of church music had declined. That this was so was due to a relative relaxation of religious tensions, to the general adoption of a temperate middle-of-the-road order in ecclesiastical processes with a consequent diminution of the significance of the evocative quality of music, to the stress laid on Bible-reading by Puritans and the Authorised Version of 1611, to the cult of the pulpit orator, and to sheer neglect.

From the middle of the sixteenth century the musical foundations of cathedrals and the greater collegiate churches had been existing on increasingly inadequate subsidies and the climate of the Jacobean period was not such that these could be made more adequate. Church music more and more centred on London, where a succession of composers was constantly required to celebrate royal occasions. The only new festival added to the calendar was held annually on 5 November, and this was regarded without disfavour among church musicians in general.[2] Otherwise they had little to be enthusiastic about.

Bishop Bridgeman's Injunctions for Chester Cathedral[3] for 12 July

[1] C. van den Borren, *The Sources of Keyboard Music in England*, p. 214.

[2] e.g. at Chester, 1618, Thomas Jones being organist: 'Given to the organist to drinke with the musike that playd the 5 of Nov in the quire vjs.' Bridge, op. cit., p. 79.

[3] G. T. O. Bridgeman, *The History of the Church and Manor of Wigan*, Chetham Soc., 1888, pp. 276–80.

1623 show how disastrously standards had fallen. 'Item. Because the great negligence of the petty Canons or Singing Men hath done much wrong to God's service, and brought the Church into contempt and obloquy, it is decreed and strictly enjoyned every member of the Quire, namely, the petty Canons, clerks, organist, and choristers, that from henceforth they do not absent themselves from Divine service any day (above 6 weeks in one year, which are allowed them for their necessary occasions to be absent) upon pain of 2d. to be forfeited by him that shall be absent for every service in this Church. And every one of them that shall come tardy after the Confession is said, or goe out before the end of divine service shall forfeit 1d. for every such default. And because the defects of the organist, or his neglect in tutoring the choristers, hath unsufferably impeached and impaired the service of God, and almost utterly spoyled the children, he is therefore (besides the censure now to be laid upon him) admonished to present reformation; with protestation that if sensible amendment be not found in the education of the choristers before Michaelmas next, he shall then be utterly deprived of his place in this Church, and another put therein.' But Bridgeman was not unaware that the singing-men had a strong case for a wage increase: 'Item. Because the use and service of Cooke, Cater [Caterer], Butler, Baker, and other such offices is now extinct, it is ordered and decreed that the pensions allotted to those officers shall from henceforth be divided among the petty canons and singing men for the betterment of their wages; which is now too mean to maintain them, considering their charge of wife and children, and seeing they are so diligently to attend divine service as they can hardly by any other vocation procure a competency for their sustenances.'

Eleven years later Archbishop Neile of York, as anxious to restore the proprieties of a Catholic form of worship as his friend Laud, wrote a gloomy account of the condition of music in the cathedrals and parish churches of the Northern Province to King Charles; on Chester he reported as follows:

'And there is by this occasion another inconvenience, that at the same time there is double service in ye same church. The service with Voices and Organs in the Quire, and ye reading service in ye body of the church. And when, in either place, any part of the service yt is prescribed is omitted, or mutilated, ye answere hath been, that the one giveth way to ye other, and what is omitted in ye one is read in ye other part of the church. The Litanie is scarcely ever heard on Sundays in ye Cathedrall church; and *Te Deum*, *Benedictus*, ye Litanie, *Magnificat*, etc., are seldome said or sung in most of ye churches of ye Diocese, but Psalmes sung instead thereof.'[1]

[1] ib., pp 368–9. Thomas Jones, appointed in 1614, was still organist and remained in office until 1637.

In the Collegiate Church of Manchester there were, reported Neile, 'neither singing men, nor quiristers, nor organ fitt to be used'. Psalm-singing encouraged some benefactors to give new organs to churches and the authorities to dispense with choristers. At All Saints, Wigan, for example, a new organ was erected in 1623 (it was destroyed in 1643) but while mention is made in the church records of psalm-singing there is none of the choir. And even when the ancient dignities were maintained, as at Christ Church Cathedral, Dublin where, at Easter, 1637, two sackbut and two cornet players were hired to accompany the choir—Bishop William Bedell objected to a service 'attended and celebrated with all manner of instrumental musick, as Organs, Sackbutts, Cornetts, Violls, etc., as if it had been at the dedication of Nebuchadnezzar's golden image in the plain of Dura'. When Giles Tomkins took over the duties of organist at Salisbury from the madrigalist John Holmes in 1629, he found not only that he could not get into his appointed house because Holmes's mother refused to move but that there were no choristers to teach.

With the suppression of the choral service by Parliament in 1644, the great era of English church music came to an end. Before the curtain came down John Barnard, a minor canon of St. Paul's Cathedral, issued his *First Book of Selected Church Musick*, a collection purporting to contain the services and Anthems (both 'Full' and 'Verse') used in the cathedral and collegiate churches of the Kingdom. The composers represented in this anthology included those then regarded as of classical quality, for Barnard excluded all who were living at the time of compilation: most have retained their status. They were Batten,[1] Bevin, Bull, Byrd, Farrant,[2] Gibbons, Giles,[3] Hooper, Morley, W. Mundy, Parsons,[4] Shepherd, Strogers,[5] Tallis, Tye, Ward,[6] Weelkes, White, and Woodson.[7] Barnard intended to supplement his *First Book* with others in which contemporary composers should be represented, but the intention was not fulfilled. After the Civil

[1] Adrian Batten (d. 1637), chorister at Winchester under John Holmes, was successively Lay Vicar at Westminster Abbey (1614) and joint organist (with John Tomkins) of St Paul's Cathedral. Batten was one of the first English composers consistently to use bar-lines.

[2] Richard Farrant (d. 1585?), sometime Master of the Choristers at St. George's Chapel, Windsor.

[3] Nathaniel Giles (*c.* 1560–1633), successively organist of Worcester Cathedral, and Master of the Children at Windsor and the Chapel Royal.

[4] Robert Parsons (d. 1569), Gentleman of the Chapel Royal 1563–9, when he was succeeded by Byrd.

[5] Nicholas Strogers, composer of church and instrumental music (keyboard pieces, *In Nomines*, etc.) of whose life nothing is known.

[6] John Ward, musician in the household of Sir Henry Fanshawe (1569–1616), who was a friend of Prince Henry and Remembrancer of the Exchequer. In Ward's *First Set of English Madrigals* (1613) there is a *Mourning Song in memory of Prince Henry*.

[7] Leonard Woodson, Lay Clerk of St. George's Chapel, Windsor, in 1605, and organist of Eton College, 1615–*c.*41.

War a volume of words of anthems as sung in St. Patrick's Cathedral, Dublin, was printed by Stephen Buckley at York in 1662, and two years later a further collection of the words of commonly used anthems was issued by James Clifford, also a minor canon at St. Paul's.

The Ayre and its Composers

Until the seventeenth century there was no reason for specialisation in the field of composition. But when James I came to the throne (by which time the status of musicians not on the ecclesiastical pay-roll had risen to near parity with those who were) there was a variety of opportunity. Thus there was one group of composers mainly known as experts in lute music or in songs with lute accompaniment; another group concerned with consort music; a third group active in the dramatic field; as well as those which belonged to the polyphonic tradition in either or both of its vocal departments. There was, of course, much overlapping; but composers sort themselves out pretty well by their principal spheres of activity.

If the madrigal represented the high point in Elizabethan musical culture, then the chief glory of the Jacobean era was the ayre (closely pursued by the fantasia). The ayre, its form and function long anticipated, united voice and verse with a rare felicity, and vocal melody for the first time in English music allied itself to a flexible and suggestive type of accompaniment—that of the lute. For this the popularity of the lute and its wide cultivation was responsible. Behind the ayre was the social prestige of the poet and, as has been seen, the setting of certain poems was sometimes at the instance of particular patrons. While a long English tradition underlay the ayre there were, as in the case of the madrigal, influences from Italy. John Dowland, for instance, was well acquainted with both Marenzio and Croce (possibly also with Gesualdo), and John Cooper, or Giovanni Coperario as he was to be known, spent some years in Italy, while the regard in which the skill of Italian solo singers was held was expressed after his visit to Venice in 1608 by Thomas Coryate.[1]

The ayre served two functions. It was, on the one hand, like the later *Lied*, an integral part of domestic music. On the other it was essential to public secular entertainment. The cult of the masque by King James I and the development of this particular art-form under the superintendency of Ben Jonson encouraged a new look at the relationship between words and music with some awareness of what was happening in Italy. The new factor in Italian song was declamation, and it was introduction of the

[1] *Coryat's Crudities,* 1611, p. 250.

declamatory style into the English ayre that gave to it a fresh vitality. A declamatory element was occasionally introduced into the madrigal—as in Wilbye's *Weep, weep, mine eyes* (1609), but was easier to manipulate in the ayre. It will be encountered in ayres by Dowland, Ferrabosco, Coperario, and Robert Jones, where consideration for the word implies concern not only for its meaning but also its spoken characteristics, of rhythm and even of pitch. Italian music was widely known through manuscript collections and in 1613 the London publication of Angelo Notari's *Prima Musiche Nuove*, by William Hole, served as a stimulus to those eager to be in the van of progress. The Preface to Notari's work described the current techniques of Italian singing style. In 1625 Notari, who had lived for some time in London as a singing-teacher, was appointed Musician for the lute and voices at Court.

In 1613 Nicholas Lanier (1588–1666) was one of the composers employed in the preparation of the 'Squires' Masque', for the wedding of the Earl of Somerset, and his setting of one song [Ex. 5] shows the main

5.

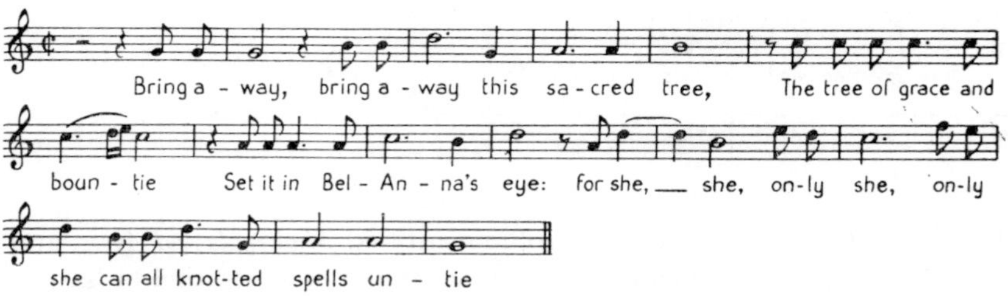
Bring a - way, bring a - way this sa - cred tree, The tree of grace and
boun - tie Set it in Bel - An - na's eye: for she, she, on-ly she, on-ly
she can all knot-ted spells un - tie

properties of recitative. Five years later the same composer was reported as having set a precedent. Referring to the Masque presented in Lord Hay's name for the benefit of the French Ambassador, Ben Jonson observed: 'The whole Masque was sung after the Italian manner, stylo recitativo, by Master Nicholas Lanier; who ordered and made both the scene and the music.'[1] Be this as it may, Lanier, who became art adviser to Charles I, was greatly interested in Italian music which he got to know at first hand when he was sent by Charles I on a picture-buying expedition in 1625. During this period another composer studied Italian style with care. This was Walter Porter, a Gentleman of the Chapel Royal in 1616,

[1] The note was not in the 1617 quarto of the text but added to the folio of 1640. By this time Lanier had established himself beyond doubt as the pioneer of recitative in English with his setting of *Hero and Leander*. The authority for this is Roger North's *Memoirs of Musick* and *The Musicall Grammarian*, quoted in McD. Emslie, 'Nicholas Lanier's Innovations in English Song', *M. & L.*, 41, no. 1, 1960, p. 13.

who was reported to have been a pupil of Monteverdi[1] and whose music—in the following example patently inspired by Italian contacts—shows characteristics of the *nuove musiche*. [Ex. 6a and b.] Porter published his

6a.

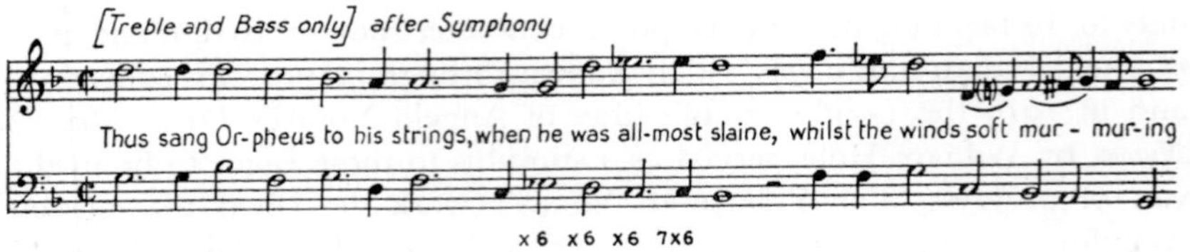

6b.

Orpheus and Euridice, in 1632, in a volume entitled *Madrigals and Ayres*, and assigned the parts to five voices and to an ample orchestration of harpsichord, lutes, theorbos, bass viol, and two violins or viols. Appropriately the volume was dedicated to a much-travelled diplomat, John Digby, first Earl of Bristol. In his preliminary notice *To the Practitioner* Porter showed how far attitudes to singing had advanced during the early years of the seventeenth century:

'. . . let me intreate you to play and sing them true, according to my meaning, or heare them done so; not in stead of singing, to howle or bawle them, and scrape in stead of playing, and performe them falsely and say they are naught; In so doing if they were nere so good, you'd spoyle them; for I must tell you, a Composer, when he hath set a Song with all the art he can, hath done but halfe the worke, the other halfe is the well performing or expressing that in singing or playing which he hath done in composing . . .

[1] See Pamela J. Willetts, 'A Neglected Source of Monody and Madrigal', *M. & L.*, 43, no. 4, 1962, p. 329.

'I have exprest in the part of the *Harpsecord*, the *maior* and *minor* sixses, by Flats and Sharpes, the figures I have put over the head of a thorow Base . . . in the Songs which are set forth with Divisions, where you may find many Notes in a place after this manner in rule or space,

they are to expresse the Trillo: I have made use of these *Italian* words, because they shall not mistake, and sing them, if they were expressed in English, being mixed amongst the other wordes, *Tace*, which is, that the Voyces or Instruments, are to be silent, or hold their peace, till such or such things be performed, also the word *forte*, which is strong or loud, I have set before most of the Songs; *Toccatas*, *Sinfonias*, and *Rittornellos*, which besides the delight and varietie they beget, they are good for the respiration of the voyces, for which end they are used . . .'

Like all such Prefaces, Porter's foreword is a statement of intention and a guide to current thinking and, indeed, action. The expressive values of music became increasingly broader during the Jacobean period so that by its end it was not only the content of song which mattered but also the way in which singers mastered the arts of expression (which also included skill in decoration). It was fortunate that the principal composers of ayres were adaptable and versatile, and consistently endowed with high talent. A number of the leaders of the school were intimately connected with the drama of the period and it was this connection that did much to develop and diversify the solo song.

As with the madrigal there is no particular starting-point. The ayre emerged, running for a time in double harness with the part-song. In his autobiography Thomas Whythorne refers to his own practice of singing songs to the accompaniment of virginals or lute. But it was the Areopagite discussions of the 1580's that directly led to the detailed consideration of the structure of poetry and its relationship to music which distinguished the composers of ayres. The central figure among these composers was Thomas Campion (1567–1620), since he was both poet and musician, though by profession, being a doctor of medicine, neither. Campion, the friend of Thomas Nash (a supporter of the Areopagus movement), acknowledged his own debt to the immediate past by addressing epigrams to Philip Sidney and Spenser, and his standing as a poet was recognised in 1593 by a complimentary reference by George Peele. Campion indeed is outstanding as a suave lyrical writer whose verses are tailor-made for musical setting. He had firm ideas as to how words should be set and the address printed before the joint *Book of Ayres* of 1601 (with Philip Rosseter), which is probably Campion's work, preaches the virtues, so ably demonstrated by him in his settings, of brevity and simplicity. Campion published four more books of ayres and provided texts for other composers.

Campion was a friend of the fourth Earl of Cumberland, for whom he wrote the text of an Entertainment[1] given at Brougham Castle, in Westmorland, on the occasion of King James's 1617 progress to his Scottish dominions, and it was in Cumberland's London house that many of Campion's ayres were first heard. It is probable that works by Anthony Holborne and the Dowlands were also the result of Cumberland's hospitality and encouragement, while the Earl's sister, Anne Clifford, pupil of Samuel Daniel, further extended the family interest in the arts. Campion was the friend of these composers as also of Robert Jones, Ferrabosco, Coperario, and Philip Rosseter—to whom he bequeathed his estate. Campion's talents, and his happy gift of being able to synthesise classical precision with lyrical feeling, were widely appreciated and he was commissioned to write the texts of four important masques. He also compiled a brief treatise entitled *A new way of making Foure parts in Counter-point* (1618?), in which is implied the acceptance of a key system in teaching method.

Campion was an amateur, yet respected by and exercising a strong influence on his professional colleagues. Chief among these was John Dowland (1563–1626), the outstanding member of the school, who may have come from Dublin.[2] Dowland's reputation was European. Skilful as lutenist, he spent some part of his youth in the service of the English Ambassador in Paris. The fact that he became a Catholic apparently militated against employment at the Court of Elizabeth in his case, but he was welcomed in Germany, first by the Duke of Brunswick—whose connection with English music is otherwise attested by titles of two *Fitzwilliam Virginal Book* pieces—and then by the Landgraf of Hesse.[3] From Germany he went to Italy. After an interim period in London Dowland became Court Musician to the King of Denmark, from whose service he retired in 1606 after which he settled permanently in London to act for some time as lutenist to Lord Howard de Walden. Although neglected by those in authority, according to Henry Peacham, he was appointed to a place at Court in 1612 which passed to his son Robert on his death. Dowland, who

[1] Set by George Mason, organist of Trinity College, Cambridge, after 1612, and John Earsden.

[2] 'From Silent Night', in *A Pilgrimes Solace*, 1612, is dedicated 'To my loving Countryman Mr. *John Forster* the younger, Merchant of Dublin in Ireland.'

[3] The library of the music-loving Landgraf Moritz (ruling from 1592 to 1627), who was specially commended by Peacham for his musical skills, contained Weelkes's *Madrigals* of 1597 and Rosseter's (and Campion's) *Ayres* of 1601, as well as collections of instrumental music by William Brade and Thomas Simpson.

was a contributor to East's *Psalms* (1592), issued his *First Booke of Ayres* in 1597 and this collection was the first positively to allow the supremacy of the top vocal part in which bar-lines were placed. This collection was issued five times during Dowland's lifetime: certain slight alterations in the 1603 edition are interesting since they make for an easier performance. Of the songs in the collection some at least owed to the tradition of folk-music, to which *Now o now I needs must part* (the 'Frog Galliard') indubitably belongs. In the *Second Booke of Songs* (1600), marked by advances both in melodic and accompanimental organisation, the celebrated *Flow, my tears*, or *Lachrimae*—a pavan style piece which became immensely popular[1] —appeared. Three years after the *Second Booke* the third appeared. In the interval that occurred before a final anthology of similar works was published Dowland issued his *Lachrimae Or Seaven Teares figured in seaven passionate Pavans, with divers other Pavans, Galiards, and Almandes* for instruments, in five parts (1605) and a translation (1606) of the *Micrologus* of Andreas Ornithoparcus, an early sixteenth-century theoretical work by a German scholar. In 1612 Dowland's last set of ayres (apart from three printed by his son in a *Musicall Banquet*) was published under the title *A Pilgrimes Solace* (with accompaniment for lute and viols).

Dowland's reputation depends on some seventy or eighty songs of highly individual quality, and a style which grew more certain and expressive with each publication. His genius lay in a capacity for synthesis. He did not entirely forsake the contrapuntal habits of his predecessors nor did he accept the conventions of the *nuove musiche* without reservations. He did, however, free the voice from too close involvement in contrapuntal textures and thus enhanced the power of the vocal line to develop expressively. At the same time, by allusive undercurrents of counterpoint, he gave variety and therefore independence to the accompaniment. He could use chromatic harmony the more effectively because it had melodic logic behind its inception, and his adoption of declamation was affected by the circumstances of the particular case rather than by any *a priori* theorising. [Ex. 7.] Although Dowland achieved early popularity for his lighter pieces, which often suggested a take-over of popular dance idiom, his more expressionistic essays established his longer reputation.

A pioneer, but without successors, Dowland suffered the fate of all such. Somewhat out of step with his English contemporaries, he was, as has been seen, neglected; and criticism assailed him. To this he referred in the bitter-toned preliminary address to *A Pilgrimes Solace*. He had, he said, 'found favour in the greatest part of Europes, [*sic*], and been printed in

[1] *Lachrimae* is mentioned by Thomas Middleton, Ben Jonson, Beaumont and Fletcher, Philip Massinger, and John Webster, and was arranged for virginals by Byrd and Farnaby.

7.

O let me li-ving die. O let me li-ving, let me li - ving, li-ving die.

eight most famous cities beyond the seas, viz.: Paris, Antwerpe, Collein, Nurenburge, Franckfort, Liepsig, Amsterdam, and Hamburge . . . Yet I must tell you, as I have been a stranger, so have I again found strange entertainment since my return, especially by the opposition of two sorts of people that shroud themselves under the title of musicians. The first are some simple Cantors, or vocal singers . . . who give their verdict of me behind my back, and say what I do is after the old manner. The second are young men, professors of the lute, who vaunt themselves, to the disparagement of such as have been before their time (wherein I myself am a party) that there never was the like of them. To these men I say little because of my love and hope to see some deeds ensure their brave words, and also being that here under their noses hath been published a book in defence of the Viol de Gamba,[1] wherein not only all other the best and principal instruments have been abased, but especially the lute by name . . . Perhaps you will ask me why I that have travelled many countries and ought to have some experience, doth not undergo this business myself? I answer that I want ability, being I am now entered into the fiftieth year of mine age secondly because I want both means, leisure and encouragement . . .'

The Jacobean was an exploratory era, and Dowland nobly expresses the doubts that afflicted many who felt that the traditional picture of the universe was 'all in pieces, all coherence gone'. The same kind of attitude is to be found in some of the ayres of Ferrabosco, Coperario, and John Daniel (b. 1562), brother to Samuel Daniel, who himself was a student of Italian affairs and an acquaintance of Giovanni Battista Guarini, author of *Il Pastor fido*. Like Dowland, John Daniel was an exponent of the expressive use of chromatics—indeed, he pursued this practice to an extreme, and thus looks forward to the tragic manner of Purcell: [Ex. 8a and b]. Daniel had some of the literary talent of his brother and was the only composer other than Campion to add a verse dedication of his own making to a set of ayres—his *Songs for the Lute, Viol, and Voices* (1606). This set is otherwise unique in being inscribed to a young woman—to 'Mistress Anne Grene, the worthy Daughter of Sir William Grene of Milton,

[1] Captain Tobias Hume's *Musicall Humors*, 1605.

Knight.' The prefatory poem of dedication is of great charm and affection. The Grenes like the Daniels belonged to Somerset.

8a.

8b.

3(ii)

Daniel succeeded his brother as censor of the plays performed by the children of the Queen's Revels in 1618. A number of prominent composers of ayres—including Robert Jones, Campion, Ferrabosco, and Coperario—were closely associated with dramatic entertainment, a circumstance that helped to maintain a directness of approach that was and long remained the norm for English song-writers.

Popularisation of Traditions

At this juncture two standards begin to be established. On the one hand there is the grave, scholarly, tradition of Byrd and Gibbons, attached to the theoretical doctrines of Morley and other writers on music, which led to the detached, uncompromising artistry of Dowland; on the other a utilitarian convention deriving from the function of entertainment. Lute and virginals music, and dances arranged for fiddlers or for consort playing, furnished private music-lovers with material of not too great difficulty and ideal for recreational use. Two-thirds of the ayres, full of grace and charm, were also light-weight and half-way towards balladry. [Ex. 9.] In seventeenth-century England the two worlds of sacred and profane—described in Donne's *Satires*—lived together, but insofar as music had been

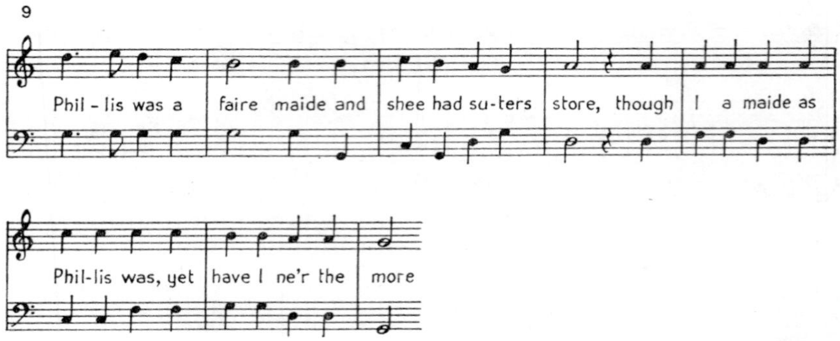

concerned the religious and philosophical speculations which had underwritten its cultivation for so long had kept them apart. Resistance to archaic principles grew stronger during the Elizabethan period, and by the time James I ascended the throne (and partly because of this) there was a considerable market for the trivial and the bawdy. The 'new music' in Britain was often new in attitude rather than in style.

Excerpts from folk-music, from ballads, from street-airs have already been noticed. The programme element was indigenous in the madrigal and was extended through the figurations available to the virginalist. Captain Tobias Hume, adventurer and eccentric and composer of one of the most memorable of English songs—*Fain would I change that note*, made vigorous experiments in pursuit of novelty in his *Musicall Humors*. Here is a 'Soldier's song', with apt accompanimental noises—an 'Imitation of Church Music, singing to the organs, but here you must use the Viol de Gamba for the organ'—and various dynamic markings—with an instruction to play *col legno* on one occasion—in the instrumental pieces in the volume. But the most important figure in the wider popularisation of music was Thomas Ravenscroft.

Ravenscroft, a chorister at St. Paul's under Edward Pearce, and Music Master at Christ's Hospital between 1618 and 1622, was an industrious musician of little original creative talent but with an astute eye for an expanding market. There was, he appreciated, a wider public than that served by the anthologies of madrigals and ayres. Thus he combed through the popular repertoire of catches and other sociable ensemble music and issued *Pammelia* and *Deuteromelia* in 1609, and *Melismata* (*Musicall Phansies Fitting the Court, Citie and Country Humours*) in 1611.

The intention of these collections was defined in the Introduction to *Pammelia*, where Ravenscroft thus advertised the 'Catches, so generally affected (I take it) *quia non superant captum*, because so consonant to all ordinary musical capacity, being such indeed as all such whose love of music exceeds their skill cannot but commend, such also as all such whose skill in music exceeds their love of such slight and light fancies cannot either contemn or condemn. Good art in all for the more musical, good mirth and melody for the more jovial, sweet harmony mixed with much variety, and both with great facility: harmony to please, variety to delight, facility to invite thee. Some toys, yet musical, without absurdity: some very musical, yet pleasing without difficulty, light, but not without music's delight: music's pleasantness, but not without easiness. . . .'

Ravenscroft cast his net wide, coming up with pieces in dog-Latin and battered French, in English and non-English. Some were psalmodic and puritanical, others were macaronic and satirically papistical. Propriety and impropriety [Ex. 10] meant that items could be chosen for

10

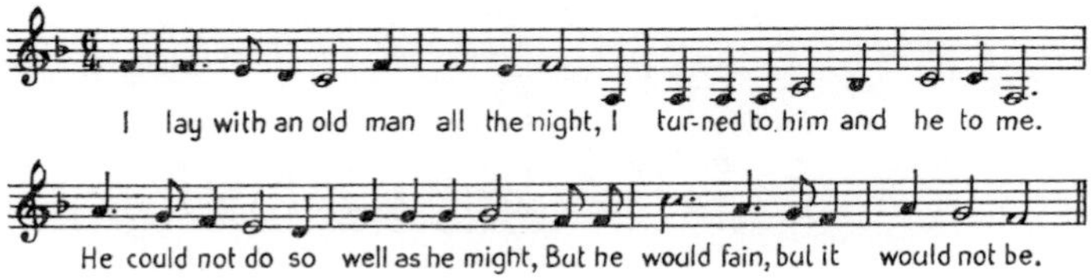
I lay with an old man all the night, I tur-ned to him and he to me.
He could not do so well as he might, But he would fain, but it would not be.

11

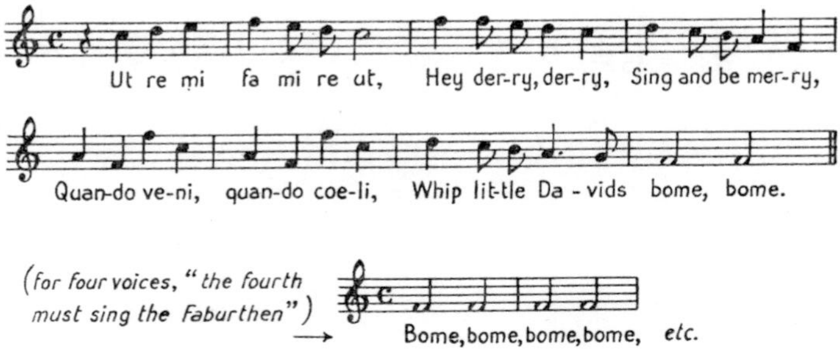
Ut re mi fa mi re ut, Hey der-ry, der-ry, Sing and be mer-ry,
Quan-do ve-ni, quan-do coe-li, Whip lit-tle Da - vids bome, bome.
(for four voices, "the fourth must sing the Faburthen")
Bome, bome, bome, bome, etc.

various types of company. Like all pedagogues of his period Ravenscroft was ardent in solmisation [Ex. 11]. He also enjoyed counterpoint and *Pammelia* (No. 74) shows a quodlibet of country dances on a ground. Some of Ravenscroft's more respectable selections, as 'Three Blind mice', have, through juvenile usage across the years, been the only connection for the vast mass of the English nation with the Golden Age of English music.

In 1614 Ravenscroft published *A Briefe Discourse*, a text-book of musical theory according to the by now defunct mensurable system, 'to the benefit of all *Students* [of music], and the Contentment of all *Affectors* thereof in this my native *country*, and especially in the *Metropolis* thereof, which gave first life and breathing to my poore Endeavours'. Ravenscroft was an excellent blurb-writer. He also had useful connections so that *A Briefe Discourse* is puffed by preludial poems by Nathaniel Giles, Thomas Campion, Martin Peerson, Thomas Pearce, William Austin, a literary barrister of Lincoln's Inn, and John Davies, of Hereford. Ravenscroft gave enticing, if not entirely relevant examples to illustrate his thesis 'in the Harmony of 4 Voyces, *Concerning the Pleasure of 5 usuall* Recreations: 1 Hunting, 2 Hawking, 3 Dauncing, 4 Drinking, 5 Enamouring'. The third section contained a Fairies' Dance across which Falstaff begins his metamorphosis into the drunken poet of Purcell's *Fairy Queen* [Ex. 12]. In the

12.

final section (in which John Bennet's help was enlisted for the composition of the last item) Ravenscroft indulged in a by now established practice of Londoners of mocking their provincial cousins. *Enamouring*, 'vor Dreble, Meduz, Denor, and Bazis', pictured (1) Hodge Trillindle to his Zweet hort Malkyn, (2) Malkinz anzwer to Hodge Trillindle, (3) Their Gongluzion, (4) Their Wedlock. A similar cycle, *The wooing of John and Joane*, was composed by Richard Nicholson.[1]

Ravenscroft is now remembered chiefly on account of his *The Whole Booke of Psalmes*: with the Hymnes Evangelicall; and *Songs* Spirituall [*sic*] . . . with such severall Tunes as have beene, *and are usually sung in England, Scotland, Wales*, Germany, Italy, France, and the Netherlands . . .' This was published in 1621. But his principal service to native music was the provision of material for commonplace use. His catches were immediately useful in taverns, in which the English male voice choir and the music club were born, and his lead was followed by John Hilton II,[2] author of a transitional set of *Ayres or Fa La's for Three Voyces* (1627), and editor of *Catch that Catch can* (1658), a much loved collection of contrapuntal ribaldry that was often re-printed.

In various ways English music moved towards new principles. But there was no one composer of the stature of, say, Monteverdi, to gather together the different tactical views and to compress them into one strategic order of the day. Most native composers of talent were inclined to look over their shoulders and to remind themselves of the academic certitudes that had for so long guaranteed good craftsmanship but which could prove severe obstacles to initiative. From time to time genius overcame these obstacles, but genius showed spasmodically and, as in the case of Dowland, was even suspect. Up to a point the determining factor in the rate of progress was the level of musical appreciation at Court, where the most funds were available for investment in the arts.

The Court Masque

King James and Queen Anne (whose first entry into London was the cause of introducing Danish music to the ears of the citizens of London[3]) were unfortunately inexpert in music and their eldest son, Prince Henry,[4]

[1] Two part-books extant in the Cathedral Library, Carlisle. These were copied by Thomas Smith (1614–84), later Bishop of Carlisle, when a student at Queen's College, Oxford, for a glee club, of which other members were Henry Edmondson, also of Queen's, and Roger Smith, who, like Nicholson, was a member of Magdalen. See Jeffrey Mark, 'The Song-Cycle in England: some early 17th century examples', in *Mus. T.*, Apr. 1925, pp. 325–8.

[2] Probably son of John Hilton (I), second organist of Lincoln Cathedral before becoming organist of Trinity College, Cambridge (1594–1612); a contributor to the *Triumphes of Oriana*.

[3] '. . . to delight the Queen with her own country music, nine trumpets, and a kettle drum, did very sprightly and actively sound the Danish march;' T. Dekker, *At the Entertainment provided to greet King James I and Queen Anne in the City of London*.

[4] A pupil of Alfonso Ferrabosco (II), who dedicated to the Prince his *Ayres* of 1609.

who was keenly interested, died before he had opportunity to influence the course of events. Yet the King was a keen supporter of the masque. The Court Masque became the focal point of cultural activity to which virtually all kinds of music were attracted and through which they developed so far as the limitations of the form allowed. It was, perhaps, a tragedy for British music that the masque never effected union with the growing traditions of Italian opera. To this point the Almoner to the Venetian Ambassador drew attention when, after seeing Ben Jonson's *Pleasure reconciled to Virtue*, in 1618, he observed that 'spoilt as we are by the graceful and harmonious music of Italy, the composition did not strike us as very fine'.[1] Full of potential, it went haphazardly across the Jacobean and Caroline period[2] until, its primary purpose nullified by the march of political events, it virtually ceased to function. Nevertheless its echoes lingered on.

In the masque of the early seventeenth century many conventions coalesced. The form derived from the traditional pageant and was contrived to serve a complimentary purpose. Plot was of little consequence; so long as an allegorical theme could be turned into a secular hymn of praise for the monarch that was sufficient. The form of words, on the other hand, became increasingly important and the texts of Campion, Chapman, William Browne of Tavistock, and, above all, Ben Jonson, contain some of the most exquisite lyrical verse of the age. Nor were they deficient in comedy, for it was a poor masque that did not entertain. It should be remembered that the highest point in the Jacobean masque was reached in *The Tempest*, in which, however, the dramatist, being under the influence of the popular theatre rather than of the Banqueting Hall in Whitehall, was able to unify the dramatic and lyrical elements according to his own design. If the poet took pride of place in the ordering of the masque, then the scenic artist came a close second. In this connection it was fortunate that Inigo Jones (many of whose designs are preserved at Chatsworth) was available.

The performance of a masque was generally undertaken by courtiers and court ladies (whose back-stage behaviour caused eyebrows to be raised even in an uncensorious society) and therefore had something of the character of amateur theatricals. The masquers—some of whom encouraged the practice in their remote manor-houses in the provinces—were in fact taking part in a ritual. Their chief activity as a team was concentrated in the group of stately dances, arranged by professional directors

[1] Venetian State Papers, XV, p. 110.

[2] A late example of a masque in the provinces was that written by Sir Aston Cokayne, and presented at Bretby House on Twelfth Night, 1639. See S. Glover, *History of the County of Derby*, 1829, II, pp. 159-162.

such as Thomas Giles and Jerome Herne, that was itself defined as the masque. These dances were in reality tokens of fealty. But the masquers were happy finally to relax with their guests in taking part in the popular dances of the day—the revels, galliards, corantos, lavoltas, and so on. Under the influence of Ben Jonson a third group of dances was introduced, those of the antimasque, which were assigned to professionals. In the preface to his *Masque of Queens* (1609) Ben Jonson wrote how 'her Majesty had commanded me to think on some dance or shew that might precede hers and have the place of a foil or false masque'. The antimasque was both dramatic and musical gain, and became an increasingly important part of the entertainment. In some cases the masque disappeared altogether, as in the case of *The Irish Masque at Court* (1614), the propriety of which was questioned by John Chamberlain in a letter to Sir Dudley Carleton (5 January 1614). 'The masquers', he wrote, 'were so well liked at court the last week, that they were appointed to perform again on Monday; yet their device, which was a musical imitation of the Irish, was not pleasing to many, who think it no time, as the case stands, to exasperate the nation, by making it ridiculous.' It was safer to stick to witches and satyrs (figures who, with their dances, were borrowed by Shakespeare from Jonson's *Masque of Queens* and *Oberon* (1611) for *Macbeth* and *The Winter's Tale*), fairies, apes, baboons, drunkards, alchemists, or those figments of the new scientific imagination that Jonson thought up for his space-exploratory *News from the New World discovered in the Moon* (1621) and called by him 'Volatees'.

Music was an important part of the masque, but it was by no means the most important. The composer was disciplined by the requirements of the occasion and hardly enjoyed the freedom of movement or the stimulus of intellectual discussion that flourished in the privacy of the enlightened patron's chamber. Nevertheless he was able to branch out in two directions: he could exploit tone-colours and he could extend his rhythmic energy through the music for the antimasque. He was also well supplied with competent performers, since the royal choristers and instrumentalists were at his disposal.

The music for a masque, as for the contemporary drama, was intended, insofar as it was an integral part of the scheme, to be evocative, and its composition and arrangement were largely entrusted to experienced specialists. The chief contractors for the ayres were Alfonso Ferrabosco, Campion, Lanier, and Coperario (whose fee of £20 for the songs in *The Squires' Masque* of 1613 is some indication of the generous emoluments available to composers.[1]). Ferrabosco enjoyed the friendship and warm

[1] Cf. payments made in respect of the *Merchant Taylors' Entertainment* of 1607 (the three chief singers—John Allen, Thomas Lupo, and John Richards—received respectively

approval of Ben Jonson, whose testimonial to his colleague—supported by two sets of commendatory verses in other places[1]—in the preface to *Hymenaei* (1606) is marked, as Gifford observed, not only by enthusiasm but also by tenderness: 'And here', he wrote, 'that no man's deservings complain of injustice (though I should have done it kindlier, I acknowledge) I do for honour's sake, and the pledge of our friendship, name Master Alphonso Ferrabosco, a man planted by himself in that divine sphere, and mastering all the spirits of music. To whose judicial care, and as absolute performance, were committed all those difficulties both of song and otherwise. Wherein, what his merit made to the score of our invention would ask to be exprest in tunes no less ravishing than his—Virtuous friend, take well this abrupt testimony and think whose it is. It cannot be flattery, in me, who never did it to great ones, and less than love and truth it is not, where it is done out of knowledge.'

Extant settings of the lyrics of the masques are but a minute part of those that were made; but the general character of those that do remain is on the side of clarity and directness. Neither Ferrabosco nor Coperario proceeded much further than accomplished fluency. On the other hand the exigencies of theatrical presentation led towards balladry (sometimes, as in the *Irish Masque* and *The Gypsies Metamorphosed* (1621) ballads were directly introduced) and, therefore, to a more stream-lined type of song that carried over into Restoration England and beyond. Coperario wrote for Campion's Masque of 1613 a lively piece, sung by John Allen or Lanier, which commences as follows:

13.

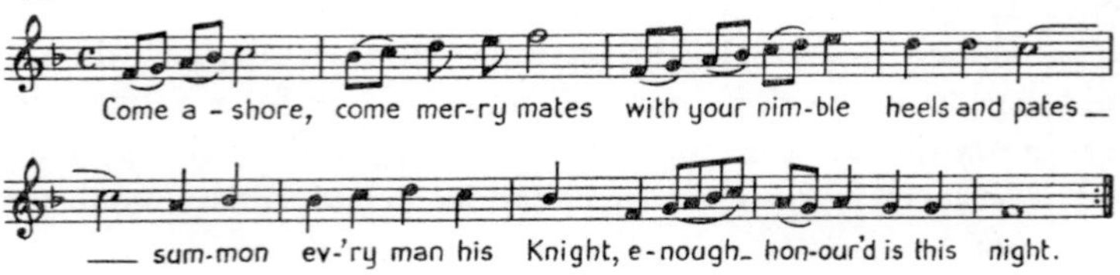
Come a - shore, come mer-ry mates with your nim-ble heels and pates —
— sum-mon ev-'ry man his Knight, e-nough — hon-our'd is this night.

£4.0.0, £3.0.0, and £3.0.0; Coperario, for setting the songs, £12.0.0; 'Powle's singing men', £1.5.0; Robert Bateman and Stephen Thomas—treble violins—£1.0.0; the King's trumpets and drums, £3.0.0; the Prince of Wales's trumpets and drums, £1.0.0; six (wood) wind instruments, £10.10.0; and John Bull, organist, £2.0.0) and of the Middle Temple and Lincoln's Inn Masque in honour of Princess Elizabeth in 1613 (£45 to Robert Johnson for 'music and songs' . . . and for the services of John and Robert Dowland, Philip Rosseter and Thomas Ford as 'musicians'); Nichols's *King James' Progresses*, 1828, and E. K. Chambers, *Elizabethan Stage*, III, p. 262.

[1] *Epigrams*, 130, *On His Book* (for *Ayres* of 1609), 131, and *To the Same*.

This kind of easy mellifluity was cultivated by Campion; it pervades the Mason and Earsden songs of the Brougham Castle Entertainment; and distinguishes the theatre songs, whether for the plays of Shakespeare, Jonson, or Beaumont and Fletcher, by Robert Johnson, Lanier, and John Wilson. Choral music ranged between the madrigal and the catch, and here the music was accommodated to its setting by extraneous devices. Thus the part-singers were disposed in the *Entertainment at Cawsham House* (1613): 'Here standing on a smooth greene, and environed with the Horse-men, they present a song of five parts and withall a lively silvan-dance of sixe persons: the Robin Hood-men faine two Trebles, one of the Keepers with the Cynick sing two Countertenors, the other Keeper the Base; but the Traveller being not able to sing, gapes in silence, and expresseth his humour in Anticke gestures.' In the *Masque of Flowers* played at Whitehall on Twelfth Night (the favourite season for court masques) the attendants on Silenus and Kawasha were assigned effective four-part, and four-square, part-songs that would not misfit into the operettas of Gilbert and Sullivan.

The orchestral interludes, and dances, for the masques gave full opportunity for extravagance. In *Lord Hay's Masque* (1607) the instrumentalists to the right of the scene comprised 'Basse and meane lutes, a Bandora, a double Sack-butt, and an Harpsichord, with two treble Violins; on the other side somewhat nearer the skreene were plac't 9 violins and three lutes, and to answere both the Consorts (as it were in a triangle) sixe Cornets, and sixe Chappel voyces, were seated almost right against them, in a place raised higher in respect of the pearcing sound of those Instruments . . .' The effectiveness of the music was enhanced by the placing of the musicians, over which much care was invariably taken. Thus before the second scene of William Browne's *The Inner Temple Masque* (1614) a curtain was drawn back to show 'an artificial wood', and hillocks upon which 'were seen eight musicians in crimson taffety robes, with chaplets of laurel on their heads, their lutes by them, which being by them touched as a warning to the nymphs of the wood, from among the trees was a heard [a] song.' During the first antimasque 'the music was composed of treble violins with all the inward parts, a bass viol, bass lutes, sagbut, cornamute, and a tabor and pipe.'[1] After the first and before the second antimasque a lyrical interlude in which Circe entices the ship-

[1] Cf. *Pleasure reconciled to Virtue*, where for the entry of Comus Jonson required 'a wild music of cymbals, flutes and tabors'. This performance, amply described by Orazio Busino, employed twenty cornets and trumpets for the royal entry music and there were (Busino reported) twenty-five to thirty violins (i.e. strings). In *Britannia Triumphans* (1637) by Davenant, the fantastical element was represented realistically by a 'mock music of 5 persons . . . one with a viol, the rest with Tabor and pipe, Knackers and bells, Tongs and key, Gridiron and shoeing horn'.

wrecked Ulysses required that 'Presently in the wood was heard a full music of lutes, which descending to the stage had to them sung this following song, the Echoes being placed in several parts of the boscage.'

The composers of the instrumental music for the masques included Thomas Lupo,[1] Mark or Robert Bateman,[2] Edward Pearce,[3] Robert Johnson,[4] and John Adson.[5] The largest surviving collection of such music is contained in B.M. Add. Ms. 10444, but numerous pieces found their way into the lute and virginals books. A few pieces were published, notably in John Adson's *Courtly Masquing Ayres composed to 5 and 6 parts for Violins, Consorts and Cornets* (1611, reissued 1621), and in Thomas Simpson's *Taffel-Consort, Ersten Teil* (Hamburg 1621).[6]

The composers of the instrumental parts of the Jacobean Masque were, perhaps, the principal innovators of that time, for, in transferring the capacity to react to external stimulus—familiar enough in madrigalian music—to the sphere of the consort, they not only rationalised the significance of tone-colours but also explored the further possibilities of instrumental characteristics and techniques. Their work was supplementary to that of the composers of fantasias and of dance suites, from whom they derived as much as was relevant to their purpose, and gave opportunities not offered by chamber music *per se*. Thus the new music of the Jacobean era is summarised best by such antimasque items as:

14.

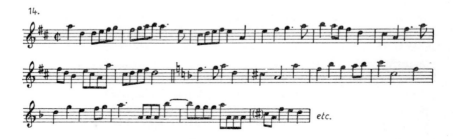

[1] One of many members of this family active at that time; presumably Thomas who was appointed 'composer for our violins' in 1620 and who died in 1638, being succeeded as 'ordinary musician' by his son Theophilus, and as composer for the violins by Estienne Nau.

[2] Mark Bateman was a royal trumpeter; Robert, not among the court musicians, appears in continental publications.

[3] Possibly Edward Peers, Gentleman of the Chapel Extraordinary, 1603.

[4] See p. 209.

[5] (d. 1640) cornet and recorder player, at one time a City Wait; see p. 122 fn. 2.

[6] This collection (four parts and figured bass) included seven pieces by Simpson, five by Dowland, four by Moritz (i.e. Maurice) Webster (d. 1636), lutenist and violist, and single items by Robert Bateman, Alfonso Ferrabosco, Edward Johnson, and Robert Johnson.

15.

The masque was a courtly entertainment, but the robust tastes of the Jacobean Court did not admit of any over-refinement. The development of the antimasque introduced satire and pure buffoonery and maintained a healthy connection with popular drama, with the extended jig, and also the still vital folk-drama. On his progresses through the Kingdom James I felt less inhibited than when surrounded by ambassadors at Whitehall (not that he entirely subdued his untamed inclinations even there, for there was at least one occasion on which he was too drunk to survive to the end of a performance) and the masquing entertainments put up by his subjects were almost entirely antimasque. In 1617 Ralph Assheton,[1] of Whalley, in Lancashire, was one of the masquers at Court. On 18 August of the same year the King, who spent some time visiting the alum mines in the neighbourhood, was entertained at Houghton by Assheton. Assheton's friends and retainers put up a fine show, 'dancing the Huckler, Tom Bedlo, and the Cowp [Cap] Justice of Peace', and displaying the familiar antics of such other familiar figures of country fun as Robin Goodfellow, Old Crambo,[2] Jean Tospot, and Dolly Wango. Sir John Finett, master of ceremonies to the King, played the 'Cap Justice' with great success.[3] This contrasted strongly with what had been expected of an Elizabethan country house entertainment. There was a rumbustiousness running through all Jacobean music, a fact that influenced the ultimate direction of dramatic music—and one which gave concern to the Puritans. In 1641 George Wither wrote as follows in his *Hallelujah*: 'So innumerable are the foolish and profane songs now delighted in (to the dishonour of our language and Religion) that Haleluiahs and pious Meditations are almost out of use and fashion; yet, not in private only; but at our public feasts and civil meetings also, scurrilous and obscene songs are impudently sung, without respecting the reverend Presence of Matrons, Virgins, Magistrates or Divines.'

James I was not one of the more notable music-loving monarchs, but his reign rather than that of Elizabeth covered what has hitherto been

[1] Kinsman of Ralph Ashton, see p. 128 fn. 1.

[2] Cf. Ben Jonson, *Fortunate Isles*: 'A pretty game! like Crambo, Master Skogan.'

[3] *History of the Borough of Preston*, II, p. 358.

defined as the Golden Age in English music. Many of the greatest masters were active during the first quarter of the seventeenth century and some of the most distinguished collections of native music belong to that narrow period. Lute anthologies, and madrigal and ayre collections have been detailed. So too have some of the major works within the field of chamber music, to which—because in this field there proved to be more continuity than in any other—further reference will be made. Most important of all, perhaps, were the virginals books. One book of such music, *Parthenia*, was published; but the great manuscript collections were repositories of the most distinctively original music composed by British musicians during the period under review.

Music for Virginals

The cult of virginals music commenced in earnest during the reign of Henry VIII and by the end of the sixteenth century the instrument was as a necessity in the middle and upper reaches of society. Although the virginals were so enthusiastically cultivated in Britain, instruments, as in the case of the lute, were imported, from Italy, Germany, or the Netherlands. As was the case with all later keyboard instruments it was considered a suitable medium for the refinement of young women, as Thomas Whythorne (who also draws attention to the fact that it served as an accompanying instrument for solo songs) makes clear in his autobiography. Being a household instrument the virginals, again like the lute, maintained its usefulness by giving access to music popular in other terms. Dance music, popular songs and ballads, airs from theatre and masque, adaptations of church pieces, and of fantasias originally laid out for consort, formed a large part of any anthology. But composers were quick to see two latent possibilities. More ready to respond than the organ, the virginals appealed to the professional virtuoso. On the other hand, its sensitivity was such that it could provide a new range for imaginative excursion. In contrast with the brilliance of Bull stands the poetic refinement of Giles Farnaby. No sooner, however, had music for the keyboard reached the summit of achievement, most familiarly recollected by the so-called *Fitzwilliam Virginal Book*, than it died away, leaving no succession. Such sporadic behaviour is a feature of British musical history: the one word which is not generally applicable, therefore, is development. British music (and perhaps it is none the worse for it) belongs to a permanent condition of existentialism.

The *Fitzwilliam Virginal Book*—once the property of John Christopher Pepusch (whose wife, the singer Margarita de l'Epine, found Bull's variations on *Walsingham* too much in advance of her own excellent harpsichord technique for comfort of execution) is the most noteworthy collection. Almost certainly copied by Francis Tregian (?1574–1619), a prominent member of a Catholic family from Cornwall, this collection comprises almost 300 pieces, among which are the keyboard masterpieces of Bull, Byrd, Peerson, Philips, and Richard and Giles Farnaby, as well as examples by Tallis, Blitheman, Morley, J. Mundy, Ferdinando Richardson, Robert and Edward Johnson, some lesser composers, and by Sweelinck. Some of Byrd's Fitzwilliam items are repeated in the volume copied by John Baldwin, lay Clerk of Windsor, in 1591 and known as *My Ladye Nevells Booke* (42 items) after Hawkins's surmise that the book had been made at Byrd's request for a pupil of that name. *Will Forster's Virginal Book* (78 items) was completed in 1624, and *Benjamin Cosyn's Virginal Book* (98 items) at about the same time. Cosyn was organist of Dulwich College from 1622–4 and organist of the Charterhouse from 1626–43.

Two small Scottish collections are of importance in showing some development independent of the main southern stream. These are the *Clement Mitchell Virginal Book*[1] (1612), with twelve pieces (four by Byrd), and the *Kinloch Ms.*,[2] also of fourteen pieces of which six are by William Kinloch, a Scottish composer writing under the influence of Byrd, who is also represented in the same collection.

The latest extant collection is the *Elizabeth Rogers Book* (dated 1656 and containing seventy-nine pieces). All of these collections—representative of a very much larger number once made but not now existing—and the supplementary manuscripts to be found in British and foreign libraries are reasonably comprehensive and cover the repertoire of many years. But the authentic style lived on until the eve of the Restoration, being preserved by Thomas Tomkins whose last dated pieces belong to September 1654.[3]

Many pieces for virginals repeated and extended principles of composition already familiar. But in adaptation of existing material or form the composers showed an awareness of the primary consideration that an arrangement should sound like an original composition. This was due to the fact that, like all great masters of keyboard music, they thought with their fingers. Thus a distinctive style of apt decoration and figuration is to be found. Exuberance in decoration is a feature of the more ambitious works in variation form, especially of Byrd and Bull, and it is sometimes to be felt that such exhilaration in dexterity outstrips musical discretion; as

[1] Property of the Earl of Dalhousie.

[2] This volume contains also forty Psalm tunes arranged by Andrew Kemp.

[3] Paris Conservatoire, *Manuscrit Réservé 1122*: see Stephen D. Tuttle, *Thomas Tomkins, Keyboard Music* (*Musica Britannica*, V), London, 1955.

in Bull's *Walsingham* and Byrd's *O Mistris Myne* (both in the *Fitzwilliam Virginal Book*). On the other hand, when such zest is allied to imaginative perception the results are charming. Orlando Gibbons, whose control was immaculate, was adept at sketching in allusive middle parts—rather in the manner of the lutenists—which never crowd the canvas but invariably add to its attractiveness. This is evident in his arrangements of dances. From the point of lay-out the most consistently successful composer was Giles Farnaby, whose judgement was unerring when it came to the overall design of a work. It would be difficult to give any set of variations by any of his contemporaries a higher place than that merited by *Put up thy dagger Jenny*—a felicitous survey of the kinder values of keyboard music—and *Rosa solis*, in which the euphonious high cheer of rapid progressions of sixths suggests Brahmsian practice. In development of variation form the English composers were ahead of most of their contemporaries elsewhere. It is possible that Cabezón became aware of the English predilection for the method when he visited England in 1554 with Philip II of Spain, and that in due course the English followed his lead in the treatment of secular material for keyboard variation.[1] The English variations at their best were not merely decoratively interesting but conspicuous for a remarkable poetic insight, such as distinguishes Farnaby's *Pawles Wharff*.

The most perceptive of composers, Farnaby,[2] was a master of the miniature, and in his brief and Schumannesque essays in self-analysis—his *Dream*, his *Rest*, and his *Conceit*—he rebuts Ravenscroft's foreigner who considered the English as better at imitation than invention. In the same class of delicate fancy are the two gentle, rain-washed, pieces of Martin Peerson, *The Fall of the Leafe* and *The Primerose*. At the other extreme of fancy are the various excursions into the field of programme music made by Byrd and Mundy. There was, of course, nothing new in the adoption of the principle of mimesis—it was fixed in vocal music and was being increasingly exploited in the course of the popularisation of the madrigal (see p. 194)—but its extension to the keyboard encouraged further consideration of the expansive capacity of the keyboard. The classic pieces of this genre are John Mundy's *Fantasia* in the form of a sequence of meteorological commentaries on English weather, Byrd's *The Bells, The Battell*, and *The Earle of Oxfords Marche*, and Bull's and Farnaby's versions of *The King's Hunt*. All of these pieces are onomatopoeic, and more curious than convincing. Yet in their composers' realisation of the contrasted melodic

[1] van den Borren, op. cit., pp. 205–6.

[2] A composer of Cornish origin, Giles Farnaby (b. *c.* 1565) published a book of *Canzonets to Four Voyces* in 1598, and contributed to East's *Whole Book of Psalms*, 1592. From 1602–8 Farnaby lived as a household musician to Sir Nicholas Sanderson, in Lincolnshire. See A. E. B. Owen, 'Giles and Richard Farnaby in Lincolnshire', *M. & L.*, 42, no. 2, 1961, pp. 151 ff.

and percussive qualities of the keyboard they are evidence of an eagerness to establish rather than to follow precedent. One further venture in the search for new sonorities is represented by Farnaby's piece *For two virginals*.

Englishmen Abroad

The Jacobean period was as fertile in music as in poetry and drama—that both flourished together was both inevitable and fortunate—and it was one in which English musicians were able to hold their own abroad. Indeed it is the one period in which certain aspects of English music were accepted as exemplary. The work of Philips, Deering, and Bull, in the Netherlands, of Dowland in various parts of Europe, and the publication of Thomas Simpson's *Opusculum neuerer Paduanen* (Hamburg 1617) and *Taffel Consort* indicate something of the welcome accorded to English musicians on the Continent. A better index to the capacity of English music to operate in the foreign market is contained in the wholly European career of William Brade (1560–1630).

Of Brade's life in England nothing is known. At the age of thirty-four he appears as a court musician (viol-player) at the Danish Court. He was here for two years, returning for a second period of seven years in 1599, which meant that he was a colleague of Dowland. His second departure, in 1606, was the probable cause of the request of Christian IV of Denmark for another English musician on his staff. Through the good offices of Prince Henry, Francis Cutting was sent to Copenhagen. Towards the end of his life Brade served yet again in Denmark, from 1620 to 1622. Otherwise, however, he was occupied in Germany. During his first intermission he was in Berlin, patronised first by Johann Georg and then by Joachim Friedrich of Brandenburg. Between 1608 and 1610, and 1613 and 1615, he was employed by the City of Hamburg, and in the intervening years by the Court of Schaumburg. Next we meet him as Kapellmeister to the Court of the Archbishop of Magdeburg, which entailed his living in Halle, where Samuel Scheidt was active at the same time. From Halle he moved back to Berlin, where his generous emoluments and allowances indicate the value set on his work. Brade's publications included *Newe ausserlesene Paduanen, Galliarden etc.* (Hamburg 1609); a similarly entitled work in six parts (Hamburg 1614); *Newe ausserlesene liebliche Branden*, etc. (Hamburg and Lübeck 1617); *Melodieuses Paduanes, Chansons, Galliards*, etc. (Antwerp 1619); *Newe Lustige Volten, Couranten, Balletten*, etc. (Berlin 1621). Other dances by Brade were published in anthologies compiled by Zacharius Füllsack—a lutenist and trombonist colleague of Brade at Hamburg—and Christoph Hildebrand.

Brade continued the tradition of the English school, his works being nearly related to those of Adson, blending melodic attractiveness, [Ex. 16]

16.

and rhythmic variety and ingenuity with contrapuntal expansion whereever possible. He had a sure ear for the true sonorities of the string ensemble, [Ex. 17] and in acclimatising himself to German practice patently

17.

wrote with violin rather than viol in mind. He introduced the branles (i.e. *Branden*), the volta, and the mascherade to Germany, where these dances were hitherto unknown. The influence of Brade affected a generation of German composers of whom the most notable was Johann Schein, Cantor of the Thomasschule from 1615 to 1630.

Brade was one, albeit the most celebrated, of a large number of English instrumentalists active in north Germany during the reign of James I, others being Daniel (?) Norcombe, Valentine Flood, John and Clement Dixon, Jack Jordan, and (?) Rowe.[1] Whether these musicians emigrated for political or religious reasons is not even speculable. It is, however, clear that, what with the court establishment and the musical staffs of the municipalities, there was in England a tendency, as in eighteenth-century Germany, to produce too many performers for too few jobs.

[1] See Meyer, op. cit, p. 139.

Caroline Taste

The old order in English music effectively came to an end with the death of Orlando Gibbons. The accession of Charles I, whose musical interests, despite his training and his exercises in composition,[1] were less lively than those in painting, meant little overt change. Henrietta Maria brought among her retinue of servants a number of French musicians[2] for her Catholic Chapel, but they were so unpopular that life was made unbearable by native servants of the Court, and their impact was less than that occasioned by the later Francophilia of Charles II. Nevertheless Ben Jonson felt it politic to assume a healthy union between 'French air and English verse' in his commendatory poem *To Edward Filmer, on his Musical Work, Dedicated to the Queen*,[3] while the masque was accommodated to French principles. During the increasingly critical years of the reign of Charles I the tendency to secularise music continued unabated; but, apart from chamber music, the quality of composition hardly appreciated. Partly, perhaps, because of the foreign entanglements of the royal family since the time of James I English musicians on the whole became more insular. They also found it difficult to resist an innate tendency towards conservatism. There was, during this period, no composer of the stature of Byrd, or Gibbons: at best the official composers were but of the second rank.

Richard Deering came home during the reign of Charles I and was appointed Organist to the Queen and one of the King's 'Musicians for the lute and voices', but no works by him were published in the last five years of his life. His reputation, attested by Peacham, remained high and he accumulated support even among the Puritans for the solemnity of his sacred music. He was a favourite composer of Oliver Cromwell; a collection of his *Cantica Sacra* was published by John Playford in 1622; and his fame was still recollected with some nostalgia by Thomas Mace as late as 1676. In the public sphere, however, the most influential composers were Henry (1596–1662) and William Lawes (1602–45). Both of them, through the assistance of Coperario's patron Lord Hertford, were pupils of that master and his colleagues in the royal music. The Lawes's originated in Wiltshire, sons of a vicar-choral in Salisbury Cathedral, and were established in London in the early part of the Caroline period. Both specialised in secular music, Henry mainly for the voice, William for instruments.

[1] See example on p. 208.
[2] See de Lafontaine, op. cit., p. 59.
[3] Filmer's *French court-aires*, '. . . their ditties Englished', 1629. The minuet character of some of the melodies anticipates a favourite post-Restoration pattern in English music.

Henry's mastery of declamatory song was adduced by John Milton and Robert Herrick, and the testimony of the former that

> *Harry* whose tuneful and well measur'd song
> First taught our English Musick how to span
> Words with just note and accent . . .[1]

and an epigrammatic recommendation from the latter, have led to an overestimate of his musical value. Henry and William Lawes were contributors to the masques and, insofar as they produced airs on the one hand and dances on the other, continued the patterns already set. Both, however, bridged the gap between the Jacobean masque and the quasi-opera of the Restoration and were among the formative influences on Matthew Locke, Pelham Humfrey, and Henry Purcell. Henry wrote the songs for Thomas Carew's *Coelum Britannicum* (1633) and Milton's *Comus* (1634). This, the most distinguished of masques from the point of view of poetry—in the tradition of William Browne rather than of Ben Jonson—was played at Ludlow Castle, Shropshire, in honour of the installation of Lawes's friend the Earl of Bridgewater as Lord President of Wales. William, in conjunction with Simon Ives,[2] wrote the instrumental pieces for *Coelum Britannicum* and for Davenant's *The Triumphs of the Prince d'Amour* (1636). Henry maintained his close connection with the drama, collaborating with William Cartwright[3] and, in 1656, with Cooke, Coleman, Locke, and Hudson, in Davenant's *Siege of Rhodes*.

The dissolution of the ayre, as understood by the Jacobeans, was a

18.

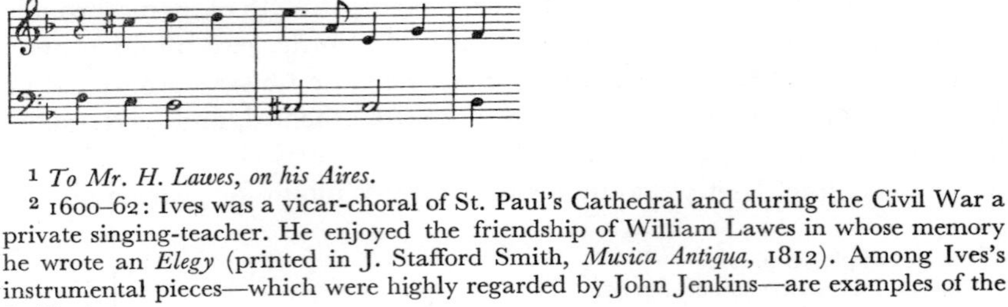

[1] *To Mr. H. Lawes, on his Aires.*

[2] 1600–62: Ives was a vicar-choral of St. Paul's Cathedral and during the Civil War a private singing-teacher. He enjoyed the friendship of William Lawes in whose memory he wrote an *Elegy* (printed in J. Stafford Smith, *Musica Antiqua*, 1812). Among Ives's instrumental pieces—which were highly regarded by John Jenkins—are examples of the *In Nomine*.

[3] *Comedies . . . by Mr. William Cartwright . . . Ayres and Songs set by Mr. Henry Lawes*, 1651.

slow and gradual process and although declamation was upheld as a new principle, composers were reluctant to dispense entirely with the ravishment of beguiling melodic contours. Thus Lawes, like Lanier and Coperario, compromised. On the other hand, the public theatre and the demands of popular entertainment in general indicated to the composer the claims of the ballad, with which Robert Johnson especially came to an agreeable working arrangement. A certain delicacy of sentiment may be observed in an example of the compositional competence of Charles I, in which the style of his tutor is evident, but also the strengthening claims of modern tonality [Ex. 18]. A song by Johnson—by far the most interesting dramatic song-writer of the first half of the seventeenth century—shows how successfully he could get the best of all worlds [Ex. 19].

19.

Care charming Sleepe, thou Ea-ser of all woes, Mo-ther to death sweet-ly thy life dis-pose
Piano
on this af-flic - ted wight fall like a cloud in gen-tle showers

Dramatic advance is best looked for in the increasingly popular *Dialogue*, rather than in the ayre, for the design of the former gave more obvious opportunity for characterisation. The progress of the dialogue—

20.

Al-le lu - - ia, Al-le-lu - ia, Al-le-lu - - ia, Al - le - lu -
Al-le-lu - - ia, Al-le-lu - ia
- ia, Al-le-lu - .- ia, Al - - le - lu-ia,
Al-le-lu - ia, Al-le-lu - ia Al-le-lu - - ia, Al-le-lu-ia,

an esteemed part of private musical practice and a frequent aid to consideration of matters of Puritan propriety—is an important pointer to English opera on the one hand and English oratorio on the other. The dialogue developed naturally from polyphonic method, as shown by Deering's *Justus cor suum tradidit* with its antiphonal *alleluias* [Ex. 20], and was incorporated with the masque as a device equally effective in verse as in music. Mason and Earsden made use of an elementary form of dialogue in the Brougham Castle Entertainment of 1618. Robert Ramsay, like Mason, organist of Trinity College, Cambridge, took the form a stage further in *A dialogue betweene Saul: ye witch of Endor, Samuell's Ghost*[1] (soprano, tenor, and bass) and achieved a miniature cantata, concluded by a trio [Ex. 21]. The characterisation is striking, and the subject thus

21.

enshrined in musico-dramatic form was used by other composers on the way to Handel's *Saul*. Most Caroline and Commonwealth composers

[1] Attributed to Nicholas Lanier in B.M. Add. Ms. 22100: see also Basil Smallman, 'Endor Revisited: English Biblical Dialogues of the Seventeenth Century', *M. & L.*, 46, no. 2, 1965, p. 137.

practised the dialogue, and minor composers whose success in the form was considerable included the younger John Hilton, (*Juno, Venus, Pallas, and Paris* for week-days, and *God, Satan, Job's wife, and Messenger* for Sundays). *Job* was later set in particularly dramatic manner by Matthew Locke. Hilton also anticipated Handel in a version of the Judgment of Solomon, that has its affinities with the relevant section in the oratorio of *Solomon*.

22.

Solomon and 2 Harlots
1. HARLOT
Jus-tice dread Sov-reigne
Jus-tice dread Sov-reigne
hum-bly I im-plore
2. HARLOT
False, false is thy cla-mour,
false all thou hast said

7

English Baroque

Music for Strings

DURING THE reign of Charles I a significant change took place in the relationship between vocal and instrumental music, and in the first case between music for choral groups on the one hand and solo singing on the other. Just as choral music, having reached a climax during the middle of the sixteenth century, continued to subsist on a well-established tradition for a considerable period, so that created by the ratification of the consort of viols and the popularisation of the fantasia also lasted well beyond its Jacobean culmination. For some short time instrumental music took first place in musical affairs in Britain; a condition not again to be encountered until the twentieth century.

Across the final troubled years of Charles I and the period of the Commonwealth protection of the national musical tradition depended almost entirely on private enterprise. It has already been seen how the standards of church music had declined. There were, as in the case of Thomas Tomkins at Worcester (whose house was wrecked by a parliamentary cannonade in 1643), or Edward Gibbons at Exeter (who loaned Charles I £1,000 on account of which he was, it was said, subsequently deprived of his estates), one or two musicians of distinction whose hardy constitutions enabled them to outlive their contemporaries and so to continue the traditions of their youth beyond their anticipated period; but younger musicians found that opportunity lay elsewhere than in the Church and the majority of Caroline organists were, in comparison with their predecessors, of mediocre talent. When a man held an ecclesiastical appointment it was increasingly important to cultivate private connections. This pattern of development had, of course, been apparent for a long time. The idea that Puritans were altogether inimical to music has long been jettisoned.[1] They disapproved of liturgical music because they disapproved of the Liturgy. They took exception to public performances—in which music might or might not have place—that appeared to give rise to behaviour that might be thought unwarrantable. Zeal led to excess—as is inevitable in revolutions. But certain parts of culture not only remained unscathed but actually grew stronger. Principal among these was chamber music.

An interesting manuscript volume which was the property of a Staffordshire family in the first half of the seventeenth century serves as a good index of modest middle class taste in the provinces, and illustrates how the circle of amateur interest was widening. A collection of ayres, dances, country-dances, and other instrumental pieces, it shows the change in emphasis in domestic music that took place towards the middle of the seventeenth century and introduces the names of composers at that time widely fashionable. The volume in question belonged first to Richard Shinton, of Wolverhampton, and passed to his son (?) Thomas (who was alive in 1628). In 1633 an inscription

Richard Shinton this booke did owe:
And John Congreve the same doth know.

denotes a family later to become well known through the dramatist William Congreve. Other Congreves who wrote their names into the volume were Elizabeth,[2] Martha, Mary, and Richard. The vocal part of the collection includes ayres by Richard Martin[3] and John Dowland[4] and some, among which is a beautiful, psalm-like, setting of *My mind to me a kingdom is*, which are anonymous. The pieces for strings are in two parts (the treble facing one way, the bass the other, for the convenience of the players) and, as might be expected when the family was concerned to find music within its playing capacity, are relatively simple. They also had been selected with a view to their entertainment value. The country-dances include 'Oxford Senior', 'Nothings', and 'Tumblinge Tom', which belong to the repertoire of the violin rather than the viol. Otherwise there are a piece for orpheoreon and bass entitled *The Echoe*, which is an early study in dynamic contrasts, simple dance movements by Davis Mell, John Jenkins, and John Banister, as well as suites by Mell and George Hudson. Of the pieces by Mell one, a Sarabande, has some interest on account of

[1] Notably by Percy A. Scholes, in *The Puritans and Music*, 1934.

[2] f. 45, 'Elizabeth Congreve writ this:
You that are constante to unconstancee
Be now or never constante unto me.'

[3] *Change thy mynde*, also in Robert Dowland's *Musical Banquett*, 1610, for two voices.

[4] *Sleepe, wayward thoughts,* and *Wilt thou, unkind,* published in *The First Booke of Songs or Ayres*, 1597.

its not otherwise unfamiliar melodic contour: [Ex. 1]. Mell was the first virtuoso violinist in England and it would seem that in Wolverhampton the strictures of Anthony à Wood on chamber music players (he was writing of those in Oxford) were ignored.[1]

1.

Mell, Jenkins, Hudson, and Banister were among those composers who carried music over the hazards of the political upheavals of the mid-century and helped to create the Restoration style, which was more the consequence of evolution than is sometimes granted.

Like the brothers Lawes, Davis (or David) Mell (1604–62) was born near Salisbury, where his father was a servant of the third Earl of Pembroke, the patron of many poets, dramatists, and artists. At the age of twenty-one Mell, who had first been apprenticed as a clock-maker, appears as one of the court violinists present at the funeral of James I. He established a considerable reputation as a player, later being praised by John Evelyn and Anthony à Wood and advantageously compared, in point of tone at least, with the German virtuoso Thomas Baltzar.[2] Mell was more fortunate than some after the execution of Charles I, for, in having trimmed his sails to the prevailing wind, he was able to describe himself in a petition to Oliver Cromwell as 'Gentleman of His Highness' Musique'. This petition concerned the advisability of setting up a national college of music and was addressed to the Lord Protector through the 'Committee of the Council for Advancement of Musicke'. Mell was among those in attendance at the funeral of Cromwell, but at the Restoration he returned to Court as private musician to the King, directing the royal band of

[1] '. . . for they esteemed a Violin to be an instrument only belonging to a common fiddler, and could not endure that it should come among them, for feare of making their meetings to be vaine and fidling'. Thomas Mace also considered it to be an unseemly instrument. But in 1660 John Playford could describe it as 'a cheerful and spritely instrument much practised of late'. See F. W. Galpin, op. cit., p. 94. The Shuttleworth family accounts show that there were no such inhibitions as here described so far as they were concerned, for in January 1621 '2 fiddles' were purchased for 6s. 8d., while in July '1 violin' was bought for 4s. This being a year of re-stocking a new lute with case was added in October at a cost of 25s.

[2] See p. 223.

violins jointly with George Hudson. Works by Mell were published in *Court Ayres* (1655) and its reissue as *Courtly Masquing Ayres* (1662), and also in publications of John Playford.

Like Mell, George Hudson (d. *c.* 1672) exercised more influence as performer and teacher than as composer. He was not only a violinist and lutenist but also a singer and in 1641 was appointed musician 'for the lute and violin extraordinary'. During the Civil War, his credentials being considered satisfactory, he also became a 'Gentleman of His Highness' Musique' and a subscriber to the petition above-mentioned. At this time he collaborated with Henry Lawes, Matthew Locke, and Charles Coleman in providing music for Davenant's *Siege of Rhodes*.[1] At the Restoration Hudson was appointed a 'violin in the private music' of Charles II, and, a few months later, Composer to the King. In 1665 he was a member of the select band of strings then superintended by John Banister. In the last year of his life Hudson, a Member of the Corporation of Music,[2] was assisted in the administration of this body by Thomas Purcell and Pelham Humfrey.

Mell and Hudson were important figures in the professional emancipation of secular musicians and in the establishment of a sense of collective purpose. So too was John Banister, whose activities—belonging principally to the Restoration period—will be outlined later. John Jenkins, on the other hand, was by far the most important composer of the transitional period. Born in 1592 and dying in 1678, Jenkins both witnessed and contributed to the biggest changes ever to take place in English music. When Jenkins was born, in Maidstone, Kent, Morley's *Madrigalls to Four Voyces* had not yet been published; before he died Henry Purcell had already been appointed Composer in Ordinary for the violin at Court. During the lifetime of Jenkins a new class of patron came into its own, and new and correlative attributes within music itself.

Jenkins became a virtuoso on the lute and the bass viol. His performance on the latter was much to the taste of Charles I, on whose staff he served, however, as lutenist. Jenkins was an agreeable person—'of easier temper than any of his faculty, he was neither conceited nor morose, but much a gentleman and had a very good sort of wit, which served him in his address and conversation, wherein he did not please less than in his composition'.[3] An equable disposition served Jenkins in good stead during the Civil War and he was employed first by the Dering (Deerham) family in Norfolk and then by their neighbour Sir Hamon L'Estrange. In

[1] See p. 235.
[2] See p. 229.
[3] Roger North, *Memoires of Musick*, pp. 85–94; see also *The Musicall Gramarian*, ed. by Hilda Andrews, London, 1926, pp. 21–6.

1660 Jenkins lived with Dudley, Lord North, at Kirtling, Cambridgeshire, whose son Roger, a lawyer and author of the *Memoires of Musick*, was Jenkins's most famous pupil. In 1660 Jenkins became a royal musician again and although his advanced years made it difficult for him often to attend to his nominal court duties he was allowed by his colleagues to retain his office, more or less honorifically. His last years were spent in the household of Sir Philip Wodehouse at Kimberley, Norfolk, where he died. He was, said Anthony à Wood, 'the little man with the great soul'.

Jenkins was a prolific composer. Apart from a few topical contributions to Henry and William Lawes's *Choice Psalms* (1648)[1] and John Hilton's *Catch that Catch can* (1652, 1658) his remaining works are instrumental. A few pieces were published in Playford's *Musick's Recreation on the Lyra-Viol* (1652), *Court Ayres* and *Musick's Hand-Maid* (1663)[2], but by far the largest part of his output was contained in manuscript. Many works appeared in various collections, thus testifying to their great popularity.

The starting point for Jenkins was the fantasia and there are more than a hundred works by him in this form, ranging from those in two to those in six parts. There are also two six-part *In Nomines,* further evidence of the strong conservative trait that marked instrumental music in the pre-Commonwealth era. When working for the Caroline Court Jenkins preserved the intimate content of the familiar fantasia. His polyphony (as enterprising and unexpected as that of Locke, see p. 232–3) was complex and designed for intellectual appreciation. As late as 1654 Jenkins was still composing in this idiom,[3] even though he and his colleagues had otherwise forsaken it. So far as he himself was concerned he was also a master of popular idioms—his dance-tune arrangements were legion—and his fantasias from time to time were infected with a tunefulness that hitherto had made only fitful appearances in this form. The most popular of Jenkins's smaller pieces was the six-part 'Bell Pavin', so named on account of its programmatic nature. Both in arrangements and in the less polyphonically extravagant of the fantasias the influence of the continuo style was apparent. In later life Jenkins composed many suites and other works for two violins and bass, denoting Italian influence, that may be regarded as prototype sonatas [Ex. 2]. Modernity in Jenkins was partly a matter of formal clarification, partly of melodic definition, and partly of harmonic direction, but principally of an appreciation of instrumental character. 'Notwithstanding that Jenkins was so excellent a master, and so skilful

[1] In Part II is Jenkins's *An Elegiack Dialogue on the sad losse of his much-esteemed Friend*, *Mr. William Lawes.*

[2] A set of dances was said to have been published in Amsterdam in 1644 (A. Goovaerts, *Histoire et bibliographie de la typographie musicale dans les Pays-Bas,* Brussels, 1880) but no copy is in existence.

[3] Meyer, op. cit., p. 218.

2.

a composer for the viol, he seems to have contributed in some degree to the banishment of that instrument from concerts, and to the introduction of music for the violin in its stead. To say the truth, the Italian style in music had been making its way into this kingdom even from the beginning of the seventeenth century; and though Henry Lawes and some others affected to contemn it, it is well known that he and others were unawares betrayed into an imitation of it; . . .'[1]

Apart from a preference for the violin and an increasingly less tentative handling of the *basso continuo* other foreign conventions were making advances in English music. Dynamic markings were used by Walter Porter, and in instrumental music by George Jeffreys and John Hilton. The latter also gave indications of tempo in one three-part fantasia.[2] The 'echo' effect was also gaining ground, exploited by Thomas Mudd, William Lawes, and Maurice Webster. In short, instrumental music was becoming deliberately expressive. Thus it was falling into line not only with foreign models but also native vocal music. At the same time it was developing a public *persona* (concerts were coming into fashion among the middle class during the Commonwealth period) and growing in virtuosity. Thus the type of figuration favoured by Jenkins, Ives, Hingston, and others in numerous showpieces featuring the gamba represented a new departure in the direction of a *concertante* style.

[1] Hawkins, *General History of Music*, IV, p. 62. Hawkins, somewhat misled by a manuscript annotation, erroneously wrote: 'In compliance therefore with this general prepossession in favour of the Italian style, Jenkins composed twelve sonatas for two violins and a bass, with a thorough bass for the organ, printed at London about the year 1660, and at Amsterdam in 1664; and these were the first compositions of the kind by an Englishman.' A similar statement occurs in Burney's *History*, III, p. 408.

[2] See Meyer, op. cit., p. 213.

The reputation of English chamber musicians abroad was continued through the period of Civil War and Commonwealth by Benjamin Rogers (1614–1698), whose fantasias and consorts, similar in style to those of Jenkins, found their way to the Courts of Austria and Sweden,[1] and by a number of other English composers who, like Young, were respectfully alluded to by Jean Rousseau, of Paris, in his *Traité de la Viole*. Young was chamber musician to the Archduke of Austria and his reputation depends almost entirely on a collection published by Michael Wagner, of Innsbruck, in 1653. This was entitled:

> // SONATE // à 3. 4. e 5. // Con alcune Allemande, Correnti e Balletti // a 3 // *di* // GUGLIELMO YOUNG INGLESE // DEDICATE AL SER.MO *ARCIDUCA* // FERDINANDO CARLO // D'AUSTRIA.

Young (who may have spent some time in the archducal service in the Netherlands, wherefore he was sometimes described as Joungh) was the first English composer to publish works under the title of Sonata and they show to what extent he had been influenced by foreign models, both Italian and German. His pieces are expressive, sometimes marked with directions regarding speed and dynamics. At the same time they carry the uncompromising harmonic characteristics of the English tradition, and retain the polyphonic quality of the native fantasia. Of Young's Sonatas, which are accompanied by a basso continuo throughout, three are for two violins, six for three, one for four, and one for five. They are, in general, cast in three or four contrasted movements. The *Canzona* is constant in all the Sonatas; there are examples of alternating adagio and allegro sections; and most contain 3/2 or 6/4 movements of sarabande or courante type. Apart from the printed works[2] Young is represented by smaller, popular pieces of similar vigorous character to those of Jenkins, Lawes, Ives, and other contemporary composers in manuscripts at Uppsala, Oxford, and Manchester. It is possible that Young left England on account of being Catholic. If he is to be identified with the William Young appointed as flautist and violinist to Charles II in 1660[3] he returned in 1660.

[1] '[The queen of Sweden] desired to heare Whitelocke's musick, whom he sent for to the castle; and they played and song in her presence, wherewith she seemed much pleased, and desired Whitelocke to thanke them in her name: she said she never heard so good a consort of musicke, and of english songs; and desired Whitelocke, at his returne to England, to procure her some to play on these instruments which would be most agreeable to her.' Bulstrode Whitelocke, *A Journal of the Swedish Ambassy* . . . 1653–4, 2 vols., London, 1772, I, p. 481; see also I, p. 304, and II, p. 462.

[2] See also *Musical Banquet*, I, 1651, and *Musick's Recreation on the Viol, Lyra-way*, 1669: Playford advertised a set of three-part Fantasias in 1669, but these were not published.

[3] See W. G. Whittaker, 'William Young', *The Dominant*, July-August 1929, p. 19.

As has been signified already the bass-viol was zealously cultivated from the early years of the century and its popularity was increased through the preference of Charles I for this instrument. The acknowledged master of bass-viol music during the middle years of the century was Christopher Simpson, a performer and composer of Yorkshire origin who enlisted in the Royalist forces under the Duke of Newcastle in 1643, but resigned military commitments when taken into the household of Sir Robert Bolles. The Bolles family had houses in London and at Scampton, in Lincolnshire. Simpson was an able composer and reckoned by Thomas Mace, in *Musick's Monument* (1676), as the equal of Jenkins and Lawes. He wrote fancies and concertante pieces in the manner of Jenkins (among his works is an allusive *Months and Seasons* for one treble and two bass viols) and many highly accomplished and apt solo pieces for viola da gamba. His special distinction as a composer lay in his exploitation of the variation (divisions) form. The general enthusiasm for the viola da gamba is indicated by the fine collection in the Watson Library, Manchester, which contains pieces by Simpson, William Young, Alfonso Ferrabosco, Thomas Gregory, Jenkins, Simon Ives, Hudson, Coleman, William Lawes, and other composers of lesser distinction. The solo viol, with its variations on folk-tunes, its dance movements, preludes, programmatic pieces, and arrangements, took over from the virginals (some music came from virginals sources), and partly explains the diminution of the keyboard repertoire. As with the virginals, those who wrote for the viol were quick to realise its distinctive properties. (Ex. 3).

3.

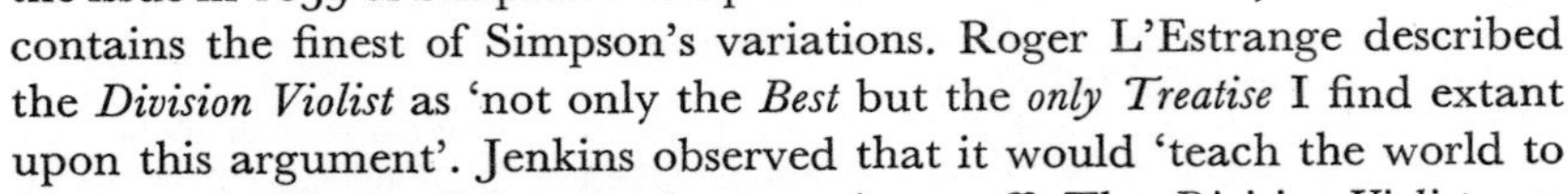

The seal was set on the respectability of the viol in musical circles by the issue in 1659 of Simpson's comprehensive *Division Violist*, a work which contains the finest of Simpson's variations. Roger L'Estrange described the *Division Violist* as 'not only the *Best* but the *only Treatise* I find extant upon this argument'. Jenkins observed that it would 'teach the world to play', and Charles Coleman also gave it a puff. The *Division Violist* was reprinted in 1667, and again in 1712. Simpson modified Campion's *Art of Discant* for Playford's *Brief Introduction* of 1660, and in 1665 published his *The Principles of Practicle Musick*. This work, dedicated to Sir John St. Barbe (a pupil together with Sir John Bolles), also ran through many editions, the ninth and last appearing as late as 1732. On its course it was mentioned by Purcell as 'the most ingenious book I e'er met with upon this Subject'.[1]

One part of the English musical tradition was thus maintained across the disorders of civil strife and repressive government, but it emerged at the time of the Restoration in the form of a compromise. Chamber music was by now much more designedly popular in character, the result of the gradual shedding of contrapuntal ballast and the taking on board of rhythmic and harmonic idioms of wider appeal. The debt owed to private patrons during this period was considerable, but at the same time much damage was done to the musical life of the country.

Dislocation of Musical Life

Echoes of days and nights that threatened disturbance came from many sources, not least from the records concerning the waits. In 1640 the Wigan Borough Court Leet Rolls[2] recorded as follows:

> Wee present William Wood of Wigan Naylor for beating a drum twixt twelve and one a Clock in the night tyme to the disturbance and terror of his Majesties Leige [*sic*] people.

Wood was sentenced to six hours in the stocks in the Market place for thus distressing the inhabitants of the borough with unwelcome and untimely music that was unlicensed.[3] But he petitioned that he was only doing his civic duty by 'beiting of the drome', for he only did it 'to call any fellow soldiatrs together, being warned to bee at Ormechurch bee eight of the Clock upon pene of deth'.

The position of waits became insecure as municipal treasuries became depleted. Already in Doncaster, owing to the poor state of the town's finances, their allowance—like the pension of the lecturer of the Parish Church—had been reduced.[4] In 1645 the waits of Leicester lost their employment during the siege of the city.[5] Those of Manchester were more

[1] *Art of Descant,* in Playford; *Introduction,* 13th edn.

[2] Vol. I, 1626-91, f. 54b and f. 61.

[3] Cf. Petition of Ralph Marsh and Laurence Taylor 'that whereas your petitioners for some years last past (according to ancient costume) have in the morneinge for the winter tyme only, with there instrumentes of musicke gone through the said towne, by permiccione of the said towne, to the great comfort of divers persons living therein', they asked to be allowed to continue, 'desiring the Ancient Charter of the Inhabitates'. The petition was granted provided 'that they divyde the money by them gotten'. ib., f. 61.

[4] *Calendar to the Records of the Borough,* IV, 17 May 1639.

[5] They were reconvened at the Restoration and in 1668 their number was increased to five. Later one more was added and a team of six was maintained by the city until extinction in 1836.

fortunate but they were reminded by the Court Leet Jury of their primary function of acting as Officers of the Watch.[1] It was more than twenty years before the Manchester waits received a more pleasant instruction, to 'play through the town every Thursday in the evening . . . according to ancient custom'.[2]

The dislocation of the lives of secular musicians of the rank and file from 1640 and for the next twenty years was severe. 'Heathen' festivals, such as May-day, and 'papistical' occasions—Christmas, for example—were interdicted, and a parliamentary proposal of 1642 that ballads in honour of Cromwell's 'great deeds' at Worcester and Edgehill[3] should be substituted for carols was received without enthusiasm. During the later years of Charles I the unpopularity of Archbishop Laud had generated a stream of pro-Parliament ballads, but the increasing austerities imposed by the Puritans drove the ballad-makers in the other direction. Illicit songs of warm royalist sentiment flourished underground—not always very far—during the Interregnum. Such compositions were not confined to the limited field of popular ballad, for satirical verses by the royalist poet and philosopher, John Birkenhead, were set by Henry Lawes.

The most severe interruption of the free-lance musician's activities came with the suppression of stage plays and interludes. The first move towards such prohibition came in 1642. In the following year the state of musicians who had hitherto depended on theatrical commissions was described as follows: 'Our musike that was held so delectable and precious that they scorned to come to a tavern under twenty shillings salary for two houres, now wander with their instruments under their cloaks (I mean such as have any) to all houses of good fellowship, saluting every room where there is company with '*Will you have my musike, gentlemen?*'.[4] On 13 December 1648 a Captain Betham was appointed as Provost-Marshall and enjoined to seize upon all ballad-singers, and to suppress stage plays. In 1656–7 an 'Act against vagrants and wandering idle dissolute persons' threatened severe measures against any 'fiddlers or minstrels [who should] be taken playing, fiddling, and making music, in

1 'This jury doth order that whereas there hath been formerly allowed certain number of waits to go through the town in the dead time of the night whereby hath been prevented many dangers not only of night walkers and robberies, but also great danger of fire discovered and prevented, and other general benefits accruing thereby to many hereafter. It is ordered that Henry Reynolds, Alexander Williamson, with some others assistants as waits aforesaid, shall, according to former custom, serve this town for their pains, to ask and receive once every quarter the gifts and allowance of every inhabitant.' *Manchester Court Records*, IV, p. 8.

2 ib., V, p. 99.

3 *Certaine Propositions offered to the consideration of the Honourable Houses of Parliament*, no. 6, quoted by W. Chappell, *Popular Music of the Olden Time*, II, p. 416.

4 *The Actor's Remonstrance or Complaint for the silencing of their Profession*; see Chappell, op. cit., p. 417.

any inn, alehouse, or tavern . . .' The lot of the out-of-work musician in search of casual employment was hard.

Under such conditions as obtain in a society split by revolution and continuing civil dissension it is only artists of acknowledged distinction or those who are opportunists who can survive. After the outbreak of the Civil War the royal musicians were dismissed. Some, like William Lawes, who was killed at the siege of Chester in 1645,[1] Christopher Gibbons, Christopher Simpson, and Henry Cooke, joined the royalist forces. A few, among them William Howes, Davis Mell, John Hingston, and Benjamin Rogers, showed more or less active sympathy with the Puritan cause. Howes was a fellow petitioner with Mell, Jenkins, and Hingston in 1656 for the institution of a national college of music. Hingston, a pupil of Orlando Gibbons, was household musician to Oliver Cromwell (whose appreciation of music was considerable) and he was also appointed as State Organist by the Lord Protector. Rogers was the recipient of a state pension, and his Bachelor's Degree at Cambridge was conferred after the University had received a direct instruction from Cromwell (28 May 1658). At the time of the Restoration, however, none of these musicians had such strong convictions as to refuse reinstatement in the musical establishment of Charles II.

Among the leading members of the profession those who suffered most were the organists of the cathedrals, collegiate chapels, and larger parish churches. Arthur Phillips, Elway Bevin's successor at Bristol, fled the country in 1640, and became private organist to Queen Henrietta Maria in exile.[2] William Child, also a native of Bristol and a pupil of Bevin, organist of the Chapel Royal since 1634, a favourite of Charles I and composer of a set of *Psalms of three voyces . . . with a Continuall Base* (1639),[3] retired to the country, and, it is said, took up farming. Walter Porter and Richard Portman, respectively Master of the Choristers and organist at Westminster Abbey, were dispossessed, the latter maintaining himself by private teaching. John Hilton lost his place at St. Margaret's Church, Westminster. When he died, in 1657, his colleagues, anxious to do him honour, the singing at burials being silenced as Popish—'sang the anthem in the house over the corpse before it went to Church, and kept time on his coffin'.[4] Old Thomas Tomkins, having endured the des-

[1] Commemorative elegies (for three voices) by Henry Lawes, John Cobb, organist of the Chapel Royal, Simon Ives, and Capt. Edmund Foster, appeared in the *Choice Psalmes* of the brothers Lawes in 1648.

[2] Phillips, composer of *The Requiem; or Liberty of an Imprisoned Royalist*, was succeeded by Thomas Deane.

[3] 'Composed after the Italian way' (manuscript note in B.M. Add. Ms. 31460).

[4] Ms. notes of Anthony à Wood, quoted by Jeffrey Pulver, *A Biographical Dictionary o, Old English Music*, London, 1927, p. 236.

truction of his home during the first siege of Worcester, eventually retired to his country estate in 1656. Choral services were effectively silenced by 1644, and even when musicians retained their place, as Thomas Deane, organist at Bristol Cathedral, and Henry Loosemore, organist at King's College, Cambridge (where the lay clerks were also kept on by the Fellows),[1] their duties were hardly more than nominal. Worst of all was the wanton destruction: the organs at Canterbury, Chichester, Exeter, Peterborough, Westminster Abbey, St. Paul's Cathedral, and in many other churches were destroyed at the beginning of the Civil War. Those that survived—unless, as at Salisbury, the Dean and Chapter dismantled the instrument and packed it away for the duration—were taken away after an Order in Council, of 9 May 1644, that declared that '. . . all organs and the frames or cases wherein they stand in all churches and chapels shall be taken away, and utterly defaced, and none hereafter set up in their places.' In the churches of the land the music was reduced to metrical psalms and responses sung congregationally. The lead was taken by the Parish Clerk who, using a pitch-pipe to give the note, had his place in the lowest tier of the three-decker pulpit (as at Shotwick and Baddiley Churches, in Cheshire.) For a long time after the Restoration small churches could not afford organs. Under these circumstances priceless collections of service-books were dispersed or destroyed.

New Openings

Oxford became an important centre for music-making during this period. When Charles I transferred his capital to that city in 1641 a number of his musicians followed him. Among them was John Wilson, one of the ablest practical musicians of the age. Informal music meetings in private houses, as of Edward Lowe, organist of Christ Church, and in various colleges, flourished continuously, and by 1656 the concert life of the city was enlivened by the frequent presence of the German virtuoso violinist, Thomas Baltzar, of Lübeck. Baltzar was at the time a guest of Sir Anthony Cope, who lived near Oxford. In due course, as John Evelyn relates, Baltzar was engaged for private recitals in London.[2] In the meantime the practice of organising concerts appeared as potentially profitable to Edmund Chilmead, an Oxford scholar who was ejected from his chaplaincy by the Puritans and took refuge in London, where he helped to lay the foundations of concert life.

The way in which music was then finding a new centre and a new

[1] See J. E. West, op. cit., p. 115.

[2] *Diary*, 4 March 1656.

function (in that a non-participant audience was increasingly a factor to be reckoned with) was an influence of importance in the shape that it would take in the future. External influences, from continental music, were to prove significant, but not more so than the changes that took place as a consequence of social upheaval. The traditional music, whether associated with Church or Court, took a battering; but music itself increased rather than decreased in popularity. Not least of all because, as in other times of stress, when alternative forms of entertainment were diminished, it offered one of the few means of relaxation and recreation. At this point the emergence of an enterprising publisher was timely.

John Playford (1623–?1686), descended from a Norfolk family, was active as a bookseller in London by 1648. Three years later he decided to expand the general publishing business he had started with the issue of musical works. Nothing had been published in England since Child's *Psalmes* of 1639 and it was evident that there was considerable opportunity. Playford, respected by musicians and amateurs of music alike, numbering among his friends Samuel Pepys, Henry Lawes, John Hilton, and the Purcell family, was shrewd. With a keen sense for what was saleable he published *The English Dancing Master* (1651), three books of *Select Musicall Ayres and Dialogues* (1653),[1] *The Introduction to the Skill of Musick* (1654),[2] and many other works of similarly popular appeal. All went into many editions.

Developments in Scotland

The enterprise of John Playford was an incentive to John Forbes of Aberdeen who, having bought the stock of a lately deceased local printer, went into music-publishing in that city in 1656. The progress made in England during the late sixteenth and early seventeenth centuries for political reasons was not possible in Scotland. Until Forbes commenced business as a music publisher virtually nothing of importance had appeared except for Edward Miller's *Scottish Psalter* (1635), with its characteristic treatment of some psalms in 'Reports'. In 1662 Forbes issued a collection entitled *Cantus: Songs and Fancies* (2nd ed. 1666, 3rd ed.

[1] (a) *Ayres for a Voyce alone to the Theorbo, or Basse Violl*; (b) *Choice Dialogues for two voyces to the Theorbo, or Basse Viol*; (c) *Short Ayres or Songs for 3 voyces, so composed, as they may either be sung by a voyce alone, to one instrument, or by two or three voyces*. The composers were John Wilson, Charles Coleman, Henry Lawes, William Welds, Nicholas Lanier, William Smegergill *alias* Caesar, Edward Coleman, and Jeremy Savile.

[2] Source material from *Rules how to compose* (G. Coperario, *c.* 1610), Dowland's translation of Ornithoparcus, *A New Way of Making Fowre Parts in Counterpoint* (Campion, *c.* 1619), *A Brief and Short Introduction to the Art of Musicke* (E. Bevin, 1631), and *The Principles of Musick in Singing and Setting* (C. Butler, 1636). See Lillian M. Ruff, 'A Survey of John Playford's "Introduction to the Skill of Musick" ', *The Consort*, no. 22, summer 1965.

1683). He included 'a considerable number of excellent choice *Italian songs* and *English Ayres*, all in three Parts', but also a small number of Scottish songs.[1] The composer of these was Thomas Davidson, director of the Sang Scule of St. Nicholas, Aberdeen.

The re-establishment of musical life after the spoliation of the Catholic institutions of Scotland was accomplished better in Aberdeen than elsewhere in Scotland, although the *Skene Lute Book* (with some Scottish items) testifies to occasional private initiative.[2]

The metrical Psalm was the means of revivifying the Sang Scules, which considerably broadened their range of activity during the seventeenth century. The first harmonised Psalter in Scotland was issued in Aberdeen in 1625, and before long the St. Nicholas Sang Scule (marked on Gordon of Rothiemay's map of Aberdeen of 1661) extended its functions to instrumental music. The directors before Thomas Davidson were Patrick Davidson (1603) and Andrew Melville (1636). There was also in the city the Sang Scule of St. Machar of which Gilbert Ross was Master between 1628 and 1641. It was in Aberdeen that John Abell (1650–1724), a singer of European renown, was born. And it was in Aberdeen that the shape of a musical society first began to appear.[3] After the death of Thomas Davidson musical instruction in Aberdeen was entrusted to 'ane stranger . . . weell expert in Musick.' This was Lewis de France. In 1683 he left Aberdeen for Edinburgh and in 1691 was prevailed upon to go to Glasgow where the Sang Scule was reported as 'altogether decayed'.[4]

In the meantime Scottish folk-tunes (some of which had hidden under pious texts in the *Buke of Godly Songs* [1st ed. 1599., 2nd ed. 1621]) were, as Pepys observed, becoming popular in London, and even stimulating Englishmen to write pseudo-Scottish music.[5]

Restoration

There was abundant musical energy during the period of the Commonwealth. The Restoration of Charles II was the cause of general release of this energy. The cheerful anticipation of the musical is indicated by

[1] Cf. B.M. Add. Ms. 36484, in the hand of David Melvill (Melvine).

[2] Music from this collection was published, with an introduction by William Dauney, in 1838.

[3] See H. G. Farmer, *Music Making in the Olden Days*, London, 1950.

[4] See Millar Patrick, *Four Centuries of Scottish Psalmody*, 1949, pp. 121–2.

[5] See R. Chambers, *Songs of Scotland prior to Burns*, Edinburgh, 1862—Introduction, pp. xiii–xiv. J. Playford's *First Book of Apollo's Banquet* contained 'several new Scotch tunes', as also *Dancing Master*, 1651, *Musick's Delight*, 1666, and H. Playford's *Wit and Mirth, or Pills to Purge Melancholy*, 1698, culminating in *Original Scotch-Tunes*, 1701.

Pepys, who relates how he with Matthew Locke, (Thomas) Purcell, and others enjoyed an evening in a riverside coffee house where they sang 'brave Italian and Spanish songs, and a canon for eight voices which Mr. Lock had lately made on the words—*Domine, Salvum fac Regem*'. The festivities in connection with the Restoration in Cambridge sent the waits of the borough to the 'top of King's College Chapel, where they played a great while'.[1] The waits of Sheffield (who had been paid two years' wages in 1659) came into their own again and their activities during the rest of the seventeenth century show not only how functions which had been forbidden were revived, but also how their standing was restored and how they improved civic affairs with banquet-music in the by now familiar German bourgeois manner.

In 1662 the town waits received 2s. 'for going about the Town on the ffaire Evening'. In the same year there was spent 2s. 6d. 'among the Lords officers at the Reareing of the Maypole', while in respect of 'Ringing upon the 5th of November and on the King's Brithday,' 17s. 6d. was expended. In 1668 3s. was paid 'to the Whaits for playing att ye faire'. On 13 May 1687 it was agreed that 'Jeremiah Ward, Thomas Unwyn and . . . be the Whaits of the towne and shall have 20s. a piece for the yeare following and each man a cloake and a badge, which cloakes they are to restore to the towne if they leave the towne within three years, their badges [a set of three cost £2. 0. 0. in 1688] whensoever'. In 1694 part of the cost of new instruments (£4. 0. 0.) was borne by the Burgesses, and in that year the waits received additional remuneration of 3s. 6d. for 'playing at the last [Trustees'] dinner'. In 1703 the 'Musitioners' of Sheffield were George Dowler, Thomas Stubbins, and William Wilburne.[2] The rehabilitation of the companies of municipal waits meant a revivification of popular music, and the publishing activities of Playford made possible the preservation both of tunes proper to the waits and also of countless ballads. The former often served as basis to the latter, in accordance with a familiar and ancient British practice of writing verses to existing melodies. Examples of music of the waits are given by Chappell,[3] while a published song of *c.* 1700 gives a lively picture of the waits of York. [Ex. 4].

In that the waits represented the popular tradition in British music and that to them was owed a great deal of credit both for the esteem in which music was held and the cross-fertilisation of the different kinds of music practised, it was fitting that those of London should greet King

[1] F. A. Keynes, op. cit., p. 50.

[2] *Sheffield Constable Accounts*, 1615–77. (The account of Ralph Staire and John Goddard, Constables of Sheffield) and the *Burgery Accounts*.

[3] *Popular Music*, II, pp. 549–51: music from London, Colchester, and Chester Waits, with references to Worksop, York, and Bristol.

4.

In a Win-ter's Morn-ing, long be-fore the Dawn-ing, e'er the Cock did crow, or
Stars their light with-draw, wak'd by a Horn-pipe, pret-ty play'd a-long York Ci-ty, by th'
help of o'er-night's Bot-tle, Da-mon made a Dit-ty, but hav-ing none of A-pol-lo's
Hu-mours, take what fol-lows, tho ye God till mel-lows, a dull and hea-vy Fel-low,
Words a - ny Cat - gut Scra - per, with a Kit and rul'd_ Pa - per,
Soon can set to Mu-sick, but some tunes to fit, with un-forc'd ea-sy Rhyme, good
Sense and yet keep Time, wou'd Pose a Dry-den, and make Sing Song Tom to sweat.

Charles II on his return from exile. The Entertainment (written and planned by John Ogilby, the royal cosmographer) given in honour of the occasion on 22 April 1661 was of large scale and involved not only the official waits but practically all available musicians in London at the time. The music was composed by Matthew Locke.[1]

Charles II, in spite of having inherited a lute from John Wilbye, was no expert in music, as his father had been, but he was enthusiastic that it should serve its proper function in the machinery of court life. He was aware that style in music had changed and he was insistent that English composers should accommodate themselves to the standards to which he had become accustomed in France. At the same time he was gratified when music kept near to the melodic and rhythmic simplicities that provided the foundation of the plain man's appreciation of music. Charles II was no high-brow, but he esteemed excellence in achievement, and he allowed his musicians a free hand. During his reign, because music was underwritten by the public in theatres, dancing schools, and concert rooms, as well as privately by an increasingly aware middle class, the whole scope of music became broader. The music of the Restoration Court, unlike that of the Jacobean or Caroline Courts, was the music of the bourgeoisie—to which class the more successful composers belonged.

The reconstitution of the Royal Music in 1660 gave secure places to some who had been dispossessed during the Civil War. Christopher Gibbons, John Wilson, who had been Choragus at Oxford University since 1656 and had published a loyal requiem in his *Psalterium Carolinum*[2] of 1657, William Child, who lived to the great age of ninety, Thomas Blagrave, William Blagrave, John Jenkins, Edward and Charles Coleman, George Hudson, Davis Mell, Nicholas Lanier, and Henry Lawes, were the principal musicians who had served the Court before the Civil War. But there were newcomers. Among them were John Hingston, as Keeper of the Organs, Henry Cooke, a Captain in the Royalist Army, Thomas Baltzar, Henry and Thomas Purcell, father and uncle respectively of Henry II, Pelham Humfrey, Matthew Locke, the repatriated William Young, and John Banister, son of one of the waits of the Parish of St. Giles-in-the-Fields, and a violinist of distinction. There was, in fact, an impressive array of experience and talent at the Restoration Court. The two immediate objectives were the restoration of the music of the Chapel Royal, and the institution of a band of violins similar to that at the French Court. Henry Cooke was made Master of the Chapel Royal

[1] See *Music for His Majesty's Sackbuts and Cornetts* transcribed A. Baines, London, 1951; also Eric Halfpenny, 'The "Entertainment" of Charles II', in *M. & L.*, 38, no. 1, 1957, pp. 32 f.

[2] *The Devotion of His Sacred Majestie in his Solitudes and Sufferings, rendered in Verse, set to Musick for three voices with an Organ or Theorbo.*

(Christopher Gibbons and Edward Lowe[1] being joint organists) and as such had the main responsibility for rebuilding the main structure of English musical education.[2] 'Composers for the violins' in 1660 were George Hudson, Matthew Locke and Henry Purcell I (in the place of Angelo Notari). In 1662 Henry Purcell I succeeded Henry Lawes, but three years later the whole matter of selecting and instructing the violinists was committed to John Banister. Cooke, Banister, and Locke were the main figures in the musical renaissance that commenced with the return of the King. Each was more influential than his own individual musical talents would seem to have suggested. It is apparent that what they may have lacked in genius (although Locke was not far short of genius) they made up for with administrative ability and wide knowledge of music of various styles, and an eagerness to instil into music the general intellectual curiosity that characterised the age.

Cooke was a singer and friend of John Evelyn, who, well versed in the subject, described him as 'esteemed the best singer after the Italian method, of any in England'.[3] In 1656 he sang the part of Solyman in Davenant's *Siege of Rhodes* (q.v.). As Master of the Choristers of the Chapel Royal he taught John Blow, Michael Wise, Pelham Humfrey, William Turner, and Henry Purcell. All of these pupils made rapid progress as composers under Cooke's guidance, and Blow, Humfrey and Turner, distinguished themselves in the joint composition of a 'Club' Anthem, while Humfrey was represented by five anthems while still 'one of the Children of His Majesties Chapel' in the second edition of Clifford's *Divine Services and Anthems* of 1664. Shortly afterwards Humfrey was sent to France by the King, and, according to Pepys, returned 'an absolute Monsieur'. In 1666 Humfrey joined Thomas Purcell and Locke as a composer for the violins. Five years later he became Master of the Choristers on the death of Cooke. He also succeeded Cooke as Warden of the 'Corperacion for regulating the art and science of Musick', an important body which observed some function as a Trade Union. It had been instituted by Charles I in 1636.[4]

[1] (*c.* 1619–52) chorister at Salisbury, organist of Christ Church Cathedral, Oxford, in 1630, and Professor of Music at Oxford, 1661. Lowe was the author of *Some short directions for the performance of Cathedral Service*, Oxford, 1661.

[2] A music book formerly in the possession of John Walter, a child of the Chapel, and now in the Cathedral Library at Chichester, gives examples of exercises choristers were expected to master *c.* 1680.

[3] *Diary*, 28 November 1654.

[4] The first Marshal of the Corporation was Nicholas Lanier. See *Orders of a Musical Corporation*, 1661–79. B.M. Harl. Ms. 1911. 'Acts and orders at an assembly of the Marshall Wardens and assistants of the science of Musique holden at Durham Yeard in the Strand in the County of Midd[lesex] upon the 31th [*sic*] day of August in the nineteenth Yeare of the Reigne of our Sovereigne Lord King Charles the Second.'

Banister, who was a close friend of Pepys, had also taken part in the performance of *The Siege of Rhodes* (one of his colleagues in the violin section on both occasions was Baltzar) and in 1661 he too was sent by the King to France. On his return he was appointed to Mell's place at Court, and later he took over that formerly occupied by Baltzar. After twelve years at Court Banister, piqued by the promotion of a less competent Frenchman, Louis Grabu, and a consequent diminution of his own authority, and by financial disorders, left the King's service and set himself up as an impresario. In the issue of the *London Gazette* of 26–30 December 1672 the following advertisement appeared: 'These are to give notice, that at Mr. John Banister's House, now called the Music School, over against the *George Tavern* in White Fryers this present Monday, will be Musick prepared by excellent Masters, beginning precisely at four of the Clock in the afternoon, and every afternoon for the future, precisely at the same hour'.[1]

If Cooke and Banister were not to be reckoned among the major composers of the period, Matthew Locke certainly was. Of the first generation of Restoration musicians he was the most versatile and accomplished, and the one who most clearly came to terms with the new situation.

Locke (or Lock), born in Exeter in 1622, was a chorister in the cathedral under Edward Gibbons (where his name and initials were carved on the organ screen in 1638 and 1641).[2] In 1648, possibly in the retinue of Prince Charles, he visited the Continent, of which expedition there is a memento in 'A collection of Songs made when I was in the Lowe Countries.'[3] The composers named by Locke were Galeazzo Sabbatini (to whose *Sacrae Laudes* of 1626 he had access), J. Rosetta, and F. Buonaventura di Rogliano, alias Francesco Costanzo. The *Seconda Prattica* and *stile concertante* principles of the motets collected in 1648 exercised a strong influence on Locke [Ex. 5*a* and *b*]. In 1653 he collaborated with Christopher Gibbons in the composition of the music for Shirley's masque *Cupid and Death*. In 1656 his *Little Consort of Three Parts* was published as an exercise in educational music. This collection of suites in the current style was dedicated to William Wake, the Exeter musician who was to become a Gentleman of the Chapel Royal in 1663. Locke referred to Wake as 'an intimate friend and great Master in Musicke' and it was for his pupils that these pieces were composed. In 1656 Locke had a second commission for dramatic music, being invited to collaborate in the score

[1] For further details of this important development in Restoration London, see my *The Concert Tradition*, Routledge, 1965, pp. 34 f.

[2] See Murray Lefkowitz, 'Matthew Locke at Exeter', *The Consort*, no. 22, 1965, pp. 5 f.

[3] B.M. Add. Ms. 31437.

5a.

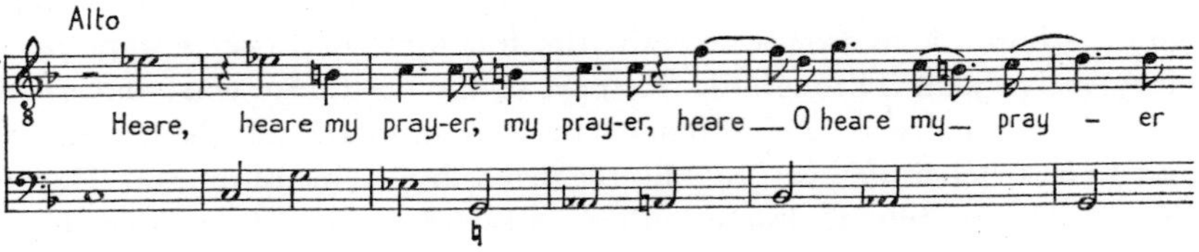

5b.

of *The Siege of Rhodes*. Not only did he write part of the music but he took an active part in the performance as the Admiral. A quick rise to relative fame saw him in the company of the elder Purcell and Samuel Pepys on a notable evening in 1660; and later that year he succeeded John Coperario as one of the court composers. In this capacity he provided the waits of London with the music they played during the Coronation procession. Locke composed church music, some for the Chapel Royal, some—settings of Psalms—for extra-liturgical performance by certain 'virtuoso ladyes in the city',[1] and some for the Roman Catholic Chapel maintained for the Queen, Catherine of Braganza.[2] Having been converted to Roman Catholicism, Locke became organist of the Queen's Chapel (this appointment appears to have aroused the envy of the Italians employed there, but he stuck it out). In 1673, Locke, whose readiness to expound his views on music had already been shown in an essay of 1666 in answer to critics of his setting of the *Kyrie* and *Credo*, published a text book, *Melothesia*. This work dealt with performance from figured bass, and as such is the first of its kind to be known[3]—and contained lessons for harpsichord and organ.

[1] Roger North, *Memoires*, p. 96.

[2] 'The services and music of the Queen's Chapel were a source of much curiosity to the Englishmen of the Court.' Edith M. Keate, *Royal Palaces of England*, London, 1911, p. 264.

[3] William Penny, *Art of Composition, or, Directions to play a Thorow Bass*, c. 1670, was mentioned in a catalogue of Henry Playford; but no copy is extant.

At the same time he replied to an essay regarding the necessity for rationalising musical notation by Thomas Salmon,[1] an industrious clergyman whose admirable reasoning caught the full force of Locke's sometimes vituperative pen. Throughout this part of his life Locke was concerned in various theatrical undertakings, to be considered in their context, and as a teacher he was highly regarded by John Blow and Henry Purcell, both of whom closely studied and made copies of examples from his works.

The main feature of Locke's music is its adventurousness. When he practised the fantasia style he did so in the light of an advancing system of tonality and under the influence of ambient foreign idioms and new instrumental characteristics. Akin to William Lawes and like him keeping an eye on the traditional outlines and polyphonic nature of the fantasia, Locke moved towards a highly expressive personal manner of expression. He was no pedant and departed from the stricter principles of fugal imitation as it suited his convenience—but he knew what was a good subject [Ex. 6]; he gave a more specifically non-vocal edge to his melodic

6.

2 Viols da gamba

contours; he rubbed themes together with refreshing audacity in respect of the resultant harmony; and he trod the chromatic path in the footsteps of John Daniel and the Italians [Ex. 7]. In his chamber music—much of

7.

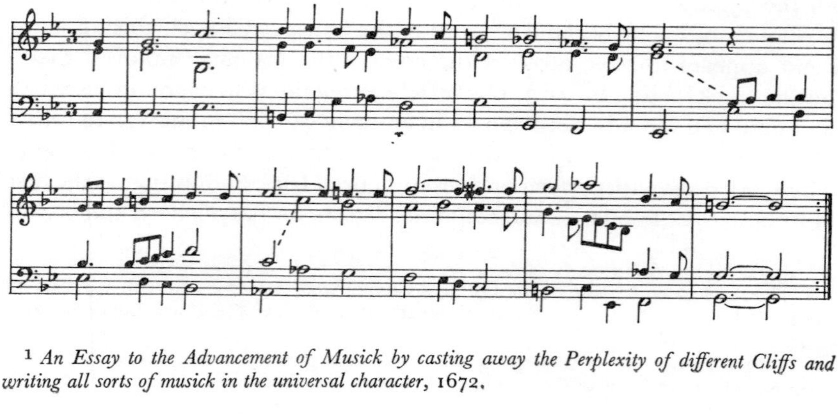

[1] *An Essay to the Advancement of Musick by casting away the Perplexity of different Cliffs and writing all sorts of musick in the universal character*, 1672.

it charmingly personalised by attribution (as the two-part Fantasia 'for severall Friends', or the canon 4 in 2 on 'A Plaine Song given by Mr. William Brode of Hereford [16]54')—Locke gave architectural character to the Suite or 'Concert' (e.g. Fantasia, Pavan, Air, Courante, Sarabande, Gigue). He was on occasion sensitive to the virtues of thematic reciprocity between movements [Ex. 8].

8a.

8b.

In the field of liturgical music Locke added a new dimension. Unhampered by Puritan prejudice and disinclined to believe that Elizabethan methods were still the best he worked with the freedom allowed by figured bass and within the sphere of the refined and purposeful declamatory style encouraged in Italy and increasingly in vogue in private sacred music in England. It was in this connection that the sacred song or dialogue, intended not for liturgical use but for private performance, was emancipatory, as is demonstrated in Locke's vigorous and striking vocalisation in

9.

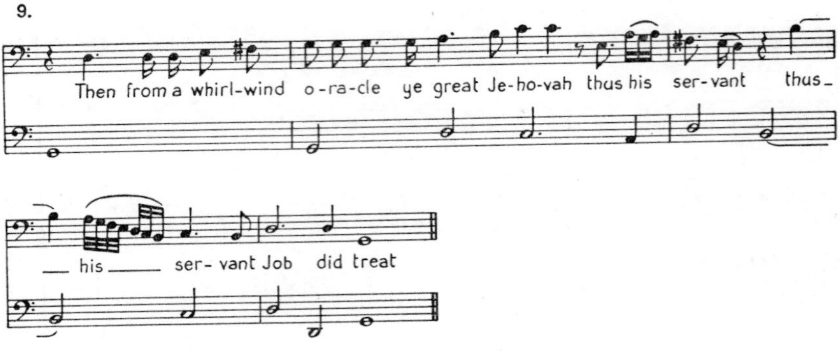

Job [Ex. 9]. In the final bars of this section the composer would appear to have had a singer of the capacity of John Gostling[1] in mind [Ex. 10].

10.

North, who was suspicious of Locke's Italian style, rightly commented on his 'robust vein'. The same writer observed further how Locke's deepest interest lay in the fusion of dramatic with musical expression so that he 'conformed at last to the mode of his time, and fell into the theatrical way and composed to the semi-operas divers pieces of vocal and instrumental entertainment with very good success, and then gave way to the divine Purcell and others'.

Music in the Theatre

It is a paradox that English opera should first have struck out towards independence in an era which saw an almost complete black-out of dramatic entertainment. In fact the virtual cessation of public musico-dramatic activity gave opportunity for the principals in this field to take a firm and fresh look at the general situation. The masque had completed its traditional course with the extravagances (there were twenty unrelated

[1] *c.* 1650–1733; Gos(t)ling was a Gentleman of the Chapel Royal from 1679 and subsequently a Minor Canon at St. Paul's Cathedral where his quarterly stipend was £4 2s. 0½d. (St. Paul's Cathedral, Salaries, Augmentations, 1686–96).

antimasques, each more exotic than the last) of *Salmacida Spolia* in 1640. The emphasis in this, the work of William Davenant who had succeeded Jonson as Laureate in 1639, was on the dance, as in the French *ballet de cour*. The music was composed by Louis Richard, a French musician with an established place at Court. The Civil War gave to Davenant—a zealous Royalist in the confidence of Henrietta Maria—opportunity (for which he was grateful) to spend some time in France when Cardinal Richelieu was establishing Italian opera, and when spectacular productions at the Théâtre du Marais were showing the possibilities of the *tragédies à machines*. The earliest of such productions was Corneille's *Andromède* (1650), in which new scenic ploys enhanced the enchanting effects already evident in the fusion of Italian opera and French ballet that had taken place through the association of Italian and French musicians. Davenant, who had obtained royal authority to build his own theatre behind the Three Kings Tavern in Fleet Street in 1640, awaited his chance to experiment in England. After capture by the Parliamentarians—he would have been executed but for the intervention of the music-loving John Milton and Bulstrode Whitelocke—and brief incarceration in the Tower of London, Davenant found means of getting round the proscription of dramatic entertainment. Players were smuggled into noble houses. A particular rendezvous for drama-lovers was Holland House, in Kensington. Sometimes, according to Aubrey, bribery enabled surreptitious shows to take place at the Red Bull. When Davenant projected something more ambitious, however, he applied for permission to furnish a 'representation or entertainment of declamation and music, after the manner of the ancients'. This was back to the Florentine principles of half a century before.

In May 1656 Davenant, permission being granted, staged his enterprise at Rutland House, and tickets cost 5s. per head. The 'First Dayes Entertainment' was a sequence of speeches and dialogues interspersed with songs and instrumental pieces. The composers were Henry Lawes, Charles Coleman, Henry Cooke and George Hudson, while Edward Coleman and his wife (one of Locke's virtuoso 'Ladies' (?)) were the principal singers. Mrs. Coleman is the first actress recorded in the history of the English theatre. In the same year *The Siege of Rhodes*, with music by the composers of the 'First Dayes Entertainment' as well as Matthew Locke, was also shown at Rutland House. A feature of this (of which the music has not survived) was the sets designed by John Webb, a pupil of Inigo Jones. This was the first occasion on which scenery was used in a public theatre in England.

At this point contact is again made with the masque. Davenant was concerned for the professional theatre. The masque belonged to the sphere of amateur theatricals. But since this was the case no objections had been made against the presentation of a work in this form by Shirley in 1653. This was *Cupid and Death*, with music by Locke and Christopher Gibbons, which was produced by a dancing-school master, Luke Channell, for the benefit of the Portuguese Ambassador. Shirley's *Contention of Ajax and Ulysses*, an occasional piece for school use, was produced at about the same time. In these entertainments recitative—being thought particularly suitable for amateurs—had an important role and it was within this casual tradition that this important part of operatic structure was nurtured. In due course the variegated masque, de-aristocratised and passed through the dancing-school and young ladies' seminary, ran into the conventions established by Davenant to produce the quasi-operatic works of Henry Purcell.

The Siege of Rhodes, against which protests were made, became the subject of a Government Commission in 1658.[1] Not intending to have his ambition frustrated nor his fortunes impaired, Davenant tempered enthusiasm with discretion and returned to tableau presentation of two stories of such realistic quality that they could capture an audience without action. He produced *The Cruelty of the Spaniards in Peru* (with music probably by Locke[2]) and *The History of Sir Francis Drake*, both of which included interspersed songs and appropriate instrumental pieces, and anticipated the secular oratorio of the eighteenth century rather more than they resembled operas.

However, with the Restoration, the period of caution and subterfuge was over. Davenant, now playing at the theatre in Lincoln's Inn Fields, traded in his old Charter for a new one from Charles II, which was granted in 1663. Then, with Christopher Wren as architect, he built a new theatre in Dorset Gardens,[3] which specialised in spectacular entertainments. Meanwhile Thomas Killigrew had used a similar patent to that granted to Davenant to build the Theatre Royal in Drury Lane.

The renewal of public entertainments meant jobs for many who had suffered long hardship. On 26 October 1663 Edward Hayward wrote to Sir Edward Nicholas, Master of the Revels (who was too ill to do the work himself), suggesting intercession with one of the Secretaries of State for the full implementation of the function, as 'the validitie and power of that offies is much enervated and weakened by the many years forced absences of the royal authority'. Hoping to act as Deputy Master Hayward asked 'that [the Master] may enjoy all ancient priviledges at Court, the ordering

[1] G. Mabbot to the Lord Lieutenant of Ireland, 28 December 1658: 'A Committee of the Councell to consider by what Authoritie the opera in Drury Lane is showne in imitation of a play, and what the nature of it is.' B.M. Lans. Ms. 823, f. 180.

[2] A 'Symeron's dance', attributed to Locke, is in *Musick's Handmaid*, 1678.

[3] Closed in 1709 after the Haymarket Theatre had become established.

of maskes in the Innes of Law, halls, houses of great personages, and societies, all Balls, Dancing Schools, and musick, except his Ma[jesty']; Pageantry and other public tryumphes, the severall feasts commonly called Wakes, where there is constantly revelling and musick; cockpitts, fencing and fencing schooles, and houses, where attended with minstrelsy, singing and dancing, together with the ordering of all momeries, fictions, disguises, scenes and masking attire. . . .'[1] Hayward received the appointment, with its powers of patronage and censorship.

The Siege of Rhodes, as Pepys observed,[2] was familiar after the Restoration, but developments in France were followed with growing interest. Corneille and Molière ensured that in French opera words would hold the superior place to music, which was interludial though coming more into its own in the ballets, the scores for which were composed by Lully. At the same time spectacle was immensely important and when *Psyche*, by Corneille and Molière, assisted by Quinault, and with music by Lully, was put on in 1671 the stage of the Palais Royal was rebuilt at great expense. In 1673, Thomas Shadwell, long an admirer and adapter of Molière's plays, adapted *Psyche* for production at Dorset Gardens. Shadwell appreciated the manner in which—as in Shakespeare—music can grow out of a libretto to expand action and realise atmosphere. The care which he took in this respect is indicated in his Preface. The instrumental music for *Psyche* was composed by Giovanni Battista Draghi, the vocal music by Locke who added his own comment when the vocal pieces were published.[3] Regarding his pieces, which were described as 'Soft, easy and agreeable' to the poetry, he said that in them 'you have from Ballad to single Air, Counterpoint, Recitative, Fuge, Canon and Chromatic Musick; which variety (without vanity be it said) was never in Court or Theatre till now presented in this nation'. The energetic self-advertisement both of Shadwell and Locke was, no doubt, stimulated by the presence in London of the French composer Robert Cambert (whose pupil, Louis Grabu, was appointed Master of the King's Music in 1665) and by the performance of Pierre Perrin's opera *Arianne et Bacchus*, to music by Grabu, at Covent Garden Theatre. In 1674 Cambert directed a performance of the masque *Calisto* by John Crowne and Nicholas Staggins (William Young's successor in the court band, who, a royal favourite, was made Professor of Music at Cambridge in 1684). Although Crowne paid a high tribute to Staggins, the interest of *Calisto* lies in the orchestra that Cambert assembled. This comprised two harpsichords, two theorboes, four

[1] B.M. Add. Ms. 19256.

[2] *Diary*, 20 May 1662; 1 October 1665.

[3] *The English Opera*, 1675, pub. T. Ratcliff and N. Thompson, Ms. of Music of *Psyche*, Fitzwilliam Museum, Cambridge, 24H19. Suite from *Psyche*, arranged by G. Bush and F. Harvey, published by Novello (1957).

guitars, three bass viols, four trumpets, timpani, four recorders, four oboes (the first use of oboes in England?) and an augmented band of strings.[1]

While opera thus began to claim a place, revitalisation of an older tradition brought into prominence the play with music. In 1663 Davenant revised *Macbeth* to the taste of a Restoration audience,[2] while Channel and Josias Priest arranged the dances, and Locke contributed incidental music (which has not survived in any kind of authentic version). After Davenant and Dryden had tampered with *The Tempest* this too was transformed into an opera by Shadwell in or about 1674.[3] Again Locke was the composer. The introductory comments in the text of this version of *The Tempest* indicate the major change that had taken place in the presentation of drama with music. The theatre was Dorset Gardens.

'The Front of the Stage is opened, and the Band of 24 Violins with the Harpsichords and Theorbo's which accompany the Voices, are plac'd between the Pit and the Stage. While the Overture is playing, the Curtain rises, and discovers a new Frontispiece, joined to the great Pilasters, on each side of the stage.'

The music for *The Tempest* was the work of a team. John Banister and Pelham Humfrey set the songs of Ariel; Pietro Reggio composed 'Arise ye subterranean winds'; Draghi and Locke were responsible for the instrumental music.[4] Locke's contribution included an Introduction (influenced by the French overture), a number of dances similar to those in the suites but ranging rather further afield. In addition to galliard, sarabande, corante, gigue, there are a gavot, a 'Lilk'—i.e. lilt, a minuet, and a rustic air, as well as a canon, and a curtain tune. The latter is a summary of all the effects considered by Locke to be appropriate to expressive—in this case programme—music. The opening bars, built on an expanding scheme which sends treble up and bass down, strongly

[1] See Arnold Goldsbrough, 'Purcell as an Instrumental Composer', in *Eight Concerts of Henry Purcell's Music* (Festival of Britain), London, 1951, p. 35.

[2] 'The Tragedy of *Macbeth* . . . being drest all in its finery, as new cloaths, new scenes, machines, as flyings for the witches, with all the singing and dancing in it . . .', Downs, *Roscius Anglicanus*, 1708, 1789 ed. pp. 42–3.

[3] '. . . having all new in it; as Scenes, Machines; particularly, one scene painted with myriads of *Ariel* Spirits; and another flying away with a table, furnisht out with fruits, sweet-meats, and all sorts of viands, just when Duke *Trinculo* and his companions were going to dinner; all things perform'd in it so admirably well, that not any succeeding opera got more money'. ib. p. 44.

[4] Humfrey's music is in the Library of the Paris Conservatoire Rés. F.1090/11753; Locke's was issued with that of *Psyche* in 1675. See M. L. Pereyra, '*La Musique écrite sur la Tempête d'après Shakespeare par Pelham Humfrey*', in *Bulletin de la Société Française de Musicologie*, II, 1920, pp. 75–85; see W. Barclay Squire, 'The Music of Shadwell's "Tempest",' in the *Musical Quarterly*, October 1921. Two suites from Locke's music for *The Tempest* arranged by W. G. Whittaker were published by O.U.P. (1934).

resemble the opening of Cousin Kemble's 'Flatt Consort' except that the tonality is major and not minor. The note values diminish as the storm approaches and increase as it abates. Locke produces an orchestral tremolo, and is generous with dynamic markings—'louder by degrees', 'violent', 'soft', 'loud', 'soft and slow by degrees'. He had hitherto introduced occasional instructions in his chamber music; thus in 'A Concert of 4 Parts'[1] he alternates 'loud' and 'soft' in a movement entitled 'Courante Ecchos' (f. 44b); prefaces another movement with 'soft and slow' (f. 49); and instructs the players in the concluding, homophonic, bars of a Fantasia (f. 52) to 'drag'. Locke also collaborated with Elizabeth Settle (*The Empress of Morocco*, Dorset Gardens, 1671) who with Shadwell was an energetic provider of plays with music for the Restoration stage.

Reaction and Progress

Locke died in 1677 and his death effectively marks the division between the old and the new. Modern music had come into its own, and Locke was its chief architect. The passing of cherished traditions was lamented by some, not least of all by that delightful, eccentric and inventive character of staunchly conservative views, Thomas Mace.[2] In *Musick's Monument—or a Remembrance of the best Practical Music* (1676) he wrote:

Old Dowland he is Dead; R. Johnson too;
Two famous men; great masters in my Art;
On each of Them I had more than one part,
Or two, or three; They were not single-soul'd,
As most our Upstarts* are, and too too bold.
Soon after them, that famous man Gotiere[3]
Did make me gratefull in each noble ear;
He's likewise gone.
I know I have some friends which yet do live,
But are so few, can scarcely make one thrive:
My friend Jo. Rogers, He's the only man
Of fame; . . .

* Some pitiful thin composers of this age.

[1] B.M. Add. Ms. 17801.

[2] Sometime chorister of Trinity College, Cambridge, Mace (*c.* 1613–?) married a Yorkshire woman and retired to the City of York during the Civil War. A notable performer and teacher he concentrated on instruction after fracturing both arms. In later life he was afflicted with deafness, the onset of which stimulated him to invent a lute with fifty strings. In 1675 he wrote a pamphlet on the highways of England.

[3] Jacques Gaultier, a Frenchman, arrived in England in 1617; his place as court lutenist was filled by John Rogers after the Restoration. A few pieces by Gaultier were included in Lord Herbert of Cherbury's Lute Book.

The virtues of the old forms were extolled in detail and Mace implied some at least of the defects of the new: 'We had', he wrote,

'our Grave Musick, Fancies of 3, 4, 5, and 6 Parts to the Organ; Interposed (now and then) with some Pavins, Allmaines, Solemn, and Sweet Delightful Ayres; all which were (as it were) so many Pathettical Stories, Rhetorical, and Sublime Discourses; Subtil and Accute Augmentation; so Suitable, and Agreeing to the Inward, Secret and Intellectual Faculties of the Soul and Mind; that to set them forth according to their true Praise, there are no words sufficient in Language; yet what I can best speak of them, shall only be to say that they have been to myself (and many others) as Divine Raptures, Powerfully Captivating all our unruly Faculties, and Affections (for to Time) and disposing us to Solidity, Gravity, and a Good Temper; making us capable of Heavenly, and Divine Influences.

'The Authors of such like Compositions have been divers famous English Men, and Italians; some of which, for their very great eminency, and worth, in that Particular Faculty, I will here name, viz. . . . Mr. Alfonso Ferrabosco, Mr. John Ward, Mr. Lupo, Mr. White, Mr. Richard Deering, Mr. William Lawes, Mr. John Jenkins, Mr. Christopher Simpson, Mr. Coperario, and one Monteverde, a Famous Italian Author; besides divers, and very many others who in their late Times, were All substantial, Able and Profound Composing Masters in this Art . . .

'Then again, we had all those choise consorts, to equally-sized instruments (rare chests of viols) and as equally performed: for we would never allow any performer to over-top, or out-cry another by Loud Play; but our great care was, to have all the parts equally heard; by which means (though sometimes we had indifferent or mean hands to perform with); yet this Caution made the Musick lovely, and very contentive.'

There was still a market for the 'contentive' music, but the lute, once a badge for the gallant, was now a weapon for the refinement of young ladies. 'You will', it is remarked in *Mary Burwell's Instruction book for the Lute* (*c.* 1668 and 1671), 'do well to play in a wainscot room where there is no furniture, if you can; let not the company exceed three or four, for the noise of a mouse is a hindrance to that music. . . . You must keep your nails short, without a brim of black velvet (as we call it). You shall pare your nails and not with your teeth, which is a great nastiness.'[1]

While Thomas Mace looked back with a not altogether unjustified regret, the amateurs in London—as Pepys and Evelyn show—were busily bringing themselves abreast of fashion. Patriotism might baulk at the political convolutions of the age which threatened too many too close

See Thurston Dart, article in *Galpin Society Journal*, no. 11, May 1958.

associations with the Continent; but there was no bar against music from abroad. Pepys admired Draghi and enjoyed the serenading music of those Italian singers who performed one autumn evening in 1668 for the Queen. Pietro Reggio, colleague of Locke in respect of *The Tempest* music, exercised especial influence. Once employed by Queen Christina of Sweden in Rome, he was in touch with current Italian fashion. In London, and Oxford, he became a popular singing-teacher, and his Italian songs and duets were at least serviceable guides to the art of bel canto. He was, however, employed from time to time as copyist and in the books he assembled for his patrons in London are excerpts from Rossi, Carissimi, Strozzi, Marini, and Albrici. The appetite for Italian vocal music was large and colleagues of Reggio were also employed in making collections. Thus music by Cavalli, Cesti, and Stradella was also made available.

As has been seen, English composers were sometimes reluctant to forsake well-trodden paths and persevered with the fantasia long after Charles II expressed his distaste for its severities. Instrumentalists who were imported pointed the way to new techniques. Among them were Gerhard Diessener, once a member of the court music in Kassel and a student of Lully in Paris, and the Italian violinist, Nicola Matteis. There is a copy of a 'Mr. Disseners Sonata' in Locke's hand in B.M. Add. Ms. 31437. Both Diessener and Matteis, much admired virtuosi, played an important part in the establishment of a regular concert life in London, ratified the advanced techniques of violin playing by their compositions, and settled down as assimilated Englishmen. In 1696 Matteis composed an Ode for St. Cecilia's Day.

Pupils of Henry Cooke

It was a stimulating age in which to be brought up as an apprentice musician. Of the pupils of Henry Cooke those who achieved most distinction were John Blow and Henry Purcell. William Turner (1651–1740), a fine counter-tenor, was both industrious and respectable. Michael Wise (1648–87), more talented than Turner and like him favourably noticed by Charles II, was neither industrious nor respectable, and as organist of Salisbury Cathedral was noted as given to 'Prophanenesse, Intemperate Drinking, and other Excesses'.[1] He died after a quarrel with his wife, in an affray with a night watchman, leaving behind a number of quite splendid anthems as well as works of a contrasting character [Ex. 11]. In addition to being organist at Salisbury, Wise was a Gentleman of the Chapel Royal and Charles II so esteemed his organ-playing that he gave him authority

[1] Charge of the Chapter of Salisbury Cathedral (1683) quoted by Betty Matthews, *The Organs and Organists of Salisbury Cathedral* [n.d.], p. 17.

to play in any church that the King might be attending. Of Wise's anthems one, *How are the mighty fallen*, is outstanding by reason of its controlled poignancy. This much sung work (it appeared in many contemporary collections of anthems) anticipated Handel not only by reason of the text.

11.

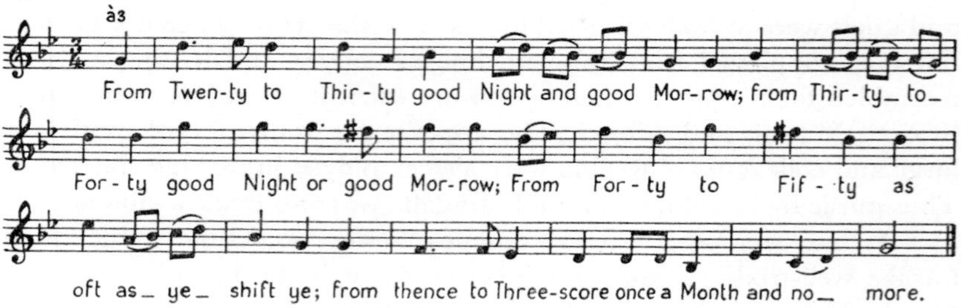

Blow was a model of decorum; a fact which has tended to obscure the fine quality of his best works, and the variety of the rest. It was Henry Purcell himself who, in an excess of gratitude, took for example a canon[1] by Blow and stated that 'this very Instance is enough to recommend him as one of the Greatest Masters in the World'. What Blow did was to assemble the disparate elements of Restoration music and to discipline them to better purpose, within certain contexts, than most of his contemporaries. He was a native of Newark, in Nottinghamshire, where it is likely that he received his early training in the local song school. A chorister at the Chapel Royal—no doubt enrolled through impressment, which was revived in order to replenish the Chapel choir—he took full advantage of Cooke's training and would appear to have continued his musical education with Christopher Gibbons and John Hingston. At the age of twenty he was appointed to the King's Private Music, as virginalist, and at the same time to the organistship of Westminster Abbey, in succession to Albertus Bryan. Bryan was a notable performer, being described as 'that famously velvet-fingered Organist', and Blow also gained a high reputation as a virtuoso. The quality of Blow's performance is not on the whole adequately reflected in his keyboard music, even allowing for the fact that the written form of such works represents little more than a basis for impro-

[1] A Canon from the Service in 'Gamut' said to have been sent to Cardinal Philip Howard in Rome, together with works by Purcell, by Ralph Battell, Sub-dean of the Chapel Royal. Reference to this appears in the preliminaries to *Amphion Anglicus*:

His *Gloria Patri* long ago reach'd Rome;
Sung and rever'd too in St. Peter's dome;
A Canon will outlive her jubilees to come.

visation. Blow composed dances, airs, preludes (based on forms familiar through the string repertoire of the period) and variations on a ground—an increasingly popular pattern—for harpsichord; and miscellaneous short pieces for organ, variously entitled 'Voluntary', 'Vers', or 'Prelude'.[1]

In 1676 Pelham Humfrey died and Blow (who had witnessed his will) succeeded him as Master of the Chapel Royal, and also as 'composer . . . for voyces in ordinary' to the King. At this time Henry Purcell was one of Blow's pupils, a fact recorded on Blow's memorial in Westminster Abbey. Other pupils of Blow included Daniel Purcell, William Croft, Jeremiah Clarke, Daniel Roseingrave, and Bernard Gates. In 1677 Blow was given the Degree of Doctor of Music by the Archbishop of Canterbury, the first instance of the use of this ancient legatine privilege in modern times. Two years later he resigned his post at the Abbey in favour of Purcell (to resume it on Purcell's death), but in 1687 he took over the Almonership of St. Paul's Cathedral. That appointment was then vacant by the death of Wise. As Almoner—with a stipend of £47 13s. 4d. and a rent allowance of £28 13s. 4d. a year—Blow acted as musical adviser to the cathedral. During the building of the new church the organistship was in abeyance. The post was filled in 1695 when Clarke was appointed. In 1703 he took over the Almonership on Blow's retirement from the office.[2] It will be seen that Blow controlled a large part of the official music of the Church and State, which is shown by the character of his major works. He died two years before Handel first came to England.

The secular character of the reign of Charles II was reflected in the accepted function of the Anglican anthem (or the Roman motet). Pepys, Evelyn, Roger North—the most conspicuous amateurs of the day, as well as the King himself, regarded the anthem accompanied by orchestra as a civilised form of entertainment,[3] under which conditions—as also in the case of the Italian cantata or oratorio—the possibility of producing distinguished music is not necessarily diminished. Occasions of national importance called for ecclesiastical celebration. William King, one of the Oxford musicians active during the Commonwealth, Christopher Gibbons, Child, Cranford, a singer at St. Paul's, William Lawes, and Pelham Humfrey, among others, dutifully memorialised the Restoration of the Monarchy, and various royal pregnancies, in transitional style, and under

[1] See John Blow, *Selected Organ Music*, ed. by A. V. Butcher, Hinrichsen ed.

[2] Salaries, Augmentations, etc., 1686–96, and Receipt Book, 1710–68, St. Paul's Cathedral.

[3] When the King went to Windsor he took a number of instrumentalists with him in order to sustain the anthem adequately (e.g. six and an organist in 1671, and fourteen in 1674). But there was opposition to the manner in which the liturgy was upset and in 1691 the Chapel Royal services were ordered to conform to normal collegiate church use, with 'solemn music'; see Wyn K. Ford, 'The Chapel Royal in the Time of Purcell', *Mus. T.*, November 1959, pp. 592–3.

the disadvantage of not yet having adequately trained choristers at their disposal. They also often had to wrestle with jejune texts.[1] Blow, beneficiary of the choir-training skills of Henry Cooke, the student of Carissimi as well as of the traditional English method, had the talent to synthesise the various influences in occasional works that were in an appropriately grand manner. He composed more than a hundred anthems; among them were works to mark the Coronations of James II, and William and Mary, the frustration of the Turnham Green assassination plot of 1696, the re-opening of St. Paul's Cathedral in 1697, the Treaty of Ryswick, by which the war against Louis XIV was concluded, and the opening of the new Chapel at Whitehall in 1698. Such works—verse anthems, with interpolated 'symphonies' for strings—were soberly dignified, neither lacking in controlled expressiveness nor in regard for textual exposition. Blow calculated choral effects with precision, and a sense of fitness for occasion prevented him from running riot with the Baroque formulas that may be found in certain of his more exuberant essays for solo voice. Sometimes he could achieve a poignancy—exposed through the judicious balance of discord and chromatics—that is absolutely compelling, as, for instance, in the Latin *Salvator Mundi*.[2]

The Restoration Anthem reached its peak in the magnificent set ordered for the Coronation of James II in 1685. In all there were eight anthems for this occasion: Purcell's *I was glad* and *My Heart is inditing*, Turner's *Come, Holy Ghost* and *The King shall rejoice*, Henry Lawes's *Zadok the Priest*, Child's *Te Deum*, and three pieces by Blow: *God spake sometimes in visions*, *Let Thy Hand be strengthened*, and *Behold, O God our defender*.[3] Of these the first is an opulent piece, designed with an expansive symphony and interpolated ritornelli for strings, and utilising all the resources and permutations of eight vocal parts. Such monumental music was rare anywhere at that time. It was part of Blow's genius that he could not only command such eloquence, but that he could do so in a manner which is both public and personal. Although *God spake* is a 'verse' anthem, the verse sections are all in ensemble. This is also the case in Purcell's *My Heart is inditing*.

The anthem extended into the ode, a form of official composition that had come into being since the Restoration, although its antecedent may be seen in the Scottish anthem of Orlando Gibbons (see p. 175). Matthew Locke had provided the prototype of the ode in the 'New Year's Song'

[1] The dynastic and political significance of such works are treated by Franklin B. Zimmerman, in 'Social Backgrounds of the Restoration Anthem', in *Bericht über den internationalen musikwissenschaftlichen Kongress, Kassel, 1962*, Kassel, 1963, p. 27.

[2] Ed. by H. Watkins Shaw, pub. Hinrichsen.

[3] See *Coronation Anthems*: *Anthems with Strings*: ed. by A. Lewis, H. W. Shaw, *Musica Britannica*, VII, 1953.

entitled 'All things their certain periods have', but it was brought to maturity by Blow and Purcell in the 1680's. The first of Blow's works in this genre was, however, not for a royal occasion, but for the University Act at Oxford in 1678 (the performance did not take place until 1679). This piece had a splendid text by Abraham Cowley, the temperament of whose verse shows marked affinities with that of Blow's music, which in this work is shown at its most graceful and melodious. Blow composed at least sixteen welcome songs for the Court, and a number of odes for St. Cecilia's Day, which became regular fixtures in the English musical calendar after 1683, performances at first being given in the Hall of the Stationers' Company. Of these, that for 1684, *Begin the Song*, is a splendid example of Blow's robust manner of statement and his appreciation of the individual capacities of his singers. (The usual singers for the odes both of Blow and Purcell were John Abell, Alphonso Marsh, John Bowman, William Turner, and John Gostling.) Apart from his felicitous treatment of detail Blow was a master of the simple effect, and his broad sweeping tunes in three-time are magnificently 'English' in an accepted sense. But, like Handel, who may well have learned how to adapt himself to the taste of the English from examination of Blow's works, he could turn almost negligible material into something both musical and memorable [Ex. 12].

12.

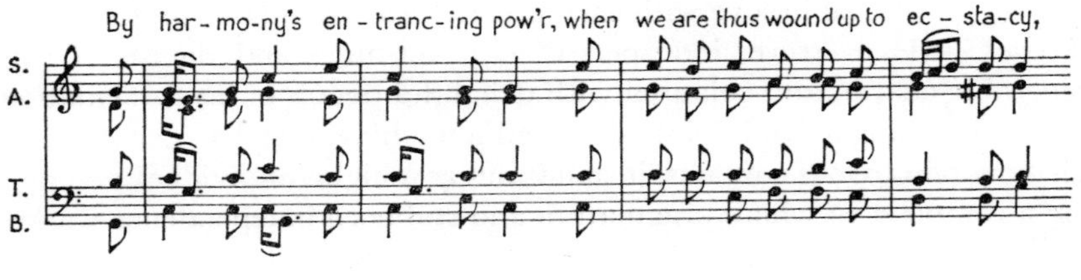

Blow's songs, many of avowedly popular character, were published in numerous collections, including the *Theatre of Music* (1685), which he edited jointly with Purcell, *Harmonia Sacra* (1688) and *Amphion Anglicus* (1700). An important work collateral with solo song (or secular cantata) was his *Ode on the Death of Mr. Henry Purcell* for two counter-tenors, two recorders, and continuo.

Although he wrote settings for plays by Nahum Tate, Nathaniel Lee, Thomas Durfey, and Aphra Behn, he did not take more than a passing interest in the professional theatre. At the same time a court commission to provide a masque stimulated Blow to compose a work which properly belongs to the exiguous tradition of English opera. This was *Venus and Adonis* composed some time after 1680. The role of Venus was played by Mrs. Mary Davis, one of Davenant's actresses and one of the King's mistresses. Her quality as an expressive singer was fully tested by Blow, who reserved for this occasion his most advanced turns of phrase. The crisis of the music occurs when Venus thus laments the death of Adonis [Ex. 13]. The affinity with Purcell is close, and the likelihood that

13.

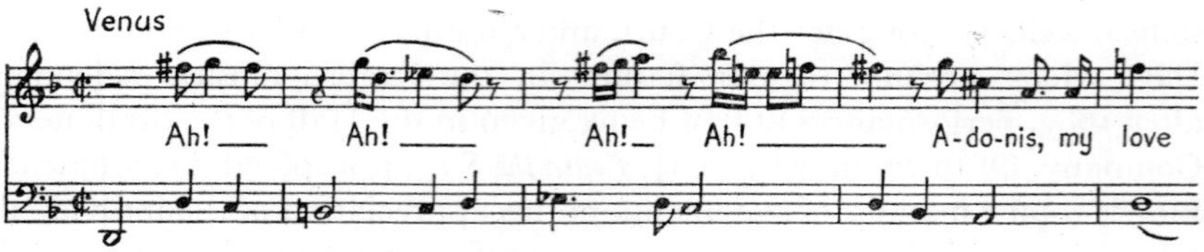

when writing *Dido and Aeneas* he had his master's work in mind is strong. As in Purcell's opera there is also in Blow's masque a hunting scene, with evocative music that suggests acquaintance with the programme music of Locke. While Venus and Adonis are the principals in Blow's score and neatly personalised by shape of phrase and harmonies that often are rich in emotional significance, there is also Cupid. The part of Cupid was given to Mrs. Davis's daughter, known honorifically as Lady Mary Tudor. She had her opportunity to amuse the audience in the scene in which she taught her fellow Cupids to confuse the love equations by making the wrong people fall in love with each other. *Venus and Adonis*, prefaced by a French style overture, interspersed with act-tunes and dances of considerable charm, and coloured with delightful details of instrumentation, owes something to Lully's influence and something to Italian cantata, but, shaking off obvious contacts, it stands out as a highly individual parergon by a composer in whom pragmatism and stubborn independence worked in effective alliance. Blow knew what his patrons required—or thought they required. He knew what he wanted to do, to extend the frontiers of music where the scale or character of a work encouraged imaginative experiment. His harmonic acerbities were not the result of incompetence (as is implied by Burney's censorious examination of Blow's 'crudities'), but of musicianly initiative. In the final issue he tried to arrange a compromise between realism and idealism in an environment growing less favourably disposed to the latter.

Purcellian Background

Regarding a composer whose high rank is universally acknowledged, two arguments are propounded to account for his existence. On the one hand he is seen as beyond natural explication, a member of a predestined hierarchy. On the other hand he is regarded as the inevitable consequence of a socio-technical pattern of events. The first argument was formerly applied with some vigour in the case of Henry Purcell. So long as the theory was maintained that after Byrd and Gibbons nothing happened in British music until Purcell appeared, the argument was both attractive and persuasive. It helped to confirm the cyclical theory of British music—which was formerly seen as a general, unremarkable plain relieved by occasional and unaccountable peaks. It also helped to endow the rare genius with magical properties and incidentally to assure the latter-day Philistine that his antipathy to the arts was well founded. While it is going too far to say that if there had been no Purcell there would have been a composer of equal talent to have occupied his place, it is only justice to his immediate predecessors and his contemporaries to point out that the accomplishment of Purcell was the result of his consideration and application of ideas and techniques that were held and practised in common. The points of style that are catalogued distinctively as Purcellian are individually to be discovered in the works of many other composers. What Purcell alone possessed was an indisputable authority—which was magnanimously granted by his contemporaries.

Here we return to a fundamental. Music was an accepted part not only of the social structure but also of the social argument. The age of Purcell was one of discussion and debate, and the musical form of the Dialogue was symbolic. It was the era of experiment in which the Royal Society emerged, in which Newton and Boyle, Hooke and Halley, flourished. On another level it was utilitarian so that journalism appeared as a vital form of literature, and Dryden perfected the influential art of satire. During the last part of the seventeenth century the foundation of modern capitalism was established, and the question of the exercise of ultimate power was posed not only between King and Parliament but also between the nascent political parties, of Tory and Whig. The political division was reflected in numerous ballads and songs.[1] Between the death of Charles II, in 1685, and the Revolution of 1688, which was precipitated by the arrogance and stupidity of James II, democratic determination—crystallised in the registered objections to the royal policies which were collected against a request of the King in 1687—appeared as a potential factor in national affairs. The people of England had rejected Roman Catholicism and its implications, and moved towards a more patent and

[1] E.g. *A Tory came late through Westminster-hall: A New Song made by a Person of Quality, and sung before his Majesty at Winchester: To the Tune of Cock Lawrel*, London, 1683, and *A Tory, a Whigg, and a Moderate Man: Words by Mr. Durfey to a pretty French Tune*, London, 1705?

aggressive nationalism. In the war against France the Royal Navy was seen to be the saviour and safeguard of the country's fortunes.

The principal musicians of this era formed a close corporation, sharing duties and ideas, and—as Banister demonstrated—prepared to argue their rights. Charles II often avoided paying his musicians. They, for their part, protected themselves by putting their talents at the disposal of the public on a larger scale than hitherto. By the end of the century the concert was an effective factor in the musical life of the community. Not only did it provide opportunity for the composer and the performer; it stimulated the practising amateur. In the age of discussion music received its fair share of attention. There were pro-Italian, pro-French, pro-English cliques, while the general run of music-lovers contented themselves with following the most convenient current fashion, and accepting whatever might come their way. The catholic taste of the most notable amateur of the age, Thomas Britton, the coal-merchant of Clerkenwell, whose concerts began in 1678 and continued until his death in 1714, is shown in the titles in his library.[1] In the Dedication to *Dioclesian* Purcell wrote as one who recognised that while xenophobia had no place in a musician's nature the propitiousness of circumstances depended on perpetual vigilance: 'Musick', he wrote, 'is but in its nonage; a forward child, which gives hope of what it may be hereafter in England, when the masters of it shall find more encouragement. 'Tis now learning Italian, which is its best master, and a little of the French air to give it somewhat more of gayety and fashion. Thus, being further from the sun we are of later growth than our neighbouring countries, and must be content to shake off our barbarity by degrees . . .' In the Preface to the *Sonatas of III Parts* of 1683, Purcell had paid a larger tribute to Italian music.

Purcell was fortunate to be born into a lively age, to have been accompanied through his apprenticeship by progressive, thought-provoking teachers. He was fortunate to have been so temperamentally adjusted that he could absorb teaching without being submerged by it (as, up to a point, Gibbons was by that of Byrd), that he could sieve his experience of other men's music and utilise only what was essential, and that he could, as Bach, attune his spirit to the climate of period and place without prejudice to his ultimate claims on wider appreciation. Purcell is a twentieth-century composer through survival and not merely revival.

It is clear that Purcell had opportunity, but so had other composers in his milieu. He, however, possessed the one distinctive mark that distinguishes the pre-eminent creative talent, that of authority. He was, up to a point, invested with some degree of authority by family tradition; for it was not unhelpful to have been born within the environment of the

[1] See Hawkins, *History*, V, pp. 79–86.

royal music. He attained high mark in his profession without undue effort and took full advantage of his official positions. He held the unqualified respect of his colleagues and gained the suffrages of the public—of a wider public than had existed in relation to the earlier English masters. 'My father', wrote Burney, 'who was nineteen years of age when Purcell died, remembered his person very well, and the effect his anthems had on himself and the public at the time that many of them were first heard; and used to say, that no other vocal music was listened to with pleasure, for near thirty years after Purcell's death; when they gave way only to the favourite opera songs of Handel.'[1] Purcell was in touch with society as a whole. His works, highly functional and reflecting a variety of interests, satisfied different social requirements. Equally they mirrored social conditions. More importantly the greatest of them possessed a rare quality of human sympathy. This quality distinguished Purcell as the first truly dramatic composer in the British tradition, and underlines the climactic position he came to occupy in seventeenth-century music. The whole intellectual ferment of the seventeenth century in England centred on personal issues, rights, and responsibilities, within the framework of a national structure. Posthumously, Purcell became a symbol. He was elected to a place of supreme honour. He was named the national composer. So he remains (some part of the modern Purcell cult is, unconsciously maybe, connected with a current nostalgia for a relinquished prestige in other fields than that of music). But the nature of his nationalism is not what it might seem; for the art of Purcell had no limitations by reason of exclusiveness.

Purcell composed a great deal of music, but few wholly integrated major works. Since there was no local precedent for these he can hardly be held culpable for not doing what he saw no reason to do. On the other hand few composers have dug so deep within limited areas. Purcell lived in the age of Defoe and in his exercise of realistic appreciation of character and situation and in his capacity for apt, accurate, sometimes trenchant, observation he displayed similar qualities. In the day to day routine of a Restoration composer practices akin to those of journalism were necessary. And the best composer was he who was the most professional.

Henry Purcell

Henry (1659–95) was the son of Thomas Purcell, who took a place as a tenor in the Chapel Royal when it was reconstituted and who remained in the royal service until his death in 1682. In 1672 Thomas was Warden of the Corporation of Music, and early in the next year he was appointed

[1] *History*, III, p. 479.

Groom of the Robes—a useful source of additional income and a token of the respect in which he was held in court circles. Thomas's brother Henry, who had sung in Davenant's *Siege of Rhodes*, was also a Gentleman of the Chapel Royal, an office which he doubled for the last three years of his life with that of Master of the Choristers of Westminster Abbey. Henry I died in 1664, and was buried in the Abbey cloisters.

As a chorister in the Chapel Royal Henry II was instructed in the theory of music and its practical application on the widest scale. This included the tuning and maintenance of instruments. A Chapel Royal chorister was also educated in other faculties and, like a grammar school pupil, was given a working knowledge of Latin. When Henry's voice broke he was put under Hingston in his office as Keeper of the King's instruments. From this he graduated to tuning the Abbey organ and to copying organ parts for the use of Blow, then organist. In 1677 Purcell succeeded Matthew Locke as a composer in ordinary for the violin (Locke's death is commemorated in an *Elegy* published in *Choice Ayres*, 1679). Two years later he took over Blow's post as organist of Westminster Abbey, after which he filled the vacancies caused by the death of Edward Lowe (1682) and John Hingston (1683) and thus became an organist of the Chapel Royal and Keeper of the King's instruments. In 1689 he was confirmed in his place in the private music of William and Mary. Among his fellow composers therein, in addition to Blow, were John Banister II, an early exponent of Corelli and a friend of Thomas Britton; Robert Carr, a lightweight contributor of flute pieces to popular anthologies; William Turner; and Charles Coleman II. In the field of composition the competition was not severe; the commissions, on the other hand, were. The history of a generation is written in Purcell's occasional pieces, as well as some details of more personal significance.

Expanding techniques and larger resources allowed not only more relevance to circumstance within the texture of music, but also a greater degree of independent aesthetic development and significance. Purcell saw the modes out and modern tonality in.

In his revision of Playford's *Introduction* for the twelfth edition (1694) Purcell excluded the chapter on modes and stated the modern tonal situation. 'There are', he wrote, 'but two *Keys* in Musick, viz. a *Flat*, and a *Sharp*: not in relation to the place where the first or last Note in a Piece of Musick stands, but the *Thirds* above that note. To distinguish your *Key* accordingly, you must examine whether the *Third* be *sharp* or *flat*, therefore the first Keys for a learner to Compose in ought to be the two *Natural Keys* which are *A re* [A] and *C fa ut* [C], the first the lesser, the last the greater Third; from these all the other are formed, by adding either *Flats* or *Sharps*.'

Purcell was the first English master of a balanced orchestral ensemble, for to the string and harpsichord band instituted by Charles II, flutes, oboes,[1] trumpets, and drums were added as needed, and as well as string there were notable wind instrument virtuosi. There were some excellent singers available, and Purcell was as quick to take advantage of their abilities, as they were to renew the spirit of vocal music. Among these singers were the first immigrant castrati, the most famous being Giovanni Francesco Siface.[2]

Purcell's music falls into two main categories, sacred and secular. These may be subdivided. Sacred music included works in the polyphonic tradition (for on serious occasions English church music was, and continued to be, measured by the standards of the by then classical composers) and according to the revitalised verse anthem convention, as well as settings of Latin psalms, and songs and scenas for more or less private use. Among the monumental items within this category are the anthems for the Coronation of James II, the *Te Deum and Jubilate* in D, for the St. Cecilia's Day service in St. Bride's Church, Fleet Street, in 1694 (for long considered one of Purcell's most important works), and the Funeral Anthem for Queen Mary—*Thou knowest, Lord*—of the same year.

The secular music embraces the official odes and welcome songs, the dramatic works, a large number of songs, cantatas and other vocal ensemble music, including a plentiful supply of bawdy material, miscellaneous canonic studies, instrumental chamber music both of the old fantasia order and in the new Italian style, and a limited amount of keyboard music. Of this very little is for organ. In this department Blow was Purcell's superior. It is possible to deduce that both from this and from the relative proportions of the general list of music that Purcell's main interest was in secular music; a fair conclusion if we assume that Purcell, as a not untypical citizen of his time, wore his religious convictions lightly. He also carried his political opinions with discretion so that there was no impediment to his singing the praises of Charles II, James II, and William and Mary.

The first of Purcell's odes was said to have been composed in 1670, when he was one of Cooke's precocious choirboys. Ten years later, by now one of the official composers, he wrote a 'Song to Welcome home His

[1] 'French hautboys' introduced by Cambert in 1674 were naturalised by 1678 when they were adopted for the Horse Grenadiers. In 1681 Purcell used the oboe in *Swifter Isis* and some years later the instrument, still described as the 'ffranch hoboy', was illustrated in Randle Holme's *Academy of Armory*. After 1690 Purcell used oboes consistently in his larger works, and after 1695 instruction books for the instrument began to appear.

[2] Giovanni Francesco Grossi, or Siface (1653–97), sang in the Papal Choir in Rome before coming to England in 1679. He was appointed to the staff of James II but returned to Italy in 1688, seen off by a complimentary keyboard piece, *Sefauchi's Farewell*, by Purcell.

Majesty from Windsor'. This, and other of the early essays of the same kind, owed a good deal to the form of the verse anthem and used the same resources, of solo voices, chorus, strings, and harpsichord. Welcome songs for the King and for the Duke of York were dutifully produced in the two years following; in *Swifter Isis, Swifter Flow* (1681) the orchestra was enlarged to include flutes and oboe. By 1683 Purcell had got the hang of the thing and in that year the uncovering of the Rye House Plot gave him an opportunity to handle a text which offered dramatic possibilities. This was *Fly, bold rebellion.* In the same year there were odes for the marriage of Princess Anne to Prince George of Denmark and for the celebration of St. Cecilia's Day. In 1685 the King's return from Winchester was marked by a setting of a piece by the dilettante poet and miniature-painter Thomas Flatman. In this, the last of Purcell's works for Charles II, the chorus and orchestra collaborate in a more distinctively Italian manner, and this relationship begins to connect the manner of the Purcellian ode with that of the Handelian oratorios. The chorus 'Welcome, welcome, welcome home', for instance, has a strong flavour of Handel. The brief reign of James II occasioned three welcome songs. In the 1686 ode, *Ye tuneful Muses*, Purcell aptly incorporated the melody of 'Hey then, up we go', which also appeared in that year's edition of *The Dancing Master*, and in every collection of popular tunes up to and beyond its apotheosis in *The Beggar's Opera.* A master of counterpoint Purcell subjected this melody to all kinds of varied treatment after his more serious inclinations had been satisfied in the *fugato* of the prefatory symphony. In 1687 *Sound the Trumpet* appeared; a spacious piece with an extended ground bass to accommodate a tenor solo, and a chaconne that was subsequently transferred to *King Arthur.* In 1689 Queen Mary's birthday was greeted by *Now does the glorious day appear*, of which the text was by Thomas Shadwell, whose political reliability was preferred by the authorities to the brilliance of Dryden. Dryden had lost his laureateship after the Revolution and was replaced by Shadwell.

In all Purcell wrote six birthday odes for Queen Mary. In addition to those by Shadwell he set texts by Durfey, Sedley, and Tate, the latter succeeding Shadwell as Poet Laureate in 1690. In these odes, Purcell, showing increasing mastery over the resources at his disposal and a just balance between the Italian, French, and English styles, reached the height of his powers in the field of ceremonial music. The crowning work of this series was the last, *Come ye sons of Art*, in which the orchestration comprises recorders, oboes, trumpets, drums, as well as strings, and harpsichord.

During this fertile period Purcell also composed the most splendid of his St. Cecilia odes, *Hail bright Cecilia* (Nicholas Brady). In this Purcell was directly addressing the concert-going public of London and he shows almost every facet of his astonishing skills. The texture is held together with a splendour of contrapuntal effect, as in the *fugato* episodes of the overture, of the wide-ranging chorus 'Soul of the World' and of the finale, while once again, in the bass solo 'Wondrous machine', he displays his affection for and conquest of ground bass. Not only is this a study in ground bass, but also an example of the *da capo* aria, which Purcell, together with his brother Daniel, helped to nationalise. The text of this ode gave opportunity for onomatopoeic allusions by instruments, while the spread of mood within the text permitted intensive treatment of ideas covering the area between the festal and the pathetic. Broadly speaking, if—as has been claimed—Purcell may be regarded as a 'Romantic' composer, *Hail, bright Cecilia* (in which he himself sang the alto solo ''Tis Nature's voice') is justification for the proposition.

Other commissions for odes (which may be seen as the effective starting-point for the British chorus-with-orchestra popular tradition and also as the foundation of the English works of this nature by Handel) included one in 1689 for Louis Maidwell's school, one in 1690 for the Society of Yorkshiremen in London, and another for the centenary ode, *Great parent, hail*, for Trinity College, Dublin. For this the words were by Nahum Tate, who was a graduate of the College.

On one side of the ode lay the province of church music, on the other that of what in England was loosely called Opera. The fact that these were all closely inter-related is one reason why neither Purcell nor any of his contemporaries arrived at one consistent, extended, architectonic form. The undogmatic attitudes that created this condition and were engendered by it resulted in the virtual still-birth of *dramma per musica* in England and in the eventual magnificent compromise of the Handelian oratorio. Handel owed much to Purcell, but both were indebted to those patrons of the closing years of the seventeenth century who appreciated both drama and music but preferred that the one should not unduly impede the other. Charles II turned his Chapel into a concert-room (for different reasons neither James II nor William approved the practice) and when music was added to a play it was usually on the understanding that it was incidental. Purcell, however, was a great dramatic composer: possibly the greatest who never in fact composed an opera.

The first six years of the reign of William and Mary constitute, perhaps, the most critical period in British music, for during this time the overall pattern of cultural life which still obtains was established. Patronage, though still nominally vested in the Court and the aristocracy, passed for practical purposes into the hands of the bourgeoisie. In this pattern opera found no lasting place: the comedy of manners, edged with satire and laced with salacity, did; so too did the spectacular musical. After his first engagement in the theatre in 1680, which produced, among other movements for Nathaniel Lee's *Theodosius*, a fine sacrificial scene which has been salvaged as a viable concert item in a modern edition, Purcell contributed a variety of songs, duets, occasional choruses, overtures and dances, to some forty plays of which the authors included Aphra Behn, Dryden, Settle, Durfey, Congreve, Southerne, and Crowne, and of which the plots were based sometimes on Shakespeare and once on Molière (*The Female Vertuoso*, from *Les Femmes savantes*, by Thomas Wright). The fertility of Purcell's invention brought forth movements such as the Trumpet Overture to *The Indian Queen*; the dances for *Abdelazer*—the rondeau of which is the basis of Britten's *Young Person's Guide to the Orchestra*; songs like 'Music for a while' (*Oedipus*), 'Nymphs and Shepherds' (*The Libertine*) and 'I'll sail upon the dog-star' (*A Fool's Preferment*); and such consistent yet varied episodes as appeared in *Timon of Athens* and *The Indian Queen*. This music was conceived in the first place as entertainment (patrons were in the habit of going to the theatre early to listen to musical performances in no way connected with the subject of the play). Thus we may discover an affinity between the famous *Abdelazer* rondeau, and a popular jig, Downfall of the Ginn'[1] [Ex. 14]. Secondly it fulfilled the ancient function

14.

of inducing a state of fantasy. Purcell was equal to any situation. His overtures, not dramatically relevant, were in themselves of high musical interest; his songs could have the irresistible, negligent charm of 'I attempt from love's sickness to fly', the intimate passion of the duet 'My dearest, my fairest' (*Pausanias*); or the popular, ballad idiom of 'Twas within a furlong of Edinboro' Town' (*The Mock Marriage*); while the interpolated Masques—as in *The Indian Queen* and *Timon of Athens*—could effectively evoke both the dramatic and the exotic.

[1] From *The Third Book of the Most Celebrated Jiggs, Lancashire Hornpipes, Scotch and Highland Lilts, Northern Frisks, Morris's* . . . (J. Walsh, *c.* 1736).

Purcell moved into the theatrical field along traditional lines. He attempted little that had not been attempted before, except in the application and expansion of the dramatic possibilities inherent in a richer and more varied style. In three works Purcell almost arrived at an opera. If *Dido and Aeneas* (*c.* 1689), *King Arthur* (1691), and *The Fairy Queen* (1692) are to be numbered—as they are—among the classics of opera it is not because they are operas, but because each is instinct with the genius of a composer whose natural capacity for exposing and analysing the human situation in terms of music was so much greater than any particular principles of construction could contain. Eager, ebullient, energetic, Purcell moved from comedy to tragedy and met the challenge of public taste with a sympathetic independence that raised him to a pinnacle of fame and affection, and he resolved his imaginative problems by paradox. There is an analogy of outlook between Purcell and Mozart (who balanced conflicting styles and wrought a masterpiece out of the improbabilities of *Die Zauberflöte*). Purcell also possessed the objectivity of Mozart, a similar skill in concentrating meaning within a melodic phrase, and a comparable sense of opportunism. He was, however, so far as may be judged, somewhat better at organising his private affairs. Purcell accepted conditions as they were; in so doing he captured the adventurousness of an epoch, while leaving his comment on the general fate of humanity in terms that transcended its commonplaces. Some part of this achievement relates to the function of the musician in post-Restoration England. The effective principle was that of craftsmanship. The methods of Henry Cooke (inherited from long tradition) led to competence in execution on many fronts.

A commission to compose a score for a school for girls called for the same display of musicianship as any other. For a musico-dramatic work for amateurs in general there were helpful examples in the existing repertoire. Thus *Dido and Aeneas* is in the line of Jacobean masques, on the one hand, and of the derivative but more plot-conscious *Cupid and Death* and *Venus and Adonis* on the other. So far as girls' schools were concerned there was a precedent in Thomas Dufett's *Beauties Triumph*, which had been compiled for Jeffery Banister's and James Hart's 'New Boarding School' in Chelsea in 1676.

The libretto for *Dido and Aeneas* was written by Nahum Tate. The court scenes, and the episodes of witches and of sailors, were ingrained in English amateur—and professional—theatricals. Storms and hunting scenes were generally commonplace, and, if he so desired, Purcell had effective music by Locke and Blow to guide him. The picturesque details are etched in (with his miniscule ensemble of strings and harpsichord) with enough realism to convince the audience of the appositeness of the music but with sufficient imagination to indicate a strong perception of the value of allusiveness. Thus the witches' dances, compounded from Locke and Lully, carry the idea of sinister fate more effectively than the vocal music assigned to the witches. In the forefront the witches are figures of comedy, but instrumental rhythms and gestures dispel the comedy. The music of the Sailors in Act III is as bouncy as their mood and turns a convention in instrumental music—illustrated by examples from Blow and Ziani[1]—into a kind of folk-song. Purcell had a ready talent for scene-setting (perhaps the most effective example is the premonitory flourish of the hunting motiv at the end of Act I); but *Dido and Aeneas* stands out less by the exercise of this talent than by the treatment of the principal characters and by the unification of the whole work by comprehensive tonal schemes. In respect of the latter the first Act centres on C minor-major, the second on F minor-major and D minor-major and the third on B flat major-G minor.

Dido and Aeneas is a fragile masterpiece. Fortuitously assembled around a libretto that is more purposeful and effective for the kind of occasion for which it was constructed[2] than is often allowed, it eludes permanence. It has the quality of a dream—the Restoration 'opera' deliberately stood at one or more remove from realism—but one in which the crisis holds an abiding relevance. The death of Dido is no tragedy, but it has an aching poignance: the end of love is more painful than the end of life and it is this particular pain which Purcell suspends above his most famous ground bass. The method is Italian but the treatment is English. Dido's Lament—like the whole of the opera—is an expansion of speech into music. This was the end at which the Restoration composer aimed. Purcell achieved it more effectively and consistently than the majority of his contemporaries. Not only did he appreciate the significance of verbal rhythm and inflection and the hidden currents of emotion that run beneath the surface of the word but he understood equally the emotive properties of melody. Thus his vocal melodies are viable in themselves, even though their richness only stands fully revealed when drawn through the logical processes of speech. 'When I am laid in earth' exemplifies this: wordless and orchestrated in un-Purcellian timbres it serves as an eloquent national homage piece; but only when it is sung does it reach finality.

In 1690 Purcell was brought into collaboration with Dryden for the first time in respect of a piece for the theatre. This was *Amphitryon* and the author, as he noted in his Introduction, was impressed by the reception given to the music by 'the numerous Quire of Fair Ladies' who attended

[1] See quotation from *Venus & Adonis* (Blow) and *La schiava fortunata* (Ziani) in J. A. Westrup, *Purcell*, 1937, p. 119.

[2] *Dido and Aeneas* was based on an earlier work by Tate, *Brutus of Alba*, 1678.

the performance. He invited Purcell, therefore, to take up the libretto of *King Arthur*, a work which was intended to be operatic from the start. Dryden was the only important man of letters in England at that time who was genuinely interested in the potentialities of opera as an art-form. His views are expressed in the Preface to *Albion and Albanius*, a patriotic piece designed (with Betterton's aid in respect of the machines) for Charles II, but not performed until James II was on the throne, and at a most unfortunate time—during the Monmouth rebellion. Dryden accepted the conventions both of Italian and French opera but appreciated the fact of the popularity of pieces such as *The Tempest* (success of which stimulated him in the first place to try his hand at an opera), and, doubting whether any Englishman had the necessary skill to compose an effective score for *Albion and Albanius*, invited Louis Grabu to try to do so. He had misgivings, but after the performance he went out of his way to cry up 'Monsieur Grabut . . . [who] has so exactly expressed my sense in all places where I intended to move the passions that he seems to have entered into my thoughts and to have been the poet as well as the composer. This, I say, not to flatter him, but to do him right; because amongst some English musicians, and their scholars who are sure to judge after them, the imputation of being a Frenchman is enough to make a party who maliciously endeavour to decry him.[1] But the knowledge of Latin and Italian poets, both which he possesses, besides his skill in music and his being acquainted with all the performances of the French operas, adding to these the good sense to which he is born, have raised him to a degree above any man who shall pretend to be his rival upon our stage. When any of our countrymen excel him, I shall be glad, for the sake of old England, to be shown my error; in the meantime, let virtue be commended, though in the person of a stranger.'

Grabu failed to measure up to Dryden's protestations. He was by any standards a dull composer and his inability to set English words was self-evident. A satirical poem on the subject of *Albion and Albanius* is quoted by Hawkins.[2] At the same time the Chaconne with which Grabu concluded the second Act and other dances, as well as the air for 'Fame', were not without their influence on Purcell.[3] In 1686 Lully's *Cadmus et Hermione*[4] was given in London by a French company, but without arousing more than the passing interest indicated in a letter from Pere-

[1] Later in the *Preface* Dryden writes: '. . . though the enemies of the composer are not few, and that there is a party formed against him of his own profession, I hope, and am persuaded that this prejudice will turn in the end to his advantage'.

[2] *History*, IV, pp. 396–7.

[3] See E. J Dent, *Foundations of English Opera*, 1928, pp. 166–70.

[4] A dance from this work was borrowed by Purcell and inserted in the scene of *The Tempest* where it follows 'Arise, ye subterranean winds'.

grine Bertie to the Countess of Rutland: the music was satisfactory, but the spectacle was inferior. This was top of the list of priorities in the London theatre, and next was the text. The more enlightened concern of Dryden for operatic properties was therefore valuable to Purcell who in 1691 found the fullest opportunity he had so far had in the design of *King Arthur*.

The text, first written as sequel to *Albion and Albanius*, was both fantastic and heroic. It allowed Purcell to invade the realm of fairyland, and the spirits of Grimbald and Philidel (the one of earth, the other of air) and their attendants provoked delicious light-hearted, yet ethereal music,

15.

[Ex. 15] that seems the idealisation of the pastoral strain of which Purcell was equally the master [Ex. 16]. A sense of landscape (apparent in the

16.

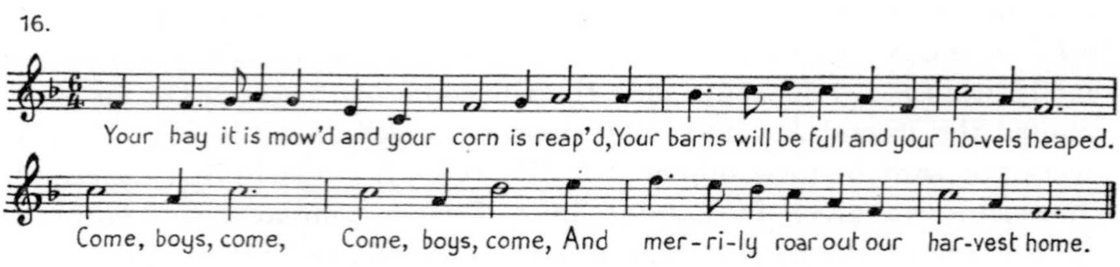

English madrigal but therein circumscribed by the limits of form and forces) pervades many of Purcell's scores. In the third Act of *King Arthur* he explores the element of *Antartica*, not only by means of vocal and instrumental *tremolo* but also of harmony. In his selection of chords—the result of contrapuntal emancipation but also of a capacity to perceive the cumulative effect in terms of general and particular colour—Purcell pays tribute to the individuality of his great English predecessors and at the same time symbolises his own strength of thought. While *King Arthur* thus captivates the imaginative ear by its variegation, it also strikes the common understanding. Purcell, and this is one of his virtues, never neglected his social context for long. Thus seventeenth-century patriotism was more than adequately served by the vigour and self-confidence of 'Come if you dare' and the gentler movement of 'Fairest Isle.' Both songs quickly passed into the national heritage.

King Arthur was a compromise between what Dryden thought an opera should be and what the public wanted. Thus it is inconsistent plot-wise and of necessity sporadically exotic. The fifth Act is a masque, comprising discontinuous episodes. Purcell's original score did not survive as a whole so it is not possible to recreate the work with any certainty of authenticity. At the same time it is to be performed and understood as a musico-dramatic unity. This is not so in the case of the remaining quasi-operas. *The Fairy Queen* is known by excerpts, especially by a suite of dances that lead straight to the heart of the matter. For *The Fairy Queen* was a sequence of masques and antimasques draped loosely round a typical paraphrase of Shakespeare's *A Midsummer Night's Dream*, which in its original form contained many elements also exploited in the Jacobean masque. *The Fairy Queen* is plotless. But it is full of lively characters, some animal, some human, others mythological. Purcell sets out an engaging sequence of character-sketches. These are in the familiar forms of song—sometimes with appended chorus, duet, dance, and overture or symphony. With Purcell one should never look for what is not there. In a show-piece such as *The Fairy Queen* the end was entertainment to which aesthetic theories had little relevance. Dryden makes it quite clear that the true author of an opera was the librettist. The composer was an auxiliary. Purcell was too busy to complain at this state of affairs even if he had felt so inclined. His job was to provide music: and this he did with a prodigality that exasperates. This prodigality, of course, was part of the Baroque, and no composer was more truly Baroque than Purcell. The character, however, is modified. Purcell showed what is frequently claimed to be properly English—a sense of humour.

The Fairy Queen spills over into many fields. There is music for night, which includes a languishing chorus akin to the finale of *Dido*, and a dance which, taking a point from Locke, is a canon 4 in 2. There is music for morning—for the sun-god Phoebus—of which the overture is exhilarated by an introductory flourish on the kettle-drums. The seasons of the year are reviewed, the personification of winter being accomplished through an ingenious disposition of a chromatic-scale ground that sooner or later grips every part in the score. There is a Falstaffian scene involving a drunken poet and a brace of tormenting fairies; another familiar set-piece in the Corydon and Mopsa hay- and love-making episode; an exotic diversion in a Chinese episode; and visits to animal farm which bring up an elegant piece for swans and a grotesque dance for monkeys which, as other pieces of informal ballet, stem from the pantomimic element embedded in English medieval music and regularised by the long tradition of the masque. *The Fairy Queen* also includes the tender simplicity of 'If love's a sweet passion' and the Handelian scintillation of 'Hark the ech'ing air.' It is fair to assume that among the audience that first saw *The Fairy Queen* at Dorset Gardens in the spring of 1692 there was no one who did not feel that at some point in the performance there was music peculiarly agreeable to his personal taste. The first performance cost a great deal of money and the anonymous author contrasted the state-subsidised production in other countries with that in England which depended on private initiative.[1] Nevertheless, the work was re-polished and several times repeated during the next year.

The standard of acting in the London theatre was high; that of dancing was passable; but insofar as the art of singing was concerned there was nothing comparable to the virtuosity of the Italians. 'I despair', wrote the author of *The Fairy Queen*, 'of ever having as good voices among us, as they have in Italy.' The ballad-type songs of Purcell—engaging in their simplicity and directness—suited native singers and set a pattern which Handel and Arne followed. But Purcell's optimism that singers of high calibre would appear if they had the right kind of music to sing is indicated by his thorough adoption of Italian manners in his later dramatic pieces, especially in the songs and arias (including the *da capo* formula) in *The Indian Queen* and *The Tempest*.

Purcell's dramatic music is the finest written by any English composer. It contains sensibility, humour, sympathy. It is at once comprehensible and elusive; of its period but transcending it. It has elegance and scholarship, but it is spontaneous and often vulgar. It sprawls over forty pieces, each of which was cooked up for a mixed audience. It is a beginning and an ending. From the point at which Purcell left it English opera might have developed. That it did not was due to lack of creative talents in part and to the pressures of new patronage. After Purcell's death royal interest in music was casual: the pulse-strings of the art were operated by private hands. The British thereafter got the music they deserved. Purcell came in when music was being adjusted to the new pattern of society. He helped to establish it in a fresh situation. In the widest sense he was a popular composer; the first great English master who was so to be described.

[1] See Westrup, op. cit., p. 75.

Purcell was in many ways a conservative. That is to say, he conserved. This was part of his strength. Thus in deference to the example of Locke and Christopher Gibbons[1] and against the expressed views of Charles II, he wrote fantasias and *In Nomines*. The fantasias (three in three, nine in four, and one in five parts), composed in 1680, were purely English. They preserved the intimacies of the involved counterpoint that had delighted generations of private musicians, yet continued the humanistic impulses contained in the moods mirrored in the expressionistic harmonies and changes of texture of Locke. The craftsman's pleasure in the solution of specifically technical problems is apparent in the *Fantasia upon one note*, in the two severe *In Nomines* (in six and seven parts respectively), and in the Chaconne in G minor (a key frequently used by Purcell) which is in the same manuscript as the fantasias.

The powerful pull of English expressionism as developed through the calculated disposition of activating dissonance marks all Purcell's work. Thus while the anthems pass through the French and Italianate phases which characterised the extended verse anthem, the listener is frequently drawn to evocative passages that depend for their dramatic relevance on a reconsideration of earlier statements of musical fact. [Ex.

17.

[1] The three-part Fantasias by Locke and Gibbons in B.M. Add. Ms. 31635 bear the note 'All the Fanta in this book of Mr. Locks Exd. by Mr. Purcell's score book.' The final item in the book is by 'M. Henry Purcell'. That Purcell had studied the consort music of Gibbons or Coperario, and even copied some, is adduced by Thurston Dart in Purcell and Bach', *Mus. T.*, 1963, p. 31.

17]. Beside Purcell, of course, stood John Blow. Outside the formal anthem for the Royal Chapel or the Abbey[1] Purcell also provided abundant material for private use. There are sacred songs (of which *The Blessed Virgin's Expostulation* and the *Evening Hymn* were published in Playford's *Harmonia Sacra*, I, 1685, II, 1693) to texts by Tate, Cowley, George Herbert, and Bishop William Fuller; in which all the resources of the developed lyrical and dramatic solo song are exposed; but also stricter canons and metrical psalms; and there is one scena which acts as another link between the sacred dramatic dialogue of the mid-seventeenth century and the oratorio of Handel. This is 'In guilty night' (*Saul and the Witch at Endor*), an extension of the treatment of the same subject by Lanier and/or Ramsey.

Purcell's mastery of vocal music was supreme, and his solo songs, ranging from the easy charm of Colonel Heveningham's 'If music be the food of love' (three settings) or Durfey's 'On the brow of Richmond Hill', across the dramatic insight of 'From silent shades' (a supremely sympathetic exposition of the idea of the traditional 'mad' song) to the funereal ecstacies of the elegies, are among the undisputed masterpieces. Yet they represent the end of the tradition that had started far back in the sixteenth century. Beyond Purcell the solo song generally became stylised or found its level in the field of popular music. Song in domestic experience was beginning to feel the stern competition of instrumental music.

The Italian sonata was soon to sweep the market. Purcell anticipated this and bent the mood of English chamber music to relative conformity with new principles in the twelve *Sonatas of three partes: two violins and bass: to the organ or harpsichord* of 1683. Without dance movements these works, admitting the significance of the keyboard instrument, are of the *Sonata da Chiesa* pattern. Here the twenty-four year old Purcell laid out his intention. He 'faithfully endeavour'd a just imitation of the most fam'd Italian Masters . . . He is not asham'd to own his unskilfulness in the Italian Language; but that's the unhappiness of his Education, which cannot justly be accounted his fault, however he thinks he may warrantably affirm, that he is not mistaken in the power of the Italian Notes, or elegancy of their Compositions, which he would recommend to the English Artists . . . It remains only that the English Practitioner be enform'd, that he will find a few terms of Art perhaps unusual to him, the chief of which are these following: *Adagio* and *Grave* which impart nothing but a very slow movement: *Presto Largo*, *Poco Largo*, or *Largo* by itself, a middle movement: *Allegro*, and *Vivace*, a very brisk, swift, or fast movement: *Piano*, soft.'

[1] In respect of performing practice see Watkins Shaw, 'Purcell's Bell Anthem and its Performance', *Mus. T.*, 1959, pp. 285–6.

In 1697 Purcell's widow published a second set of ten such Sonatas (described as for four parts, only because the harpsichord was now regarded as independent). Of them, the ninth, known as the 'Golden' Sonata, is familiar.

One great age of British music was preluded by the issue of *Musica Transalpina*. A hundred years later a fresh influence from Italy provided the stimulus for another notable era.

8

The Age of Handel

Lament for Purcell

THERE HAVE been few musicians whose deaths have been more deeply mourned than that of Henry Purcell; his supremacy in England was regarded as absolute. On 28 November 1695 the *Post Boy* noted: 'Dr. Purcel was Interred at Westminster on Tuesday night in a magnificent manner. He is much lamented, being a very great Master of Musick'. A fortnight later Gottfried Finger—a Moravian composer working in London since 1685—gave a memorial concert at the Concert Rooms in York Buildings which included his *Mr. Purcel's Farewel* ('with other variety of Musick'). A little later John Dryden wrote his *Ode on the Death of Mr. Henry Purcell.* Other poets paid their tribute. The most affecting was that of Henry Hall, formerly organist at Exeter and subsequently of Hereford Cathedral, and a composer of some stature.[1]

To the Memory of my Dear Friend Mr. Henry Purcell
Hail! and for ever hail, Harmonious Shade!
I lov'd thee Living, and admire thee Dead,
Apollo's keep at once our Souls did strike;
We learnt together, but not learnt alike:
Though equal care our Master might bestow,
Yet only *Purcell* e're shall equal *Blow*:
For thou by Heaven for wondrous things design'd
Left'st thy companion far behind.
Sometimes a HERO *in an Age appears*;
But scarce a PURCELL *in a Thousand Years.*[2]

[1] See Rev. Arthur Bedford, *The Great Abuse of Musick*, ded. to the S.P.C.K., London, 1711, p. 219: 'Dr. *Blow*, and Mr. *Henry Hall*, have not left their equals behind them'; and example of Hall's work on pp. 293–4.

[2] *Orpheus Britannicus I*, 1698. Hall contributed another poem to *Orpheus Britannicus II*. See also Franklin B. Zimmerman, 'Poets in Praise of Purcell', *Mus. T.*, 1959, pp. 526–8.

Hall had been a fellow-chorister with Purcell in the Chapel Royal. In a number of testimonials to the worth of Purcell the names of Giovanni Bassani and his pupil Corelli were introduced, symbolising the current fashion in instrumental music. The conservatives deplored the new influence from Italy and, mistakenly, held up Purcell as a defender of the narrow nationalism that they preached. Thus lamented Rev. Arthur Bedford: 'Our *Musick* began to equal that of the *Italians*, and exceed all others. Our *Purcel* was the Delight of the Nation, and the Wonder of the World, & the Character of Dr. *Blow* was but little inferior to him. But when we made not that use thereof which we ought, it pleas'd *God* to show his Resentment, & put a *Stop* to our Progres, by taking away our *Purcel* in the Prime of his Age, & Dr. *Blow* soon after. We all lamented our Misfortunes, but never consider'd them as Judgments for the *Abuse* of this *Science*; so that instead of growing better we grew worse and worse. Now therefore *Musick* declines as fast as it did improve before'.[1]

Purcell, of course, had acclimatised Italian style without sacrificing the virtues that reposed in the English tradition. The tragedy for English music was that he did not live long enough to overlap the London career of Handel. So far as composition was concerned the interregnum between the death of Purcell and the coming of Handel was largely a time of lost opportunity: so far as the general condition of music in society was concerned it was quite otherwise. It was, indeed, an era of remarkable expansion. The release of energy initiated at the Restoration and the extension of cultural opportunities made possible by a wider sharing of the national wealth, the development of technical processes and the pattern of a more democratised society, all led to an infinitely broader base for the cultivation of music.

The Music Trade

By far the most important development in the propagation of music was in the field of publication. Between 1650 and 1686 this was largely monopolised by John Playford, who not only issued new works but also retailed those in print from the beginning of the seventeenth century as well as many collections of foreign origin. For the most part Playford, employing Thomas Harper, William Godbid—whose widow Anne continued in business with Playford's nephew John—and others, published works printed from movable type distinguished by lozenge-shaped notes. John Playford I was succeeded by his son Henry, in partnership with Richard Carr. Henry Playford and Carr remained in business until 1707 and among

[1] Bedford, op. cit., p. 196.

their principal publications were Purcell's Sonatas, the St. Cecilia music of 1697, *A Choice Collection of lessons for the Harpsichord or Spinnet* (1696), *Orpheus Britannicus*, and *Amphion Anglicus* (1700). The younger Playford suffered more competition than had his father and, reviewing other prospects for profitable enterprise, went into concert promotion both in London and Oxford and expanded his business by dealing also in pictures and prints. Other publishers contemporary with Henry Playford were Samuel and Benjamin Sprint, John Hudgebut, John Clarke, John Crouch, and Thomas Cross, while John Hare, John Young, John Cullen, and John Walsh all set up their businesses before Playford's was wound up.

Thomas Cross (son of the engraver Thomas Cross, *c.* 1644–85?) regularised the process of engraving music from metal plates, his earliest known work being Purcell's Sonatas of 1683, which he engraved for John Playford. For nearly half a century Cross set a standard in engraving that was not surpassed and rarely equalled by any of his contemporaries. From the publisher's point of view the value of engraving lay in its cheapness. John Walsh took full advantage of this technological development and, showing enterprise in every direction, rapidly established an unassailable position. Coming into the field in 1695 and setting up at the Golden Harp and Hautboy, off the Strand, Walsh had an intuitive grasp of the principles of private enterprise. Having surveyed the potential market he issued numerous cheap instruction books, of music for flute, violin, and voice; then he followed with anthologies of songs, harpsichord pieces, excerpts from theatre pieces, and, in due course, operas. He published sonatas (including those of Corelli) and other chamber music, and by 1703 his catalogue included almost a hundred items. In twenty-five years the number of Walsh's publications rose to six hundred, and his fortune was made when he began thoroughly to exploit the music of Handel. When Walsh enjoyed his first spectacular success with the first issue of *Arie dell' Opera di Rinaldo* Handel observed that he would prefer that the next time he and Walsh should change their functions. Walsh recognised the value of advertisement and the utility of musical periodicals (e.g. *The Monthly Mask of Vocal Music* and *Harmonia Anglicana*). He imported foreign publications and, when it was practicable, pirated editions. Since competition was keen—there being perhaps some twenty other music publishing enterprises—Walsh kept his prices down and by so doing made a vast range of music more generally available than ever before. His business career spanned the years between 1695 and 1736. He was succeeded by his son John who continued the concern for another thirty years, when it was handed over to William Randall and John Abell.

There was also a reasonable prosperity in the manufacture, retail, and maintenance of musical instruments. Luke Pippard, one of John

Walsh's apprentices, set up such a business in Covent Garden in convenient proximity to Will's, Tom's, Button's, and Bickerstaff's Coffee Houses. John Young had premises at the west end of St. Paul's Churchyard. Ralph Agutter—who advertised *Twelve Sonatas (newly come over from Rome) in 3 parts: Composed by Signeur Arcangelo Corelli* in September 1695—occupied a house near the Concert Room in York Buildings, off the Strand. In 1707 Agutter, no doubt feeling the keen breeze of competition, left London to explore new territory where concert life at least was beginning to flourish. On 13 May the *Edinburgh Currant* advertised:

'Ralph Agutter of London, lately come to Edinburgh, Musical Instrument-maker, is to be found at Widow Pool's, perfumer of gloves, at her house in Stonelaw's Close, a little below the Steps; makes the Violin, Bass Violin, Tenor Violin, the Viol de Gambo, the Lute Quiver, the Trumpet Marine, the Harp; and mendeth and putteth in order and stringeth all those instruments as fine as any man whatsoever in the three kingdoms, or elsewhere, and maketh the Virginal, Spinnet, and Harpsichord, all at reasonable rates.'[1]

The general pattern of musical life at this time was determined by the public concert, to the organisation of which the citizens and musicians of London had devoted a large part of their superfluous energies. The professional went into this field of activity with the intention of making money. Not only were fees to be picked up and profits to be accumulated by the principals, but there was opportunity for useful publicity (which was assisted by the newspapers) and for prospecting for pupils. The amateurs were able to keep in touch with musical developments in general and to hear the best virtuosi from abroad. In increasing numbers performers, singers, and composers from all parts of Europe flocked to England, and sometimes went on to Scotland or to Ireland.

Banister was the pioneer of the public concert, but his musical evenings were weighted on the social side. Patrons went not only to listen but also to take part. A notable amateur participant in the early musical meetings was Ben Wallington, who 'got the reputation of a notable bass voice, . . . set up for a composer, and has some songs in print.'[2] Concerts were given in dancing schools and taverns—the latter providing accommodation for musical societies for many years to come, and in the Halls of the City Companies. The St. Cecilia's Day odes were performed in the

[1] Quoted by R. Chambers, *Domestic Annals of Scotland*, 3 vols., W. and R. Chambers, Edinburgh and London, 1861, III, pp. 325–6. In 1712 Agutter moved to Newcastle upon Tyne, where he had family connections: see *Newcastle Courant*, 30 April 1712.

[2] Roger North, op. cit., pp. 107–8. Songs by Wallington were published in Playford's *The Musical Companion*, 1673, and other similar works.

Hall of the Stationer's Company. Supplementing these entertainments were private functions in the town houses of the nobility, some of whom engaged musical advisers who made themselves responsible for the hire of orchestral players. Old Thomas Mace had proposed the erection of a concert-room in *Musick's Monument*: his specification was characteristically ingenious and impracticable. It was not until 1685 that premises were adapted for the purpose of concert-giving. These were in York Buildings, and the initiative came from a group of musicians who were 'determined to take the business [of promotion] into their own hands.'[1] By the time of Purcell's death York Buildings was a focal point for music-making, and sometimes served as a supplementary salon to the Court, it being on occasion convenient to entertain visiting royalty there. A rival music-meeting, derived from that formerly held in conjunction with York Buildings in Bow Street, was set up in Charles Street in 1692. Away from the centre there were concert-rooms at Sadler's Wells, at Lambeth Wells, and Richmond Wells, and at Islington; and when the race-meetings took place in Nottingham some of the evenings were filled in by musical performances; while concert interludes (to develop into the interpolated concerto performances of Handel's oratorios) were included in theatrical performances.

Britain and Europe

Baltzar and Matteis paved the way for foreign artists. Among those who followed and established themselves in London were Gerhard Diessener, Gottfried Finger, Johann Wolfgang Franck, and John Christopher Pepusch. Finger, who was a prominent member of the musical community in London, and, like Matteis, composed a St. Cecilia's Day ode, was for some time director of the concerts at York Buildings. He went back to Germany in 1702, piqued by being placed after John Weldon, John Eccles, and Daniel Purcell, in a competition for the setting of Congreve's *The Judgement of Paris*. Franck, formerly at the Court of Ansbach and a successful composer of operas for the Hamburg theatre, spent a season in charge of the Charles Street concerts.

Pepusch, son of a clergyman in Berlin, arrived in London about 1700, and after a period of free-lance work established himself as a regular theatre musician, superintending and adapting works for Drury Lane and (after 1713) Lincoln's Inn Fields Theatres; as a Kapellmeister, being engaged in that capacity part-time by the Duke of Chandos in 1712; as a scholar—he was one of the founder members of the Academy of Ancient

[1] North, op. cit., p. 112.

Music in 1710 and a zealous student of musical history and theory; and as a teacher, his instructions being contained in *A Treatise on Harmony, containing the chief Rules for composing in two, three, and four parts*, issued anonymously in 1730 and, with revisions, in 1731. In 1713 he became a Doctor of Music at Oxford University, his exercise a timely ode for the Peace of Utrecht. A voluminous composer, Pepusch left many airs, songs,[1] catches, sonatas, concertos, and Latin motets; but his principal claim on posterity is in his arrangements for *The Beggar's Opera* of 1728. In 1737 Pepusch became organist of the Charterhouse. An amiable man and a fine teacher —as the long and distinguished list of his pupils testifies—Pepusch was conscious of the educational responsibility of the musician. Thus, recognising the need for improvement in the general standard of violin playing, he published duets for two violins intended as prefatory exercises to the sonatas of Corelli which he edited for Walsh. He made an abortive attempt to set up a Music School for promising children[2] (an offshoot of the Academy of Ancient Music and a forerunner of the Royal Academy of Music). And, but for the accident of shipwreck, would have joined Dr. Berkeley in his project in the Bermudas in 1724. Pepusch was an honoured member of the musical community but he did not possess the temperament to set the Thames on fire. That, perhaps, made for a comfortable life: so too did his wife's fortune of £10,000.

Among other German visitors during the last years of the seventeenth century were August Kühnel, the viol da gamba player of Zeitz and Kassel, and Jacob Kremberg, who appeared at a concert of 'new music' at Hickford's Dancing School in 1697. The Germans not only played their own works, but also frequently prided themselves on their skill in propagating Italian music. Among the large number of Italians who appeared at concerts (their names were not always given in newspaper announcements) the most conspicuous were the opera singer Margarita de l'Epine, who arrived in 1693, stayed on and eventually married Dr. Pepusch in 1718; Francesco Geminiani, a pupil of Corelli who did more than anyone to build up the Corelli cult in Britain after his arrival in 1714; and Pier Francesco Tosi, who established himself as a singing-teacher and concert impresario in London in 1718. Niccola Haym, an Italian cellist and librettist of German descent, took up residence in London at the beginning of the eighteenth century and among other functions fulfilled that of musical director to the second Duke of Bedford.

A letter from Haym to Humfrey Wanley of 14 June 1705 relates to a concert held in the house of Gasparo Visconti, an Italian violinist resi-

[1] Including two sets of *Six English Cantatas*, words by John Hughes and others (*c.* 1710 and 1720).

[2] See Hawkins, *History*, V, p. 347.

dent in London and usually known as Gasparini (hence some confusion with Francesco Gasparini). In a further letter of 30 August Haym asks Wanley for the return of some sonatas for organ by Bernardo Pasquini as well as a cantata of his own.[1] In a manuscript collection, dated 1706, now in the possession of the Leeds City Library but formerly the property of Lord Irwin (Edward Machel Irwin, 1686–1714), of Temple Newsam, Leeds, there are arias by Giuseppe Montuoli, of whom Irwin may have been a pupil. The gentry were being introduced to a wide variety of Italian music.

British musicians were by no means aggravated by the influx o foreign colleagues and rivals. They provided their own virtuosi, among whom the most famous was John Shore, the trumpeter, whose playing inspired the trumpet obbligati of Purcell; while composers such as Nicholas Staggins, Vaughan Richardson, William Turner, William Croft, John Eccles, John Blow, John Barrett, Daniel and Henry Purcell provided a large part of the concert repertoire. But the most powerful influence was that of Corelli, who acquired a higher reputation, and one that lasted longer, than anywhere else in Europe.

It is possible that Matteis first played sonatas by Corelli in public in London. These sonatas had, of course, become a regular part of the programmes at Thomas Britton's; while Thomas Shuttleworth, of Spitalfields made copies of them before they were available in print in England, and gave to his more talented son Obadiah (a virtuoso organist) an enthusiasm for this master.[2] Niccola Haym also promoted the cause of Corelli and prepared an edition of his sonatas for Estienne Roger of Amsterdam. A striking testimony to the attraction of the English to Corelli is the career of James Sherard, who, as Giacomo Sherard, in 1701 and 1711 published sets of Sonatas for two violins and bass with Roger that drew from Hawkins the reasonable comment that 'an ordinary judge, not knowing that they were the work of another, might mistake [them] for compositions of this great master.'[3] Sherard, a native of Leicestershire and brother of the scientist William, was a doctor and botanist of distinction and a Fellow of the Royal Society. Music was his hobby and, since he was acquainted with the Duke of Bedford, it is likely that his introduction to Estienne Roger, who published his Sonatas, was through Haym.

It is probably no more than coincidence that another Englishman of the school of Corelli also came from Leicestershire. This was Robert

[1] See Haym's letters in B.M. Harl. Ms. 3779.

[2] So Obadiah Shuttleworth published in 1726 *Two Concertos being the first and eleventh solos of A. Corelli, as they are made into concerto's . . .*

[3] Op. cit., II, 1875 edn., pp. 678 and 806.

Valentine, one of a large and influential dynasty of musicians settled in the city of Leicester by 1683. Robert, son of Thomas Valentine, musician and freeman, appears to have spent the greater part of his working life abroad. In the early years of the eighteenth century it seems that he was patronised by Sir Thomas Samwell, a landowner of Northamptonshire and later Member of Parliament for Coventry. Samwell was a dedicated lover of music and art and toured extensively in Europe, penetrating as far as Dresden where he collected a portrait of the court musician Pierre Bufardin. There is evidence to suggest that Robert Valentine came across a number of German composers of the early eighteenth century, particularly those, like Reinart, Schickard, Seits, and Quantz, who wrote for the flute, on which Valentine himself was an expert performer.[1] If so it may well have been in the company of Samwell, to whom Valentine dedicated his Opus II Sonatas for flute (or violin) and cembalo. These were published in Rome in 1708, the composer being designated as Roberto Valentine, *inglese*, when the Sonatas were reissued a year or two later in Amsterdam. Valentine worked for some years in Rome and a set of divertimenti for two flutes[2] dedicated to Giovanni Gastone, Grand Duke of Tuscany, shows acquaintance with one of Handel's Italian benefactors. Valentine was an agreeable composer with a facility for meeting the requirements of the expanding company of amateur flautists and oboists, and his works were published in Rome, Amsterdam, and in London, while the disposition of extant manuscripts in Sweden and Northern Germany shows that he enjoyed a general and enviable popularity during his lifetime. Valentine made no pretension to profundity, but had a considerable talent for developing charming melodic outlines. these were often flown over the lightest of harmonic supports, as shown, for example, in the last movement of a flute (or oboe) concerto [Ex. 1].

1.

But the Italianate Valentine was not unmindful of the succinct virtues of English melody, which was brought to the notice of German amateurs in this manner: [Ex. 2]. A composer, and violinist, who alternated between England and Italy—sometimes it was suggested as a Secret Service agent—

[1] See p. 372 fn. 2.
[2] Assisi, Biblioteca Communale, A. fol. 2.

was William Corbett, whose travels are indicated in the titles of his Opus VIII Concertos, otherwise known as *Le Bizarrerie Universali.*[1]

2.

The process of adaptation of Italian instrumental style and the institution of Italian opera in England were not easily achieved. The established English composers of the transitional period were content to follow their own inclinations. Since genius passed with the death of Purcell there was (apart from the ageing and individualist Blow) only talent left to cope with the situation. And attempts to make major changes were sometimes essayed by composers of less than average competence. Thus the way was left clear for speculative composers from Europe.

Composers of the Reign of Queen Anne

The principal native composers of the reign of Queen Anne (whose personal concern for music was slight) were John Eccles, Daniel Purcell, Richard Leveridge, Ralph Courteville, Jeremiah Clarke, John Weldon, and William Croft. Thomas Tudway, an ex-Chapel Royal chorister and from 1705 Professor of Music at Cambridge. was also a composer, and as such never at a loss for a *pièce d'occasion.* But he was of more importance as a musicologist whose invaluable work in collecting, classifying, and annotating the church music of the classical age of English music has already been mentioned.

John Eccles, successor to Nicholas Staggins as Master of the King's Music in 1700, was the son of a music teacher who became a fanatical Quaker and, on concluding that music was one of the vanities of the world, abjured his art and turned cobbler. John had no such inhibitions and carved out a profitable career for himself as a purveyor of songs to the theatres. He was one of the most prolific of song-writers and in the last year of his life Henry Purcell was glad to have his co-operation in the provision of a score for Durfey's *Don Quixote.*

Among Eccles's works is a setting of Congreve's *Semele,* the text—except for emendations later made by Pope—being that used by Handel.

[1] See my *The Concert Tradition,* p. 83.

A further link with Handel is Eccles's collaboration with John Dennis in *Rinaldo and Armida* (1699), an heroic quasi-opera in which Dennis, basing his libretto on Tasso, was strongly influenced by Dryden. Songs by Eccles appeared in every collection of the first part of the eighteenth century and achieved enormous popularity. In his official capacity he composed odes, and that which graced the first official birthday of Queen Anne—*Inspire us, genius of ye day*—was commenced with the intention of celebrating King William.[1] Three books of *Theatre Musick* by Eccles were published between 1698 and 1700 and other music of his, together with pieces by Henry Purcell, Robert King,[2] James Paisible,[3] Weldon, Tenoes,[4] Gasparini, Finger, and others, was published in an Amsterdam collection of 1738.[5] Eccles's most original contribution to the music of his time was his score (incomplete) for *Semele*, written in 1707; but this serious attempt to create a truly English form of opera from the dramatic principles inherent in the techniques of Purcell never received a performance.[6] At the end of his life Eccles retired to Kingston-on-Thames and devoted himself to his recreation of angling; he went up to town only to supervise the annual birthday and new year odes.

Daniel Purcell, like his brother, was a chorister in the Chapel Royal (being noted as among those who attended at Windsor in 1678). In 1688 he was appointed organist of Magdalen College, Oxford, which post he relinquished in 1695 when he returned to London. During Henry's last illness Daniel appears to have taken over some of his commissions and he rapidly gained popularity as a theatre composer. In this field he was prolific: he contributed music for the last Act to *The Indian Queen*, 'Mr. Henry Purcell being dead'; he collaborated with Jeremiah Clarke and Leveridge in various undertakings; and in 1705 he wrote music for *Orlando Furioso*, for the opening of the new theatre in the Haymarket. While he was still at Oxford Daniel composed a setting of Thomas Yalden's *Ode for St. Cecilia's Day* (1693), Yalden also being a member of Magdalen College. In London he wrote a succession of ceremonial works which included further settings of St. Cecilia odes—the text of one being by Joseph Addison—and pieces in honour of King William's return from Flanders in 1697 and Princess Anne's Birthday in 1700. Purcell engaged

[1] This work (B.M., Add. Ms. 31456) has some fine solos, of 'transitional' character for Elford (see p. 278). Damascene and Williams.

[2] Who took Banister's place in the Royal Band in 1680, and was licensed to give concerts in 1689.

[3] Of French extraction, member of the royal band and a well-known composer.

[4] S. Tenoe, singer, singing-teacher, and concert-promoter.

[5] *Duos Anglois de differents Maîtres à 2 Flutes ou Violons* (Livre Second). In this 'Hark the ech'ing air' (*The Fairy Queen*) is described as an 'Allemande de Mr. Purcello'.

[6] See Stoddart Lincoln, 'The First Setting of Congreve's "Semele",' *M. & L.*, 44, April, 1963, p. 103.

in concert promotion[1] and in 1713 he returned to church music, being appointed organist of St. Andrew's, Holborn.[2] In his capacity of church musician Daniel wrote a number of verse anthems and published a useful set of *The Psalmes set full for the Organ or Harpsichord as they are plaid in Churches and Chappels in the manner given out*; *as also with their Interludes of great Variety* (1718). Daniel Purcell had a reputation as a humorist and this side of his personality is not disguised in his popular songs, on which his posthumous fame depended. He has, of course, suffered from being his brother's brother. There is an affinity between the two styles. Daniel was a persistent composer of grounds, and his attitude to word-setting was similar to that of Henry [Ex. 3]. If Daniel is here a little more loose-limbed he is certainly not unaware of the asperities that could toughen

3.

the texture of the casual song. In some respects, perhaps, Daniel shows the direction that Henry might have taken had he lived in the more placid days of Queen Anne. Daniel could handle the *da capo* form as to the manner born: Alessandro Scarlatti himself could hardly have improved on the smooth competence of [Ex. 4].

[1] *The London Gazette*, of 31 March 1712, advertising a concert in Stationers' Hall for 3 April.

[2] On his death in 1717 Henry's youngest son, Edward (1689–1740) applied unsuccessfully for the post, Maurice Greene being appointed. He also failed to obtain the vacancy caused shortly afterwards when Greene went to St. Paul's. Edward became organist of St. Margaret's, Westminster, in 1726.

4.

Daniel Purcell's most interesting work is his prize piece, *The Judgement of Paris*, the score of which was published by Walsh. Here is an example of the transition in English music that was taking place to bring about what is loosely termed the Handelian style, but so far without benefit of Handel. Daniel (who dedicated his work to Anthony Henly, of the Grainge, in Hampshire) looks back and gives to Venus a magnificent air—'Stay, stay, lovely youth'—over a ground bass that is marvellously Purcellian. But he firmly marks the sturdiness of the period of Queen Anne in [Ex. 5] and demonstrates to the next generation the best kind of

5.

'patriotic' melody and its proper development in the 'Grand Chorus'—'Hither all ye Graces'. Daniel stated his principles in the Preface to *The Judgement of Paris*: '. . . There is a Justness of Composition a true Harmony of parts; The making the Notes and Airs expressive of the Numbers and meaning of the Words, the pathetique or commanding Force that stirs the Passions, which many Censurers regard no more, than some Masters in their Composures. There is a Sort of Painting in musick, as well as Poetry, which if a Master misses he may be fortunate with the unknowing, but never with such Judges as you Sr. whose Skill is too great to be imposed on by false Charms, or glaring defects or to neglect, or over look any reall Beauty and perfection.'

Ralph Courteville, son of a similarly named musician who was one of the first batch of post-Restoration Gentlemen of the Chapel Royal, was a chorister of the same foundation. In 1691 he became the first organist of Wren's new and favourite Church of St. James's, Piccadilly; the organ was one which had previously stood in the Chapel Royal and was a gift from Queen Mary. Like Daniel Purcell Courteville found a parish organistship a satisfactory, and not too time-absorbing, occupation in that it provided a basic £20 a year and left him free to take part in the general musical life of the city. He composed a certain amount of chamber music—including a set of 6 Sonatas 'composed and purposley (*sic*) contrived for two flutes'—and a large number of songs. He contributed to Durfey's *Don Quixote*, as well as to plays (and revivals) of Southerne, Tate, and Dryden.

Richard Leveridge, whose settings of *All in the downs* and *The Roast Beef of England* helped to stimulate a popular appreciation of the square-toed tunes which for long symbolised the English character in terms of music, was a bass singer. He was notable on account of the power and depth of his voice and, even if his singing style (as Hawkins averred) was crude, he was a favourite in the theatres for nearly sixty years. He sang for Blow and Purcell, and also for Handel. A prolific composer—who was associated in certain works with Daniel Purcell, Leveridge deserves particular mention on account of his music for *Macbeth* (1702), in which he sang the part of Hecate, and for the 'comic masque' of *Pyramus and Thisbe* (1716), taken from the clown scenes of *A Midsummer Night's Dream*. In 1726 Leveridge opened a coffee-house in Tavistock Street, Covent Garden.

Composers of this generation were nothing if not fluent. In view of the energy necessary for the conduct of their increasingly varied careers and for the guarantee of their incomes this is hardly surprising; but fluency can easily destroy genuine inventive ability. This was so in the case of Jeremiah Clarke, whose claim on posterity lies in a 'Trumpet Voluntary' once misattributed to Henry Purcell. Clarke was a favourite pupil of Blow in the Chapel Royal and through his master's influence was appointed to the Chapel Royal and St. Paul's Cathedral. In 1704 Clarke became an organist of the Chapel Royal in place of Francis Piggott and in the next year a vicar-choral of St. Paul's. 'He had the misfortune to entertain a hopeless passion for a very beautiful lady in a station of life far above him; his despair of success threw him into a deep melancholy: in short, he grew weary of his life, and on the fifth day of November, 1707, shot himself.'[1] The melancholic strain does not show in Clarke's compositions. Covering the usual fields of ode, anthem, catch, theatre tune, and keyboard music he displayed high professional competence, a keen appreciation of popular taste, and a disregard for any kind of doctrinaire approach. In 1695 Clarke was moved by the death of Purcell to compose a full scale elegiac ode—*Come, come along*—which was 'perform'd upon ye stage in Druery Lane playhouse'. Two years later Clarke and his fellow stewards of the annual St. Cecilia's Day celebration commissioned the text of *Alexander's Feast* from Dryden. Clarke's own setting, which has not survived, was performed three times in 1697. He composed music for various plays and for the adaptation of Fletcher's *The Island Princess* with Daniel Purcell and Leveridge. Whether for voice or instrument Clarke could turn out charming melodies that were ideal for the growing company of musical amateurs whose aim was to accomplish no more than would give them a passport to the sociable musical evening. 'The bonny grey-eyed morn', written for Durfey's *The Fond Husband*, was a top favourite for many years and its lease of life was extended when Pepusch picked it up for 'Tis Woman that seduces all Mankind' in *The Beggar's Opera*. On the whole Clarke was indifferent to the words that he set and even the most salacious of texts was taken in his stride and laid out against a genteel, neatly-turned tune [Ex. 6]. The truth is that a certain indifference was setting in: music was prefabricated and sold to the highest bidder.

6.

Young Co-ry-don and Phyl-lis sate in a love-ly Grove con-
-triv-ing crowns of li-lies, re-peat-ing tales of love, And
some-thing else but what I dare not what I dare not what I dare not name.

[1] Hawkins, *History*, V, p. 58.

The great demand for sociable, saleable, pieces on the part of publishers was reducing the quality. Clarke, who wrote anthems for the Coronation of Queen Anne and the victory of the allies at Ramillies, admirably exemplifies the journalistic quality of the post-Purcell composer and among his harpsichord pieces are many that, by reason of their captions, qualify as rapidly processed news items: for instance, Marches for the Duke of Gloucester, King William, the Dukes of Ormonde and of Marlborough, the Emperor of Germany and the Prince of Denmark (Queen Anne's husband). The last is the famous 'Trumpet Voluntary'. Some of Clarke's pieces were published in *Ayres for the Harpsichord or Spinett*, which he published in 1700 in conjunction with Blow and Croft; many remained in manuscript. The vogue for 'trumpet' pieces was partly explained by the popularity of John Shore; but also by a more conscious sense of nationalism and pride in military achievement.

John Weldon and William Croft were prominent church musicians, whose temperaments and abilities were well suited to the broad, respectable tenets that prevailed in the Church of England at the beginning of the eighteenth century. Weldon, a native of Chichester, was a pupil of John Walter, of Eton College, and, it is said, of Henry Purcell. In 1694 he became organist of New College, Oxford, after which he succeeded to similar posts at the Chapel Royal and St. Bride's Church, Fleet Street. In 1715 he was appointed 'second composer' (Croft being the first) to George I, by whose command he also became organist of St. Martin's-in-the-Fields (to which the King presented the organ) in 1726. After early commissions for the theatre Weldon forsook this province and after 1708 devoted himself to song-writing, to chamber music, and to music for the Church. Something of an academic composer, Weldon's works hardly rise above a decent competence. Under the title of *Divine Harmony* he published six solo anthems for Richard Elford, a famous counter-tenor of St. Paul's Cathedral and the Chapel Royal, who was later to take part in the first performance of some of Handel's *Chandos Anthems*. Croft was born in Nether Eatington, Warwickshire, and as a chorister of the Chapel Royal was yet another protégé of Blow, by whose good offices he was elected to the organistship of St. Anne's, Soho (the name of this church is remembered in Croft's most famous hymn tune). In 1700 Croft was Master of the Children of the Chapel Royal and on Blow's death he succeeded him as organist of Westminster Abbey. In the same year, 1708, he became a Doctor of Music at Oxford, his exercise consisting of settings of odes by Joseph Trapp[1]: it was published under the title *Musicus Apparatus*

[1] *The Tragedy of King Saul: written by a Deceased Person of Honour* (Playford 1703) was by Trapp and has certain affinities with the libretto of Handel's *Saul* (see 'Die Bedeutung des Saul', *Händel-Jahrbuch*, Leipzig, 1959, pp. 76 f.).

Academicus. Croft wrote relatively little secular music, and even in what he did write he tended to fall into a mood of gravity [Ex. 7]. His extensive

7.

output of anthems—some of the best being issued in *Musica Sacra* in 1724—represents the highest point to which Anglican church music reached during the first quarter of the eighteenth century, and served a useful function in bringing church musicians back to a reconsideration of the traditions of English polyphony.

Synthesising the techniques of his predecessors, Croft was able to give a new dimension to the 'anthem', taking it in the general direction of the Handelian oratorio, but (so far as is known) without reference to Handel's early essays in that genre. Like Thomas Roseingrave (see p. 291) Croft evolved a large-scale form related to and collateral with the familiar verse anthem. A magnificent example is *Give the King Thy Judgements, O Lord*,[1] in six extensive movements. The first begins with a finely measured declamation over a pedal [Ex. 8*a*]. In the second section Croft moves with vigour later to be associated perhaps, with, Parry [Ex. 8*b*]. This is succeeded by a counter-tenor solo, against which a solo-stop effect as from the organ voluntary lends contrast: with its typical repetition of figures

8a.

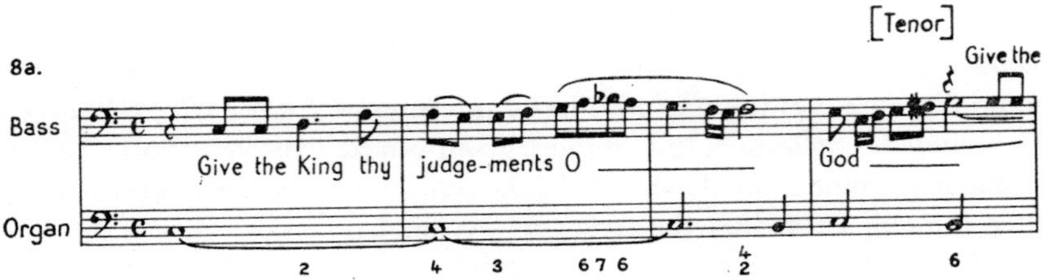

[1] B.M. Add. Ms. 17861, dated 13 July 1727.

8b.

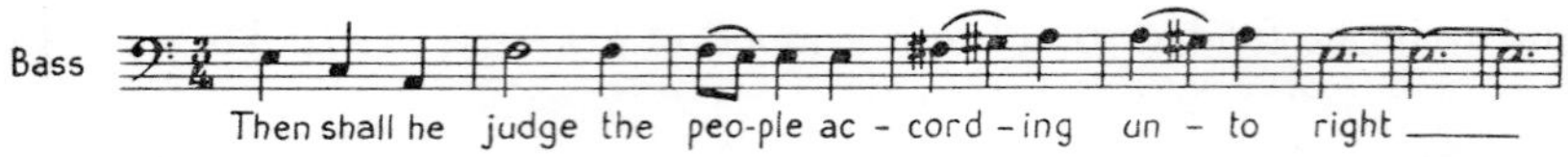

this is an especially well-integrated piece of writing [Ex. 8*c*]. A Purcellian flourish—again accommodated over a tonic pedal—[Ex. 8*d*] goes into a

8c.

8d.

recitative in C minor, tempered by an *ostinato* bass, in which key this homophony relives the past and looks sideways at *Israel in Egypt* [Ex. 8*e*]. The whole is concluded, in C major, by an ornate five-part chorus culminating in a 'Handelian' Amen. Of all the composers who came immediately after Purcell, Croft had the strongest personality.

A friend of the scholar and composer Henry Aldrich[1] (Dean of

[1] According to Charles Avison Aldrich introduced works by Palestrina and Carissimi into the services of the Church of England: see *An Essay on Musical Expression*, 2nd edn., 1753, p. 97.

8e

Counter~
~tenor
His do - mi - nion shall be al - so from ye one sea to ye o - ther
Tenor
His do - mi - nion ..
Bass I
His do - mi - nion ..
Bass II
His do - mi - nion ..

Christchurch, Oxford) Croft seems to have had antiquarian interests; some time before 1712 he undertook at his own expense the restoration of the monument in Norwich Cathedral to the Elizabethan musician William Inglott, who succeeded a Thomas Morley as organist in 1587.[1] In 1726 Croft published two volumes of anthems in *Musica Sacra*: from this the Burial Service used at State Funerals is taken. In respect of the verse 'Thou knowest, Lord' in this service, which remains in Purcell's setting, Croft simply observes that Purcell's version could not be bettered.

The Opera Situation

The idea that the British were inferior to other nations in respect of musical invention (suggested by Ravenscroft) had been gaining currency across the seventeenth century. The case of Italian opera hardened it into a doctrine. From the date of the opening of the Opera House in the Haymarket the ambitious native composer was forced on the defensive: the chances of his achieving a reputation among the influential and wealthy were attenuated. There was a further difficulty. The aristocracy was divided in enthusiasm. Some, fresh from European cultural experiences, wished to see opera firmly established in London.[2] Others disliked Italian singers, and in the course of a few years their dislike became infectious.

'And upon the 9th of *April* 1705 Captain Vantbrugg open'd his new Theatre in the *Hay-Market*, with a Foreign opera, Perform'd by a new Set of Singers, arriv'd from Italy; (the worst that e'er came from thence)

[1] William Inglott (1554–1621) composed two pieces in the *Fitzwilliam Virginal Book*.

[2] The chances of opera of any kind being performed anywhere else in Britain were remote. On 17 January 1700 *The Flying Post* reported that 'the opera Dioclesian was acted at Norwich, by Mr. Dogget's Company, the Duke of Norfolk's Servants, with great Applause, being the first that ever was attempted out of London'.

for it lasted but 5 days, and they being lik'd but indifferently by the Gentry; they in a little time marcht back to their own Country.'[1]

The first Italian opera to be performed in London was *Gli Amori d'Ergasto* (*The loves of Ergasto*), a pastorale. The programme-book gave the libretto in two languages, the English translation facing the Italian original (by an unknown librettist). The composer, however, was no Italian but an opportunist German, Jacob Greber, a friend of Margarita de l'Epine and her accompanist on the occasion of her debut at Drury Lane on 29 January 1704. (In Nicholas Rowe's *Poems on Several Occasions*, 1714, de l'Epine was described as 'Greber's Peg'.) Disenchanted by his English reception Greber left for Germany, taking the score of his opera with him.[2] For the time being the Italophiles contented themselves with a compromise. Thomas Clayton, a member of the King's band between 1692 and 1702, visited Italy and, having fetched up with Haym and Charles Dieupart,[3] speculated in 'an opera after the Italian manner, all sung' at Drury Lane (16 January 1705). This was *Arsinoe*, *Queen of Cyprus* (Italian libretto by T. Stanzani, English version by P. A. Motteux), for which Clayton adapted Italian music or composed in a pseudo-Italian style. The cast included Catherine Tofts, the best of English sopranos of the period and one who could command a fee of £500 a season, and Leveridge.[4] *Arsinoe*, despite twenty-four performances, was indifferently received; but the promoters persisted. On 10 April 1706 a version of Buononcini's *Camilla*—a European success since its Naples première in 1696—was produced at Drury Lane; the music being arranged by Haym and the English text by Owen MacSwiney. When revived during the next season this opera was sung half in English and half in Italian in order to accommodate the singers, who now included the contralto Valentini, as well as Mrs. Tofts's great rival, Margarita de l'Epine. On 15 March 1707 Clayton's *Rosamond*, an original work to an insipid libretto by Joseph Addison, was also played at Drury Lane.[5] A month later *Thomyris*, *Queen of Scythia*, a pasticcio of airs by Alessandro Scarlatti, Buononcini, Steffani,

[1] *Roscius Anglicanus*, p. 64.

[2] Copy in National Library, Vienna.

[3] French violinist, harpsichordist, and composer, resident in London from *c.* 1700. A notable player of Corelli's Sonatas, Dieupart owes his chief fame to the fact that his *Six Suites de clavessin* (Roger, Amsterdam) were known to and used by Bach, whose first English Suite (prelude) is based on the Gigue from Dieupart's first suite which is also in A Major.

[4] For details relating to contracts to musicians for and general costs of the early operas see Allardyce Nicoll, *XVIII Century Drama*, 1700–50, London, 1925, pp. 270–92.

[5] '. . . 'tis observed that this Opera, for the Beauty of its Diction, exceeds many *English* Performances of the Kind; but being very ill set to Musick, it had not the Success due to its Merit'. *The Poetical Register: or, The Lives and Characters of the English Dramatick Poets*, London, E. Curll, 1719.

Gasparini, and Albinoni, was put on in the same theatre, and in the next year Dieupart arranged the words for *Love's Triumph* (from Ottoboni's *La pastorella*, with music by Scarlatti and others). By now the taste for opera in this form had developed somewhat and in 1710 the opera-going public was prepared for a full-scale opera according to the authentic tradition. On 21 January Buononcini's *Almahide*—the libretto based on Dryden's *Almanzor and Almahide* and *The Conquest of Granada by the Spaniards*—was performed at the Haymarket with an all-star cast: Valentini, Nicolini, Cassarini, Lawrence, Margarita de l'Epine, Isabella Girardeau. Between the Acts there were intermezzi in English, in which the singers were Dogget, Mrs. Lindsay and Mrs. Cross. *Almahide* was played twenty-four times up to 1712, and the airs were published by Walsh, who had been encouraged by his previous successes with issues of songs from *Camilla*, *Arsinoe*, *Rosamond* and *Thomyris*.

On 27 February 1712 Gasparini's *Hamlet* (published by Walsh), first produced in Venice in 1705, was given, with Nicolini in the title role and with l'Epine, Girardeau, and Mrs. Barbier in the cast. It had six more performances.

Soon afterwards there was a spirited attempt to provide *opera seria* to a home-made libretto in English. The author of *Calypso and Telemachus* (Haymarket, 25 May) was John Hughes;[1] the composer, the German Johann Ernst Galliard, a one-time pupil of Steffani's. In his Preface Hughes described his opera as 'an Essay for the Improvement of Theatrical Musick in the English language, after the Model of the Italians'; regarding Galliard he observed that he 'has offer'd a much more prevailing Argument than any I cou'd urge, to shew that the English Language is capable of the most agreeable Graces of Harmony.' But Hughes was backing a loser. Handel, whose *Rinaldo* had been produced at the Haymarket on 7 March 1712, was on the scene. During these energetic years of operatic speculation an unsuccessful attempt to extend the influence beyond London is said to have been made when Clayton went to Dublin in 1709 at the invitation of Philip (later Duke of) Wharton, a well-known Jacobite, with the intention of establishing 'opera in the Italian manner' there; but—either because of Clayton's incompetence as a composer or Wharton's eccentricities (he was some-time president of the Hell-Fire Club)—the venture never got off the ground.

Exotic Traits in British Music

During the first twenty or thirty years of the eighteenth century the conflict between native and Italianate musical styles was acute, tending

[1] An enthusiast for music and one of those who attended Britton's concerts, Hughes was also one of Handel's first English friends.

in some respects to take on a class-conscious aspect. Thus opera was cultivated by the aristocracy and aspirant bourgeoisie and deplored by the Pietists,[1] while the rest of the community looked to more homely fare for nourishment and recreation. Handel himself was conscious of two contrasting attitudes and he found his own way to sublimate the tension that they caused. In so doing, by way of compromise, he established himself as a British composer.

Italian opera was exotic. But there were exotic traits in music nearer home. Scottish, Irish, Welsh, and English provincial tunes were kept in view in London during Tudor times. In the Purcellian period they began to stage a vigorous comeback, and Henry and Daniel Purcell made arrangements of Scottish tunes. In 1701 Henry Playford published a volume of *Original Scotch-Tunes*. In or about the same year an unaccustomed piece of authentic pentatony appeared (without publisher's imprint)—[Ex. 9]. Further impetus to the import of Scottish culture into

9

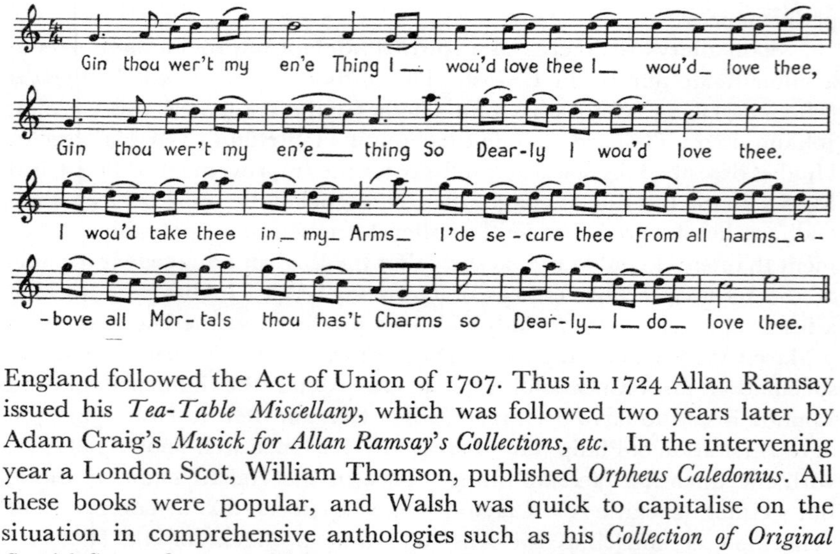

England followed the Act of Union of 1707. Thus in 1724 Allan Ramsay issued his *Tea-Table Miscellany*, which was followed two years later by Adam Craig's *Musick for Allan Ramsay's Collections, etc.* In the intervening year a London Scot, William Thomson, published *Orpheus Caledonius*. All these books were popular, and Walsh was quick to capitalise on the situation in comprehensive anthologies such as his *Collection of Original Scottish Songs* of *c.* 1720. The reputation of Scottish music was enhanced by the talents of Mrs. Barbier and Mrs. Robinson who made hits out of *The Bush aboun Traquair* and *O Bessy Bell* and *Mary Gray*, and John Abell and Alexander Gordon. Abell, born in Aberdeen and, it is thought, a Chapel Royal chorister, was employed at the English Court until the Revolution

[1] 'As *Whoredom* is encourag'd in these *Operas*, so *Drunkenness* meets with some *Encomiums*', Bedford, op. cit., p. 113.

of 1688, after which he held a miscellany of appointments at European courts (he was Intendant at the theatre in Kassel) before settling again in London in 1701. Commended among others by Congreve, Abell gave concerts in London and also in Scotland, choosing his programmes from many different schools and performing in a variety of languages.[1] He died in 1724.

While Scottish national music thus enjoyed a small renaissance, that of Ireland also began to reassert its identity. The temporary pacification of the country by the Treaty of Limerick (1691) led to a more relaxed mode of town- and country-house living and ancient traditions were stirred by the activities of the remaining harpists. Of these the most notable was Turlough Carolan (1670–1738), who, under the patronage of Irish and Anglo-Irish alike, composed many songs—some affected by current Italian idioms that had seeped into Dublin—which were to pass into the realm of folk-song. In or about 1721 John and William Neale, the first music-publishers in Dublin, issued a set of *Carolan's Tunes*.[2] In respect of Wales the Eisteddfod tradition was yet again revived—at Llandegla in Denbighshire. Even if this was concerned with poetry rather than with music (except that the two were always interdependent in Wales) a proper concern for indigenous culture developed in spite of the indifference of the by now half-English gentry. Towards the middle of the century many famous airs—such as *Meillionen* and *Morfa Rhuddlan*—were published after the versions of John Parry.[3] A year after Handel's death Welsh musical culture was stimulated again in the classical manner.[4] Handel himself showed awareness of British folk-music: of Scottish in the dances of *Ariodante*; of Irish in the *Forest Music* composed on the occasion of his Dublin visit of 1741–2; and of Welsh in the introduction to the ritornello of 'Happy we', in *Acis and Galatea*, of the melody *Codiad yr haul*. This he may well have learned from his colleague Powell, the Welsh-born London harpist.

Churches, Organs, and Organists

All this activity was on one side of British music. On the other was church music in which also new attitudes were crystallising. Between opera and liturgical music there was a divide, which grew wider and deeper as the

[1] See John Abell, *A Choice Collection of Italian Ayres . . . sung to the Nobility and Gentry in the North of England; and at both Theatres in London*, London, W. Pearson, 1703.

[2] Only extant copy (title-page and pp. 1–5 wanting) in National Library of Ireland.

[3] *q.v.* p. 349.

[4] 'Be it known that a Eisteddfod of the Poets and Musicians of Wales will be held at the Bull in Bala Town, on Whit-Monday and Whit-Tuesday in 1760. It will be held under the same rules and in like manner as the ancient Eisteddfod of Caerwys in the days of Queen Elizabeth . . .' *Philomath's Almanack*.

years passed. Between popular song and hymnody, on the other hand, an accommodation was reached, so that by the middle of the century it became often difficult to distinguish the one from the other.

During the reign of Queen Anne the place and character of the music of the Church of England were settled by tacit agreement between the interested parties. The State Church provided a convenient set of imprecise theological principles that caused a minimum of offence and discouraged fanatical inclinations. Moral precepts—derived from reaction against the amorality of the Restoration Court—were inculcated in the parishioners by a tolerably well-educated set of ministers who, aspiring to higher social ranks, found sacramentalism inconsistent with middle-class ambitions. The new churches built in London as a consequence of the Fifty New Churches Act of 1711 were, of course, designed more or less exclusively for the purpose of preaching. The separation of music from ceremonial was indicated also by the erection of west-end galleries—as at Wigan by instruction of Bishop Stratford—'for the use of such persons within the parish as had and should attain to some competent skill in singing, to the end that by sitting together they might the more easily perform their separate parts . . .' There was by now a sense of religious toleration, though this was relative in respect of practising Dissenters, and a reasonableness that soon sank into indifference. The uncertainties of the long period of Reformation and the secularity of the Restoration era had provided challenges to musicians and in both epochs there was church music of distinguished quality. When the accent fell on respectability creative talent ceased to react to any marked degree. At the same time developments within the music of the Church of England were important: their consequences remain to the present day.

The impoverishment of musical foundations outside London during the latter part of the seventeenth century was considerable, and this led to a marked diminution in the quality of the musicians in charge of them. Thus of the organists and choirmasters practising in the cathedrals during Handel's lifetime few call for more than cursory mention. The wholesale destruction of organs by the Puritans had been a grievous blow. In many parish churches in the country organs did not come back until the nineteenth century, their function being filled by church bands with more enthusiasm than ability. The musical direction was entrusted to the Parish Clerk who—if there was no band available—pitched the hymns and (since sets of books were prohibitive in cost) gave them out line by line. The most notable of Parish Clerks was William Knapp (1698/9–1768),[1] whose *Sett of New Psalm Tunes and Anthems in Four Parts, with an introduction to Psalmody*

[1] Of Poole. See Rev. S. E. V. Filleul, *William Knapp*, in *Dorset Nat. Hist. and Arch. Soc. Proc.*, 1907.

after a plain and familiar manner (1738) and *New Church Melody* (1753) contain the essential details of parochial music of that age. The feature of this music is the demotion of the old metrical psalm and its gradual replacement by the hymn: a process which may be said to have started with the *Select Psalms and Hymns* prepared for St. Margaret's Church, Westminster in 1697. One or two characteristic hymn-tunes by Knapp remain in present-day hymnals and serve to remind that on such modest foundations the English provincial choral society was at least in part built. One of the best attended churches in the Kingdom was St. Nicholas, Newcastle upon Tyne, and Charles Avison wrote of the moving effect of the congregational singing, in which the voices of seamen predominated. 'I cannot but own', he said, 'that I have been uncommonly affected with hearing thousands of Voices hymning the Deity in a style of Harmony adapted to that awful occasion.'[1] The need for a popular hymnody was appreciated by many composers, but the limitations of the form leave little distance between the amateur composer—like Knapp—and the highly-trained professional—such as Croft, or for that matter Handel.

In the post-Restoration period organ-building lay principally in the hands of the Harris family (Renatus I and II, Thomas, John, and John Byfield, son-in-law of the last) and of Bernard Schmidt (known as Father Smith) and his descendants and successors. Thomas Harris had spent the Commonwealth years in France; Schmidt was, as the name suggests, a German immigrant. While the quality of the pipe-work of these builders was high the instruments that were built in London and some of the provincial cathedrals and larger parish churches were small and without pedals.[2] (Father Smith's organ at St. Paul's Cathedral had a toe-pedal mechanism that operated some of the pipes otherwise controlled from the manuals and Burney reported that Handel was grateful to practise on it on account of the opportunity afforded for pedal practice; but this was exceptional.) The largest of the early eighteenth-century organs was that built by Renatus Harris[3] for Salisbury Cathedral in 1710. This comprised four manuals—Great, 'Borrowed' Great for which separate stops provided for transference from the Great, Choir, and Echo, thirty-three speaking stops, and a 'drum pedal tuned to CC'. Mostly, however,

[1] Quoted in *The Works of William Mann*, 1811, III, p. 385.

[2] At St. Nicholas, Newcastle upon Tyne Renatus received £300 for erecting an organ of six to eight stops in 1676. In 1699 the City Corporation added a trumpet, and fifty years later Snetzler added a Swell manual to the existing Great and Choir. In the same year the Corporation ordered a 'sweet stop' (i.e. hautboy). *Dedication of the Re-Constructed Organ at St. Nicholas, Newcastle*, 1911.

[3] Renatus Harris, Smith's keen rival, had put in a tender to build the organ in St. Paul's. His intentions were contained in *A Proposal for the Erecting of an Organ in St. Paul's Cathedral, over the West Door, at the Entrance into the Body of that Church*, Renatus Harris, n.d. after 1710.

organists made do with instruments of chamber music proportions. The Swell Pedal was introduced by Abraham Jordan for the instrument at St. Magnus's Church, London Bridge, in 1712. Jordan was also the builder of the organ in the Duke of Chandos's Palace at Canons, which was installed in 1720.

A provincial builder of some importance was Thomas Swarbrick—of German descent—of Warwick, who was responsible for instruments in St. Michael and Holy Trinity, Coventry; St. Mary, Warwick; Lichfield Cathedral; Holy Trinity, Stratford-on-Avon; and St. Saviour, Southwark. Regarding the organ in St. Michael, Coventry, Sharp wrote that 'The celebrated Handel performed once or twice upon the organ and gave his decided testimony in favour of its excellences; particularly commending the Double Diapason, Vox Humana, and Bassoon Stops. The Swell is much admired for its compass, sweetness, and admirable effect, and there was formerly also a Swell in the Choir Organ, a circumstance of very unusual occurrence.'[1]

The relatively modest nature of the English organ, the slender use to which it needed to be put during Divine Service, and the fact that its mastery meant little in the way of additional emolument meant that no school of organ-playing and composition in any way comparable to that of Germany was created. John Robinson (1682–1762), a pupil of Blow, organist of St. Lawrence, Jewry, in 1710, of St. Magnus, London Bridge, in 1713, and of Westminster Abbey in 1727, was a 'florid and elegant' performer and his performances gratified large numbers of people who otherwise avoided church-going as much as they could. In his Introduction to Boyce's *Cathedral Music*[2] Hawkins remarks how formerly the voluntary between the psalm and the First Lesson was a slow and solemn movement, intended 'to compose the minds of the hearers, and to excite sentiments of piety and devotion. Mr. Robinson introduced a different practice, calculated to display the agility of his fingers in Allegro movements on the Cornet, Trumpet, Sesquialtera, and other noisy stops,[3] degrading the instrument, and instead of the full and noble harmony with which it was designed to gratify the ear, tickling it with mere airs in two parts, in fact solos for a flute and a bass'.[4] Robinson married William Turner's daughter

[1] Sharp, op. cit, p. 55.

[2] Vol. I, 1788, p. ii. Cf. Bedford, op. cit., p. 247, where advice is given to church authorities, 'That they do not choose a Man who gets his Maintenance by teaching to play upon the *Spinnet* and Harpsichord.'

[3] Cf. Thomas Tudway (B.M. Harl. 7342, Introduction to vol. VI): 'And as Organs have been infinitly improv'd since 50 or 60 years by additional stops, which imitate almost ev'ry instrument of pipe or strings; so are they become . . . a very ornamental & ye most beautiful structure that was ever erected in ye Church . . .'

[4] Cf. Mus. Ex. 8*c*, p. 280.

Ann (an opera singer) by whom he had a daughter who sang the name-part in Handel's *Belshazzar* in 1745.

Another organist of nimble spirit was Obadiah Shuttleworth (*c.* 1675–1734) who succeeded Philip Hart at St. Michael's, Cornhill, about 1724. Hawkins reported his talents also with disapproval, since he was 'a mere harpsichord player, who having the advantage of a good finger, charmed his hearers with such music as was fit alone for that instrument, and drew after him greater numbers than came to hear the preacher'.[1] Shuttleworth's successor was Joseph Kelway (d. 1782), a pupil of Geminiani and a champion of the music of Domenico Scarlatti, who moved to St. Martin's-in-the-Fields in 1736 where his powers of improvisation attracted the attention of Handel.

But it is Thomas Roseingrave (1690–1766) who stands out most prominently among the organists of his generation. The son of Daniel Roseingrave (*c.* 1650–1727), who was a pupil at the Chapel Royal in its richest period and subsequently organist of Gloucester, Winchester, Salisbury, and the two Dublin cathedrals, Thomas was educated in Dublin and in Venice, where he became acquainted with the Scarlattis.[2] Roseingrave was responsible for the London production of Domenico Scarlatti's *Narciso* in 1720. Five years later he became organist of Handel's parish church, St. George's, Hanover Square. Roseingrave, as will be shown in particular, had a strain of genius. He also suffered from a neurotic disability so that after 1737 (when his matrimonial ambitions perished for the same reason as those of Jeremiah Clarke) he was obliged to seek a quieter life in Dublin where his brother Ralph was by now organist. Almost a hundred years after his death Thomas was thus described: 'It seems, however, that Roseingrave, the really great organist of St. George's, Hanover Square, was the only English composer who left behind him, besides an unequalled reputation as an extemporary player in the Church style, a body of compositions which, although long neglected and nearly forgotten, are of that sterling excellence and durability of style usually considered the attribute alone of the organ compositions of a Handel or of a Bach.'[3] This, of course, is overstating the case but Roseingrave's *Voluntaries* and, more particularly, his *Fugues*, vigorous in counterpoint, enterprising in harmony, and purposeful in design, are nearer to the

[1] ib. Cf. Hawkins's approval of William Boyce, 'who well understood the nature and genius of the organ, [and] seldom played on any other stop than the stopped diapason, and on that in three and four parts, in a style suited both to the place, and the occasion;' and of the "voluntary movement on the Diapasons" with which Handel introduced a Concerto, 'which stole on the ear in a slow and solemn progress', op. cit., V, p. 413.

[2] Roseingrave published an edition, the first in England, of *Forty-Two Suits* [*sic*] by *Domenico Scarlatti* 1728.

[3] *Musical Standard*, 21 May 1864, p. 333.

stronger traditions of English instrumental music of the earlier schools than almost anything else of their period.[1]

By reason of the popular antipathy to Italian opera, of the large increase of musical activity among a wider section of the community, and the prevailing and generally restricting attitude of the Church, it will be seen that English music towards the end of the reign of Queen Anne tended to contract in intrinsic interest. Purcell could be regarded as the peer of the great European composers. His successors were not of that class, but the situation has been presented in such a way that Handel's role has to some extent been misinterpreted. What really mattered was that Handel, in almost every particular, knew how to deal with the situation as he found it. It is of particular interest to refer again to Tudway. In his Introduction to vol. VI of his collection he describes what in effect were the origins of Handelian oratorio. But first he reproves his fellow-countrymen for their arrogance and insularity.

'. . . The truth of all this is; the skill of composing is much more general, and greatly improv'd, And ye composers of secular Music, are become much greater Masters than ever was known before . . . I must, tho I should offend some of my country men, needs say: to compose an Opera, is a very great and Masterlike work, and ye greatest of all secular performances in Music; wch few genius', ev'n among ye Italians, can reach; But I don't in ye least question, by that time these musical representatives have been a few years longer in England, and ye present encouragement continue, by ye countenance of so great a Number of our Nobility and Gentry, it will appear we have Genius's in England strong enough for y^r^ work; However this cant be done, by despising of 'em, as many of our Masters do, who obstinately deprive yourselves of ye means of obtaining to ye perfection of them.

'Our Countryman Mr. Henry Purcell, who was confessedly the greatest Genius we ever had, dy'd before these musical representatives came upon ye stage in England; He wou'd have been so far from despising them, that he would never have eas'd till he had equall'd, if not outdone them; And did by ye pow'rs of his own Genius, contrive very many, and excellent compositions of divers kinds for ye stage; But that which set Mr. Purcell eminently above any of his contemporaries was yt Noble Composition, ye first of its kind in England, of Te Deum and Jubilate, accompanied with instrumental music; which he compos'd principally against ye Opening of

[1] Cf. *Fifteen Voluntaries and Fugues for the organ*, ed. by A. V. Butcher (Hinrichson ed.); *Ten Organ Works*, ed. by Peter Williams (Stainer & Bell); *Compositions for Organ and Harpsichord*, ed. by Denis Stevens (Pennsylvania State University Press). Not surprisingly Roseingrave was rejected by Hawkins who described his works as 'harsh and disgusting, manifesting great learning, but void of eloquence and variety'. *History*, V, p. 176.

St. Pauls but did not live till that time; However it was sung there severall times since, before Her Majesty Queen Anne upon ye great Events of her Reigne. . . .'

Tudway underlined the evocative quality of performances in which the singers were supported by 'Great organ', trumpets, and at least thirty or forty other instruments. Musical works of this nature were not in any sense ritual but, independent of the normal liturgical scheme, accepted in their own right. The occasional anthem of earlier times, from which the Purcellian Te Deum in part descended, was according to normal usage. Tudway saw the emergence of a new kind of musical work which evaded easy classification:

'Mr. Crofts and Mr. Hendale [Handel], both by ye Queen's Order, have likewise with great Art and good success compos'd ye like pieces, of Te Deum and Jubilate, which were perform'd before Her Majesty, on Publick Occasions, with great Applause; These 3 compositions are all of the kind at present were ever made in England; your Lordship will distinguish that such like pieces as these are only proper in ye church for great Occasions . . . [and] therefore are not strictly call'd Church Music, although, they are upon ye same divine Subject.'[1]

The end of the War of Spanish Succession came when Thomas Roseingrave, twenty-two years of age, was in Italy. In December 1712 he composed just such a work as Tudway describes—'not strictly "Church" Music', but 'upon some divine Subject'. The work (contained in Tudway's collection) was headed 'For ye Peace 1713'. Entitled *Arise, shine, for thy light is come*, it comprises a setting of *Isaiah*, 60, vv. 1, 2, 3, 10, 15, 16, 18, for solo voices, choir, and the then statutory festival orchestra of two trumpets, two oboes, [bassoon(s)] strings, (harpsichord, and organ), in eight extended movements centred on C major. This is a virtuoso work, illuminated by a brilliant sense of orchestral scoring, and of considerable significance.[2]

Roseingrave had absorbed the current Italian oratorio style and used it to great dramatic effect, demonstrating precisely the point that Tudway had made—that defiance of techniques developed elsewhere was unhelpful to the cause of English music. Roseingrave put on an Italian dress and hoped to regularise its use in England. Thus after a fine symphony of

[1] Like Purcell's Service those of Croft and Handel were in D major. Tudway notes that Croft's works were performed twice before Queen Anne 'at ye Chapell Royal at St. James's on days of Thanksgiving, and thrice, at St. Paul's on ye like Occasions with instrumental music'. Handel's Service was 'by the Queens Order for ye Thanksgiving On ye Peace, 1713, And perform'd in St. Paul's Church'.

[2] First performance since Roseingrave's time at the Handel Festival, Göttingen, 1966, in a performing edition published by Boosey and Hawkes.

ninety bars which won the esteem of Burney, Roseingrave introduced the voices [Ex. 10*a*]. The mood of *Epinicion* extends and culminates in an

10a.

fine and evocative passage [Ex. 10*b*]. The second movement in C minor is

10b.

equally stylish and affecting by reason of melodic and harmonic allusions [Ex. 10*c*]. These follow a tenor solo (C major) 'And ye Gentiles'; a soprano solo in 12/8 time (G major) with intricate interweaving of solo voice and solo oboe; a verse à 3, *alla breve*, setting of 'Thou shalt know' leading to a broad, homophonic, choral sequel; a dramatic bass solo 'violence shall no more be heard in thy land' (4/4, B flat major); and a final 'Grand Chorus'

10c.

—'But thou shalt call thy walls salvation'—that is sustained by the ritornello motiv of the opening symphony, and has similar *Adagio-Allegro* alternations to those of Handel's 'Worthy is the Lamb'.

In this occasional piece by Roseingrave the character of English oratorio is clearly, if fortuitously, defined. The choice of text is relevant to later development and in this connection it may be observed that those parts of the *Book of Isaiah* that were to capture Handel's attention some thirty years later were stimulating a good deal of activity during the reign of Queen Anne. Thomas Tudway composed a verse anthem also entitled *Arise, shine* for the Chapel Royal on a section of Chapter 60, and in his collection is also Henry Hall's *Comfort ye my People* (*Isaiah*, 40, vv. 1–7, 9), a dramatic setting, concluding with a fine six-part exposition of the climactic words 'Behold your God', which also hints at the pattern of things to come [Ex. 11*a* and *b*]. It was in 1712 that Pope, conjoining Isaiah and Virgil, published his Sacred Eclogue—*Messiah*.

11a.

11b.

The Coming of Handel

Such was the situation in Britain when Handel arrived to take measure of its possibilities and to exploit them. That he was able to do so was due as much to his personal as to his musical qualities: it was also due to the fact that as a German he became *persona grata* at a German court. In the best sense of the word Handel was an opportunist. Because he was and because of his incredible industry he was able to become a British institution.

The image of this institution has provided the British people with a somewhat distorted version of Handel's personality and, it may be said, also of his music. It is well to remember that he was, by birth, a particular kind of German. He was a Saxon, and, like many in his part of Germany, he had—from his mother's side of the family—a certain amount of Slavonic blood in his veins. The Saxons are proud and provincial; often gifted to the point of succeeding in undertakings without any demonstration of undue effort; quick in repartee, humourous, and engaging. The Saxons are generous and hospitable. The Saxon dialect (or one of its branches), which was an impediment to acceptance in other parts of Germany, was of no consequence abroad, so paradoxically a German from a Saxon city could sometimes make himself more easily at home in foreign parts than in another German state. Handel, son of a successful surgeon, was brought up to bourgeois standards. His career was a progress towards the full realisation of those standards in the most congenial climate. In the long run he made himself at home in England, but, true to type, he did not forget his first loyalties. Thus after his death a considerable part of his wealth returned to relatives and to the University, in Halle where he was born.

Trained in the sound principles of composition and musicianship that belonged to the ecclesiastical and civic traditions of Germany, and represented in Halle by Wilhelm Zachau who was his first teacher, Handel, aware of the greater exhilaration of music in Dresden, Brunswick, Hanover, and Hamburg, and of the profits to be made through opera, made a grand tour of inspection before achieving the ambition of every young composer of his generation—a trip to Italy. At the age of twenty-one, with many works and some successes behind him, Handel arrived in Florence. He spent nearly four years in Italy, during which his engaging manner gained influential friends and patrons, and the quality of his by now almost completely Italianate music won the approval of many admirers. The climax of his sojourn in Italy was the acclaim given to *Agrippina*, the opera composed for the Carnival season in Venice at the end of 1709. Through the good offices of Agostino Steffani, sometime Kapellmeister at Hanover but now engaged in weightier affairs, Handel was appointed as his successor. In general an office of this nature was attractive, affording prestige on the one hand and generous opportunity to travel on the other.

Aware of conditions in England through contacts he had made both in Germany and Italy, Handel's intention to visit the country is hardly likely in the first place to have extended beyond the limits of the expedition undertaken in 1710. As in Italy he showed interest in musical life in general and he made congenial social connections. He was lucky to be introduced to the company that assembled weekly in Thomas Britton's loft in Clerkenwell, when a cross-section of aristocracy and bourgeoisie, aided by a representative group of London professional musicians, provided programmes that stretched from the English classics—from the Elizabethans to Purcell—to the contemporary and also gave a good insight into English attitudes to music. Among those who were regular at Britton's evenings were some who, inspired by Italian and French precedents, founded an 'academy'—the Academy of Vocal (and instrumental) Music in the year in which Handel arrived. Among the promoters were Henry Needler, a civil servant, Pepusch, John Ernest Galliard—a former protégé of Steffani in Hanover who had been brought to England by Queen Anne's husband, Prince George of Denmark, and had achieved a respectable place among English musicians—and Bernard Gates, a Gentleman of the Chapel Royal since 1708. The performances of the Academy were sustained by the choristers both of the Chapel Royal and St. Paul's

Cathedral. During his first visit to London Handel was approached by Aaron Hill—poet and dramatist and now manager of a company about to transfer from Drury Lane to the Haymarket Theatre—with a commission to provide an opera. The result was *Rinaldo*, fifteen performances of which in 1711 gave to the fashionable audiences who heard it some idea of what an opera in the Italian style really could be. The star of the cast was Nicolini who sang the aria 'Cara sposa', which Handel considered one of the best he ever wrote. In March Nicolini's troupe took *Rinaldo* to Dublin, the first time an Italian opera was given there. From the publication of *Rinaldo* Walsh made £1,500, while William Babell, twenty-one years old, a member of the Royal Band, helped both himself and Handel by making arrangements of items for harpsichord and for amateurs.[1] All in all, therefore, it is not surprising that Handel left London with some reluctance, for there were many who pressed him if not to stay permanently then to return as soon as he conveniently could.

The Establishment of Handel

In the event Handel came back in the autumn of 1712 with the operas *Il Pastor Fido* and *Teseo*, both of which were played at the Haymarket, but, for various reasons, without the success that had attended *Rinaldo*. No matter, Handel—though still on leave of absence from Hanover—allowed himself to be taken into the main-stream of London music so that the idea of permanent residence in England grew stronger. Indeed it became irresistible. After the performances of the *Birthday Ode* and the *Utrecht Te Deum and Jubilate* at St. Paul's Cathedral, the reception of these works, and the grant of a pension by the Queen, the undertaking to go back to Hanover was conveniently set aside. Handel was an opportunist.

In the Baroque period composers, broadly speaking, were content to base their own style on one that was common property throughout Europe. Handel's music was founded on Italian principles (which were, of course, effective in the German music of his youth) and infected by German provincial idiom. His first English works belonged to England only because they were performed there. But a composer's style develops in particular

[1] Published in *Suits of the Most Celebrated Lessons* (J. Walsh and J. Hare, 1717). Babell received more notice in Germany than in England. He was 'ein sehr berühmter, nunmehro verstorbener Clavicymbalist und Componist zu London, [der] hat in zwey Büchern verschiedener Autoren choisirte Trio für Instrumente ediret'. (Walther, *Lexikon*, 1732); and 'war ein Schüler von Händeln, geb. in London, und soll, nach Matthesons Berichte im vollkommenen Kapellmeister, auf der Orgel seiner Meister noch übertroffen haben. Man hat noch eine Sammlung der berühmtesten Lessons für Klavier unter seinen Namen'. (Gerber, *Lexikon*, 1790). The information probably came in the first place from Handel to Mattheson.

directions according to environment. Attention to convention and to day-to-day requirement affects the shape and indeed the content of music; especially when, as in Handel's case, the composer is sensitive to and frequently analytical of current taste. Handel was disinclined to live in discomfort. He regarded his profession as one which could afford him a relatively high standard of living: therefore he considered the relationship between his music and his public carefully. He was an astute businessman —with the good sense to cover his more speculative ventures with safe investments. This is one side of the picture, represented statistically by the extensive risks he took with his capital in regard to opera promotion and by the handsome fortune which he accumulated across the years and, after prudently seeking professional advice, disposed in sound stocks. Against this is to be noted the extreme warmth of Handel's generosity, both to persons and to institutions, and his concern for people with whom he came into contact.

During the reign of Queen Anne there were in London sufficient Germans—both musicians and others, for Prince George had encouraged immigration—for one such as Handel to feel himself at least not far from home. He could, for example, if he desired, attend a Lutheran service at the German Chapel that was maintained by the Queen at St. James's Palace. As a practising musician he found tolerance among the majority of his English colleagues who were well used to a cosmopolitan membership of their profession. When the Elector of Hanover became George I of England (this transition caused Handel some unease on account of his broken contract) there was a new influx of Germans. Their influence on music was to remain for more than a hundred years.

Handel, being the kind of person he was, concerned himself less with the question of nationality than with the wish to accommodate himself to the patterns of society. That he did so partly explains the enthusiasm that developed for his music, the course that his music took, and the respect, growing in the end to veneration, for his person. Handel revolutionised British music on a wide front; more than any other composer at any time. As a citizen he made a contribution to the reshaping of social responsibilities.

As a composer his work lay in these fields; of opera, occasional music, instrumental music, oratorio, and popular music. In each case he depended on people and on institutions, and the relationships that were developed give a comprehensive view of British music during the half-century in which the rest of Europe was otherwise adjusting itself to a new order of music.

Handel composed operas until 1741, by which time Italian opera, because of the feuds attendant on its provision, the presumption and general behaviour of Italian star singers,[1] strong reaction against an unintelligible language, and the popularity of ballad opera, was now out of fashion. Handel undertook the writing and direction of opera in the first place because he was conscious that the form offered the best opportunities to use his gifts and because it was backed by powerful supporters. *Rinaldo* was revived in honour of the Coronation of George I and *Amadigi*, also patronised by King and Court, was composed for the same season of 1714. At this period Handel appears to have been living with the Earl of Burlington, under whose sponsorship *Silla* was probably given a private performance. Burlington spread his interest wide over the arts and under his roof Handel had opportunity to conduct instrumental performances (others took place under the patronage of the Duke of Rutland, and Lords Essex and Perceval), and to meet the principals in English letters, art, and architecture.

The taste of the English in the theatre continued to centre on plays of many different types, and, according to the tradition established in Restoration times, on plays with music. Italian opera as such was being cultivated on stony ground.

Addison's *Rosamond* had been a serious attempt to show up the absurdities of Italian opera but only succeeded in demonstrating the incapacity and unwillingness of the English to provide a viable and attractive alternative. John Hughes, who was acquainted with Handel and the author of the libretto of Handel's English cantata *Venus and Adonis*, wrote the libretto for *Calypso and Telemachus* as propaganda for English opera. In 1722 Daniel Bellamy's private production of *Love Triumphant* (in a girls' school) attempted without much success a fusion of opera and masque into a 'pastoral opera'. In 1727 Lewis Theobald—the butt of Pope—published the libretto of another operatic hybrid, *The Rape of Proserpina*, and in his Preface he repeated formerly adduced arguments concerning the merits of English in respect of musico-dramatic works and went on to lambast those managers who were unable to spend adequately on scenic devices because of the extravagant salaries paid to foreign singers.

The nobility, however, were not easily put off and, since a taste in opera was a useful symbol of cultural prestige, they persisted. Opera became a hobby; an expensive hobby. In 1719 a Royal Academy of Music was set up under the governorship of the Duke of Newcastle, and with

[1] Cf. Henry Fielding, *Pasquin*, 1736, Act IV, Sc.1:
Thou wilt not suffer eunuchs to be hired,
At a vast price to be impertinent

and, *Epilogue*.

With soft Italian notes indulge your ear,
But let those singers, who are bought so dear,
Learn to be civil for their cheer at least;

twenty Directors to supervise its activities. Singers were brought from Italy and Germany. While Handel was expected to be the principal composer, others, of potential attraction to the public, were invited to contribute works. In 1720 Giovanni Buononcini was persuaded to come from Rome. On and off he remained in London for twelve years, eventually assuming the not entirely happy position of chief counter-attraction to Handel. In 1720 Handel produced *Radamisto*; later in the year came Buononcini's *Astarto*; in the following year a curious three-man opera *Muzio Scevola*, Handel writing the last Act in succession to a first Act by Filippo Mattei and a second by Buononcini. Before 1728 Handel composed *Floridante*, *Ottone*, *Flavio*, *Giulio Cesare*, *Tamerlano*,[1] *Rodelinda*, *Scipione*, *Alessandro*, *Admeto*, *Riccardo I*, *Siroe*, and *Tolomeo*, for the Royal Academy.

By now the writing on the wall was clear to read. That the compulsion on the aristocracy to attend the opera was lessening is indicated by the Account Book of Lady Mary Wortley Montagu which shows her expenditure on opera for four seasons as follows:

1724	operas	£3 3s. 0d.
1725	operas	£2 12s. 6d.
1726	operas	£1 1s. 0d.
1727	operas	10s. 6d.[2]

A manuscript Song Book of 1733[3] shows a preference on the part of Lady Mary and her sisters for a different kind of music—e.g. *To all you lady's now at Land*, *The lass of Patie's Mill*, *It was within a furlong* [*of Edinboro' Town*], etc. The ballad was firm in the affections of the British,[4] and so too was the ballad opera.

Ballad opera was a natural consequence of what had gone before. But it was the combination of easy and familiar music, pointed, coarsely

1 'They write from the King's Theatre in the Haymarket, That the Company of Singers lately arriv'd from Italy, continue performing Mr. Handel's new celebrated Opera, call'd Tamerlane, with such great applause from the Nobility, and all the Audience, that 'tis order'd by the Royal Academy to be play'd 6 Weeks successively. The Italian Words in the said Opera, are truely translated into English Verse, and Engrav'd under the Musick, which was never done before in any other Opera.' 'From Mr. J———'s Letter, London, Nov. 10', *Newcastle Courant*, 14 November 1724.

2 Sheffield Central Library, *Wharnecliffe Muniments*, 508.

3 ib., 506.

4 In spite of: 'The *Ballads*, which are sung in most, & sold in all the *Market-Towns* of this Nation, are a dreadful Instance of this *Corruption*; & the *Tunes* being fitted to a *vulgar Capacity*, are frequently learn'd by those who are not able to pay for a better *Education* . . . It is an endless and an impossible Task to give a full Account of all these *scandalous Songs & Ballads*, which swarm in Town & Country, & by the cheapness of the Price seem wholly intended to debauch the poor, as well as the rich . . . [of Playford's *Musical Companion*] . . . *Drinking* is almost perpetually encourag'd . . . Many of the *Love Songs* are scandalously debauch'd with *Smut*; and living a *Maid* is look'd upon as a great Folly.' Bedford, op. cit., pp. 64–5.

humorous, and satirical verses, and the general guying of *opera seria* in *The Beggar's Opera*—the 'Newgate pastoral' of John Gay's inspired invention—that really set the ball rolling.[1] After the first performance of *The Beggar's Opera* at Lincoln's Inn Fields on 29 January 1728, there was, predictably, a flood of works of similar genre. Gay's sequel, *Polly*, intended for 1729, was disallowed by the censorship—it awaited performance until 1777. In 1729 Theophilus Cibber staged a version of Allan Ramsay's *Gentle Shepherd* as a pastoral-musical-comedy entitled *Patie and Peggie*, Henry Carey revised *The Contrivances* to conform to the new pattern, William Chetwood's *The Lover's Opera* was put on at Drury Lane, and Essex Hawker's *The Wedding* (for which Pepusch arranged the music) at Lincoln's Inn Fields. Also in 1729 Charles Johnson's *The Village Opera* was played successfully at Drury Lane and after thirty years it was re-written by Isaac Bickerstaffe as *Love in a Village*, in which form and with the lyrics set to airs by Handel, Arne, Festing, Geminiani, Boyce, and others, it renewed its former popularity and went on to father many works of similar rural and sentimental character. Among other authors who busied themselves with ballad opera in the decade following Gay's first notable production the best-equipped were Henry Carey and Henry Fielding, whose sporadic thrusts at opera and opera singers helped to reduce that entertainment further in common esteem.

Handel soldiered on. At the beginning of 1728 the original Royal Academy closed down and was replaced by a new organisation, for which Handel again went to the Continent to engage singers. In December he produced *Lotario*. In successive years there followed *Poro*, to a text by Metastasio, *Ezio* and *Sosarme*, *Orlando*, *Arianna*, *Ariodante* and *Alcina*, *Atalanta* (for the wedding of the Prince of Wales), *Arminio* and *Giustino*, *Berenice*, *Faramondo*, *Serse*, *Imeneo* and *Deidamia*. This, the last of Handel's operas, was produced in January 1741. It had but three performances. The day of Italian opera in England, it appeared, was over.

Handel's thirty-year effort to persuade the English into accepting a European fashion against their inclinations was an heroic performance. One less conservative would have accepted the situation long before the logic of the balance-sheet made retreat inevitable. Because he refused to give in—despite the internecine warfare that divided high society into pro- and anti-Handel factions, the intervention of guest-composers as reputable as Hasse and Gluck, and the havoc caused to his physical and mental health—Handel was able to add to his pre-1728 masterpieces at least half-a-dozen major contributions to the field of opera in his last

[1] *The Beggar's Opera* was played in Dublin and Glasgow in 1728, in Jamaica in 1733, in New York and other American towns in 1750; its influence was enormous, possibly greater than any other single musical work (except *Messiah*) that came from England.

decade of work in this sphere. But they were increasingly irrelevant to the condition of British music except insofar as the popular airs, marches, and overtures, through Walsh and through exploitation in the Pleasure Gardens, became in the widest sense popular. On the musical side Handel developed his ready appreciation of the possibilities of character-drawing through the aria, and of scene-painting by means of orchestral colour. Valorous work in German opera-houses over the past forty years, and more recently by British and American individuals and institutions, has brought the Handel operas back on to the stage, where—given a reasonable chance—they help to correct the faulty impressions of the composer that were allowed to accumulate out of exaggerated regard for his other activities.

The age of Handel saw the development of a corporate sense on the part of orchestral players, and the emergence of some sort of solidarity was due on the one hand to the increased opportunities for public performance that were forthcoming and, on the other, to the challenging properties of the music that was to be played. Concerts were given at Court, in taverns as formerly, at Hickford's Room off the Haymarket, at the room in Brewer Street, Soho, that was taken over on the closure of Hickford's Room in 1729, in Vauxhall Gardens after 1732 and, when available, in the theatres. The enthusiasm for instrumental music that appeared in the latter part of the seventeenth century intensified during the eighteenth, under the influences of visiting virtuosi and professors, of the agreeable qualities of the sonatas and concertos especially of Corelli[1] and his disciples and imitators, of the appreciation of playing standards among both native professional and amateur performers, and of the exhilaration of the wide-ranging instrumental works of Handel. Professional players followed various regular commitments and were ready to undertake free-lance work and also to risk their reputations if need be on solo exhibitions and to reinforce their earnings from the profits on well-advertised benefit concerts.

While the taste of the concert-going public was conservative the fact that a concert was an entertainment was rarely lost sight of; thus novelty of one sort or another was welcome so long as the structure of established forms remained inviolate. An advertisement in the *Daily Journal*, for 25 February 1732, for instance, displayed: 'For the benefit of Mr. Angel and Mr. Cook, . . . at Lincoln's Inn Fields . . . A Concert of VOCAL and INSTRUMENTAL MUSICK *By the Best Hands*, In the manner as it was perform'd at Dresden, by the King of Poland's Command.

[1] Writing of Corelli, Geminiani, Handel, Vivaldi, etc. Rev. John Trydell remarked '. . . how chaste and perfect their Compositions are. And their intrinsic merit may, perhaps, ever challenge the foremost place, as long as the love of Harmony shall prevail in the World'. *Two Essays on the Theory and Practice of Music*, Dublin, 1766, p. 44.

The Performers are to be in the Character as follows:—The Harpsichord by Columbine, Violoncello by Harlequin, Bassoon by Scaramouch, Double Bass by Pierot, Singing by Diana and an Indian King, Violins by a Spaniard, a Roman, an Hungarian, a Persian, a Turk, a Polander, an Arabian, a Muscovite: the Tenor by a Highlander, the German Flute by a Satyr, French Horns by Forresters, two Shepherds Hautboys, and others. The Concert of Performers will consist of between 40 and 50 of the best Hands. Places will be kept on the stage for Gentlemen and Ladies performers, who are willing to play between the Acts, in proper Habits as they please.'

Ten years later the *Daily Advertiser* (22 February 1742) carried: 'For the Benefit of Mr. Brown[1] at the Castle Tavern in Paternoster Row, this day . . . will be performed a concert of vocal and instrumental musick. Particularly an Organ Concerto by an Eminent Master, a Concerto on the Bassoon by Mr. Miller, a solo on the German Flute by Mr. Ballicourt and a Solo and several Concertos on the Violia [*sic*] by Mr. Brown, The vocal parts by Mr. Beard and Mr. Lowe.'

A select list of the notable players who crossed Handel's path shows how international the field of London instrumental music was. Corbett (see p. 272) was leader of the Opera Orchestra from 1705 to 1711, and he was vigorous in promotion of the Corelli style. In 1714 Francesco Maria Veracini, accounted one of the leading violinists in Europe, came to London to lead the same orchestra in succession to Corelli's pupil Castrucci. In the same year Geminiani, later to move to Dublin, arrived. He had a high reputation as a teacher, and among his pupils were Matthew Dubourg who was later to greet Handel in Dublin, Michael Festing, and James Nares. Geminiani, also a pupil of Corelli, did as much as anyone to embed his master's works in the English repertoire, and his own concertos and sonatas served as models to many English composers among them Avison of Newcastle, Stanley, John Hebden, and John Humphreys. Other immigrant musicians to play significant rôles in the development of instrumental music included Giuseppe Sammartini of Milan, oboist in the opera in 1723 and subsequently chamber musician to the Prince of Wales; Charles Weidemann, a flautist who towards the end of his life accumulated a large collection of music which he edited for court functions for George III; Giacomo Cervetto, cellist; and Johann Friedrich Lampe, bassoonist who married Thomas Augustine Arne's sister-in-law and subsequently directed orchestral performances in Edinburgh and Dublin. During the whole of this period Dublin benefited from the vice-regal music sponsored from the castle and produced in John Clegg one of

[1] Leader of the King's Band and an intimate friend of Handel: see Burney, *Commemoration, 1785*, p. 48.

the finest violinists of the day. He was as well known in London as in Dublin. The acknowledged leader among English orchestral players was Michael Festing, who, according to Burney, 'acquired a weight and influence in his profession, at which hardly any musician of his class ever arrived'.[1] It was Festing, moved by the death of a popular colleague—the oboist Jack Kytch—and the plight of his dependents, who founded as a provident society the (after 1789 Royal) Society of Musicians. Among those who lent powerful aid to this society in its formative years was Handel, who made donations to it during his lifetime and posthumously through his will. His bequest of £1,000 was the largest contribution received to that date.

Handel's response to the opportunities afforded by the pattern of concert-giving, the special occasion, and the technical abilities of his friends and colleagues, is seen in the *concerti grossi* (especially op. 3, 1734, and op. 6, 1739), in the *Water Music* and *Royal Fireworks Music* suites of *c.* 1717 and 1749 respectively, and in the sonatas which he consistently spread over his English career. Handel's vocation as teacher (of the royal children in the first place, but he had other pupils) and performer is mirrored in his keyboard music of which the most original and important is contained in two sets of organ concertos (op. 4, 1735–6: op. 7, 1740–51). The latter belonged more or less intimately to the department of oratorio, through the popularisation of which Handel exerted (and continues to exert) a massive influence. The antecedents of the fully developed Handelian oratorio were mixed: Italian cantata, oratorio, and opera, German church music, and the English dialogue of the seventeenth century and the anthem and its extensions as described on pp. 279–80; the Bible and a derivative tradition of sacred verse and drama; and the English theatre. The whole corpus of Handelian oratorio, of course, stretches over a wide territory, so that apart from the personal stamp of the music there is little in common between the lyrical *Susanna* and *Theodora* on the one hand and the heroic *Samson* and *Jephtha* on the other, or between *Israel in Egypt* and *Messiah.* The reason for these broad distinctions lies in Handel's reaction, firstly to the different textual stimuli, and secondly to the estimated appreciation of his audiences. Essentially oratorios developed as a response to the frequently expressed demand for an English form of opera—from which Hughes at least did not exclude the propriety of utilising what was adaptable from Italian convention. On the side of the main stream Handel did indeed construct at least one English opera, *Semele,* an adaptation of Congreve's libretto. But even *Semele* is difficult to make entirely convincing on the stage because of the difficulty of integrating the choruses and accommodating the chorus singers.

[1] *History*, IV, p. 669.

Handel was an empiricist. He worked according to no set theory but under the spur of necessity—the necessity to meet actual or estimated demands. Moreover he had the particular genius that can see the potentiality of any medium that is to hand. Handel appreciated what his literary associates were driving at, and he had access to the expert singers of the Chapel Royal. The foundation on which the oratorio was built was in fact the Chapel Royal, whose singers (like those of St. Paul's) were available to be hired by responsible organisations subject to the license of their Dean.[1]

As 'Kapellmeister' to the Duke of Chandos Handel composed the twelve *Chandos Anthems*—works of considerable variety and flexibility and calling for those qualities of independence and interpretative insight which the Chapel Royal singers were accustomed to display. The names of the principal singers were written into the autograph of the sixth Anthem (which was incorporated into the 1732 version of *Esther*) by Handel: among them was Bernard Gates. In 1719 or 1720 *Acis and Galatea*, a secular serenata based on Gay's poem, was produced. In August 1720 *Haman and Mordecai*, in which Alexander Pope had a hand and which had as literary antecedent Racine's *Esther*, was given under the patronage of the Duke. At this point the 'anthem' (and *Haman and Mordecai* appears to have been so described)[2] left its moorings, moving towards opera and away from any possible liturgical connection.

The years passed. Handel composed the Coronation Anthems in 1727. The Academy of Ancient Music[3] flourished and a leading figure in its activities was Bernard Gates, now responsible for the Children of the Chapel Royal. Members included Hughes and Weely, two singers detailed as fellow participants in the sixth Chandos Anthem. *Haman and Mordecai* (now named *Esther*) was performed at the Crown and Anchor Tavern for the Academy of Ancient Music, on 23 February, 1732. A number of choristers later to become famous as exponents of Handel, or otherwise,

[1] Cf. Expenses of Academy of Vocal Music 1725/6–31 (B.M. Add. Ms. 11732). 'A Coach for ye Children [of St. Paul's] 2/0', and Regulation of 1798 (the Children [of the Chapel Royal] continued to 'assist at Oratorios in Lent, as long as those performances maintained their ecclesiastical character entire'). 'When the boys return home from singing at the Oratorios, the antient music, or any other concert, public or private, in the evening, they shall have a coach to carry them home, and shall have a good supper—and in winter a fire—at their return'; quoted in E. Sheppard, *Memorials of St. James's Palace*, 1894, II, p. 320.

[2] *The Weekly Journal*, 3 September 1720, referred to the opening of the Duke of Chandos's Chapel 'with an Anthem on Monday last' (29 August).

[3] Typical programmes of the Academy (note the division into 'Acts') were: 31 January 1733—First Act; *Psalm*, Palestrina; *Madrigal*, Marenzio; *Psalm*, Colonna. Second Act; *Madrigal*, Paolo Petti; *Psalm*, Colonna; *Motet*, Lupi: Third Act; *Psalm*, Palestrina; *Madrigal*, Marenzio; *Magnificat*, Colonna; *Non nobis Domine*, Byrd: 19 December 1734– *Motet*, Pepusch; *Cease not thy Mourning*, Farmer; *Where art thou, wanton*, Morley; *Judgment of Solomon, in the Manner of an Oratorio*, Charissimi [*sic*]. Word-books, formerly the property R. J. S. Stevens and E. F. Rimbault, in the Leeds City Library.

took part in this performance, in costume, including John Randall (Esther), John Beard (Priest), and Samuel Howard and Thomas Barrow (chorus). Further performances took place on 1 and 3 March. On 20 April a pirated version of *Esther* was presented at York Buildings. On 2 May a royal command performance at the Haymarket was directed by Handel. This performance was affected by a ruling of the Dean of the Chapel, Bishop Edmund Gibson (in office from 1721 to 1761). Gibson was a disciplinarian, zealous for the good order and reputation of the Chapel Choir, and the injunctions drawn up and promulgated by him in the document of 1728 relating to the 'Decent and Orderly performance of a Divine Service' were relevant to the maintenance of high musical standards.[1] It is not surprising that he tempered his permission for the singers to take part in *Esther* with an instruction that there should be no acting. If, however, he had not so decreed oratorio would have taken a different course. As it was the presence of a trained and static body of singers ensured that the choral element would be prominent in the form of oratorio that became acceptable. At the same time the adaptability of the singers was encouragement to Handel to treat the chorus with flexibility and imagination.

The year 1732 may be seen as decisive; for the desire for English words to be used in preference to Italian (expressed directly to Handel by Aaron Hill at the end of the year) was recognised as exploitable. So too was another of Handel's existing scores. *Acis and Galatea* was revived at Lincoln's Inn Fields in quasi-opera form with Susanna Arne singing the part of Galatea. The same young singer appeared also in a 'new English opera . . . after the Italian manner', *Amelia*, the words by Henry Carey, the music by Lampe, who continued his collaboration with Carey in a series of popular ballad operas. Not readily disposed to see unauthorised versions of his works taking place Handel himself gave a performance of *Acis and Galatea*, augmented by some numbers taken from his earlier Italian cantata on the same subject. Meanwhile the idea that oratorio was likely to prove successful occurred to Willem de Fesch, a Dutch musician resident in London, who in conjunction with William Higgins prepared *Judith*, which was given at Lincoln's Inn Theatre at the beginning of 1733. In Lent, 1733, Handel provided the oratorio public with *Deborah*, the subject of which may have been provoked by Maurice Greene's *Song of*

[1] It seems that there had been some slackness in performance, '. . . It is hereby ordered that ye several members of ye Quire do joyn in singing the Psalms, Services, and Choruses with a due application and with a proper and decent strength and extention of voice'; and also in selection, 'And ye precentor . . . shall take care to chuse only such unto their number as have good voices and suitable capacitys, and shall not only instruct them in ye grounds of Music, but also qualify them in due time to bear their part in the Verse Anthems'. Sheppard, op. cit., II, pp. 215–16.

Deborah and Barak, a piece composed for the 'Apollo' Academy; and later in the year he completed *Athaliah* in time for performance in Oxford on 10 July. During his visit to Oxford Handel organised five subscription concerts in the Sheldonian Theatre. As a result of this series of events the enthusiasm of the music-lovers of Oxford was sufficiently stimulated to look for more suitable premises for such performances, and in 1742 the scheme for a Music Room was launched: the Room itself, in Holywell Street (now part of the Faculty of Music of the University), was ready for occupation in 1748.

In 1734 Handel was challenged as an oratorio composer by the peripatetic Niccola Porpora whose *Davide e Bersabea* was performed at Lincoln's Inn Fields. It was revived a year later but was quickly extinguished by Handel's rich programme of *Esther*, *Athaliah*, and *Deborah*, which were further enhanced by the inclusion of organ concertos. The popularity of the concertos as played by the master himself was a factor in the consolidation of the cult of oratorio. The point was made by William Mann: '. . . if any of my readers are old enough to recollect how the great Handel executed that kind of Capriccio, which he usually introduced upon the Organ between one of [*sic*] the Acts of his Oratorios . . . , he will, I believe, agree with me, that words cannot more perfectly express the supreme excellency of that performance, than the opinion I have translated from this Swiss Critic [J. J. Rousseau]. For myself, I own that the superior manner, in point both of vocal and instrumental Performers, by which his Oratorios have been since executed in Westminster Abbey and elsewhere, cannot compensate for the want of that solo, now alas! to be heard no more'.[1] In later years Handel did not hesitate to intersperse his oratorios with concertos by other instruments than the organ; while in *Saul* he made organ concertos integral to the score.[2]

Between 1735 and 1737 Handel composed *Alexander's Feast*, a fine and colourful setting of Dryden's poem (adapted by Newburgh Hamilton); the Anthem for the marriage of the Prince of Wales and Princess Augusta of Saxe-Gotha at St. James's;[3] and the Funeral Anthem for Queen Caroline,[4]

[1] *The Works of William Mann*, III (*Essays, Historical and Critical on English Church Music*), pp. 305–6.

[2] First *Symphony* (revised and more familiar form) and *Symphony* in Act II.

[3] 'The marriage service was read by the Bishop of London (Dr. Edmund Gibson), Dean of the Chapel Royal, and after the same was over a fine Anthem was performed by a great number of voices and instruments'. Quoted by Sheppard, op. cit., II, p. 72. No doubt as in the case of the Wedding Anthem of 1734, Handel held a rehearsal of the music in the presence of the King and Queen and other members of the Royal Family.

[4] 'The Anthem to be sung in Westminster-Abbey at the Funeral, it's reckon'd will take up an Hour in performing. The Musick, which will be exceeding grand and solemn, is compos'd by Mr. Handel, and the Words by Dr. Green.' From several London papers, 10 December, *Newcastle Courant*, 14 December 1737.

in which he pertinently quoted from his recollections of German chorale. In this period he also revised his Italian oratorio of 1708, *Il Trionfo del tempo*. Other ideas were taking shape but a severe illness in 1737—some kind of thrombosis attack accompanied by a severe bout of depression—held up activity for some months in 1737, during which he went to recuperate at Aix-la-Chapelle.

In 1733 the preacher John Henley proposed that the subject of Saul[1] would make a fitting theme for a St. Cecilia's Day celebration. At the beginning of 1736 Aaron Hill published one Act of *Saul: A Tragedy* in the *Gentleman's Magazine*. In the summer of 1738, to a libretto prepared by Charles Jennens, Handel wrote the score of his *Saul*. As usual, working in haste he borrowed a trio sonata and turned it into the opening symphony, and, in the first place, intended to incorporate the *Funeral Anthem*. No sooner was the score of *Saul* complete than he went straight on to *Israel in Egypt*, taking into this work, unique by reason of the pre-eminence of the chorus, an unused item from the sketches for *Saul* and ideas culled from Stradella (and possibly Urio). *Saul* and *Israel in Egypt* were the novelties for the 1739 oratorio season. Later that year Handel returned to classical English poems and, lightening the choral texture somewhat in view of the unfavourable reception of *Israel in Egypt*, composed the *Ode on St. Cecilia's Day* (Dryden) and *L'Allegro, il Penseroso ed il Moderato* (Milton).

The Apotheosis of Handel

At this point Handel, being fifty-five years of age and by now resigned to abdication from his other vocation of opera-composer, was inclined to call it a day. On 8 April 1741 he gave a farewell concert, the programme comprising the two most recent choral works. At the end of August, however, he took up his pen again. By 14 September *Messiah* was complete. By 29 October the score of *Samson*, from Milton by Newburgh Hamilton, was ready. Almost immediately Handel set off for Dublin—by way of Chester where a rehearsal of *Messiah* took place. On arrival in Dublin he superintended a series of subscription concerts which began on 18 November. For some years past works by Handel had been performed in aid of various of the city's charities. An invitation to pay a personal visit came from the Duke of Devonshire, Lord Lieutenant, and the intention was that the new oratorio should be given in the recently opened music hall designed

[1] Other works which lie in the background are Abraham Cowley's *Davideis* (1656), to which Jennens referred in the Word-book of Handel's Oratorio; Dr. Joseph Trapp's *The Tragedy of King Saul*, and, on the musical side, the dramatic dialogue settings by Nicholas Lanier, Robert Ramsay, Henry Purcell, and Benjamin Lamb, of *In guilty night*.

by Richard Cassels and also in aid of charity. The first performance of *Messiah*, on 13 April, was one of the most notable of all first performances, for it fortuitously set down a new concept: that music of this character could exert a moral influence. The original impulse for this work may have come in part from Alexander Pope, or from Thomas Roseingrave, or, for that matter, from Henry Hall. Handel's ideas, like those of many composers (Beethoven being the most conspicuous example), took time to mature. Often, as in the case of *Messiah*, the idea broke the surface in response to an occasion. The circumstances surrounding the Dublin invitation enabled the libretto of *Messiah*, as developed by Jennens, to assume a particular relevance. From then on, despite an initial coolness in London on the part of the pietistic, *Messiah* became the fulcrum of all the charitable movements that sprang up in Britain from the time of its creation. The particular charity in which Handel himself was personally interested was the Foundling Hospital, where for many years he directed or appeared at an annual performance of *Messiah*.

By now an honoured national figure (a British citizen by Act of Parliament in 1727), with his statue by Roubiliac a feature of the Gardens at Vauxhall, Handel entered upon the last fruitful decade of his composing life. It was a decade in which nationalism as such became a determining factor in the life of the community, and from time to time Handel was called upon for celebratory music. In 1743 the victory of the British, Hanoverian, and Austrian troops at Dettingen called for a *Te Deum*.[1] In the same year the operatic *Semele* and *Joseph and his Brethren* were completed in time for the next oratorio season. In 1744 a secular 'oratorio', *Hercules*, complemented *Belshazzar*. The Rising of 1745 called for an *Occasional Oratorio*, performed in 1746, and the heroic *Judas Maccabaeus*,

[1] A concert given in 1743 (of which the programme is in the Leeds City Library) contained as Act II an *Ode on the Birthday of the Prince of Wales* by John Travers (*c.* 1703–1758) which concluded with a Latin chorus—the words of which apparently represent first thoughts for the National Anthem which was first sung two years later:

O Deus optime
Salvum nunc facito
Regem nostrum;
Sit laeta victoria,
Comes et gloria,
Salvum jam facito
Tu Dominum.

Exurgat Dominus;
Rebelles dissipet,
Et reprimat;
Dolor confundito;
Fraudes depellite;
In te sit sita spes
O! Salva Nos.

which enjoyed considerable success in its first season, and has continued to do so for no very apparent reason beyond the relative ease with which its choruses can be managed. In 1749, as has been said, the Peace of Aix-la-Chapelle produced the *Royal Fireworks Music*.

The oratorio audience by now had a solid core of middle-class patronage, but it claimed the prerogative to be fickle. Support fluctuated: *Messiah* was sure of a full house but new works less so, and *Theodora*, following *Joshua* and *Alexander Balus* (perf. 1748) and *Susanna* and *Solomon* (1749), called for wry comment from the composer when he saw the empty seats at Covent Garden in 1750. There remained one oratorio to write: *Jephtha* (an oratorio to a text by John Hoadly on this subject was composed by Maurice Greene in 1737). This noble work was completed with difficulty, for Handel's eyesight was failing badly, but it was completed. It was produced at Covent Garden on 26 February 1752.

Although afflicted with near-blindness and generally deteriorating health, Handel remained active to the end of his life.

> 'Mr. Handel Perform'd the Messiah at Covent Ga Apr. 6th 1759—Playd a Concerto upon the Harpsecord, and Dy'd on the 14th of the said April, in the 75th year of His Age—Quite sensible to the last.'

The anonymous writer of this notice prefaced it with an elegiac poem, *Spoken upon the Death of George Frederic Handel Esq.*, which illustrates the change that had taken place in English sensibility; partly as a consequence of the mid-century attitude to oratorio.

> To Melt the Soul to captivate the Ear
> (Angels his melody might deign to hear)
> T' anticipate on Earth the Joys of Heav'n
> Was Handel's Task, to him the pow'r was giv'n.
> Ah! when he late attund Messiahs praise
> With sounds Celestial with Melodious Lays
> A last farwel [*sic*] his languid Looks exprest
> And thus methinks th' enraptur'd Crowd addrest
> Adieu! my dearest Friends and allso you
> Joint sons of sacred Harmony adieu!
> A wisp'ring Angel prompts me to retire
> Bids me prepare to meet th' immortal Choir
> O! for the glorious Change, great Handel cry'd
> Messiah heard his Voice, and Handel dy'd.[1]

Handel was not only the first English composer accepted during his lifetime as a national figure (Purcell's apotheosis, due to external circum-

[1] B.M. Add. Ms. 33351, f. 24.

stances, on the whole was posthumous); he was the first composer of any kind whose works were intuitively thought to be expressive of and appealing to national sentiment. During his life in England political, economic, social, and religious values interacted and the pattern that formed was one which remained. The monarchy, despite the frequent personal demerits of the Hanoverians, had popular support; but its powers were more and more reduced so that decision-making rested increasingly with Parliament. Growth in the national income, mercantile development, the early signs of an Industrial Revolution that began to show a new energy in towns such as Birmingham and Manchester, spread prosperity over a wider field. Handel's librettist, Charles Jennens, was one beneficiary of industrial expansion, inheriting his considerable wealth from his father who was an iron-master in the Midlands. Patriotism was strengthened by memories of the victories of Marlborough, by the suppression of the Stuart risings in 1715 and 1745, and by military successes during the War of Austrian Succession. For almost two decades in the middle life of Handel, however, national consolidation was the more readily achieved through the peaceful premiership of Robert Walpole. Handel saw the establishment of the English novel, its picaresque traditions turned by Richardson, Fielding, and Smollett (for whose *Alceste* Handel sketched music that was re-hashed for *The Choice of Hercules*) towards social criticism. He was part of a many-pronged movement that led towards a greater realisation of the necessity for less social injustice, associating with William Hogarth (a member of the Academy of Vocal Music[1] and a fellow-Governor of the Foundling Hospital) and Thomas Coram. Collateral with the dissatisfaction that caused men to inaugurate charitable foundations and to build hospitals was a cultivation of sensibility (in the poetry of Matthew Green, John Dyer, and William Collins) that led the middle-classes towards sentimentality. It was dissatisfaction with an establishment that often appeared content to leave things exactly as they were that brought into being the Methodist movement. In one way or another Handel's life and music comprehended all these phenomena. Thus it was that, taking advantage of every opportunity offered to him and making others where they previously did not exist, Handel achieved his peculiar eminence.

Expanding Opportunity

British music owed much to Handel, but he in turn was indebted to a general extension of musical enterprise that would almost certainly have taken place without his residence in England. For in the eighteenth

[1] Noted as Subscriber no. 69, 8 May 1729 (B.M. Add. Ms. 11732).

century the means of expansion were to hand in a large and ever-growing stock of printed music and in the dispersal of excellent teachers and orchestral leaders (usually foreigners who found the competition in London too great) throughout the Kingdom.

By the time of Handel's death the beginnings of musical education for infants was under way.

In, or about, 1744 one of the fundamental books of infant musical instruction was issued: *Tommy Thumb's Pretty Song Book*—with a charming frontispiece showing a little flute player with his two admiring sisters(?). The instructional purpose of the volume was indicated by this quatrain:

The Childs Plaything
I recommend for Cheating
Children with Learning
Without any beating.
(N. Lovechild)

Some of the basic nursery songs are here to be found. Some which were in common use no longer are. For instance,

Piss a bed
Piss a bed
Barley Butt,
Your Bum is so heavy
You can't get up.

or

We are all a day
With drinking ont;
We are all a day,
With drinking ont;
The Piper kisst
The Fidlers Wife
And I cant sleep
For thinking ont.

After a decade the process of selection had removed the ruder examples of children's songs, and an advertisement in *The Northampton Mercury* for 23 April 1759 showed why. '. . . Nancy Cock's dainty-fine Song-book was for all Little Misses and Masters; to be sung to them by their Nurses, till they can sing them themselves—with a suitable Picture to every Song'. A tribute to the musical virtues of the nurses was emphasised some time before 1767 when *Mother Goose's Melody* was published: 'We cannot', according to the Preface, 'conclude without observing, the great probability there is that the custom of making *Nonsense Verses* in our schools was borrowed from the practice among the old *British* nurses, they have, indeed, been always the first preceptors of the youth of this kingdom and from them the rudiments of taste and learning are naturally derived. Let none therefore speak irreverently of the ancient maternity, as they may be considered as the great grandmothers of science and knowledge.'

This was a period in which in large towns (still maintaining their own waits) instrumental and vocal concerts multiplied, and in which large-scale choral festivals began. The renewed concert life of Edinburgh, that owed much to the Germans, Beck and Crumden, who organised events at the end of the seventeenth century, flourished greatly—as Allan Ramsay noticed—[1]and a regular Musical Society came into being in the city.[2] At the same time there was similar activity in Glasgow and Aberdeen, in which Musical Societies were also established. An Instrumental Music Society was founded in Dublin in 1710 and collaboration with the already existing singing-clubs maintained by the cathedral singing-men (similar clubs were maintained by cathedral singers in Hereford, York, Lincoln, Lichfield, and Chester) led to the formation of a Charitable and Musical Society in 1723. The experienced musicians who controlled the instrumental performers in Dublin in the first half of the century were Johann Kusser, Kapellmeister to the Lord Lieutenant, and his successor Matthew Dubourg, who was in office from 1727 until 1765. Charles Avison, Novocastrian by birth but educated in Italy, organist first of St. John's and then of St. Nicholas's Church, made Newcastle a very considerable musical centre. There had been a concert tradition in the city since the beginning of the century, based on a close association between church and civic musicians similar to that in, say, Leipzig. Regular series of subscription concerts started in 1736—although benefit concerts are recorded before that time. So the *Newcastle Courant* of 14 August 1736 advertised:

> At the ASSEMBLY-ROOM, on Wednesday will be perform'd a CONSORT [*sic*][3] of vocal and instrumental MUSICK. To begin at Six o'Clock.
>
> Tickets, at 2s. 6d. each, may be had at Mrs. Hill's and Mrs. Pratt's in the Flesh Market, at Mrs. Banson's, and at the Sandhill Coffee-House.
>
> N.B. The first Subscription CONSORT will be held on Thursday the 26th Instant, at the Assembly-Rooms; & Tickets for the Season, at One Guinea each, will be deliver'd at the Door.

[1] In *The City of Edinburgh's Address to the Country*, 1716, and *To the Music Club*, 1721.

[2] See Edinburgh Musical Society Minutes, 1728–95 (4 vols.), and *Index to the Music*, Edinburgh Central Public Library.

[3] In Northumbrian dialect 'concert' may still be heard as 'consort.'

Avison worked in Newcastle for more than thirty years. His efforts affected the neighbouring towns, as Durham, where concerts were also established. His own works, and those of a close colleague, John Garth, of Durham, show eloquently how taste in the north-east changed from Baroque to Classical (see pp. 334–5).

By 1744 regular concerts were also taking place in Manchester. In the Manchester programmes the overtures, from operas and oratorios of Handel alike, took pride of place, with the Concerti of Corelli strong runners-up.[1]

The Oratorio Cult

As early as 1717 the three choirs of Worcester, Hereford, and Gloucester were meeting for combined performances and by 1724 the Three Choirs Festival existed officially as a charitable undertaking similar to the Sons of the Clergy Corporation in London which had sponsored large-scale musical performance since 1698.[2] Taking a lead from the Utrecht celebration at St. Paul's the works occasioned by the Treaty were prominent at the Three Choirs Festival for some years. By 1739 other works by Handel took their place, but so too did compositions by Boyce (conductor of the Festival from 1737 for some years) and Maurice Greene. Between 1730 and 1740 the organist at Gloucester was Barnabas Gunn, formerly at St. Philip's Church, Birmingham, whose connection with Handel is indicated by the fact that Handel was a subscriber to his *Two Cantatas and Six Songs*. There was also a strong Handel cult in the south and west of England. At Salisbury a musical festival—'for the Benefit of the Toun Music, assisted by several bands from Bath, etc.'—was instituted in 1744, the guiding light being James Harris,[3] a gentleman of independent means and

[1] See *Manchester Collecteana*, 2, 'Places and Institutions', Manchester, 1867, pp. 73–5.

[2] The Charity had begun in 1674, when Stewards were appointed, but it was twenty or so years before the music took precedence over the Sermon (which in 1738 was preached by the Dean of Worcester). See *A Complete List of the Stewards, Presidents, etc. belonging to the Royal Corporation for the Relief of the Poor Widows & Children of Clergymen, from the Grant of the Charter by King Charles II, July 1, 1678*, comp. by William Freeman, London, 1733. This Festival had a northern counterpart in 1722, when, on 14 September 'the Sons of the Clergy had their Anniversary Meeting here [Newcastle], and were honour'd with the Presence of the Lord Bishop. Two fine Anthems were sung by the Choir of Durham in our great Church . . .' *Newcastle Courant*, 15 September 1722.

[3] Harris wrote an essay on aesthetics (*Three Treatises*, 1744) in which he annotated his argument by Handelian references: '. . . in the natural or inanimate world, music may imitate the slidings, murmurings, tossings, roarings, and other accidents of nature, as perceiv'd in fountains, cataracts, rivers, seas, etc.; the same of thunder; the same of winds, as well the stormy as the gentle. In the animal world it may imitate the voice of some animals, but chiefly that of singing birds; it may also faintly copy some of their motions. In the human kind, it can also imitate some motions [f.n. As the walk of the giant Polypheme, in the pastoral of Acis and Galatea] and sounds [f.n. As the shouts of

acquainted with Handel through his kinsman the Earl of Malmesbury. In 1748 and also in 1749 *Acis and Galatea* was performed. For the next three years *Samson* took pride of place, though in 1752 *Judas Maccabaeus* and parts of *Messiah*[1] had been added to the programme. In 1753 *Judas Maccabaeus* was repeated, and in the four succeeding years *Joshua*, *Hercules*, *Esther*, and *Saul* respectively were given. From Salisbury the Handel influence spread out to Bath (where Handel spent a holiday in 1751), Bristol, and Devizes.

In 1759 performances of *Messiah* were given at the Senate House in Cambridge on 17 May (conductor John Randall, then Professor of Music in the University), and in the Sheldonian Theatre in Oxford on the first Thursday of July (conductor William Hayes). On 18 September *Acis and Galatea* was performed in Coventry for the benefit of Capel Bond, organist of St. Michael's and Holy Trinity Churches from 1750 to 1790, and a pioneer of oratorio in a number of Midland towns. To make this occasion a success no expense was spared and solo singers and instrumentalists were brought down from London.[2] Between the acts were a solo on the violin by Thomas Pinto,[3] and concertos—one for the bassoon by Miller,[4] one for the trumpet by Adcock, and one for the hautboy by Thomas Vincent.[5] A week later an ambitious performance of *Messiah* took place in the village church in Church Langton, Leicestershire, which was promoted by the Rev. William Hanbury,[6] the vicar of the parish. 'More than two hundred coaches, chariots, landaus, and post-chaises brought a genteel audience'; so that 'neither perhaps had any Church in England so splendid a congregation'. We read further that 'the number of beautiful ladies was very great, which occasioned the meeting to be afterwards much talked of on their account'; while 'the music, on so solemn a subject,

a multitude, in the coronation anthem of God Save the King, etc.]; and of sounds, those most perfectly, which are expressive of grief and anguish [f.n. . . . for grief, in most animals, declares itself by sounds, which are not unlike to long notes in the chromatic system. Of this kind is the chorus of Baal's priests in the oratorio of Deborah, *Doleful tidings, how ye wound, etc.*] p. 30. At a later point Harris wrote of 'Handel . . . whose genius having been cultivated by continued exercise, and being itself for the sublimest and most universal now known, has justly placed him without an equal, or a second.'

[1] A Ms. score made from the parts and the original property of John Matthews, lay vicar in Salisbury Cathedral, is discussed by Watkins Shaw in *M. & L.*, 39, April 1958.

[2] Advertisement in the *Northampton Mercury*, 10 September.

[3] 1714–83, of Neapolitan birth, a notable soloist and orchestral leader (Three Choirs Festival, Drury Lane and Haymarket Theatres, Edinburgh, Aberdeen, and Dublin).

[4] A frequent performer at subscription concerts and member of the Ranelagh Gardens Orchestra; according to Burney the best bassoonist of the day. (*History*, IV, pp. 663 and 665).

[5] *c.* 1720–83; pupil of Sammartini, notable for quality of his tone; composer of *Six Solos for a Hautboy, German Flute, Violins, or Harpsichord* (Op. 1) and other works. Vincent was a member of the Royal Band from 1725.

[6] *The History of . . . the Charitable Foundations at Church-Langton*, London, 1767, pp. 80 f.

by so good a band, was most affecting . . . ; an eye without tears I believe could hardly be found in the whole church'. After the performance the company adjourned to a great booth for venison, pasties, ham-pies ('of more than a yard diameter'), and other delicacies.

The proliferation of oratorio performances had the most profound effect on British music. It is, indeed, doubtful whether any other single type of music, virtually the work of one composer, ever achieved so much; for Handelian oratorio democratised music. Not only did it bring great music to a vast part of the population previously disfranchised but it involved a great cross-section of the community in the practice of music. Oratorio in England may have begun on a ducal estate in 1720. Forty years later it was, by popular consent, the property of the people. The extent to which it affected musical appreciation and stirred the ambitions of the modest is indicated by William Mann, who, in a section entitled 'Village Practitioners', writes: 'For these, since the rage of oratorios has spread from the Capital to every Market Town in the Kingdom, can by no means be satisfied unless they introduce Chaunts, Services, and Anthems, into their Parish Churches, and accompany them with, what an old Author [Thomas Mace] calls, *Scolding Fiddles*, squalling Hautboys, false-stopped violoncellos, buzzing Bassoons; all ill-tuned and worse played upon, in place of an Organ, which, if they had one, they would probably wish to improve by such instrumental assistance. The tintamarre which this kind of squeaking and scraping and grumbling produces, I will not pain my Reader by bringing stronger to his recollection. . . .'[1]

Handel was also responsible for a sub-division in the profession of singing: by 1759 the 'oratorio singer'—a particularly English phenomenon—was going strong, secure in the knowledge that as many engagements awaited him or her as could be undertaken. 'Handel', wrote Hawkins, 'was not a proud man, but he was capricious: In his comparison of the merits of a composer and those of a singer, he estimated the latter at a very low rate.'[2] The Italian singers he imported were always liable to be taken to task by the master, who used them because he was required to do so by his promoters and also because English singers competent in the Italian style were few and far between. Mrs. Tofts had left the stage (she married an acquaintance of Handel, Joseph Smith, Consul in Venice) before he arrived. Mrs. Barbier took the place of Mrs. Tofts and was engaged for *Il Pastor Fido* in 1712. She also sang in 1713 in *Teseo* and when *Rinaldo* was revived on 9 May it was 'for Mrs. Barbiers Benefit'; she sang the title role. In 1717 Mrs. Barbier, hitherto kept at home by her parents, eloped and after her marriage returned to the stage, but for Rich at Lincoln's

[1] Mann, op. cit., p. 388.
[2] *History*, V, p. 300.

Inn Fields, where she mostly sang in pantomime. Anastasia Robinson, later to become the Countess of Peterborough, was the finest English singer in the Italian style of her period; she was unusual in that at public concerts she was able to accompany herself on the harpsichord. Mrs. Robinson made her first appearance on the opera stage in a pasticcio, *Cresus*, in 1714. When a performance of another pasticcio, *Arminio*, was put aside for her benefit later in the season the house 'was as full as possible could be'.[1] Mrs. Robinson, who sang subsequently in *Rinaldo*, *Amadigi*, *Muzio Scevola*, *Floridante*, *Ottone*, and *Giulio Cesare*, as well as in operas by composers other than Handel, was the only English singer who was able to match up to Cuzzoni and Senesino as a box-office draw, and to accumulate a large fortune. After her marriage and retirement from the opera-house in 1723 she behaved as a *grande dame* and, in keeping with her acquired rank, held a salon at her house at Parson's Green where she entertained, among others, Buononcini and Maurice Greene. Apart from Alexander Gordon, John Beard, and William Savage (who sang as 'the boy' in *Alcina* in 1735) the only other native-born singer to appear in an opera by Handel was Richard Leveridge—for whom Purcell had composed 'Ye twice ten hundred deities' in *The Indian Queen*. Leveridge, a bass singer, took part in the first production of *Il Pastor Fido*. But Italian opera was not his métier and he too transferred to Rich's management at Lincoln's Inn Fields where he was more at home in pantomime: 'he had no notion of grace or elegance in singing; it was all strength and compass'.[2] A sportsman, whose skill as a ballad composer was not inconsiderable, Leveridge was prepared as late as 1730 to back himself for £100 against any bass in England.

John Rich, son of Christopher Rich one-time controller of Dorset Gardens, Drury Lane, and the Haymarket Theatres, was the most influential impresario of the eighteenth century, and as such responsible for launching many singers. In 1714 he opened the new Lincoln's Inn Fields Theatre where, recognising a public reaction against five-act tragedy and comedy alike, he developed pantomime and ballad opera and in so doing furnished opportunity for English singers whose chances at the Haymarket became almost non-existent as wave after wave of foreign virtuosi came over. At Lincoln's Inn Fields, as also at Drury Lane, masque, now hardly distinguishable from pastoral opera, was kept alive. Pepusch wrote the music for Hughes's *Apollo and Daphne* while William Turner was responsible for that for *Presumptuous Love* (an intermezzo inserted into a version of *The Comedy of Errors*) in 1716, but the hey-day of the eighteenth-century masque was some twenty years later, by which time Rich had taken over the management of Covent Garden.

[1] Colman, *Opera Register*, 1712–34; see *Händel-Jahrbuch*, Leipzig, 1959, p. 201.
[2] Hawkins, op. cit., V, p. 183.

There was by now a new school of English singers whose aspirations were not primarily in the direction of Italian opera. There were the three daughters of Charles Young, organist of All Hallows Church, London: Cecilia, who married Arne, Esther; wife of Charles Jones of the Royal Band; and Isabella, wife of J. F. Lampe. Cecilia was a member of Handel's opera company in 1735, and she sang the part of Athalia in the first performance of that oratorio; Esther, attached to Covent Garden in 1739, took part in *Semele* in 1744, doubling Juno and Ino; Isabella, who was also a singer at Covent Garden, toured a good deal with her husband and she sang in *Acis and Galatea* in Dublin in 1749 and in Edinburgh two years later. There was Arne's sister Susanna, who married Theophilus Cibber in 1734. Mrs. Cibber had, so it was said, a small voice. That she was able to rival the Italians was due to her powers of interpretation. Brought up in the atmosphere of the theatre, she developed into a great tragic actress, and she was able to inform her singing with a powerful sense of relevance. Referring to her famous performance of 'He was despised', Burney observed that, 'by a natural pathos and perfect conception of the words, she often penetrated the heart, when others, with infinitely greater voice and skill, could only reach the ear.'[1] Mrs. Cibber was greatly respected by Handel who, it is thought, wrote the parts of Micah (*Samson*) and Daniel (*Belshazzar*) with her in mind. Another actress and singer with a high reputation for affecting interpretation was Kitty Clive (of Irish descent), for whom Arne composed some of his Shakespearian settings and whom Handel chose for the part of Delilah in the first performance of *Samson.*

Of the male singers of this generation the most conspicuous were John Beard and Thomas Lowe, tenors, whose emergence helped to spell the end of the *castrati*. Beard was an old chorister of the Chapel Royal and a pupil of Gates, and his virile singing of a hunting song by Galliard, 'With early horn', established him as a general favourite. He had a strong voice which he managed with great musicianship. After singing for Handel in *Alexander's Feast*, *Acis and Galatea*, and *Atalanta* in 1736, he became a first choice for oratorio, and was principal tenor in *Israel in Egypt*, *Messiah*, *Samson*, *Judas Maccabaeus*, and *Jephtha*. Thomas Lowe, whose reputation was enhanced by his singing of Arne's Shakespeare songs, was said to have had a better voice than Beard, but to have been less of a musician. Nonetheless he was also esteemed by Handel and engaged for *Samson*, *Susanna*, *Joshua*, *Solomon*, and *Theodora*.

All these singers, like the Italians and Germans Handel continued to employ, came to oratorio by way of the theatre; but each one was notable for his or her ability to bring language to life. The effect on Handel of collaboration with them was to simplify melodic style, to allow the singer

[1] *Commemoration*, 1785, p. 42.

room for interpretative movement within the recitative, arioso, or aria—the latter no longer the formalised *da capo* type of the opera convention. Perhaps *L'Allegro* most of all shows the understanding that Handel developed for the character of English music as it was popularly understood.

So far as the art of singing was concerned in England there were two main streams: the Chapel Royal (and cathedral) tradition on the one hand; the theatre (and pleasure gardens) tradition on the other. Through John Beard the two streams met, and the next generation of soloists who sang during Handel's last years formulated from the two a distinctive oratorio style, which in due course was also to be affected by the increasingly sentimental attitude of the audience. Isabella Young, a pupil of Gustav Waltz (Handel's bass), one of three grand-daughters of Charles Young who became singers, was the most notable Handelian contralto, or mezzo-soprano, of Handel's last years. She took part in the first performance of *The Triumph of Time and Truth* in 1757, after which (as the inscription of her name in the conducting scores of the oratorios in Hamburg shows) she was a regular performer in the annual Lenten Series. Isabella Young, who also played Handel's organ concertos in public, married John Scott in 1757, after which she was billed sometimes as Mrs. Scott, but more often as Miss Young. Charlotte Brent, daughter of an alto singer who had taken the part of Hamor in the first performance of *Jephtha* in 1752 and a pupil of Arne, made her first stage appearance in Dublin in 1755 and subsequently she was taken on at Covent Garden by Beard. Outstanding in the role of Polly in *The Beggar's Opera* (the part that carried sopranos to fame more than any other), Charlotte Brent proved as versatile as her distinguished predecessors in the role—Mrs. Cibber and Kitty Clive—and like them she sang Handelian parts with distinction. She carried on the tradition, appearing at Three Choirs Festivals and provincial performances for some years after Handel's death. Others to further what could now be called the oratorio tradition were Robert Hudson, a tenor singer in St. Paul's and the Chapel Royal and an occasional singer at the pleasure gardens, who took part in the Handel Commemoration of 1784; John Soaper, also a singer in the choir of St. Paul's; Champness, a bass singer whose career stretched from the 1750's until the Commemoration; Wass, a Chapel Royal singer who appeared with Beard at the 1755 Worcester Festival; Benjamin Mence, a London clergyman; John Saville, for almost fifty years a vicar-choral of Lichfield Cathedral; Price, a counter-tenor at Gloucester; Matthews, a well-known bass soloist in Oxford where he was a university officer and to be found in the 1784 Commemoration Choir; and Charles Reinhold, a former choirboy of St. Paul's (he was the son of Thomas Reinhold, of Dresden, who followed Handel to London in 1731) who also lived on to take part in the

Commemoration. Finally there was Frasi, the Italian soprano who came to London in 1743 and, mastering the English language and the 'clear and simple' English style of singing, stayed on to be a favourite in oratorio performances all over the country for a period of twenty years. Such were the principal singers who ensured continuity in the oratorio style of performance.

Composers Contemporary with Handel

The pattern of Handel's career suggests a growing complacency in the British attitude to music, and it is apparent that during his lifetime a reluctance to look outward developed. The days in which informed amateurs kept abreast of continental music and in which promising students were encouraged to study abroad were, for the time being, largely past. Of the better-known composers of the period only one, Charles Avison, studied in Italy. The remainder were trained at home. Without an aristocracy able to subsidise music on the European scale, and with patronage much more a matter for the bourgeoisie, English composers not unnaturally accepted the limitations of bourgeois taste; a composer who held an official position considered himself to belong to the middle-class and adopted its standards. Music was regarded on the one hand as recreational, on the other as utilitarian. Necessarily then it became increasingly insular; because of its insularity it was for the most part ignored abroad.[1] Yet a great deal of music was written and despite the industry of Handel it was not easy to keep up with the demand. There was a market for church music, anthems and services for the major establishments and hymns and psalms for country churches and chapels. The development of music clubs, especially outside London, in which amateur instrumentalists met together, ensured sales for sonatas and concertos of no more than moderate difficulty. Theatrical entertainments required a steady flow of songs and overtures, while nightly concerts at Vauxhall, Marylebone, and Ranelagh (from 1742), and at Gardens which opened in the provinces in due course, acted as a further stimulus to production. Circumstances conspired to favour efficient composers, and of these there was no lack. As for genius, that was a term reserved to Handel. By implication genius in music was mostly to be found outside Britain. This supposition grew stronger until it became a cardinal point in English philosophy. The stronger it grew the more necessary it became to import

[1] Maurice Greene, however, was described as 'unter die grössten Organisten der Zeit' in Mattheson's *Der Vollkommende Capellmeister* (1739). Handel may have primed Mattheson; but it is possible that Wych the British Ambassador in Hamburg—like Handel a subscriber to Telemann's *Musique de Table* (1734)—may have urged the claims of his country's music.

a quota of foreign composers. By the end of the century the outlook for a British composer was somewhat bleak.

The most substantial English composer of the Handel era was Maurice Greene (*c.* 1695–1755) who, filling some of the most profitable public offices, was an effective influence in the whole field of English music. The son of a London vicar, Greene was educated as a chorister of St. Paul's Cathedral, of which he became organist in 1718. Friendly with Handel, Greene used to invite him to play the organ at St. Paul's[1]; subsequently, however, this friendship is said to have diminished on account of Greene's sponsorship of Buononcini. On the death of Croft Greene became organist and composer of the Chapel Royal. In 1730 he succeeded Tudway as Professor of Music at Cambridge and five years later was appointed Master of the King's Band on the retirement of Eccles. Greene had charm and knew how and where to use it. Benjamin Hoadly, Bishop of Salisbury and then of Winchester, was a friend, and Hoadly's son, John, wrote the libretti of his oratorios and pastoral operas. The Countess of Peterborough entertained him and helped him towards his appointment as Master of the King's Band. Greene was frequently a visitor at Newcastle House—his volume of settings of Spenser's *Amoretti* is dedicated to the Duchess of Newcastle—where he was able to meet another regular guest, Buononcini. Pope not only allowed Greene (who like Pope was deformed) to set his *Ode to St. Cecilia* for his Doctor's exercise in 1730 but emended the text for that purpose. In his last years Greene was able to live in ease and some dignity on a Surrey estate bequeathed to him by a lawyer uncle.

Despite his social inclinations Greene threw himself wholeheartedly into musical life. He helped to found the Academy of Vocal Music—from which he retired when his friend Buononcini was said to have passed off a composition by Lotti as his own. Having left one Academy—taking the St. Paul's choristers with him—he founded another, in the Apollo room of the Devil tavern. A friend of Festing (whose son married Greene's daughter), he supported the institution of the Society of Musicians. In 1741 another society, in the affairs of which he became involved, was founded, for the performance of madrigals.

The originator of the Madrigal Society was an ex-attorney, John Immyns,[2] who had been a pupil of Pepusch and a member of the Academy of Vocal Music. The programmes of the Academy (see p. 304) had already pointed to a keen madrigalian interest. Immyns' sole interest was in 'ancient' music and his Madrigal Society was after the pattern of Nicholas

[1] '. . . their Royal Highnesses the Princess Anne and Princess Caroline came to St. Paul's Cathedral and heard the famous Mr. Handel (their musick-master) perform upon the organ;' *Applebee's Weekly Journal*, 29 August 1724.

[2] Copies of madrigals made by Immyns *c.* 1740 are in the Fitzwilliam Museum, Cambridge.

Yonge's, but the members included representatives of the working class. 'They were', said Hawkins, 'mostly mechanics; some, weavers from Spitalfields, others of various trades and occupations;'[1] and they were reasonably competent in sight-reading, having come to music by way of parochial psalmody. Having settled down to regular activity Immyns persuaded Greene to allow choristers from St. Paul's to assist. Apart from this Greene had his own interest in older music and devoted much time to the preparation of a collection of anthems[2] and services, which, since it was unfinished at the time of his death, was passed on to William Boyce as the foundation of *Cathedral Music*. In this manner the revival of interest in the former glories of English music began to gather momentum rapidly during the latter half of the century. The Madrigal Society survives, the oldest of musical societies with a continuing life.

However much Greene may have been interested in the music of former times, as a composer he belonged essentially to his own age. Textural procedures of the Elizabethans were picked up by him from Croft and he was capable of expressing pathos as in *Lord, let me know mine end* or *Lord, how long wilt thou be angry* (from his *Forty Select Anthems in Score*, 1743); but the tempering of Elizabethan acerbities denied the splendid tension of the former age. Greene's solemnities are nearer to the Wesleys than to Byrd and Gibbons. In his verse anthems he aimed at and often achieved comeliness of design, while at his most magniloquent he could—with a climactic 'bell' motiv—range himself beside the greatest of his contemporaries [Ex. 12*a* and *b*].[3] If this has a Handelian ring so too has

12a

[1] Op. cit., V, p. 349.

[2] John Alcock (1715–1806), who was a chorister at St. Paul's and organist of Lichfield Cathedral (1750–60), had already begun such a collection in 1735 but on hearing of Greene's intention passed over to him what he had already prepared.

[3] B.M. Add. Ms. 17861, 'copied by S. Porter [1733–1803; a native of Norwich, chorister at St. Paul's and organist of Canterbury Cathedral from 1757 to his death] while he was an apprentice to the Dr.'

12b.

the *siciliana* movement, 'By the streams that ever flow', quoted by Hawkins[1] from a St. Cecilia ode.

As an instrumental composer Greene distinguished himself by the clarity of his writing. His overtures[2] are melodically alive and their diatonic directness is characteristic of an idiom that ran through English orchestral music and into the first essays in symphonic expression. His harpsichord music is elegant, even witty, and ideally disposed for the instrument.[3] Here, as in his songs, Greene shows an appreciation of Italian deftness that, it was sometimes thought, escaped Handel in his keyboard works. In general, whether writing for organ or harpsichord, English composers steered clear of the alleged 'heaviness' of Handelian idiom. This desire to achieve elegance was expressed also in song-writing. Here

[1] Op. cit., V, p. 331.

[2] *Six overtures* (Walsh *c.* 1745), and Overture for *Florimel* (?1737), and *New Year's Odes* (1739, 1745, 1746).

[3] *A collection of lessons for the Harpsichord*, John Johnson (1750?), *A* [*second*] *Collection of lessons for the Harpsichord* J. Walsh [n.d.].: for a discussion of Greene's harpsichord music as well as that of other composers, see C. Vere Pilkington, 'A Collection of English 18th Century Harpsichord Music', *P.R.M.A.*, 83, 1956–7, p. 89.

Greene was frequently insouciant, and always graceful [Ex. 13]. His

13.

talent, however, shows its limitations when, as in the *Amoretti* of Spenser, he tries, cantata-wise, to cover a larger canvas. These songs represent Greene's support for the thesis that English poets should provide subject matter for English composers.

The theory that English composers lost their identity under the influence of Handel is not wholly tenable. Considering the processes through which music passed in the hands of Blow, Croft, Roseingrave, and Greene it is reasonable to assume that the character and quality of native music would have been very much as it was by the middle of the century even if Handel had gone back to Germany after his first visit and stayed there. On the other hand it is clear that Handel learned a good deal from English practices and adjusted his own style accordingly. This was particularly so in respect of song, in which one English-born composer was outstanding by any standards: Thomas Augustine Arne.

Arne walked by himself. His antecedents to music were irregular; he held no official appointment of importance; he concentrated on popular music; he was a Roman Catholic; and he offended against the canons of respectability. John Stafford Smith, who knew him, summed him up as 'a conceited Papist, an evil-living man, but a God-gifted genius for melody'.[1] Having been at school at Eton, Arne was put apprentice to a lawyer. During the three years of this apprenticeship he learned the violin and then turned to Michael Festing for more advanced tuition. Lessons with Festing were all the professional teaching he had: for the rest he was self-taught. This fact relieved him of theoretical considerations and ensured that a natural independence was strengthened.

His sister's success in Lampe's *Amelia* in 1732 encouraged Arne to provide her with further material in similar vein. He re-set Addison's *Rosamond*, which was produced at Lincoln's Inn Fields in 1733. There followed other essays in theatre music which succeeded so far as to persuade the management at Drury Lane to commission Arne to compose music for an adaptation of Milton's *Comus*[2] made by John Dalton. This

[1] See W. A. Barrett, *English Glees and Part-Songs*, London, 1886, p. 267.

[2] An operatic version of *Comus*, entitled *Sabrina*, prepared by Paolo Rolli, had been put on at the Haymarket in April 1737. This, presumably *pasticcio*, was not successful and only three performances were given.

was staged at Drury Lane on 4 March 1738, the principal singers being Arne's sister, his wife (since a year), Kitty Clive, and John Beard. The work was immediately approved and in its first season enjoyed eleven performances. It 'afforded such general and permanent delight, that the melodies were sung all over the Country'.[1] Arne, reducing Italian extravagance but retaining the felicities of Italian vocal practice together with the spontaneity and rhythmic verve of the Purcellian tradition, and keeping within earshot of the popular successes of Clarke, Daniel Purcell, and Eccles, caught the lyrical quality of the text and produced a sequence of recitatives and arias (some *da capo*, others not) that aptly caught the changing moods of Milton's (or Dalton's) verse. In reflection of the rural scene the songs show indeed a quality of impressionism, contrasting with the firmer character of the Overture and the interspersed dances. Two years after the appearance of *Comus* Arne wrote the music for Congreve's *The Judgment of Paris* for Drury Lane, and for *Alfred* (James Thomson and David Mallet), a 'Masque' produced in August, at Cliveden, for Frederick, Prince of Wales. In the first place Arne composed five numbers and the finale, 'Rule Britannia', but across the next fifteen years he altered and added to the original version so that in 1756 he gave a performance in Dublin that was advertised as 'sung in the manner of an Oratorio'.[2] The patriotic fervour of 'Rule Britannia' is repeated in some of the airs of *Eliza* (1754) [Ex. 14*a* and 14*b*], of which the romantic text—by Richard Holt—anticipates that of Edward German's *Merrie England.*

14a.

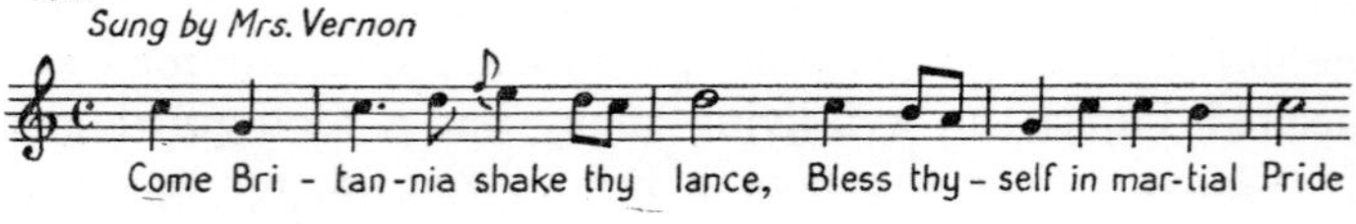
Sung by Mrs. Vernon
Come Bri - tan-nia shake thy lance, Bless thy - self in mar-tial Pride

[1] *The Harlequin*, 16 May, 1829, quoted by Julian Herbage in Introduction to *Comus* (*Musica Britannica*, III, 1951).

[2] In his 1759 edition of *Alfred*, Mallet noted that the following verses, referring to the 'King across the water', were written by Lord Bolingbroke for 'Rule Britannia':

Should war, should faction shake thy isle,
And sink to poverty and shame,
Heaven still shall on Britannia smile,
Restore her wealth and raise her name.

How blest the Prince, reserved by fate
In adverse days to mount thy throne!
Renew thy once triumphant state,
And on thy grandeur build his own.

His race shall long, in times to come,
So Heaven ordains, thy sceptre wield;
Revered abroad, beloved at home;
And be at once thy sword and shield.

14b.

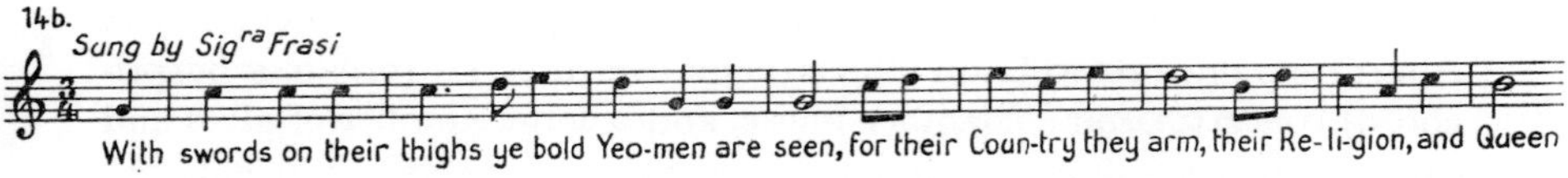
Sung by Sigra Frasi
With swords on their thighs ye bold Yeo-men are seen, for their Coun-try they arm, their Re-li-gion, and Queen

In 1740—with the revival of *As You Like It* at Drury Lane in December—Arne began his Shakespearian settings with 'Under the greenwood tree'; 'Blow, blow, thou winter wind'; 'When daisies pied'; and 'When icicles hang by the wall'. In 1741 he composed songs for *Twelfth Night* and *The Merchant of Venice*. Five years later came the extensive score for *The Tempest*, which concluded with a Musical Entertainment called 'Neptune and Amphitrite'. For the interpretation of these songs Arne depended on Kitty Clive and Thomas Lowe.

In 1742 Arne and his wife went to Dublin where—overlapping Handel's visit—they remained for two years. The Arnes were appreciated in the Irish capital and returned in 1755–6 and 1758–9. The first of Arne's two oratorios—*The Death of Abel* to a libretto prepared by Arne himself from Metastasio's *La Morte d'Abele*—was performed in the Smock Alley Theatre in Dublin on 18 February 1744.

On his return to London Arne composed a comic opera *The Temple of Dullness* (from Theobald) for Drury Lane, where in addition to his duties as composer he took over the leadership of the band. As prolific as he was said to be profligate, Arne composed a vast amount of music—much of it ephemeral—for the theatre and from 1745, when vocal music was added to the programmes, also for Vauxhall, Ranelagh, and Marylebone Gardens. In 1759 he became a Doctor of Music of Oxford University and in the following year he transferred from Drury Lane to Covent Garden, where *Thomas and Sally* (Isaac Bickerstaffe), with its delightful *buffo* tunes, scored an immediate success. Bickerstaffe also wrote the libretto for Arne's second oratorio, *Judith* (1761), in which, it is said, female voices were used in oratorio chorus for the first time.

Like Handel Arne studied the market prospects with some care. After Handel's death there was a swing-back to Italian opera (to be discussed in the next chapter) and Arne promptly provided Covent Garden with *Artaserse*, which he followed two years later with *L'Olimpiade*, also to a libretto by Metastasio. *Artaserse* was successful and its airs passed into the popular tradition, but its successor was not. Among his later undertakings were a revival of Purcell's *King Arthur* (Drury Lane, 1770), to which, after reference to the crudity of Purcell, he added a fine three-movement Overture (G ma., *con spirito*, with prominent 'cuckow' motiv; G mi., *Largo*, showing stern use of harmonic minor scale and expressive *appogiature*; G ma., 'patriotic' *Side-drum March*) and other numbers of his own; an Ode for the Shakespeare Jubilee at Stratford-on-Avon in 1768;

and a setting of William Mason's *Caractacus* (Covent Garden, 1776). Apart from one or two Latin motets, eight overtures, six (organ or harpsichord) concertos, some chamber music, and a large number of glees and catches, Arne's music—in all a vast output—was exclusively devoted to the theatre and the several Gardens. This hindered his reputation. Insofar as the 'learned' composers were concerned Arne was an outsider[1]: he was not taken seriously because, unlike many of his contemporaries, he did not take himself seriously. It is odd, therefore, that he alone among English composers—since, as it was said, he lacked 'grandeur of thought'[2]—should come down to posterity complete with his title of Doctor. This was granted on his competence as a composer of sacred music.

Having defied academic criticism in his own day and, since his private life was said to have been irregular, ridden through the moral censure of the nineteenth century, Arne has been carried across two centuries by a handful of songs that have proved imperishable. This degree of immortality was earned by his genius for melody. Living among singers, Arne understood what the voice could do—his judgement in gauging the comfortable limits of fioriture, the proper length of a sustained note, the effectiveness of a change of register, the balance between vocal line and instrumental accompaniment, was inerrant. He is for the singer always a grateful composer. 'Arne', says Barrett, 'was the first native musician who placed our claim to musical excellence on a level with that of the Italians themselves, then the approved good masters of the melodic art, by adopting and improving their style of composition, excluding from it what has justly been deemed an excess of refinement, and preserving only its real and permanent beauties. To this it may be added that his own claim to originality is indisputable'.[3] His originality consisted of this; that he understood the aesthetic ideals of those about him and brought them to significance. He was, of course, a far more varied and subtle composer than has often been allowed, and not averse from experiment. Indeed, as has been seen, he found it expedient to experiment from time to time

Arne's songs became part of the folk-music tradition and he himself

[1] 'Arne found detractors in his own day chiefly among those of his own profession who were jealous of his powers, or who were unable to distinguish the difference between the moral character of a man and the expressions of his genius.' W. A. Barrett, op. cit., p. 202.

[2] Burney, *History*, IV, p. 674.

[3] Op. cit., pp. 201–2. Cf. Gerber's *Lexikon*, Leipzig, 1790: Arne 'ist seit 1730 den Engländern das, was [J. A.] Hiller den Deutschen ist. Herr Mag. Ebeling sagt von ihm: die Engländer haben ihm ihre besten Opern zu danken. Er hat viel Erfindung und Gefühl, einen gefälligen Gesang, fleissige Bearbeitung und macht von den Zierrathen vernünftigen Gebrauch. Von dem gewöhlichen Schlendrian in Ansehung der Form der Arien mit da Capo, mit langen Passagien und Cadenzen, geht er mehrenteils als'.

rarely lost sight of the impulses of the tradition as he knew it. For this example [Ex. 15][1] allies itself with *The crost couple*, familiar in Restoration

15.

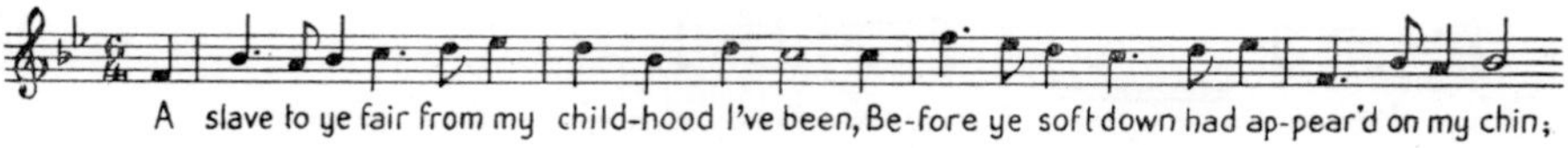
A slave to ye fair from my child-hood I've been, Be-fore ye soft down had ap-pear'd on my chin;

times, while *The Highland Laddie* [Ex. 16][2] recalls Arne's early predilection,

16.

The low-land lads_think they are fine, But oh_they're vain and id - ly gau-dy

as remarked by Burney, for turning out pseudo-Scottish numbers. Since Arne is often spoken of in the same breath as Purcell, on whom, however, he had a perverse judgement,[3] it is not surprising that he found it natural often to go in the same direction [Ex. 17]. This excerpt shows a frequent

17.

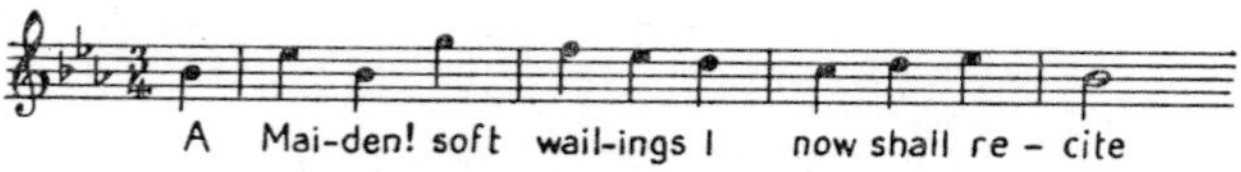
A Mai-den! soft wail-ings I now shall re - cite

mark of identification in Arne, the interval of the sixth. The last quotation from a setting of a poem 'selected and alter'd from Gay's *Pastorals*' draws attention to the fact that Arne was not unwilling to fall in with the current tendency to revalue (and sometimes rewrite) the works of the most famous of English poets. And he was honest enough to state his reasons for textual emendation. Thus in his version of Suckling's *Honest lover whatsoever* he observed: 'N.B. The original Poem (tho' admirable in its kind) being in too unequal measure for Musick, Mr. Arne was oblig'd to get several of the lines alter'd.' In the same volume of *Lyric Harmony* Suckling's *Why so pale and wan, fond lover* and Waller's *Go lovely rose* appear, as well as lyrics based on Chaucer and Prior. In *Vocal Melody II* Chaucer is represented again, with his *Recantation* ('From sweet bewitching Trials of Love'). Arne (like Schubert) had the gift of being able to capture the essential atmosphere of a poem and to transfer it to musical terms. Thus in 'By dimpl'd Brook' (*Comus*) the precision of the pastoral fancy of the poet is exactly conveyed by the elegance of the melody [Ex. 18]. This song illustrates Arne's sense of timing—in respect of the concluding phrase of each

[1] From *The Muses Delight*, Liverpool, 1757.

[2] ib. This air was a favourite of Sheridan who adapted it to the words of 'Ah! sure a pair', in *The Duenna*.

[3] See letter from Vincent Novello to Josiah French, B.M. Add. Ms. 33965.

18.

By dim-pl'd Brook, and Foun-tain Brim, The Wood-Nymphs deck'd with Dai-sies
trim Their mer-ry mer-ry Wakes and Pas-times keep:

of the first two verses. [Ex.19]; his contiguity to Handel [Ex. 20]; and an

19.

What hath Night to do with Sleep? What hath Night to do with Sleep?

20

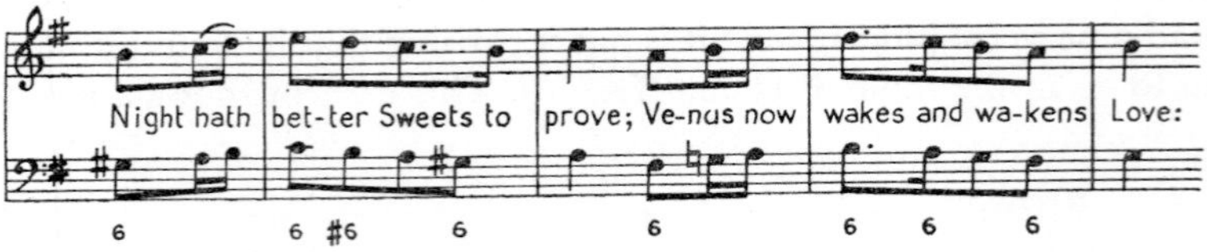
Night hath bet-ter Sweets to prove; Ve-nus now wakes and wa-kens Love:
6 6 ♯6 6 6 6 6 6

affinity with Schubert in his effective relaxation of the strophic form, for the last verse, for an extension of his lyrical fancy. The side-tracking of the melody into A minor is neatly done, but it serves to underline a textual allusion. Arne, thought deficient in 'harmony' by some of his critics, was in fact masterly in manipulating his tonalities so as to achieve the greatest effect with the minimum of effort. He may have looked towards Italy but occasionally he might seem to have the feeling for harmony of a German: this is suggested by the sombre under-chording of both settings of *Come away, Death*.

The Shakespeare settings in particular show how much Arne visualised a song setting as a composition for voice and instruments. The colour of the piccolo in *Under the greenwood tree*, and of the flute in *When daisies pied*, the triplet figuration of the violins in *Tell me where is fancy bred*, and the manner in which the instrumental ensemble in general is allowed equality in the expression of sonority indicate how judiciously Arne assembled his sounds. In the Funeral Music of *Romeo and Juliet* he shows an appreciation of the relevance of dark instrumentation, just as in the introduction to his *The Morning Cantata*, where flute (or piccolo) combines with second violin and viola, he shows the aptness of a contrasting combination. The score of *Elfrida* (William Mason and George Colman), of 1772, shows all Arne's pastoral fancy in a sequence of delicately scored bird songs in which the manner is almost that of Haydn in *The Seasons*, while the rhythmic definition of the air 'Hark compleating our Prophetic strain, the Fleet hoof rattles o'er the plain' looks across two centuries to a composer whose affinity with Arne often seems close—Benjamin Britten. There is also landscape music of great charm in *Eliza*, particularly in the song written for Beard, 'The woodlark whistles through the grove', and in the muted horns and strings that suggest 'Gentle Breezes, Silent Glades'. Originality in scoring marked *Artaserse*, in which a large orchestra, including clarinets, was employed.[1] At this point the development of the orchestra in England ran out of English hands, for a year after the production of *Artaserse* John Christian Bach arrived.

Arne, whose pupils included the singers Charlotte Brent and Harriet Abrams, evolved a style that influenced English composers until well into the nineteenth century. But few of those who acquired his manner possessed his judgement or his versatility. Some part of his talent was inherited by his son Michael (his 'natural' son, according to Burney) who has been remembered on the strength of a characteristic Vauxhall Gardens piece: *The Lass with a delicate air*. Like his father the contributor to many theatrical productions, Michael Arne has, however, a stronger claim to attention than his works by themselves demand.

It was Michael Arne who took the music of Handel back to the German people. On 30 September 1771 he gave a performance of *Alexander's Feast*, together with a piano concerto, and a song from his father's *Artaserse*, sung by Miss Venables—now happily recovered from a throat infection.

On 9 September the *Hamburgischer Correspondent* announced:

'Dem geehrten Publico . . . wird hiermit angezeiget, dass . . . am Montage, den 23sten September, Herr Arne aus London das von dem berühmten Handel componirte Oratorium genannt Das Alexanderfest, . . . aufführen wird . . . Auch wird Herr Arne sich mit einem Flügel Concerto hören lassen und Mademoiselle Venables eine Aire mit obligat Trompette aus der vortrefflichen Oper, genannt Artaxerxes, von Dr. Arne in London singen . . .'[2]

On 21 September there was a further announcement communicating the change of date of the performance:

'Der Herr Arne benachrichtigt hierdurch das geehrte Publicum, dass er sich wegen einer überkommenen Unpasslichkeit der Demoiselle Venables am Halse genöthigt findet, das Concert vom 25.September bis zum

[1] See Julian Herbage, 'The Vocal Style of Thomas Augustine Arne', in *P.R.M.A.*, 78, 1951–2, p. 93.
[2] *Hamburgischer Correspondent*, 1771, no. 146.

30. dieses zu versetzen. Die Billets vom 23sten gelten denn also auf den 30sten September'.[1]

Arne stayed on in Hamburg and the next news of him came on 4 January, 1772, when a mixed programme of Italian and English arias and cantatas, and piano concertos, was advertised:

'Mit hoher Obrigkeitlicher Bewilligung wird Mittewochs, den 8ten Januar 1772. in dem Concertsaale auf dem Kamp ein Concert gegeben werden, worinn *Miss Venables* einige Italienische und Englische Arien und Cantaten singen wird. Herr Arne wird sich mit Flügel-Concerten hören lassen, und auf eine Italienische Arie singen. Billetts zu 1 Mk. 8 ssl. sind bey Hn. Arne im Schuster Mehrdorfs Hause in der Filterstrasse, und in Herrn Dreyers und mehrern berühmten Caffeehäusern, zu haben.'[2]

On 15 April Arne gave a private performance of *Messiah*—the first performance in Germany—and its success prompted him to give a public performance. This again was delayed on account of Miss Venables's indisposition.

'Auf Verlangen . . . wird Herr Arne Donnerstags, den 14ten dieses, das Oratorium: Der Messias, welches am 15ten April in dem Privat-Concerte des Herrn Arne . . . mit vielem Beyfall ist aufgeführet worden . . . öffentlich abermals aufführen . . . Der Beschluss wird mit dem grossen Coronation Anthem von Händel, welches ebenfalls schon . . . aufgeführet worden ist, gemacht werden'.[3] Notices in the *Hamburgischer Correspondent* on 13 and 19 May advised postponement of the performance until 21 May. Thus Michael Arne made his signal contribution to Anglo-German relationships, and helped to restore Handel to the German tradition.

William Boyce was born in the same year as Thomas Arne, and was also an important figure in a transitional period. He was, however, less sensitive than Arne to fluctuations in taste and changes in style and maintained a sturdy conservatism. He was well described by Burney as an 'honest composer'. But his influence was strong in many directions and in his role of conductor he made an effective contribution to the popularisation of choral music. His *Cathedral Music* (1743)—the conclusion of the labours in research of Alcock and Greene—was a practical means of safeguarding the traditions of English church music of the sixteenth and seventeenth centuries. It remains to be said that Boyce's expectations in respect of *Cathedral Music* were at first disappointed: the cathedral

[1] 1771, no. 153.
[2] 1772, no. 3.
[3] 1772, no. 74.

churches by and large had but a slender concern for the heritage of the past.

Boyce was a choir-boy at St. Paul's and became a pupil of Greene. After serving his apprenticeship to Greene he accumulated organistships in London and added to his emoluments by teaching music in girls' schools. During the early part of his career he went to Pepusch for lessons in composition, and his talent was recognised in 1736 by his appointment to the Chapel Royal as composer. In 1758 he added to this office that of organist. In 1735 Boyce took over the direction of the annual Festivals of the Sons of the Clergy from Greene, with whom he remained on friendly terms until Greene's death. It was his success in this undertaking no doubt that brought him the invitation to conduct the Three Choirs Festival[1] in 1737. He maintained this connection with the Festival for a number of years and his anthems were in the programmes until the end of the century. His visits to Gloucester brought him into contact with Martin Smith, the cathedral organist, whose son—John Stafford Smith— was to become one of Boyce's most receptive pupils. The concern for musical scholarship[2] and for the evaluation through performance of the works of previous generations shown by Pepusch, Immyns, Croft, Greene, Alcock, and Boyce, was conveyed to Stafford Smith who became, virtually, the first English musicologist. Boyce appears to have been a sound teacher, combining patience and friendliness, and he was greatly esteemed for his personal qualities: '. . . Pray', said Jonathan Battishill, Boyce's sometime deputy at the Chapel Royal organ, as he lay on his deathbed, 'place me near that great man, Dr. Boyce'.

Arne, like Greene and others, was sometimes tetchy so far as Handel

[1] The close connection between the two festivals is indicated by the fact that in 1745, 'Dr. Greene, Master of His Majesty's Band of Musick, with several of the Gentlemen belonging to the Chapel Royal, Westminster Abbey, and St. Paul's, set out for Gloucester, where they are to meet the Gentlemen belonging to the Choirs of Worcester, Hereford, and Gloucester, in order to perform at the last mentioned place . . . a Grand Concert of Musick, both Vocal and Instrumental, for the Benefit of poor Clergymen's Widows and their Children'. *Gloucester Journal*, 29 May 1745.

[2] Boyce possessed, among other works, Morley's *Introduction*, Dowland's translation of Ornithoparcus, Elway Bevin's *Art of Music and Canons, A Treatise concerning the lawfulness of Instrumental Music in holy Offices* (Dodwell, 1700), J. F. Lampe's *The Art of Music* (1740), 'Curious Pieces for the Organ or Harpsichord, composed by Tallis, Byrd, Dr. Bull etc.', and sonatas and concertos by Henry Symonds, Hebden, Samuel Wesley, Philip Hayes . . . Lockhart, Elizabeth Turner, Felton, Chilcot, Burgess, Avison, Hebden, Jackson, Overend, Bates, Icleman, Flecton, Defesch, Burney, Nares, and P. Wise. see 'A Catalogue of the Truly Valuable and Curious Library of Music, late in the Possession of Dr. William Boyce . . . Consisting of all Dr. Greene's Curious and Valuable Manuscripts, with the greatest Variety of Excellent Compositions for the Church, Chamber, and the Theatre, ever yet offer'd to Sale . . . sold by Auction by Messr. Christie and Ansell at their Great Room, Pall Mall, Wed. April 14, 1779 and the Two following Days': copy in Leeds City Library.

and his reputation were concerned. He, however, had the confidence to back his own talents and to display them in a style which owed relatively little to Handel. Boyce, on the other hand, sat back in reverent wonder at the genius of one who could, as he is reported to have said, 'take Pebbles, and convert them to Diamonds'. As a composer he was content to pursue an equable course through charted waters. He was, of course, an official composer, and this curtailed his freedom of action to a certain extent. He wrote many anthems and services, and a few have retained their place in the cathedral service lists, their merit reposing in their propriety. He composed an oratorio, *David's Lamentation over Saul and Jonathan* (John Lockman), for the Apollo Academy in 1740, and another—*Solomon*[1]—in 1743. For many years he contributed new year's and birthday odes to the existing repertoire. Twelve Sonatas (*c.* 1745) for two violins and bass were immediately successful and were played for many years. The *Eight Symphonys* (*c.* 1760), containing the instrumental introductions to earlier odes, were also well received. Boyce did not limit his interests and he was a prolific composer for the theatre, the one-act entertainment *The Chaplet*, of 1749 (Moses Mendez), achieving a considerable popularity. Boyce also knew how to turn out a compelling tune—the one that proved durable was *Heart of Oak*, from *The Harlequin's Invasion* of 1759 (a pantomime by Garrick for which Boyce, Michael Arne, and Theodore Aylward wrote the music). He was kept fully occupied, in many directions, and he published relatively little during his lifetime. Towards the end of his life he sadly realised that he was outmoded. Hawkins describes what happens when a revered older master suddenly appreciates that time does not stand still: 'Mr. *Boyce* had lying by him, the new-Years' and birth-day odes which he had composed during the time he had filled the station of master of the royal band. The overtures to these he thought would be well received, and, about the year 1770, he published twelve of them. They are very original and spirited compositions, and abound with elegant airs, and the evidence of deep skill and learned ingenuity. The taste of the people at the time of the publication of these was very unpropitious to their success: they had the misfortune to meet with the compositions of [J. C.] *Bach* and [C. F.] *Abel* which had already gotten possession of the public ear'. Thus disappointed Boyce refused to consider publication of other works during the remainder of his life. Like Beethoven he suffered from deafness: the consequence, however, was different with him than with Beethoven, causing him to retain the idiom that pre-dated the onset of the misfortune.

We have then in Boyce a foil to Arne. The contrast between the two is best seen in their attitude to orchestral music; Boyce sticking closer to

[1] The well-known and rather insipid air 'Tell me, gentle Shepherd' belongs to *Solomon*.

the French overture and its Baroque properties, Arne moving more readily towards the Italian *sinfonia*, sonata form and the *galant* style.[1] Boyce's court duties kept him busy in the form that was favoured on official occasions (and so it continued well into the next period) and sanctified by Handelian usage; Arne, elevated by the freer atmosphere of the theatre, preferred gaiety, abandon, and colour. Arne used his instrumental timbres with imagination. With Boyce the detail of orchestration was a secondary matter—perhaps this too was caused by his deafness. In some of his scores he gave the exact constitution of his playing strength—which averaged out at six first and second violins, two–three violas, three–four cellos, three–four double-basses, with oboes and bassoons, and flutes, trumpets, and timpani as required by the nature of the works. The approach generally characteristic of the period is indicated by the note to a score of *Saul and Jonathan*; 'the hautboys with the violins excepting when they go too high, then take them eight notes for a bar or two as you find occasion. Observe the same if they get too low. I speak only in regard to the Overture'.[2]

Boyce, however, was too good a musician not to be aware of what was going on in the world, and signs of *galant* idiom, derived from compositions of the Milanese school of symphonists,[3] may be perceived in the 1770 set of overtures. But in general the instrumental works of Boyce are marked with vigour, fine, plain-spoken melodies kept in place by firm rhythm and secure basses. He had a preference for quick rather than slow middle movements—as also his master, Maurice Greene—but he was capable of unsuspected excursions into the unfamiliar. Thus in the 1770 *New Year's Ode* overture he enchantingly demonstrated that those who considered him incapable of appreciating what was new were wrong [Ex. 21].

21

[1] See the character of the *Sinfonia* to *Alfred* and of the *Eight Lessons for the Harpsichord* (*c.* 1743).

[2] See *Preface* (p. xxii) to *William Boyce—Overtures*, ed. by Gerald Finzi, *Musica Britannica*, XIII, London, 1957.

[3] See C. L. Cudworth, 'The English Symphonists of the Eighteenth Century', in *P.R.M.A.*, 78, 1951–2, p. 35.

A third composer born in the same year as Arne and Boyce was Charles Avison, already noticed for his pioneer work as a concert promoter in Newcastle upon Tyne. Avison, encouraged by the success of his concerts, was a busy composer and his concertos were welcome additions to the repertoire. The concertos, about fifty in all but some being re-arrangements,[1] were spread across the middle years of the century, from 1742 to 1764, and were designed to conform with the principles of Geminiani, Avison's friend and probably his teacher. It was Geminiani who tried but failed to persuade Avison to accept appointments in Dublin and Edinburgh. The reputation Avison enjoyed is further indicated by his refusal of two other offers: at York Minster in 1734 and at the Charterhouse on the death of Pepusch in 1752. In addition to his concertos Avison also wrote three volumes of sonatas for harpsichord 'with accompanyments for two violins and violoncello' (1756, 1760, 1764).

Avison's sonatas are of great interest in that in them may be seen for the first time in England a realisation of new principles both of execution and design. Thus in the *Advertisement* to the *Six Sonatas* (op. 5) of 1756 Avison stated: 'In regard to the Harpsichord; the Manner of Playing as described by the Term *legato*, or chaining the Passages, by some *spirited Touch of the Finger*, is much more suitable to the style of these Pieces, than That of the *Staccato*, or invariable marking of the Note *by means of the Wrist*'; while in that of op. 8 (1764) he noted that 'the Sonatas of Scarlatti, Rameau, and Carlo-Bach, have their *peculiar* Beauties. The *fine* Fancy of the Italian . . . the *spiritual science* of the Frenchman . . . and the German's *diffusive Expression* are the distinguishing Signatures of their Music.' The sonatas of Avison are 'scientific'—he was a fine fugue writer—but highly expressive, and marked by diversity of form and of figuration—a feature of which is a predilection for crossing the hands in the manner of Scarlatti. His *fantasia* style (as in the fine third Sonata of op. 5 where it is attached to a sternly German fugue) is of the manner of C.P.E. Bach, and his awareness of formal organisation of a new order is demonstrated in op. 5, no. 2, where two formulae [Ex. 22*a* and *b*] proceed through a

22a.

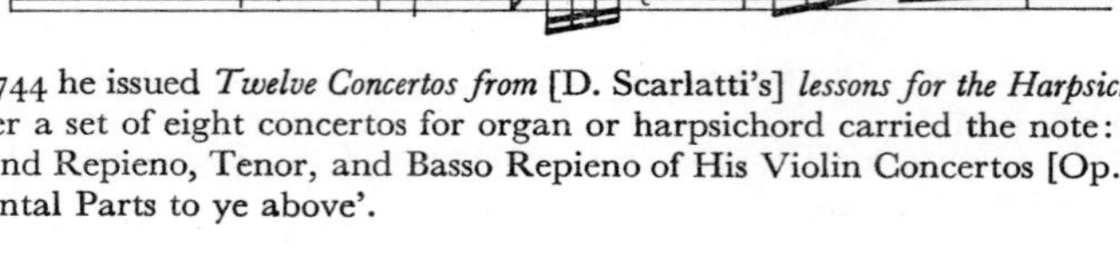

[1] In 1744 he issued *Twelve Concertos from* [D. Scarlatti's] *lessons for the Harpsichord*; three years later a set of eight concertos for organ or harpsichord carried the note: 'N.B. The 1st and 2nd Repieno, Tenor, and Basso Repieno of His Violin Concertos [Op. 2] are the Instrumental Parts to ye above'.

22b.

development section (G major, E minor, A minor) to a recapitulation (*b* returning in the subdominant) and a coda. Avison's breaking of new ground was not without its effect locally, for John Garth (1722–1810), organiser of the Gentlemen's Subscription Concerts in Durham in 1759, who collaborated with Avison in issuing an English edition of Marcello's Psalms (1757), also brought out a set of similar sonatas 'for the harpsichord, pianoforte, and organ' (*sic*), about 1768. Certainly Garth knew what he was about, and the Gentlemen of Durham must have felt that they were well in the van of progress.

23.

Avison was a powerful figure in the musical life of north-eastern England, but he had a wider influence through his critical treatise, *An Essay on Musical Expression* (1752). In this work he made pertinent practical observations, especially on orchestral playing; speculated on the philosophic issues concerning the nature and function of music and its relation to natural phenomena; applauded the quality of the works of Caldara, Marcello, and Geminiani; and allowed himself the privilege of judicious criticism of Pergolesi's *Stabat Mater* and of Handel, who, he considered, wrote too much too fast. Avison was the first English musician to affect musical criticism in the knowledgeable manner of Mattheson, and his enlivening and constructive discussion of current styles was a healthy corrective to such works as the Rev. Arthur Bedford's *Temple Musick* (1706) and *Great Abuse of Musick* (1711) and Richard Browne's *Medicina Musica* (1722), which were widely read but almost entirely deficient in informed criticism. Avison's *Essay* (stimulating to James Harris, see

p. 313) provoked an answer in the form of *Remarks on Mr. Avison's Essay on Musical Expression* (1762), anonymous but known to be the work of William Hayes.[1] Avison responded to Hayes with a second and revised edition (1753) of his work (including a Reply) with supplementary material on the music of the ancients by the ecclesiastical historian John Jortin. It is, perhaps, noteworthy that Avison's considerations extended to the *Quarter Tone* which he described as 'amazingly powerful in rousing the Passions'. He referred, however, to reports from the orient and not to microtonal experiments on Tyneside.

Other composers of this generation included Samuel Howard, John Stanley, James Nares, and William Felton, each of whom made his mark on the musical life of the community without, however, stepping far enough away from the steady conventions to stir more than minority interest at the present time.

Howard, who as a choirboy sang in the *Esther* revival of 1732, was a pupil of Pepusch and graduated to organ-stools in the city, and to Drury Lane Theatre. On the one side he assisted Boyce in the compilation of *Cathedral Music* and wrote hymn-tunes and a small number of anthems; on the other he contributed to the popular repertory of song through his pantomimes (*Robin Goodfellow*, 1738, *The Amorous Goddess*, 1744) and his melodies for the Gardens. Howard set a new standard in patriotism, for 'brought up in the Chapel Royal, [he] preferred the style of his own country to that of any other so much, that he never staggered his belief of its being the best in the world, by listening to foreign artists or their productions.'

John Stanley also 'cultivated the style in which he was originally instructed'; but with a high competence. His *concerti grossi* (op. 2, 1742)[2] are strong in outline, vigorous in respect of rhythm, and the fugal movements (Handelian in their lack of pedantry) are as good as any composed by an English composer of that generation. Stanley was not unaware of the demands of changing attitudes and the *concertino* group of his concerti was concentrated in subsequent arrangements into a harpsichord (or organ) part. His posthumous fame depended on the concerti, but his output was both large and varied. He composed hymns and anthems, songs, cantatas, solos for flute and harpsichord, three sets of organ voluntaries (1748, 1752, and 1754), odes, oratorios,[3] and operas.[4]

[1] 1706–77; a native of Worcestershire, chorister at Gloucester Cathedral, and subsequently organist at Shrewsbury, Worcester Cathedral, Magdalen College, Oxford. Hayes, who was elected Professor of Music in Oxford University in 1742, was a prominent oratorio-conductor in the provinces and helped to establish the Three Choirs Festival.

[2] See Gerald Finzi, 'John Stanley', in *P.R.M.A.*, 77, 1950–51, p. 63.

[3] *Jephtha*, 1757; *Zimri*, 1760, *The Fall of Egypt*, 1774.

[4] *Arcadia*, librettist Robert Lloyd, 1761, for the marriage of George III and Charlotte Sophia, and *Teraminta*, librettist Henry Carey, who was a friend and admirer of Stanley.

Stanley was a conspicuous figure in the musical life of London. Blinded by an accident at the age of two, he overcame this disability to a remarkable extent; so that his capacity as performer on harpsichord and organ (he also played the violin) became legendary. He was taught by Greene and at the age of twenty-one was appointed organist at the Temple Church, retaining his earlier post of organist at St. Andrew's, Holborn. His organ recitals attracted many of his colleagues (including Handel) and his direction of concerts at the Swan and Castle taverns guaranteed their success. A fashionable teacher and supported by his wife's substantial fortune, Stanley was able to live outside London near Epping Forest through which he delighted in riding his horse.[1] When Handel's sight began to fail it was recommended to him that he should take Stanley into partnership. A year after Handel's death Stanley did direct the oratorio performances, first with J. C. Smith as partner and then, after Smith's retirement in 1774, with Thomas Linley. Five years later he succeeded Boyce as Master of the King's Band. The fact that he had a personality that was at once powerful and agreeable enabled him to make good use of his creative talents. These, to be truthful, were somewhat limited and in his *Zimri* there is a fatal run-down of the Handelian conventions. The oratorios of Stanley as of J. C. Smith were no more than pastoral entertainments to vapid libretti devoid of any sense of drama. Thus Smith in *Paradise Lost* (1760) in an aria recalling the shadow of 'Scenes of horror' in Handel's *Jephtha* [Ex. 24]. Stanley never even rose

24.

[1] See 'John Stanley' in *Vestiges*, no. 13, April–May 1957, Vestry House Museum, Walthamstow, Essex.

to this level. But if his vocal music was unprovocative his literary style was not. In his Preface to his Cantatas of 1742 (to his own words) he put up a patriotic performance, remarking that the rulers of Italy—in contrast to those of the past—were now 'keeping the Minds and Consciences of Men under the Cloud of Ignorance and Superstition [rather] than to illuminate them with the knowledge of polite Arts'. But he despaired of his own prejudiced countrymen for, 'The Slender Regard that is usually paid to Works of this Nature, when they have not the sanction of a foreign Name, will, we hope, be a sufficient Excuse for our introducing the following Cantata's into the World with the Ceremony of a Preface, the Design of which is not so much to bespeak its Approbation, as to shew how little the Performances of other Countries are entitled to that Pre-Eminence which is at present so greatly allow'd them.' A week after his death Stanley was commemorated at St. Andrew's Church, Holborn, where he had been organist for more than half-a-century. The memorial voluntary was 'I know that my Redeemer liveth.'

James Nares was another who owed his early education to the Chapel Royal. After his voice broke he studied with Pepusch and at the age of nineteen became organist of York Minster. He held this office for twenty-two years. In 1756 he took Greene's place as organist at the Chapel Royal, while in the next year he succeeded Gates as Master of the Children. Said to have been a fine choir-trainer Nares is important not only as a composer but also as an educationist. His keyboard music—commencing with *Eight Sets of lessons for the Harpsichord* (1747)[1]—was deliberately aimed at the teacher of modest capacity to whom *Il Principio, or A regular Introduction to playing on the Harpsichord or Organ* (1759) would have been invaluable, for it consisted of a graded system of lessons.

'It has', wrote Nares in his Preface, 'long been matter of Wonder to Lovers of Music that no regular Introduction to the Art of Harpsichord playing has ever been offered to the Public. A Work of this kind would be very Usefull, particularly in Boarding Schools: not such an Introduction as should be confined to the meer Rudiments of the Science, but rather a set of Lessons so adopted and disposed as to conduct the Scholar step by step from the first Essays of playing to the Execution of difficult Music.' The work, added the author, was 'the result of many Years experience, and a carefull Attention to those obstacles and difficulties which it is intended to remove and alleviate'.

[1] The list of subscribers included Beard, Boyce, Cramer, Defesch, Gates, Greene, Handel, Hayes, Pepusch, Randall, Stanley, Weideman, Worgan; but also organists at Birmingham (Gunn), Derby, Doncaster, Durham, Grantham, Hull (William Avison), Newcastle (Charles Avison), and Wakefield. In such towns the parish church organist, sometimes, as in Newcastle, appointed and remunerated by the Corporation, was assuming the role of local music director.

In the event the pieces, miniature sonatas of three (sometimes two) movements disposed in three *Essays* (C, F, and G, major) and eight 'easy' *lessons* (D, B flat, F, G, D, B flat, E flat, and A major), are rather more than beginners' pieces and quickly require a fair technique. They are, however, rewarding and to be placed among the best things of their period. Nares handled his material with a light touch, and had clearly looked at the keyboard works of Rameau whose *Principles of Composition*, in an English version, was recommended to students by Avison[1]. Here, for example, is Nares in *Badinerie* mood [Ex. 25], while here is the true quality

25.

(Essay III)

of a *Rondeau* [Ex. 26]. Like Avison Nares was a student of 'Expression', and the last of his lessons ends with a charming *Pastorale* movement.

26.

During the era of Handel great changes took place in the relationship between musician and society. These changes were assisted by Handel's influence, but would have taken place without him, since their causes lay in the structure of society itself. The musician was largely freed from the claims of royal or aristocratic patronage and was aware that his welfare depended on the support of a wider public, through 'those Entertainments, where the public Ear should always be consulted'.[2] This public, brought together at popular concerts or at more formal subscription concerts, got what it wanted. Hence the flood of theatrical pastiches, of ballads, and of concertos. But rapid development was not always in the interests of quality, hence Avison commented, 'how often does the Fate of a Concerto depend on the random Execution of a Set of Performers who have never previously considered the work . . .'[3] So far as the solo

[1] Op. cit., p. 81.
[2] ib. p. 86.
[3] ib. p. 151.

concerto was concerned one type stood out prominently—the organ concerto. The popularity of this stemmed primarily from Handel's works, but was extended by similar works (original or arranged) by many composers,[1] among whom the one who enjoyed the widest celebrity was William Felton. A native of Shropshire Felton was educated at Manchester Grammar School and St. John's College, Cambridge. After graduation he became vicar-choral (later minor canon) of Hereford Cathedral, to which he was attached for the rest of his life. Stimulated by the existence of a music club in Hereford and by the triennial Festival, Felton, whose neat fingering on the harpsichord was remembered by Burney from hearing him play in Shrewsbury, devoted himself to musical composition. Ecclesiastical emoluments out of proportion to the duties required were by now supporting a new type of clergyman, whose usefulness (if any) was likely—in the provinces—to be somewhat removed from theology. Felton published five sets of organ concertos between 1744 and 1760, as well as *8 Suites of Easy Lessons for the Harpsichord* (op. 3, 1747-52). The facility that Burney noted in execution is conveyed through Felton's compositional techniques, which are recognisably Handelian, and if his more extensive movements are guilty of digression they do show an appreciation of texture and of the relationship between solo instrument and ensemble. Felton, like most of his contemporaries, had an ear for melody and his popularity in his lifetime depended on the so-called 'Felton's Gavotte'—an *Andante* with *Variations* from Concerto No. 3, op. 1 (1744). This *Andante* (later adapted to an improbable text and destroyed in the process) is charming and fluid, and shows how new conceptions of lightness in design and simplified harmonic structure were beginning to work even on a staunch conservative [Ex. 27]. As tended to be the case

27.

[1] See C. L. Cudworth, 'The English Organ Concerto', in *The Score*, no. 8, September 1953.

with other items engaging public affection this movement was kept alive by a legend as much as by its intrinsic quality. 'Felton's Gavotte' was said to have been played by the supporters of the Young Pretender on their leaving Manchester in December 1745[1] and at the execution of the Jacobite Jeremy Dawson in the same city during the following year.

Felton, as has been said, was representative of a new type of dilettante in Holy Orders. Hanbury belongs to this group, so too the Rev. John Mainwaring. Like Felton, Mainwaring was a graduate of St. John's College, Cambridge (of which he became a Fellow in 1748), and he held a country living at Church Stretton, Shropshire. Mainwaring aspired to being a man of letters and, not being inhibited by a little learning in special fields, covered a wide territory. Thus: 'He published, without his name, a judicious life of Handel, and would have offered his remarks on painting and sculpture, but he thought the market was already overstocked . . .'[2] *The Memoirs of the Life of the late George Frederick Handel: To which is added a catalogue of his works, and observations upon then* (1760) was an invaluable prop to the later cult of Handel in Britain.

[1] A Ms. Concerto by Felton was performed at a subscription concert in Manchester on 23 July 1744. Since many of the subscribers to the series of 1744–5 concerts were Jacobites it is possible that the legend grew from that fact. See *Remains, Historical and Literary*, Chetham Society, Manchester, vol. LXXII, 1867.

[2] J. Cradock, *Literary and Miscellaneous Memoirs*, 4 vols., London, 1828, I, pp. 189–90.

9

The Age of John Christian Bach

Conservatism

DURING HANDEL'S lifetime British music was, insofar as this may ever be possible, democratised. The process continued so that by the end of the century the practice and appreciation of music was probably more widespread than in any country in Europe. For this expansion there was a price to pay, and, on the whole, it was paid by the native composer who more and more was denied the kind of protection afforded by the continental system of aristocratic patronage. Such patronage of this order as there was centred in the Court, and George III, while the first of the Hanoverians to pass as an Englishman first and a German second, either rested happily on boyhood memories of Handel or, encouraged by his Queen, engaged court musicians from Germany. At the same time, however, the King was no passive patron. He was ready to express his views and to exert his influence. Thus he sent a memorandum to Lord Carmarthen regarding a programme submitted to him from the Ancient Concerts: 'Lord Carmarthen's List of Musick for next Wednesday is very excellent and meets with the Approbation of those whose opinion on the Subject He wished to know; His introducing Mrs. Billington if He can get Her to sing pathetick Songs and not to overgrace them will be doing an essential service to the Concert.'[1]

In 1749 Geminiani had sadly noted a decline in musical taste in Britain. In his *Introduction to a good Taste in Music* he wrote: 'when I came to *London*, which was thirty-four years ago, I found Music in so thriving a State, that I had all the Reason imaginable to suppose the Growth would

[1] St. James's, 3 March 1786; B.M. Egerton Ms. 2159, f. 57.

be suitable to the excellency of the Soil. But I have lived to be most miserably disappointed; for, though it cannot be said that there was any Want of Encouragement, that Encouragement was ill bestowed. The Hand was more considered than the Head; the Performance than the Composition; and hence it followed, that instead of labouring to cultivate a Taste, which seemed to be all that was wanting, the Publick was content to nourish insipidity'.[1] Twenty years later John Hawkins, writing on behalf of the Academy of Ancient Music—now finding an annual subscription of two-and-a-half guineas inadequate to maintain its standards because of the easy money performers could obtain at popular concerts, stated cause and effect for what the conservatives regarded as a continuing decline. He looked with concern at 'that satiety or indifference which attends the hearing of music calculated for the *present hour*, and not intended for posterity'.[2] The consequence was that '. . . the compositions of this day are almost solely in the *major* third, and their structure little better than divided counterpoint, and what is still worse, on a *monotonic* bass; nor are the compositions, which some effect to admire, less liable to the objection of uniformity in respect to their several *divisions* or strains—For reasons, which no one is willing to aver, Adagio-Music is exploded, and we are content to forego the Majesty and Dignity of the *Largo* and Andante movements, with all the variety arising from the interchange of different airs and measures, for the noise and rattle of an unisonous *Allegro*, to which no name can be given, or the intoxicating softness of that too oft iterated air, the *Minuet*'.[3] Hawkins returned to his charge in 1788, in his Preface to Boyce's *Cathedral Music*, protesting that J. C. Bach and C. F. Abel had abdicated their responsibilities as serious musicians by living 'by the favor of the public', by cultivating two styles, 'the one for their own private delight, the other for the gratification of the many'.

'Yet these, too, had their fate; the multifarious productions of *Bach* and *Abel*, their *Trios*, *Quartettos*, and *Quintettos*, as they are called, together with their *Periodical Overtures*, were heard, and consigned to oblivion; but their style of writing in a great measure survives. We no more hear the solemn and pathetic Adagio, the artful and well-studied Fugue, or the sweet modulations of the keys with the minor third: all is *Allegro* and *Prestissimo*, and, if not discord, such harmony as the ear sickens at hearing. Such music Mr. *Handel* was used to listen to and laugh at, and comparing it to a game at cards, would exclaim, "Now D is trumps, now A", in allusion to those vulgar transitions from the key-note to its fifth, with which such

[1] Quoted by Avison, op. cit., pp. 105–6.

[2] *An Account of the Institution and Progress of the Academy of Ancient Music with a Comparative View of the Music of the Past and Present Times*, by a Member, London, 1770, p. 20.

[3] ib. p. 16.

sort of music, especially when accompanied with French horns, abounds.'

The period thus covered may have been one of vulgarisation—Hawkins's view has been accepted by many subsequent writers—but it was exciting. A great deal was taking place and, as happens when public opinion gets to work on the arts, taste was volatile. Against a background of conservatism there was a conspicuous taste for novelty. 'Scarcely had the life of Handel terminated, when the latest powers of instruments became better known; and as encouragement was offered, men arose, who enlarged (by extraordinary practice) those powers, while, in some instances, improved mechanism * was called in to aid the growing advancement. *Witness the substitution of the piano forte for the harpsichord, and the various additions to harps, horns, flutes, trumpets, and serpents, by pedals, keys, and other ingenious contrivances . . .'.[1] The pianoforte, the symbol of the new music, made unspectacular progress at first. William Mason, the poet, wrote enthusiastically to Gray on his acquisition of such an instrument in Hamburg in 1755, but by 1767 it was still going through the adoption process. A Covent Garden playbill in that year announcing a benefit concert for Miss Brickler on 16 May concluded—'Miss Brickler will sing a favourite song from Judith, accompanied by Mr. Dibdin on a new instrument called Piano-Forte.'[2] The great master of the pianoforte in London at this time was John Christian Bach, whose first performance of a concerto for it apparently took place in 1768. The popularity of the piano was in large measure due to Silbermann's former apprentice Johann Christoph Zumpe, who settled in London at about the same time as Bach. He invented what was known as the 'English Single Action'. Mason possessed an instrument by Zumpe to whom Laurence Sterne also made reference in his *Letters from Yorick to Eliza* (1773).

John Christian Bach

Christian Bach, the youngest son of Johann Sebastian and Anna Magdalena, was twenty-seven when he arrived in England in 1762. Since 1756 he had lived in Italy, latterly occupying the post of cathedral organist in Milan, and, as had Handel before him, had acclimatised himself to the atmosphere of Italian music. England, a magnetic country to all continental musicians,[3] had clearly come into mind as a possible centre for

[1] 'A Slight Sketch of the Present State of Music in London', in *The Quarterly Musical Magazine* and *Review*, III, 1820, pp. 400–8.

[2] Quoted in *An Illustrated Catalogue of the Music Loan Exhibition . . . at Fishmongers' Hall*, June–July 1904, Novello, 1909.

[3] 'The greatest part of the foreign musicians who visit London remain there: for as that great city is actually a PERU to them, they do not choose to deprive themselves of the lucrative monopoly which they there enjoy, in regard to their own profession.' M. d'Archenholz, *A Picture of England*, English edn., Dublin, 1791, p. 235.

fruitful activity. In 1761 John Christian somehow became acquainted with John Lockman's *Ode on the Auspicious Arrival and Nuptials . . . of Queen Charlotte* and set it to music. He also composed a birthday ode with choral writing which, for one who had not directly been engaged in English musical affairs, was a surprisingly good shot at an acceptable 'English style' [Ex. 1]. A year later, with Handel's example in mind, he reached

1.

London, there to direct the Italian season of opera at the Haymarket. The management of this house was now in the hands of the singer Colomba Mattei, in whose home Bach lodged until her departure from the Haymarket and from England in 1763.[1] Bach, advertised as 'Mr. John Bach, a Saxon Master of Music', succeeded Gioacchino Cocchi.[2] His first London opera was *Orione* in which he was well served by the soprano Anna Lucia de'Amicis. *Orione*, in which Bach showed how drama within music could be realised by abstention from the *da capo* principle and by heightened orchestral colour, was a success and ran for three months. It was in this opera that clarinets made their first official public appearance in London. (The clarinet had been introduced as a novelty into various concert rooms from time to time during the preceding twenty years.) After *Orione* came *Zanaida* which ran for the rest of the season. At this point Bach was appointed music master to the young Queen. His court duties resembled those of Carl Philipp Emanuel at Potsdam and Berlin in that he was required also to accompany the King's flute playing. For reasons which by now are apparent Bach's career as an opera composer in London was chequered. After his first operas (stimulated by Arne's attempt in the same genre?) he waited two years when *Adriano in Siria* was a relative failure. Two years later a subject of more British interest, and treated as a dramatic poem by William Mason in 1759, inspired *Carattaco*,

[1] The Haymarket as an opera-house had been badly—sometimes dishonestly—managed for at least a decade. It continued a precarious course until 1785 'with various degrees of injury to the proprietors, when it entirely sunk under the accumulated weight of lawsuits, factious cabals, and distresses of every sort.' E. Waters, 'A Statement of Matters relative to the King's Theatre' in *The Quarterly Musical Magazine and Review*, 1, 1818, pp. 239–63.

[2] Composer to the King's Theatre since 1757 and of about a dozen operas. Cocchi, who composed a number of ceremonial works, among them one for the wedding and Coronation of George III, was a reputed singing-teacher, and he remained in England until 1773 when he returned to Venice.

which enjoyed greater esteem. But Bach, like Handel, appreciated the peculiar British situation and as much as possible disentangled himself from Italian opera in London, preserving his place in the European field, however, by composing *Temistocle* (1772) and *Lucio Silla* (1776) for Mannheim, and *Amadis des Gaules* (1779) for Paris.

When Bach ceased to be Mattei's paying guest he shared a house with Carl Friedrich Abel—one of Johann Sebastian's Leipzig pupils. Abel, who had come to London to give concerts in 1759, was a noted gamba player, but also an excellent harpsichordist, and able to give creditable performances on other instruments as well. He was chamber musician to the Queen, and also busy as a concert promoter. Bach joined Abel in this venture and together they took over from Cocchi at Spring Gardens and regularised the fashionable subscription concerts at the Soho house of Mrs. Cornelys. Bach and Abel imposed a symphonic pattern on the Cornelys concerts and after ten years installed themselves in the Hanover Square Rooms,[1] to remain a principal centre of music in London for a century.

Between them Bach and Abel—who entertained the eight-year-old Mozart during his London visit of 1764–5—built the *galant* symphony and concerto into the metropolitan pattern of concert-giving. While they enjoyed great success in London, however, their influence was slower to work elsewhere, for in the provinces—other than in Leeds where Herschel was as much a pioneer as Bach in London—traditions sometimes were difficult to uproot. Bach was a master of the *galant* style and in his hands the formal structure of the opening symphonic movement appears both as assured and yet fluid. This inventiveness extended to orchestration and he was capable of the most original effects—as in the contrast between muted and *pizzicato* strings in the symphony for double orchestra (op. XVIII, no. 5) and the use of independent wind and of solo viola in op. XXI, no. 1. Bach, like Handel, was an Italianate composer: but he also retained German traits, notably in an expressive fugue on BACH and in the implied tragic implications of the slow, C minor, movement of op. VI, no. 6. But Bach also saw himself as a British composer.

In 1763 he published *Six Concerts pour le Clavecin*, dedicated to Queen Charlotte, and the finale of the last of this set demonstrated a pretty show of loyalty in a set of variations on a by now familiar tune [Ex. 2]. Bach

2.

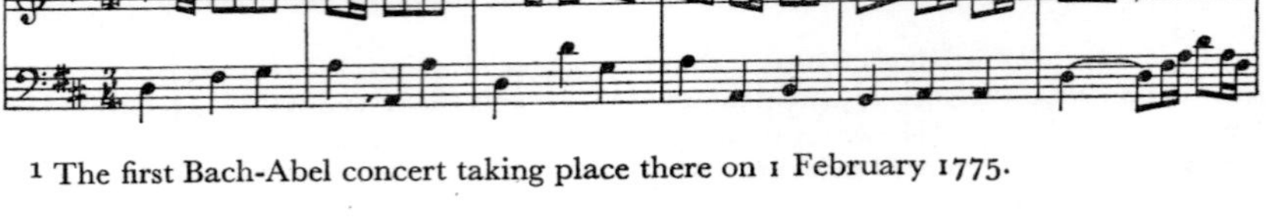

[1] The first Bach-Abel concert taking place there on 1 February 1775.

enjoyed writing such variations—useful for the purpose of introducing him to the public as an exponent of the pianoforte—and in his op. XIII, no. 4 he exploited the vogue for Scottish folksong in variations on *The Yellow Hair'd Laddie*;[1] though by the time Bach had finished with it there was not much of the Caledonian element left [Ex. 3]. He had, however, no need to

3.

Solo (Var. 4)
tr
tr

add a British label to his popular works. He quickly adapted himself to the conventions of ballad opera and made delightful, and surprisingly varied, contribution to the Covent Garden pasticcios, *The Maid of the Mill* and *The Summer's Tale*, and to *The Flitch of Bacon*. *The Maid of the Mill* was based on Samuel Richardson's novel *Pamela*, libretto by Isaac Bickerstaffe, and the music arranged by Samuel Arnold. The overture was by the Earl of Kelly, the second aria by 'the late Elector of Saxony'; other composers drawn on were Arnold, Bach, Galuppi, Giardini, Hasse, Jommelli, Pergolesi, Philidor, Piccinni, Domenico Scarlatti, and Vinci. The printed score (R. Bremner) carried the following notice: 'N.B.—That none may pretend ignorance, Notice is here given, That who ever Presumes to Print, or write out for Sale, any song in This OPERA, will be Prosecuted by the Author and the Proprietors, with the utmost rigour of the Law.'

The Summer's Tale, attributed to Richard Cumberland, was also arranged by Arnold, who drew on the composers featured in *The Maid of the Mill* (both works were produced in 1765) and also Boyce, Howard, Lampe, and Stanley. *The Flitch of Bacon* came thirteen years later at the Little Theatre in the Haymarket directed by William Shield. Like Arne Bach had an intuitive sense of what was vocal and what was not (he was also a singing-teacher, his best-known pupil being Mrs. Weichsel for whom he wrote many songs) and he often showed a nice capacity for reading into an English poet's intention. Two items from *The Summer's Tale* nicely anticipate the manner of Sullivan [Ex. 4 and 5]. On the other

4.

Sung by Mr. Mattocks
vl.
vl.
So pro-found an im-pres-sion I bear ____ of the Maid who was once my fond choice

[1] A favourite source-book of the period was James Oswald's *The Caledonian Pocket Companion* (*c.* 1747). Among Bach's works for Tenducci and the Pantheon concerts were arrangements of *The Broom of Cowdenknowes* and *Lochaber*.

5.

hand Bach could also manage to affect the sturdier but popular church style and a setting of Rev. W. Dodd's *Let the solemn organ blow* for *The Christian's Magazine* is as good a hymn-tune as any composed in the 1760's.

John Christian Bach became as much an Englishman as Handel. Among his friends and familiar acquaintances were Thomas Gainsborough (in whose company he was once robbed by highwaymen[1]), Sir Joshua Reynolds, John Zoffany, George Colman, Richard Brinsley Sheridan, Horne Tooke, John Wilkes, Lord Abingdon, Sir William Young, Governor of Dominica, and Lady Glenorchy. Prolific in all fields, personally popular, and the projector of concerts that were famous throughout Europe, Bach should have made a great impression on the musical life of the country of his adoption. In that he was one of the principal architects of modern English orchestral playing and that without his years of concert management the impulse which was to lead to the foundation of the Philharmonic Society would hardly have sprung to life he accomplished much. But his reputation declined quickly: in the end he was defeated by the memory of the Saxon composer whose place he had tried to take. Bach forgot to pay sufficient respect to a by now broadly based choral tradition.

Ambitious Projects in the Provinces

'To go to the fountain head, we must quote the personal example of our venerable SOVEREIGN himself, who has done much to perpetuate by his own partiality the love of Handel among his subjects, and all that remains of the nervous, sound, noble, and majestic style of performance which is acquired by the study of that composer.'[2]

Opportunities for studying that composer were multiplying. During Handel's lifetime word-books of individual oratorios were published in

[1] See W. T. Whitley, *Thomas Gainsborough*, London, 1915, pp. 117–19, where Bach's evidence before the Recorder at the Old Bailey, which led to the conviction of two criminals, is quoted.

[2] *The Quarterly Musical Magazine and Review*, 1818, I, p. 7.

Bristol, Salisbury, and Dublin, as well as in London. About 1760 a collection of libretti of 'All the Favourite Oratorios' was available from 'the Booksellers of Oxford, Gloucester, Worcester, Hereford and London'. In 1767 T. Lesson, of Doncaster,[1] issued a similar collection for the benefit of northern Handelians. That the general enthusiasm for the oratorios was well under way at this time is attested by the subscribers to the edition of the scores published by William Randall (Walsh's successor after 1766). *Messiah* appeared in 1766, and as other oratorios followed they were welcomed by many provincial organists, and by musical societies in Kirkheaton, Saddleworth, Sheffield, and Halifax ('at the Old Cock'), in Yorkshire, and in Blackburn ('at the Plume of Feathers'), Wigan, and Oldham, in Lancashire, as well as in other places.

The city of Chester had a particular association with Handel. Not only was the rehearsal of *Messiah*, arranged by Edmund Baker,[2] remembered but also an organ recital by Handel's organist Maclaine.[3] Musical events were promoted thereafter by Edward Orme, a gifted painter, a Freemason, a 'conduct' of the cathedral, and from 1765 to 1776 organist. On 23 April 1751 there was a benefit concert for Orme (Arne's Overture to *Alfred* was among the works played); on the following day a benefit for Wightman, a local violinist and oboist; three days later a third such concert was given for John Parry of Ruabon, the blind harpist to Sir Watkins Williams Wynn, who had played to Handel and was a familiar figure in the concert rooms of Britain.[4] This was to all intents the first festival in Chester. In 1758 Orme conducted a grand concert in aid of the Infirmary. The next great occasion was in 1772. *Messiah*, *Samson*, and

[1] The force behind music in Doncaster at this time was Edward Miller (1731–1807), pupil of Burney and protégé of Nares. The Records show that instrumental music in Doncaster was still municipally supported: e.g. '13 May, 1763. Ordered that if Mr. Miller, the organist, will undertake to instruct the corporation band of music to play upon the hautboy and bassoon the Corporation will be at the expense of the instruments'. *Calendar to the Records of the Borough of Doncaster*, vol. 4. Miller discovered the talent of F. W. Herschel (1738–1822); see E. Miller's *History of Doncaster*, 1804, p. 162.

[2] Baker was previously organist of St. Chad's Church, Shrewsbury. He was a friend of Thomas Arne and the teacher of Charles Burney. See H. Owen and J. B. Blakeway, *History of Shrewsbury*, II, p. 226.

[3] 5 November 1741: 'Yesterday arrived in his way to Dublin, Mr. Maclaine, who was invited to play on our Cathedral organ, this day, on wh he performed so well, to the entire satisfaction of the whole Congregation, that some of the best Judges in Musick said, they never heard the organ truly played on before; and his performance was allowed to be very masterly and in the finest taste.' Quoted from *Adams' Chester Courant* in *Faulkner's Journal*, 3–7 November 1741.

[4] Parry (1710?–82) was born at Bryn Lynan, near Nevin, and was engaged as family harpist at Wynnstay, Ruabon, the home of the Wynns. In addition to *Antient British Music* (1742) he also published *A Collection of Welsh, English and Scotch Airs* (1761), and *British Harmony, being a Collection of Antient Welsh Airs* (1781). Sir Watkin Williams Wynn (1749–89) was M.P. for Denbighshire, a friend of Reynolds and Garrick, and a generous contributor to the Welsh School in London.

Judas Maccabaeus, supervised by Orme but conducted by Hayes, were given in the cathedral on 16, 18, 19 June, while on 17 June there was a miscellaneous concert in the Exchange. In 1783 there was a five-day festival, with *Messiah*, *Jephtha*, and *Judas Maccabaeus* in the cathedral, *Acis and Galatea* and a miscellaneous concert in the County Hall, where there were balls each evening, and on the last day, 20 September, a public breakfast, with rounds and catches. Further Handel festivals followed in 1786, 1791, 1806, and 1814.[1]

It was, however, in Yorkshire that the major extension of the Handelian influence took place. The centre of activity was Leeds where public musical performances were first noticed by the *Leeds Mercury* in 1726. It was not, however, until 1741 that programme details were given. In that year and the next John Parry gave harp concerts, with 'several pieces of Corelli's, Handel's, Geminiani's, and Vivaldi's', a 'Grand Organ Concerto of Mr. Handel's', and English and Scottish airs. While secular music was taking root in the social life of the city the cause of music in church was being furthered by John Carr, a splendid organist, in office at the parish church from 1713 until 1756. His successor, Mr. Crompton (of Rochdale), took over the organisation of secular concerts and by 1763 designed a plan for a series of twelve subscription concerts at the Assembly Rooms. The programmes of these concerts during the next two or three years were among the most progressive in England, London not excepted. There were not only overtures by Handel, and concertos by Avison, Corelli, Handel, and Geminiani, but also symphonies and concertos with clarinets, with 'favourite pieces for Clarinets, French Horns, and Bassoon'.[2] Crompton had persuaded Herschell to become secretary of the Leeds concerts, and Herschel, with German wind-band music experience behind him, was eager to promote the cause of wind music in general and of the clarinet in particular.

On Tuesday 27 September 1767 the *Leeds Intelligencer* noted that 'On Sunday last being His Majesty's Accession Purcell's grand Te Deum and the grand Coronation Chorus were performed in the Chapel of Holbeck in this parish with great applause.' At the end of the year it was noted in the same journal that 'On Christmas Day that part of Messiah most proper for the occasion, was performed by the singers of Holbeck Chapel, to a very crowded audience, with universal applause.' This appears to be the beginning of *Messiah* performances as a part of the English Christmas festivities. Enthusiasm for this oratorio was now running so strong that from 9 September 1768 a series of eighteen fortnightly performances, to be given in the Assembly Rooms, began. At this juncture

[1] See J. C. Bridge, *A Short Sketch of the Chester Musical Festivals*, 1772–1829, Chester [n.d.].
[2] First mentioned in the programme of a benefit concert for Herschel in May 1765.

Leeds had established a claim to supervise or assist other towns in their Handelian endeavours. Thus on 9 May 1769 principals from Leeds went to Holmfirth to strengthen the local talent. In October of that year there was a two-day Handel festival, in Trinity Church, Leeds, in aid of the Infirmary.

On 12 October, *Judas Maccabaeus* was performed, and on the next day *Messiah*. This occasion drew together the best performers from a wide area. Singers came from Doncaster (where oratorios were given in the parish church as a suitable entertainment during the race-meetings), Wakefield, Beverley, York, and Lichfield; extra orchestral players from Manchester, and an organist from Halifax.[1] In 1772 Crompton, to whom Leeds owed much, went to Lancaster, his place being taken by Jobson of Wakefield, who had already appeared in Leeds as violinist and conductor. Jobson not only directed the oratorio performances but taught one of the best Handel singers of the period, Miss Harwood, who made a great reputation in London—the first specialist Handel singer from the provinces to do so.

The installation of a new organ, built by Snetzler,[2] in St. Paul's Church, Sheffield, in 1755 was the occasion of the first 'public entertainment' in that church and city and so successful was it that 'the inhabitants (were) resolved to have the like annually'. The next recorded performance took place in 1769, *Messiah* being given at the church and *Acis and Galatea* in the theatre. The instrumental performers numbered ninety-eight, the singers 160. A word-book of a performance of *Saul* in Sheffield in 1774 is extant in the Sheffield City Library.

Handel Commemoration at Westminster Abbey and its Influence

Few composers escape diminution of reputation during the twenty years or so after their deaths. Handel was one of the few: his reputation soared as enthusiasm for choral singing intensified, especially in the provinces. During this period the large-scale 'festival' performance of oratorio was established; as a result of this and the growing cult of choral music in London the intention to hold a centenary Commemoration of Handel in Westminster Abbey and the Pantheon developed. The Commemoration,

[1] See Emily Hargrave, 'Musical Leeds in the Eighteenth Century' in *The Publications of the Thoresby Society*, vol. XXVIII, Leeds, 1928, pp. 320 ff.

[2] Johann (John) Snetzler (*c.* 1710–1800), a German organ builder, settled in England in 1740. Among his famous instruments were those built for the first *Messiah* performance in Dublin, for Chesterfield Parish Church (1741), Aberdeen Musical Society (1752), King's Lynn Parish Church (1754) St. Martin's Church, Leicester (1774), Halifax Parish Church (1765), and Rotherham Parish Church (1777).

under the patronage of George III, took place in May 1784 and involved upwards of 500 performers, among whom were representatives of every important provincial music centre. The Directors of the Commemoration included the Earl of Sandwich and Sir Watkin Williams Wynn. The former was a well-known Handelian and the principal patron of the Concerts of Ancient Music which were founded in 1776,[1] and of Joah Bates[2] who directed the Ancient Music and also the Handel Commemoration. Sir Watkin Williams Wynn, a co-founder of the Ancient Concerts, as has been seen, came to the project of a Handel festival in London with experience of those in Chester behind him. The Handel Commemoration, described in detail by Burney in 1785, was a success and similar events took place in the Abbey in 1785, 1786, 1787, and 1791.[3] Of the first participants in the 1784 Festival some emigrated to America, there to develop an independent Handel cult: among them were the violinists Alexander Reinagle—who directed the City Concerts in Philadelphia, Jean Gehot—who established himself in New York, and George Gillingham—for a time leader of Reinagle's orchestra in Philadelphia. A number of English organists and choral experts (including Josiah Flagg, William Selby, and Raynor Taylor) also emigrated to the States at this time, taking with them scores of the oratorios. The Handel choral cult took root especially in Boston.

The Westminster Abbey performances had an enormous influence in England, in large towns and small. The inspiration given to communities with but modest resources is illustrated by the following notice of a performance in Lancashire: 'For the Benefit of Mrs. Russell organist will be performed on Wednesday, October 20, 1784, in the Chapel (All Saints) in Little Bolton, the Grand Miscellaneous Pieces, as performed before His Majesty, at the Commemoration of Handel, in Westminster Abbey and at the late festival in Liverpool, with so much applause. The overture in Esther, Dettingen Te Deum, a Funeral Anthem, composed on the death of Queen Caroline; Duet, Air, and Chorus, in Judas Maccabaeus;

[1] The concerts continued from 1776 to 1848. The guiding principle was that no music written within the last twenty years should be performed at any concert.

[2] 1741–99; born in Halifax and taught music by Hartley and Wainwright, organists in Rochdale and Manchester respectively, before going to Eton and Cambridge. Bates, secretary to Lord Sandwich and a Civil Servant, was an amateur musician, but influential.

[3] 'I have just received the Duke of Leeds's note enclosing the letter addressed to Him by his brother Directors of the Ancient Concert on this subject of resuming the Festival at Westminster Abbey; it having subsided for those two last year's was not at my instigation but from the trial of Mr. [Warren] Hastings in Westminster Hall. If the Duke of Leeds can find means of securing certain Days for the Musical Performances in Westminster Abbey I shall most willingly attend them, and considering how thoroughly the Public as well as the House of Peers seem tired of the Attendance in Westminster Hall I should not think this difficult to be effected.' Note by King George III, from the Queen's House, 27 February 1790. B.M. Egerton Ms. 2159.

and parts of the Oratorio of Israel in Egypt. The whole to conclude with the Coronation Anthem. Principal Instrumental Performers, Messrs. Buckly, Burr, Barker, Wainwright, Hutchinson, Entwistle, Nicholson, and Mr. Wainwright, from Liverpool;[1] Principal Vocal Performers, Messrs. Heywood, Houghton, Travis, Nield, Bradley, Radcliffe, Miss Wrigley, and Mrs. Russell. The Chorus Singers from Hey, Oldham, Shaw, etc. End of the 2nd Part, a Concerto, by Mr. Nicholson. The Band will be large and the Chorusses remarkably full, accompanied with Kettle Drums, Trumpets, Hautboys, Bassoons, Double Bass, and every other Instrument requisite. The doors to be opened at Ten and begin exactly at Eleven o'clock in the forenoon. Tickets, at Two Shillings each, to be had at the Horse Shoe, the Boar's Head, and the Swan Inns, in Bolton. N.B. Nothing will be taken under full price during the whole Performance'.[2]

In Leeds a month later a three-day festival (the programme being drawn from the Westminster Abbey performances) took place. Miss Harwood, now described as 'principal at the Antient Concerts in London and at the Festival of the Three Choirs', made a triumphant home-coming, while to make the 'chorus as full as possible the double bassoons, trombones, and double drum' used in London were hired. The newspaper looked for sensation and found it, for the 'roll of the Double Drums in the dead march in "Saul" almost rivalled the tremendous voice of nature when terribly shaking the spheres'.

The popularisation of music thus continued at a rapid pace until by the beginning of the nineteenth century Britain could, in some respects, be justly described as one of the most musical countries in Europe. It would have been difficult, however, then to have discovered any common denominator of taste. The progress of music under the social, ecclesiastical, and moral principles and prejudices that obtained made consistency on the creative side impossible. The native composer then became a realist, submitting himself to the exigencies of the situation and aiming no higher than common-sense prompted. This being the case the non-professional, dilettante musician, or music-lover, was often left to take an initiative. This was particularly the case in Scotland where composers were mostly found among those least affected by religious inhibitions—the 'gentry'. Lord Colville of Ochiltree, the twelfth Earl of Eglinton, David Foulis, and Alexander Baillie, were all practising composers. A much more important figure was Thomas Erskine, who succeeded as sixth Earl of Kelly in 1756.

[1] After the installation of an organ in St. Peter's Church, Liverpool, in 1764 musical festivals became practicable, the first taking place in 1766, towards which the Borough Council subscribed £40. In 1786 a music hall was built in Bold Street to accommodate an audience of 1,300. See *Liverpool Bulletin*, vol. 7, 1959, p. 8.

[2] Quoted in *Bolton Evening News*, 17 July 1875.

Symphony-Overture and Music for the Theatre

Kelly went to Germany, where he 'shut himself up at Mannheim with the elder Stamitz, and studied composition and practised the violin with such serious application that, at his return to England, there was no part of theoretical or practical music, in which he was not equally versed with the greatest professors of his time'.[1] Kelly was a popular composer, his minuets, songs, and 'overtures', being unreservedly welcomed at Ranelagh and Vauxhall and at provincial concerts; his importance lies in the fact that he brought the Mannheim symphony into the ambit of British music. His most celebrated piece in the modern manner was the overture to *The Maid of the Mill*, which clearly shows its antecedents and the composer's grasp of symphonic principles [Ex. 6*a* and *b*]. In or about 1762 Kelly

6a.

6b.

published *Six Overtures in 8 parts, and a thorough bass for the harpsichord, Opera prima*, in which it seems that he saw fit occasionally to re-write his master's works in a more modern style.[2] Other symphonic works by Kelly appeared in a series of *Periodical Overtures* issued by Robert Bremner as nos. 13, 17, 25, and 28 (this being the *Maid of the Mill* Overture). In

1 Burney, *History*, IV, p. 677.

2 C. L. Cudworth, 'The English Symphonists of the Eighteenth Century', in *P.R.M.A.*, 78, 1951–2, p. 31.

No. 25 there is a complex of dynamic markings which show the substance of the complaint of the conservatives, that although the 'new stile of composition lately cultivated in Germany . . . pleases by its spirit and a wild luxuriancy, which makes an agreeable variety in a concert (it) possesses too little of the elegance and pathetic expression of Music to remain long the Public Taste'.[1]

Bremner, the publisher, was hardly less important than Kelly and Bach and Abel in naturalising the symphony. Having established a prosperous music-publishing and selling business in Edinburgh he determined to set up in London, where he arrived in 1762. (In that year he purchased the *Fitzwilliam Virginal Book* at the sale of Pepusch's Library and presented it to Lord Fitzwilliam.) He (and others) issued the parts of the symphonies of Stamitz, Dittersdorf, Filtz, Holzbauer, Haydn, and Mysliveček, which were not only the staple fare of the Bach-Abel Concerts but were acceptable to musical societies in many parts of the country.

The symphony, however, was regarded none the less as a foreign preserve. English composers were inclined to compromise, either with older styles, or with the easy charms of the Pleasure Gardens idiom. Conservative standards prevailed at Court, where, although the King regularly imported players for the Royal Band from Germany, Handel still held sway. This resulted in curious quasi-symphonic studies being prepared for those occasions for which musical performances were obligatory. Normally a royal Suite at the Court of George III comprised an Entrada, followed by a medley of minuets and marches. The Entrada was often supplied by the Introduction and Allegro of a Handel Overture. If not it could be extracted from Hasse, Geminiani, Pugnani, Sammartini, or Kelway, or newly composed by the current director of the Court Concerts and Balls, Charles Weidemann, whose own contributions show a not always easy partnership between the old and the new.[2] Many of the minuets were amateur essays, sometimes of considerable charm and sometimes written by members of the Royal Family.[3] Marches from German regiments were popular, as also those composed by Bach and Abel. On the whole the orchestral music furnished at royal parties was more in line with popular standards than with those encouraged at the Bach-Abel Subscription Concerts. To these English composers in general had little chance of entry: 'The cold reception that anything under the title of English meets with is enough to deter them from doing anything

[1] J. Gregory, *The State and Faculties of Man*, Edinburgh, 1765, p. 180.

[2] e.g. the Entrada 'For Her Majesty's Birthday 1775', R.M. 24.i.17, which contains music of this kind used between 1761 and 1787.

[3] Princess Augusta was a harpsichordist, the Prince of Wales a cellist, the Duke of Cambridge a violinist, and the Duke of Cumberland a flautist; all were competent to take part in the concerts, two a week, given at Buckingham House.

at all.' So said John Potter—who stuck to song-writing for Vauxhall Gardens—in his *Observations on the present state of music and musicians, with general rules for studying music, to which is added a scheme for erecting and supporting a musical academy in this Kingdom* (London, 1762).

The truth is that the successful English composers of the period were too busy ever to be able to stand back and look closely at what they were about. Sometimes, paradoxically, they found themselves batting on a too easy wicket. At least half-a-dozen composers more or less contemporary with Christian Bach possessed decided talents—which got lost in fugitive pieces for the theatre.

Thomas Linley (1733–95), a pupil of Thomas Chilcot, organist of Bath Abbey and a promoter of oratorio performances, had the advantage of working in a city where there was a lively and independent instrumental tradition. The Pump Room Orchestra had been established as early as 1704, and theatrical performances were also frequent. Linley became well-known as a singing-teacher, and in 1774 he went to London to take up partnership with Stanley in the direction of the Lenten oratorio seasons. A year after commencing this office in London Linley composed some of the songs for Sheridan's[1] *Duenna*, which, running for seventy-five nights, established Linley as a theatre composer. He was joined in this enterprise by his son Thomas (1756–78), who had studied with Nardini in Florence and became intimate with Mozart. The younger Linley was responsible for the Overture to *The Duenna*. Both Linleys were accomplished melodists in the manner of Arne. The elder Linley's symphony-overtures were effective extensions of that master's procedures, but marked by a refinement derived from Italian *sinfonia* models. Among his miscellaneous undertakings were a newly orchestrated version of *The Beggar's Opera* (Drury Lane, 1779), a rehash of *King Arthur* entitled *Anthea and Emmeline* (1784), with original music by Linley added to that previously supplied by Purcell and Arne. The Overture to *The Gentle Shepherd* was a composite work. The elder Linley wrote the first movement [Ex. 7],

7.

[1] Sheridan was Linley's son-in-law, having eloped with Elizabeth Ann Linley (1754–92), a famous soprano, in 1773. Other members of this talented family were Mary (1758–87), Maria (1763–84), also singers, Ozias Thurston (1765–1831), organist, and William (1771–1835), author, civil servant, and composer. Linley family letters are in the Bath Municipal Library, see C. Black, *The Linleys of Bath*, London, 1926, also W. Wade, 'Some Bath Musicians', in *The Bath Critic*, vol. 2, no. 3, March 1952, pp. 108–9.

but for the second used part of a galant violin concerto by his dead son [Ex. 8].

8.

Samuel Arnold (1740–1802), an ex-chorister of the Chapel Royal, was an opportunist. A pupil of Bernard Gates and James Nares, he was asked by John Beard to compose for Covent Garden. In 1765 he was responsible for the supervision of the music for *The Maid of the Mill.* Not only did this entail selection and composition of airs but also the arrangement of instrumental music to accompany stage action— the first time this had been done in such a work since Purcell's time. Arnold contrived this to Beard's satisfaction and it was appreciated that his talent for such work was considerable. He was employed at Covent Garden until 1776 when George Colman took him over to the Little Theatre in the Haymarket. Arnold wrote or arranged music for forty-three works, from which a number of symphony-overtures survived. Eight were published as Op. 8. Arnold, like Sullivan, was at his best when least in earnest; but he found it difficult entirely to escape from his antecedents. Although he was permanently connected with the theatre, and from 1769 was lessee of Marylebone Gardens, he climbed up the conventional ladder. He composed oratorios (*The Curse of Saul*, 1767, and *The Prodigal Son*, 1773, being the most successful), became a Mus.D. at Oxford in 1773, succeeded Nares as organist of the Chapel Royal in 1783, took over Stanley's share of the direction of the oratorios on Stanley's death, and was appointed conductor of the Ancient Music in 1789. Four years later he succeeded Benjamin Cooke as organist of Westminster Abbey. But Arnold is best known for his continuation of Boyce's *Cathedral Music* and his edition (running to forty volumes) of the works of Handel. This, the first collected edition of the works of any master and the symbol of that master's final conquest of the British, was presented to Beethoven on his death-bed.

Arnold's general abilities were considerable, but his creative gifts relatively slender. And it went against his dignity to give them full rein.

Charles Dibdin (1745–1834), on the other hand, had no doubts about the direction he should take. The twelfth of fourteen children of the parish clerk of Holy Rood Church, Southampton, he became a chorister in Winchester Cathedral and was instructed in the rudiments of music by Peter Fussell (later to succeed James Kent, the anthem-composer, as organist). He had practical experience in the amateur concerts that took place weekly in Winchester, where he appeared as solo singer, and he developed so strong an affection for Corelli that he scored *Concerti grossi* from parts to find out how the harmonies worked. Although an aspirant composer Dibdin decided that professional instruction was superfluous. 'The music I have,' he said, 'was strongly in my mind from my earliest remembrance, *and I knew that no master could at any time have been of the least service to me*'.[1] On the death of his father he went to London to live with an elder brother, Thomas, a sailor and the inspiration of his most celebrated song, *Tom Bowling*. Charles tuned harpsichords for a living and managed to publish a set of ballads with Thompson, who gave him three guineas for the copyright. By dint of perseverance he established connection with Rich and Beard and, with the additional help of the Earl of Sandwich, became a chorus-singer at Covent Garden. In 1762 he wrote both words and music of *The Shepherd's Artifice*. Three years later he took the part of Ralph in *The Maid of the Mill*, and for some years he acted in pieces of his own composition. Dibdin composed for Covent Garden, but also Drury Lane, Sadler's Wells, the Haymarket, and the Circus. In twenty years he contributed to more than 100 dramatic pieces. His popularity as a writer of ballads congenial subjects, many of a more or less realistic nature, was such that he could safely set up 'Entertainments' of his own in London and tour the British Isles. Possessed of enormous energy Dibdin wrote novels, a *History of the British Stage*, a number of didactic works for young musicians, and an account of his *Professional Life*. (His private life was so pock-marked by scandal that it was best left unwritten.) His *Musical Tour* (Sheffield, 1788) gives an admirable and racy account of provincial musical life. Dibdin composed about 1,000 songs, but, being frequently in disagreement with his employers, lived near to penury. He laid no claim to scientific musical excellence but his acute sense of what the public wanted enabled him to leave behind a mass of what were for many years not unjustly regarded as 'typically English' songs. Although Dibdin was a minor master his melodic distinction was undeniable, e.g. [Ex. 9] even if there were those who tried to deny it. 'I am indeed told', wrote Dibdin in the Dedication of *The*

[1] *Memoir* by George Hogarth, in *The Songs of Charles Dibdin*, 1842, p. xiv.

9.

Sung by Mrs. Wrighton
How weak the Maid whose led a - stray

Padlock to Garrick, 'there are some who affect not only to doubt my having Set the Musick of the Padlock, but even to name the Composer, some Italian Master (God knows who) that I stole it from . . .' It may well be that Haydn had Dibdin's example in mind when writing his *Sailor's Song*, which has its affinities with pieces in Dibdin's *From Yo, Yea, or the Friendly Tars* (1777) and *The Islanders* (1780). Of his overtures, those to *The Padlock* (1777),[1] *The Blackamoor* (1770), and *The Institution of the Garter* (1771) were issued in orchestral parts.[2]

A year younger than Dibdin, James Hook (1746–1827), of Norwich, had a similarly unpretentious attitude to musical composition, but he had enjoyed a firmer education and was thus able to express his fertile ideas with professional competence. Hook was a pupil of Thomas Garland, organist of Norwich Cathedral—himself a pupil of Maurice Greene. Since his father, a cutler, died when he was eleven Hook was compelled so early to put his talents on the market. He taught, copied music, tuned harpsichords, and took part in local concerts. When he was seventeen or eighteen he went to London, where he entertained the guests at a tea-shop with recitals on the organ. As a composer of light music he first became prominent with a Prize Catch for the Catch Club; in the same year, 1765, he composed a Mannheim-type overture for *The Sacrifice of Iphigenia*, a pantomime performed at the theatre in Richmond. Two years later Hook was installed by Arnold as organist and composer at Marylebone Gardens, and in 1774 he took up similar appointments at Vauxhall, where he remained for fifty years. In the course of a long career Hook composed, it is estimated, some 2,000 songs. He also composed organ and harpsichord concertos—he performed such a concerto nightly at the Gardens concerts —and some piano music. The latter included an instruction book, the *Guida di musica*, the outcome of his long experience of teaching both privately and also in a girls' school in Chelsea. Hook, now remembered only by the deft contours of *The Lass of Richmond Hill*, took in every change of style that occurred in England from Handel to Haydn, finding the norm of his own style at the point at which J. C. Bach and the Earl of Kelly touched English music. Hook was the one truly *galant* writer in the

1 *The Padlock*, together with *The Maid of the Mill* and an anonymous *Midas* (1762, Dublin), was in the repertory of an English Company which played in St. Petersburg in 1771–2. See E. W. White, *The Rise of English Opera*, London, 1951, p. 76.

2 A large number of Dibdin's printed works, as well as some important Mss. remains, are held in the Local History Department of the Southampton Public Library.

English tradition; but this inclination towards the elegancies in no way precluded his symphonic structures from showing a native impulse of singable melody. He had, said Leigh Hunt, 'a real though small vein of genius, which was the better for its being called upon to flow profusely for Ranelagh and Vauxhall'.

Dibdin and Hook arrived as composers by an unconventional road. So too did William Shield (1748–1829), who achieved an equal popularity in the field of theatrical and entertainment music, and a rather superior reputation outside this field. Shield was born at Swalwell, near Gateshead, in Co. Durham. His father, a local singing-teacher, died when he was nine and the boy was put to work with a boat-builder. As with Hook, musical talent showed early and the young Shield, encouraged by his employer, Edward Davison, was much in demand as a violinist at Tyneside concerts. He had the good fortune to receive tuition from Avison, who in due course arranged for him to lead the Newcastle subscription concerts. Shield also played at the Summer concerts in Spring Gardens in Newcastle. From that city he moved first to Scarborough and then to Stockton-on-Tees, to lead the theatre orchestras. At this period of his life Shield was fortunate in making the acquaintance of John Cunningham and Thomas Holcroft, lively figures in the dramatic history of the period, and Joseph Ritson, antiquarian and authority on folk-song and ballad. All agreed with Shield that the practice of bending folk-music to the conventions of art-music—as generally done at that time—was to be deplored.[1] He also became acquainted with Luigi Borghi, a violin and viola player who led the second violin section at the Handel Commemoration in 1784, and Fischer the oboist. Both these players advised Shield to go to London, where—when he had followed their counsel—he found employment in the orchestra of the Italian Opera, first under the leadership of Giardini and then of Wilhelm Cramer.

In 1775 Shield published his Op. 1, a set of *Six duettos, five for two violins, and one for two German flutes*. Three years later *The Flitch of Bacon*, for which he edited and arranged the music, was put on at the Haymarket. In the same year he was appointed to the staff of Covent Garden. Over the next twenty years he produced scores for some thirty 'operas', some of which derived from legend (*Robin Hood*, 1784), some from heroic episodes in English history (*The Siege of Gibraltar*, 1780, and *Richard Cœur de Lion*, 1786), some indirectly from fiction (*Aladdin*, or *The Wonderful Lamp*, 1788). In 1789 *The Grenadier* was cancelled as likely to prove too provocative. This was a piece based on the French Revolution, but 'when

[1] See *Rudiments of Thorough Bass*, London, *c.* 1815, p. 35, for a reference to the right and wrong ways of setting *The Keel Row*, one of the 'Border' songs that Shield learned in childhood.

the flame of liberty in Paris seemed to be converted into hell-fire, and patriotic men into demons, Mr. [Thomas] Harris [stage-manager at Covent Garden] very prudently thought it advisable not to touch upon the subject.'[1] Shield was the master of the sturdy, immediately memorable, melody, and songs like *The Arethusa* and *The Ploughboy* typify his approach. Both songs have, of course, crossed the boundary and qualified by general assent as 'folk-songs': the second of these is sponsored by Britten in an arrangement that nicely recalls the carefree quality endemic to such routine balladry. Shield's overtures were compounded from diverse elements. The Mannheim manner—passed on to him through Cramer—is evident; so too is the Italian manner, favoured by many British composers of the period; in the overture to *Rosina* (1783) he drew on a popular symphony by the Viennese composer Vanhall, whose works were widely used in England. He was never inclined to forego a reference to folk-song and the overture to *Rosina* ends with a vivid arrangement of *Coming through the Rye*. In 1791 Haydn went to Covent Garden to hear *The Woodman*, and reported the audience behaviour, against which the eighteenth-century musical director in the theatre had to operate, in uncomplimentary terms. The Overture to *The Woodman* is typical and one of Shield's best. In the first movement realism is induced by the sound of bugle horns. The succeeding *Larghetto e Affetuoso* has a lazy charm [Ex.10], while the finale is a rollicking Rondo.

10.
Larghetto e affetuoso

Outside the theatre Shield was in frequent demand as a performer and he was a member of the Royal Band. In 1795 he played at York House in the company of Haydn,[2] whom he revered and with whom he once travelled from London to Taplow.[3] In 1817 he became Master of the King's Music. Shield was under no illusions about the value of his music for the theatre, but he retained his earlier ambitions and sometimes indulged them by writing chamber music. After his early venture into

[1] *Recollections of the life of John O'Keefe* (written by himself), London, 1826. John St. John's *The Island of St. Marguerite*, for which music was composed by Thomas Shaw, was also banned (after one performance on 13 November in the same year) on account of the offence that might be caused by references to the Fall of the Bastille.

[2] 'Salomon led the band, amongst whom were Cervetto, the elder Parke, Shield, myself, Dance, Blake, and Haydn who presided at the piano-forte.' W. T. Parke, *Musical Memoirs*, 2 vols., 1830, I, p. 196.

[3] Shield, op. cit., p. 69.

this field there appeared *Six Duets for two Violins* (op. 2), *c.* 1780, *Six Quartettos, five for two violins* (op. 2), *c.* 1780, *Six Quartettos, five for two violins and a tenor and a violoncello, and one for a flute, violin, tenor and violoncello, c.* 1780, and *Six trios for violin, tenor, amd violoncello* (1796). The last set was written in memory of the Scottish painter Jacob More (1740–83) 'as a Token of Gratitude for the Services he rendered to the Author During his Residence in Rome'. The last movements of the first and third Trios show examples of lively writing in 5/4 time [Ex. 11*a* and *b*]. 'These', said the

11a.

11b.

composer in his Advertisement, 'have amused some of the most distinguished Professors, both in England and in Italy'. These works are also remarkable for the unusual interest of their viola parts. Shield was an attractive personality, a keen professional musician zealous for the reputation of his profession, and alive to the needs of musical education. He was of modest origin and he never lost his modesty; nor did he forget the significance of music to the people at large. He believed in folk-song not because he rediscovered it, but because it had been a part of his early life. He subsequently lost no opportunity to furnish his audiences with folk-music expressed in as accurate form as was possible. In 1791 he visited his native village, where his mother still lived. He took the opportunity then of collecting songs of the neighbourhood, remarking when he published them: 'These hitherto neglected flights of fancy may serve to augment the collector's stock of printed rarities, and may perhaps prove conspicuous figures in the group of national melodies.'[1]

The English symphony-overture was a by-product of theatrical entertainment and practice matched up with theory. Thus the British composer would have agreed with Trydell's view that '. . . musical Sounds do of themselves, that is to say, merely by the Sound, suggest our Ideas. Chiefly those of the Passions, as Desire, Aversion, Joy, Sorrow, & the like. And this they do by their acuteness or gravity: by Chromatic Notes, or half tones, which belong not to the Harmony of the Key.

'These last particularly express the Violence, or abruptness of Passion, when they ascend; and weakness and despondency when they fall. The changes or abatements of the Passion are discovered by the crowding of brisk Notes, or by the sudden transition into slow. Lastly, the flat and sharp Keys have their peculiar and proper Objects. The first being expressive of every plaintive and tender Sentiment, the sharp third discovering Joy and elevation of Mind.'[2] This, of course, was a restatement of continental philosophy, but British composers, working it out for themselves, rarely aspired higher than the needs of the moment required. It is thus that very few came within measurable distance of J. C. Bach and only a small number of symphonies were published in score. Of those that were some of the most charming were composed by William Smethergell, organist of St. Mary-at-Hill and All Hallows, Barking. Smethergell enjoyed performances of his works at Vauxhall Gardens, where Hook was one of the few musicians of the time to try to protect the English composer. About 1780 Smethergell published *Six Overtures in Eight parts* ('violins, hoboys, horns, tenor, and bass [bassoon]')—previous to which he had issued six concertos for harpsichord or pianoforte (*c.* 1775). About four years after the appearance of the first set of overtures a second set was published. Thus Smethergell became the only English composer to publish two such sets of works. The second set even ran to a second edition in 1794.

Smethergell's symphonies are characteristically English in the fluency of their melodies, in their three-movement form (op. 5, no. 4 deviates by having only two movements), in the sedate quality of their minuets or of the *Siciliano* in op. 5, no. 1, in the vigour and rhythmic energy of the

[1] See Richard Welford, *Men of Mark 'twixt Tyne and Tees*, London, 1895, III, p. 392.
[2] Trydell, op. cit., p. 97.

concluding allegros or rondos, and in the character of their scoring. The *Larghetto* of the E flat symphony (op. 2, no. 6) has an eloquent bassoon solo, for instance, and for twelve bars of this movement the music is sustained only by wind. Smethergell was a neat formalist (he owed something to Jommelli, whose Symphony XIV containing a celebrated Chaconne he had arranged for keyboard in 1780), careful in his disposition of tonalities. He was precise with dynamic markings—as in the *f* and *p* contrasts and the *crescendo* which comes to a climax on the dominant of the dominant in the first movement of op. 2, no. 1, and the *fp.* markings of op. 5, no. 4. Furthermore Smethergell understood the difference between a theatre overture and a concert-room symphony and his scores often indicate a high degree of sensibility. Hence the last of his overtures, in A major, begins with a charming *Allegro pastorella* [Ex. 12]. The finale to this overture is an engaging rondo that moves along a syncopated course as if in Magyar vein.

12.

Social Music

The quarter-century which came after the death of Handel was a crucial period in the history of British music, for the pattern which then crystallised determined the conditions under which music would develop, or fail to develop, for the next hundred years. The oratorios of Handel represented an ideal. They were an incentive to the prosperous to give donations to charity; they were an encouragement to many who hitherto had enjoyed no musical franchise to exercise their talents and their imaginations; they were, as the immediate post-Handelian oratorio scores show, a frequent cause of impediment to the composer. It was left to Haydn, inspired by English performances, to carry the oratorio form into new channels. For the many the oratorio was serious music. At the other extreme was the vast accumulation of ephemeral music which at its best was unpretentious and at its worst negligible.

Within these limits there was a wide range of activities promoted by particular social groups, or even cliques. The superior concerts of Bach and Abel entertained the discriminating, the privileged, and those who had social ambitions. Provincial concerts organised in emulation of the London concerts were inevitably described as gentlemen's concerts. In both cases it became understood that European, and especially German, composers were to be preferred to British composers. It is a paradox that whereas in Handel's time the English singer had briefly come into his or her own, in the time of Bach the clock was put back and a new race of foreign singers and players became established at the expense of native artistes. These developments were the consequence of economic expansion, of general affluence, and of the demands of national and local government, and of business and industry. The spread of responsibility in a society from which absolutism had largely disappeared and which was on the way towards a particular kind of democracy made it inevitable that the fine arts would take a secondary place in the considerations of the effective rulers of society. British music therefore became a monument, and not an entirely inglorious one, to private enterprise.

The great choral tradition of the British, as it has lately been understood, really began in the period under review; to the extent that then it was first effectively organised. The festivals have been dealt with. But side by side with them were groups of singers whose efforts were invaluable in supporting a love of choral singing. In the body politic the Freemasons were an increasingly influential body and their rituals and convivialities called for music of one sort or another. So '. . . the music for laying of Foundation Stones should play some solemn air; for lively tunes are indecorous and unsuited to this stage of the proceedings. Pleyel's Hymn, Haydn's National Anthem, Handel's Minuet in Samson, or a slow march, would be considered appropriate . . .' while 'the songs for social occasions were usually on Masonic subjects, as printed in the old Books of Constitution, and other works; and although the poetry is sometimes not of the choicest kind, yet several of them may class among the best compositions of the day'.[1] In 1763 Thomas Hale, of Darnhall, Cheshire, compiled an anthology entitled *Social Harmony* for the use of Masons in the northern counties. In a volume which contains part-songs by Purcell, Eccles, Blow, Travers, Greene, Arne, and Handel, and a setting of a poem[2] by Handel's friend Charles Legh of Adlington, there are to be found an

[1] Rev. G. Oliver, *The Book of the Lodge*, London, 1856, pp. 53 and 179.

[2] *The morning is charming*, à 3, the music by Mr. Ridley, organist of Prestbury.

Ode Sacred to Masonry by William Hayes [Ex. 13]: as well as an anonymous

13.

piece which unconsciously asserts again the ancient principle of faburden [Ex. 14].

14.

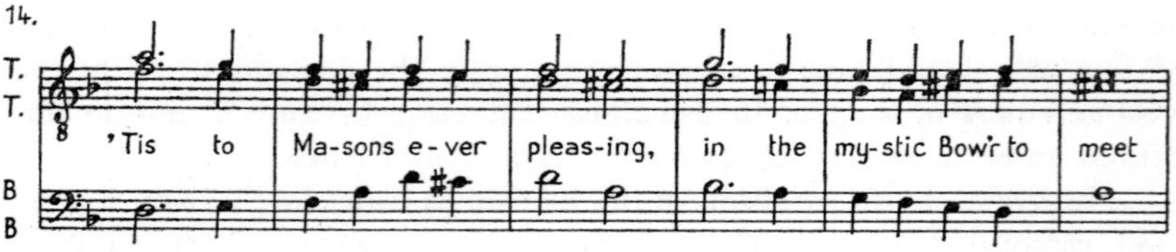

Evangelical Influence in English and Scottish Church Music

The Church of England, apart from the festivals organised by enterprising local committees and the resident cathedral organists, had virtually nothing to show during this period, nor for many years to come. Musicians whose livelihood depended on the Church built up extensive teaching practices and, if they were inclined to composition, issued collections of keyboard pieces. It is only in this field that such musicians found outlet for originality. The anthems and services of the period rise no higher than the faded proprieties of James Kent of Winchester, of Gainsborough's friend, William Jackson of Exeter (who, however, was also a theatre composer), and Benjamin Cooke, of the Chapel Royal and Westminster Abbey. To be landed for life in a totally unmusical environment could bring grievous disillusionment to some who had set out in life with the highest hopes. John Stanley's pupil, John Alcock of Lichfield, relates how the daily services at Lichfield often had a congregation only of one old woman, how the Passion Week services were discontinued, how 'there was not a Book in the Organ-loft fit for Use, but what I bought, or wrote myself (for which I never was paid one Halfpenny)', and how his playing the organ in a cold cathedral brought on the rheumatism.[1] Alcock gave up his post at the cathedral and became organist of parish churches, in Sutton Coldfield and later in Tamworth. Pupils of Greene were to be found in one or two key places. John Camidge,[2] also a pupil of Handel, was organist of York Minster from 1756 to 1803, during which time he developed secular music in the city and inaugurated the Handel Festival which led to the great Yorkshire Festivals. Camidge published glees, songs, and a set of *Six Easy Lessons for the Harpsichord.* Another pupil of Greene was Hook's teacher, Thomas Garland, who held office at Norwich Cathedral from 1749 for a period of fifty-nine years. He too exercised a strong local influence. Greene's successor at St. Paul's Cathedral (who also served for a long period—from 1755 to 1796) deserves notice. John Jones, a Welshman, was deficient in the faculties necessary for cathedral practice[3]; but he was quite one of the most original and enterprising of harpsichord composers of his day. His *Lessons for the Harpsichord* (1761), in which dynamic markings unusually appear, are technically ambitious and wide-ranging in imaginative exploration, alluding to but not quoting from the characteristics of both Welsh and Scottish folk-music. A prolific composer of single and double chants, Jones was the author of that chant which so affected Haydn when he heard the Charity Children at St. Paul's in 1791. 'No music', wrote Haydn, 'has for a long time affected me so much as their innocent and reverential strains.'

The music of the Church of England was out of touch both with the main stream of music and with the people. But invigoration of the tradition of sacred music was coming from the Methodists, whose influence was to prove increasingly powerful especially in the northern parts of the country. The inspiration of Methodist hymnody came from John and Charles Wesley, who, having been affected by the singing of the Moravians with whom they first came into contact when missionaries in Georgia, recognised that singing and evangelism were inseparable. John Wesley wrote the words of hymns, many of which he translated from German sources, but it was Charles, responsible for more than 6,000 original hymns, who really laid the foundations of evangelical hymnody. John

[1] Preface to *Anthems,* 1771.

[2] Camidge (*c.* 1734–1803), former choirboy at York, was organist of Doncaster Parish Church in 1755. He was succeeded at York by his son Matthew (1764–1844) and he by his son, John (1790–1859).

[3] 'Jones . . . appears not to have been worthy of the situation, for he was not capable of doing the duty for a length of time after the appointment: and as he could not play from score, he employed himself in arranging the Anthems in two lines.' *The English Musical Gazette,* 1 January 1819.

Wesley's first London Meeting House, on the site of a disused iron foundry near Moorfields, was established in 1739. Three years later *A Collection of Tunes Set to music as they are commonly sung at the Foundery* was issued. A feature of this collection was the number of adaptations of German tunes. In 1746 another volume appeared, *Hymns on the Great Festivals and Other Occasions*, to which J. F. Lampe, one of Wesley's converts, contributed twenty-four tunes. The demand grew and in 1753 a larger anthology of more than 170 hymns was assembled by Thomas Butts and published as *Harmonia Sacra or A Choice Collection of Psalm and Hymn Tunes*. The music was taken from many sources: the popular airs of the day, including those of Handel and Arne, were adapted, while the collections of such private charitable institutions as the Foundling, Lock, and Magdalen Hospitals were drawn on. In 1761, since the supply was not equal to the demand nor were any of the existing hymnals entirely acceptable, John Wesley prepared a book of his own: *Select Hymns with Tunes annext*. 'I want', Wesley wrote, 'the People called Methodists to sing true the Tunes which are in *Common Use* among them.' By now, although they were maintained in degenerate form in the Church of England, the old metrical Psalms were largely a relic of the past. The hymns, with pietistic, emotional, even erotic, tendencies in the texts, were more immediately significant, and their significance was enhanced by the contemporaneity of the tunes. Naturally these tunes were frowned on by the musically critical, but to the under-privileged they were a gateway to a new province of emotional experience. Thus we may discover the new connection between sacred and secular as contrived by fervent Methodism in a swinging tune that fortuitously puts the ancient hocket device to work again [Ex. 15]. Here is precedent for clergymen who try to modernise the Faith by loans from the popular market.

15.

Enthusiasm for hymn-singing resulted in the extension of musical education among the poorer members of the community and in the further development of choral singing. (See pp. 411 f.) It remains to be said that the enthusiasm for hymn-singing engendered by Methodism also had its early effects in Scotland, where a movement towards better church choirs was initiated by an English Methodist, Thomas Channon, when stationed on military duty in Aberdeen. Channon, released from army duties by a sympathetic commanding officer and supported by the local laird, began his task of teaching Scottish choristers to sing 'in the reformed way' at the parish church in Monymusk. Channon progressed not without opposition but the fame of his choir spread, and in 1755 he gave a performance with a church choir of twenty-two sopranos and altos, thirty tenors, and eighteen basses in Aberdeen. The conservatives in the Kirk took grave exception to the new methods of singing in parts, and to the introduction of new music. But they were overwhelmed by the sheer enthusiasm that Channon engendered. Aberdeen capitulated, then Edinburgh, then Glasgow. Choir lofts were built and steps were taken to appoint singing-teachers, to issue tutors, and new psalm books. One of the architects of Scottish church music of the new dispensation was the first singing-teacher appointed by the Corporation of Glasgow to Hutcheson's Hospital. This was Thomas Moore, who had built up a considerable reputation in the field of popular musical instruction in Manchester. When he had arrived in Glasgow, Moore published *The Psalm Singer's Pocket Companion*, and in 1761 he followed this with *The Psalm Singer's Delightful Pocket Companion . . . Illustrated with great Variety of Tables, Scales, and Initial Lessons*. Thereafter Scottish publishers found that works of this order were a profitable investment: the future of the choral tradition in Scotland was thus guaranteed.

Aids to Popular Musical Education

While the evangelicals were making the music peculiar to them more popular (and less respectable) there were those who were intent on settling a hitherto often disreputable form of music-making into the ways of respectability. The practice of singing catches—those entertaining by-blows of the madrigal tradition—had continued from the early seventeenth century. In 1761 a Catch Club[1] was established, promoted by an *ad hoc* committee of earls, generals, and esquires. The Earl of Sandwich was a prominent member of this body which, after the formulation of rules of procedure, was, in 1762, designated the Noblemen and Gentlemen's Catch Club. The first Secretary of the Club—which was to enjoy royal patronage when in 1784 the Prince of Wales became a member—was Thomas Warren. The Catch Club was characteristically English and was to music as the M.C.C. was to become in regard to cricket. In fact,

[1] A Catch Club had existed in Dublin since one was established by the cathedral singing-men in 1679–80.

by the time the Club was set up, the catch had lost its early contrapuntal enterprise, for the glee (a part-song for male voices) had assumed a greater popularity. In 1763 the Club sought to stimulate professional interest in its activities and to encourage English composers by offering annual prizes, one for the two best catches submitted, one for the two best canons, and one for the two best glees. Meetings took place at the Thatched House Tavern, a regular rendezvous for musicians. The Catch Club and the Glee Club, which was independently founded in 1783, as well as the Edinburgh Catch Club founded in 1771, gave a great impetus to social music-making and a large number of composers—some of whom will be separately noticed—profited by the welcome given to their works when they were published.

As a consequence of the general diffusion of interest education in musical theory and practice was more zealously cultivated, and fresh opportunities offered themselves to composers. By the 1780's the convention, that has persisted, that English musicians are best employed in pedagogy was firmly set. It has been seen that the better-known keyboard composers were zealous, and even methodical, in supplying a demand. Other evidences of energy dedicated to the cause of instruction are frequent. The needs of church choristers were met by a sequence of books, based on psalm-tunes (decorated à la mode), anthems (often anonymous and trivial), chants, and occasional canons. Where money was tight a good deal depended on willing copyists, such as those in the remote north-west who were responsible for *William Sewell's Book of Psalmody, Culgarth, Cumberland, taught by Arthur Smith*, 1772, and a similar collection of the same period attributed to John Collinson.[1] Some of the published volumes, like *The Leicestershire Harmony* (*c.* 1760), 'by an eminent Master of the County of Leicester', were in the first place intended for regional use. Others, which had proved invaluable guides across the years and had run into numerous editions, were more widely used. Among these proved companions to church choristers were John Screeve's *The Divine Musick Scholar's Guide*, *The Psalmist's Recreation*, and *The Complete Psalmodist*, all first issued about 1740 but fully influential twenty, thirty, and forty years later.

A comprehensive volume such as *The Complete Psalmodist* (sold at 4s.) contained: a Preface, combining an exposition of the divine origin of music with a potted musical history and useful hints regarding the best instruments to purchase and the names of recommended dealers; a section on rudiments (including valuable advice on ornamentation), harmony, and, more briefly, counterpoint; an Alphabetical Dictionary; and, finally, the music in score. The preliminaries to such volumes serve

[1] Both volumes in the Public Library, Barrow-in-Furness.

as an index to the average of musical knowledge and appreciation within their period. For instance, it has been observed that the pianoforte was late in establishing itself in Britain. One year after J. C. Bach's reputed first performance in London John Arnold, compiler of *The Complete Psalmodist*, writing in the second edition, described the instrument with a certain degree of imprecision as follows:

> Forte, loud
> Forte & Piano, loud and soft.
> N.B. There are Harpsichords of this Kind, etc. of about 70 or 80 Guineas Price, which play Forte and Piano.

As a companion volume for secular choral singers Arnold issued a collection of catches, glees, etc., *The Essex Harmony* (5s.), which also ran through many editions. Nor were amateur (and would-be professional) solo singers without assistance in respect of technical instruction. There was Domenico Corri's (1746–1825) *Select Collection* (*c.* 1779)—the result of Corri's tuition from Porpora and his experience as a fashionable singing-teacher in Edinburgh where he had settled in 1771. Towards the end of the century Samuel Webbe anticipated Kodály's method of encouraging security of vocal technique by issuing *Forty-two Vocal Exercises in Two Parts . . . Designed for the Assistance of those who wish to sing at Sight and as a Sequel to L'Amico del Principiante, Being twenty-eight short sol-faing exercises for a single voice* (R. Birchall, n.d.). Provision was also made for singers of tender years by Granville Sharp in *A Short Introduction to Vocal Music . . . a little treatise, intended for the use of children* (1767–77).

On this level elementary string players were also coming in for attention. Benjamin Blake (1761–1827), himself largely self-taught, played the viola in the Italian Opera from 1775 and from 1789 to 1810 was music-teacher in a school in Kensington. He was a member of the Band of the Prince of Wales and, as the first acknowledged specialist viola player, was much in demand for private concerts. His pedagogic publications included three volumes of duets for violin and viola (*c.* 1780, *c.* 1782, *c.* 1785), under the general heading of *A Musical Dialogue between master and scholar*, and three solos for viola (with accompaniment for cello). Blake understood his job, and his pieces could well be put into service today. William Smethergell was also active in the educational market, and among his last publications was *Six Easy Solos for a Violin, with figured bass, harpsichord or violoncello . . . for the Improvement of Juvenile Performers* (*c.* 1795). John Gunn (*c.* 1765–*c.* 1824), of Edinburgh, published a *Theory and Practice of fingering the Cello* in 1789, and a flute tutor (of which there were many by various composers) four years later.

The Valentines of Leicester (see p. 271) were especially active in and about that city during the whole of the eighteenth century. The most prominent members of the family were Henry III (b. 1708) and John (1710–91),[1] who were pioneers of concert-giving in Leicester and also in Matlock Bath. John, who kept a music shop in Leicester, was a busy composer. His marches[2] were extremely useful, as William Gardiner testifies. His *Duets for French Horns* and his *Eight Easy Symphonies* were even more useful, since they were composed with the limitations of young and provincial players in mind. The *Eight Symphonies* were advertised as 'with Solos for the Different Instruments interspersed through the Whole; being an Introduction to playing a Concert, Designed for and Dedicated to all Junior Performers[3] and Musical Societies by John Valentine of Leicester'. All but one (no. 3) of the symphonies have three movements, but Valentine loaded them in favour of local taste. Thus there are marches in nos. 1, 4, 6, and 7; minuets in nos. 2, 3, 4, 5, 7, and 8; a gavotte in no. 2, a giga in nos. 5 and 7, a rondo in no. 6, and a siciliana in no. 8.

The final name to be added to the list of musical educators active during the early symphonic and sonata era is that of Theodore Smith, whose working life covered the last thirty years of the century. Smith was early in the field of the pianoforte duet and may very well be regarded as its progenitor, for his *Trois Sonates en duo, qui peuvent être exécutées per deux Personnes, sur un Cleveçin ou Piano Forte* (op. 1, 4) appeared between 1775 and 1780, published in Berlin by Hummel. Smith, as an Englishman who worked in Germany (between 1775 and 1784), reversed the normal practice: what was more, he was described by Gerber as 'ein sehr gefälliger und angenehmer Komponist'. His first set of duets was not only apparently the first in England (where they were re-issued) but also in Germany, anticipating the *Drey Sonaten für Clavier als Doppelstücke für zwey Personen* of C. M. Müller by a year or two. After returning to England Smith wrote songs for Vauxhall Gardens, and a few hymns for the Ebury Chapel, of which he became organist, but his output mainly consisted of elementary keyboard and chamber music. In *A Musical Directory* (*c.* 1780) he gave

[1] Others included Henry II, organist of St. Martin's Church in 1701, who was the father of Henry III and John; Henry IV (1726–95); Henry V (1750–1821); Henry VI (1775–1826); Robert II (d. 1816); Ann, who published violin or flute and pfte. sonatas; and Sarah, who became organist of St. Martin's Church in 1800.

[2] Marches, minuets, and arias by 'Valentine of Leicester' are contained in an interesting volume in the British Museum (Add. Ms. 34074). In addition to these there are selections from Arne, Boyce, Handel, and 'Signor' Bach, but also from the German composers Reinart, 'Schicht', 'Seits', who possibly had contact with Robert Valentine while he was in Europe (see p. 271).

[3] Cf. William Gardiner (1770–1853), *Music and Friends*, London, 1838, I, p. 14, referring to his boyhood in Leicester: 'though so indifferent a performer on the violin, I undertook to establish a junior musical society, to play overtures and symphonies, of which I took the lead. Our pieces were Valentine's Marches, Humphreys' Symphonies, and as much as we could play of Handel's and Corelli's Concertos.'

helpful information to beginners on ornamentation and treatment of dynamics. It is sad that this interesting if shadowy figure is remembered only as the teacher of William Horsley. Smith, it was said, was 'a musician of mean capacities and of brutal mind. The five years of Horsley's association with this creature was a period of terror and neglect'.[1]

Theodore Smith, slenderly honoured for his work in Germany (and posthumously only adequately noticed in German reference books), no doubt worked off his frustrations on William Horsley. There was a fair taint of Philistinism in the atmosphere of London when he returned and success too often and too easily attended indifferent work. But it was increasingly difficult to escape from England. At the beginning of the century a few English musicians were able to take their talents abroad, there to capitalise them. Towards the end of the century the traffic was, to all intents and purposes, one way.

[1] W. A. Barrett, op. cit., p. 290.

10

Changing Values

DURING THE latter half of the eighteenth century the British composer was shown various directions he might take. In virtually every case the composer considered the limitations imposed upon him and took only tentative steps towards emancipation. For the first but not the last time 'modern music' became a point of contentious argument and various voices, some more eloquent than others, were being raised to defend the proprieties of an established, respected, and, indeed, national tradition. Among them the most powerful was that of John Hawkins (1719–89) who, as has been seen, was adamant in regarding Handel as the end of musical excellence. Charles Burney (1726–1814), on the other hand, took Handel as the beginning of an era that grew more and more golden as music became increasingly 'refined'. Burney and Hawkins, whose attitudes symbolised the new concept of a division of music into past and present, were in some ways the outstanding figures in English music during the period in which they lived, imposing on it at least a new awareness of critical values. They were the first English writers to achieve eminence on account of scholarship in the hitherto unconsidered field of musical research. The major work of each was a *History of Music*, and, as luck would have it, the issue of that of Hawkins in 1776 coincided with the publication of the first volume of Burney's. Neither author was greatly pleased with the other.

Hawkins, apprenticed first to an architect and then to a lawyer, set up as a young man on his own account as an attorney in London. His musical interests in the first place were those of an amateur, and as such he was a regular member of a number of concert clubs. He was a friend of John Stanley (who set a number of his poems) and an acquaintance of Handel. A member of the Academy of Ancient Music and of the Madrigal Society he also frequented literary gatherings. An associate of Burke, Goldsmith, and Samuel Johnson—by whom he was described as 'unclubbable'—Hawkins took a keen interest in literary criticism and issued an edition of Izaak Walton's *Compleat Angler* (1760) and assisted in the preparation of a re-issue of Hamer's edition of the *Works of Shakespeare* (1771). Hawkins was enabled to devote much of his time to the scholarly pursuits that were congenial to him on account of his marriage in 1753 to an heiress. Nevertheless he was not inactive in his own province of the law and in 1761 he was appointed to the Middlesex bench of magistrates. Two years later he became Chairman of the Quarter Sessions and in 1772—after some not entirely judicious canvassing on his own behalf—was knighted. Across the years Hawkins built up a large library (largely destroyed by fire in 1785) and prepared his *magnum opus*, the *General History of the Science and Practice of Music*, which comprised five volumes. Among his other works were two pamphlets, *Memoirs of Steffani* (1740) and the *Account of the Academy of Ancient Music* (1770), his introduction to Boyce's *Cathedral Music* (1789), and a *Life* and an edition of the *Works* of Samuel Johnson (both 1789), of whose Will he was an executor.

Hawkins may have been, and some of his contemporaries said he was, an unattractive person, but his judicial training served him in good stead as a historian. He collected material and where he felt incompetent either to interpret or to evaluate it he relied on the technical competence of those with more adequate qualification. Hawkins had as collaborator and 'devil' John Stafford Smith, who will be seen to have been a guiding spirit of Hawkins's *History* and also prominent in English musical life.

Charles Burney was of Scottish descent, his great-great-grandfather, James Macburney, having come to England among the followers of James I. He was born in Shrewsbury, the son of a portrait painter. The family was musical and Charles's brother James was organist of St. Chad's Church, in Shrewsbury. 'His extemporaneous voluntaries [were] in the lighter manner of Handel's organ concertos, on whose admirable school his taste was formed, and the brilliant execution of his fingers on the echo stops, will not be forgotten by the few organ amateurs who survive to remember him in his best days.'[1] Charles went to school in Chester when his father moved to that city, became a pupil of Baker at the cathedral, and had the good fortune to see Handel on the occasion of his celebrated visit. At the age of sixteen Burney was back in Shrewsbury, where he was tutored by his brother. He heard Felton and Hayes play the organ in the town and was a violin pupil of Nicholas Matteis[2] who had

[1] H. Owen & J. B. Blakeway, *A History of Shrewsbury*, 1825, II, pp. 226–7.

[2] Son and pupil of Nicola Matteis. He played the violin for a time in the court orchestra in Vienna. After returning to England he settled in Shrewsbury, teaching music and French. He died *c.* 1749.

settled there. Back in Chester in 1743 he met Arne, by whom he was taken to London as an apprentice.

Burney renewed acquaintance with Handel in whose orchestra he played. Recommendation from Jacob Kirkman,[1] the harpsichord maker, brought Burney an appointment as musical instructor to Fulke Greville, a wealthy and well-connected amateur. He learned to move with ease in polite society and acquired an elegance of manner that was as remarkable as Hawkins's lack of it. After some years as organist—from 1751 to 1760 he worked at St. Margaret's, King's Lynn—Burney, by now married and with a family, returned to London. There he set up as a harpsichord teacher and was successful in establishing a prosperous clientèle. Active as a composer[2] Burney kept his eye on the trends of the day so that in 1766 he prepared a version of Rousseau's *Le Devin du Village* for performance at Drury Lane. Burney's interest in this highly popular piece had been aroused when he visited Paris in 1764. On that occasion he had visited various musical institutions and collections of music, which stimulated him to think in terms of a large-scale study of music. In 1769, having graduated as Mus.D. at Oxford, he began seriously to prepare to undertake his *History of Music*. In June of the next year, having eased his way by letters of introduction, he made a tour of France and Italy. Two years later he visited the Low Countries, Germany and Austria. Wherever he went he was agreeably received by prominent musicians and scholars and his impressions of his experiences were duly noted against the day when they should be turned into literature.

Accounts of the two tours were collected into *The Present State of Music in France and Italy*, etc. (1771) and *The Present State of Music in Germany, the Netherlands, and the United Provinces* etc. (1773). Engagingly written, informative as guide books in general, and an excellent introduction to European musical life, these volumes were widely approved.[3] Not least by Burney's close friend, Johnson, who took them as a model for his *Journey to the Western Isles of Scotland* (1775). The first volume of *A General History of Music* was sent into the world with a dedication (written by Johnson) to the Queen. The remaining volumes appeared in 1782 (II and III) and 1789. In 1785 the *Account of the Musical Performances* at the Handel Com-

[1] 1710–92; Kirkman (formerly Kirchmann) came to England from Strasbourg as a young man and worked for a Flemish harpsichord manufacturer, Hermann Tabel. On Tabel's death Kirkman married his widow and took over the business which he expanded. About 1773 he took his nephew Abraham into partnership, and soon afterwards the firm was also making pianofortes.

[2] Burney published a considerable amount of chamber and keyboard music. His Harpsichord or Pianoforte Duets (1777, 1778) were once accepted as the first such music to be published: as has been seen he was preceded by Theodore Smith.

[3] Joel Collier's [i.e. John Laurens Bicknell, The Elder?] parody, *Musical travels through England,* was also approved, reaching a fourth edition by 1776.

memoration,[1] with valuable first-hand reminiscences of the master, was published. A compulsive writer, Burney engaged in much periodical work and in his old age he contributed the whole of the articles on music to Abraham Rees's *Cyclopaedia.*

Burney, not entirely content to receive only minor offices—such as the organistship of Chelsea Hospital which he held for the last thirty years of his life, was a noteworthy personality in London. He worked at high pressure, his enthusiasms leading him far afield from music, but he was eminently sociable. He entertained and was entertained by the principals of both social and intellectual life. He discoursed fluently—particularly on astronomy (he lived in Sir Isaac Newton's old house and had an observatory on the roof), literature, and drama. He was, said Mrs. Thrale's friend, Murphy, 'a most extraordinary man; I think I don't know such another: he is at home on all subjects, and upon all so agreeable! he is a wonderful man'. Burney's parties were famous. There could be met Johnson—often fulminating against the musical proceedings, the Thrales, Gabriel Piozzi, who was to marry Mrs. Thrale, James Bruce, the African explorer—sometimes with Africans in attendance, Joshua Reynolds, Russian princes, German baronesses, and ambassadors; there could be heard the music, now in fashion, of Abel, Schobert, Schroeter,[2] Eckardt, Sacchini, Müthel—a duet for two harpsichords by whom Burney thought 'the noblest composition of its kind in the world'. John Stanley played for Burney's guests; so did Cervetto,[3] Giardini, Barthélemon,[4] Fischer, Crosdill, Pacchierotti,[5] and other then celebrated Italian singers. And Burney's devoted family helped to look after guests. Of his daughters Fanny achieved fame as the authoress of *Evelina,* which, in addition to being a work of distinctive charm, is also an aid to musical appreciation, and—as Second Keeper of the Queen's Robes—as occasional confidante of the ageing and eccentric George III. Burney, brought up on Handel, Arne, Felton, Geminiani, Corelli, Tartini, Scarlatti—'that wild but masterly composer', lived through the age of Christian Bach, was a frequent companion of Haydn when he visited London, came gradually to

[1] German translation by J. J. Eschenburg published (Berlin and Stettin) 1785.

[2] On 1 January 1782 the *Gentleman's Magazine* (p. 46) announced the death of 'Signor Christian Bach, musick-master to the Queen, Mr. Schroeter performer on the piano forte, succeeds Mr. Bach in the above appointment at Buckingham-House.'

[3] James Cervetto (1747–1837), son of Giacomo Cervetto (1682–1783), a popular cellist and composer.

[4] François Barthélemon (1741–1808), French violinist, persuaded to England by the Earl of Kelly in 1764. Barthélemon married Mary Young, singer and niece of Mrs. Arne and Mrs. Lampe.

[5] Gasparo Pacchierotti (1744–1821), Italian male soprano, who sang in London on a number of occasions after 1778.

understand the true stature of Mozart,[1] revised his first unfavourable views of Sebastian Bach through Samuel Wesley's advocacy, and was able to salute Beethoven—some of whose works he heard in 1803 for the first time, played by a Miss Tate—as 'amongst the first musical authors of the present century'.

Burney had an insatiable appetite for life. His charm was carried naturally, and his youthfulness (reflected in Reynolds's portrait) was beguiling. 'Here's Mr. Burney', said Mrs. Piozzi—as she then was—at a Salomon concert, 'as young as ever'. He was a Fellow of the Royal Society of Arts, and a Fellow of the Royal Society, thus giving the appearance of being what he aspired to become—a Universal man. Burney is remembered as a historian. His main achievement, however, lay less in his writing than in his destruction of a social barrier. Burney was the first professional musician to gain acceptance as a 'gentleman': his career gave dignity to a profession that was then, even more than now, undervalued. If he had had his way the musical profession would have been otherwise strengthened, for in 1774 he and Giardini put a proposal to the Governors of the Foundling Hospital that this institution should become a *conservatorio* similar to those which had been based on charitable foundations in Naples and Vienna. The Governors turned down the suggestion.

Nevertheless Burney himself would have expected to have received first acknowledgment on account of his contribution to the literature of music. He was less a scholar than a first-rate feature-writer who had the gift of vivid description. When he writes of Handel whom he knew he brings him to life. When he steps aside from his narrative to animadvert on the inelegance of German peasant women, the tiresome behaviour of postilions and postmasters, the majesty of the Danube, or the obstructiveness of Prussian frontier controls, he lights up a whole canvas. When he relates his interviews with the great—with princes or electors, or with Metastasio, Gluck, or Hasse—he engages the reader in their company by his accurate reporting and the vitality of his prose. He lays his prejudices on the table and makes no pretence at objectivity. Always looking for subjects to stimulate his own interest, he spices his observations with an effervescent enthusiasm. His music-travel books—worthy companions to those of von Uffenbach and Reichardt—deserve Johnson's encomium. The *History* is another matter. At his best Burney wrote lucidly and with a sense of humour—at his worst (and he tired as he grew older but refused to stop writing) he could be very heavy-handed. So too for that matter could Fanny, whose later writings have none of the point and quality of *Evelina*.

We return to Burney in relation to Hawkins. The latter was indus-

[1] See C. B. Oldman, 'Dr. Burney and Mozart', in *Mozart-Jahrbuch, 1962–3*, Salzburg, 1964, p. 75.

trious and, so far as possible, exact. His work (amplified by the scholarship of Stafford Smith) was fundamental to an English musicological approach. He was a painstaking writer and, as he himself wrote in an unusually free moment of Thomas Morley, 'his compositions seem to be the effect of close study and much labour'. Burney, on the other hand, wore his sometimes inexact learning[1] prestigiously and was really more concerned with what was going on around him. Thus he wrote, for example, of the works of Weelkes, Wilbye, Kirbye and Thomas Bennet [*sic*]:

'Of these four composers, the best madrigalists of our country, many productions have late been revived at the Concert of Ancient Music, and Catch-Club, where, by the perfection of performance, effects have been produced, of which it is probable the authors themselves, even in the warm and enthusiastic moments of conception, had but little idea so that from the care, accuracy, and expression, with which they are sung by the performers of these well-disciplined societies, it may perhaps with truth be said, that they are not only renovated, but rendered much better composition than the authors intended them to be.'[2]

Burney's friend, the Rev. Thomas Twining,[3] read the manuscript of the second volume of the *History* and wrote to him that he found it 'prodigiously entertaining'. The comment is fair, and in that he was able to combine instruction with pleasure Burney was performing an invaluable service in the broader ranges of English music.

Hawkins was primarily an antiquarian; Burney saw himself as a composer; the two basic interests are reflected in their respective prose-writings. The next two most influential names in the important pioneer group of musical scholars are those of Stafford Smith and Samuel Wesley, each of whom was also a composer; the one of reasonable talent, the other of something approaching genius. Each added an extra dimension to the compositional techniques of the period and anticipated important aspects of reforms that took place a century later.

John Stafford Smith and Musica Antiqua

John Stafford Smith (1750–1836) as a chorister of the Chapel Royal was a pupil of Nares and Boyce. He became a useful tenor singer and a com-

[1] See Elizabeth Cole, 'Stafford Smith's Burney' in *M, & L.*, 40, no. 1, 1959, p. 35, for an account of Smith's marginal corrections and observations in his copy of the *History*. This is now in the possession of the Royal College of Music.

[2] *History*, III, p. 123.

[3] Thomas Twining (1735–1804), rector of Colchester and an Aristotelian scholar, was a keen musical amateur. His Letters (*A Country Clergyman of the Eighteenth Century*, London, 1782) make an interesting commentary on the music of the period. Twining was a friend of the poet Gray who influenced him to appreciate early Italian music.

petent organist and, after serving as a Gentleman in the Chapel Royal and a member of the choir of Westminster Abbey, ultimately succeeded Samuel Arnold as organist and Master of the Children of the Chapel Royal in 1802. By this time, however, he had established himself both as a composer and as an authority on ancient music. He sprang into prominence in the former capacity when awarded a prize by the Nobleman's Catch Club in 1765. This became a habit and his catches, canons, glees, or odes figured regularly in the Honours List of the Club for the next fifteen years. In the limited field of music of this order Smith was justly regarded as a master. A large number of pieces were published by E. T. Warren (see p. 405) and in miscellaneous collections, while independently he issued five sets of glees. An early admirer of 'Tommy' Arne's genius for melody, Smith took this as his fluent guide. He was often capable of nice touches of humour, as shown by his agreeable discussion of parliamentary practice in his catch *The Debate* (a favoured set of words concerning the dignities of the Speaker of the House of Commons, also previously set by Joseph Baildon). Even in his lighter essays, however, Smith was inclined to look back—or sideways at the manuscripts accumulating in his study. Thus he could produce a three-part canon from one traditional London Cry ('Sweet Lavender') and set it above another ('Ground Ivy') used as a ground bass, or a 'Canon in Subdiapente, 2 in 1, on a plainsong' [Ex. 1]. Among his manuscript remains[1] are genuine attempts to recreate the

1.

[1] B.M. Add. Ms. 31809.

madrigal. Two examples are settings of an anonymous *Flora calleth forth each flower* and (though this is incomplete) of Thomas Lodge's *Rosalind's Madrigal.* As a composer Smith fortuitously claims his place in history for quite another reason. A member of the Anacreontic Society[1] (founded in 1766), he composed for his fellow members a suitable ode—*To Anacreon in Heaven.* In 1814, the music, having crossed the Atlantic, was adapted to other words and as *The Star-spangled Banner* reached a wider public. In the craft of composition Smith was an earnest student and a good teacher. His *Introduction to the Art of Composing* is in the library of the Royal College of Music (Ms. 2097); his most distinguished pupil was John Goss.

As a pupil of Boyce Smith had opportunity to examine examples of old music in his master's collection. That his enthusiasm was aroused early is clear by the fact that he was only in his twenties when he selected, transcribed, and annotated works of the sixteenth and seventeenth centuries and handed them to Hawkins. In 1779 Smith went into the business as musical scholar on his own account and issued *A Collection of English Songs*; but his outstanding achievement was *Musica Antiqua* (1812), in which he introduced his fellow-countrymen to many of the forgotten glories of their heritage. *Musica Antiqua* moved away from the central choral tradition and contained early keyboard music, madrigals, ayres, and movements from the Jacobean masques. Its full intention was defined on the title-page, as 'A Selection of Music of this and other Countries, from the commencement of the twelfth to the beginning of the eighteenth century; comprising . . . Motetts, Madrigals, Hymns, Anthems, Songs, Lessons and Dance Tunes some of them now first published. . . .' It constituted a valuable repository of knowledge for the better part of a hundred years. Smith had his own views on editorship, as is shown by his version of Purcell's *Grand Te Deum: alter'd and digested . . . also adapted for the organ or harpsichord only.* But he cast the net wide and, through his *Ten Select Voluntaries*, brought back to organists pieces by Gibbons, Blow, Purcell, Greene, Boyce, and—in token of filial piety—James Martin Smith. While among his annotated manuscripts

[1] The Society lasted until 1794. Its meetings were fortnightly and were held at the Crown and Anchor which was also the headquarters of the Gloucester Society—Smith was a Gloucester man.

are transcriptions of works by Dowland, Campion, Rosseter, Leveridge, Purcell, Lampe, and Buononcini, and extracts from E. Jones's *Welch Airs* (1783). His library of more than 2,000 items was dispersed after a sale in 1853. Among the precious items contained in this collection was the *Mulliner Book*. This with other of Smith's material was at one time the property of Joseph Ritson, whose *English Songs* (1783) and *Ancient Songs from the Time of Henry III to the Revolution* (1792) gave further impetus to the consideration of late medieval and Renaissance music.

Hawkins and Burney reviewed music that to them appeared as antique with curiosity and a sense of gentlemanly superiority. Smith, on the other hand, was guided by enthusiasm tempered by modesty and like Boyce he was concerned to make his researches of practical consequence. Reconsideration of the past was, of course, one facet of the age and musicians looking back towards the 'Gothic' were in line with practitioners in other fields. So far as literature was concerned Thomas Gray, Thomas Percy, Thomas Warton, Thomas Tyrwhitt, and George Ellis were engaged in the transcription, editing, and annotation of folk-poetry, balladry, and early specimens of English literature, and in so doing were preparing the ground for the Romantic revolution symbolised by *Lyrical Ballads* in 1798. Gray was also greatly interested in music. In architecture Sanderson Miller, Horace Walpole, James Wyatt, and Browne Willis were busy investing their imagination and skills in a renascence of the Gothic style. It is, then, hardly surprising that some musicians should have developed similar attitudes; nor that in the end they should have come up with a renewed respect for contrapuntal techniques. It was Samuel Wesley who recognised that Sebastian Bach represented the *ne plus ultra* of contrapuntal excellence and his championship of that master was one of the most remarkable, and profitable, accidents in the record of English music. But Wesley was more than an advocate for another man's work—he was a highly original composer in his own right. If he had enjoyed better fortune—as he himself recognised—and better health he could have risen to very high rank. Instead of this he passed into relative oblivion leaving behind a legend, a reputation for eccentricity, and a handful of distinguished works.

The Wesleys and the Bach Revival

Rev. Charles Wesley, brother of John the founder of Methodism, who has already been noticed as a hymn-writer, was a friend of Beard and Stanley and a keen connoisseur of music. He admired the music of Corelli, Geminiani, Handel, and also of Purcell. His wife, Sarah, of Welsh extraction, was said to have been a good singer, especially competent in the arias of Handel. That their sons should be musical was not surprising. Neither was it surprising that they should show signs of precocity. Most of the Wesleys did. Charles Wesley (1757–1834), the elder of the two sons to be considered here, was alarmingly forward as a performer on the harpsichord and in due course was placed under Joseph Kelway for tuition. Samuel (1766–1837) was even more precocious and his gifts in interpreting the keyboard works of Handel and Scarlatti, in extemporisation and in original composition, were so outstanding that those experienced in these matters spoke of the arrival of an English Mozart. The Hon. Daines Barrington, who had examined the infant Mozart on behalf of the Royal Society, performed the same service in respect of the younger Wesley.[1] Samuel composed an oratorio, *Ruth*, between the ages of six and eight; an indiscretion he did not repeat. He had his first lessons in music in Bristol, but when his father moved to London he became a pupil of William Cramer.

At the age of eleven Samuel played on the organ at a Bach-Abel concert. He was commended on that occasion by Arne, whose generosity to young musicians at least was not inconsiderable. A year later and for the next seven years the two brothers organised subscription concerts in their house, which were patronised by an influential body of fashionable well-wishers.[2] Charles and Samuel appeared both as performers and composers, and the one published sets of six quartets in 1779 and of six organ concertos in 1780, while the other issued eight sonatas for harpsichord or pianoforte in 1780 and a further collection of three in 1785. Many works remained in manuscript, among them more concertos by Charles and the first of Samuel's two *Odes on St. Cecilia's Day* (1779). During this period Samuel, temporarily converted to Roman Catholicism, composed a *Missa de Spiritu Sancto*, which he inscribed to Pope Pius VI.[3] This eccentricity, however, was not so disturbing to the Rev. Charles Wesley (who had insisted that his sons were thoroughly educated in a general way) as the possibility that his sons might adopt music as a career. This seemed the more likely in 1786 when the boys were summoned to Windsor Castle to play selections from Handel to George III.

Reluctantly, Charles Wesley senior consented to his sons becoming professional musicians, oddly insisting only that they should not accept appointments at Court. This condition cost Charles the organistship of St. George's Chapel, Windsor. Neither brother was ever able to advance far along the road of professional preferment and both remained organists

[1] See Daines Barrington, *Miscellanies* (ed. by J. Nichols), London, 1781.
[2] Details of these concerts are in B.M. Add. Ms. 35017.
[3] 22 May 1784.

in lesser establishments, music teachers in girls' schools, and private practitioners. Samuel was further handicapped by periodical phases of mental instability, the result of an accident in 1788 in which he damaged his skull.

Charles Wesley did not in any way live up to his early promise and neither his few later compositions nor his professional activities were of any great consequence. With Samuel it was otherwise. He was a prolific composer (relatively little, however, being published), writing a large amount of organ and other keyboard pieces, glees and allied works, anthems and motets, songs and duets, chamber music, overtures and concertos, and even operatic fragments.

At the same time Samuel enjoyed an enviable reputation as organist and was in demand in various parts of the country. He also caught the first genuine wave of enthusiasm for popular education and gave series of public lectures both in London and in Bristol. In the course of his life Wesley built up a large stock of out-of-the-way information. But what he acquired interested him primarily for its musical content; thus it is that his comments were invariably relevant to the creative aspect of music.

'The Library of the ancient Concert abounds in the works of all the best composers since counterpoint was established: and from such a treasury the musical public might be perpetually supplied with new Antiquities—qualified into relicks, so long remembered, they're forgot. But unhappily because some certain pieces have always (and deservedly) received universal approbation they are re-iterated so injudiciously that were they not indeed of the most sterling excellence the patience of subscribers would surely have long since failed; whereas were but a few of the noble productions with which their Library teems brought forward, and which now lie mouldering on its shelves, it would prove a fillip to the Institution of the Concert, a Renovation of its primeval energies.'[1]

Wesley, unlike Burney, was not one who placed implicit faith in the superior virtues of the musicianship of his own time. Therefore he preached that in respect of the orchestration of *Messiah* Handel knew better than his improvers—an unusual point of view then and for a long time to come.

'No musician in his senses' [he wrote] 'will question the solid judgement and refined taste of Mozart: but infallibility is not to be found on this side of the Alps though some folk still believe it may on the other. Mozart duly appreciating and admiring Handel's unrivalled Oratorio of the Messiah in his zeal for extending and augmenting its wonderful effects, essayed an improvement by the additional various wind instruments,

[1] Wesley's lectures, B.M. Add. Ms. 35015, f. 225 v.

throughout the whole work; but certainly this zeal was "not according to knowledge" for the majority of movements in this Oratorio need no other accompaniments than what their immortal author deemed proper and necessary . . .'[1]

Wesley ranged widely. Contemporary music enthralled him equally with that of the masters of the past; he transcribed excerpts from Purcell,[2] but did not fail to note down a barrel-organ tune that pleased him.[3] The focal point of his researches was, however, the music of Bach. To this he was introduced in the first place by August Friedrich Kollmann[4] and George Pinto.[5] Wesley responded immediately to the genius of Bach and set out to become acquainted with as many of his works as possible. He was further indebted to Karl Friedrich Horn,[6] who had 'a vast quantity of his compositions that have never seen the light; among the rest, Stupendous Trios for the Organ, which he used to play thus: his right hand played the first part on the Top Row of the Clavier; his left the 2nd part on the 2nd Row, and he played the Bass *wholly* upon the Pedals. There are Allegro Movements among them, and occasionally very brisk notes in the Bass Part, whence it appears that he was alike dexterous both with hands and feet'.[7]

On 11 June 1808 Wesley arranged a concert at the Hanover Square Rooms, at which 'several admired compositions of the celebrated Sebastian Bach were performed', and a year later he organised the first performance in England of *Jesu, meine Freude*. In 1810, in conjunction with Horn, he issued through R. Birchall *A Trio* [*Six Trios*] (*J. S. Bach*) *composed originally for the Organ . . . adapted for three Hands upon the Piano Forte*, while between 1810 and 1813 he published his *New and Correct Edition of the Preludes and Fugues of John Sebastian Bach with an Introduction*. Among his intentions at this time was also an English edition of Forkel's *Life of Bach*, which, how-

[1] ib. f. 63.

[2] 'Purcell bears a close analogy with Shakespeare in his rare faculty of exciting mental emotion of every kind, by his magic and marvellous modes of expression, on all occasions. He is, indeed, a superb acquisition to our country . . .' Letter to Vincent Novello of 1830.

[3] Add. Ms. 31239.

[4] 1756–1829; a Hanoverian who was appointed to a post in the German Chapel at St. James's Palace in 1784. In 1799 he published one of the '48' in an *Essay on Practical Harmony*. In the same year he projected an edition of the '48'.

[5] 1786–1806; violinist and pianist, and composer of great talent. Among his compositions is a pianoforte sonata dedicated to his friend, John Field, and published by Birchall in 1803. Pinto was a pupil and protégé of Salomon.

[6] 1762–1830; he arrived in England in 1782 and was set up as a music teacher by the Saxon Ambassador, Count Brühl (a subscriber to the Wesley concerts), and in 1789 became one of the music teachers at Court.

[7] Letter of 17 October 1808, to Benjamin Jacob, in *The Bach Letters of Samuel Wesley*, London, 1875, p. 7.

ever, did not appear until 1820.[1] Wesley was tireless in his championship of 'St. Sebastian' and gave many organ recitals to promote his aims. He was the leader of a group of players who shared his zeal, among them Benjamin Jacob (1778–1829) and Thomas Adams (1785–1858), while he communicated his enthusiasm to his son, Samuel Sebastian, who continued to spread the influence of Bach in the years to come. Other supporters of the cause of Bach who were influenced by Wesley were Samuel Webbe, William Crotch, and Vincent Novello.

At the head of Wesley's compositions stands the motet *In Exitu Israel*, a strong essay in eight-part writing, inspired by the plainsong *cantus firmus*[2] and infused with the sonorous energy of Bach, without parallel in England in the period in which it was written and to be ranked among the major achievements of English music. Wesley had a rare control of contrapuntal movement and, at the same time, an understanding of the relationship between the horizontal and the vertical aspects of choral music, as is shown in the fine ending of *Anima nostra*[3] [Ex. 2]. Of similar quality to

2.

In Exitu Israel are the *Carmen funebre* (*Omnia vanitas*) and *O magnum mysterium*. As a composer of instrumental music Wesley was variable, but rarely dull, and in many pieces he gave a prescription which, alas! too few were willing to dispense. Thus there may be noted the modernity of the modulations and the original treatment of suspensions in the second of the *Three Fantasias* for organ,[4] the chromatic freedom of subject and

[1] This was prepared not by Wesley, but by A. F. Kollmann according to a letter from Wesley to his friend Emmet.

[2] See *Dixit Dominus* à 3, also on a plainsong theme, B.M. Add. Ms. 14340.

[3] Add. Ms. 14340, with note to score, 'Nb. Organo comitante vel tacente, ad libitum.'

[4] *A Series of Progressive Studies*, Josiah Pittman, Chappell (1882). Book 2 contains *Six Petites Suites de Pièces*; Book 7, *Three Fantasias*; and Book 12, *Three Preludes and Fugues and March*, by Wesley.

counter-subject of the C minor fugue of *Three Preludes and Fugues and March*, the Mendelssohnian ease of the G minor prelude from the same set—which terminates with *Non nobis Domine*, and the bold linear gestures of a trio for two flutes and pianoforte[1] [Ex. 3].

3.

Wesley was a prominent figure on the musical scene, but his merits were appreciated only by a few.[2] Among these were Vincent Novello and it was through the energy of Novello and his circle that Wesley eventually became an effective influence. It was one of Novello's young friends who wrote the warmest epitaph on Wesley:

'His whole soul was music; he was the unsophisticated child of nature, of warm affections and impulse. Had he perceived less keenly, or felt less warmly, he might have preserved himself from many of the errors which chequered his career. Still he was the first great devotee of the unpopular Bach in England; as such we remember him with a hearty benison to his memory, and gratitude for his musical example, for he was essentially a gentleman, kind, affectionate and encouraging to young musicians.'[3]

The Impact of Haydn, Mozart, and Beethoven

In the long run the resuscitation of English music of the sixteenth and seventeenth centuries, the renewal of interest in Purcell to which Smith and Samuel Wesley were also parties, and the unveiling of the works of J. S. Bach were to prove the outstanding achievements of the closing years

[1] A two-movement work: I *Andante—Allegro*; II *Andantino* (theme and variations); B.M. Add. Ms. 48302.

[2] 'The genius of Samuel Wesley has had a most extraordinary influence on art in this country, but to the shame of our countrymen, he is better appreciated, through his works, which are numerous in the extreme, and they are widely disseminated—in Germany.' *Freemasons Magazine and Masonic Mirror*, 28 January 1858, p. 159.

[3] 'Progress of Bach's Music in England', Edward Holmes, in *Mus. T.* (reprinted from *Fraser's Magazine*), June 1851.

of the eighteenth and the opening years of the nineteenth centuries. Hardly less important was the centralising tendency that brought into being the Philharmonic Society in 1813.

During their later years the Bach-Abel Concerts were liberally supported by Willoughby Bertie, fourth Earl of Abingdon. This nobleman, a radical in politics, a friend of John Wilkes, and a supporter of the principles of the French Revolution, was not only a patron of music but an excellent flautist and a versatile composer. He was, indeed, a composer of original views, and in his reputed eccentricities well in the van of progress. In *A Representation of the Execution of Mary Queen of Scots in Seven Views* (1790) and in *A Selection of Twelve Psalms and Hymns* he foreshadowed later romantic intentions by attempting to 'unite the sister arts of music, poetry and painting'; while his political views were given expression in music through his selection and setting of strongly democratic texts.

In the score of *Mary Queen of Scots* are included four engravings which Abingdon illustrates by skilful association rather than directly programmatic method. Since he maintains a basic A minor tonality through the first three movements, and continues the second section into the third, he achieves a consistency of atmosphere that is enhanced by an eclectic use of idioms, and some finely judged orchestration. Horns and trumpets are employed sparingly but with significance. The mood of the first section, with a slender anticipation of Mendelssohn's 'Scottish' Symphony ('Going to the Place of Execution'), is settled by this heavy tread [Ex. 4*a*].

4a.

As Queen Mary is seen 'on her knees at prayer' a psalm is sung by chorus [Ex. 4*b*]. The proximity to the Mozart of the *Requiem* is heightened by a

4b.

splendid emancipating cadence in C major to the words 'Libera me'. The final movement of the work, in A major, to illustrate the 'Execution', is a realistic march 'from' the scaffold. Abingdon is a very interesting composer, but he lived in the wrong place at the wrong time.

After the death of J. C. Bach the formerly joint concerts were controlled by Abel, but with the substantial backing of Abingdon, who was said to have subsidised them, between 1785 and 1793, to the extent of £1,600. The concerts were now designated the Professional Concerts and led by William Cramer. Although ranking first in point of prestige, these concerts were rivalled by those engineered by Gertrude Mara and Johann Peter Salomon at the Pantheon, in Oxford Street.

Salomon arrived in England in 1781, having become redundant at Rheinsberg, in Germany, when Prince Henry of Prussia dismissed his orchestra, of which Salomon was leader. Salomon played in the orchestra of the Professional Concerts but resigned his place after a disagreement. Thereupon he set himself up as impresario. Those who were progressive in their tastes in England had fallen under the spell of Haydn. His works were included in the Bach-Abel programmes, and those of the Leeds Subscription Concerts,[1] and were extensively published by William Forster. Feelers were put out to Haydn that he should visit London as early as 1787. The Professional Concerts organisers saw in a Haydn visit an opportunity of recovering lost ground and Lord Abingdon and Cramer took appropriate action to bring it about. Learning of this development, Salomon, using the publisher John Bland as his agent, tried to outbid his rivals. It was not until after the death of Prince Nicholas Esterházy, however, that Haydn felt it possible to travel to London and when finally he did, in 1791, it was as a result of Salomon's insistence. In order to make sure of his man Salomon went to Vienna to lay out the attractive terms of a proposed contract. Haydn was to receive £50 for each of twenty performances, and the takings (each guaranteed up to £200) of two benefit concerts.

When Haydn reached London the Professional Concerts and Salomon's concerts were on one side of the metropolitan musical spectrum. On the other, and in pious opposition, were the Ancient Concerts (the performances under royal patronage now designated King's Concerts). In between was the Italian Opera, transferred to the Pantheon since the destruction of the King's Theatre, by fire, in 1799. A proposal to build a second house for Italian opera had been mooted by Sir John Gallini[2]—

[1] First mention of a Haydn *symphonia* in the fourth of the 1779–80 series, when the programme also included an overture by Arne, symphonies by Bach and Schwindl, concertos, by unnamed composers, for violin and harpsichord, and songs.

[2] Italian dancing-master, who had been stage-manager of the Haymarket Theatre. He married the sister of the third Earl of Abingdon, and built Hanover Square Concert Rooms.

who had hoped to induce Haydn to compose an opera—but scotched by George III. There were still the Gardens concerts and the popular pastiches, ballad-operas, and pantomimes, at Covent Garden and Drury Lane. Under these circumstances it was difficult to assemble anything like a consistent and well-disciplined permanent orchestra. Salomon, however, managed to get together a force of thirty-five to forty players for the Haydn concerts of 1791–2, and if the master was taken aback by the independence and lack of *esprit de corps* of his players, he was impressed by their responsiveness and by the generosity of his patrons and admirers. He made many friends. Among them were Mrs. Schroeter, widow of Bach's successor, for whom he developed a romantic regard; Mrs. Hunter, wife of John Hunter, the surgeon, and authoress of most of the texts of his English cantatas; Lord Abingdon,[1] and William Shield. During the time of Haydn's first stay in England the directors of the Professional Concerts, unable to persuade Haydn away from Salomon, brought over Ignaz Pleyel (a pupil of Haydn) to direct their concerts; while Salomon also introduced Gyrowetz (resident in London since the French Revolution had caused him to leave Paris) to his prospectus as associate conductor with Haydn.

In 1794–5 Haydn was again in London and once again was lionised. Salomon moved his concerts from the Hanover Square Rooms during this year and presented them at the Haymarket Theatre, where they were entitled 'Opera Concerts' and were distinguished not only by the presence of Haydn but also by the appearances of many virtuosi performers, among whom Clementi, Jan Ladislav Dussek,[2] Domenico Dragonetti,[3] J. B. Cramer, and Giovanni Viotti[4] were prominent.

Haydn appreciated that the English did much, by their approbation and enthusiasm, to increase his reputation. He found London a congenial environment in which to compose, the National Anthem stimulated him to the production of *Gott erhalte Franz den Kaiser*, and the performances of the Handel oratorios to consideration of that genre. So far as the English were concerned he left behind a fund of good-will, a conception of the potential of the modernised orchestra (symbolised in the 'London'

[1] In 1795 Haydn devised pianoforte or harp accompaniments to Abingdon's *Twelve Sentimental Catches and Glees* (*c.* 1795) and he set two numbers of Needham's *Invocation of Neptune* at Abingdon's suggestion (B.M. Add. Ms. 9284).

[2] 1760–1812; Bohemian pianist and composer and sometime pupil of C. P. E. Bach, who worked in London between 1790 and 1802. He was much regarded by Haydn who wrote of his talents in glowing terms to Dussek's father. Dussek junior married the daughter of Domenico Corri, she being a professional singer in London, in 1792.

[3] 1763–1846; Italian double-bass player who migrated to London in 1794.

[4] 1755–1824; Italian violinist and composer, who came to London in 1793. He directed performances at the Italian Opera, being responsible for the first London performance of Gluck's *Alceste* in 1794.

symphonies), a regard for Vienna as an international music centre, and a determination on the part of some to reform conditions that, in the field of instrumental music, were little short of chaotic. On the other hand, the reputation and the adulatory cult of Haydn made it difficult for English composers to live in the same musical atmosphere.

Apart from Hook, who has been mentioned, and William Crotch, to be noticed at a later point, there were two composers who came directly and evidently under the influence of Haydn. These were Thomas Haigh (1769–1808)—a *Favorite Symphony in 9 parts* being the direct consequence of Haydn's tuition—who eked out a living by making arrangements of his master's works for incomplete ensembles, and John March (1752–1828). March was a lawyer and an amateur, who organised amateur orchestras in Salisbury, Canterbury, and Chichester. He himself played the viola and his sense of orchestration was advanced. For instance, he gave considerable play to the violas, he released the double-bass from the bondage of subordination to the cellos, and he exploited the sonorities of the wind instruments. Among his works are a programme symphony, *La Chasse*, and a string quartet 'in imitation of Haydn's Op. 1'. Unlike his English contemporaries, he wrote extensive slow movements, and like Haydn, was often inclined to use variation form within the symphonic structure. One of the difficulties of assembling and assessing English music of this period is that so much sprouted in inaccessible places and, having done so, rapidly went to seed. Thus one discovers a quite impressive 'Viennese' symphony movement in the overture to John Davy's (1765–1824) score for Joseph Holman's *What a Blunder* (Haymarket, 1800). Davy, a pupil of Jackson of Exeter, had a ready pen and a facile temperament. His preference for bouncing 6/8 tunes and his sub-Handelian technique for dealing with choruses—of peasants, nuns and friars, etc.,—and his ingenuous jingles of words and notes in musical comedy place him less among the disciples of Haydn than among the precursors of Sullivan.

5.

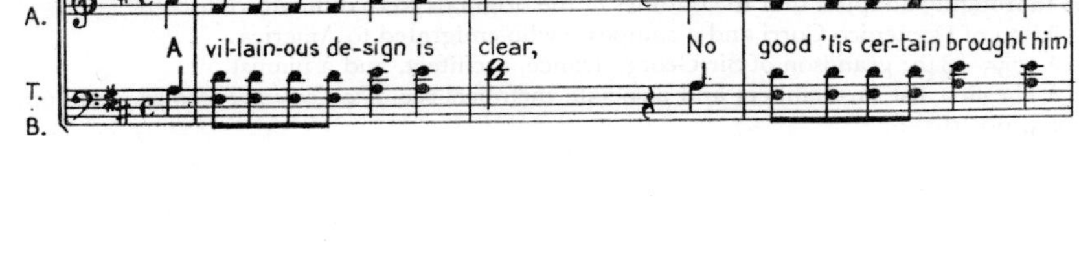

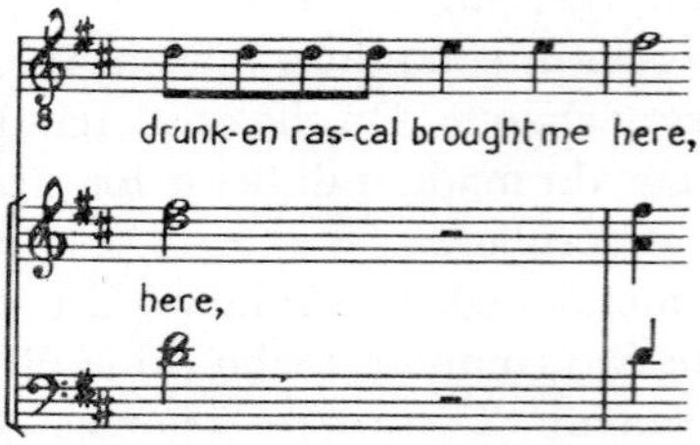
drunk-en ras-cal brought me here,
here,

While Haydn was responsible for a changed attitude towards music, especially so far as the amateurs were concerned, there were in England disciples both of Mozart and Beethoven. Among those who cultivated the music of the former the principal was William Ayrton[1] (1777–1858), Samuel Arnold's son-in-law, who, as director of the music of the King's Theatre, was responsible for the first English productions of *Cosi fan tutte* and *Die Zauberflöte* (1811), and *Don Giovanni* (1817).[2] Ayrton was a writer of some talent, too, and possessed of organising acumen. A friend of Salomon, he was long concerned to improve both the standard of music, and its status in England. Salomon and Ayrton began to plan for yet another Academy of Music. As they were thus engaged, three leading players, J. B. Cramer, Philip Corri,[3] and William Dance,[4] were promoting another scheme—to restore 'to the world those compositions which have excited so much delight, and [to] rekindle in the public mind that taste for excellence in instrumental music which has so long remained in a latent state'. At a meeting held in Samuel Chappell's drawing-room in New Bond Street on 17 January 1813 the proposal was welcomed by the representative group of musicians who attended in response to the initial circular. The Philharmonic Society was founded.[5] A year after its foundation the Society gave the first English performance of the 'Eroica' Symphony.

Apart from the disadvantages laid on certain aspects of musical development by the general structure of society (and the ultimate lack of a more or less absolute aristocratic control of patronage), the insular situation made compositional progress on a broad front improbable.

[1] Ayrton was the son of Edmund Ayrton (1734–1808), pupil of Nares at York Minster and his successor as Master of the Children of the Chapel Royal. The Ayrtons were prominent in Yorkshire and Edmund's brother and nephew were organists of Ripon Minster.

[2] Henry Bishop, after seeing these performances, envisaged Mozart in English for the English. Unfortunately the adaptations of *Don Giovanni* (as *The Libertine*) and *Figaro* were so thoroughly adapted that the outlines of the originals were difficult to discern.

[3] Son of Domenico Corri and a composer who emigrated to America.

[4] 1755–1840; grandson of Sir George Dance, architect, and a pianist.

[5] For first list of members and associate members see *The Concert Tradition*, London, 1965, pp. 167–8.

British Mozartians

The British appreciated musical genius the better when aware of the personality that contained the genius. Handel established himself in the general affection of the nation not only on account of the quality of his music but also because of his public image. The same was true of Haydn, who fitted so amiably into an English setting. Mozart, insofar as his reputation in Britain was concerned, was at a disadvantage. His solitary visit as a boy soon faded from the memory of all but a few, and if he was recollected it was generally as a yardstick, by which to measure home-grown infant prodigies, such as the two Wesleys and William Crotch. If Burney is taken as the guide to Mozart's reputation in England, it will be found that for long he had reservations about the composer's 'experiments' in his instrumental works (a number of which were published in London) and that it was not until he became acquainted with the vocal music and operas that he recognised the true quality of genius. And this was after Mozart's death. It was, in the end, Haydn who convinced him.[1] Owing to this late start in appreciation English composers for the most part were left in ignorance of the new potentialities of musical method and design. Thomas Linley was exceptional in his meeting with Mozart; but then he was but a boy and so was Mozart. Towards the end of Mozart's life, however, a small group of devoted Mozartians from Britain was assembled.

Between 1784 and 1787 Michael Kelly (1762–1826), Stephen Storace (1763–96) and his sister Nancy (1766–1817), and Thomas Attwood (1765–1838) were to be found in Vienna. All were on terms of friendship with Mozart. Kelly, the son of a Dublin wine-merchant, showed talent as actor and musician when a boy, and, after lessons from Philip Cogan (a friend and protégé of Clementi), Michael Arne and Rauzzini (and others), and several successful appearances on the Dublin stage, was sent to the Conservatorio in Naples. He sang in various Italian theatres until in 1783 he took up an appointment in the Court Theatre in Vienna. In 1786 he sang the parts of Basilio and Don Curzio in the first performance of Mozart's *Nozze di Figaro*. The part of Susanna was taken by Nancy Storace, who, like Kelly, had been a pupil of Rauzzini. Nancy and Stephen were the children of Stefano Storace, a Neapolitan double-bass player attached to the King's Theatre in the Haymarket, and an English mother. Stephen's abilities were as notable as his charm of manner. He was an accomplished violinist by the age of ten; he had artistic facility that enabled him in due course to design the sets for his own operas; he was well-read. 'Had [he] been bred to the law,' said Richard Brinsley Sheridan (who after his marriage to Elizabeth Linley lodged for a time in Storace's father's home), 'nothing could have prevented him becoming Lord

[1] See C. B. Oldman, op. cit., p. 77.

Chancellor.' In his teens, through the generosity of his father, Stephen went to study in Naples; Nancy, who had made her debut in London in 1777, accompanied him. Like Kelly the Storaces displayed their talents in various Italian cities before arriving in Vienna, where Nancy was engaged at the Court Theatre at a seasonal salary of £500. Nancy's charms captivated the Emperor (as in due course they were to captivate Mozart). Stephen, without previous experience in the field, was commissioned to write an opera, *Gli sposi malcontenti*. He was then invited to compose another. This was *Gli Equivoci*, the libretto by da Ponte out of Shakespeare's *Comedy of Errors*. After his return to England Storace used a trio from this work for *No Song, no Supper*, and two songs and a chorus for *The Pirates*. The fourth member of this British colony in Vienna, Thomas Attwood, owed his opportunity to the Prince of Wales,[1] whose skill in and knowledge of music was considerable. An ex-chorister of the Chapel Royal, under Nares and Edmund Ayrton, he came into prominence at a chamber concert at Buckingham House and the Prince (whose enthusiasm for music was not always so readily matched as in this case by readiness to pay for its provision) dispatched him also to Naples. Unlike Kelly and Storace Attwood went to Vienna particularly to take lessons from Mozart, who was said by Kelly to have had a high opinion of his capacity. Life passed pleasantly and not unprofitably in Vienna, as is described by Kelly in his lively *Reminiscences*[2] (ghosted by Theodore Hook, the literary son of James Hook), while it is clear that Mozart hoped that through these diverting and enterprising companions he would be able to negotiate a long-desired return to London.[3]

In 1787 the party went back to England; Kelly and Nancy Storace with sufficient testimonials to their gifts as singers to ensure acceptance by the English; Stephen Storace with evidence of success as a composer of elegance and theatrical adaptability; Attwood with exercise-books filled with essays marked and corrected by Mozart.[4] High hopes and ambitions then faced the bleak prospect of the English situation. Attwood disappeared into a parochial organ loft and undertook music teaching at Court until in 1796 he was chosen to succeed John Jones at St. Paul's Cathedral.

On his return from Vienna Attwood hankered after the theatre and

[1] See Dedication of *St. David's Day* (1800) to the Prince of Wales; also C. B. Oldman, 'Thomas Attwood, 1765–1838', *American Choral Review*, 1965, vol. 8, no. 2.

[2] Published 1826.

[3] See letter of Leopold Mozart, 1–2 March 1787, in *Letters of Mozart and his family*, ed. by Emily Anderson, London, 1938, III, p. 545; and Heinz Wolfgang Hamman, 'Mozarts Schülerkreis', in *Mozart Jahrbuch*, 1962–3, p. 125.

[4] See C. B. Oldman, 'Thomas Attwood's Studies with Mozart', in *Gedenboek . . . D. F. Scheurleer*, The Hague, 1925; 'Two Minuets by Attwood with Corrections by Mozart', in *Music Review*, VII, 1946, p. 166.

in 1792 he composed the score for John Rose's *The Prisoner* at the King's Theatre. In this, as in three subsequent works for which he was responsible, he made use of tunes by Mozart. Attwood was prolific in this department of music and contributed to more than thirty so-called operas. He also composed some admirable and cultivated keyboard music in which he carried his Viennese reminiscences with efficient charm. The master's voice is to be heard in the first movement of the B flat Sonata contained in Storace's admirable *Collection of Original Harpsichord Music* (1787–9) II [Ex. 6]. This versatility has been overlooked for it is as a church composer

6.

that Attwood has generally been recollected. It is difficult to believe either that his heart was in this department of music or that his church compositions were in any way other than mediocre. He enjoyed prestige, however, and to his appointment at St. Paul's he added the organistships of George IV's Chapel at Brighton and of the Chapel Royal. Otherwise Attwood was one of the founder members of the Philharmonic Society and among the first in England to fall under the spell of Mendelssohn. Between 1826 and 1832 he directed many Philharmonic concerts. He was regarded as a specialist in Viennese music and was responsible for the interpretations of as yet unfamiliar works by Mozart and Beethoven. He introduced the great symphonies of the last period of the former and the Fifth Symphony of the latter to London audiences. As was to become increasingly the case with British composers in the nineteenth century, Attwood's practice of composition was impeded by the calls of teaching and official business.

Kelly continued his career as a singer and for twenty years was in demand at London concerts and provincial festivals. He was also principal tenor at Drury Lane. Among tenors in England he was exceptional in not having to fall back on falsetto for his high notes.[1] His farewell appearance, appropriately enough, was in Dublin in 1811, where, in deference to the nationalist-romantic fervour that was developing, he sang his own *The Bard of Erin*. In addition to these activities Kelly, who lived in sin and

[1] The use of falsetto by English tenors was adversely commented on by Haydn.

contentment with the famous soprano Mrs. Crouch, acted as manager of the King's Theatre, put together the music (some of it his own) for sixty-two dramatic pieces, and kept a wine-shop. Sheridan suggested he should advertise himself as a 'Composer of Wines and Importer of Music'. In respect of the English 'operas' of the day this was fair comment. 'His own airs,' wrote George Hogarth, 'though slight, are always elegant; and his knowledge of the Italian and German schools, not very general among the English musicians of his day, enabled him to enrich his pieces with many gems of foreign art.'[1]

Storace was the most able of the group and had he enjoyed greater opportunity to use his gifts, better health, and a longer life, could well have achieved lasting distinction. As it is he must rank among that large number whose attainment was incommensurate with early promise. Storace was by aptitude and training a man of the theatre and his intuitive capacity for matching situation with appropriate music was considerable. On his return to England he pinned his hopes on the Italian Opera at the Haymarket and in 1788 his *La Cameriera astuta* played for three nights. But an Italian manager was not disposed to see an Englishman—even if of Italian origin—breaking in on what was virtually a closed shop. Nor was he willing to see Nancy establishing herself in the King's Theatre.[2] She had sung in one opera there, Paisiello's *Gli Schiavi per amore*, which had been directed by Stephen and had been warmly commended by the Prince of Wales. Disheartened, the Storaces retired to Bath, where Stephen busied himself as artist, but after a brief period of recuperation they were back in London. Stephen adapted Dittersdorf's[3] *Doktor und Apotheker*, for which an English text had been prepared by James Cobb. At this juncture, in view of the success of Shield and Arnold in particular, he saw his future to lie, if anywhere, in the field of English opera.

In 1789 *The Haunted Tower*, the libretto also by Cobb, was played at Drury Lane. Nancy sang in what was an outstanding success for both of them and henceforth she was one of the regular singers in that theatre. The success of this work encouraged Sheridan, then manager of Drury

[1] *Memoirs of the Musical Drama*, London, 1838, II, p. 446.

[2] 'My sister's success in London upon the whole has been as much as we could expect—though she has had great opposition from the Italians—who consider it as an infringement on their rights—that any person should be able to sing that was not born in Italy—at present she gains ground very fast—we have done the *Gave Generose* under another title with very great success—it has been performed to near 20 bumper houses—she is re-engaged for the next season at an advanced salary—& likewise at the ancient concerts—I am likewise to compose an opera.' Letter from Storace to Sir Robert Murray Keith, H.M. Ambassador in Vienna. B.M. Add. Ms. 35538, f. 258.

[3] Storace knew both Paisiello and Dittersdorf personally. During his years in Vienna a performance of a string quartet was given by Haydn (vl. 1), Dittersdorf (vl. 2), Mozart (viola), Vanhall ('cello), Paisiello being among the audience (*The Harmonicon*, 1828, pp. 2–3).

Lane, to put on *No Song, no Supper*, a piece which he had earlier refused but which Kelly wished as an after-piece (*No Song, no Supper* lasts for just over an hour) to *The Beggar's Opera* for his benefit on 26 April 1790. It proved Storace's most popular work. In the six remaining years of his life it was performed a hundred times at Drury Lane alone. *No Song, no Supper* was popular in the provinces and by 1792 it had reached America, being played in Philadelphia. A year later it was performed in New York and in 1795 an English resident company, managed by an Edinburgh man named Williamson, presented it to audiences in Hamburg. The same company had previously played that other notably exportable opera, Shield's *The Shamrock* (retitled *The Poor Soldier*), which was a pasticcio of Irish melodies. Storace's other outstanding works were *The Siege of Belgrade*, adapted in large part from Martin y Soler's *Una Cosa rara*; *Dido, Queen of Carthage* (1792), which was based on Metastasio's libretto but of which the music no longer exists; *The Pirates* (1792); and *The Cherokee* (1794)—'the first operatic western'.[1]

Storace knew better than any of his English contemporaries what opera was, or could be. Disliking the provincial hybrid that passed as opera in London, and taking Mozart's *Die Entführung* as his example, he introduced to the theatre a more cohesive form of opera which—even if he followed current practice by drawing on the works of others—allowed a dramatic sense to infuse the music. He was also the first English composer to introduce operatic ensembles that were an integral part of the dramatic development of opera. An enchanting example is the trio, 'Knocking at this Time of Day', in the first Act of *No Song, no Supper*, while the 'Jolly Friars' chorus in *The Iron Chest* (1795) and the following excerpt from *The Pirates* anticipate the gift of Sullivan of lifting insignificance to significance through a perception of the comedy inherent in the commonplace [Ex. 7]. Storace was an inspired melodist and like Arne contrived to nationalise

7.

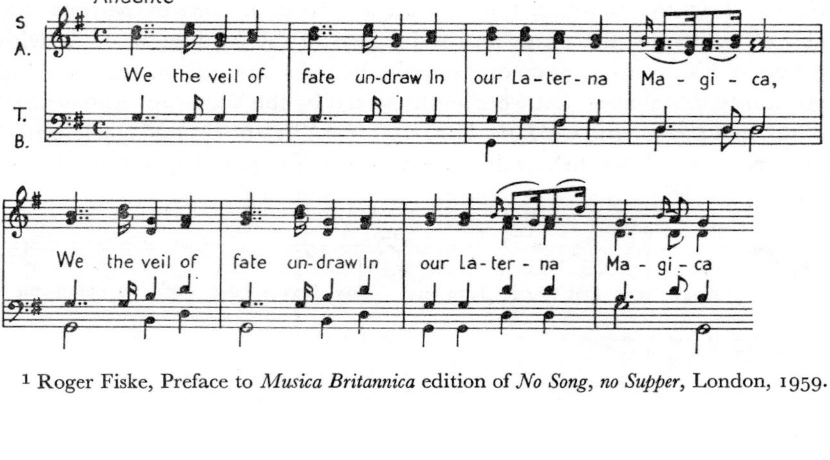
Andante
S
A.
T.
B.
We the veil of fate un-draw In our La-ter-na Ma-gi-ca,
We the veil of fate un-draw In our La-ter-na Ma-gi-ca

[1] Roger Fiske, Preface to *Musica Britannica* edition of *No Song, no Supper*, London, 1959.

Italian characteristics. His melodic gift shone in his overtures, in which he wrote sonata-wise with consistent competence, and his ease within a European environment is shown by the Polonese of the Overture to *My Grandmother* (1793) [Ex. 8]. Storace handled the orchestra with taste [Ex. 9]

8.

9.

and not infrequently with an ear for affecting sonorities—as in the contrast of octave strings with high, sustained woodwind chords redolent of Mendelssohn in the Overture to *The Haunted Tower*. Into this score are also introduced off-stage horns. Storace's operas were in sympathy with contemporary fiction; they were historical—threatening as in *The Iron Chest* to evoke 'old England', fantastic, sentimental, exotic. This, of course, was true of other operas popular in England at that time; but Storace had the talent and the technique to demonstrate the appropriate classification—even if, as in the Dance of Turkish Soldiers and Women in *The Siege of Belgrade*, he found the familiar *alla turca*, as used by Mozart, the easiest pointer to the terms and seductions of the Middle East. As with others of his group Storace occasionally bent formulas from the school of sensibility into shapes that were avidly seized by the Victorian *petits maîtres*. Thus, in a *Lamentation of Marie Antoinette* (1793) he anticipated a celebrated and sentimental Scottish psalm-tune of later date [Ex. 10]. Otherwise, as

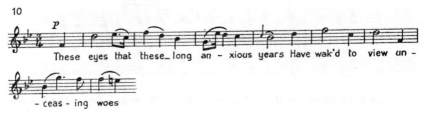

10

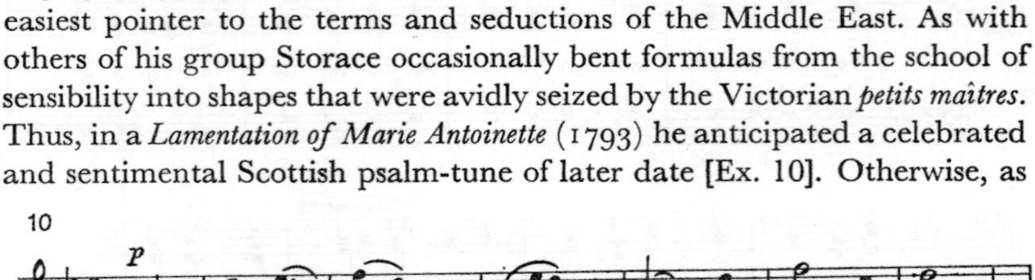

a song-writer, he could anticipate the *Lied*-composer's aptitude for conveying atmosphere in an instrumental interlude [Ex. 11].

11.

During the last quarter of the eighteenth century what had previously appeared (in Arne, for example) as patriotism turned into imperialism, and in many dramatico-musical works, or in independent programmatic orchestral pieces, new-found techniques, as well as those of earlier establishment, were pressed into propaganda. In 1795 François Barthélemon's daughter Cecilia composed a graphic overture—with much noise but little music—to celebrate *The Capture of the Cape of Good Hope*, while four years later Attwood published a very dull piece, an *Overture to the Mouth of the Nile*, and an equally dull march for the Stock Exchange gentlemen who formed the First Regiment of Loyal London Volunteers. There was a rising interest at this time in the progress of British fortunes in India, where imperialism was being secured by Richard Wellesley, brother of the Duke of Wellington, and son of the Earl of Mornington. The right mood for the times was struck by Joseph Mazzinghi (1765–1844), a pupil of J. C. Bach, and William Reeve (1757–1815) in *Ramah Droog* (1798). This was an opera set in India (and live elephants were brought on to the stage). Its ideological function is clearly set out in an opening chorus of (bad) Indian and (good) British soldiers. The words (and the music) of the Finale set the standard for much main-stream English poetry-cum-music in the succeeding century.

Sacred to Freedom's glorious cause
Britain the sword of Justice draws,
A lesson to the admiring world
Oppression from his seat is hurl'd.

Against this, however, may be set *The Favourite African Song taken from Mr. Park's Travels set to music* [anon.] *the poetry by the Duchess of Devonshire* (pub. J. Dale), which ends:

The white man far away must go,
But ever in his heart will bear
Remembrance of the Negro's care.
Go, white man, go
But with thee bear
The Negro's wish, the Negro's pray'r,
Remembrance of the Negro's care.

On the whole, English composers, unsubmissive and reluctant to abandon every native tradition, came to terms with the *nuove musiche* of the seventeenth century more sensibly than with that of the late eighteenth century. In the former period the political, national, and social destinies of the people were in a relatively uncertain condition and change was in the air. Nearly two centuries later the situation was otherwise. Britain was secure, powerful, and, in large measure, socially stable. The Industrial Revolution was well advanced though its worst consequences were still some way ahead. So far as a large part of the nation was concerned change was unwelcome. Conservatism in music, which of all the arts was the one most deeply rooted in the social organisation, was inevitable. To help to maintain it the style of Handel was always available. It took not only musical skill of a high order but also a good deal of moral courage to try to run against the prevailing tide of taste. Those who tried did so at their own peril and were either shunted off into a siding, like the Wesleys, promoted to official positions where they could do no harm, like Attwood, or consigned to an early grave, like Storace. As has been seen England was not short of infant prodigies and the career of him who was in some ways the most prodigious of all, William Crotch (1775–1847), shows how hard it was for any but the toughest of plants to survive.

Indigenous Musical Forms

Crotch was the son of a Norwich carpenter who combined musical interests with his practical skills and built a chamber organ for domestic use. It was recorded by Crotch himself that he played in public, in Norwich, in February 1778. At the beginning of November in that year he was taken to Cambridge 'where he played on all the College and Church organs to the astonishment of the gentlemen of the University.'[1]

[1] *London Magazine*, April 1779.

A month later he was in London, where he was heard by J. C. Bach and commanded to appear at Buckingham House. Quite properly he played *God Save the King*,[1] as well as other tunes. The infant Crotch was kept in London for some months and then taken on tour through the British Isles. He was given full publicity treatment, it being noted in the advertisements how he played *God Save Great George our King* and the affecting air, *Hope, thou nurse of young desire*, at the age of two years and three weeks. Crotch was dragged from town to town, appearing in public houses for two hours each morning and 'in the evening, if desired'. He also included in his programmes 'Voluntaries of his own composing'. In January 1782 there were newspaper reports that he had died. They were, however, false. 'Master Crotch', corrected the *Leeds Intelligencer* of 15 January, 'is *not* dead as mentioned in several papers, but alive and in good health at Ayr in Scotland'.

It was about this time that Crotch visited Leicester, where he was taken to meet William Gardiner. 'He was brought first to our house', wrote Gardiner, 'and played upon the piano-forte as he sat upon his mother's knee. At that time there were not more than two or three piano-fortes in the town or neighbourhood; mine was esteemed a good one, made by John Pholman, I suppose in Germany, and before any were made in England. Upon this instrument Crotch first exhibited his extraordinary talent in Leicester. I laid before him Handel's organ concertos, which, without difficulty, he played at sight. He was a delicate, lively boy, and, next to music, was most fond of chalking upon the floor'.[2]

When he was ten years old Crotch played to old Stanley who patted his head and expressed the hope that one day he would conduct a Handel Commemoration. A year later the boy was in Cambridge, now employed as assistant to John Randall and playing the organ regularly at King's and Trinity Colleges, and Great St. Mary's Church. His oratorio, *The Captivity of Judah*, was performed in Cambridge at the end of the summer term of 1789. A year later he succeeded Thomas Norris as organist of Christ Church, Oxford, and in 1797, on the death of Philip Hayes, he became Professor of Music. It would be unkind to say that that was the end of William Crotch, but in many ways it was. His creative talent dwindled into glees, anthems, a handful of keyboard pieces, and a dreary oratorio, *Palestine*, from which one chorus 'Lo, star-led chiefs' has survived into present-day cathedral service-lists.

Crotch, like Wesley, was an energetic lecturer (his crying-down of

[1] '. . . it had not only been often played to him on the organ by his father, but has been most frequently administered to him as a narcotic during the first year of his life.' Dr. Charles Burney in *Account of an Infant Musician*, read before the Royal Society, 18 February 1779, published in *Philosophical Transactions* for 1779, vol. XXIX, 1780, p. 183.

[2] op. cit., I, p. 33.

Mozart was deplored by Burney) and prepared to cover a good deal of ground. Since he did not confine himself to select, university audiences but broke into the field of popular education, at the Royal Institution, he achieved something of value in respect of the stimulation of extra-mural studies. He was a member of the Philharmonic Society and in 1822 was elected Principal of the newly founded Royal Academy of Music, a post which he held until his death. But the composer that was in Crotch never came to life.[1]

The insularity of British music is best shown in the glees (and allied works for male voices) which were the hard core of Georgian middle-class musical experience. Thousands were composed and not one single composer whose name survives from that age avoided adding his contribution to the pool. The glee, a source of social contentment in public houses throughout the kingdom, was an agreeable miniature form, ideally requiring a neat ear for melody, an eye for correct harmonies, a sense of 'expression', and some appreciation of English literature. It called for competence but not genius. Thus there was a large company of amiable composers whose talents were well suited to the requirements. Among professional musicians (other than those already named) who were admitted to the Catch Club, were the following, whose distinction lay almost solely in their ability to meet the demand for glees: Samuel Webbe, Charles and William Knyvett, R. J. S. Stevens, Samuel Harrison, Joseph Corfe, John Callcott, and William Horsley. Among amateurs the most prominent were Henry Harington and the Earl of Mornington.

In the middle ranges of musical life the best-known glee-composers were useful and influential and if as composers they did not push out far into the unknown they helped to stimulate a general competence in and respect for music itself. Samuel Webbe (1740–1816), acknowledged as the founder of the 'modern' glee and its chief exemplar, left fatherless in infancy and motherless in his thirteenth year—one year after he had been apprenticed to a cabinet-maker, pursued his self-education so zealously that he became fluent in Latin, French, Italian, Spanish, Czech, and Hebrew. As a craftsman he was one day required to repair a harpsichord. Promptly he learned to play it and, having given demonstration of his capacity to play 'by ear', he enlisted the aid of Charles Barbandt, organist of the Bavarian Embassy Chapel, who was prepared to give him lessons. Webbe's only professional appointment was that of organist of the Sardinian Embassy Chapel, for which he composed a number of simple Masses. Otherwise he was devoted to the affairs of the Catch Club—of which he

[1] The Norwich and Norfolk Record Office holds 14 vols. by Dr. A. H. Mann relative to a proposed biography of Crotch (Ms. 11200–11 and 13) as well as musical Mss., water-colours (Crotch was an accomplished artist), letters, pocket-books, and memoirs.

became Secretary in 1794—and of the Glee Club[1]—to which he acted as Librarian. A prolific composer, Webbe was esteemed for his imaginative handling of the glee and for his competence in catch and canon. He was of an amiable disposition and was rare in the profession of music in that he had no enemies. His son, Samuel (*c.* 1770–1843), followed in his father's footsteps and, also achieving high place among glee-composers, eventually settled in Liverpool. There he was organist of St. Nicholas's Church and of the Roman Catholic Chapel in Toxteth Park. The Knyvetts were a musical family over several generations. The first to reach a moderate eminence was Charles (1752–1822), a native of Norfolk, who became Gentleman and subsequently organist of the Chapel Royal. He was an alto singer and in conjunction with the famous Handel tenor Samuel Harrison (1760–1812) established the Vocal Concerts in 1791. Knyvett's elder son, also Charles (1773–1852) and a pupil of Webbe, was for many years organist of St. George's Church, Hanover Square, while William (1779–1856), the younger son, became, like his father, a Gentleman of the Chapel Royal. He also was appointed composer to that foundation. Richard Stevens (1757–1837) was a chorister of St. Paul's and subsequently organist of the Temple Church and of the Charterhouse, and Gresham Professor of Music. Joseph Corfe (1740–1820) was not only organist of Salisbury Cathedral but also an excellent singer (he was principal tenor in the Handel Commemoration of 1784) and a pioneer educationist, issuing popular editions of the works of Handel and Purcell as well as treatises in singing and on the art of thorough bass. Corfe was succeeded at Salisbury by his son Arthur.

John Watt Callcott (1766–1821), son of a Kensington builder, was yet another self-educated musician who held various organistships in London. Industrious and thorough, Callcott took the craft of composition seriously (in 1791 he applied to Haydn for lessons) and was highly regarded in glee-loving circles. His general knowledge of music was wide and he was among those chosen to lecture at the Royal Institution. Encouraged in his early years by Benjamin Cooke and Samuel Arnold, Callcott developed his interest in choral music through the Academy of Ancient Music. A founder-member of the Glee Club, he was one of its leading composers. William Horsley (1774–1858), a pupil of Theodore Smith, was befriended by Callcott (whose eldest daughter he married) and succeeded him as organist of the Asylum for Female Orphans. Horsley held other organistships, was a founder member of the Phil-

1 Arising out of meetings held in the home of Robert Smith, in St. Paul's Churchyard in 1783, this Club was founded in 1787. The members did not restrict themselves to the enjoyment only of glees but listened to Samuel Wesley playing Bach or, later, to Mendelssohn playing Mendelssohn. The Club was dissolved in 1857.

harmonic Society, organised a glee society euphoniously known as the Concentores Sodales, and composed, in addition to many glees, church music, pianoforte sonatas, and also three symphonies. One work of Horsley which merits notice—and performance—is a twelve-part anthem in, he supposed, the 'old English style'. If this is refined down mainly to dominant and tonic harmonies it shows a splendid appreciation of the medium and some striking placing of contrasted choral textures.[1] When Mendelssohn visited Britain in 1829 he became very friendly with the Horsley family.

All these musicians, excellent as they were, were painfully insular. Their own capabilities were consciously or unconsciously harnessed to the Handel myth so that techniques of the classical school were alien to them. The limitations of the glee, however, were such that the amateur—in other departments of music being rapidly outpaced by the professional—could still show an equal skill with his professional colleague. Thus Henry Harington (1727–1816), a physician of Bath (later Alderman and Mayor), was able to command a leading place among the popular composers of the period. His interest in music was aroused when he was an undergraduate at Oxford, where William Hayes ran a catch club. In 1784 a Harmonic Society was inaugurated in Bath[2] to which Harington was both Composer and Physician. Garrett Colley Wellesley (1735–81), created Earl of Mornington in 1760, appeared from a castle in Co. Meath as a small boy unusually talented in playing the violin, the harpsichord, and the organ. His gifts were such that it was put out that when in due course he approached Thomas Roseingrave and Geminiani for help in composition they sent him away with the flattering information that he already knew all that they could teach him. Wellesley graduated as M.A. from Trinity College, Dublin, and in 1757 he established an 'Academy of Music' in the city. To the choral section of this society women were admitted—an unusual concession for those times. In 1764 Mornington was elected the first Professor of Music in his University, which conferred on him (and also on the Rt. Hon. Charles Gardiner) the degree of Doctor of Music. Mornington divided his time between London (where he was much concerned for the musical welfare of his young kinsmen, Samuel and Charles Wesley) and Dublin. He composed anthems for St. Patrick's Cathedral, Dublin (for many years the pious custom prevailed of commencing all services with a work by Mornington), and glees, catches, and so-called madrigals.

The glee and catch societies aimed at maintaining an English tradition. The madrigal impulse was still—albeit faintly—alive when they

[1] *Hosannah! to the Son of David* (1797, revised 1837), B.M. Add. Ms. 23914.
[2] There were also a Bath York House Catch Club and a Bath Catch Club.

came to be established, and the point should again be made that the madrigal never quite died out. Its outlines were simplified and rationalised in the seventeenth-century catch and in such easily singable trifles as the near-madrigals of Ravenscroft (see p. 194), and it was from the popularity of both that eighteenth-century composers were able to draw. One of the prime functions of the Noblemen's Catch Club was to temper choral enthusiasm with refinement. The scabrous words in which Henry Purcell and Wise had delighted were—officially at any rate—out. Refinement was now often allied with scholarship and, as has been seen, an interest in the arts of a bygone age was an established mark of gentility. The glee composers therefore ransacked British poetry and the principal collections show a wide range of selection. There were, for example, settings of lyrics by Shakespeare, Ben Jonson, Philip Sidney, John Lilye, Nicholas Breton, John Dryden, William Shenstone, and Robert Burns. Callcott, whose antiquarian interests led him to an abortive scheme for a *Musical Dictionary*, was inspired by the works of Ossian and Thomas Chatterton—even though little of inspiration is apparent in his settings. He and Stevens also made extensive use of Evans's *Collection of Ballads* (1784). Stevens, however, was the notable Shakespearian and among his works are settings of *Ye spotted snakes*, *Sigh no more ladies*, *Blow, blow thou winter wind*, *It was a lover and his lass*, and, the most evocative and popular, *The cloud-capt towers*. Collaterally with this literary exercise went the re-copying and re-issue of many genuine madrigals. None was more assiduous in this than Edmund Thomas Warren (d. 1794; later known as Warren-Horne), Secretary of the Noblemen's Catch Club from its inception until 1794. Warren made copies of many madrigals for the Ancient Concerts[1] and in 1790 published a set of *Madrigals for 3 Voices and revised, corrected, and put into score*, while other examples appeared in Warren's famous collection (625 numbers) of *Catches, Canons, Glees*, etc. which was published serially between 1763 and 1794. Other collections intended for glee clubs (and their guests on Ladies' Nights), such as *Catches, Canons, and Glees* (J. Sibbald, Edinburgh, 1780) and *Amusement for the Ladies* (Longman and Broderip, *c.* 1800) spread the opportunity for the general singing of madrigals. In 1811 the Madrigal Society offered a prize for the best piece written 'after the manner of madrigals by Bennett, Wilbye, Morley, Ward, Weelkes, Marenzio . . .'. The first prize-winner (1813) was William Beale, for *Awake, sweet morn.*

The glee was confined by the prevailing standards of middle-class taste and correctness. It was further confined by being essentially for male voices (though through the cult of the male alto a reasonably wide range was practicable). The best of the glees—those, for instance, of Webbe

[1] Mss. now in R.C.M. Library.

and Stevens—are fluent and graceful but with the music rarely showing more than a superficial connection with the chosen text. Humour now qualified by propriety penetrated some glees—as Callcott's famous and once topical *Have you Sir John Hawkins' hist'ry?*, but sensibility easily declined into sentimentality. Spofforth's *Hail, smiling morn*, the harbinger of every part-song for a hundred years, is the classic instance. From Spofforth came two sets of quasi-glee settings of nursery rhymes; cosy, but by no means unattractive pieces collected into *The Newest Christmas Box, containing a variety of Bagatelles . . . for Juvenile Amusement.*[1] The smoothness of the typical glee permeated almost all branches of British music during the Victorian era, and the male-voice pieces currently popular in competitive festivals and Eisteddfodau are in direct line of descent. There is already an ominous familiarity about the 'sturdy' English melodic style, thus reduced [Ex. 12], as also about the teetering elegance of this [Ex. 13].

12.

13.

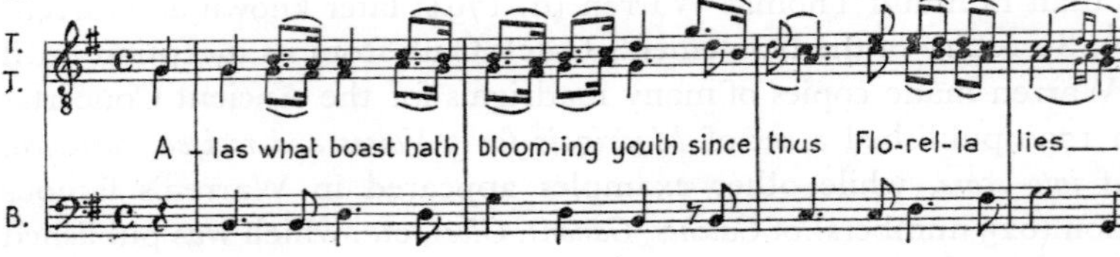

There is an irrelevance in such music. Irrelevancy became the principal demerit of British music for many years to come.

Although the glee—which was to be found in ensemble numbers of British operas of the late eighteenth century—was an entirely localised form, its development had some significance in a wider setting. It popularised the cult of sensibility and in so doing founded that of sentimentality. Harmony *per se* was upgraded and a special value was attached to the

[1] Cf. James Hook's similar *A Christmas Box containing the following Bagatelles . . .* (J. Bland). Spofforth also composed *The Twelfth Cake, a Juvenile Amusement*, consisting of little ballads, which would find some to appreciate its didactic prettiness in infant schools of today. It deserves its place at least in the history of music in education. So too does *The Child's Introduction to Thorough Bass, in Conversations of a Fortnight, between a Mother and her Daughter, of ten years old* (London, Baldwin, Cradock, and Joy, 1819).

sonorous values of chords and chordal progressions. Side by side with this went the extension of the influence of the pianoforte. This took place on two planes: of manufacture, and of composition. The former was particularly connected with the name of Broadwood.

The Pianoforte and its Composers

In the early part of the eighteenth century a Swiss cabinet-maker, Burkhardt Tschudi, set up in business in London. Having joined forces with a harpsichord maker he successfully established himself independently in this field. In 1761 a Scotsman, John Broadwood (1732–1812), became one of his employees. Following a familiar precedent Broadwood married his employer's daughter and in due course became principal of the firm. 1773 the firm was in business as Shudi and Broadwood. In 1795 it became John Broadwood and Son. In 1773 Broadwood, taking the instruments of the London-based Johann Zumpe as model, turned his attention to the making of square pianos. Zumpe had been successful with these on the market for a decade. Broadwood, who had a talent for invention, was even more successful, for he was able to improve on his predecessors' technological methods. By 1781 he had made his first grand piano and three years later he patented the damper and piano pedals. In 1788 he departed from a harpsichord principle by doing away with a continuous long bridge and by introducing a separate bridge to carry the bass strings. Broadwood's improvements were universally adopted.

Up to 1776 Broadwood had been assisted by Robert Stodart I (d. 1797?). In that year Stodart founded his own business and contributed to the development of the grand piano. He it was who combined harpsichord and piano actions into a two-manual instrument. His 'new invented sort of instrument, or *grand pianoforte*, with an octave swell, and to produce fine tones, together or separate, at the option of the performer', aroused much interest in 1777. Stodart was succeeded by his son William and in 1795 William was granted a patent for a 'new invented *upright grand pianoforte*, of the form of a book-case'. This represented the final domestication of the piano, and a growing tendency to regard it as a piece of furniture was reflected in the variations played on the 'book-case' motif. The firm of Stodart made admirable grand pianos—a number of which are still in use—and in 1820 developed the revolutionary principle of metallic bracing. In the previous year Robert Stodart II (nephew of Robert I) emigrated to America where in partnership with William Dubois he founded the firm of Dubois and Stodart on Broadway, New York.

The official *coup de grace* was given to the harpsichord in 1795, for in that year its place in the orchestra for the performance of the King's Birthday Ode was surrendered to the grand piano. In October of the same year the piano was publicly heard in Leeds for the first time, when David Lawton, organist of the parish church and conductor of many subscription concerts, played an unspecified piano concerto. That the piano advanced in public favour was due to the pertinacity and publicity campaigns of the manufacturers on the one hand, but to the interest of players and composers on the other. From the early 1770's it had been discreet to advertise suitable keyboard music as for harpsichord or piano, and the convention continued until the end of the century. Among the pioneers of pianoforte technique the most important was Muzio Clementi (1752–1832).

The claim of Clementi to be considered as an Englishman is as strong as Lully's to be counted as a Frenchman. He was fourteen years old when an English visitor to Rome noticed his musical talent and sought and received permission to take him back to England. This visitor was Peter Beckford, a sportsman, a dilettante, and nephew of William Beckford, of Fonthill Abbey fame. Young Clementi lived with Peter Beckford in Dorsetshire for four years, during which time his studies were supervised by his patron. From Peter's care Clementi passed to William's and three years more of study were undertaken at Fonthill. By 1773 he was ready to appear in public, being first advertised as 'the young Roman'. In 1777 he became cembalist to the Italian Opera in London and four years later his reputation as a piano virtuoso brought invitations to various European cities. In Vienna Clementi met Haydn and, at the instigation of Joseph II, took part in a competition with Mozart. Clementi admired Mozart's *cantabile* style of playing. For his part Mozart disapproved of Clementi's merely 'mechanical' efficiency—the result, it was later said, of playing on English instruments.

For twenty years, except for a visit to Paris in 1785, Clementi worked in London: as conductor, performer, teacher, and businessman. The ablest of his English pupils was J. B. Cramer.[1] But the most celebrated of all his protégés was the Irishman, John Field (1782–1837).[2] Clementi was in business as a musical instrument dealer and manufacturer and publisher, and, after initial disappointments and set-backs, brought himself to a state of enviable prosperity. In 1802 he set off again on a European tour, taking with him his apprentice and pupil Field. The tour took in Paris, Vienna, and St. Petersburg—where Field remained. Back in Germany in 1807 Clementi gave lessons to Ludwig Berger and Meyerbeer

[1] Son of Willem, and founder of the pianoforte and music-publishing house of J. B. Cramer & Co.

[2] See pp. 463–6.

and renewed his acquaintance with Haydn. He also met Beethoven and made provision for his firm to publish certain of his works. Although he made several more journeys to the Continent (adding Moscheles to his list of pupils), Clementi, who was one of the founders of the Philharmonic Society, spent the last twenty years of his life in England, dedicating them principally to composition and to the conduct of his business undertakings. He died in Evesham, in Worcestershire, to which he had retired, and was buried in the Cloisters of Westminster Abbey. Clementi & Co. was taken over on Clementi's death by Collard and Collard, which in turn was eventually absorbed into the Chappell Piano Company.

Clementi was a seminal influence in the whole development of music. He was the first composer fully to understand the stylistic implications of the instrument and the first consistent master of the sonata principle as applied to pianoforte music. Brought up to play Scarlatti, he so altered the course of the sonata that Beethoven gratefully acknowledged his genius, and insisted on the invaluable quality of Clementi's Studies, of which the most famous and most widely used were the set of one hundred designated as *Gradus ad Parnassum* (1817).

As a composer Clementi ranged widely. A solid contrapuntal technique—which gives a distinctive resoluteness to his surviving symphonies—is to be seen in the fugues of *Trois Sonates . . . et Trois Fugues* (op. 5), published in Paris in 1780. In these works—nearer to Schumann in spirit than to Bach—there is a marked individuality in the shaping of the subjects which is found to lead to dramatic exploitation of thematic material. In the first of these Fugues, in B flat major, there are sweeping tonality changes which range as far from base as D flat minor. Not perhaps surprisingly Clementi was an excellent parodist, as he demonstrated effectively, and sometimes with tongue in cheek, in his *Musical Characteristics, or a Collection of Preludes and Cadences for harpsichord or pianoforte, composed in the style of Haydn, Kozeluch, Mozart, Sterkel, Vanhal,*[1] *and the Author* (op. 19, *c.* 1790). Clementi wrote sonatas in the approved manner, with accompaniment for violin and violoncello, but when he had taken full measure of the capacity of the piano, and his own to deal with it, he threw aside this convention—and emancipated the piano. Even in his earliest works, the charming *Six Sonatas* (op. 1, 1780) dedicated to Peter Beckford, there is evidence of a maturity of thought, and, *pace* Mozart, one notes the frequent direction to play *legato*.

Clementi amplified the sonata by raising the status of the 'development' section, which in his hands rarely descended to triviality but never

[1] A Vanhal Sonata printed by Storace ends with a *Rondo all'Inglese*, a tribute to English popular taste by a Viennese composer (an acquaintance of Burney) who enjoyed great esteem in Britain.

overstayed its welcome. So far as proportion was concerned Clementi had a truly classical touch. A precise writer, he discouraged extempore ornamentation (as Avison had done before him) and in op. XII, No. 1 he puts the appropriate warning signal—*senza ornamenti*—at one point. Above all Clementi penetrated the poetic nature of the piano. Thus he holds the end of the exposition of the first movement of op. 3, No. 1[1] in mid-air [Ex. 14]. His large-scale slow movements are not only poetic

14.

but also instinct with power. [Ex. 15] The reason for Beethoven's appre-

15.

ciation of his stature may also be gauged by the opening of the F major Sonata printed in Storace's *Collection* I. [Ex. 16] The popularisation of

16.

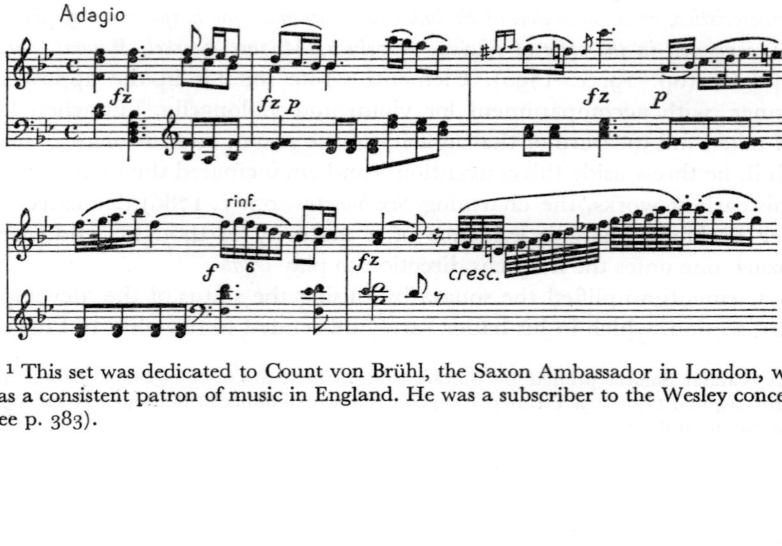

[1] This set was dedicated to Count von Brühl, the Saxon Ambassador in London, who was a consistent patron of music in England. He was a subscriber to the Wesley concerts (see p. 383).

the piano meant exactly what it said and Clementi (whose business was to sell instruments and music) noted Broderip and Wilkinson's issue of *Twelve Original German Waltzes*, by Mozart. These had separate accompanying parts for tambourine, triangle, and other percussion, and Broderip and Wilkinson had on show 'also an elegant Assortment of Tambourines, Triangles, Cymbals, etc., made light, for the Ladies'. Clementi was not going to be left behind in this explosion of a female percussion band movement and his op. 37 Waltzes of 1797 are full of original good humour, and some complexity. In the fourth of the set, in G major, Clementi interjects stormy, and syncopated, sections in G minor, B flat, and E flat, and in the ninth he runs amok with nail-dangerous *glissandi*—ten times the score is marked 'sliding with one finger'. The waltz was well established in Britain by the turn of the century, other collections coming from A. Betts, J. Dale, T. A. Rawlings, and James Sanderson, who inscribed a set to the Princess of Wales.

The Spirit of Change

Broadly speaking the general effect of conscious romanticism was to release a spirit of nonconformity. Since, however, British composers who held official posts were constrained by their environment to side with the conformists, the main stream of music flowed along without dramatic interruption to its progress. Music, in fact, was beginning to be a thing apart—a polite recreation, or a formal ritual necessity, in no way to be connected with the way of life of the effective guardians of the soul of the nation. Concert life in the provinces, as will appear in the next chapter, became a second-hand version of that in London and audiences lost their capacity for participation and independent criticism. None the less there was another side to the picture. Nonconformity showed during the last years of the eighteenth century in two ways: in a powerful surge of effort by the working-classes, and by a realisation of regionalism and local patriottism. Behind both lay politically or socially inconvenient influences that in due course were turned aside having for the most part been diverted by the drearier canons of good taste.

Public concerts as established during the eighteenth century, according to a familiar principle of evolution, derived from those hitherto sponsored by the nobility. In due course, when the working class became conscious of a sense of collective responsibility and indeed of latent power, the process of evolution extended further. The chapels and churches of the industrial north had their choirs and their bands. Their repertoires included not only psalms and hymns but also the choruses of Handel, and the anthems of Croft, Greene, Kent, and even Purcell and Boyce. There developed numerous music clubs and from them a great deal of the strength of the nineteenth-century choral tradition in northern England stemmed. Thus: 'In the parish of Eccles about 1792 was formed the quarterly meetings, or club, of the choirs of Eccles Church, Monton Chapel, Ellenbrook Chapel, and Swinton Chapel, and at each place they formed a Monthly Club for the practice of vocal and instrumental music, principally oratorios of Handel, Haydn, and other eminent composers. At the quarterly meetings it was arranged what should be performed at the next meetings.'[1]

Such clubs became widespread and were the source not only of enthusiasm for musical activity but also of accurate training, particularly in sight-reading. Handloom weavers, spinners, colliers, public-house keepers, clerks, schoolmasters, parish officials, an occasional village doctor, and their wives combined together to furnish their communities with the best music that lay within their capacity. Picked singers (and sometimes players) from these local clubs were invited to participate in the larger regional, oratorio festivals at Manchester, Liverpool, Birmingham, Chester, York, Newcastle, and in the cities of the Three Choirs. If one wished to refute the accusation that the English were unmusical one could do worse than choose the following incident:

'Mr. James Cordwell . . . and several other Lancashire chorus singers, were engaged to sing at a festival at St. Nicholas's Church, at Newcastle upon Tyne; Mrs. Shepley and some other female singers were engaged to sing there. There were no railways then, only one stage coach, and all the seats in this were occupied. They started [from Swinton] about six o'clock on Sunday night. These veterans said there was nothing for it but walking, consequently they set off and walked all Sunday night and got well into Yorkshire by day light on Monday morning. To make matters worse it rained most of the night. They called at a roadside inn, got breakfast, a good rest, and dried their clothes, then set off and walked all day and part of Monday night, and got to Newcastle about two o'clock on Wednesday afternoon, wet, weary, and tired. They went straight to St. Nicholas's Church, and found the principals, band, and chorus, rehearsing *Israel in Egypt*. The chorus was rather unsteady.' The Lancashire singers took their places, and then, 'the rehearsal went on afterwards to the conductor's entire satisfaction'.[2]

The musical education of the growing but as yet small industrial centres of the north was often in the hands of those who had come up to

[1] William Millington, *Sketches of Local Musicians and Musical Societies*, Pendlebury, 1884, p. 11.

[2] Millington, op. cit., p. 17, referring to the Festival of 1824.

authority by an unconventional route. In 1784 the Overseers of Breightmet, near Bolton, paid £1 1s. od. so that a blind boy, William Lonsdale, should have a violin. Lonsdale not only mastered the violin but also the Harmonious Musical Glasses,[1] and he developed a profitable turn in which 'without any assistance whatever' he performed 'on four musical instruments at once, in an astounding manner peculiar to himself, viz., the violin, double drum, French horn, and triangle; and also gave his imitations of the French horn and bassoon.'[2] Lonsdale, having acquired another technique, became organist of Bolton Parish Church; from which office he was dismissed when, confusing his functions, he played the congregation out of matins with a 'jig'. The radical side of provincial thought showed itself in the issue of political ballad:

Cursed be the wretch that bought and sold
And barters liberty for gold.
For when election is not free
In vain we boast of liberty.
And he who sells his single right
Would sell his country if he might . . .[3]

or parody:

God save great Thomas Paine,
His Rights of Man explain,
To ev'ry soul;
He makes the blind to see
What dupes and slaves they be,
And points out liberty,
From pole to pole.[4]

or in contemptuous comedy at the expense of metropolitan life:

I went to the Opera, I think 'twas the place;
I did not much like it, but I may want taste.
Such squeaking, and squatting, and dancing by name;
Talk of legs, I came out, I was really asham'd.[5]

The coming of a new social order meant that an older one was in decline.

[1] Among many inventors of armonica type instruments credit should be given here to the Irish eccentric, Richard Pockrich, whose musical glasses, 'as large as bells', were popular from 1744.

[2] J. C. Scholes, *Memorials of the Bolton Parish Church Organs*, Manchester/Bolton, 1882, p. 46.

[3] 'Carey's Wish', published in *The New Wigan Warbler, Fifty Choice Songs* (Wigan, 1818).

[4] *Civic Songs* (n.d., no imprint), Leeds Central Library, pp. 36–7.

[5] 'London Sights', in *The New Wigan Warbler*.

The token of decline was the movement (already established in literature) to collect folk-music. As has been seen, William Shield was a pioneer in this field, while George Thomson (1757–1851) of Edinburgh, collaborator with Burns and, in his commissions for arrangements, with Haydn, Beethoven, and Weber, busied himself in the issue of British folk music on a generous scale. So far as regional folk-music was concerned a notable example was *Popular Cheshire Melodies* (Chester, 1798), of which the editor was Edward Jones, harpist to the Prince of Wales, a friend of Burney, and one of that long line of Welsh harpers who strove to preserve the integrity of their own tradition while enriching that of their neighbours.

Edward Jones (1752–1824),[1] *Bardd y Brenin*, published his own versions of Welsh music[2] and was a prominent figure at the Eisteddfodau at Corwen and Bala in 1789, in Carmarthenshire in 1819, and in Wrexham in 1820. During the reign of George III St. David's Day was celebrated at Court, and in London there was a flourishing Gwyneddigion Society to which the organisers of the Llangollen Eisteddfod (January 1798) applied for support. The London Welshmen, among whom were many of strong radical and nationalist opinion, were prepared to back the national festival, but only if it were run in a more business-like way. Contents (both in poetry and music) must be announced in advance, and so too must subjects for competition. It was agreed to advertise arrangements and conditions in the Chester and Shrewsbury newspapers. The Bala Eisteddfod of September 1789 was floated on London subscriptions.

Respectability, however, soon settled on the affair. The vital impulses that inspired Morgan John Rhys, editor of the near-republican *Y Cylchgrawn Cymraeg*, dried up and were only kept alive in occasional pamphlets and popular ballads. Many of these reflected opposition to military service and to the methods of the press-gang. By 1821 the Eisteddfod (held this year in Caernarvon) was patronised by the nobility and the dignitaries of the Church. The Marquis of Anglesey gave a speech. There was a 'discourse on the History of Music in Wales'—and the way to sing was demonstrated by the Bath Harmonic Society. There was penillion singing; but there was also oratorio.

The romantic properties of Welsh culture were realised by Samuel Arnold, whose four-movement overture to James Boaden's *Cambro-Britons* (March, Andante, Andante, Rondo) includes two harps in the second and fourth movements, and 'Union pipes' (bagpipes) and harp in the third. The orchestration also included triangle and tambourines, while

[1] Jones (not to be confused with Edward Jones [1768–1813], of Caerphilly, harpist and pupil of Sackville Gwynne, Glanbrân, Llandovery) left numerous manuscripts, literary and musical, now in the possession of the City of Cardiff Library (Ms. 4.130); see Tecwyn Ellis, *Edward Jones, Bardd y Brenin* (in Welsh), University of Wales Press, Cardiff, 1957.

[2] E.g. *Cynghansaid Cymry*, 'Old Welsh Crowd', with twenty-four variations (*c.* 1780).

the Land of Song was memorialised in a 'Chorus of Angels', accompanied by two flutes and bassoon. In the 'Scottish or Caledonian' overture to *Love and Money*, a pastiche, Arnold included the air of *Ar hyd y nos*.

The harp, too, had symbolic significance in Ireland.[1] The national music revival that culminated—somewhat ingloriously—in the drawing-room confections of Tom Moore (aided by Sir John Stevenson), developed first within a turbulent and heroic movement for national independence and unity. This urge began when Dean Swift, a member of the ruling class, took the part of the dispossessed and the oppressed, and assumed formidable proportions when Protestant generosity of spirit, and the leadership of Grattan and Flood, led to the formation of the Irish Volunteers and to the inauguration of an independent Irish Parliament in 1782. 'Ireland', said Grattan, 'is now a nation. In that character I hail her, and bowing in her august presence I say *Esto perpetuum*.' But the question of the Irish Catholics, the just but fruitless demands for recognition of their civic rights, and the bitter determination of Wolfe Tone and the influence of French republicanism gave a new dimension to nationalism. 'The truth is, I hate the very name of England. I hated her before my exile and I will hate her always.' Thus there was a nation within a nation, and in 1798 a rising that resulted in the withdrawal of parliamentary independence from Dublin in 1800 and an Act of Union with Britain that gave the British complete control of the reins of administration again. Thereafter the cultural vigour of Dublin declined for many years and with it a musical tradition of long, if chequered, standing all but died.

Writing in 1766 Trydell said: '. . . there is no such Thing as *Irish* music since the Trade hath been opened with Italy, nor is it, I believe, settled whether there be such a Thing as a Taste for *Irish* Music among us: Except the little Remains, or Reliques preserved in the few *Irish* Airs, which have miraculously survived the Change of Times, and withstood the Power of Novelty, and Weight of Numbers, can make the Claim.' Moreover—speaking for the small group of partly expatriate people of quality in Dublin—'The very kind Reception Music hath met from us, proves beyond Contradiction that we have a Taste, and this too for *Italian* Music. Every Gentleman among us as truly judging of *Italian* music and Performances, as if he had made the Tour. This is a good Step towards Imitation of the same, wherever we shall have it in our Power to compose . . . Why may not an *Irish* Author express his own sense, as I may say, in *Italian* Language: that is, compose his Music on the Principles of the *Italian* Taste, or any other he may choose to imitate, or possibly which

[1] Irish folk-music was occasionally exploited by composers: e.g. Wagenseil's *A Lesson for Harpsichord or Pianoforte . . . to which is added a favorite Irish air, Gramachree Molly with Variations* (C. & S. Thompson, London, *c.* 1770).

he may invent?'[1] That, broadly speaking, was the way of Mornington, of Stevenson, and of the abler Philip Cogan, Doctor of Music of Trinity College, and pupil of Clementi. Cogan walked so far over to accommodate his talents to the taste of English patrons that, in the Rondo of the Second Sonata of his op. 7, he introduced the melody of Shield's 'The Ploughboy'. It may be that John Field did 'express his own sense' in a foreign idiom; but by the time he did so he was, from an Irish point of view, hardly an Irishman at all.

Trydell, resident and isolated in the metropolitan and superficially brilliant life of Dublin, was unaware of Irish music. That is, of the tradition maintained by the itinerant harpers. The classical master of the Irish harp was Turlough Carolan (d. 1738). But across the middle years of the century the tradition was maintained by Denis Hempson (1695–1807),[2] Echlin O'Kane, Catherine Martin, and Arthur O'Neill (1734–1816). Hempson and O'Kane played in Ireland and in Scotland and before the Young Pretender. During the period of renascent nationalism the harpists, Catholic and Protestant and from north and south alike, were a rallying point for political sentiment and the organisation of harp contests served a dual purpose. These, which were counterparts to the Welsh Eisteddfod, took place at Granard, Co. Longford, in 1781, 1782 and 1785, and in 1792 the most famous of all was held in Belfast. Among those present at the Belfast gathering was Edward Bunting (1773–1843), who drew this picture of the then venerable Hempson, who

'realised the antique picture drawn by Cambrensis and Galilei,[3] for he played with long crooked nails, and in his performance, "the tinkling of the small wires under the deep notes of the bass" was particularly thrilling, took the attention of the Editor with a degree of interest which he can never forget. He was the only one who played the very old—the aboriginal—music of the country; and this he did in a style of such finished excellence as persuaded the Editor that the praises of the old Irish harp in Cambrensis, Fuller, and others, instead of being, as the detractors of the country are fond of asserting, ill-considered and indiscriminate, were in reality no more than a just tribute to that admirable instrument and its then professors'.[4]

Inspired by Hempson and the other harpists, Bunting, who owed a great deal to Arthur O'Neill,[5] determined to collect the ancient airs of

[1] Op. cit., pp. V–VI (Dedication to Rt. Hon. John Ponsonby, Speaker of the Irish House of Commons).

[2] Hempson really did live to this ripe old age.

[3] Bunting refers later (p. 30) to Vincenzo Galilei's statement, derived from Dante, in *Dialogues on Ancient and Modern Music*, that the harp was brought to Italy from Ireland.

[4] *The Ancient Music of Ireland*, Dublin, 1840, p. 3.

[5] Master of the first Belfast Harp Society, 1807–13.

Ireland and of the Irish language. He did valiant service and was indeed the first thorough field-worker in the British Isles. He issued three important volumes of national music (with English words) in 1796, 1809, and 1840. It was largely on Bunting's researches that Moore based his much more famous *Irish Melodies* (1808–34); but Moore, the one-time rebel, was seduced from his first allegiance by the blandishments of London society and his version of the national melodies, domesticated by his polished lyrics and the correct harmonisation of Stevenson and, later, of Henry Bishop, sailed into popularity under false pretences. By this time the Irish language was practically proscribed, the country was once again an English province, and the opportunity to renew the whole concept of music in Ireland was lost. John Stevenson composed glees, and music for operas that were played in Dublin, was knighted by the Lord Lieutenant in 1803[1], and eleven years later was appointed as organist and musical director at Dublin Castle. The last state of Irish music was infinitely worse than the first.

1 'By the College presented with a Doctor's degree,
By the State dubb'd a Knight—for composing a glee.'
Concert Strictures revised, anon., Dublin, 1805.

II

Mass Culture

Idealism

A NATIONAL music, of course, does not exist. What is considered as such is the distillation of contrasting conventions into a fresh essence of greater or lesser palatability or distinction. So long as British music—with its strong vocal inclinations—kept Italian procedures in sight, the consequences were as often as not more rather than less beneficial to composers. Until halfway through the Georgian era Italian influence was powerful. Then the Germans—led by the denationalised Handel—took over, and effective control of musical affairs in London, and in due course in parts of the provinces, often passed into the cousinly hands of the expatriate *Kapell-* or *Konzert-meister*. The British are not by temperament over-given to taking music seriously. For the better part of a century, however, they were obliged to do so. Now there is nothing wrong in taking music seriously; but it must be the right music, and for the right reasons. In the nineteenth century a strong dose of German idealism, prescribed by a dominant school of men of letters and periodically stirred by Queen Victoria and her Consort, was taken with increasingly uncomfortable after-effects. Rank and file musicians learned to swear by the German classics, and, when it was possible, went to Leipzig with the intention of becoming classics in their own right. None of them did. Some might have done, given reasonable conditions and encouragement, had they either gone elsewhere or else stayed at home. There is one exceptional case, that of Hugo Pierson, who went to Germany, stayed there, and became a German composer.

It is conventional to take a gloomy view of an age in which the top composer was William Sterndale Bennett, and in which Henry Smart was even counted as a composer at all. Yet an account of individual composers and their general lack of substantial achievement gives an inadequate picture. The nineteenth century, in one or two particulars, was an outstanding period in the history of British music. It was a revolutionary era. The top people finally lost the remains of cultural prestige and a large part of their power of control (vestiges of influence naturally lingered), and the prevailing standards of taste came from below rather than from above. During the reign of Queen Victoria, music became a matter of mass culture. The revolution, however, was a temperate one, and the fierce enthusiasm for musical experience that burst out in hundreds of towns and villages was modified by a sense of discrimination, implanted firstly by tradition and secondly by widening opportunities for education.

Tradition still meant one thing: oratorio. The one notable musician of Sheffield, Joseph Taylor (1730–1811), was remembered because 'he was the first public person who introduced oratorios into the town, and as a tribute of esteem, honourable both to the givers and receivers, performances of sacred music have yearly been presented for the benefit, the profits of which, in age, infirmity, and blindness, enabled him to live comfortably'.[1] Under the influence of oratorio local composers sprang up, one of them, John Hall, wrote *The Resurrection* and *The Redeemer* for performance in the Duke of Norfolk's Hospital Chapel. By now, however, there was a serious renewal of doubt concerning the propriety of oratorios, and by 1819 oratorio performances were excluded from St. Paul's Church—the venue for many years—'the use of the church having been refused by the perpetual curate, the Rev. Thomas Cotterill'.[2] Perpetual curates, and their superiors, exercised a strong control over popular taste and it strengthened as religious belief and moral virtue were seen as concomitant. Their views, reinforced by the views of Dissenters, gained wide circulation as education, first promoted as a charity, spread, and as popular journalism expanded.

It will have been realised that in the last two hundred years a convenient measure of the musical life of the British people is the reputation of Handel. Thus he emerges in the *Chester and North Wales Magazine* of April 1813:

'Some Thoughts upon Oratorios'

'The celebrated Handel was the first who introduced *Oratorios*, or sacred performances, at our theatres, two nights in each of the weeks during Lent; to the exclusion of historical or profane representations; and, *originally*, oratorio was confined, solely, to SACRED PIECES. The music of Handel is, indeed, admirably adapted to fill the mind with that sort of devotional rapture which, in the commemoration of the sufferings of our

1 *The Register and Chronological Account of Occurrences and Facts of Sheffield*. Sheffield, *c*. 1830.
2 ib.

blessed Lord and Saviour, as men, we ought to admire, and, as Christians, to *feel*. There can scarcely, however, be any thing more improper, than the *melange* which is now dignified with the appellation of SACRED MUSIC; but what would make an infidel *shudder*, can hardly make a christian *blush*. At one time, the audience is presented with "I know that my Redeemer liveth", and, at another, with the wandering transitions of a female maniac —with "Pious Orgies", and the "Soldier tired"—"Holy, Holy, Lord God Almighty", and "Mirth, admit me of thy Crew"—"Lord of Eternity", —and "Hush ye pretty warbling choir"—"Hallelujah", and the "Prince unable"—thus are the public alternately amused with a celebration of Omnipotence, and a song of amorous dalliance; the attributes of the Deity, and a Bacchanalian rhapsody; Te Deum and L'Allegro; the sufferings of the MESSIAH, and the ravings of *Mad Bess*.—If this is piety, what is irreligion? If it is solemnity, what is ridicule? If it is reverence, what is contempt? Is it thus, then, we are to consider HIM "who covereth himself with light as with a garment; who stretcheth out the heavens like a curtain; who layeth the beams of his chambers in the waters; who maketh the clouds his chariot; who walketh upon the wings of the wind?" Is the Majesty of Heaven to be insulted by a derisive eulogy, which does the same honor to Alexander as to the ALMIGHTY; to Acis and Galatea, as to the REDEEMER OF MANKIND; mingling, in the same strain of preposterous celebration, the heathen mythology and the Christian faith? Let us no more boast of the suppositious reformation of manners and principles in this country: of the progress of religion; and of the advantages of divine revelation; when we can thus impudently offer that insult to the MOST HIGH GOD, which the unenlightened worshippers, in the rudest ages of Pagan barbarity, would not have dared to pay to the manufacture of his own ingenuity.'

The general effect on would-be oratorio-mongers was discouraging, but not sufficiently discouraging to prevent some who should have known better from writing works which were in conformity with these sentiments. This was the result of idealism misapplied.

On the other hand there was a stream of idealism, touched off by pragmatic Romanticism, that proved much more beneficial.

A great deal of the musicality of the British was at all times siphoned off into literature. Particularly was this the case at the end of the eighteenth and the beginning of the nineteenth centuries. Burns, himself half a musician, was a direct inspiration to musical Europe. Another farm-labourer turned poet who inclined to music was John Clare, whose manuscript collection of popular tunes—to play on the fiddle—is in the Northampton Library.[1] Coleridge, Shelley, Keats and Leigh Hunt were

[1] Ms. 12.

virtually within the province of music and (together with Charles Lamb) they met at the point at which music for the people became a soluble problem in musical logistics. They were all friends of Vincent Novello (1781–1861), to whom more than anyone the credit for the so-called 'Renaissance' at the end of the century was justly due.

Coleridge and Shelley were ardent folk-song enthusiasts. Of the latter Thomas Medwin wrote: 'Shelley was particularly fond of music and delighted in her [Mrs. Williams's] simple airs, some of which she had brought with her, in memory, from the East. For her were composed the exquisite lines, "I arise from dreams of thee", adapted to the celebrated Persian air sung by the Nautch girls, "*Tazee be tazee no be no*", and the Arietto which has been admirably set by an English composer,—"The *keen* stars are twinkling".'[1] Shelley was devoted to the music of Mozart, and when he went to the first London performance of *Don Giovanni*—he went as the guest of Thomas Love Peacock—his enthusiasm was great. For *Figaro* it was even greater. 'The profusion and unity attainable in opera by a genius exulting in his mastery enthralled Shelley, and he felt the quality expressed by Hazlitt: "Mozart's music should seem to come from the air, and return to it. Next time he set forth on a long poem his spirit would be aided by the spirit of this musician." '[2] Keats was similarly alive to Mozart. His school days under John Clarke at Enfield, however, brought him into contact with other composers:

> But many days have passed since last my heart
> Was warmed luxuriously by divine Mozart;
> By Arne delighted, or by Handel madden'd;
> Or by the song of Erin pierc'd and sadden'd:[3]

Leigh Hunt's thoughts on these and other composers were finally epitomised and epigrammatised in *The Fancy Concert* of 1845; his tribute to Vincent Novello in the *Sonnet to Henry Robertson, John Gattie and Vincent Novello* of 1818. The company that assembled in Novello's hospitable drawing-room in Oxford Street, Percy Street, or Shacklewell Green, shared a variety of interests—in drama, literature, water-colour painting, as well as music—and were politically persuaded to a conviction that works of art should be made generally available, particularly among the working classes. The publication of cheap editions of the classics of literature and the extension of interest in works, especially those of the Jacobean dramatists, that had hitherto been hardly more than dissertation material for scholars, inculcated into Novello the ambition to spread a wide musical

[1] *Life of Shelley*, 2 vols., London, 1847, II, p. 126. For Shelley's appreciation of folk-song see also *History of a Six Weeks' Tour*, 1817, p. 105.

[2] Edward Blunden, *Shelley*, London, 1946, p. 176.

[3] *Epistle to Charles Cowden Clarke*, September, 1816.

culture by similar means. His missionary zeal was encouraged by Leigh Hunt who, having occasion to write to him in 1817 concerning the purchase of a piano for Shelley, observed: 'I would have Mozart as common in good libraries as Shakespeare and Spenser, and prints from Raphael.'

New Publishing Ventures

Novello, the son of an Italian emigrant, was a pupil of Samuel Webbe at the Sardinian Embassy Chapel. In 1797 he became organist of the Portuguese Embassy Chapel, where his term of office was distinguished by the first English performances of the Masses of Haydn and Mozart. An all-round musician (he was able to read full scores at sight at the piano), Novello conducted the Italian Opera Company at the Pantheon, helped to found the Philharmonic Society—which he also conducted on occasion—and played the organ at the Westminster Abbey Festival of 1834. At this festival his daughter Clara (who in 1832 had taken part in the first English performance of Beethoven's *Missa Solemnis* at Thomas Alsegar's house) made her first oratorio appearance in London.

A dearth of music suitable for liturgical use in the Catholic Church led Novello thoroughly to investigate the library of his friend Christian Ignatius Latrobe—a Moravian minister with many German contacts who was host to Haydn in 1791—from which he emerged not only with scores of Haydn and Mozart, but also of Pergolesi, Jommelli and Caldara. In 1811 Novello, finding no publisher to accommodate him, went ahead on his own and independently published *A Collection of Sacred Music*. In this the organ part was realised and not presented as formerly only with figured bass. There followed: in 1816, *Twelve Easy Masses*; in 1822, *The Evening Service*, etc.; and in 1825 his greatest editorial achievement—the five volumes of *The Fitzwilliam Music*, which were eulogised by Charles Lamb in an unsigned article in *The New Monthly Magazine*. Between 1826 and 1832 Novello published *Purcell's Sacred Music*, some of which would otherwise have been lost for ever in the fire at York Minster in 1829. In that year the Novellos made their celebrated expedition to Salzburg,[1] to present Mozart's sister with a sum of money collected from English admirers of the master. During their visit they also met Mozart's widow and the whole occasion set Novello's favourite pupil, Edward Holmes, on the course that was to lead him to the composition of the first English biography of Mozart.

Novello's active life in London lasted until 1849, when, after a brief

[1] See *A Mozart Pilgrimage: being the Travel Diaries of Vincent and Mary Novello . . .* transcribed and compiled by Nerina Medici di Marignano, ed. by Rosemary Hughes, London, 1955.

period as organist of the Roman Catholic Chapel at Moorfields (the Pro-Cathedral for London), he retired to Nice. He was held in respect and affection by a wide circle of friends and the hospitality of his home was extended to such visiting luminaries as Mendelssohn (letters from him to Novello are extant), Fétis, and Liszt. His talents (which did not lie in the field of original composition although he composed a large number of works) were inherited by his children. Of these Mary (1809–98), a pupil of Mary Lamb, who married Charles Cowden-Clarke, compiled a celebrated *Concordance to Shakespeare*, translated a number of important musical treatises, edited *The Musical Times* from 1853 to 1856, and wrote numerous instructive essays on music in general. On her father's account, and fifty years after his Austrian pilgrimage, she was welcomed in Salzburg where she went in order to write an account of the festival. Clara (1818–1908) was one of the great European sopranos of her age and if she inspired audiences by the purity of her Handel interpretations she also surprised them by the catholicity of her taste. In 1856 she took part in the inauguration of the Crystal Palace, and one year later she sang in the Philharmonic concerts conducted by Wagner.

Mary Sabilla Novello (d. 1904) also embraced a singing career, but, handicapped by ill-health, was compelled to abandon public performances and to confine herself to teaching and to occasional literary work. The most important of the children of Vincent Novello, from the long-term view, was Joseph Alfred (1810–96), the eldest son.

Alfred (as he was known) was a well-known bass singer. (It was when he was in York, as apprentice to a local Catholic organist, that Vincent took the opportunity to visit the city and to investigate the Purcell holdings in the Minster library.) In 1829, however, he decided that his true vocation was not in singing, and he commenced as publisher in Frith Street, Soho. His initiative and perseverance (against the opposition of other publishers and the impediment of government taxation 'upon knowledge'—to the repeal of which his exertions led) in due course resulted in the issue of popular choir pieces in *Novello's Choral Handbook* at 3d. a page, of the items in Mainzer's *Singing for the Million*, in penny numbers, and, after 1846, of the standard oratorios in monthly parts—each part costing 6d. Novello also founded *The Musical Times* in 1844. In the best Victorian tradition Alfred did good and prospered. The good he did, however, was enormous and, in the broadest sense, it is doubtful whether any two men have ever done more for the cultivation of music 'amongst the least wealthy classes'[1] in Britain than did Vincent and Alfred Novello.[2]

[1] See Mary Cowden-Clarke on her father's sense of mission in *The Life and Labours of Vincent Novello*, London, 1863.

[2] The history of the firm is available in *A Century and a Half in Soho*, London, 1961.

By coincidence, in the very year that Vincent Novello embarked on music publishing another firm was launched. For on 23 January 1811 *The Morning Chronicle* announced:

'Chappell & Co. beg leave to acquaint the nobility and gentry that they have taken the extensive premises lately occupied by Goulding & Co., 126 New Bond Street, and have laid in a complete assortment of music of the best authors, ancient and modern, as well as a variety of instruments, consisting of Grand and Square Piano-fortes, Harps, etc., for sale or hire.'

The active spirit behind this announcement of intention to maintain a breach in the otherwise solidly 'residential' New Bond Street was Samuel Chappell, who took into partnership John Baptist Cramer and Francis Tatton Latour, who, like Cramer, was a well-known music teacher. Chappell's interests, unlike those of Vincent Novello, were in contemporary music, and in 1813, on the suggestion of Cramer, he put his rooms at the disposal of those who called the meeting at which the Philharmonic Society was inaugurated. Within six years the reputation of the firm was such that Beethoven (concerned for the publication of his works in London) could say in a letter to Ferdinand Ries that '[Cipriani] Potter says that Chappell in Bond Street is now one of the best publishers'.

Samuel Chappell died in 1834. The business was continued by his widow, Emily (in 1840 'E. Chappell' was music seller to the Queen), assisted by her two elder sons, William (1809–88) and Thomas (1819–1902). In due course the third son, Arthur (1825–1904), joined the firm. William Chappell (who went into partnership with Beale and Cramer in 1844) was a scholar rather than a publisher, but his business affinities helped him to appreciate that musical scholarship was best served when there was a serviceable end-product. He inspired the foundation of the Musical Antiquarian Society (1860) 'for the publication of scarce and valuable works by the early English Composers' and for five years acted as treasurer and publications manager. He was succeeded in these offices by his brother Thomas. Between 1838 and 1840 William edited and issued his *Collection of National English Airs*, expanded into the invaluable *Popular Music of the Olden Time* (1855–9). Thomas Chappell was a businessman in the mould of John Walsh. He had an unerring instinct for recognising what the public wanted. As a purveyor of light music he felt it necessary personally to demonstrate the somewhat suspect polka in the 1840's; through his youthful enthusiasm Chappell's purchased Balfe's *The Bohemian Girl* in 1832, and made a fortune, which was mightily increased when the operettas of Sullivan were brought into the firm's list. Tom Chappell, through whose enterprise the St. James's Hall was erected (see p. 484), also acted as agent for readings by Charles Dickens, who summarised the family as 'speculators, though of the worthiest and most honourable kind'.[1]

A third firm to come into existence at about the same time, and to exert a considerable influence on musical life during the nineteenth century and to continue to the present day, was that of Boosey's. The music firm of T. Boosey and Co. was an offshoot of a book-selling and publishing concern controlled by Thomas Boosey which throughout the last decade of the eighteenth century specialised in the importation and issue of foreign works. In 1796, for instance, there was published an English version of Schiller's *Kabale und Liebe*, in London and Leipzig, jointly by T. Boosey and A. Reinicke. Such contacts as he had made through books encouraged Boosey to extend his interest to music and when the music section was formed in 1816, under the management of Boosey's twenty-one-year-old son, also Thomas, it underlined its function as importer of foreign music. In 1820 Boosey published Forkel's *Life of Bach*, and five years later Thomas Busby commended the enterprise of Mr. Boosey in supplying Italian, French and German music.[2]

It will thus be seen that the music publishers who took the place of those who had flourished during the eighteenth-century surgence of activity reflected three main facets of interest: the traditional choral repertoire; the masterpieces of contemporary, or recently dead, continental masters; and musicology. All were part not only of a popular movement in music but also in education, and the links between musical and other forms of instruction, especially in the adult field, were strong. This returns us to a frequent point of departure: music and morals: in the nineteenth century musical experience—the thesis being warmed up for secular application out of the utterances of the Early Fathers (and some of the later ones)—was considered licit if it made people, particularly of the lower orders, better. Thus George Hogarth in 1818 quoted a 'late writer' as saying:

'In the densely peopled manufacturing districts of Yorkshire, Lancashire, and Derbyshire, music is cultivated among the working classes to an extent unparalleled in any other part of the kingdom . . . a well-chosen and well-performed selection of sacred music is listened to by a decent and attentive audience of the same class as the performers, mingled with their employers and their families.

'. . . They are no longer driven by mere vacuity of mind to the beer-shop, and a pastime which opens their minds to the impressions produced by the strains of Handel and Haydn, combined with the inspired

[1] See *The Chappell Story 1811–1961*, London, 1961.

[2] *Concert Room & Orchestra Anecdotes*, London, 1825, 3 vols., III, p. 99.

poetry of the scriptures, means something infinitely better than the amusement of an idle hour . . .'[1]

Adult Education

The principle of self-help so far as music was concerned swept through Britain. The focus of ambition was the great musical festival, which, as has been shown, often worked on a regional basis. The foundation of adult education was religion, so that in 1798 William Singleton, a Methodist, and Samuel Fox, a Quaker, combined to institute classes in Nottingham. In 1804 the formation of the Bible Society gave extra stimulus to the movement. In 1816 Dr. Pole established an Adult School in Leeds, and in 1842 that inaugurated by Joseph Stamp in Birmingham joined hands with other interests to support the ambition that led to a University College on the one hand and to a Midland Institute—in which a music department was a prominent feature.[2]

The field of choral music, kept fertile by small-town organists and interested amateurs, was crossed by Alfred Novello and then by Joseph Mainzer (1801–51)—a radical refugee from reactionary Europe after 1848, John Hullah (1812–84) and John Curwen (1816–80), whose public spirit, energy, and pedagogic abilities were efficacious to a remarkable degree. By the middle of the century there were few towns without choral societies—in which the working class was strongly represented—and, what is more, the capacity for sight-reading was strong. The extent of the zeal for musical self-education is reflected in the fact that on 18 April 1837, 600 people assembled in the Mechanics' Institute, Salisbury, to hear a Mr. Biddlecombe lecture on singing.

Apart from those larger towns in which musical activities had steadily developed through the latter part of the eighteenth century, many institutions represented the general increase in corporate music-making up to 1855. All were under-pinned by Adult Schools, Mechanics' Institutes, church and chapel choirs, and miscellaneous classes; as for example the Psalmody classes at Broughton Ferry, the Cold Higham Singing Class, the weekly class in the Islington Working Man's Institute, the Bradford Classical Harmonists who met in the Mechanics' Institute, and the Trinity Choral Classes in Southwark.

1 *Musical History, Biography and Criticism*, London, 1838, 2 vols., II, p. 274.

2 The foundation stone of the Midland Institute was laid by the Prince Consort on 22 November 1855. 'I remember the time,' wrote Arthur Godlee, 'when we had penny classes in the violin. Large numbers attended and the backs of the students were used as music stands for those sitting behind them. It was a crude state of things and a good part of the time was occupied in getting the instruments tuned.' *Birmingham Institutions*, ed. by J. H. Muirhead, Birmingham, 1911, p. 339.

Choral Societies and Festivals

There were founded in the first half of the century: Coventry Union Choral Society (1813),[1] Edinburgh Harmonists' Society (1822),[2] Blackburn Choral Society (1829), Burnley Choral Society (1834),[3] York Choral Society (1837),[4] Bedford Musical Society (1837), Stockport Choral Society (1840), Glasgow Choral Union (1843), Wigan Choral Society (1847),[5] Norwich Choral Society (1853), Huntingdon, and St. Neot's Choral Society (1854), Carlisle Choral Society (1854),[6] At Newcastle upon Tyne the tradition of Avison was carried on by his successors—his son, also Charles, Thomas Thompson (1777–1834)[7] and Thomas Ions (1817–57).[8] The latter gave a new stimulus to music on Tyneside—where latterly the natives had rested on the past fame of the festival—by founding the Newcastle Sacred Harmonic Society. The most remarkable choral achievement of this period, perhaps, was in the distant Shetland Islands. At Lerwick a musical minister, Thomas Barclay, and precentor, William Merylees, saw to it that the parishioners were competent vocalists. In 1835 a fee-paying school under the aegis of the Moravians (or United Brethren) was opened and one of the masters was John George Glass (1810–54), a keen musician, who set himself the task of founding a choir—and later an orchestra. Glass rehearsed each section of his choir individually on the first four days of the week, assembling them for a full rehearsal on Fridays: 'in 1848 he began the series of practisings which ceased only with his life . . . The first work

[1] Music in Coventry benefited from the energy of Edward Sims, organist of St. Michael's Church from 1828. His influence was memorialised by George Eliot, whose love of music grew from early experiences in Coventry.

[2] New societies abounded in Edinburgh: e.g. Institute for the Encouragement of Sacred Music (1817), Professional Society of Musicians (1819), The Edinburgh Choral Union came into being in 1858.

[3] Also a Choral Union in 1843.

[4] A York Music Society for the support of subscription concerts had been founded in 1786.

[5] Conductor, Thomas Graham, organist of parish church 1844–67 and previously of Chapel for Deaf and Dumb, Old Trafford, Manchester. In 1847, there were 55 members. Late attendance incurred a penny fine; absentees were expected to pay 3d. Some members, having run up debts of 5s., were known to pay them off in instalments. The parish church at this time had a children's choir, the boys dressed in surplices, the 'singing-girls' in 'special bonnets and spencers and shoes provided at the cost of the parish'.

[6] First performance of *Messiah* in Carlisle at third annual concert (1857)—with 'full orchestra'.

[7] Horn-player in Theatre Royal, Newcastle, at the age of twelve, and subsequently a pupil in London of Clementi and J. B. Cramer. Organist at Newcastle Festival, 1796 (under patronage of Prince William of Gloucester), 1814, and 1824.

[8] An amateur until his appointment to St. Nicholas's Church in succession to Thompson. A pupil of Moscheles and assistant conductor to Sir George Smart at Newcastle Festival of 1842.

he set his choir to . . . was Mendelssohn's "Elijah", then newly published. It is curious to think of, that "Elijah" was put in rehearsal in the Shetland Isles the same year it was first performed in Birmingham, and I question whether it was then known at all in Scotland. After the "Elijah" came the "Messiah", "Judas Maccabaeus", "Dettingen Te Deum" . . .'[1]

Taking into account all the circumstances that led to this proliferation of choral activity it is not surprising that the uniformity long since imposed by the cult of Handel was intensified. The choral festival in the provinces was a steady source of income for such venerated Handel directors as Thomas Greatorex and George Smart, for the top singers, and for orchestral players. Of these latter there were too many in London and too few in the provinces where the subscription concerts in many places came to an end at the end of the eighteenth century, simply because amateurs were no longer able to keep pace with the demands of the new orchestral music. As the festivals increased in number so did critical interest in provincial choral standards grow. 'The inhabitants of the Southern counties of England,' wrote Busby, 'have scarcely an idea of the taste and zeal with which music is cultivated and encouraged in the North.' He added how at the sixteenth amateur music meeting, at Sheffield in 1824, 'London dilletantes who attended their Concerts were astonished.'[2]

The end of the Napoleonic Wars gave patriotic incentive to music-making and in the Minute Book of the Chester Musical Festivals,[3] a resolution was noted on 24 May 1814, 'that a grand Musical Festival shall be held in the City on the 27th September next to celebrate the glorious success of His Majesty's Arms in conjunction with those of the Allies and the happy termination of the Wars.' The costs of the festival (covered by two-guinea subscriptions for five performances, single tickets at half a guinea, and donations) were enormous. On the vocal side there were payments of £420 to Mme Catalani, £160 to Mrs. Salmon, £220 10s. to Mr. Bartelman, £220 10s. to Mr. Braham, £63 to Mr. Kellner, £21 to Mr. Garbett, £120 2s. to chorus trebles, £89 15s. 6d. to tenors, £75 17s. 6d. to counter-tenors, £110 8s. 6d. to basses. The glee singers who performed at the 'Public Breakfast' received £3 10s. and '2 Chorus Singers in Chester' £4 4s. The total sum expended on singers was £1,508 17s. 6d.

[1] See *Arthur Laurenson*, his letters and literary remains, ed. by C. Spence, London, 1901, pp. 4–11.

[2] Op. cit., III, p. 136. There was a Sheffield Musical Festival in 1805. In 1809 the Yorkshire Music Society performed in Sheffield, in 1810 in Leeds, in 1812 in York, and then in rotation—with Hull coming in in 1833—until 1845. In 1822 subscription concerts were given in the Theatre. Six years later a more ambitious scheme was launched as the Yorkshire Choral and Sheffield Subscription Concerts, in the Music Hall. The Patrons included the Earl of Harewood and Sir George Sitwell. Programmes included works by Beethoven (Symphony 1), Calcott, Bishop, Moore, Haydn, Romberg and Mozart.

[3] Chester City Library 78, 106.

On the instrumental side £105 went to Greatorex, the conductor, £251 6s. to violinists, £72 4s. to 'Tenors' (violas), £108 3s. to cellos, £91 7s. to double-basses, £44 2s. to bassoonists, £43 1s. to oboists, £12 12s. to flautists, £31 8s. to clarinettists, £47 5s. to horn players, £49 7s. to trumpeters, £36 12s. to trombonists, £7 7s. to 'single drums', and £31 10s. to 'double drums'. In all instrumental fees were £931 4s.

In accordance with a familiar principle of inflation festival costs increased so that in 1821 the expenses were—Vocal, £1,564 1s.; Instrumental, £1,221 3s. In this year *The Chester Chronicle* questioned the demands of Mme Camporese in the nicest terms: 'We are sorry that anything like dissatisfaction should have been expressed by this lady, after the very liberal treatment she experienced from the Committee. We believe she only gave five songs in the Church [Cathedral], for which she had 150 pounds, enough in all conscience we would have thought. The air of Italy, however, as connected with pecuniary matters, has unquestionably a bracing tendency.' The Committee, however, conscious of their cultural duty to city and county, went forward, heedless of cost, to prepare for the next festival. This took place in 1829. By now the instrumentalists accounted for £1,776 16s. (including fees for two serpent-players who were engaged this year), the singers for £1,250 5s. That was the last Chester Festival for fifty years.

The most sought after conductor for the festivals of that period was Sir George Smart (who presided at the pianoforte), and when he directed the Newcastle Festival of 1824 (the same festival to which the Lancashire singers mentioned on p. 412 walked) his salary was £157 10s. Other payments included Braham £189, Miss Stephens £189, Mrs. Salmon £168, Mori, the leader of the orchestra £50, Robert Lindley (senior), principal cellist £35, Nicholson, the oboist £25, Erskine of Birmingham, second oboist £20, Henshaw, organist of Durham Cathedral, assisting Thompson (whose fee is not quoted) £12. Rank and file players received between £3 3s. and £7 7s., while chorus singers ranged between £1 1s. and £5 5s. The boys of Durham Cathedral did well with £3 3s. apiece; but the one boy from the Catholic Chapel (Newcastle?) had to be content with 15s. In the main the front orchestral desks were occupied by London players. Behind them were players from Newcastle (some from the theatre band), Edinburgh, Scarborough (the Theatre), York, Leeds, Sunderland, Gateshead, and (brass players) from the Royal Dragoon Guards. Singers were drawn from the north-eastern towns for the most part (a few were 'volunteers') but strengthened by the contingent from Lancashire. The choir totalled 117, the orchestra fifty-five. Payments to the chorus singers were, of course, in place of wages lost through absence from work.[1]

[1] Details from a copy of Sir George Smart's List (Newcastle City Library).

Press advertisements make it clear that the tradesmen of Newcastle approved the festival as bringing business to the city, and private householders were not backward in offering rooms to let. No stone was left unturned to meet all requirements, even those that might occur some months later. Mrs. Laidlaw, for instance, a midwife, announced her services as being available in Edinburgh. Against the advertisement an anonymous Newcastle annotator observed: 'This is a well timed address at a Musical Festival, where ladies may have had the full enjoyment of the fascinating duets which are so often performed.'

Place of honour in all the festival programmes was naturally reserved for Handel (*Messiah* now being given—as at Newcastle in 1824—with Mozart's additional accompaniments), but the miscellaneous evening concerts were beginning to show a wider range. At Liverpool in 1805 there were to be heard a 'Grand Overture' by Haydn, a symphony by Mozart, a concerto by Dragonetti, and Purcell's *Ye twice Ten Hundred Deities* (sung by Bartleman). If in the next year the citizens of Chester were held mostly to a diet of Handel, Boyce, Croft, and Pergolesi (though Haydn's *Creation* was also performed), by 1814 they were able to hear the overtures to *Lodoiska* (Cherabine [*sic*]) and to *Zamberflotte* [*sic*]. Seven years later a *sinfonia* by Beethoven was played, while Braham and Kellner, backed by the festival choir, presented an excerpt from Purcell's *King Arthur*. At the 1826 Birmingham festival the 'Jupiter' symphony and Weber's *Freischütz* Overture were played, while vocal excerpts from Rossini's *Semiramide* and Weber's *Oberon* gave the audience a fair prospect of what was almost *avant garde*. These examples of modern music were, however, judiciously separated by familiar songs by Arne and glees by Stevenson and Stafford Smith.

During the 1820's and 1830's provincial festivals abounded—in Yorkshire, Norfolk, Shropshire, at Oxford, Cambridge, Liverpool, Manchester, Brighton, Reading, and so on. But in the next decade some streamlining had to take place. In 1840 the singers at Shrewsbury (where a festival had run spasmodically since 1790, in conjunction with the Musical Society formed in 1785) agreed to accept a cut in their fees. A year later they refused, and there was a deficit of nearly £100. 'The principal singers', it was reported in *Eddowes's Journal*, 'also received a larger sum for their services—having last year accepted engagements much under their usual terms. Still we think they are much too well paid, and if festivals are to succeed, these professionals must lower their pretensions . . . We are informed that Miss Birch, Miss Hawes, and Mr. Phillips, received somewhere about fifty pounds each, and the other principals some little less . . .' Noting that the chorus singers brought from Manchester earned £4 each for a five-day stint, the reporter concluded:

'There is a sad inequality in the pecuniary remuneration connected with these engagements.' In 1824 the Norwich Festival showed a profit of £2,411. In 1827 this was reduced to £1,372. Three years later the profit was but £236. In 1833 it stood a little higher, at £448. In 1836, however, there was a loss of £231.

The intensification of music among the working classes was nowhere more marked than in Wales—where town and country met, where one valley was as it always had been and the next defaced by the mining engineer. Past and present fired a new, sometimes bitter, nationalism. The Eisteddfod became a national institution. Unfortunately the Anglo-Welsh element diminished the intrinsic quality of the first large-scale Eisteddfodau and the tastes of the alien landlord further restricted a proper development. The paradox was that while the Honourable Society of Cymmrodorion in London was attempting to preserve the Cymric culture in its purity (for instance, at the Eisteddfod held at the Freemasons' Tavern on 22 May, 1823), the Eisteddfod in Wales was beginning to forfeit its birthright. Thus at the Cardiff Eisteddfod of 1834: 'The concourse exhibited society in all its diverse shades and gradations from the peer to the peasant, and whilst the metropolis contributed its fashionable and most distinguished characters, the rural beauty of our sunny and laughing vales hastened likewise to give a roseate grace to the feast, and the hardy tenants of our bleaky hillsides teeming with hidden treasures and a nation's wealth crowded to the spot of attraction, even from the steeps of rugged Snowdon'.[1]

The President of the Eisteddfod was the Marquess of Bute, who held a house-party at Cardiff Castle and whose progress to the opening ceremony was accompanied by trumpets playing 'Men of Harlech'. On the side of Welsh music there were prizes for 'the best New Air in a Welsh modulation', for 'the best Variations on any Welsh melody', for 'the best English verses to any Welsh melody'. There was a 'miniature silver harp . . . with a gratuity towards travelling expenses to the best proficient on the single-stringed harp', which was awarded to Edward Watkins of Merthyr, a blind harper, who played *Serch hudol* 'with admirable skill'. The prize for the best performance on the treble-stringed harp went to Hugh Pughe of Dolgellau. There was a medal for the best singer who accompanied him/herself on the harp, 'according to the manner of Gwent and Dyfed'. There were also exhibitions of *Penillion*, 'according to the North Wales manner'.

On the other hand the fashionable concerts at the Town Hall were monopolised by London principals—Braham, Mrs. Knyvett, Miss Stevens, each of whom sang a bastardised Welsh item, and Lindley. At the final concert the National Anthem threw up a new, and macaronic text:

1 *Glamorgan, Monmouth & Brecon Gazette,* 23, 30 August 1834, reporting the Gwent and Dyfed Eisteddfod and Musical Festival.

Long may old Cambria share
His love and royal care!
God bless the King!
May he attune the lyre,
And every hand inspire
To sing with soul of fire
God save the King.

The second verse was in Welsh.

From this point the Welsh National Eisteddfod maintained its continuity throughout the nineteenth century (and, of course, to the present day), but, with one eye continually kept on London, it progressed somewhat ambivalently. The great John Thomas—the greatest harpist of the period—won the triple harp prize at Abergavenny in 1838 but then took the road to London, whence he frequently journeyed to give recitals in Europe. The ambitious and the enterprising had to follow this course. At home the Welsh built their choirs, and composers (unknown outside Wales) taught themselves to satisfy the choral needs of the Principality. The 'choral art in Wales depended upon a small group of composers who were wise enough to take the level of the working people, indeed they were all men of the people, and did not qualify themselves first as professional musicians by college or university training'.[1] Among the pioneer composers of Wales were Ambrose Lloyd, Tanymarian, Owain Alaw, Ieuan Gwyllt, and Gwilym Gwent. While such composers tried to find an expression of the national feeling for music compatible with the sentiments of the workers in the valleys of the south, there were those like Maria Jane Williams who were collecting and editing the traditional songs of the country. It was the beginning of an heroic struggle to preserve and strengthen a culture against odds. In the years to come the English were to benefit—more than they deserved.

Professional Standards

There is no doubt of the vitality of provincial music during the reigns of George IV and William IV and the early years of that of Queen Victoria. There was, however, a two-fold weakness in the situation. On the one hand this lay in the variable quality of the teaching of '. . . the people, [who] though desirous to learn, are of course ignorant, and therefore receive *any* instruction rather than none—and their teachers, though anxious to comply with the desires of their pupils, are not always very well informed

[1] John Graham, *Century of Welsh Music*, London, 1923, p. 16.

on the subject they propose to teach and still less frequently able systematically to impart what knowledge they do possess'.[1] On the other hand the non-existence of permanent orchestras and of opera outside London was a grievous handicap. This meant that it was only in the capital that any kind of adequate attention could be given to the increasingly exacting works of European extraction. The focal body in London was the Philharmonic Society, and the dominant name that of Beethoven, for the sustaining of whose reputation the Society deserved as much credit as any in Europe. To be just, however, the discovery of Beethoven as a great composer was due in the first place, not to metropolitan musicians, but to the amateurs of Leicester, and to publishers of enterprise. The Abbé Dobler, Chaplain at Bonn, a violinist and occasional conductor of the Electoral orchestra,[2] came to Leicester as a refugee in 1793. William Gardiner writes: 'On arriving at Leicester he sought my acquaintance and with the assistance of Mr. [John or Henry] Valentine, the professor, [the E flat Trio of Beethoven] was first played in the year 1794, many years previous to its being known in London. How great was my surprise on hearing this composition, accustomed as I had been to the smooth, swimming harmonies of Corelli, the articulated style of Handel, and the trite phraseology of the moderns! for at that time we had only one symphony of Haydn, and not a note of Mozart. What a new sort of sensation, I repeat, did this composition produce in me! It opened a fresh view of the musical art, in which sounds were made to excite the imagination entirely in a different way.'[3] The first English publisher to undertake a work by Beethoven was William Wennington who issued the canzonetta *La Tiranna* in 1799. During Beethoven's lifetime 128 of his works were published in England, the most important coming from Clementi, Birchall, Goulding and Boosey.[4]

The Philharmonic Society was persistent in urging commissions on Beethoven, and its officers visited the master from time to time. In 1815, Charles Neate,[5] pianist and pupil and friend of Field, who was the first to play the 'Emperor' Concerto in England, went to Vienna to try to persuade Beethoven to write three overtures for the Society. In the end Beethoven sent the score of the already written *Ruins of Athens* Overture. In 1818 the Philharmonic commissioned two symphonies and invited the composer to come to London. In this year Cipriani Potter was in Vienna, taking lessons from Beethoven's old master Emanuel Förster and spending

[1] G.F.G., 'On the Influence of Patronage on Art' in *The Musical Union*, no. VIII, 24 June 1845, pp. 53–4.

[2] In which Salomon and Bernhard Romberg played.

[3] William Gardiner, op. cit., I, p. 113.

[4] See Alan Tyson, *The Authentic English Editions of Beethoven*, London, 1964.

[5] 1784–1877; obituary in *Mus. T.*, May 1877.

some time with Beethoven, who was good enough to correct his exercises. Potter, said Beethoven, 'is a good man and has a talent for composition'. As will be seen, Beethoven's opinion on Potter's ability in this direction was by no means unwarranted. Potter's own memories of this acquaintanceship are vivid—'The favourite medium by which Beethoven expressed his ideas was the Italian; his pronunciation of that language being better than his French or German; for having resided the greater part of his life in Vienna he had imbibed the Viennese pronunciation, which is considered the worst in all Germany; and indeed is only to be supported on the stage, and as a patois dialect; the natives considering it a vehicle for wit and humorous amusement'. Regarding Beethoven's music he set a *caveat* before his timorous contemporaries, for whom 'classical' standards were already refrigerated: 'Musicians should be more careful in hazarding a hasty opinion of the works of so great a master.'[1]

Beethoven did not, however, compose the symphonies that were wanted by the Philharmonic. Nevertheless, in 1822, after an embassy by Ferdinand Ries on behalf of the Society, exclusive rights in the intended Choral Symphony were thought to have been secured by an advance of £50. In spite of this the first performance of the work took place in Vienna, the English première, under Smart, being given on 21 March 1825. Faithful to the end, the Philharmonic Society gave a donation of £100 to Beethoven on his deathbed.

The cause of new music was furthered (against conservative reservations) by the continued belief on the part of continental virtuosi and composers that England was a gold-mine. Spohr, who admired the string playing he encountered in England, came in 1820. He conducted the Philharmonic Orchestra[2] and presented the Society with the score of his Overture in F.[3] Four years later the fourteen-year-old Liszt played in London—a test theme for extemporisation being provided by Smart. In 1825 Liszt ventured into the provinces and played at two concerts in Manchester.[4] Liszt was also in England in 1827, 1840, and 1886, and taught a number of English pupils, of whom Walter Bache was the first and Frederic Lamond the last. In the first concert at Manchester at

[1] 'Recollections of Beethoven, with Remarks on his Style', in *The Musical World*, 29 April 1836, pp. 101–6.

[2] Regarding Spohr's defiance of tradition by conducting not, as Smart, from the piano, but with a baton, see Henry Pleasants, *The Musical Journeyings of Louis Spohr*, Oklahoma, 1961, pp. 204–6.

[3] See *Catalogue of the Musical Mss. . . . deposited by the Philharmonic Society of London*, B.M. 1914. These Mss. include works by Beethoven, Cherubini, J. B. Cramer, François Fémy, Haydn, Mendelssohn, Neukomm, Pleyel, Potter, Spohr, and Weber.

[4] Theatre Royal, 16 and 20 June: the orchestra, directed by R. Andrews, 'at the Grand Piano Forte', numbered forty players. See Francis Hueffer, *Half a Century of Music in England*, 1837–87, London, 1889, pp. 97 *et seq.*

which Liszt appeared there was a second performance within the week of 'the highly celebrated Overture to *Der Freischütz*, composed by C. M. von Weber'.

In 1825 Smart, accompanied by Charles Kemble, Manager of Covent Garden, travelled to Germany to invite Weber to write an opera for Covent Garden. Weber came to London in the next year, with the score of *Oberon*. He conducted one Philharmonic concert, and his *Jubel-Ouvertüre* was played by the Philharmonic on 29 May 1826, a few days before his death at the Smarts' house. After Weber came Mendelssohn, both breaking and winning hearts on the occasion of his first visit in 1829. His Symphony in C minor (no. 13), played at a Philharmonic concert on 25 May 1829, was the start of an ambitious career in England where his influence in the end was probably more profound than in his native country. Alone and unknown, Wagner reached London in 1839. He came back sixteen years later, as guest conductor of the Philharmonic. Berlioz's name was bruited in London in 1843 when, on 9 March, *The Musical World* flew a kite. 'It is rumoured that M. Berlioz, the highly-prized French composer is preparing a new Symphony for the Philharmonic Society, which, it is said, he will conduct in person.' It was, however, not for another four years that Berlioz did pay the first of his two visits to London, and then at the invitation of the conductor Jullien.[1] Berlioz returned to London in 1851 to serve on the music jury set up in connection with the Great Exhibition. He stayed on to conduct concerts for the New Philharmonic. Of the other great composers of the first half of the nineteenth century, Chopin was the last to visit Britain, arriving in 1848, through the invitation of his Scottish pupil, Jane Stirling. Another British pupil, at whose London home he gave his first public recital, was Adelaide Sartoris, daughter of Charles Kemble, who, before her marriage, had achieved distinction as a singer and had undertaken the title role of Bellini's *Norma* in Venice. In 1848 Chopin refused an invitation to play at the Philharmonic Society on the grounds that 'they have only one rehearsal—a public one'.[2]

From the first the Philharmonic concerts attracted strong support, but the fact that orchestral players (except for the wind) were expected to give their services aroused strong feelings. In 1815 a number of players seceded and established a short-lived enterprise known as *The Professional*. To meet an emergency the Philharmonic directors were compelled to retreat from first principles and to engage substitute players on professional terms. Thus, the original players flocking back to the body they had temporarily deserted, the rebellion was broken. Another cause of dissen-

[1] See Hueffer, op. cit., pp. 151 *et seq.*, and A. W. Ganz, *Berlioz in London*, London, 1950.

[2] A. Hedley, *Selected Correspondence of Fryderyk Chopin*, London, 1962, pp. 315–16. Chopin was altogether unflattering about the Philharmonic Society performances.

sion was the feeling that British musicians were getting a raw deal. In 1823, Harrison's and Knyvett's Vocal Concerts having come to an end, a series of British concerts were organised, the conductors being Smart, Attwood, and Bishop. The programmes, however, were particularly dull, and it is small wonder that the venture folded up.

At this juncture the Royal Academy of Music, developed from Burney's project by way of a proposition by T. A. Walmisley in which the Philharmonic Society would directly have been involved, began its career. Inspired by Lord Burghersh[1] (aided by other of the nobility and the Archbishops, and given royal approval by George IV), the Academy began as half-conservatory, half-charity-school, under far from ideal conditions. 'I had forgotten', wrote the Rev. John Miles, Head Master, shortly after the opening in 1823, 'to mention to your Lordship the practising upon more than one instrument in the same room. There are three pianos and a harp in the largest room, and two pianos in another; and I understand from the boys that, at first, they found the noise of the different instruments unpleasant: but now, I find, they experience no interruption from the various sounds; as that caused by the instrument at which the boy sits so overpowers the others, as regards his ear, that he scarcely hears it; and certainly it has this advantage, that it makes each boy attentive to his own work.'[2] The first Principal of the Academy was Dr. Crotch. Among his senior colleagues were Attwood, Greatorex, Shield, Smart, William Horsley, and J. B. Cramer. Bishop, F. Cramer, Clementi, and Potter were on the teaching staff as well as the principal London orchestral players.

After three years Lord Burghersh, stating that the promoters of the institution 'were prompted in their exertions to establish it, by the desire of enabling the genius of this country to compete with foreigners, and thus to place the musical talents, so generally to be met with throughout the British empire, in a situation to divide with the numerous professors from abroad the enormous sums of money, yearly expended in this country for the enjoyment of music', appealed, on 5 August 1825, to the Government for assistance. 'We hope', he said, '[that] His Majesty's Government will not refuse to grant us a sum of from £400 to £500 a year, which would

[1] 1784–1859: succeeded as Earl of Westmorland in 1841. Burghersh, who played the violin, studied music under Charles Hague (1769–1821), Professor of Music at Cambridge. He studied also under Zeidler in Berlin and Mayseder in Vienna. A diplomat by profession, Burghersh became Ambassador in Berlin in 1842, and in Vienna in 1851. His wife was the third daughter of the Earl of Mornington. Mss. of his compositions (including some not negligible symphonies) are in the B.M. He was highly esteemed in Berlin and when his death was reported the military bands paraded there to play Beethoven's 'Funeral March' in his memory.

[2] W. W. Cazalet, *The History of the Royal Academy of Music*, London, 1854, p. 173.

cover the amount of the rent and taxes, in the house [4 Tenterden Street, Hanover Square] we at present occupy.'[1]

In April of the next year—the Academy having by now been granted a Charter—Lord Liverpool, Prime Minister, replied to Burghersh and in so doing set a precedent which was to last for a long time.

'We feel', wrote Liverpool, 'it is quite impossible to do more for the National Academy of Music than to give them the expense of their Charter, which you state to be £300.

'We have no fund to advance for any such Institutions without going to Parliament. This would subject the Institution to parliamentary investigation, and discussion, and we should not know on what principle to regulate any grant.

'The National Gallery for pictures and statues stands upon quite a different footing: the pictures are visible and solid wealth (if discreetly purchased), as little variable in their value in the course of years as lands, funds, or any other property. The public can at all times estimate their value; and the only loss is that attendant upon all dead property—that of interest.'[2]

Superficially music was in a flourishing condition, but when it came to the crunch due recognition of its place in the community was lacking. That meant that orchestral music and opera, of which the expenses were as always on the increase, were always vulnerable. To obviate disaster the sensible thing to do was to study the relationship between programme and receipts. The Philharmonic, having gained a reputation and a following, remained in the clear, but other concerts were spasmodic. There was also crisis in the field of choral music.

'The Constitution of the Philharmonic Society', observed Samuel Wesley, 'has proved a powerful engine of support to instrumental musick and to its performance in the most correct manner: it is, however to be regretted that the same attention to effect is not directed to the vocal as to the instrumental department: the voices are continually overpowered by the weight of the band; the wind instruments perpetually predominate; the voice of the singer is drowned, he becomes consequently careless (as he very reasonably may), and the composition, however excellent, is utterly ruined.'[3]

The Ancient Concerts—still directed by members of the House of Lords—ran on into the nineteenth century, but with little vitality remaining—too little even for the performance of Handel's oratorios. After 1804, the concerts, previously given in Tottenham Street and then the Concert

[1] Cazalet, loc. cit.

[2] ib. p. 174.

[3] Lecture at Royal Institution, 1828; B.M. Add. Ms. 35015, f. 225 v.

Room of the Opera House, took place in the Hanover Square Rooms. In 1832 the Sacred Harmonic Society was founded in order to rectify the choral situation. The conductor was Joseph Surman, who remained in office until Michael Costa[1] took over in 1847. True to period the Sacred Harmonic Society presented oratorio on a large scale. The first performance of *Messiah* given by the Society (in Exeter Hall) involved 300 performers. When Mendelssohn's *St. Paul* had its first London performance on 7 March 1837, the number had risen to 500. In 1847 the Society gave a forgotten work of Handel—*Belshazzar*—and the revised version of *Elijah.*[2] *Elijah* was given on 13 April 1847. It was repeated on 23, 28 and 30 April. At the performance on 23 April, the Queen and Prince Albert were present and 'at the end of the performance, Her Majesty and Prince Albert, rising to depart, were loudly and repeatedly cheered; and, subsequently, a tremendous cheer was given for Dr. Mendelssohn'. This was Mendelssohn's tenth and last visit to London, and he brought with him on this occasion the fifteen-year-old Joseph Joachim. The Sacred Harmonic Society flourished across the middle years of the century—being responsible for the first Handel Festival at the Crystal Palace in 1857—but was dissolved in 1882. During its existence the Society built up a magnificent library of music and books, which passed into the keeping of the Royal College of Music.

Musical Journalism

As music was in one way or another popularised, a hitherto peripheral profession—that of musical journalism—developed rapidly, and by the middle of the century the music critic had become a figure of significance. Opportunities for such writers multiplied from the beginning of the century. The *Spectator* (for which Edward Taylor, friend of Spohr and organiser of the Norwich Festival, wrote), the *Atlas* (1826), and *Fraser's Magazine* (1830) encouraged the belletristic writer. The *Quarterly Musical Magazine* (1818), *The Harmonicon* (1823), and *The Musical World* (1836), dealt in musical matters of general interest, while others covered forgotten details of musical history in a more or less accessible manner. *Mainzer's Musical Times* (1842) and *The Musical Times* (1844) were particularly geared to technical concerns, especially relating to choral singing. Under the Novello-Cowden-Clarke influence *The Musical Times* balanced technical discussion with whimsical studies in musical aesthetics. Concurrently

[1] Michael Costa (1808–84), born in Naples, came to England in 1828. By 1832 he had so far established himself as to be appointed by Monck Mason as musical director at the King's Theatre. He became a leading conductor, directing the Philharmonic Society (1846–54), the Sacred Harmonic Society (1848–80), the Birmingham Festival (1849–82) and festivals at Bradford (1853) and Leeds (1876). Costa, also a composer, was knighted in 1869.

[2] First performed at Birmingham Musical Festival, 28 August 1846.

greater consideration was given to music in the daily papers. For many years the music critic of *The Morning Post* was the many-sided Welshman, John Parry (1776–1851) of Denbigh—singer, composer, editor of Welsh music, and Eisteddfod conductor.

The senior writer on music was William Ayrton (1777–1858), whose sound practical skill found expression in his directorship of the King's Theatre and whose zeal for musical education led to his establishment of *The Harmonicon* and his contributions to *The Penny Cyclopaedia* and Knight's *Pictorial History of England.* George Hogarth (1783–1870) was a Scotsman and before coming to London took a lively part in the musical life of Edinburgh—he was joint secretary of the 1815 Musical Festival in that city. In 1836 Hogarth's daughter Catherine married Charles Dickens, by whom he was invited in 1846 to act as music critic to *The Daily News.* Hogarth wrote for numerous other journals and also a number of invaluable books. As Secretary of the Philharmonic Society he undertook a History of the Society on the occasion of its Jubilee in 1862.

Ayrton and Hogarth were useful, and utilitarian writers. So far as style was concerned, however, Edward Holmes, devoted friend of Keats since their schooldays together, the friend of all Vincent Novello's friends, was the master. Pitched in a key mid-way between those of Lamb and Leigh Hunt, his prose is consistently readable. He had an allusive mind that enabled him to colour his style without, however, disturbing its intention. And he had a gift for the compelling phrase.

Of Bach he wrote: 'Beyond any musician, he lived remote, in the futurity of his art.'[1] Of the Mozart Sonata in E flat [K. 282] he observed:

'Although this work may be called a child's Sonata, the marks of the lion are visible in it.'[2] His sympathies were wide—too wide for H. F. Chorley[3]—and spilled out into life. His feeling for the human predicament

[1] 'Progress of Bach's Music in England', *Mus. T.*, June 1851. Holmes was much influenced by S. Wesley, and he took every opportunity to listen to Bach: hence in August 1837 he wrote to Leigh Hunt that 'it is not unlikely that you might come out and meet us at St. Katherine's Church (or Chapel) in Regent's Park on Thursday afternoon at 4 to hear a new fugue or prelude of his for the organ—and several of Bach's Trios, Adagios, Pedal fugues etc. played by a young girl [Miss Stirling, a pupil of Holmes who was then organist at Poplar Church], whose wonders of execution combine such meaning—presence of mind and skill of hand as amount to genius and the greatest wonder of all is that she has no vanity and is sensible only of her own deficiencies.' Cf. *The Musical World*, 25 August 1837, p. 173, which describes the performance.

[2] 'Thematic Catalogue of Pfte. Works of Mozart', *Mus. T.*, July 1851.

[3] 'As a musician, his knowledge was deep, if somewhat prejudiced. He had incoherent passions for particular composers, in whom he could see no fault. There was no keener lover of Bach than he, and yet the other day he was engaged in the recommendation of M. Berlioz just as fervidly—owning no short-comings, admitting no defects . . . As a critic, Mr. Holmes more willingly lent himself to praise than to blame.' *The Athenaeum*, 5 November 1859, p. 605.

brought affectionate words for the 'old grey-headed artists in their armchair days revolving speculations of flight to America'.[1] His eye was keen and as a travel-book *A Ramble Among the Musicians of Germany* (1828; published anonymously and by some attributed to Vincent Novello until he denied authorship) is easy and attractive. His masterpiece was his *Life of Mozart* (1845). In this book Holmes pioneered a new style in musical biography and began to tilt the scales against the pseudo-heroic. 'We do not', he commented in *A Ramble*, 'wish to know the great performances of great men, we wish to know their *little* actions, how they walked, looked, and spoke, their crooked habits and peculiarities; and to know that Mozart had a restless and nervous fidgetiness in his hands and feet, and seldom sat without some motion of them, makes him more present to us than the most laboured picture.'

Henry Fothergill Chorley (1808–72) and James William Davison (1813–85) finally, and rather disastrously, settled the music critic in his place as an arbiter of taste. The one was a member of the staff of *The Athenaeum* (1830–66) the other of *The Times* (1846–79) as well as editor of *The Musical World* (1844–85). Chorley, of a Lancashire family of Quakers, was musically more or less untrained. Friendship with Felicia Hemans—as well as other literary figures—turned him towards a literary career which continued side by side with that of music critic. An upholder of the proprieties, Chorley manfully withstood the shock of the music of Berlioz, Schumann, and Wagner, and advised his composing countrymen to avoid such excesses of incontinence and incompetence. Chorley's large literary output included a number of libretti. One, adapted from Tennyson, was *The May Queen*, for Sterndale Bennett; another, pseudo-Welsh, was *The Bride of Neath*[2]—a Victorian idyll of Glamorgan village life—which John Thomas set for the Swansea Eisteddfod of 1863. Davison, whose mother was an actress, first studied law but his aptitude for music, sharpened by lessons from W. H. Holmes and G. A. Macfarren, turned him away from the Bar. Friendship with Sterndale Bennett and Mendelssohn ratified him in his decision to embrace a musical career. This was initially in the field of teaching (in 1859 he married Arabella Goddard, who was among his piano pupils), but gradually he got a foothold in that of journalism. In the course of a long life Davison maintained more or less intact the principle that he had taken up at the outset. Mendelssohn was the ideal of good sense and good music, while Sterndale Bennett was the one English master worthy of the highest recognition. Davison fought for

[1] *Mus. T.*, editorial, May 1852.

[2] An interesting work in that Thomas tried to harness his style to folk-song (e.g. the use of the melody *Nos galan* and the principle of *penillion*), but his technical resources were painfully limited.

Bennett. He also defended the rights of English musicians in general. But the direction which European music appeared to be taking filled him with despair. As music critic of *The Times*—and one who involved himself in musical politics—Davison brought that paper into the centre of the musical arena. In so doing he materially assisted in the establishment of a body of authority in the musical life of London which was well-placed to keep heterodoxy in check.

Victorian Composers—Lives and Works

During the first half of the nineteenth century the strong tendencies to sit on the past and to popularise choral music, coupled with the centralisation of orchestral music and the absorption of playing talent by the 'classics' and the works of continental composers of greater or lesser note and the diminution of native opera by Italy and Germany, left the native composer without much in the way of adequate opportunity or stimulus. Above all there was the increasing pace of life. 'One must', wrote Berlioz in 1853, 'have seen the rush, the turmoil of the musical life of favourite artists in London, to get a fair idea of it.

'More curious still is the life of the professors who have been established in England for years past, such as Mr. Davison, his admirable pupil Mrs. Goddard, Messrs. Macfarren, Ella, Benedict, Osborne, Frank Mori, Sainton, Piatti. They are always running about, playing, conducting, either at a public concert, or at a private musical soirée, and they scarcely have time to greet their friends through the window of their cab as they cross the Strand or Piccadilly.'[1]

The first of the magisterial figures in English nineteenth-century music was Sir George Smart (1776–1867). The son of George Smart, double-bass player and publisher, he was brought up within the authentic Handel tradition. His father had seen Handel conduct and he, as a Chapel Royal chorister, was the pupil of Ayrton. Smart was an organist, but, more importantly, a violinist, and as such took part in Salomon's concerts. At one of these he deputised for an absent timpanist and received a lesson in drum-playing from Haydn. In 1811 Smart directed concerts in Dublin and was knighted by the Lord Lieutenant. A founder member of the Philharmonic Society, he undertook many of its concerts; but his talent lay especially in the field of oratorio. He introduced Beethoven's *Mount of Olives* to London in 1814 and was also responsible for the first English performance of Mendelssohn's *St. Paul*, at Liverpool, in 1836. Smart had a finger in almost every pie. He was organist and composer of the Chapel Royal, a professor in the Royal Academy of Music; he taught singing (he was sought out by many who wished to acquire a Handel

[1] A. W. Ganz, *Berlioz in London*, London, 1950, p. 175.

technique) and included among his pupils Henriette Sontag and Jenny Lind; he was one of the editors of the Musical Antiquarian Society, and in this role issued the madrigals of Orlando Gibbons, while for the Handel Society he prepared a score of the *Dettingen Te Deum*. Smart promoted the cause of Mendelssohn and Weber, and was largely responsible for posthumous memorials to each; the Mendelssohn Scholarship on the one hand, the Weber statue in Dresden on the other.

Above all, however, Smart was the inspiration of the provincial festivals. He was punctilious in administration, authoritative,[1] yet genial with the large bodies of performers assembled for these occasions, and a master of large-scale choral effect. He directed festivals over the years in Bath, Bury St. Edmunds, Cambridge, Derby, Dublin, Edinburgh, Hull, Liverpool, Manchester, and Newcastle upon Tyne, as well, of course, as in London. A wholly admirable character—whose regional activities made possible those of Henry Wood and Malcolm Sargent in due course—Smart endowed the vocation of the administrative musician with a fitting dignity. As a composer, although he rode into popularity on the strength of his general reputation, he was negligible. More than that he was a menace. For a certain facility enabled him to combine the stolidity acquired from a basic misunderstanding of Handel with the sentimentality already seen to have insinuated itself into Storace, and (if church music is taken into account) Attwood. The nadir of Victorian music was reached long before Queen Victoria came to the throne: in Smart's *An Acrostic Elegy on the much Lamented Lord Nelson* (1815).

Smart, perhaps, did not set out to be a composer. Cipriani Potter (1792–1871), on the other hand, did. He just missed being a very good one. The reason for his relative failure lies almost certainly in the English attitude, considerably strengthened during the Victorian era, that English music, for practicable purposes, did not exist.[2] Moreover, Potter lacked the

[1] In 1833, in preparation for the Liverpool Festival, he sent a memorandum to Dragonetti: 'You are not to perform at any Concert etc. within 40 miles of Liverpool for a fortnight before the Festival there; or to suffer your name to be announced for any concert within that distance until after the Festival at Liverpool.'

[2] As is well known, the alleged unmusicality of the English at this time was an article of faith with many (not all) Germans. A characteristic observation is that of Georg Weerth: 'Wehe dem, der dies Konzert [a private concert in Yorkshire] anhören musste! Erhabener Geist, du gabst ihnen alles, du hast ihnen Shakespeare und Milton gegeben, du gabst ihnen die Westminsterabtei, damit sie alle grossen und kleinen Menschen komfortabel begraben können, du gabst ihnen Flotten und Meere, du gabst ihnen Indien und China, du hast sie gross gemacht vor allen Völkern. Erhabener Geist, du gabst ihnen alles—nur keine Musik!' *Streiflichter auf Old England*, Leipzig, 1963, p. 21. Weerth, on an industrial visit, stayed in Bradford in 1843. His principal musical memories were of 'God save the Queen' and 'Rule Britannia' and of carol-singing of which he gives a charming and humourous picture. He was a year or two too soon to witness a revival of music in Bradford almost entirely inspired by his fellow-countrymen. (See p. 535.)

hall-mark of Leipzig, with the aid of which Sterndale Bennett duly nosed into the first place among his English contemporaries.

Potter was an infant prodigy, and, as the result of his father's teaching, a competent pianist by the age of five. His later studies in piano technique were from Joseph Woefl, pupil both of Haydn and Mozart, and in counterpoint and composition from Attwood, Calcott, and Crotch. His interests were thus strongly affected by Vienna, and in 1817—after certain early compositions had been given a hearing at the Philharmonic Concerts—he went there. After a period of study with Förster he made a tour of Italy, returning to London in 1821, in which year he was the soloist in Mozart's D minor Concerto at a Philharmonic concert. At this juncture Potter enjoyed a sufficient degree of recognition[1] in fortifying him for what he took to be his life's work. During the next decade he applied himself to composition (while living on his performing and teaching engagements). He wrote ten symphonies, most of which were played at Philharmonic concerts. These are large-scale, highly competent, and distinctive works, which at the very least deserve occasional exhumation—if only to show what English music was, and what it might have become. Potter often stood not ignobly in the shadow of Beethoven [Ex. 1]. A strong sense of the

1.

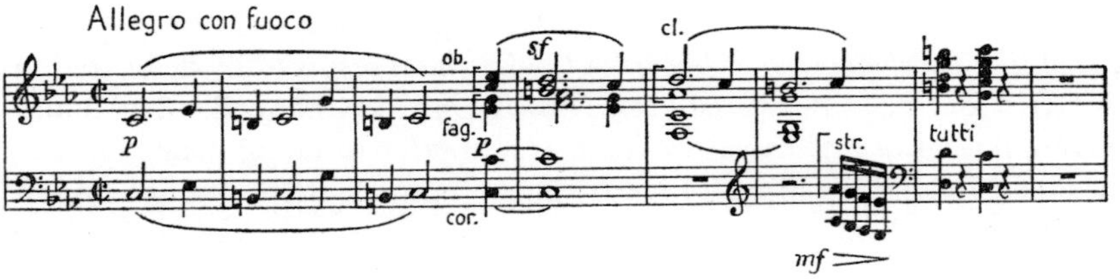

dramatic distinguishes his tonal and rhythmic structures, and in respect of the latter Potter stands out a mile from his contemporaries at home. His affection for Mozart left its mark too. In the first of the following examples the first four bars (which follow an introductory *Maestoso*) show evolutionary harmonic tendencies also to be noticed in Weber and Spohr [Ex. 2*a*].

2a.

[1] 'In early compositions he met with kinder critics in Germany than he did in his own country.' *The City Press*, 15 July 1871.

The lineage of [Ex. 2*b*] is unmistakable. When the two impulses met—

2b.

of Mozart and Beethoven—Potter developed on the one hand a *Gemütlichkeit* and on the other an *Enthusiasmus* that show a strong affinity with Schumann. This affinity is especially marked in the pull of syncopation across the 3/4 bars of the Scherzo of the Eighth Symphony, in which the imagination is further nourished by ingenious and evocative permutations of tonality. The symphonies also are spacious in texture and felicitous in scoring. During his visit of 1855 Wagner conducted Potter's G minor Symphony, and gratified the composer by the care he took in its preparation at rehearsal.

Potter's output was considerable, including three Shakespeare Overtures (to *Cymbeline*, *The Tempest*, and *Antony and Cleopatra*[1]), three piano concertos,[2] and a large number of miscellaneous works for chamber ensemble[3] and piano solo.

Among a large number of works for the piano that carry the mark of competent musicianship but few signs of the strength or originality of the symphonies, the *Studies . . . in all the Major and Minor Keys Composed for the Use of The Royal Academy of Music* (*in London*) 'and respectfully dedicated to the Rt. Hon. Lord Burghersh' (two books, pub. S. Chappell, 1830) stand out by reason of a backward glance at a greater teaching collection but also their intrinsic quality. These are mood pictures, slight but not easy in execution, and often agreeably evocative. Twenty-three years later Sterndale Bennett followed Potter with a series of *Preludes and Lessons* (op. 33), in which the idea of the *Lied ohne Wörter* implicit in Potter was carried along a by-pass of Mendelssohn (see no. 19—*Prelude and Aria*) towards the miniatures of Brahms (note the warm sixths in no. 20 in G minor) and of Grieg (no. 5—*Der Schmetterling*). But the most interesting of Potter's works, in a premonitory sense, is *The Enigma: Variations and Fantasia on a favourite Irish Air for the Piano Forte in the Style of Five Eminent Artists, Composed and Dedicated to the Originals by Cipriani Potter* (pub. T. Boosey), and one may wonder whether or not a copy of Potter's piece was not once seen lying about in his father's music shop, and the pattern committed to the subconscious memory by Edward Elgar. Potter thus

[1] Composed respectively in 1836, 1837 and 1856.

[2] In D minor, 1832, in E flat (1833?); in E, 1835.

[3] See particularly the Sextet for Flute, Clarinet, Viola, Cello, Bass, Piano (solo): B.M. Add. Ms. 31786. This is a fine example of Potter's meticulous and always interesting feeling for instrumental timbres.

managed a 'Dorabella'-type vignette [Ex. 3*a*], at the end of which variation he passed to the next over an Elgarianly dual purpose mediant [Ex. 3*b*].

3a.

3b.

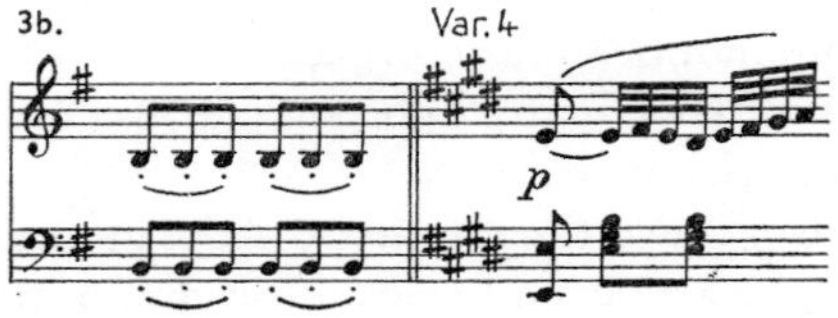

The pioneer of Beethoven's piano concertos, Potter was ready to extend a welcome to any new music of the integrity of which he was convinced and in 1857 he prepared an edition of Schumann's *Album für die Jugend*, while in 1871 he took part in the first English performance of Brahms's *Requiem*.[1]

Of a too amiable disposition, Potter was not equipped for the duties of Principal of the Royal Academy which were thrust upon him by Lord Burghersh on the resignation of Crotch in 1832. There were harassments on two fronts. Lord Burghersh, virtual dictator of the establishment, was difficult to deal with except on terms of surrender. The students were unruly—the more so because they resented this aristocratic president, whose insistence on the frequent performance of his own works was a particular cause of discontent. 'His introduction of his own compositions, to the exclusion of those of Handel, Haydn, and Mozart; his inattention to the real interests of the institution; his carelessness of everybody's time and convenience; show most clearly that his object is not so much to improve the musical art: as to draw round him a circle of which he may be the principal attraction. The professors have no power whatever, or things

[1] See fn. 1, p. 473.

would not be left in their present state. The consequences of these abuses to young men who come from the country to learn to sing, is lamentable. Expecting to be fully educated, and then introduced to the means of earning a comfortable livelihood, they enter the academy at a considerable expense; and after staying there for some time, they leave it with truly the competency to sing a few songs; but with so little knowledge of music in general, and so little power to learn quickly, or read at sight, but they must slip into poverty and obscurity, unless they resolutely begin their education over again.'[1]

Nevertheless, in its first fifteen years of existence the Academy had brought forth three musicians of distinction, Blagrove, Sterndale Bennett, and George Macfarren. Henry Blagrove (1811–72), a native of Nottingham and son of a music teacher, was a violinist. After leaving the Academy he went to Kassel to study with Spohr. On his return in 1834, he assembled a permanent string quartet (the other members being H. Gattie, J. B. Dando, and C. Lucas) and his concerts at the Hanover Square Rooms, supplementing the public recitals of chamber music organised by Potter and also by Neate, furnished opportunity for many to become acquainted with the classics of the chamber music repertoire.

William Sterndale Bennett (1816–75) was the prototype of the modern administrative musician, busy in public and even busier in private in the conduct of musical politics. He eventually built for himself an impregnable position, but in so doing destroyed his once considerable creative talent. The main part of his compositions were completed by the time he was twenty-eight.

The Bennett family had its roots deep in the soil of English music. It stemmed from Derbyshire where there were many Bennetts in the neighbourhood of Ashford in the early part of the eighteenth century. William Bennett (1732/3–1808) was a tailor. So was his son John (1754–1837), who, however, played the oboe in the church band and was a celebrated bass singer in the neighbourhood. In 1791 John was appointed a lay-clerk at King's and Trinity Colleges in Cambridge. Two sons of John were choristers at King's, and one of them, Robert (1788–1819), after apprenticeship with Dr. John Clarke-Whitfield, was elected organist of St. Peter's Church, Sheffield, in 1811.[2] Robert died when his son William

[1] Collet Dobson, 'State of the Royal Academy of Music', in *The Musical World*, 1837, pp. 20–21.

[2] Bennett was a candidate in 1810, when J. Blewitt was elected, but Blewitt withdrew from the post in 1811 to go to Ireland. (See W. T. Freemantle, *Sterndale Bennett and Sheffield*, Sheffield, 1919.) A new organ was installed in St. Peter's Church in 1805, John Mather then being appointed organist. See *Minutes of the Town Trust* (*Burgery Reports*), 1 August 1805: 'Trustees invite Master Cutler and Company and Church Burgers to guarantee with them the risk of a loss in the Music Festival for the opening of the new organ.'

was in his fourth year. The child, already seen to be musical, was put under the care of his grandfather, who arranged that he should become a choir-boy at King's, and thus maintain a family connection.

At the age of ten Sterndale Bennett was withdrawn from the choir and on account of his outstanding ability placed as a boarder in the Royal Academy at the instance of Rev. F. Hamilton, then Superintendent of the Academy. Young Bennett immediately made his mark. Attwood had him to sing in St. Paul's Cathedral. In 1828 'Master Bennett" played a piano concerto of Dussek—'and the example of one who was modestly brought forward in a Concerto of Dussek's will not be lost on the students of another generation, who will here trace the early indication of that prize talent now matured with ripening years'.[1] Bennett's lessons in composition were at first with Crotch (whose belief in the efficacy of writing double chants conflicted with Bennett's preference for essaying string quartets à la Mozart), and afterwards with Potter. Potter was a good teacher (the affinities between his and Bennett's style are to be seen both in pianoforte and orchestral textures) and characteristically he encouraged his star pupil so that in 1832 Bennett's first Piano Concerto, in D minor, was played at an Academy concert. This work, published at the behest of the Academy, is full of musical ideas and ends with a bracing scherzo-finale. In the early part of the following year this concerto was repeated—in the presence of Mendelssohn. Mendelssohn urged on Bennett the desirability of study in Leipzig, the opportunity for which came three years later.

By this time Bennett had firmly established himself in London as the white hope of English music. He had composed five symphonies, and, more important, two more piano concertos. The second concerto, in E flat, was dedicated to Potter, the third, in C minor, to J. B. Cramer. Both were given performances at Philharmonic concerts, in 1835 and 1836, with Bennett as soloist. In these strongly classical works Bennett admitted as major influences the stylistic traits of Mozart and Beethoven—the former in the nervous, but keen, character of first and last movement themes, the latter in occasional dramatic gestures. In the G major *Romanza* of the third concerto Bennett, with some finely judged *pizzicato* chords, balances the claims of his heroes. It was, however, the Mozart impulse that lasted longest. As in his D minor Concerto so in his G minor Symphony of 1837 he ruminates over the interval of the semitone. A quotation from the finale of the latter work shows also how Bennett's ideas stood still [Ex. 4].

Bennett reached Leipzig, having first accompanied J. W. Davison to the lower Rhine Festival, in the autumn of 1836. He remained in the city until the following June. His sponsorship by Mendelssohn opened all

[1] Cazalet, op. cit., p. 220.

4.

musical doors and his gifts as pianist and composer were acclaimed not least of all by Robert Schumann, with whom a lifelong friendship developed. Bennett distinguished himself by appearing in the Gewandhaus Concerts as pianist, composer and conductor, his Concerto in C minor[1] and his overture *The Naiads* temporarily raising doubts in German minds as to whether England was as unmusical as it was reported to be. Schumann, ever generous so far as young foreign musicians were concerned, was lavish with his praise for Bennett's genius: so lavish that English critics and historians have spent a hundred years in attempts to demonstrate that Schumann's critical acumen has been much overrated. A greater tribute, of course, was Schumann's dedication of one of his finest works—the *Etudes Symphoniques*—to Bennett.[2] During this first visit to Leipzig Bennett—as befitting a Yorkshireman—arranged the first cricket match ever to be played in Germany. In 1838 he returned to Leipzig, after commencing teaching at the Academy, and produced his F minor Concerto and *The Wood Nymphs* overture at Gewandhaus Concerts. Thereafter he paid one more visit to Germany—in 1842—meeting Spohr in Kassel before going to Leipzig for the last time.

At this point we see Bennett as a composer of great promise. His main talent lay in his capacity for making the notes *sound* right: a talent increased by his wide reading of the pre-classical masters and allied to the same aptitude in Purcell and Arne. Bennett was acknowledged to be a great pianist (Mendelssohn was not one to allow friendship to invade his critical faculty) and it was as a composer for the piano that he shone. On the whole, he avoided the stock figurations that are abundant in Potter's piano works, and he was judicious in his estimate of the most apt tonal relationships between keyboard and orchestra in his concertos. The best of his work lies in the evocative *Three Musical Sketches* (op. 10)—dedicated to Davison—'musical Claude Lorraines', said Schumann, the *Six Studies in Capriccio Form* (op. 11), the *Three Impromptus* (op. 12), and the splendid logic of the Sonata in F minor.[3] Schumann makes an interesting

[1] 'Last week Bennett played his C minor concerto, and was enthusiastically applauded by the Leipzigers, who have all of a sudden become his friends and admirers; indeed, he is the sole topic of conversation here now.' Mendelssohn to his sister Fanny, 24 January 1837.

[2] Bennett's Fantasy in A major (op. 16) is dedicated to Schumann; his F minor Sonata (op. 13) to Mendelssohn.

[3] For a sympathetic assessment of Bennett in this field see Geoffrey Bush, 'Sterndale Bennett: the Solo Piano Works', in *P.R.M.A.*, 91, 1964–5, p. 85.

observation, of some psychological significance, in his notice of the fourth Concerto; an observation that relates Bennett to Mendelssohn on the one hand—and to Benjamin Britten on the other: 'As though the Englishman could not abdicate his nature, water plays a principal part in Bennett's works . . . This barcarolle may be added to his other most successful compositions, the overture to the "Naiads", and his masterly sketches, "The Lake", "The Millstream", and "The Fountain" '. On the whole, however, one reluctantly concludes that Schumann did somewhat over-state his case, being captivated by Bennett's remarkable all-round competence and his personality. The works which were singled out for praise have the Mendelssohnian demerit of predictability. Comparison with Field (see pp. 463 f.) sufficiently establishes the point that whereas Field had genius Bennett had talent. Without the piano Bennett was somewhat less assured, and the overtures which were so highly esteemed at their first performance already show the concessionary attitude of the Victorian composer unwilling to push his audience into any violence of imaginative exercise.

The congeniality of Leipzig gave Bennett enormous encouragement and the feeling that he was recognised to be a composer helped him towards the assurance that he was a composer. Moreover, as a patriotic Englishman he was pleased to note that during his Leipzig period English musical stock had risen high in that city. There was Bennett himself, and Macfarren and Pierson who were credited with being worthy composers, and there were also two English singers who sang for Mendelssohn at the Gewandhaus. These were Mary Shaw, one of Smart's pupils, and Clara Novello, who were described by Mendelssohn in a letter to the Philharmonic Society in London, on 19 January 1839, as 'the best concert singers we have had in this country for a long time.' These three artists had common qualities; they cared for tonal purity and stylistic precision. These were also Mendelssohnian virtues.

The apparent 'golden mean' of Mendelssohn's own style was attractive to English musicians for many reasons. It not only combined classical propriety with romantic fancy, but it had a ready appeal for the British people as a whole. Among those who fell heavily under the influence was Charles Edward Horsley (1822–76), son of William. He met Mendelssohn at home—his father frequently acting as Mendelssohn's host in Kensington—and his talents, nurtured by his father and Ignaz Moscheles, were noted with approval by the master. Consequently he went to Kassel to work with Hauptmann and then to Leipzig where his studies were at last supervised by Mendelssohn himself. Horsley composed prolifically in the benign German environment, his largest work being the Symphony in D minor (op. 9),[1] written between November 1842 and September

[1] B.M. Add. Ms. 37234/5.

1844, dedicated hopefully to the Society of British Musicians. On the whole this is a school-symphony in the manner of the master. An opening *Andante con moto* concerns itself at first with the sonorities available from *divisi* cellos and independent bass. The first subject [Ex. 5*a*] tends to remain fussily in the same place, while the second subject [Ex. 5*b*] languishes

5a.

5b.

characteristically with the clarinet before being transferred to the cello where the leap of the sixth in the fourth bar expands with qualified ecstasy to an octave, to terminate in C major. Like Mendelssohn Horsley enjoyed writing quick movements—the third movement, the slow movement, is still *Andante con moto*, with a fatal habit of settling too readily on second inversions—and altogether he is capable of generating a sense of exhilaration. But—especially in the second movement *Scherzo* and the final *Allegro con fucoco*—there is a sense of contrivance. This was the failing of British symphonic writers until the emergence of Elgar. The wonder is, of course, that any British symphonies were composed at all. Horsley returned to England to become an organist at Notting Hill. In 1868 he emigrated to Australia, and thence to the U.S.A. His life as composer, like that of Bennett, virtually came to an end when he left Leipzig.

On his return to England Bennett settled down to teach. He was director of the Philharmonic Society from 1842. In 1848 he resigned from the Society on account of dissension with Michael Costa, but after Costa's resignation (and after Wagner's direction of the Society in 1855) Bennett resumed his connection and became its conductor. Two years previously he had, reluctantly, refused a remarkable offer to take over the conductorship of the Leipzig Gewandhaus Orchestra. In 1849 Bennett brought together all the existing threads of Bach interest in England,[1] and founded

[1] An unexpected reference to Bach occurs in a letter from Thomas Carlyle to George Grove (28 January 1853): 'Your excerpt about Sebastian Bach is worth something; and the kindness with which you communicate it is worth a great deal. I am very much obliged to you. According to "Rodenbeck's" book the visit in question occurred on the

the Bach Society: on 6 May 1854 he conducted the first performance in England of the *St. Matthew Passion.* The influence of Bach is detectable in Bennett's works, as for instance in the treatment of the opening chorale (in 4/4 against the instrumental 3/8), the reduced instrumental accompaniment to the words of Jesus in *The Woman of Samaria*, and in various keyboard pieces. The pace of professional life—as Berlioz testified—was killing; but Bennett, zealous that England should take her place among the musical nations, refused no invitation. In 1856 he was elected Professor of Music at Cambridge. Ten years later he succeeded to the Principalship of the Royal Academy. He was also busy as conductor of the principal provincial festivals. He composed when he could—which was not often. Among his works *The May Queen* and *The Woman of Samaria*,[1] cantata and oratorio respectively, enjoyed a popularity that was in inverse ratio to their intrinsic merit. Both suffered from entirely banal texts, which were not helped by tedious repetitiveness (e.g. 'I will love thee/I will love thee/ love thee O Lord/O Lord, my strength'). Bennett, however, succeeded in pleasing the public, particularly with fluent little 4/4 melodies running over a dribble of accompanimental quavers, more especially the petit-bourgeois public that dominated musical taste (especially in the provinces) during the period of Victorian affluence. The choral societies (like the churches) had come to terms with middle-class sentiment.

An unflattering view of the prevailing standards is given in the account of Bennett's Sheffield lectures of 1859. By now the practice of lectures on musical appreciation, instituted by Samuel Wesley, Crotch, and Callcott, was firmly established, and the Sheffield Literary and Philosophical Society was delighted to issue an invitation to a celebrated native of the town to repeat in Sheffield the series of talks he had given in London. Sterndale Bennett, however, was not merely content to talk. He played as well, and so may be regarded as the founder of the lecture-recital. He 'gave several illustrations from the works of Handel, Bach, Scarlatti, Mozart, Beethoven, Mendelssohn and others. As a piano-forte

"7th April" (1747), and the concert, that evening, was at the Old Schloss in Potsdam, Sansouci being just in the birth throes, and not yet born, for our objects. 7th April, 1747, that was the evening on which Sebastian tried the piano . . .'

In *The Spectator*, of 11 June 1853, Grove (disguised as 'Constant Reader') protested against Vieuxtemps's dull concept of Bach's Chaconne, saying that 'feeling, tender passionate sentiment, a burning genius, and a prodigious flow and march of ideas, are [Bach's] characteristics'.

[1] In his Preface to this work Bennett anticipates Elgar's suggestion regarding the character of Gerontius: 'With regard to the Woman of Samaria herself, it will be plainly seen that the composer has treated her as a secular and worldly character, though not without indications here and there of that strong intuitive religious feeling which has never been denied to her.'

player Dr. Bennett ranks in the first-class, and his performances last night delighted the audience . . .'[1] His lecture, on 'The state of music in English private society and the general prospects of music in the future,' while noting certain advances in native musical culture—especially through the provincial festivals, was on the whole depressing. He deplored the trivial condition of domestic music-making, and the haphazard organisation of concerts, and he observed on the general superiority of musical life in Germany. What he said was, in different words, repeated by Elgar in his famous Birmingham Lectures of 1905–6. The strength of Bennett's case was illustrated in a letter from 'A Subscriber' which appeared in the *Telegraph* on 29 April:

'At the lecture delivered last evening by Dr. Bennett, I was unfortunately very near to some ladies, who kept up a running conversation during the performance of even the most beautiful music in the programme. A gentleman said to me before I attended the lecture "Playing Bach's fugues in Sheffield will be casting pearls before swine". I scarcely thought that was a just remark respecting the members of the Sheffield Literary and Philosophical Society, but I am sorry to say that a great deal of the pleasure that I should have experienced during the exquisite performance of the first movement of Beethoven's "Moonlight Sonata" and also Mendelssohn's "Andante and Rondo Capriccioso," was prevented by such refined remarks as the following: "Well, what plaintive ditties!" "Are you taking the music all in?" "It *may* be very grand!" "I couldn't tell the difference between his playing and our Fanny's!" "Is that dress silk?" "What a gay bonnet Miss—— has got on!" &c.

'Now all these valuable remarks might be intensely interesting to those who made them, but as there is another lecture to come, I hope the remark-makers will not inflict such a punishment upon those who wish to profit by the opportunity, so rarely afforded in Sheffield, of hearing the delightful playing of Dr. Sterndale Bennett.

'I hope these few lines will spare many a lover of classical music the punishment that I have undergone.'

Sterndale Bennett, knighted in 1871, accumulated authority and through so doing enhanced the prestige of public pedagogic officers. The Principal and the Professor[2] became powerful, whereas the status of the composer and the executant (unless foreign) was implicitly down-graded. During the eighteenth century those musicians who held office at Court

[1] *Sheffield Telegraph*, 28 April 1859.

[2] By the will of Major-General John Reid (1721–1807), soldier and amateur musician, a Chair of music was set up in Edinburgh University in 1839. In a codicil to his will Reid instructed that 'in every year after his appointment [the Professor] will cause a concert of music to be prepared on the 13th of February, being my birthday'. Thus the Reid concerts were established.

were at least highly competent, and often a good deal more. William Shield died in 1829. The names of his nineteenth-century successors as Masters of the King's (Queen's) Music—now only responsible for occasional concerts with a small orchestra—are eloquent of the decline in prestige that took place after the death of George IV: Christian Kramer, François Cramer, George Anderson, Sir William Cusins. Nor was the Chapel Royal any more contributory to the musical life of the country. The office of organist, held by Attwood, Smart, Charles Knyvett, John Sale, John Goss, George Cooper, and Charles Jekyll, was a sinecure: a deputy did the work. The Mastership of the Children lost all musical relevance in the hands of relative nonentities such as William Hawes and Thomas Helmore. In 1860 retrenchment reduced the number of Gentlemen to eight. In the same year the old offices of violist and bell-ringer were discontinued. With the passing of the sense of commitment to music shown by Tudors, Stuarts, and Hanoverians alike much of the virility drained away from British music. The Queen patronized celebrity concerts—but as a public duty.

The career of Sterndale Bennett covers a period of re-adjustment and by his example other composers lost their souls while making gains in other directions. George Macfarren's (1813–87) career was similar to Bennett's. Born in London, Macfarren entered the Academy, of which he became a professor in 1834. In this year his Symphony in F minor was played at a concert of the Society of British Musicians. In 1836 a Symphony in A[1] and the programmatic *Chevy Chase* Overture[2] were heard. Two years later the *Devil's Opera*, a satirical sketch on the kind of diabolism currently fashionable in *Der Freischütz* and *Robert le Diable*, was performed at the Lyceum Theatre.[3] Further operas followed in 1846 and 1849. On 27 October of the latter year his *King Charles II* was greeted

[1] 'Mr. Macfarren's Symphony (taken as a whole) has more the air of adult and rational unity, than any previous composition of his, we remember to have heard.' *The Musical World*, 27 January 1837, p. 93.

[2] 'Mr. Macfarren's overture . . . will, in all probability, be pronounced the best piece of descriptive writing that has hitherto proceeded from the pen of that very clever young musician . . . It was tumultuously applauded'. ib., 10 February 1837, p. 124. Tumultuous applause was, it was elsewhere reported, often laid on in a spirit of partisanship by pupils from the Academy. *Chevy Chase*, however, made the grade independently, for it was included in a Gewandhaus concert in 1843.

[3] Ancillary to the Society of British Musicians an 'English Opera House' (at the Lyceum) was optimistically set up. Among the beneficiaries were John Barnett (1802–90), who composed *The Mountain Sylph* (1834), *Fair Rosamund* (1837), and *Farinelli* (1839), after which he lived for another fifty-one years without writing another opera; and Edward James Loder (1813–65) whose *Nourjahad* (1834) was the first opera performed under the auspices of the new set-up. His *The Night Dancers* (1846), 'wild, romantic, and imaginative' (Hogarth, *Memoirs*, II, p. 375), was one of a number of operas by English composers introduced by the management of the Princess's Theatre, in Oxford Street, between 1842 and 1850. This enterprise centered rather on operas in English than on English operas.

wholeheartedly and extravagantly by *The Musical World* on 3 November: 'That it is the finest and most complete operatic work of a native musician ever produced on the stage is no less universally allowed. The production of such a work and its reception must be regarded as an epoch in the history of the music of this country.' Alas! the puff was unrealistic, for ' . . . in 1851, changing the form of composition, from the great difficulty of finding any opening in this country for operatic music, he brought forward, at the National Concerts at Her Majesty's Theatre, the Cantata, "The Sleeper Awakened". The music in this work has become established among the popular favourites of the day, several of the pieces being continually sung by artists at various concerts'.[1]

Macfarren's output, despite the ultimate handicap of total blindness—which caused him to dictate his later works to amanuenses, was enormous. He made a valiant attempt to break into the field of the string quartet (the precedents were Bishop's quartet in C minor, of 1816, and examples by Barnett, Walmisley, and Ouseley) by composing six works of this order. Apart from the first, in G minor, they were, however, undistinguished and rapidly passed into limbo. The oratorio *St. John the Baptist* (Bristol, 1873), not unnaturally in an oratorio-conditioned country, took perhaps the highest place among his works. Here we see the frustrations of the would-be opera composer, for the work has every quality of English opera of the period. It also has the general failing—an absence of dramatic movement or development. Yet, despite its faults, *St. John the Baptist* is worth looking at twice. Once because it shows one part of Elgar's background, and once because it is so much livelier than the general run of English oratorios. Macfarren handled the chorus finely—like Berlioz and Elgar he never used two parts if one would do: thus his choral interjections have a compelling thrustfulness. Nor did he make of counterpoint a mere matter of duty. The splendid choral variations on Croft's *Psalm 104* which comprise no. 10 are a rare instance of a composer making really effective use of an English hymn-tune. This movement, strongly diatonic and athletic, is from the same 'English' compartment from which the best of Parry was lifted. The emergence of a new consideration of diatonic viability is urged in anticipation of Vaughan Williams—as far as motiv is concerned—in this manner [Ex. 6*a*]. The same movement (a recitative detailing the habits and diet of John the Baptist) extends diatonic influence in the interlude [6*b*] which is not immediately to be thought of as 'Victorian'. In the urgency of this excerpt the impulsiveness of Elgar is seen to be latent. Elgar is foreshadowed even more in the fourth-beat triplets, the bold tread, and the incisive part-writing of the final chorus of the oratorio. On the programmatic side (Macfarren rarely

[1] Cazalet, op. cit., p. 308.

6a.

6b.

resisted temptation in this respect) we have a 'Shofar' motiv in the overture (Macfarren prefers an interval of a fourth rather than the sixth of *The Apostles*) and a by no means ineffective *Orientale* [Ex. 6*c*] for the entry of

6c.

Salome—a lady, alas! whom Macfarren felt obliged to describe in prudent musical language.

Macfarren's interests were wide. One other aspect of his composition deserves notice. He was among the early 'social realists', albeit undoctrinaire. A history of British music that omitted mention of his part-songs, *Cricketer's Song* and *Song of the Railroads*, would be sadly lacking in responsibility.[1] Macfarren edited Purcell's *Dido and Aeneas* for the Musical Antiquarian Society and Handel's *Belshazzar*, *Judas Maccabaeus*, and *Jephtha* for the Handel Society, of which he was secretary. He wrote books (*Rudiments of Harmony* still stands the examiner in good stead in many British schools of music, even after more than a hundred years), programme-notes, and many articles. He succeeded Bennett as Professor at Cambridge, became Principal of the Royal Academy in 1876, and was knighted in 1883.

Bennett and Macfarren were major figures in a changing environment. But, despite their considerable services to British music, they were

[1] Also mentioned in the same list are E. G. Monk's *The jolly Cricket ball* and *Foot-ball Song*, and Walter Cecil's less ebullient *An Emigrant's Song*, *Mus. T.*, 1855, p. 124.

victims of circumstance. They capitulated to economic pressure and abdicated their right as individual composers to conform to accepted standards. They escaped the baneful influence of the Victorian Church, however, for not being among its servants their concern with liturgical music was slight.

Until well into the second half of the eighteenth century the Church of England gave encouragement—if increasingly sporadic—to composers. In the first half of the nineteenth century it gave virtually none. Stirred by considerations of prestige new and large organs were built—leading builders being Elliott and Hill,[1] Hill and Davison,[2] and Gray and Son[3]—and there was also a developing export trade, instruments being dispatched to various parts of the Empire and even to Russia. An intriguing note in *The Musical World*, 14 July 1837, describes organs constructed wholly from iron or brass, 'intended for the use of the newly-formed railroads at Birmingham and St. Petersburgh'. The same article—on 'English Organs and Organists'—speaks of organists in high places, 'whose ignorance of organ music, and organ effects, did not long remain the laughter and scorn of the profession, since, from its constant exhibition, the mind naturally united the ideas of imbecility and folly with the holders of such appointments.' On a lower level many appointments were cooked. Thomas Adams, for instance, one of the most distinguished members of the profession, was called in as referee at the Parish Church of Greenwich when a vacancy was to be filled. 'Mr. Adams returned one who happened to be extra-parochial, and his opinion was consequently rejected, expense uselessly incurred, and a member of the profession wantonly insulted, by the return of a lady, whose only recommendation was that of residing in the parish'.[4]

Church Music

So far as choirs were concerned almost the only satisfactory work was being done under the aegis of the Roman Catholics. With the decline of standards in the Established Church in the later eighteenth century music-lovers went in large numbers to the Sardinian, Spanish, and Portu-

[1] Thomas Elliott joined John Snetzler's foreman, W. Nutt, in 1803. In 1825 he took William Hill into partnership. The firm built many important organs during the nineteenth century, including those of York Minster (which was the subject of litigation between the Minster authorities and the firm) and Birmingham Town Hall.

[2] In 1837–8 Hill was partnered by Frederick Davison.

[3] This firm dated from 1774. After 1838 John Gray joined forces with Davison, the firm finally becoming Gray and Davison. Gray and Davison were responsible for the Crystal Palace, and Leeds, Bolton and Glasgow Town Hall organs.

[4] *The Musical World*, 17 February 1837, p. 140.

guese Embassy Chapels. The Catholics were also active in the provinces, so that Zimri Andrews, a collier and a violinist, of Pendlebury near Manchester, being 'well versed in Mass music [was] often engaged as principal second violin in performances of Masses in Catholic churches and chapels'.[1] When Weber's funeral service took place in the Catholic Chapel at Moorfields on 21 June 1826, Mozart's *Requiem* was performed. Although eminent soloists were employed (Attwood played the organ), the choir of the chapel was competent to give a splendid account of itself in the choral sections. In the Warwick Street Chapel there was also a 'well-appointed vocal band'—but 'let [the reader] wander to St. Paul's, and he would encounter poverty and slovenliness, a meagre and inefficient choir, a careless performance—neither principals nor chorus, but a make-shift for both.'[2] Things had come to such a pass in the Established Church, indeed, that when the King of Prussia, visiting London, wished to hear the choir of St. Paul's, a choir had to be impressed from elsewhere for the occasion.

At Westminster Abbey (the organist being James Turle[3]) the Dean and Chapter were misappropriating endowments particularly designated to the choral foundation:[4] in this instance for 'pricking the new tunes in the music books.' 'May it be permitted to enquire . . . when this payment was first discontinued, and who now misappropriates the money. Improvement in the musical service of our cathedrals becomes hopeless, when we find those who are most interested in the welfare of the corporations, the first and foremost to close every avenue that might tend to bring about such a desirable event. When last, we wonder, did any of the Deans and Chapters request the composition of a new service or anthem? and during the last half-century how much has been expended in purchasing new works, or employing the talents of our English composers? We would venture to say such a return, if made, would not produce a

[1] Millington, op. cit., p. 84.

[2] See 'English Cathedral Music', in *British and Foreign Review*, XVII, 1844, pp. 83–116. Cf. *The Musical World*, 17 February 1837, p. 141. 'From what daily takes place in the choir of this cathedral, the sooner the promised reform in choral matters, suggested by the Bishop of London, is put into operation, the better for the respectability of the parties attached to the corporation. One afternoon last week the choir present were two tenors and a counter-tenor! Truly, this is a mode of performing choral worship in praise of the Deity, which none but dignified members of the Establishment could stomach. The manner of chanting adopted by the choristers at this Cathedral we honestly believe to be *peculiar* to the place. So much the better; but we are sorry that the metropolitan Cathedral should afford the example.'

[3] Turle (1802–82), with G. W. Budd, edited Wilbye's works for the Musical Antiquarian Society (2 vols., 1841, 1846): otherwise he was known for the size of his hands which could cover an octave and a half.

[4] See also Rev. John Jebb, *The Choral Service of the United Church of England and Ireland*, London, 1843.

sum equal in the annual income of the poorest Dean in Christendom.'[1]

The general condition of the Church of England was deplorable and its liturgical and doctrinal deficiencies and ambiguities were the cause of the so-called Oxford Movement. One result of High Church thinking was a reconsideration of the repertoire, character, and purpose of hymnody. The desuetude into which metrical psalmody had fallen, the evangelising consequences of Methodist hymns, and a zeal for collating devotional exercise and doctrinal exposition led Bishop Reginald Heber to consecrate his lyric talent to the composition of texts for new hymns. By sometimes drawing on the great Latin hymns, which he freely translated, he opened up new possibilities that conveniently united with those being explored on the liturgical side. Heber's example was followed by Bishop Richard Mant, Isaac Williams, John Chandler, Edward Caswall, John Keble, John Henry Newman, Henry Francis Lyte, and John Mason Neale, who, between them, enlarged the whole concept of hymnody within the Church of England. New words meant new tunes and a generation of composers grew up for whom the provision of hymn tunes was a major occupation. Among the many minor musicians active in the field of hymnology Charles Steggall (1826–1905) was conspicuous. A pupil and friend of Bennett, and secretary of the Bach Society (1849–70), Steggall published a volume of *Church Psalmody* in 1849, gave two thoughtful lectures on *Music as applied to religion* in 1852, helped to found the (Royal) College of Organists in 1864, and was among those responsible for the music of *Hymns Ancient and Modern*. A few of the tunes composed during the middle and late nineteenth century were good; many were respectable; most (although esteemed by the pious and the sentimental) were indifferent. The Victorian hymn-tune, part-song, and cantata or oratorio met together in a middle territory of etiolated Puritanism and eviscerated Romanticism to form a bulwark—in due course guaranteed by ecclesiastical approval—against positive musical advance on any broad front.

The church musicians, sometimes not unwillingly, were taken for a ride. Their material circumstances improved. The choir-schools were re-constituted. The decencies of liturgy were reinstated. The cathedral churches undertook choral Mattins and Evensong. And the repertoire was restocked—with anthems and services of high respectability. But most of this music (which may still be heard) was of an unsurpassed dullness. Solid rather unimaginative organists and choirmasters, concerned with 'pure tone' and the value of sight reading, filled the cathedral, college, and parochial organ lofts and, sustained by treatises such as those of Macfarren, taught the virtue of sobriety in the Anglican manner.

[1] *The Musical World*, 24 March 1837, p. 31.

The eventual *vade mecum* of the Anglican, even of the Englishman, was the summary of half-a-century of tempered reform in *Hymns Ancient and Modern* (1860–61).

The grand master of respectability was John Goss (1800–80) who succeeded Attwood as organist of St. Paul's Cathedral. A pupil both of Stafford Smith and Attwood, Goss reduced the scholarly insights of the one and the grace of the other to what Ernest Walker justly describes as 'a very agreeable view of sedately graceful expressiveness joined to solid technical skill'.[1] Thomas Attwood Walmisley (1814–56), Attwood's godson, had more talent than Goss, but less luck. By the time he was eighteen he had written two string quartets as well as other chamber music, a Symphony in D minor,[2] and two organ concertos. Monck Mason (see p. 467) tried to persuade him into opera, but Walmisley, of considerable mathematical talent, decided to go to Cambridge. In 1833, although an undergraduate, he became organist of Trinity and St. John's Colleges and in due course found himself serving at other places of worship and playing for eight services each Sunday. Walmisley is one of the last composers in the ode tradition. In 1835 he substituted for the Professor, Clarke-Whitfield, and composed a deliberately Handelian ode for the Installation of the Marquess Camden as Chancellor of the University. He earned a hundred guineas for this, but had to pay forty per cent of his fee to Clarke-Whitfield.[3] In 1836 Walmisley was appointed Professor on the death of Clarke-Whitfield. Apart from occasional fees there was no salary attached to the office. A second Cancellarian ode—this time after the manner of Mozart—was composed in 1842. His third, and last, ode—to Prince Albert (1847)—was to a text by Wordsworth, the only official work written by him as Poet Laureate. Walmisley then found Mendelssohn a suitable model. Although he had set out with high hopes, Walmisley, immured in Cambridge that yet awaited a musical awakening, settled down to the routine of church music. His best-known work is the grave Service in D minor, still regarded as a minor masterpiece. Henry Smart (1813–79), nephew of Sir George, was organist at Blackburn before going to London. He had considerable facility in supplying exactly what was wanted, and thus enjoyed an inflated reputation.

The Reverend Sir Frederick Arthur Gore Ouseley (1825–89), son of

[1] Op. cit., p. 266.

[2] Walmisley, a friend of Mendelssohn, showed him the work (of which only one movement is extant and preserved with other Walmisley Mss. by the Royal School of English Church Music). Having learned that it was Walmisley's first symphony Mendelssohn damped the young man's ardour by suggesting that an opinion might be better passed on No. 12—a reference to Mendelssohn's own symphonic record, where what is now the first was, in fact, the thirteenth.

[3] Note by Walmisley on Ms.; information communicated by Mr. H. E. Walmisley.

a diplomat, was an oriental scholar and an amateur musician of some talent and much energy. His connections and principal interest (he only ever had one curacy) enabled him to obtain the Professorship of Music at Oxford in 1855, and a Precentorship at Hereford Cathedral. Ouseley edited the works of Orlando Gibbons, researched into early Spanish treatises, wrote text-books, instituted examinations for degrees at Oxford, and founded St. Michael's College, Tenbury. This institution (still in existence) was intended to serve as 'a model for the choral service of the church in these realms.' It is, however, more famous through the wealth of material bequeathed to it by Ouseley which constituted the basis of the present library. Ouseley composed oratorios and other ecclesiastical music. *The Martyrdom of St. Polycarp* (Oxford Mus. D. exercise, for 1854) is an outstanding example of the condition to which English music was reduced through slavish adherence to the canons of respectability. Most of the work is traced over *Elijah* (see the Angel's 'Thus saith the Lord of Hosts, before whom I serve, Be strong Polycarp', the improbable double-chorus, 'He taught impiety', and the angelic trio [S.S.A.], 'In the sight of the unwise'): but the final, fugal, double-chorus, to the word 'Amen', is a solemn study in Handelian pastiche. During the remainder of the nineteenth century a great many oratorios and sacred cantatas were written. Since they are adequately summarised in the prototypical *Woman of Samaria* and *St. Polycarp* they will receive no detailed mention.

Far more important than any of these well-meaning and virtuous men was Samuel Sebastian Wesley (1810–76), the one church musician of the period touched with genius. Wesley was the son of Samuel (his mother was Sarah Suter, with whom Samuel lived) and inherited many of his father's traits. He was, however, of a tougher fibre, and, riding over such professional disappointments as being passed over for the Windsor organistship in 1835 and the Edinburgh Professorship in 1841 and 1844, fought his way through the slough of ecclesiastical disregard for music, leaving Deans and Chapters painfully aware of his militant progress.

Needless to say Samuel Sebastian, being a Wesley, was precocious. As a chorister in the Chapel Royal he was rewarded for his solo singing by the always appreciative George IV. After acting as organist of various London churches he was appointed organist of Hereford Cathedral in 1832. Here he composed his most famous anthem, *The Wilderness*, which, however, was not awarded the Gresham Prize Medal (for which it was submitted) on the grounds that it was 'not cathedral music'. Wesley married the daughter of the Dean of Hereford and transferred to Exeter in 1835. Seven years later, having been invited to open the organ in the newly built parish church of Leeds, he took the opportunity offered to him of becoming permanent organist of the church. Active as lecturer and conductor of the Leeds Choral Society, he did much to renew the musical spirit of the city.[1] In 1849 he moved to Winchester (from where he could undertake teaching at the Royal Academy), and in 1865 to Gloucester. Having once conducted the Three Choirs Festival, at Hereford in 1834, Wesley gratefully renewed acquaintance with this institution and directed the meetings at Gloucester from 1865 to 1876. In his next to last year, he was awarded a Civil List pension of £100 a year, which he preferred to the knighthood that was alternatively proferred.

Wesley's was a restless, searching, critical and creative mind. It was his love of Bach, his considerable skill as organist, and his belief in the essential integrity of the choral tradition that turned him into a church musician. As a young man he had some experience of the London theatre, and it is possible to recognise in him a talent that, given favourable circumstances, could have enriched the music of the theatre. The most celebrated works that he composed for the Church were by nature dramatic —and so was his intervention in church affairs as pamphleteer. Wesley was 'a Radical Reformer, a rater of the Clergy, and particularly of the dignitaries of the Church'.[2] In 1845 he published his Service in E, in the Preface to which he tore apart the easy complacencies about the 'cathedral tradition.' He made rough observations on the weaker selections in Boyce's anthology, not even sparing Tallis—on the content of his Service in D minor. Wesley had his ear attuned to the sonorities of his own day (he had a special respect for the music of Spohr) and looked for ways of making use of them within the field of church music. 'It would, no doubt, be difficult to impart to the richer portions of the service all the high qualities of modern art, and yet preserve the necessary regard to the features in detail. To accomplish this is the task of the modern church musician'. In *The Wilderness* and in the Service in E Wesley gave practical expression to this thesis. Both works are vivid, and arresting. In the former Wesley shows a greater sense of the dramatic possibilities of recitative than almost any English composer since Purcell [Ex. 7]. In the latter he demonstrates that appreciation of the choral medium (supported by organ) depends on recognition of the acoustical properties of the particular kind of auditorium to be used. The opening of the 'Jubilate' is a fine instance of the intuitive understanding of the English composer for a thrilling mass of sound ready for acoustical amplification by the architect's vaulting. In both works harmonic colour is introduced with conviction (which Wesley later lost) and aptness. Wesley's compositional methods, in his

[1] In 1855 the new Town Hall of Leeds was opened by the Queen and the occasion was celebrated by the musical festival for which Bennett, who conducted the festival, composed *The May Queen*.

[2] *Morning Post*, 26 February 1844.

7.

Bass solo
For all flesh is as grass, and all the glo-ry of man as the flow-er of grass. The
Organ
grass wi-ther-eth and the flow-er there of fall - eth a - way

principal works, stand away from convention. Neither the English tradition nor the function of English liturgical music encouraged 'classical' procedures. Wesley, therefore, did not see fit to use them. Thus his works do not 'develop'—see, for example, the series of vignettes that constitute *The Lord is my Shepherd.* They grow out of the character of the words, and the words themselves promote their own allusions. In the *Service in E*, for example, there are highly original shifts (through the distant reaches of A flat and G major) in the *Gloria* of the 'Jubilate', and a wonderfully expanding passage, rising semitonally above the crotchet pulsations of the pedal, at the words 'And the third day . . . right hand of the Father' in the 'Creed'; in *The Wilderness* one notes the felicitousness of the chordal implications as 'the waters break out', in *Praise the Lord O my Soul* an elevating climactic exploitation of thesis and antithesis as represented by the contrasting bright lights of A major and F major. All these and other similar instances show a fine appreciation of the warmth of the words of the English liturgy. In his implicit recognition of the purely sensuous authority of music Wesley was ahead of his day, as also in an eclecticism that absorbs many influences—of the Elizabethans, of Handel, of Sam Wesley, of Bach, of Spohr, of Mendelssohn—without being submissive to any of them. Apart from the works named the classic examples of Wesley's style are *O Lord, thou art my God, Wash me throughly, Cast me not away*, and *All go to one place*; works in which the dominant note—rare at that time in English music—is of tragic resignation. More than once Wesley reminds us of Brahms. Like many other composers Wesley's reputation subsequently rested on his lesser works—*Blessed be the God and Father* (with, however, a splendid dramatic alternation between 'Being born again' and 'But the Word of the Lord') and the hymn-tune 'Aurelia', for instance.

Wesley's direct assault on the establishment with which he had so strong a love-hate relationship was conducted through his two contentious pamphlets—*A few words on Cathedral music* (1849) and *Reply to the Inquiries of the Cathedral Commissioners relating to the Improvement of the Music in Divine Worship in Cathedrals* (1854)—and his speeches and lectures. The reverse of Wesley's progressiveness was his perversity in preaching the virtues of unequal temperament.[1] Or, perhaps, he was again ahead of his time.

Irish Composers

The British composer of the eighteenth century was, broadly speaking, an 'insider'. Those of any distinction in the nineteenth century, on the other hand, were 'outsiders'. This is a reflection of the altered status of music within the social structure. Composers who especially suffered from a sense of 'alienation' were those who crossed the unseen but none the less definite frontiers and attempted to work within territories marked off for foreign occupation. Most of all did this apply in the treacherous domain of opera. It is significant that among those who, sooner or later, felt themselves to be cut off—or who cut themselves off—were a number of Irishmen. The influence of expatriate Irishmen was to strengthen as the Victorian era pursued its course. Because they were exiles from their own land and strangers in England the Irish developed a valuable sense of cosmopolitanism and in the long run helped to redeem England from the parochialism that settled down during the regimen of the cathedral organist school—which effectively set up barriers against any kind of reciprocal free trade.

The first of the Irish composers of note of the nineteenth century was also the greatest: John Field (1782–1837). Field's influence was out of all proportion to the extent of his compositions (those which are extant add up to no more than seventy pieces according to the most recent and authoritative computation[2]). But he it was who uncovered the poetic nature of the pianoforte and especially through his *Nocturnes* (in all eighteen) opened up an area of sensibility that Chopin and Liszt were grateful more fully to explore.

Field was in the first place the beneficiary of the Italian opera tradition that had established itself in Dublin at the Smock Alley, Crow Street,

[1] See letters by Wesley relating to Temperament in *The Musical Standard*, April, June, July 1863.

[2] Cecil Hopkinson, *A Bibliographical Thematic Catalogue of the Works of John Field, 1782–1837* (privately published), 1962. See also Alan Tyson, 'John Field's Earliest Compositions', *M. & L.*, 47, no. 3, 1966, pp. 239–248.

and Royal Theatres. His father (later to play in Bath and in the Haymarket, London) was a fiddler, and the son of an organist. Between them, father and grandfather kept John hard at it. The discipline of practice was so severe that the boy from time to time considered the desirability of running away from home. As has already been said, he became a pupil and employee of Clementi. His piano playing was an asset of the first order to his employer[1], and the opinion Clementi held of his pupil was endorsed by audiences in Paris and Vienna: 'the perfect and incomparable manner in which he performed the celebrated Fugues of John Sebastian Bach, "and which in more recent times have delighted the best judges who have heard him", excited in an especial manner the astonishment of the Parisians'.[2]

Field settled in St. Petersburg where his fame as teacher and performer was enormous. After nearly twenty years in that city he went to Moscow where, apart from a profitless European tour that took in England, in 1832, he remained until his death.

Like all the great pianoforte composers, Field's style came through his fingers—so that his works give the impression of calculated extemporisation on subconscious memories. His melodic talent derived from Italian cantilena and his style of playing was, in his own day, compared with Catalini's singing. The influence of Clementi (to whom he dedicated three sonatas) shows in general rather than in particular—in the exploratory attitude to the keyboard and in the lay-out of sonatas and concertos. In these Field was content to repeat, but not uncritically, the principles inculcated into him. Even so, in rhetorical passages in the concerto, gestures that are unmistakably based on those of Clementi are moderated to the executant style of Field. His touch 'and tone were the most perfect that it is possible to conceive. His mode of holding his hands on the instrument was worthy of imitation, his fingers alone played, without any unnecessary movement of the hand and arm, each finger striking the key with such mechanical power and nicety, that he was enabled to produce the loudest as well as the softest tones, the shortest as well as the longest notes, in equal perfection, without the slightest visible effort . . . It is true that there are those who maintain that it is necessary to make use of [instruments with an easy touch], in bravura playing: this was not Field's style, yet so charming and so successful was he in the execution of the minutest passages, that even Hummel,[3] in his best days, could only

[1] 'Field a young boy, which plays the pianoforte Extremely well', Haydn *3rd London Notebook*, ed. Robbins Landon, London, 1959, p. 301.

[2] 'Memoirs of Field', in *The Musical World*, 14 April 1837, pp. 70–72.

[3] An amusing account of Field's only encounter with Hummel is given in *The Musical World*, 20 January 1837, p. 70. This was quoted from Rudolf Hirsch, *Gallerie lebender Tondichter: biographisch-kritischer Beitrag*, Vienna, 1836.

be pronounced second to him . . . his wonderful and in some degree most lovely and dream-like trifles, acquire throughout a perfect and beautiful touch, a singing tone, and that delicate, decided, and often piquant expression so peculiar to the composer'.[1]

It is well-known that Field's example inspired Chopin, but to regard him merely as a forerunner of a greater master is unjust. Field stands immaculate in his own excellence, the first real composer ever to come out of Ireland and among British composers the one who most nearly reached perfection. In a rich age of English poetry Field was the only musician capable of uncovering a complementary vein of lyrical music. He had melodic genius but the capacity to dissolve melodic notions into the evanescent half-tones which his fingers discovered. Thus we may notice the cadenzas and melismata, the chains of thirds, the delicate arpeggiandi of the nocturnes (especially no. 7 in A and no. 10 in E), as well as the imaginative asides in harmonic ambiguity that show, for example, in no. 11 (E flat), and the richly endowed vision of [Ex. 8] to

8.

realise why Field's genius fired those among his contemporaries who looked to music to release the hidden shapes of the reflective spirit. Liszt recognised in the *Nocturnes* a 'poignant charm'. But Field was not limited to poignancy and charm. He could, in partial realisation of the character of Irish folk-song, effectively use the mood of the morning (even in a night-piece) [Ex. 9]. Moreover, as in the second and third concertos (in A flat and E flat), he could walk across the score with a histrionic gesture

9.

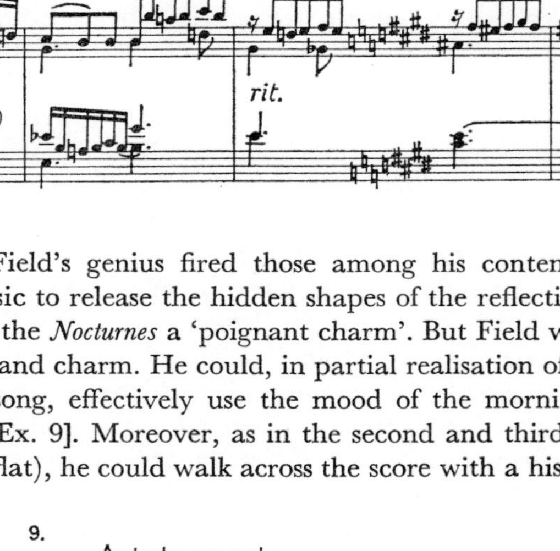

[1] *The Musical World* 14 April, 1837.

in the heroic manner but not without some mitigation of its vulgar potential.

10.

Field, praised by Schumann[1] and Liszt,[2] who, having met Field, made the striking and pertinent observation that 'he loved silence,' left no influence in Britain. On the other hand his compatriot Michael William Balfe (1808-70) did. *The Bohemian Girl* was not only to become the most widely popular of all operas in English but the most convenient point of departure for the amateur operatic societies that sprang up in the latter part of the century. In 1963 *The Bohemian Girl* was still breathing, there being one performance during that year—by the St. Mary's Choral Society, Clonmel, Co. Tipperary. There was also one performance in that year of Wallace's *Maritana* (see p. 469), by the Birmingham Co-operative Repertory Company. Balfe, son of a Protestant father who played in the Crow Street orchestra and a Catholic mother, was born in Dublin (though he spent most of his youth in Wexford) where, when he was a boy, he gave performances on the violin and pianoforte that drew packed houses. Prospects in Dublin now less alluring than formerly, Balfe went to London, where he shone first as a baritone singer. Under the patronage of a Russian aristocrat, Count Mezzara, he was enabled to study in Italy. He also spent some time in Paris, where Rossini engineered an engagement for him 1827 in as Figaro in *The Barber of Seville*. Balfe sang with success on the opera stage both in France and Italy, and also achieved success as a composer—his tunes and his orchestral textures falling easy on the general ear. He returned to England—where opera had reached a nadir in its chequered fortunes under the aegis of the tawdry Bishop,[3] who had reduced it to the lowest form of light entertainment—with a view to bringing English opera into line with continental standards. He

1 Schumann became acquainted with Field's *Nocturnes* through Henriette Voigt, who learned them from Ludwig Berger, who was also Mendelssohn's teacher.

2 *Über Fields Nocturnen*, Leipzig, 1859.

3 Henry Bishop (1786–1855), one of the founders of the Philharmonic Society, was associated with the London theatres for most of his life. He was Professor of Music at Edinburgh (1841–3) and Oxford (1848–55). A quite negligible composer, he was responsible for more than a hundred stage pieces, among which are 'operas' based on the Waverley Novels of Scott.

would—for Weber, Auber, and Meyerbeer had shown the way to London audiences—amplify the romantic repertoire. In 1835 he produced *The Siege of Rochelle* at Drury Lane. *The Maid of Artois* (with Malibran in the title role) came in the next year. And, after that, *Catherine Grey*. In 1837 Balfe provided a score for an adaptation of Beaumont and Fletcher's *Caractacus*. This hero, previously treated by Arne and Bishop (in a Drury Lane ballet in 1808), turned up again at Drury Lane in the same year, in an altered version of J. R. Planché's *Bonduca*. All Balfe pieces had the merit of dramatic viability, and the scores were consistent and logical in design, if thin in content. They were approved—and in 1838 he was commissioned to compose *Falstaff* (to an Italian libretto) for Her Majesty's Theatre.[1] This was the first such commission for a British subject since Arne's *Artaserse* (still maintained in the repertoire almost a century later).

Ambitious to revivify English opera, Balfe formed a company (and enlisted royal support) to furnish the English Opera House at the Lyceum. This failing, he took his interests back to Drury Lane, where Alfred Bunn the manager also practised as a librettist; and a very indifferent one. It was Bunn who provided the text for *The Bohemian Girl*, which, under Balfe's direction, shot into immediate popularity. Not only was it successful in Britain. It also swept across the continent—a pretty fantasy with trite but tuneful numbers that belonged to the category rather of operetta than of opera. (The waltz numbers, the slender two-chord choruses, sometimes enhanced by their punctuation [Ex. 11] showed Sullivan the direction to take.) Balfe composed opera for the Opéra Comique in Paris, was honoured by the Kings of France and Spain, entertained by the King of

11.

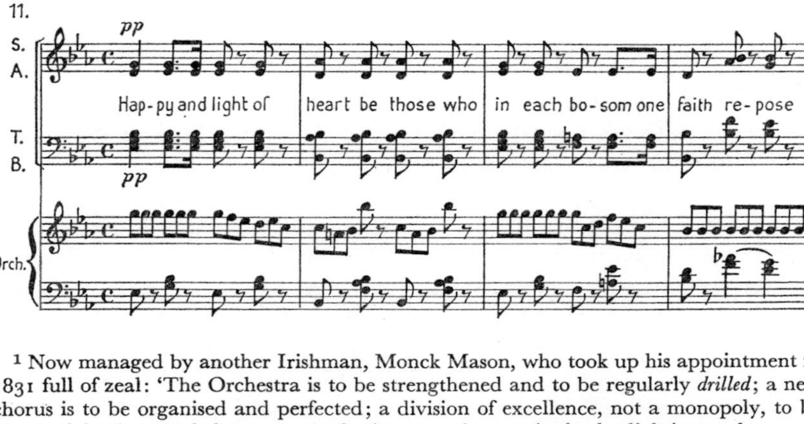
pp
S.
A.
Hap-py and light of heart be those who in each bo-som one faith re-pose
T.
B.
pp
Orch.

[1] Now managed by another Irishman, Monck Mason, who took up his appointment in 1831 full of zeal: 'The Orchestra is to be strengthened and to be regularly *drilled*; a new chorus is to be organised and perfected; a division of excellence, not a monopoly, to be observed in the vocal department; the house to be repaired; the lighting to be much improved; entirely new scenery to be furnished; the pit to be stalled . . .' *The Edinburgh Literary Journal*, 27 August 1831, p. 15.

Prussia, and fêted in St. Petersburg. His energy was prodigious. He composed in all some twenty-nine operas (as well as smaller works). He succeeded Costa as conductor of Her Majesty's Theatre (giving the first performances in England of Verdi's *Nabucodonosor* and *I Lombardi* and organising Verdi's visit to London to conduct *I Masnadieri*). He held that office until the closure of the theatre in 1852, in which year he conducted a series of orchestral concerts, the so-called 'Grand National Concerts'. In 1857 he again took up the in-and-out project of an English Opera organisation, in conjunction with the singers Louisa Pyne and William Harrison. In seven years £200,000 was spent on this scheme, and among the composers to benefit was Balfe's fellow-countryman, William Vincent Wallace.

On Balfe's death his admirers petitioned the Dean of Westminster for permission to erect a tablet in the Abbey, claiming that he 'was the first British composer to elevate the English Lyric Drama to a high position in this country; so was he also the first native subject who was able to compete on the Continent with foreign composers, and produce in France, Germany, Italy, and Spain the works of a British musician.'[1] After some years a tablet was duly erected in the Abbey; as also a mammoth statue in Drury Lane Theatre.

William Wallace (1814–65), like Balfe, exercised the fingers of the young pianist, and possibly still may do so, through arrangements of melodies from *Maritana*, his one permanently successful work, taken into the custody of pianoforte tutors. To be truthful Wallace's talent hardly rose higher than this elementary level, and it is impossible to give any satisfactory reason for the fact that *Maritana* made the grade, while other not less worthy pieces perished by the wayside. Certainly it was not the libretto, by Edward Fitzball[2] out of a Spanish novel. But then as now there is no sure guide to prosperity in the popular market; its attainment is fortuitous.

Wallace's career, however, had a certain picturesque quality which was no liability in an age which esteemed the exotic. Born in Waterford, where his father was a bandmaster, Wallace learned to play a number of instruments. In 1832 he was organist of Thurles Cathedral, which he relinquished to play the violin in the Theatre Royal band in Dublin. He went to Australia, where he gave concerts in Sydney, to New Zealand (where he narrowly escaped being murdered by the Maoris), to South America, to Cuba, to Mexico, to the United States. Giving concerts where he went, he was, so to speak, the Minstrel Boy *in proprio*.

[1] 'Balfe and Wallace', one of a series of articles reprinted from the Dublin *Evening Telegraph* and re-issued in *Irish Graves in England*, M. McDonagh, Dublin, 1888, pp. 61–2.

[2] 1792–1873; prepared texts for many melodramas and 'operas': see his *Thirty-five Years of a Dramatic Author's Life*, London, 1859.

In 1844 Wallace was in London, where he met Fitzball. The consequence of this meeting was a commission to compose the score to *Maritana*. This was an immediate success—largely because Wallace, although incapable of any real dramatic development through his slender musical resources, gave the customers what they wanted. One could pass over the banality and repetitiveness of the libretto (especially the spoken dialogue) and enjoy the composer's melody shapes and rest content over the completely static, undisturbing rhythms. His orchestration was flashy and titillating and he had a knack of drawing attention in suitably graphic terms to details of setting. Spain was an excellent stimulus to a composer like Wallace, while he could produce a tear-jerking church scene. 'Ah', wrote Fitzball, 'the Angelus! Such good fortune should admonish us to be deeply devout.' The admonition was not lost on the composer and his resultant *Angelus* was cherished in the choir stalls as well as on the stage. Plenty of choral ensembles went down well, while a certain agile charm added a veneer of apparent tastefulness. This may be noticed in the first song of *Maritana*, 'Sing, Pretty maidens, sing'—another reminder that for lightness of texture and sprightliness of movement Sullivan did not have to look overseas for encouraging precedents. Wallace, even more than Balfe, did not delude himself. He was in the field for what he could get out of it. In this he, and those of the school to which he belonged, anticipated the Lionel Barts of the twentieth century; they were, however, musically literate. The British opera composer of the mid-nineteenth century reflected the attitude of the theatre audience pretty accurately.[1] He provided an escape from reality. Thus the arrest of Lazarillo in *Maritana*, devoid of any feeling for dramatic probability, serves as opportunity for a lively *buffo* dialogue—its content superficially mentioned in the pulsing crotchets and the minor tonality [Ex. 12]. In *Maritana* Wallace turns up as the poor man's (early) Verdi. In *Lurline*, an opera commissioned by Pyne and Harrison (to whom it was assigned according to the extant agreement for half a guinea), and produced in 1860, Wallace appears as the poor man's Wagner, the libretto, again by Fitzball, being based on the Lorelei legend. The first Act—with maidens—is set in the waters of the Rhine (scenic ambition was a characteristic of English opera-house managers). Any further comparison between Wallace and Wagner is unprofitable, as

[1] It is important to remember that opera in England was an extension of normal theatrical conventions and in no sense thought of as an 'art-form' to which particular reverence should be paid. Thus, in an age in which many more people went to the theatre than formerly, the attitude to the opera was as that to drama or, more frequently, to melodrama: thus—'For the most part the spectators only wanted "the mixture as before": they were quite uncritical of absurdities and crude contradictions in the plot, which tended to run on well-established lines.' R. J. Mitchell and M. D. R. Leys, *A History of London Life*, London, 1958; 1964 edn., p. 322.

12.

Wallace's Alberich—not named except as the 'gnome'—demonstrates. [Ex. 13]. This is not opera: it is pantomime. Thus, in essentials, although

13.

sixty years had passed, English opera was very little (if any) further ahead than in the days of Reeve and Mazzinghi, and we are left still with Storace as the only real musician among the theatre composers of the age.

But these composers never (or rarely) pretended to be other than what they were. The academics, and most of the oratorio composers (whose methods were frequently those of Balfe and Wallace), did: they regarded themselves as a cut above—as 'serious' composers. The distinction proved yet another of the handicaps which the musician of the next two generations inherited. But virtue went unrewarded. Wallace, who had got rid of *Lurline* for half a guinea, had the chagrin of seeing the management net £62,000.

Outsiders

Balfe and Wallace remained outsiders on account of their cheerful lack of good taste. There remains a group of contemporary composers not of Irish stock whose reluctance to conform to the code of pious banality qualifies them at least for sympathetic consideration. This group comprised Robert Lucas de Pearsall (1795–1856), John Liptrot Hatton (1809–86), Edward James Loder (1813–65), and Henry Hugh Pierson (or Pearson; 1815–73), each of whom deserves close biographical, and psychological, exploration, for each, in his own way, was an odd man out. Two of them, Pearsall (the 'de' was added later as an affectation) and Pierson, had private funds on which to base their cultural unorthodoxies.

Pearsall, educated in law, practised as a barrister until, for reasons of health, he withdrew from this vocation at the age of thirty and settled in Mainz. There he took up the study of music—in which he had shown early aptitude—seriously, his tutor being Joseph Panny (1794–1838). In 1836 Pearsall inherited an estate near Bristol, and in this year temporarily returned to England, where his historical and musical interests combined to send him through the scores of the English madrigal school. Association with the Bristol Madrigal Society[1] gave him first-hand acquaintance with the madrigal style, and thereafter he devoted himself to this mode of composition. He was, in fact, picking up where Stafford Smith and Samuel Wesley (both, for the record, natives of Gloucestershire) had left off. He pursued the course thoroughly and his main works in this manner almost achieved what might be thought impossible: they united sixteenth-century contrapuntal gestures with Victorian harmony to the point of near credibility. The flaw in such works as *Great God of Love* and *Light of my Soul* is rhythmic debility. Pearsall understood the capability of voices and two of his works at least deserve high rank for their sureness of touch, their

[1] Founded as the result of lectures on 'English Vocal Harmony' given in Bristol in January 1837 by Edward Taylor. J. D. Corfe (son of A. T. Corfe of Salisbury), the cathedral organist, directed the Society until 1865. He was succeeded by Daniel W. Rootham (father of Cyril B. Rootham) who retained the directorship for exactly fifty years.

clarity, and the avoidance of circumlocution: these are the exquisite arrangement of *In dulci jubilo* and the warm, exciting, ten-part choral ballad, *Sir Patrick Spens*. A man of parts (he translated Goethe's *Faust* and Schiller's *Wilhelm Tell*), Pearsall tempered his antiquarian enthusiasm with judgement. Thus his neo-madrigals and his part-songs which have roots in the past have no taint of mortuary air. What has is the part-song *O who will o'er the downs so free* which enjoyed enormous popularity (and possibly still does) and may not unjustly be exhibited as the worst piece of music composed during the Victorian era. The greater part of Pearsall's life was spent on the Continent and after 1842 he resided, baronially, in a *Schloss* on the shores of the Wartensee.

Hatton's part-songs endeared him also to choral societies; but these represented for him but the inglorious end to early ambition. Hatton was born in Liverpool and after various appointments as organist in that city embarked on a career as an actor. In 1842 he united his skills as chorus-master at Drury Lane where, on the recommendation of Balfe, his operetta *The Queen of the Thames* was produced in 1844. In the same year exasperated that he could not get a production of his *Pasqual Bruno* in London, 'and not having the patience of Rooke[1] to wait 20 years, took it over to Germany, had it translated into that language,[2] and, on returning, brought me a play-bill,[3] thinking that I should be sufficiently delighted, and perfectly satisfied (as I was forced to be) at seeing my name Herr Fixhall inserted as the author of the libretto'.[4] Hatton's opera was not a roaring success in Vienna, but he not unnaturally thought it was. So far as he was concerned, in the light of experience at home, it was. 'He returned to England, and, finding that works by foreign composers had greater chances of success than those of native musicians, he published a series of beautiful songs, under the *nom de plume* of "Czapek", which is the Hungarian for "Hat on". He visited America as a solo pianist and vocalist, and met with considerable success.'[5] Having made his small mark overseas Hatton renounced his wider hopes and (one more unsuccessful opera showing him the folly of doing otherwise) concentrated on the profitable

[1] William Michael Rooke (1794–1847), Dubliner and sometime deputy leader of the band at the Theatre Royal in his native city. Associated with Drury Lane from 1821. His *Amilie* (composed in 1818) was performed at Covent Garden in 1838—also in the same year in New York, Dublin, and Philadelphia.

[2] By Joseph von Seyfried.

[3] *Pasqual Bruno*, the occasion of a benefit for Joseph Staudigl (who was to sing at Birmingham in the title role in the première of *Elijah* in 1846), was performed at the Kärntnertor theatre on 2 March 1844.

[4] E. Fitzball, *Thirty-five Years*, II, p. 158.

[5] W. A. Barrett, op. cit., p. 331. Cf. G.F.G., *The Musical Union*, loc. cit., p. 54. '. . . it is well known that no artist stands the least chance of a favourable reception in London who has not made a successful debut in Paris, or some large German town, and that even [then] his success will frequently depend upon the momentary caprice of his audience'.

sector of the home market. In addition to his part-songs he composed one oratorio; two songs, *To Anthea* and *Simon the Cellarer* demonstrate what might have been and what was. The former is a fine, integrated example of true *Lied*, the latter a Victorian pop number.

The son of John David Loder (1788–1846),[1] violinist and publisher in Bath, leader of the Three Choirs Festival Orchestra and from 1840 a professor at the Royal Academy, Edward Loder had the opportunity to pursue his musical studies in Germany: this rather by accident than design, for his original intention was to study medicine. A pupil of Ferdinand Ries in Frankfurt, Loder came back to England after some years and was commissioned to write the music for *Nourjahad.* Other romantic operas[2] followed, but it was for his songs that Loder was esteemed and subsequently overrated. In an age in which one might have expected a resurgence of song-writing, none took place. The commercial ballad, an unsavoury perversion of the former Gardens song, reigned supreme. The *Lied* was a German patent. Loder, impelled by a contract to compose a weekly piece for the publisher Dalmaine, departed so far from native precedent as to attempt to adjust the Schubert—Schumann manner to English poetry. In fact Loder's reputation has been established by historians on the strength of one song (conveniently accessible through the years in leaflet form). This was *The Brooklet,* a setting of a translation of Wilhelm Müller's *Wohin?* To attempt to rank this (*Grove,* edn. V, p. 357) as 'among the most beautiful and effective songs in existence' is nonsense. Having dismissed this waif it is fairer to look at the qualities that do stand out in Loder's brave repertoire. An early Novello collection of his songs justly described them as 'thoroughly English in character'.

This indeed they are. Despite their limitations (of text and style) they represent a point of view. Melodically effective, they give a genuine impression of emotional range—and when this is supported by accompanimental point or, rarely, harmonic colouring, they suggest the value of a judiciously administered transfusion of German blood. Loder, however, did not set his aim far beyond the reach of his potential audience. Thus we encounter the fake 'old Englishry' of *Robin Hood* (1844) and *Father Francis* (1847), the heartiness of the fictional British tar in *The British Anchor*

[1] The Loders were a musical family. John's brother was a leading piano teacher in Bath. His daughter Kate (1825–1904; Edward's cousin) became a pupil at the Royal Academy. In 1844 she distinguished herself as the soloist in Mendelssohn's G minor concerto, performed before the composer. She became a teacher at the Academy but soon after her marriage to Henry Thompson, surgeon, she gave up her professional career. It was at her home, on 7 July 1871, that Brahms's *Requiem* received its first, private, performance in England. Lady Thompson (as she now was) and Cipriani Potter played the orchestral part as piano duet.

[2] *Raymond and Agnes* (Manchester 1855) was revived by Nicholas Temperley at Cambridge in May 1966.

(1844), the fireside cosiness of the by now commercialised *Old Christmas* (1840), and the nadir of sentimentality in *The home of early years* (1835). To be truthful the banality of these texts is paralleled in German *Lied* and Loder only just missed making these and many other songs considerably greater than the texts which promoted them. In one rather fine song —Bishop crossed with Schubert—Loder does reveal a real passion; *Wake my Love* (George Soane, 1801–61) has a splendid sense of conviction in the ranging contours of the vocal line. A deft pastoral is *Philip the Falconer* (W. H. Bellamy, 1798–1862), where the accompaniment—of light, detached, chords—fits perfectly. Although this song, unvaried strophic, is too long, it has kinship with the consciously antique country fancies of Peter Warlock.

Pearsall, Hatton, and Loder, in one way or another, were at least half-committed to Germany. Pierson, a refugee from English philistinism in the by now established mould, became wholly so. The English vicarage by the nineteenth century had become one regular training-ground for rebellion; the Public School (barbarous in discipline) another. While the ancient University, now to a large extent in academic and social disarray, was liable to provoke the sensitive and the thoughtful to suicidal despair, or to wild and uproarious gestures of contempt for all the dearly-won (and badly kept) moral principles of the upper-middle classes. Henry Hugh Pearson was the son of a clergyman (who in due course became Dean of Salisbury); he was a pupil at Harrow School; and a student at Trinity College, Cambridge. At Harrow and Cambridge he associated with Percy Florence Shelley, son of the poet and himself a composer.[1] Taught music by the Salisbury Corfe, Walmisley, and Attwood, in spite of parental disapproval, Pearson set poems by Byron and Shelley.[2] After leaving Cambridge he wandered round Europe, spending some time in Leipzig, where he made the acquaintance of Mendelssohn, and in Dresden. Here he seduced the wife of the polymath J. P. Leyser (best known as a painter), but in due course made her his wife. In order to spare his family the ignominy of kinship with a lecher and a composer (the second a more disgraceful occupation than the first), Pearson changed his name, temporarily to Edgar Mansfeldt and finally and permanently to Heinrich Hugo Pierson. Armed with the commendation of Schumann,[3] Pierson sent in a late candidature for the Professorship at Edinburgh in 1844. Around this election (from which Sterndale Bennett, a strongly fancied candidate, withdrew) battle raged between the legal and medical

[1] To the extent of a setting of his father's *Hymn of Pan*, privately issued, 1864.

[2] *Characteristic Songs of Shelley*, Novello (*c.* 1839); see Alice and Burton Pollin, 'In Pursuit of Pearson's Shelley Songs', *M. & L.*, 46, October 1965, p. 322.

[3] In respect of a collection of six songs by Robert Burns (Kistner, Leipzig, *c.* 1842), in *Neue Zeitschrift fur Musik*, no. 8, July 1842, pp. 32–3.

faculties of the University and between the reactionary and the progressive factions in the musical press.[1] In the end local talent—in the person of the lawyers' favourite, one Donaldson—was rejected and Pierson, the prophet of a new dawn, installed. Within a year, however, Pierson, through a distaste for bagpipes it was said, relinquished his office and returned to Germany.

In 1852 Pierson injected new excitement into British music, choosing as his arena the traditional jousting-ground of oratorio. At the Norwich Festival of that year two works were selected: William Richard Bexfield's *Israel Restored*,[2] and Pierson's *Jerusalem*. The latter work was heralded by a massive publicity campaign, as representative of the 'new music' associated especially with the names of Schumann and Wagner. The former, which had been performed in Norwich in 1851, relied on academic decencies and local patriotism.

Jerusalem, dedicated to the Archbishop of Canterbury, was characteristically ambitious. Pierson built an effective libretto from biblical extracts. The first part deals with Christ's prophecy of the destruction of Jerusalem, His Crucifixion, and the fall of the city. The second part contains a lament over the city and the promise of its restoration. In the third the dispersed Jews are recalled from exile, the hostile armies are defeated at Armageddon, and the Johannine vision of the New Jerusalem as in the *Book of Revelation* is pictured. 'I think', wrote the composer in his Preface, 'it will be allowed that the selection from Scripture, which I have endeavoured to set to music, is one of extraordinary beauty and unusual scope; I would also remark that in this compilation a more regular dramatic action will be found than in any other of the strictly-sacred Oratorios extant,—this being affected by the interesting collocation of the different passages, without the aid of *dramatis personae*.

'I must confess that I consider all attempts to construct an Oratorio upon the basis of a modern poem as more or less futile, and, moreover, as an approximation to the secular character of the Opera, from which the Oratorios should be separated by a broad line of demarcation . . .'

Pierson's score was mostly in terms which the academic English were reluctant to accept. It is a compendium of idioms, drawn from Spohr, Gounod (whose *Messe Solenelle* was performed in London under John Hullah on 15 January 1851), Meyerbeer (cf. the 'March of Roman Soldiers'), Schumann, and Wagner. In one place only does Pierson suggest

[1] Particular support for Pearson came from Charles Lewis Grüneisen—whose father had been a friend of Schiller—music critic of the *Morning Post*.

[2] Bexfield (1824–53), an organist, published settings of poems by Shelley, Byron, and Tennyson in the 1840's, graduated as Mus. D. at Oxford with an exercise that ended with 'a *strict canon* in eight real parts, with full orchestral accompaniments'. His 'Concert Fugue' went down well at the Great Exhibition of 1851.

'Englishness'—in the choral-variation version of 'Lo he comes with clouds descending' (III, no. 41)—and even here there is an unexpected warmth of harmonic colouring. If the arias are the least satisfactory part of the work (giving little scope for dramatic development), the general intensity of mood is impressive. Pierson had the ability to expound his ideas vividly (a quality that appealed to Macfarren, who prefaced the first performance of *Jerusalem* with a long and thoughtful essay). He expended great energy; his movements are rarely rhythmically static; and he had considerable genius in epitomising action—especially in orchestral points introducing or interspersed among recitatives that themselves have considerable declamatory force [Ex. 14*a* and *b*]. The opening of the overture [Ex. 14*c*] is

14a.

14b.

14c.

as firm a statement as contrived by any composer of the age, wonderfully relevant, and—taking into account the tension of the counter-subject that appears at the ninth bar [Ex. 14*d*]—extremely well-wrought. It is fair to

14d.

say that the overture does not maintain this dramatic power. Nevertheless it is a fine achievement. So too is the oratorio, which has a fire otherwise sadly lacking in English music of the period. Although welcomed with some enthusiasm by the Norwich audience (the interpretation by Julius Benedict (see p. 486) was masterly), criticism was hostile. The 'aesthetic school', it was said, was characterised by 'vagueness and incoherency', deficiency in scholarship, and 'a mistaken view of the true and unchangeable principles of art'. Among the correspondence raised by the event one letter contained the inescapable rebuke: 'It is a curious circumstance, that, notwithstanding the perpetual whine about the dearth of English talent, and the backwardness of English artists in entering the musical arena, no sooner does an individual step forward to vindicate his native land from the reproach, than he is forthwith *pooh-poohed* and *cold-shouldered* by his own countrymen foremost of all.'[1]

Pierson went back to Germany, and wrote his incidental music for *Faust* (Part II), which was produced in Hamburg and, in part, at Norwich, in 1857. This work gained considerable popularity in Germany, and it is not difficult to see the reason. The music is steeped in German atmosphere. Carrying on from the melodrama *Manfred* by Schumann, it holds impending tragedy in the fine, dark-coloured overture (cf. Overture to *Jerusalem*) [Ex. 15*a*]. But after this, in the first item in Act I, there is all the warmth and fantasy of the woods of the Harz country. The music of Ariel and the fairies is quoted and commended by Walker[2]—even though that writer,

[1] Henry Davison, *From Mendelssohn to Wagner*, London, 1912, pp. 142 ff.
[2] Op. cit., pp. 271–2.

15a.

misunderstanding the function of the music, falls back with unnecessary and unwarrantable fervour on the former charge of 'sheer amateurism'. In this movement—the mood being valid for the Forest of Arden—Pierson shows what English composers ought to have been doing with English texts. But—as Bennett's *May Queen* so sadly demonstrates—they were generally too inhibited to realise their own potential. Pierson comes down on the side of the 'romantic' Goethe, whereas Schumann, in his *Faust*, recognised more fully the 'classical' reputation of the poet. But in so doing he realises many scenes of invincible charm, and even some with quite un-German notions of comedy written in. On the one hand there is the female voice *Chorus of Invisible Spirits of the Elements* (no. 8), which suggests something of Holst's *Rig Veda* hymnody in the enharmonic florescence of shifting triads—from D flat major to F major, and from the former towards its other wing through B double flat major. On the other hand, Pierson could be succinct or definitive, and at two points we are within the sphere of *Háry János*. The relevant titles are 'The Entry of the Emperor and his Suite' (no. 1) [Ex. 15*b*], and 'The March of the Imperial

15b.

Army' (no. 12). 'Hörst du die Trommeln fern?' asks Mephistopheles [Ex. 15*c*]. The requirements of the theatre imposed a salutary discipline on

15c

Pierson; for his purely instrumental music (as in his Shakespearian overtures), while full of experimental colour-mixtures, lacks the sharpness of utterance of the *Faust* pieces.

Forgotten, or discredited, by his native land, Pierson lived on to achieve a position of high respectability among German composers. His songs (not the most distinguished part of his output, for his genius was outside the lyrical vein) and his opera *Contarini* (Hamburg, 1872) were esteemed, but it was *Faust* which was held in greatest affection. 'Diese geniale Musik hatte damals überhaupt solche Erfolge, dass Schott in Mainz dieselbe ankaufte und der König der Belgier dem Componisten für Kunst und Wissenschaft verlieh ... Pierson zählte zu den fruchbarsten, wenn auch nicht populärsten Tonsetzern der Neuzeit.'[1]

Pierson's death earlier that year gave rise to sympathetic notices in the German press; thus H. M. Schletterer in the *Augsburger Zeitung*[2]: 'Vor mehr als dreissig Jahren kam er, ein Fremdling, zu uns, dem deutschen Geist, der deutschen Poesie, der deutschen Kunst mit schwärmerischer Neigung zugethan . . .;' but the prophet had but little honour in his own country.

It will be seen that the course traced by British music is a good deal more irregular than that of most European nations. That this is so is in considerable measure due to economic circumstances. By a paradox the more favourable these were the more disconcerting the consequences to the national music. During the period under review in this chapter the expenditure on music either indirectly or directly was enormous. The great provincial town halls,[3] with great organs, were built—without much consideration as to their function (beyond political meetings and oratorio). Singers—Clara Novello, Jenny Lind, Albani, Braham, Sims Reeves, Lablache, Tamburini principal among them—and pianists, including Moscheles and Thalberg, made fortunes. Visiting virtuosi of all sorts and visiting composers did well enough. But what to do about British composers? That was a difficulty, resolved by the determination of authority either to tame them or to starve them. The latter principle was preferred

[1] Faust was performed in the Stadt Theatre, Leipzig, in 1873, as reported in the *Neue Zeitschrift für Musik*, 1873, p. 508. The quotation is taken from a leading article in the same issue (pp. 529–32), *Henry Hugh Pierson und seine Musik zum Zweiten Theile von Goethe's 'Faust'*. For English studies of the music, see Ernest Newman, *Musical Studies*, London, 1905, pp. 88–91, and H. G. Sear, ' "Faust" and Henry Hugo Pierson', in *Music Review*, X, 1949, pp. 183–94.

[2] Quoted in *N.Z.M.*, loc. cit.

[3] E.g. Birmingham (1831–46), Leeds (1855–8), and St. George's Hall, Liverpool (1841–54) which were built partly in response to the need for accommodating musical festivals of some long standing. The organ at Liverpool was the first to be built by Henry Willis (at a cost of £10,000), and was opened on 28 May 1855 by S. S. Wesley. Liverpool was fortunate in having also a Philharmonic Hall (1846–9).

and became part of the national mythology. It is small wonder that composers, battered by the doctrines of *laissez-faire*, were hard put to it to lose neither form nor integrity. The composer's world, intelligible and manageable in the eighteenth century, was in fragments. There was a new tradition to be built.

The English are reluctant to depart from tradition, even when the purpose of the tradition is long frustrated by change. The Reform Bill indirectly touched the one musical tradition that had long outlived its usefulness. The waits were at last abolished. That they lasted so long enabled the spirit of medievalism to overlap that of neo-medievalism. In 1802 the last of the waits were appointed in Sheffield. Four years later their office was abolished.[1] In Alnwick Thomas Coward died in 1845 and his tombstone incorrectly bore the inscription, 'the Last of the Waits of this ancient Borough'. His fellow-wait was still, however, living in 1863. 'We remember seeing them both in their glory riding through the streets on a cold day in April, their yellow plush breeches all bespattered with mud, for they had been at the Freeman's Well, and the deep snow was melting into slush before the breath of spring. They had on pheasant blue coats adorned with many buttons of yellow (not gold), yellow facing, buff waistcoat, yellow plush breeches, and top boots, and white band round their hats. On the right arm each had a silver badge of the insignia of the borough (St. Michael and the Dragon) encircled by a crescent moon . . .'[2] It is as though the Canterbury Pilgrims had ridden down into the age of Victoria.

[1] *Minutes of the Town Trust*: 1 September 1802. John Dawson and William Taylor: 'also resolved that the town's musicians shall be at the discretional call of the Trustees upon any occasion which they shall think proper to demand their attendance, not to exceed four times in each year'. On 13 March 1806 the waits were discontinued.

[2] 'The Last of the Waits' (anon.), *The Alnwick Journal*, 15 June 1863, p. 185.

12

Pressure from Below

New Audiences

IT IS A sad paradox that during a period in which municipal administration was undergoing radical change—to the great benefit of the British people in terms of improved health, educational facilities, and even, in certain respects, of cultural amelioration—the ancient civic responsibilities for the maintenance of official musicians (such as they were) should have been abnegated. With the final passing of the waits the last link in the chain of commitment to the principle of supporting local music on a professional basis was broken. That for the last hundred years of their existence the waits did not amount to much—except insofar as they added to the gaiety of the community—is neither here nor there: the fact is that a precedent was cancelled. And, as is well known, in British administration most things become possible if precedents can be found actually to exist.

In the high noon of Victorian pride and prosperity the power of the Barbarians and Philistines was formidable, as was polemically remarked by Matthew Arnold in *Culture and Anarchy* (1869). The barrier to effective musical progress during an era in which opportunities for development should have been great was erected by the very people who hitherto had led music from out of aristocratic and ecclesiastical containment into the market-place. These people comprised the middle classes. 'The great middle classes of this country', wrote Matthew Arnold, 'are conscious of no weakness, no inferiority; they do not want any one to provide anything for them; such as they are, they believe that the freedom and prosperity of England are their work, and that the future belongs to them. No one admires them more than I do, but those who admire them most, and believe in their capabilities, can render them no better service than by pointing out in what they underrate their deficiencies, and how their deficiencies, if unremedied, may impair their future. They want culture and dignity; they want ideas. Aristocracy has culture and dignity; democracy has readiness for new ideas, and ardour for the ideas it possesses: of those, our middle class has the last only—ardour for the ideas it already possesses.'[1]

Behind British music there stood both democratic readiness for new musical traditions, and ardour for those that had been established. If the middle classes had moved when they could have moved, the record of music in Britain during the nineteenth and twentieth centuries would have been richer in worthy achievement. As it was, music was handed as a hostage to the twin doctrines of self-help and *laissez-faire*; composers, for the most part, vainly sought to lay hands on the ghost of middle-class taste; the creative potential of the great mass of the people of the nation was ignored; and the situation was not seriously to be looked at with a view to reparation for almost a century. For reasons which will become more obvious the simple problem of the period now under review was, who was to pay for what and for whom.

In the middle of the nineteenth century a significant need of the day was discerned by a Frenchman and a German. To Louis Antoine Jullien (1812–60) and August Manns (1825–1907) principal credit is due for the provision of orchestral concerts at the cheapest price for the greatest number. Both men aimed at satisfying that public which would have hardly been welcomed by the regular patrons of, say, the Philharmonic Society.[2] Jullien, formerly a student at the Paris Conservatoire, was a brilliant showman whose technical efficiency as a conductor and genuine love of 'classical' music were rather more than balanced by a capacity for shrewd appraisal of mass psychology and an extreme egocentricity. He was a populariser and packed audiences into his concerts at the Royal Zoological Gardens, Surrey Gardens, Drury Lane and the Lyceum. In effect, and sometimes by name, these programmes, which crossed the spectrum from Haydn and Mozart and Beethoven to popular polkas and quadrilles and which employed a mixture of regular and irregular instrumental ensembles, often of mammoth proportions, were Promenade Concerts.[3] Jullien's principal work in London was done between 1845 and 1853, when he went for a time to America.

'M. Jullien', observed *The Musical World*,[4] 'was undoubtedly the first

[1] *Education and the State* (1864), in *On the Study of Celtic Literature and other Essays*, Everyman edn., p. 186.

[2] Dissatisfaction with the policy and standard of the Philharmonic Concerts led to the formation of a New Philharmonic Society in 1852, which ran along parallel lines until 1879. The founders of the New Philharmonic were the music publisher, Frederick Beale, and the musician, Henry Wylde (1822–90), one of Potter's Academy pupils.

[3] It was in opposition to them that in 1848 Balfe's 'Grand National Concerts' were inaugurated.

[4] 26 February 1859.

who directed the attention of the multitude to the classical composers. Previous to his time, symphonies, concertos, and the higher orchestral works were reserved for the Philharmonic Society or, at best, for benefits and festivals, where the directors of musical entertainments did all they could by high charges to prevent the public from hearing good music; they had no right to cry out against the ignorance of the masses, but rather blame themselves that the masses were not better informed. M. Jullien broke down the barriers and let in the "crowd" . . . His claims, as a musical Luther, have long been acknowledged . . .'

Manns, a German bandmaster, came to England in 1854 as assistant conductor of the wind band at the Crystal Palace (now sited at Sydenham). On 21 July 1855 he was invited to become conductor. 'The number of our band', wrote George Grove, then Secretary to the Crystal Palace, 'is at present 58, but we should be very glad, if possible, to reduce it, as the expense is considered by many to be too great, and we should prefer to reduce it to 36 . . . If you should engage any of your present musicians, you must consider that *after 7 in summer and 5 in winter their time is their own for other engagements*, and this should be taken into account in fixing their pay. You must remember that, as the conductor of the band, you will be bound to do all you can to make the music *economical* as well as *efficient*.'[1]

Manns, enthusiastically backed by Grove,[2] turned the wind band into a symphony orchestra, instituted Saturday night concerts for which special trains were run from Victoria Station, familiarised the classics, installed among them Schubert as a symphonic composer, beat down the critics to introduce the fearsomely 'new' music of Schumann,[3] and in the course of half-a-century saw to it that among the first performances native works in relation to foreign stood in the ratio of almost one to two. Manns kept in touch with the by now traditional music of the people by directing gigantic triennial Handel performances, triggered off in the commemorative year of 1859, at the Crystal Palace, in which northern choirs were invited to participate.[4] Moreover, on the side of popular education he persuaded his directors in 1860 to set up the Crystal Palace Company's

[1] Quoted in H. Saxe Wyndham, *August Manns and the Saturday Concerts*, London, 1909, pp. 31–2.

[2] Grove's programme notes were an important feature of the Crystal Palace concerts, and their influence on public, critics, and teachers, was considerable.

[3] It is hardly to be believed, but it is true, that 'Chorley . . . to the end of his life made it a point to walk out of the concert-room at the beginning of the second movement of Schumann's quintette, to mark, it is said, his high disapproval of a certain chord [see 3rd beat of 7th full bar] in the eighth bar.' *H. Saxe Wyndham*, op. cit., p. 48.

[4] '. . . the stupendous volume of sound at a Handel Festival and the simple grandeur of the chords appeal to the ordinary amateur in a way that baffles description. He cannot explain *why* he enjoys the proud massiveness of it; he simply remembers it afterwards, and feels that he has been in the presence of a mysterious and inspiring "something".' Manns, in an interview, *The Strand Musical Magazine*, 1895, I, p. 404.

School of Music, which may be seen as contributory to the movement that culminated in the foundation of other music schools (see p. 494). It is not proposed here to list each one of the 103 British composers whose works were given a hearing by Manns: sufficient to say that they ran from Sterndale Bennett to Elgar, taking in Sullivan, Parry, Stanford, Cowen, and Mackenzie. Ebenezer Prout (1855–1909), better known as a theorist, was also among those indebted to Manns, and he wrote of him as follows: 'English composers owe a deep debt of gratitude to Manns. At the date when the Saturday concerts were commenced, a British prophet had emphatically no honour in his own country, and it was an extremely difficult matter for a native musician to obtain a hearing at all. But Manns, German though he was, showed far more sympathy for rising English composers than, so far as I know, any English-born conductor has ever done.'[1]

More than Jullien, Manns (being a German) followed the star of idealism. His mission was based on faith in the capacity for musical appreciation of the previously underprivileged, and his success in this mission owed considerably to the dominant philosophical tenet of the nineteenth century: that there was attainable some sort of harmony in human affairs. This was the belief of the Benthamites, of social reformers like Robert Owen and Lord Shaftesbury, of Disraeli, Darwin and Arnold. The notion that music could both symbolise and help to effect a 'harmony of interests' was tacitly understood during the nineteenth century, but more explicitly stated in Britain during the twentieth century. But there was the matter of suiting intention to deed.

If it seemed improbable that the 'crowd' could be attracted to orchestral concerts of high calibre it seemed impossible that chamber music could be popularised. Yet it was, and almost entirely because of the initiative of Arthur Chappell, whose 'Monday Pops' became a national institution. It makes sobering reading to learn that 1,500–2,000 people could regularly be assembled (at 1s. a time) for performances of chamber music; and that on special occasions—as, for instance, the hundredth concert—1,000 people could be locked out because there was no room. It had been thought that 'the very name of quartet or quintet, *a priori*, was supposed to convey to the popular mind something "bitter as coloquintada" '.[2]

The firm of Chappell was largely responsible for the financing of the building of the St. James's Hall, in Piccadilly. When it was ready for use in 1858 a pilot scheme of concerts was launched. The programmes were of miscellaneous character, and by no means exclusive of the trivialities that

[1] Quoted in H. Saxe Wyndham, op. cit., pp. 227–8.
[2] *The Musical World*, 26 February 1859.

were supposed to generate profit. On 14 February 1859, however, Arthur Chappell boldly laid down the promise of a new policy in an entirely 'serious' programme devoted to Mendelssohn. The main works were the Quintet in B flat (op. 87) and the Quartet in D (op. 44, no. 1), the players being Henri Wieniawski and Louis Ries (violin), Doyle (quintet only) and Schreuss (viola), and Piatti[1] (cello).

The enterprise was greeted with warm approval. 'After repeated proofs that the large audiences assembled every Monday in St. James's Hall are by no means hostile to what is conventionally termed "classical", but which would be at once more simply and appropriately styled good music, the directors of the Monday Popular Concerts have veered suddenly round. No longer turning a deaf ear to honest counsel, based upon plain common sense and every day experience, they now, on the contrary, seemed resolved to profit by it, and to carry out their resolutions by a more sweeping and radical change than was either suggested or meditated by their advisers. On Monday, instead of a concert of shreds and patches . . . there was an entertainment calculated alike to enchant the sense and invigorate the mind, while at the same time sufficiently rich in variety to comfort even those epicurean amateurs, who have been nourished from the cradle in intellectual delicacies . . . For the first time since the institution of the Monday Popular Concerts, singers were not allowed to press upon the audience a number of those trashy songs and ballads which they are paid for singing in public.'[2]

The following week's programme was given up to Mozart,[3] and the *Morning Post*[4] weighed in with commendation for the policy and a reproof to those who had tried to hinder it. 'The directors of the Monday Popular Concerts are therefore entitled to the warm sympathy and most liberal support of the public in their new enterprise, which, owing to many concurrent circumstances, too numerous and intricately interwoven, and, we may add, too paltry in their nature to be described in detail, is perhaps as difficult and dangerous as it is honourable.'

Chappell planned six concerts for the series, but, emboldened by the

[1] Alfredo Piatti (1822–1901) not only played at the first of these concerts, but also, in 1887, at the thousandth.

[2] *Literary Gazette*, 19 February 1859.

[3] In respect of the choice of composer the *Daily Telegraph* of 22 February observed that Mozart attracted to the opera 'not only the greatest musicians but also the most ignorant habitués of the Casino. The same can be said of no other writer, and of no other composer. The majority of educated men and women—even of those who talk about him—do not hear Beethoven very often, and do not understand him when they do. What are called "the vulgar" never hear his music at all and it would be as surprising to find a "fast" person at a Beethoven concert (except at the congenial Jullien's, where sometimes for the space of an hour, it is impossible to avoid the great symphonist) as to meet with a costermonger reading Shelley'.

[4] 23 February 1859.

reaction of press and public, extended it to thirteen. In the second year he gave twenty-seven, in the third year twenty-four concerts.[1] During this period eleven concerts were given outside London, in Liverpool, Newcastle, Edinburgh and Glasgow. The artists were the best available, whether native or foreign. In the early years they included Julius Benedict (otherwise known as a conductor, and popularly, in due course, as the composer of *The Lily of Killarney*—1862) who was the regular pianist and 'conductor', Arabella Goddard, Charles Hallé—who gave performances of all Beethoven's pianoforte sonatas in 1860, Lindsay Sloper, Clara Schumann; Sainton, Joachim, Auer, Vieuxtemps, the violinists; W. T. Best, the famous city organist of Liverpool; Lazarus, the clarinettist; and Sims Reeves, Santley, Wilbye Cooper, and Charlotte Dolby, the singers. The success of Sterndale Bennett's performance of the *St. Matthew Passion* encouraged Chappell to include Bach (and Handel) in the programmes, which in two decades widened their scope to an enviable degree. The classical composers were given full coverage. Of the modern school Brahms, Bruch, Chopin, Goetz, Goldmark, Grieg, Joachim, Onslow, Raff, Rheinberger, Rubenstein, Saint-Saëns, Schumann, and Spohr, were represented. From British composers (or those of British adoption) there were contributions from Balfe, Bennett, Henschel, Loder, Macfarren, Mellon (see p. 487 fn. 2), Thomas Pinto, and Henry Smart.[2] The Monday Pops, after 1865 alternating with Saturday Pops (immortalised by W. S. Gilbert in *The Mikado*), ran until 1898. Some part of the way they were companioned in St. James's Hall by the Tuesday afternoon concerts of John Ella's Musical Union, which, established in 1845, went on successfully for a period of thirty-five years.

The principle of doing good at a profit was written into Victorian morality. Indeed, as Robert Owen discovered when wishing to improve industrial conditions in New Lanark, without the exercise of this principle social progress would have taken place less smoothly and more slowly. Outside London the only activity likely to show a profit sufficient to warrant the original outlay was the festival—and even this undertaking had, as has been seen, become hazardous. It was, therefore, to the credit of the citizens of Liverpool that a Philharmonic Society was founded in 1840. Some ten years later, now lodged in the new Philharmonic Hall

[1] 'Mr. Arthur Chappell, by patiently submitting to losses at the commencement of his career as manager of the 'Monday Popular Concerts', and indomitable perseverance in what he knew to be a good cause, has at length succeeded in reaping the monetary profit and artistic honour from his unflagging efforts, and created an institution that can only be described as one [of] the very first in its way of which this country can boast'. *Morning Post*, 4 July 1861.

[2] See *Catalogue of Works performed at the Monday Popular Concerts*, 1859–79, Chappell, 1879; also volumes of *Analytical Programmes* published by Chappell.

opened in 1849, the orchestra comprised ninety-six players—most of them professionals from London.[1] The Liverpool Society,[2] however, had no intention of departing from the social conventions that had been enshrined in the earlier subscription concerts. Only 'gentlemen' were admitted to membership. In Manchester it was otherwise. Charles Hallé whose talents as pianist have already been noticed in connection with the Monday Pops, with a foot in Manchester since he directed the Gentlemen's Concerts in the city from 1850, founded the Hallé Orchestra in 1858. Taking his cue from the success of Chappell's undertaking in St. James's Hall, he made provision for the admittance of the less prosperous members of the community at a shilling a head. In 1860 *The Musical World* was able to report that these concerts were 'becoming the vogue with all classes, from the rich merchant and manufacturer to the middle-class tradesmen and bourgeois, to the respectable and thrifty, albeit humbler, artisans'. In other northern cities events were more sporadic, but there was a fresh outbreak of festival-giving. In 1853 the opening of the St. George's Hall in Bradford provoked a short-lived festival (triennially from 1853–9), of which Costa was the conductor.[3] In 1858 the festival tradition, which could now be properly accommodated, was re-established in Leeds, under the conductorship of Sterndale Bennett. Apart from the new Town Hall the showpiece of this festival was the organ, claimed to be one of the largest in Europe. It was resolved: 'that in further announcements of the Festival the large organ be mentioned in a prominent manner.'[4] A Town Hall was opened in Huddersfield in 1881, and this also occasioned a festival, in which the orchestra was the Hallé under its own conductor. Charles Hallé was also responsible for the first eight Bristol Festivals (1873–93), at the first of which Macfarren's *St. John the Baptist* was first heard.

[1] Cf. the orchestra for the Leeds Festival of 1858: 'This consisted of the most celebrated performers in the Metropolis together with a few artistes of repute in the West Riding. Ninety-six players were engaged and the usual twenty first, and eighteen second, violins had place; the twelve viola players (described as "tenors") and the twelve violoncellos and twelve double basses made a total of seventy-four strings. The remainder were—eight woodwind, ten brass, two drums and a harp. The timpani are not mentioned.' J. Sprittles, 'Leeds Musical Festivals', *Thoresby Soc. Misc.*, 13, pt. 2, p. 206.

[2] In 1865 Alfred Mellon (1820–67) became conductor. Already noticed on p. 486 as a composer, Mellon, who was a native of Birmingham, conducted the Musical Society of London from its inception in 1850 as a rival to the New Philharmonic until his death, and also Promenade Concerts at Covent Garden from 1860.

[3] The chorus-master was William Jackson (1815–66), son of a miller of Tanfield, a largely self-taught musician who was the first conductor of the Bradford Festival Choral Society. Jackson's compositions included an oratorio, *Isaiah*, performed in 1853 as part of the inauguration of St. George's Hall.

[4] Festival Minute Book, 31 July 1858. On the last night of the first Leeds Festival a 'People's Concert' was given—'the prices being such as would afford an opportunity to all classes of seeing the noble Town Hall, as well as listening to a choice selection of music . . . altogether 4,000 people were present.' Sprittles, op. cit., p. 207.

The record so far shows an admirable, if limited, extension of opportunities for musical appreciation. While credit is due to the promoters it is clear that—so far as the working classes were concerned—paternalism was an effective force. No doubt, under the conditions that obtained, this was inevitable. But in the long run the class division which it was hoped, by some, to mitigate was in fact strengthened. Instrumental music was made available to more people, but the charitable impulses that sustained its wider provision were barely disguised. The general run of English composers had few illusions: their aim was to satisfy the patent emotional and intellectual requirements of the respectable. For the first time in the history of British music the leading composers lost touch with the fundamentals of the art. Because he knew from personal experience what it was that had sapped the vitality of the tradition, and was able and courageous enough to adjust the balance, Elgar eventually succeeded in reconstituting the tradition.

Until the early years of the Victorian era it may have been reasonable to hold that folk-song had some validity in the general musical experience of the British. Towards the middle of the century this could no longer be maintained—except, perhaps, in the Celtic fringes. By 1850 the greater part of the people were living in industrial towns, and frequently under conditions of lamentable squalor. But industrial England, where political balladry and occupational song took on a new lease of life, was pushing up a new tradition of folk music—that of the wind-band movement.

The Wind Band

The origins of this movement were threefold. There was already a long history of military music and after the end of the Napoleonic Wars demobilisation brought numerous expert performers into the field of industry. There was the ancient office of the waits, who, as has been seen, were being deprived of civic occupation at the same time.[1] And there were the church-bands, now being demoted by the organ. In Lancashire these bands were often of ripe proportions. That, for instance, at Providence Chapel, Walkden Moor, consisted of one flute, two clarinets, two bassoons, one serpent, one cello, and frequently a trumpet. It supported a choir of eight or ten trebles, and eight men, the control of the complete establishment being entrusted to one John Berry, a pit carpenter. It is small wonder that the introduction of the organ was viewed with disfavour.[2]

[1] In 1833 two redundant waits of the City of York, Daniel Hardman and James Walker, did in fact undertake the formation of a windband of twenty-four players.

[2] 'During the past 30 years the proper orchestral wind instruments such as the flute, oboe, clarionet, bassoon, French horns, slide trumpet, and alto trombone, have been much

The patronage of wind-players by industrial corporations began in the 1820's. In or about 1825 the colliery manager to the Bridgewater Trustees established a 'reed band' at Edgfold, Worsley. John Fawcett, a shoemaker who had learned the clarinet in the Volunteers Band in his native Kendal, was engaged as teacher. In 1832 a brass band was founded in the iron works at Blaina, in Monmouthshire. By the 1840's the railway works at Swindon, Wiltshire, had a brass band. By the side of these officially supported groups, there were 'Old Bands' and 'Temperance Bands', increasingly in demand for public meetings, for festivals, 'club feasts', and processions.[1] There were also 'reed bands', especially to be found in some northern theatres and in the Belle Vue Gardens in Manchester. The quality of many of the wind and brass players in Lancashire was recognised by Hallé, who conscripted a number of them into his orchestra. This source of supply has lasted until recent times.

Gradually, mixed wind bands gave way to all brass (the technical problems of brass instruments being fewer) and in 1851 a Lancashire band gave a performance at the Great Exhibition. Two years later the first of the Brass Band Contests took place at Belle Vue, Manchester.[2] Two bands still familiar that were prominent in this period were those of Besses o' th' Barn, and Black Dyke Mills. In 1860 the first Crystal Palace Band Contest was held, attracting an entry of 170 groups.

Industrial Wales

It is generally maintained that the one indisputably musical part of the British Isles is the Principality of Wales. 'At the same time', the Welsh writer F. Griffith justly remarked, 'it is a singular fact that, whilst no country has displayed more natural aptitude for music, there is none which has made so small an impression upon the history of Art'.[3] Here is a tragic case of lack of opportunity. The native tradition rested on vocal and on harp music, and on the Eisteddfod. To become famous the Welshman had

neglected. This has been caused by the introduction of organs into churches and chapels to the exclusion of orchestral instruments and secondly to the formation of brass bands in preference to reed bands, consequently there has been very little opportunity for hearing the proper orchestral wind instruments . . . there are, in many parts of the kingdom at the present time, a great number of musical societies being formed for the practice of vocal and instrumental music, but nearly every one of them is incomplete for want of the proper orchestral wind instruments.' Millington, op. cit., pp. 41–2.

[1] For the history and ramifications of the Bolton Old Band (1803–50) see Millington pp. 107–18. Also an account of brass band music at a Temperance Festival in Leeds, in *Mus. T.*, June 1847, p. 752.

[2] A band contest attended by the Stalybridge (Cheshire) Old Band was said to have taken place in 1818, *Grove*, I, p. 915.

[3] F. Griffith, *Notable Welsh Musicians (of To-day)*, London, 1896, 4th edn., p. xi.

to leave Wales, and, if he was a composer, to subordinate his natural instincts to the cooler disciplines of the English. Thus it was that during the nineteenth century only a handful of Welshmen made the grade—out of Wales—while there remained behind teachers whose technical equipment neither matched their innate talent nor their enthusiasm. Yet, as the valleys of the south became more and more industrial, heroic efforts were made to give a new purpose to the nation's music.

The characteristic popular musical expression of the age, as in Germany in Lutheran times, was the hymn. The foundations of Welsh hymnody, and also of a new phase of Welsh poetry, were laid down by William Williams (1717–91), 'Williams of Pantycelyn', the evangelist who also did much to spread Methodism through Wales. Between 1744, when the first volume of his six-part *Aleluia* appeared, and 1787, when the final part of *Rhai Hymnau Newyddion* was published, he produced a mass of inspiring material for common use that by the beginning of the nineteenth century was endowed with a canonical authority. The propagation of religious music, which was also the music of social protest, was made infinitely easier when tonic sol-fa was adopted. The credit for making the system available to the Welsh goes to two Sunday School superintendents, Eleazar Roberts and John Edwards, whose enthusiasm was fired after hearing a lecture by John Curwen in Liverpool. In August 1861 Roberts published a set of sol-fa lessons in *Y Cerddor Cymreig*. Beside the hymn there ran the folk-song (with traditional harp melody often turned into folk-song) and the editorial work of Maria Jane Williams (*Ancient National Airs of Gwent and Morgannwg*, 1844), John Thomas (Ieuan Ddu), the schoolmaster of Treforest (*Cambrian Minstrel*, 1845), and John Owen (*Owain Alaw*), organist in Chester (*Gems of Welsh Melody*, 1860), being geared to practical rather than scholarly exercise, was invaluable in giving a sense of pride in a broad heritage of poetry and music. Since, through the Eisteddfod competitions, the composition of poetry was a popular occupation, a connection between the past and the present was maintained. It is, therefore, not improper to accept *Hen wlad fy nhadau*, the poem by Evan James, the weaver, and the music by his son James James, the innkeeper of Pontypridd, as a folk-song. First published by Owen in 1860, this work has, of course, been accepted as the National Anthem of Wales.

Most Welsh musicians of the period are virtually anonymous (or, perhaps, polyonymous). The names of four composers, however, stand out against their background.

Henry Brinley Richards (1817–85) does not take high place among British musicians, but he was among those Welshmen who helped to give some self-respect to their country's music, when this was badly needed.

Born in Carmarthen (his birth-place wears a commemorative plaque), where his father was the church organist, he was able to go to the Royal Academy in London through the good offices of the Duke of Newcastle. A pupil of Macfarren, W. H. Holmes, and Potter, he distinguished himself in the first place as pianist. In due course he became a professor at the Academy. Negligible as a composer (his principal work being *God Save the Prince of Wales*), but regarded as one with authority by reason of his London connections, Richards exerted a considerable influence on the Eisteddfod. Even more valuable was his work on national music which led to the publication of *The Songs of Wales*[1] in 1873. John Thomas of Bridgend also won his way to the Royal Academy, having gained the Triple Harp prize at the Abergavenny Eisteddfod of 1838. In 1851 he made a European tour as harpist, and in 1871 he became Harpist to Queen Victoria. A friend of Rossini and Meyerbeer, an honorary member of the Società di Santa Cecilia in Rome, the Società Filarmonica in Florence and the Philharmonic Society in London, Thomas, entitled Pencerdd Gwalia at Aberdare in 1853, took an active part in many Eisteddfodau, and his works were performed at Swansea in 1863 and at Chester three years later. In 1862 he organised a concert, for a Welsh choir of 400 voices and twenty harps, at St. James's Hall, and nine years later founded the London Welsh Choral Union. Between 1862 and 1874 in conjunction with J. Jones (Talhaiarn) and T. Olivant he issued four volumes of *Welsh Melodies with Welsh and English poetry*, and in 1873 he put out his version of *The Songs of Wales* based on previous publications of John Parry and George Thomson. An unsophisticated composer (his works include settings of poems by Welsh poets and of Welsh translations of the classical poets—including Goethe), Thomas nonetheless is an interesting one. Without the limitation set on him by the academic conventions upheld in London he might have been a good one. The same obtains in the case of his brother, Thomas Thomas (1829–1913)—or Ap Thomas, also renowned as a harpist, who was the first Welshman to play at a Gewandhaus Concert (1872). Works by Thomas Thomas (which were published in New York and Berlin) include a cantata version of *The Pilgrim's Progress* (1868).

A fourth notable Welshman to arrive at the Royal Academy was Joseph Parry (1841–1903). Born in Merthyr Tydfil, where he was put to work in the iron works at the age of ten, Parry spent some of his youth in America, his parents having emigrated to Pennsylvania. On his return he came to the notice of Brinley Richards at the Llandudno (1862) and Swansea (1863) Eisteddfodau. Through the efforts of Richards a fund, with subscriptions not only from Wales but also the U.S.A., was set up to

[1] Boosey, replaced by *The National Songs of Wales* (ed. E. T. Davies, Sydney Northcote, A. G. Prys-Jones), 1959.

subsidise Parry's further education in London. In 1878 he became the first Welshman to graduate as Mus. D. at Cambridge. Meanwhile he had taken a teaching appointment at Aberystwyth University College, from where he moved to the University College at Cardiff in 1888. In these offices his reputation was sufficient to ensure a permanent place for music in the Welsh University Colleges. Parry was a prolific composer, but in his major works he felt obliged to use a nondescript style thought to be proper to a Doctor of Music. Thus his ambition to establish a national Welsh Opera, through *Blodwen*[1] and other works, was frustrated. In the field of oratorio he was on safe ground and *Saul of Tarsus* was the principal piece at the Cardiff Festival of 1892.[2] Parry, always prone to produce too much too hastily, spread himself over symphonic works, but his posthumous fame depends on the works he could have written had he never walked along the academic road—the hymn-tunes, *Dies Irae*, *Llangeistiolus*, and *Aberystwyth*. As, however, the last-named is the noblest work of its kind composed by a British musician, Parry achieved more than many whose reputations were, and sometimes are, said to stand higher. In the course of time Parry, the greater part of his music forgotten but for convenient Eisteddfod trifles and *Aberystwyth*, became a legend.[3]

Since the nineteenth century the Welsh choir (the 'Choir in the Valley', etc.) has been romanticised. It has also tended, of later years, to romanticise itself. But there was nothing romantic about its organisation and purpose in the strenuous days of the Victorian age. The choir, an offshoot of chapel and Trade Union, was a means of maintaining self-respect. It gave opportunity for self- and communal expression; for protestation, and for a belief in values that were otherwise denied. The urge to use the native talent to the best use threw up many distinguished and devoted chorus-masters. All of them sprang from modest backgrounds. Among the best-known were Rhys Evans (1835–1917), a clothier, who made the famous United Aberdare Choir and was not content until he could give the classical choral works with adequate orchestral accompaniment; Hugh Davies (1844–1907), who left school at the age of eight to work in the brickfields, became a promoter of sol-fa classes and editor of *Cerddor y Tonic Sol-ffa* and ended his career as a Methodist minister; and Harry Evans (1873–1914), who had the ambition to establish a Welsh College of Music and conducted many choirs in Wales, and finally the Liverpool Philharmonic Choir. Evans's son became a royal physician.

[1] Text by W. Rowlands. This, the first Welsh opera, was performed at Aberdare 1886, Liverpool and Merthyr Tydfil, 1887, Cardiff, 1890, Liverpool, 1921.

[2] See W. H. S. Johnstone (rev. W. A. Morgan), *History of the First Cardiff Musical Festival*, London/Cardiff (n.d.).

[3] And the subject of J. Jones's *Off to Philadelphia in the Morning*, Penguin Books, 1951: see also E. Keri Evans (and others) *Cofiant Dr. Joseph Parry*, Cardiff/London, 1921.

And there were composers; like William Thomas Rees (1838–1904) of Bridgend, a collier until he was past thirty, the author of oratorios, cantatas, and hymn-tunes, and a prize-winner at the London Eisteddfod of 1887 for an essay concerning the necessity for improving the standard of instrumental music in Wales; John Price (1857–1930), of Rhymney, 'a child of the [Hullah] singing school and the Eisteddfod'[1]; J. T. Rees (b. 1858?) of Ystradgynlais, already an underground worker at the age of nine and a miner until he was twenty-one; and Tom Richards of Maesteg (b. 1859?). In respect of Richards, it was written how 'When he was quite a boy, a fatal accident killed his father, and left him and his eight brothers and sisters totally without means of support. Thus, having to work before reaching the age legally required, he was deprived of every means of getting education, but this did not prevent his musical proclivities from breaking forth in him while quite young . . .'[2]

The music sung by the Welsh choirs had this distinctive quality: that it enshrined the Welsh language, and even the most trite pieces are capable of making a particular and memorable impact through the intensity with which Welsh singers can invest the living word. This relationship, between music and language and between the combination of both and the realities and unrealities of daily life as it is lived, is what folk-music is about. Irrespective of whether the music itself is good, bad, or indifferent, the repertoire of Welsh music is the only one in Britain that recognises that folk-art, being a continuing action, cannot die and be resurrected. The pity of it is that as yet there has been no composer capable of lifting the Welsh language into a musical context of universal validity. There should have been, but there has not been, a Welsh counterpart to Janáček or to Kodály. The two obstructions were the pressures from England, and meagre opportunities for adequate musical education.

Music in Ireland

It is of interest to turn to a wholly contrasting situation in Ireland, where the colonial administrators and a handful of wealthy, if often nervous, landlords[3] upheld their cultural responsibilities rather more securely than their friends and relatives at home. Culture in Dublin naturally did not

[1] Griffith, op. cit., p. 186.

[2] Griffith, op. cit., p. 191.

[3] *The Spectator*, of 8 January 1866, gives an indication of the background. After the end of a spate of Fenian trials the Government were 'still, however, taking extraordinary precautions accumulating troops in Dublin and generally acting as if they either suspected danger or were afraid lest the excessive panic should lead the menaced upper classes to take matters into their own hands'. No doubt, after the philosophy of Haweis (see p. 500), it was hoped that music would 'discipline the emotions'.

mean Irish culture and the music (flavoured with oratorial nostalgia) that was practical in the city was after the pattern of London, with, however, a rather stronger Italian accent. Yet the international successes of Balfe and Wallace were sufficient to give the illusion of a separate Irish strain, and it was partly on the proceeds of a performance of *Maritana* that a school of music was instituted. The urge towards such a foundation derived from the zest of a group of practising musicians, among whom were prominent members of the Robinson and Levey[1] families, John Smith, and Robert Stewart, and the enthusiasm of certain amateurs. Of these one who merits notice is John Stanford, a lawyer and a well-known singer, and the father of C. V. Stanford.

Francis Robinson, a Yorkshireman by birth, founded the Society of 'The Sons of Handel' in 1810–11. His four sons were all musicians (forming a male-voice quartet with a special interest in German part-songs) and the youngest, Joseph (1816–98), building on the foundations laid by his father, directed large-scale choral and orchestral performances under the aegis of the Ancient Concert Society (f. 1834). A keen Mendelssohnian, Robinson gave the first performance outside Germany of the music for *Antigone* with the (Trinity College) University Musical Society, and it was for Robinson that Mendelssohn, as one of the last acts of his life, orchestrated *Hear my Prayer*. In 1852 Robinson conducted a cantata by Robert Stewart (organist of the Cathedrals, and the University, to be knighted for his services to Irish music in 1872) at Cork, and in the following year he assembled a thousand performers for an International Exhibition in Dublin. Side by side with this effusion of energy Robinson held classes in music under the auspices of the Ancient Concert Society. In 1856 the enterprise was advanced through the collective effort of teachers and patrons and the Royal Irish Academy of Music was launched. For thirty or so years its destinies were controlled by Joseph Robinson who—aided by an annual grant which the Irish members extracted from the British Parliament in 1870—built up an effective staff, predominantly of Italian and German professors.

Schools of Music in England

For practical purposes the Irish Academy got off to a happier start than that in London, of which the existence was constantly in jeopardy. By depending on fee-paying pupils the Royal Academy of Music excluded

[1] Richard Michael Levey (1811–99), violinist and composer, had a lifelong connection with the Dublin Theatre Royal. A friend of Balfe and Wallace, and an acquaintance of Berlioz's Harriet Smithson, he was the early teacher both of Robert Stewart and Charles Villiers Stanford.

much promising talent, but the income from this source was invariably inadequate to maintain a desirable standard. Until 1853 the Academy was in effect a co-educational boarding-school for pupils aged from ten to fifteen. These pupils, habited respectively in blue swallow-tail coats with 'Academy' buttons and high-waisted white frocks, were submitted to a fearsome discipline. For breaches of regulations, even the slightest, the penalty was summary dismissal. During the first three decades of the Academy's existence the relationship between the nobility who served on the Committee and the teaching staff went from bad to worse. In 1866 the latter issued a Unilateral Declaration of Independence.

The state of tension already existing was not helped by quixotic government action. In 1864 the Chancellor of the Exchequer, Gladstone (himself an amateur composer of 'sacred' music), allowed to the Academy an annual grant of £500,[1] which, however, was withdrawn when Benjamin Disraeli took charge of the Exchequer. On Gladstone's return to power in 1868 the grant was restored. In the meantime the Committee of Management decided to close the Academy and to surrender the Royal Charter. Having taken counsel's opinion and learning that this abdication was *ultra vires*, the Professors, putting themselves on half-pay until a settlement should be reached, re-opened the Academy on their own account. While the affairs of the institution were thus being re-sorted, other enterprises set out to provide musical education on a professional level. Through the interest of the Duke of Cambridge the Royal School of Military Music was founded at Kneller Hall in 1857. A proposed 'Handel College' was mooted two years later, but apart from collecting a site[2] and the offer of support from Benedict it went no further than the planning stage. In 1864–5 a National College of Music, under the direction of Henry Leslie[3] and with the assistance of a powerful group of experienced and eminent teachers, came and went. In 1874 a fusion of the functions of the Church Choral Society and the College of Church Music (both founded in 1872) resulted in a new teaching and examining institution, incorporated in 1875 as Trinity College, London. This in the first place relied on ecclesiastical goodwill and was therefore restricted to male students, who, when graduating, were required to satisfy the examiners not only in musical but also in church history. The prospectus for

[1] To be set against the grant for Schools of Science and Art, which was £87,830: or the Edinburgh Museum, which received £8,824.

[2] Given by Owen Jones (1809–74), son of the Welsh antiquary, Owen Jones (1741–1814); Jones was an architect and designer, who had been joint director of design for the Crystal Palace, and the architect of St. James's Hall. Jones's plans for the 'Handel College' were made use of in the preparation of the Guildhall School of Music in 1880.

[3] Henry Leslie (1822–96) was involved in the management of various amateur organisations, but was best known through the excellent choir that bore his name.

some years was broader than that of a musical academy and many classes were held in various liberal and scientific faculties. But Trinity College did not answer the increasingly clamant call for a national school of music, a scheme for which was already being worked out at a high level. In or about 1870 the Duke of Edinburgh—the early patron of Arthur Sullivan—took an initiative as a result of studying the *Report on Musical Education in England* that had been issued by the Royal Society of Arts some four years previously. The Report, highly critical of the Academy, supported and reflected the views of those who considered that radical reform should be undertaken in some way or other. The Duke began to collect support for a new institution and in 1873 called a public meeting to outline a scheme 'to erect a building at a cost not exceeding £20,000 for the purpose of a Training-School for Music at Kensington, in connection with the Society of Arts'. An important part of the scheme was to establish free scholarships 'in favour of particular towns and counties'. In 1875 the Prince of Wales presided over another meeting. A building was given by Charles Freake. Subscriptions came in in sufficient quantity to endow a number of scholarships. At Easter, 1876, the National Training School for Music was opened; its Principal being Arthur Sullivan (who still retained a professorial appointment at the Academy).

The promoters of the National Training School had reason to hope for governmental subvention; but none came. Thus by 1878 the position was precarious and a fusion of the School and the Academy appeared a sensible way out of immediate difficulty. But the Academy people were not disposed to entertain the idea. In 1882 the Prince of Wales called another meeting and provincial mayors were brought into the picture. George Grove 'went through the country delivering addresses, insisting upon the necessity for the College, crying shame upon the inadequate condition of English music, and carrying enthusiasm everywhere with him'.[1] On the crest of the wave of this enthusiasm and with generous endowments (in 1882–3 these amounted to £125,000), the Royal College of Music was opened on 7 May 1883. The Director was Grove,[2] who was succeeded in 1894 (when the present building[3] was opened) by Hubert Parry.

While the Royal College of Music was thus coming into existence, the Corporation of the City of London, having examined its own cultural responsibilities, detected a need for an institution that was not primarily

[1] Sir George Grove, 'The Royal College of Music' in the *Strand Musical Magazine*, 1895, pp. 83–7.

[2] On the occasion of the opening of the Royal College knighthoods were bestowed on Grove, Macfarren, and Sullivan.

[3] Made possible by the grant of the site by the Royal Commissioners of 1851 and a donation of £45,000 from Samson Fox (1838–1913) of Leeds, a prominent inventor and industrialist who was the pioneer of the acetylene industry in Europe.

for would-be professional musicians and in 1880 opened the Guildhall School of Music, with T. H. Weist Hill (1828–91), a well-known violinist, as Principal. The School started with sixty-two students. Within four years the number had risen to 2,314. Towards the end of the century Schools of Music within existing centres of adult education were established in Birmingham and Glasgow, and in 1893, through the initiative of Sir Charles Hallé, the Royal Manchester College of Music was founded.

What Hallé wrote in 1895 in some particulars has relevance at the present time:

'Personally, I had never been able to see that there was any *prima facie* advantage in confining high-class training colleges in music, or anything else, to the capital of a country. From earliest boyhood I had been accustomed to the judicious multiplication of conservatoires, and had never seen evidence that would warrant the supposition that this multiplication was disadvantageous to the art in whose interest they were founded. . . . What was true of Germany might also be true of England, which in due time might likewise have its Leipzig, Frankfurt, Dresden, and Cologne. The advances made in England since my first coming, nearly fifty years ago, were incalculably great; and in the big manufacturing towns of the north, especially, the interest taken in the higher forms of classical music . . . was so genuine and discriminating that I had long felt regret that there was no possibility of rightly developing so much native talent. Even among audiences composed chiefly of artisans and miners, I had again and again been struck with the keen discernment of good and bad, and the unquestionable musical instinct commonly revealed . . .

'It is a thousand pities that, without the kindly intervention of rich friends, only the well-to-do can take full advantage of an institution like this. Some comparatively poor students, it is true, manage to enter for a time, but cannot afford to remain long enough to do justice to their talents; while there is a large and important class never reached at all, whose wants hitherto have found no articulate voice, who have only their gifts to commend them, and to these the College is unhappily as yet absolutely inaccessible. The usefulness of any institution would be vastly impaired by so great a limitation.'[1]

The schemes thus projected for the improvement of musical education were brave but lacking in potency until such time as their purpose could be fully explored and the communal responsibilities that they invoked materially acknowledged. At a conference of the Incorporated Society of

[1] 'The Royal Manchester College of Music', in the *Strand Musical Magazine*, 1895, pp. 323–9.

Musicians (established in 1882 by James Dawber of Wigan, and Henry Hiles of Manchester) held in Plymouth in 1899, S. S. Stratton, of Birmingham, moved: 'That the time has arrived when the recognition and support accorded by the municipalities of this country to literature and painting should be extended to the art of music.'[1] This *Leitmotiv*, already familiar but falling on too many wilfully deaf ears, recurs hereafter with greater frequency.

Influences in Musical Education

A conjunction of circumstances helped to underwrite the moral arguments and prejudices that had increasingly enmeshed British music since the death of Handel. A further touch of morbidity had, of course, been added by the lamented passing of Mendelssohn, while such occasions as the State Funerals of the Duke of Wellington[2] and Prince Albert greatly assisted the cause of presumed 'serious' music. Church music began to come into its own again—but under the restrictions imposed by the general policy of recovering decencies rather than of inspiring radical changes. The hymn-tunes and anthems of Henry Gauntlett and John Bacchus Dykes, and a host of other minor composers, stand—alas!—as unmute testimony to the approved doctrine of musical sanctification by melodic martyrdom and harmonic (and sometimes enharmonic) apotheosis. Since church-going became increasingly fashionable so did hymn-books proliferate. Their general purpose was neatly outlined in a provincial collection, *The Burnley Tune-Book* compiled by Thomas Simpson (published by Pitman of London), of 1875, where the *Preface* began as follows: 'The *Burnley Tune-Book* may be said to be a collection of English Tunes by English Composers, both professional and amateur: the melodies being for the most part the legitimate outpourings of music imbued with deep musical and devotional feelings.' The widespread cultivation of choral music by the working classes (happily self-supporting) was also approved as an aid to pacification of unruly temperaments or tranquillisation of unhappy conditions. During the cotton famine that struck Lancashire during the American Civil War one Robert Griffiths, Secretary of the Sol-fa College,[3] put in a large stint of social welfare through music, which 'was brought in among other recreations to keep the people occupied and happy. Tonic sol-fa classes

[1] See *Mus. T.*, 1899, pp. 98–9.

[2] For which John Goss composed the anthem, *If we believe that Jesus died.*

[3] John Curwen's work in disseminating his principles culminated in the foundation of the *Tonic Sol-fa Reporter* (1851), the Tonic Sol-fa Association (1853), the publishing house of Curwen (1863), and the Tonic Sol-fa College (1869). In 1874 the first Tonic Sol-fa Festival took place at the Crystal Palace.

were held in mills, the machinery, idle and useless, was cleared out and turned into rooms of entertainment. Mr. Griffiths often took his choir to sing to the people. What quiet appreciative listeners they were! So polite and orderly! "that experience", says Mr. Griffiths, "awoke in me a respect for the working classes which I have never lost!" [1]

The point at which the prevailing Victorian social attitudes towards music and morality met was the Education Act of 1870. That music received any consideration at all at this time was due to the long perseverance of John Hullah (1812–84). A native of Worcester, Hullah was a pupil in London of William Horsley. Moderate early success as a composer (he set Dickens's *The Village Coquettes*, St. James's Theatre, 1836) was followed by conversion to the cause of popular musical education. Inspired by the example of Mainzer and Wilhem,[2] he argued his case for universal musical instruction with (Sir) James Kaye-Shuttleworth, with whom he was acquainted. Kaye-Shuttleworth, a doctor of medicine, was one of the architects of the social welfare state and made his mark in many fields. Through his work as secretary of the committee of council on education (1839–49) he may, however, be given chief credit for the preparatory discussions that led to the Forster Act of 1870. He was also the founder of the Training College for Pupil Teachers at Battersea (1839–40), to which Hullah was appointed music tutor. From this official bridgehead he moved forward, commencing a school of vocal music for Sunday- and Day-school teachers at Exeter Hall in 1841, and taking on similar instruction at King's College, Queen's College and Bedford College, in London. Assiduous in his labours, Hullah, also on the staff of the Academy and Horsley's successor as organist of the Charterhouse, conducted many choral functions, including those given by the children of London schools in the Crystal Palace, and delivered Royal Institution lectures of quite exceptional interest.[3] In 1872 he was appointed Inspector of Training-Schools for the United Kingdom. In the same year the London School Board appointed a supervisory teacher of singing to its schools—John Evans. In 1882 the position occupied by Hullah was, on his retirement, up-graded and one of the principal official musicians of the day, John Stainer, added to his other offices that of Inspector of Music in the elementary schools of England. There were devoted teachers who, rigorously schooled in sol-fa, did much to establish standards of musical literacy. But their efforts, contained by their own limitations of technique

[1] *Manchester Faces and Places*, 1891, vol. II, no. 11, pp. 165–8.

[2] Guillaume Wilhem (1781–1842), director-general of music in the provincial schools of Paris.

[3] See especially those dealing with Baroque music, of Germany, Italy and England, contained in *The Third or Transition Period of Musical History*, London, 1865. This volume was dedicated to Gladstone.

and experience, were subjected to powerful controls. The aim of music in education was utilitarian, to raise money, and to instil a reverence for established values in Church and State: songs were allowed which 'included some virtue or discountenanced some vice',[1] or which expatiated on the glories of the British Empire. That instruments should be introduced into schools was a proposal generally regarded with horror.[2] The views of the upper or the lower classes so far as music was concerned were expressed clearly, eloquently, and tediously by the Rev. H. R. Haweis, who saw in music—the finest 'discipline to the emotions'—the panacea for most social evils, including illegitimacy and over-population. He also well understood and expounded the dogma that musical enterprises should be self-supporting. This being taken as axiomatic, he could expound his theories: 'Let the heaven-born art of music spread,' he wrote; 'let it bless the homes and hearths of the people; let the children sing, and sing together; let the concertina, the violin, or the flute be found in every cottage; let not the only fiddle in the place be hung up in the beer-shop, the only choruses in the village be heard in the choir and at the public house. And while music refines pleasure, let it stimulate work. Let part-songs and sweet melody rise in all our crowded factories above the whirl of wheels and clanking of machinery; thus let the factory girl forget her toil and the artisan his grievance, and Music, the Civiliser, the Recreator, the Soother and Purifier of the emotions, shall become the music of the future for England.'[3] And the sovereign remedy: 'I have known the oratorio of the *Messiah* draw the lowest dregs of Whitechapel into a church to hear it, and during the performance sobs have broken forth from the silent and attentive throng . . . If such performances of both sacred and secular music were more frequent, we should have less drunkenness, less wife-beating, less spending of summer gains, less pauperism in winter.'[4]

There was another side to the educational picture. As a result of compulsory religion and contacts, through commercial and cultural interest, with Germany, music was beginning to infect the 'public schools', now

[1] Percy A. Scholes, *The Mirror of Music, 1844–94*, London, 1947, 2 vols., II, p. 617. There is a nice example of musical utilitarianism in the annals of Liverpool for 1882. In that year Samuel Crosbie (1849–1937), a schoolmaster who introduced the sol-fa notation to Liverpool, and founded the Liverpool Tonic Sol-fa Choral Society, gave a concert with his Teachers' Choral Society which raised £20 for the new Everton Football Club.

[2] See *St. James's Gazette*, 1890, regarding the provision of school pianos (already to be found in Manchester, Liverpool, Leeds, and Bradford) in London: 'What must be the feelings of the middle-class householder when he is asked to take money out of his ill-lined pocket in order that the children of "the poor" may be taught to dance and sing under the auspices of smug philanthropists.'

[3] H. R. Haweis, *My Musical Life*, London, 1898 (5th impression), p. 161.

[4] ib. p. 208. The reader is also referred to the same author's *Music and Morals* (1871), which within twelve years had run into as many editions.

reaching the high point of their influence on national life. Not unnaturally (except in the case of Christ's Hospital which was regarded as a Charity School and which maintained its ancient, strong and independent musical life) the inclusion of music within the curriculum made no appeal either to administrators of these establishments or to many of the parents. But boys who had aptitude for music, were able to survive the rigours of the post-Thomas Arnold system, and even to absorb the prevalent attitude regarding 'leadership', in due course came into the running for direction of the national musical life. Walter Macfarren (1826–1905), brother of George, an ex-chorister of Westminster Abbey, and a professor at the Royal Academy, was organist at Harrow School between 1848 and 1850, when, however, he did not have a single pupil. In 1862 John Farmer (1836–1901), who had studied music at the Conservatorium in Leipzig, was appointed to the staff of Harrow and recognised as music master a few years later. He remained at the school until 1885 when he became organist of Balliol College, Oxford. In both establishments he did much to generate a lively interest in music, and at Harrow he was responsible for siphoning the 'House spirit' (already stimulated by a football competition) into singing contests, and the communal ethos into the 'School Song'. Farmer was the composer of *Forty years on*, and other music for public school use.[1] The possibility that music might exercise a 'refining and elevating influence' occurred to Edward Thring, headmaster of Uppingham School, and in 1865 he imported to his staff Paul David (1840–1932), son of Mendelssohn's friend, the great violinist, Ferdinand David. At Uppingham community singing of school songs was balanced by opportunities for hearing and performing instrumental music, and on occasion distinguished visitors—of whom Joachim was one—were invited to contribute to the school's musical life.[2] It took a considerable time for this condition to become wide-spread in the boarding-schools, and the impact made by these institutions was at first more considerable than was warrantable by their intrinsic musical virtues.

Uncongenial Climate for the Composer

The interplay of the social, economic, and cultural facets of British life during the Victorian era so militated against the creative musician that a

[1] John Farmer (a native of Nottingham) had 'the sense and genius to write music that is wanted. How much there is written that is not wanted.' *Notts and Derbyshire Notes and Queries*, May 1895. Farmer aimed at introducing the *Liedertafel* tradition into Harrow. See article on 'School Songs' in the '*Harrow Almanack*, 1866; also 'The Musical Society' in *The Harrovian*, 10 June 1871, p. 166.

[2] Thring's sympathy for music owed much to his wife, who came from the Rhineland.

young composer reviewing his prospects within the twenty or thirty years that followed the death of the Prince Consort could only tighten his belt and hope for the best while fearing the worst. In an age in which vulgarity reached heights hitherto thought unattainable an unbridgeable gap began to separate 'serious' music from the rest. It was one of the merits of what, without disrespect, may be termed the sub-classical era of British music—from the mature Arne and Avison to the hey-day of Attwood—that a composer then could be a whole composer, his sympathies for a wide range of his countrymen made manifest in a broad expanse of varied but not quite disparate works. But with such a composer as Sterndale Bennett, for example, such diversity would have been thought impolitic. In the same sub-classical period musicians mostly learned their craft in the old way, through a form of apprenticeship. After the foundation of the Academy academic education became at least desirable, though the principle of apprenticeship actually strengthened in the organ-lofts. The Victorian composer understandably looked wistfully towards the Continent. There he could write symphonies in expectation of performance and even publication. There he could study in the opera-house, and, having learned the business of opera, stand a reasonable chance of adding to the provincial repertoire. In England the symphonic field became more and more a closed shop. Opportunity in the theatre also contracted.

In 1843 an Act for Regulating Theatres was passed by Parliament in order to do away with the worst restrictions of the 1737 Licensing Act. Between 1737 and 1843 drama, as such, had been restricted to Drury Lane and Covent Garden. The function of the Haymarket, by the terms of its license, was to provide Italian opera. When other theatres put on plays they did so with such addition of music and dancing as to satisfy the Lord Chamberlain that they were no longer plays. Hence, the considerable accumulation of entertainments with songs and interludes that led so many composers to the threshold of opera. In 1847 Covent Garden, re-decorated, opened as the Royal Italian Opera. Destroyed by fire in 1856, but speedily restored, it fulfilled this function until 1892, when as the Royal Opera House it widened its scope to include French and German (or, for that matter, any other foreign) operas to be sung in their original language. An international house, its reluctance to stage native operas (even if there was any sign of public demand, which there was not) was at once understandable and regrettable. Her Majesty's Theatre in the Haymarket also suffered destruction by fire in 1867. Ten years elapsed before opera was put on there again, but in 1892 the theatre was demolished and its successor (managed by Herbert Beerbohm Tree) made no provision for opera whatever. The plans for a National Opera at the Lyceum foundered; so too did a similar scheme undertaken at the St.

James's Theatre in 1871.[1] In 1875 James Henry Mapleson (1830–1901),[2] lessee of Drury Lane, drew up a grandiose plan for a Grand National Opera House at Westminster. Not only did he draw up plans, he began to put them into effect—only to find that faulty estimates and careless surveying and a consequent and inexorable spiralling of costs made it necessary to abandon the site, which, however, was found to be admirable for police purposes. Where there might have been an Opera House is New Scotland Yard. Meanwhile, the peripatetic company known, after its first manager and conductor's name, as the Carl Rosa[3] bravely tried to keep the operatic flag flying, not only in London but also in the provinces. The first performance by this company was, in fact, in Manchester, on 1 September 1873, when *Maritana*[4] was given. This company did something for the native composer—when, as grew more and more improbable, it could find any competent to compose an opera.

Overall, then, the position was so bad that bad music (of which there was plenty) could not make it work. Anything less than bad was liable to be seized on by the optimists and hopefully overrated. Under this light we arrive at the careers of five composers who, in different ways, would seem to have achieved some immortality, though in varying measure and for diverse reasons: Sullivan, Stanford, Parry, Elgar, and Delius—two Irish-

[1] Which amounted only to a revival of Balfe's *The Rose of Castile*, conducted by Arthur Sullivan.

[2] Mapleson studied violin and piano at the Royal Academy and singing in Italy. He managed Italian opera seasons at Drury Lane, the Lyceum, and Covent Garden, and produced Gounod's *Faust* (1863) and Bizet's *Carmen* (1878). He took touring companies to America, and in 1888 published his *Memoirs* (2 vols.).

[3] Carl Rose (*sic;* 1842–89), born in Hamburg, educated in Leipzig and Paris, settled in England after a period in the U.S.A. After years of labour in the cause of opera Carl Rose concluded that the influence of Puritanism was so strong in England that no Government would ever offer any subsidy. (See *Mus. T.*, 1887, pp. 267–9) .

[4] Which prompted the *Manchester Guardian* critic to begin his notice (3 September) with a general statement on the subject of opera in England.

'From time to time the public is reminded of the neglect of English opera, and as often some enterprising and—judging by the experience of former ventures—sanguine manager is found to attempt once again to revive or create a "national" taste for this class of entertainment. We say to create; for, though much has been done in this direction during the last half century, the fact that native composers have been compelled rather to write for the music shop than the stage—to write down to the capacity of drawing-room misses, in short, proves how little real hold opera has as yet upon the English character. Nor, indeed, is this to be wondered at when we consider how weak and often inane the plots and dialogues of the operas are. The lyric stage has never in any country done justice—except, perhaps, in the cases of the operas written for the Grand Opera in Paris—to the requirements of literary style. So long as pleasing melodies and attractive "situations" were supplied, it has scarcely been deemed necessary to give a thought to anything else. Before a "national" English opera can be founded there must be a union of the powers of the dramatist and the musician. So long, however, as operas are listened to for the sensuous pleasure derived from the music only, this class of entertainment will fail, we are sure, to obtain the favour which, under different conditions, may yet be possible in the future.'

men, two west country Englishmen, one Yorkshireman of German descent. Sullivan and Elgar belonged by birth to the lower middle-class, the one the son of an Irish-born military bandmaster,[1] the other of an organist, piano-tuner and music-shopkeeper in a provincial city. Parry stemmed from the landed gentry and Stanford from the Anglo-Irish élite of Dublin. Delius represented a strong influence in northern England—that of the immigrant Germans,[2] who were present in Bradford, where he was born, in considerable numbers. Sullivan and Elgar were, in different ways, aggressive; as conditions then were, progress or prosperity could only come to those who started near the foot of the ladder, through the skilful deployment of such aggressive qualities as might be inherent. Stanford, of the quick tongue and sudden temper, was also aggressive. In his case this is usually and too readily attributed to his Irish nature. Parry, on the other hand, not needing to fight, was a moderate reformer and behaved as he might have been expected to behave, according to the autocratic principles of his class. Delius, temperamentally the least well-endowed of the group to deal with English philistinism, became, like Pierson, a cultural refugee so that his impact on British music became fortuitous. Sullivan, Parry, Stanford, and Elgar, however, were directly influential.

Those who were pupils of Parry and Stanford sometimes allowed a sense of gratitude unduly to affect judgement and these two composers have frequently been upheld as the architects of a 'Renaissance' in English music. This, since taken as a whole the condition of the nation's music was not uniformly unhopeful, is exaggeration. By the same token there was, in the earlier years of the present century, a frequent tendency to overestimate the value of their compositions. With the advantage of perspective it is now to be conceded that Parry's 'nobility' was often plain dullness, and the brilliance of Stanford was no more than fluency, guided by an imaginative intelligence, but restrained by a faulty sense of aesthetic values. Parry and Stanford have been joined together in a partnership but this association has really benefited neither. In the long run their works, with very few exceptions, have been consigned to the scrap-heap. This is not true of Sullivan on the one hand, nor of Elgar on the other, whose survival is due to the fact that those considerations of 'good taste' which actuated both Parry and Stanford were not allowed to inhibit their aptitudes. Sullivan and Elgar were aware of what British music was, rather that what it ought to be, and worked from within its limits of acceptability. Parry and Stanford, more patently idealistic, attempted to demolish the existing local structure and, while using at least some of the same material,

[1] His mother was partly of Italian descent.

[2] Delius's father was German-Dutch, his mother German.

to build anew. Great composers—in the popular and not the partisan specialist sense—come at the end of a tradition. Those whose aim is reformation leave behind ideas which may, or may not, provide a suitable base for more eminent successors. It was not what Parry and Stanford themselves did as composers that mattered, but what they helped to make possible for those who came after.

Arthur Sullivan

Arthur Sullivan (1842–1900) performed this great service to music in Britain: unwittingly and even unwillingly he redeemed it from the bondage of sententiousness. His posthumous reputation depends entirely on his operettas, in which he demonstrated beyond doubt that ebullience and sparkle, and even wit, were valuable and (since response to them was immediate) indigenous qualities within the collective musical character of his fellow-countrymen. What he did, in conjunction with a librettist of genius, was to invert philistinism and to show, by a kind of Gilbertian paradox, that when stood upside-down it was even an asset. Sullivan (and Elgar too) had the common touch and by exercising it he helped those for whom common was the most opprobrious of epithets to appreciate that it had other, and vital, connotations. Sullivan shone as an entertainer. When he put off the motley and tried to play the tragic or even the merely solemn role he failed; sometimes dismally. Sullivan wanted to succeed where he did not, and not to succeed where he did. He symbolised a schizophrenic condition in his generation.

Acclimatised to music at home, and well experienced as a boy in the techniques of orchestral instruments, Sullivan was sent as a chorister to the Chapel Royal[1] on the recommendation of Sir George Smart. At the age of fourteen he was entered as a student at the Royal Academy of Music, where he was the first holder of the newly founded Mendelssohn Scholarship.[2] After two years, under Bennett, Goss, and O'Leary,[3] he was sent off to Leipzig,[4] where he remained for three years. By now residence in Leipzig was more or less obligatory for prospective British com-

[1] The Master of the Children was Rev. Thomas Helmore (1811–90), no great musician but a pioneer in the revival of plainsong in the Church of England.

[2] The Scholarship Fund was based on the proceeds of a performance of *Elijah*, given by the Sacred Harmonic Society and John Hullah's 'Upper Schools', conducted by Benedict, at Exeter Hall on 15 December 1848.

[3] Arthur O'Leary (1834–1919), native of Co. Kerry, Ireland, a pianist trained in Leipzig and at the Academy of which he became a professor. O'Leary was befriended by Mendelssohn and acquainted with Robert and Clara Schumann.

[4] Fellow students in Leipzig included J. F. Barnett, composer, and Walter Bache (1842–88) and Franklin Taylor (1843–1919), pianists.

posers and the solid Conservatorium tuition was imposed on all the members of the present group with the exception of Elgar, whose financial resources permitted him no more than a fortnight in the city during his formative years. Sullivan enjoyed Leipzig and his lively talents were appreciated by his tutors (see p. 509). Irish independence, however, enabled him to steer clear of the restricted areas of academicism and the first-fruits of his labours were characterised by lightness and colour rather than by 'scholarship'. In fact, Sullivan's temperament was both a blessing and a curse. It enabled him to produce music with facility, to compose fluent entertainment music (*Unterhaltungsmusik*, perhaps, fits), and to give free rein to an innate sentimentality; it vitiated balanced judgement. Stanford had some of the same temperament, but controlled by a sharper intelligence and a superior general education.

The holder of the Mendelssohn Scholarship could not have produced a happier subject for his debut as a composer. The pantomimic and melodramatic music for *The Tempest* which Sullivan wrote in Leipzig show the qualities of Mendelssohn and Schumann worked into an individual style. Manns showed sound discernment in his acceptance of excerpts from *The Tempest* for performance at the Crystal Palace in 1862, and it is not surprising that he felt impelled to repeat the music at a second concert a week later. Hallé performed *The Tempest* music later that same year in Manchester. It is the refinement and variety of the scoring that first catches the attention—notable examples being the settings of the songs 'Honor, riches', and 'Where the bee sucks'. In both songs the rather angled rhythm of the vocal line, more conspicuous in the earlier songs, is softened by the flexibility and fluency of the orchestral textures which, continually changing in detail, are to be counted as lyrical in a Shakespearian sense. Sullivan usually manipulated his gayer measures best—as in the characteristic 'Banquet Dance' of Act III, Sc. 2 [Ex. 1*a*] and the

charming Scherzo music of Act IV, Sc. 1; but in the Overture to Act IV the quality of a more richly endowed Romanticism appears [Ex. 1*b*]. This was one of Elgar's points of departure.

Accepting the organistship of St. Michael's Church, Chester Square,

1b.

London, as a small insurance against indigence Sullivan immediately turned towards the theatre and, acting also as organist at Covent Garden, was encouraged by Costa to try his hand at ballet for which, as *The Tempest* showed, he had a genuine talent. The music for *L'Ile enchantée* was written in 1864, in which year, again through Costa's good offices, he composed *Kenilworth* (text by Chorley) for the Birmingham Festival. A visit to Ireland resulted in an *Irish Symphony*, which, like *Kenilworth*, was also performed at the Crystal Palace. Of the clutch of national symphonies that came in Britain during the second half of the Victorian era Sullivan's is, perhaps, the best. He had the sense to generalise and not to particularise, and if the work reflects more of Sullivan's temperament than of the supposed character of the land of his forefathers that is fair enough: he was by way of being an Irishman. The energetic fourths of the opening, the echoes of the brass motiv in E major by the bassoon, in E flat (from where the tonality shifts to B major), the interpolated string figure that remembers the 'Dresden' Amen, the long Schumannesque, triplet-motivated, first subject of the *Allegro, ma non troppo vivace*, are finely original. So too are the *Scherzo*, looking back to Mendelssohn across *The Tempest* [Ex. 2*a*], and the *Allegretto*. In this movement the light-weight

2a.

string backcloth to the oboe solo is both delicate and subtle and the pull of the harmony towards C major a nice example of imaginative exploration [Ex. 2*b*]. One regrets, of course, that Sullivan, like Sterndale Bennett, never again really caught the first fine careless rapture.

Two years after the production of the *Irish Symphony* the death of his father occasioned the Overture *In Memoriam*. Thus far Sullivan had achieved success early, though not unwarrantably, and his standing at home was enhanced when *In Memoriam* was accepted for a Gewandhaus Concert. In 1867 Sullivan went with George Grove, a close friend, to

2b.

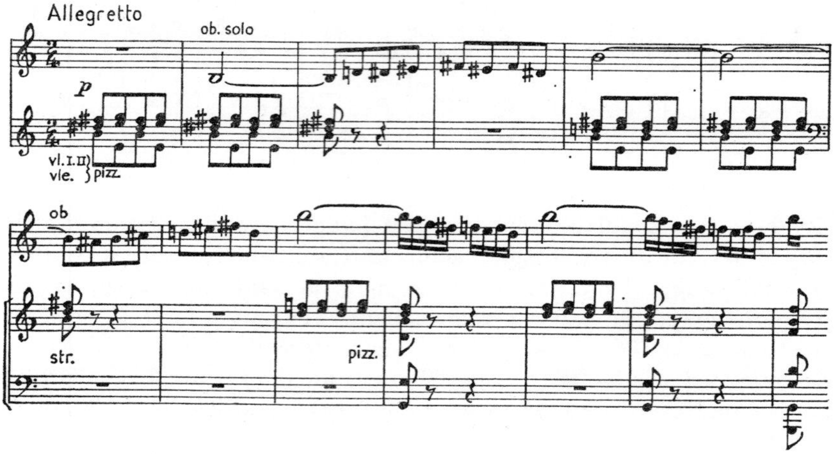

Vienna and through diligent searching there came to light the *Rosamunde* music of Schubert. This too went straight to Manns for performance at the Crystal Palace.

In later life Sullivan, a generous man, acknowledged the debt he owed to Manns and the opportunities afforded to him by Manns were a signal factor in his successful appeal to the suffrages of the wider public. The ten years from 1867 to 1877 were decisive. Sullivan became both public entertainer and moral preceptor. With one hand he wrote music for farcical operettas—of which *Cox and Box* (1867) is still to be heard and *Thespis* (1871) is significant as the first collaboration with W. S. Gilbert—and for plays (including *The Merchant of Venice*, 1871); with the other he wrote hymn-tunes (*Onward, Christian Soldiers*, once popular, now surviving in a Welsh parody—'Lloyd George knew my father'—which erodes any distinction between a sacred and profane style), cantatas, and oratorios. The overture *Di ballo* (1870) is a gay piece of this period that carries a Schubertian deftness. Sullivan's music was more than tolerable when, as in the case of *Di ballo*, it moved. He was a composer whose talents atrophied in any movement with a striking-rate below *moderato*. Unfortunately such oratorios as *The Prodigal Son* (1869) and *The Light of the World* (1873), the first a Worcester, the second a Birmingham Festival, contribution, are quite reduced to inanimity by the current requirement that sacred music should show a preponderance of semibreves and minims. *The Golden Legend* (Leeds Festival, 1886)[1] has carried the cult of white notes

[1] The work was a flop when performed in Berlin in 1887, and caught an early blast of German xenophobia—'Was macht dieser Fremde hier?' asked the *Börsen Zeitung*. (See *Mus. T.*, 1887, pp. 265–6.)

into modern times with the chorus 'O gladsome light'. But sanctimony was well served and on account of his serious music, which he alas! also took seriously, Sullivan, a royal favourite, was decorated with Doctorates, and (in 1883) a knighthood. It is unprofitable to pursue Sullivan's frequent successful forays into the field of sacred—or generally serious—music. Never able to refuse commissions, he stocked the market and satisfied the customers, but it would be difficult to discover a page of music comparable, say, with Macfarren's best. Equally it would be difficult to give pass marks to Sullivan's songs, the worst of which, such as *The Lost Chord,* touch a banality hardly reached either before or since. For a composer who relied for the most part on those classical props of the conservatorial conscience, tonic and dominant, Sullivan did very well for himself [Ex. 3].

3.

Ursula
Vir-gin, who lo-vest the poor and low-ly, If the loud cry of a mo-ther's heart
p

Dr. Paperitz, a teacher in Leipzig, who had known Sullivan as a student, was shown a score of *The Light of the World*. He remarked: 'But you Englishmen, who come here and show such promise, become utterly spoiled when you get back to commercial England. Compare Sullivan with Brahms. Of the two I think Sullivan had the greater natural musical talent; but Brahms will not write a note he doesn't think worthy of his gift . . . As for Sullivan, he settles in London, and writes and publishes things quite unworthy of his genius. He is petted by royalty, mixes in aristocratic circles, acquires expensive tastes which oblige him to prostitute his talents for money-making works. As a consequence, his modes of expression deteriorate, and England and the world are robbed of the fruit of his God-given gifts'.[1]

There is a point at which the intrinsic quality of music is of less consequence than its referential significance. Thus the demerits of Sullivan's style as evinced oratorio-wise turn into virtues where attached to texts which abound in pointed and felicitous turns of phrase, and of which a formal neatness is sufficiently marked to impose a corresponding tidiness

[1] Samuel Midgley, *My 70 Years' Musical Memories (1860–1930)*, Novello, 1930, pp. 21–2.

of pattern in the music. In 1875 Sullivan was engaged by Richard D'Oyly Carte to collaborate with Gilbert in the production of a 'dramatic cantata' for the Royalty Theatre. It was in an Offenbach season that *Trial by Jury*—with Sullivan's brother Frederick taking the role of the Judge—was first given, and it was an immediate success. The whole story of opera in England from the beginning of the century to this point shows how avid the public was for entertainment, rather than for any kind of uplift (that was the province of oratorio). It was the manner in which Sullivan appreciated and satisfied this appetite that marked him out as one of extreme perceptivity.

In 1876 D'Oyly Carte took a lease of the Opéra Comique Theatre and, backed by a business syndicate, decided to exploit the Gilbert-Sullivan combination—sometimes, in time to come, an uneasy one. In the following year *The Sorcerer* was produced, and ran for 175 nights. Its successor in 1878, *H.M.S. Pinafore*, set up a record by enjoying an unbroken run of 700 performances. In addition to this it captured the American market, though, effective copyright protection then being non-existent, the co-authors benefited less than they should have done.[1] There followed *The Pirates of Penzance* (1879), *Patience* (1881), *Iolanthe* (1882), *Princess Ida* (1884), *The Mikado* (1885), *Ruddigore* (1887), *The Yeomen of the Guard* (1888), *The Gondoliers* (1889), *Utopia Ltd.* (1893), and *The Grand Duke* (1896).

The enormous success of D'Oyly Carte's investment enabled him to open the Savoy Theatre, in 1881, and the operettas thereafter were up-graded and known as the 'Savoy operas'. Almost ten years later D'Oyly Carte was led by the siren of 'grand opera' to the rocks that had wrecked so many previous ventures, Sullivan was not unwilling to turn to a theme which he considered more proper to his standing and his talents, and, with Julian Sturgis as librettist, composed *Ivanhoe*, the first and the last English work to be staged at the new English Opera House that D'Oyly Carte had built in Cambridge Circus.

Sullivan was not sparing of himself. He undertook the superintendency of the National Training School, conducted at the major festivals,[2] and was inveterate in turning out oratorios and occasional music. During his last years he worked against the climactic and agonising phases of an incurable disease. His death was mourned as that of no other composer

[1] In 1879 Gilbert and Sullivan visited New York in order to produce the 'authorised version' of *H.M.S. Pinafore* at the Fifth Avenue Theatre.

[2] Sullivan was appointed to conduct the Leeds Festival in 1880, Costa having blotted his copy-book by his high-handed treatment of the Committee, and Charles Hallé having withdrawn his candidature since he was not to be given a free hand in choosing his orchestra. Sullivan retained his Leeds conductorship until ill-health compelled his resignation in 1898; at this year's festival he conducted Elgar's *Caractacus*.

since Handel, and he was buried in St. Paul's Cathedral. The Savoy operas are now virtually the sole reminder of Sullivan's genius, and the extent to which they owe their reputation to this rather than to Gilbert's texts is permanently debatable. It may, however, be said that in the whole history of music there has been no such partnership in which the claims of poet and composer have been so equally poised. That this is so is creditable to the latter in that his, being the second, was the more severe task.

The operas as a whole (most are still viable and some few are the mainstay of amateur and educational operatic undertakings) have certain characteristics previously written into the native musico-dramatic tradition such as it was. The atmosphere of horror and mystery backs *Ruddigore* as formerly Storace's *The Haunted Tower*. The fairies of *Iolanthe*, the bucolics of *Patience*, the exotic properties of *The Mikado*, the rumbustious

4.

patriotism beneath the traditional flummery of *The Yeomen of the Guard* are all to be found in the main stock of Covent Garden and Drury Lane at the beginning of the century. Also in line with what was conventional the Gilbert and Sullivan pieces were interspersed with spoken dialogue. What was new was the satirical tone, the holding-up to ridicule of British institutions, the topicality that brought Oscar Wilde, and the aesthetes, into the story of *Patience*, and immortalised lesser-known figures on the Victorian scene. A master of word selection and of metrical invention, Gilbert, whose pleasure in baiting middle-aged spinsters shows an unpalatable vein of sadism, proved the ideal stimulus to Sullivan's mobile talents. Because he was essentially a miniaturist and an eclectic, Sullivan succeeded in this field, whereas in those works on the serious side of his output, where a sense of tragedy or of drama would have been proper had he the capacity to convey either, he did not. Sullivan was not oblivious to the precedents of Storace, Reeve, Mazzinghi, Davy, and Attwood (see pp. 395 f.), and was content to work with a minimum of technical resources. His debts to Offenbach and to Schubert are slight, although he knew exactly when to embellish his ready-to-measure style. Thus he can add to lyrical atmosphere—as in 'The sun whose rays' (*The Mikado*)—by investing the verbal with a new and quasi-independent musical phrasing. He can cross rhythmic patterns—as in 'When I came to the Bar' (*Iolanthe*) and 'How beautifully blue the sky' (*The Pirates of Penzance*)—with minimal fuss and considerable musico-dramatic effect [Ex. 4]. He can switch tonality with unwanted freshness within an otherwise pedestrian context [Ex. 5]. A natural orchestrator, Sullivan practically never misjudges

5.

either the detail of instrumental colouring, or the relationship between instruments and voices. He had, not surprisingly, a keen ear for atmosphere and his evocations of scene—particularly in *Iolanthe* on the one hand and *H.M.S. Pinafore* on the other—are both lucid and unmistakable. So far as characterisation was concerned he was at his best in group treatment—as the 'three little maids from school' of *The Mikado*, the daughters of Major-General Stanley in *The Pirates of Penzance*, and a varied selection of naval, military, and civilian teams, to whom he allotted extraordinarily telling glee-like ensembles (which again derived from the precedent of earlier Victorian opera).

Sullivan set out to reform nothing. A completely professional composer, he accepted the conventions as they were and in one particular department showed (as in the Viennese tradition to which he subscribed with his enthusiasm) how music of significance can, given the kind of aid that a librettist of the calibre of Gilbert affords, evolve. With Parry it was otherwise. He was a man with a mission.

Hubert Parry

In contrast to Sullivan, Parry (1848—1918) was an amateur, with wide interests that stretched from poetry (which he composed in youth) to sport. The son of Thomas Gambier Parry, a Gloucestershire squire who as a painter was responsible for decorations in Gloucester and Ely Cathedrals, he was educated at Eton and Oxford. Before leaving Eton he qualified as a Mus. B. at Oxford. Having arrived in the University he made chamber music his principal musical interest. He was, said H. C. Colles in *Cobbett*, one of the first English composers of recent times to 'form his musical mind by the study and practice of Chamber music.' He set a precedent by taking as his first stringed instrument the viola. His enthusiasm led to the institution of the Oxford University Musical Club. During the long vacation, having previously had lessons from Sterndale Bennett and Macfarren, he went to Leipzig to study with Pierson. It cannot be said that this influenced his subsequent style, although the mere fact of having studied in Germany was sufficient for xenophobic reactionaries most improbably to arraign him as a dangerous Wagnerian. For some years Parry worked in an insurance company and his musical interests were dilettante. Friendship with Edward Dannreuther, the encouragement given to him after private performances of chamber works, and the acceptance of his Overture *Guillem de Cabestanh* by Manns for a Crystal Palace concert strengthened his resolve to treat composition as a vocation. Parry's close connection with Gloucester (where S. S. Wesley had been an early inspiration) resulted in a string work—*Intermezzo religioso*—being played at the Three Choirs Festival in 1868. In 1880 his first large-scale work, *Promethus Unbound*, was performed, also at a Gloucester Festival. Shelley was not admitted into the cathedral, for the performance, conducted by Parry, took place at the 'first secular concert' in the Shire Hall. Whether this ambitious work was a success or not was a matter of opinion, and critical opinion was divided. *The Times*, however, was ready to extend a welcome to a text of a choral work that was literature. With some truth the writer observed: 'English composers are frequently too forgetful of the fact that bad poetry rarely inspires good music. One of the features which at once suggest themselves to the attentive listener is the close connection of Mr. Parry's music with the words it is intended to illustrate, and it may be said of him that in more than one instance he has succeeded in giving additional force to Shelley's lines.' The critic, in the course of a long article, returned to this point: 'Here', he wrote, 'as elsewhere, Mr. Parry's music, as all vocal music should do, grows from and is inseparably wedded to the words.' As for the lineage of the orchestral music and its message—'The orchestral prelude . . . shows Wagnerian influence, perhaps more even than the vocal portions of the work. Without containing any distinct reminiscence it resembles structurally the marvellous prelude to 'Tristan and Isolde' with which it also shares the oneness of sentiment. Its motto might be, 'Ah me!, alas, pain, pain ever, for ever!'[1] Parry brought to the task of setting Shelley a feeling for declamation that had disappeared under the congestion of harmonic and rhythmic clichés borrowed from alien sources. These, Parry recognised, had choked the free flow of musical thought in England. While proposing a bold prospectus for English music in the matter of rhythmic values he also showed the vigour inherent in strong, and wide-ranging, melodic contours, which were the stronger for their abstention from chromatic persiflage. With more of rhythmic independence, and of melodic determination, contrapuntal technique began to take on a new lease of life.

Although his first major choral work was not sent off with universal acclaim (and it made little mark subsequently) Parry felt sure enough of himself to press on in the same field. Thus at the next Gloucester Festival, in 1883, he offered a spacious setting of Shirley's *The Glories of our Blood and State*, in which, correctly, Brahmsian affinities were discovered; for Parry shared with Brahms a seriousness of intention and frequent gravity of mood. His textures were carefully, and contrapuntally, woven. He avoided effect for the sake of effect. This was where he made his greatest misjudgement, for the orchestra, confined more and more to activities of secondary importance, tended to obscure what otherwise called for attentive and analytical listening. *Blest Pair of Sirens* (1887) is not free from this criticism, but the sheer vitality of the vocal writing and the generous tribute which the composer paid to the 'English Choral tradi-

[1] *The Times*, 8 September 1880.

tion' in the planning of the chorus parts have kept this work alive when most of his other works have passed away. 'This,' *The Musical Times*[1] observed, 'is a fine and scholarly piece of writing, full of excellent counterpoint, but always clear, broad, and dignified. As usual with this composer, the general style of the music reflects that of Brahms; but in this instance, it is Brahms in his more genial mood.' Within this statement are brought the majority of Parry's larger compositions. The very merits of the style to the next generation—or rather the next but one—became demerits. 'Scholarly writing' smacked of the academic mind. Parry continued to co-operate with the older masters of English literature—setting words of Milton again (in *L'Allegro ed il Penseroso*, 1890), of Pope, Tennyson, Dunbar, in festival works of cantata stature and of the seventeenth-century poets in songs and part-songs—and also with such contemporaries as Swinburne, Browning, and Bridges. Parry's larger works (which included some oratorios for which he himself wrote the libretti) were ideal for middle-class choral society use. They were earnest, sometimes pompous, and solid in literary merit. But by the composer's often pedantic approach to textural detail he made of music more a duty than a pleasure. It is, for instance, difficult to believe that Parry really understood the spirit of Milton as well as did Handel when we encounter [Ex. 6]. On the other hand when high seriousness was required by the philosophical content of the poem and detached from the 'Festival' requirements,[2] Parry could reach a high point of achievement. His finest music

6.

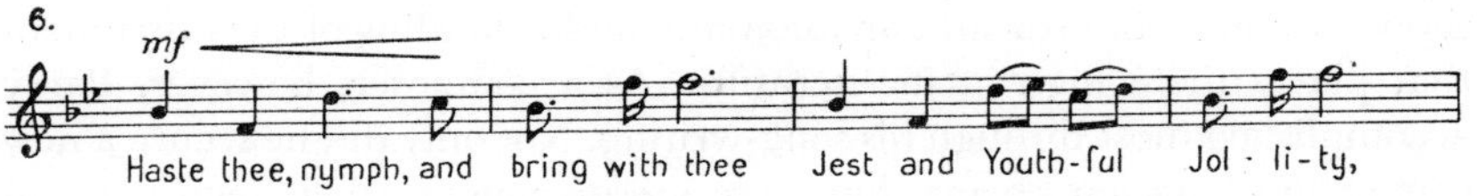
mf
Haste thee, nymph, and bring with thee Jest and Youth-ful Jol - li - ty,

is contained in the six unaccompanied motets of 1918, entitled *Songs of Farewell*, which, introspective and even tragic, are splendid monuments of the choral art.

Parry's four symphonies fail because of abstemiousness in the matter of colour and the heavy-handedness that came from an inability to refer

[1] *Blest Pair of Sirens* was composed for the Bach Choir that had been founded in 1876. This Society, conducted by Otto Goldschmidt (husband of Jenny Lind) until 1885 when Stanford took over, gave inspiring performances in its early days of the *Mass in B Minor*. (see J. A. Fuller-Maitland, *A Door-keeper of Music*, London, 1929, pp. 78–80).

[2] Cf. 'I am, to tell the truth, not very fond of Festivals. It is not that oratorios bore me, or even the new works "composed expressly", the word "expressly" here indicating the extra-special dullness supposed to be proper to such solemn occasions. These things are the inevitable hardships of my profession . . .' Bernard Shaw, *The World*, 3 May 1893.

matter to manner. Parry was one of those English composers—and he had numerous successors—who tended to hold the orchestra at arm's length as somehow lacking in the dignity with which by now choral music was re-invested. It is not to be denied that the symphonies were zestful, energetic, and marked by what used to be termed sound ideas. These ideas, however, better inhabited the borders of choral music. Thus it is that the *English Symphony* (no. 3 in C major, *c.* 1889) reads like an oratorio. The Englishness lives in the diatonicism [Ex. 7*a* and *b*]. With

7a.

I Allegro energico

7b.

III Allegro molto scherzoso

the organ Parry was more successful, and his *Chorale Preludes* and *Fantasias* show a range of interest and an idiomatic understanding of the instrument that places them high in its literature. As a composer, however, Parry accomplished most through his song-writing. Not only did he secure a new connection between poems that were meritorious on their own account and melodies apposite in respect of contour and rhythm, but he established a viable relationship between voice and piano. Altogether there are twelve sets of *English Lyrics*, of remarkable consistency. These are, nevertheless, but minor masterpieces: Parry, finding it difficult to wear his heart on his sleeve and imbued with a strong sense of caution, could never really let himself go.[1]

Parry became Director of the Royal College of Music in succession to Grove in 1894, and six years later followed Stainer as Professor of Music at Oxford. To these functions he brought authority, and a capacity for handling people was an important factor in bringing a purposefulness into the higher branches of musical education. As the author of a number

[1] For a discussion of Parry's songs, see H. C. Colles, 'Parry as Song-Writer', in *Essays and Lectures*, London, 1945, pp. 55–75.

of books on music he helped to recondition popular appreciation of the great masters, while his study of the music of the seventeenth century in the third volume of the *Oxford History of Music* was a landmark in musicological progress: not least of all because he protested 'that true genetic knowledge did not consist in dates, anecdotes, and facts, but in a first-hand familiarity with the actual compositions of the past.'[1]

Charles Villiers Stanford

Charles Villiers Stanford (1852–1924) had the gift, that Parry lacked, of a vivid imagination. Thus the best of his music touches areas that Parry would never have contemplated invading, and carries the mark of an intuitively musical personality. He was a kind of Anglo-Irish Dvorák, whose talents, however, rarely reached the fulfilment that they often seem to promise. The reason is plain; Stanford was a patriotic Irishman. As such he believed in the superiority of the Irish to the English, but, because of his social origin, felt obliged to associate himself with those among the English who held it as a high responsibility to keep the majority of the Irish in subjection. Thus Stanford's Irishness was vitiated by a disbelief in any vital form of national expression. He fell back on watery legends and comfortable fancies to please drawing-room gatherings. Thus he trod some of the way previously covered by Tom Moore. But before Ireland made any obvious impression on his music he had thoroughly schooled himself in styles that were antithetical to all that truly Irish music was. And, for that matter, to everything that English music should have been. Stanford at the present time is remembered by his surviving pupils. His services and motets are stock items in the cathedral repertoire. 'Public school' choirs still perform *The Revenge* and *Songs of the Sea* and *of the Fleet*, just as they doggedly retain Parry's *Blest Pair of Sirens* for more solemn occasions. Otherwise Stanford's music is unknown to the general public. In the gravitation of the few works that survive from a huge output one sees the pull of respectability, both social and academic: the cause of Stanford's inability fully to extend his gifts. In former times the English middle classes acted as the catalyst for musical adventure. In the days of Parry and Stanford they constituted a major impediment. To get by in the social round, the British composer needed to resemble his betters. At the end of the road of musico-social respectability was the lure of a title: for most composers knighthood was the kiss of death. It was a token of achievement in anything but creative activity.

Stanford went to school in Dublin and, supported by his father's

[1] P. C. Buck in Introductory Volume to the *O.H.M.*, 1929.

strong musical talent and enthusiasm, had lessons in composition and organ from Sir Robert Stewart. He was always sustained by the memory that his father had given supper to Mendelssohn after the first performance of *Elijah*, and he accepted Mendelssohnian values as of divine inspiration. In 1870 he went to Cambridge, to read classics, and while still an undergraduate became organist of Trinity College. Fortunate in living in Cambridge in a period in which culture was not an appendage to programmed instruction, and in which leisure and wealth gave rare opportunity to those privileged to enjoy both, Stanford broke the crust of endemic hostility to music by the charm of his personality and the allowable extravagances of his Dublin accent. He stamped his personality on the chapel services, and stirred the University Musical Society (founded in 1843) to life. He became Conductor of the Society in 1874. After meeting Joachim, Stanford determined on a course of study in Germany, and for long periods during the next three years he worked there, first with Carl Reinecke, conductor of the Gewandhaus, and then with Friedrich Kiel in Berlin. Reinecke's teaching he found restrictive, Kiel's inspiring. 'He was', said Stanford, 'a rare man and a rare master. I learnt more from him in three months than from all the others in three years'.[1] Kiel made his pupils 'work out their own salvation by criticism rather than by rule of thumb and the obeying of orders'.[2] These were the principles which Stanford himself adopted in teaching and thus broke with the practice of instruction according to strict precedent that prevailed in England. Stanford loved Germany. He revelled in the wealth of musical experience available—like Sterndale Bennett he complained that English society offered so few opportunities[3]—and came into contact with Wagner and Liszt. He made his own mark in German society and took it as a compliment when Schumann's friend Albert Dietrich, the Kapellmeister of Oldenburg, having heard Stanford's *Eight Songs from 'The Spanish Gypsy'*[4] (George Eliot) observed that they were 'not English but Deutsch'.

Unlike most of his English contemporaries, Stanford was both experienced in opera and with a natural inclination towards expression in theatrical terms. This was part of his good fortune in being a Dubliner,

[1] See H. Plunket Greene, *Charles Villiers Stanford*, London, 1935, p. 53.

[2] ib.

[3] E.g. 'We are, in music, training children, improving boys, and doing nothing for young men. In our music schools we are going ahead in improving the education and the taste of a comparatively few, and assuring the still fewer, the highly gifted, that there is nothing whatever to do after they are educated . . . We provide a mass of free scholarships, the emoluments of which end when their holders retire, and we have no posts, to give them a livelihood at the outset of their careers, which begin when education ceases.' C. V. Stanford, 'Notes upon Musical Education', in *Interludes*, London, 1922, pp. 14–15.

[4] Plunket Greene, op. cit., p. 60.

for Dublin was the only British city outside London where there was anything like a living operatic tradition and an appreciation of the fundamental art of *bel canto*. Not only Stanford bore testimony to this phenomenon, but also Bernard Shaw. Having added opera-going in Leipzig, Dresden, Berlin, and Bayreuth to his experience, Stanford began to compose an opera: *The Veiled Prophet of Khorassan* (the libretto, based on Moore's *Lalla Rookh*, by William Barclay Squire, a Cambridge undergraduate at the time).

Not surprisingly production of Stanford's opera was not practicable in England. It was, however, given in Hanover on 6 February 1881. Among other composers whose operas were given premières during the same season were Joseph Huber, Robert Emmerich, Carl Gramman, and Jules de Swert: the obscurity of their names acts as a brake on placing too much *post hoc* pride in Stanford's achievement. However, the work was well received as the *Neue Zeitschrift* of 18 February noted: 'In Hannover ging am 6 [Feb]. Stanford's 'Verschleierter Prophet' (nach Lalla Roukh) mit sehr günstigem Erfolge in Scene. Der Componist wurde wiederholt gerufen, Frl. Börs, Scholf, und Rollet leisteten vor zügliches . . .' *The Veiled Prophet* was given performances in other German opera-houses. Thirteen years later it was played, in Italian, at Covent Garden. The record of Stanford's operas speaks for itself. The second, *Savonarola*, was produced in Hamburg in 1884: a Covent Garden production in London was torpedoed by incompetent casting and insufficient rehearsal, even though the conductor was Richter. The performance was in German. *The Canterbury Pilgrims*, in which the influence of *Die Meistersinger* is to be seen, was given by Carl Rosa in 1884 at Drury Lane. Apart from an unpublished Italian opera, *Lorenza*, Stanford wrote no other for twelve years. In 1896 *Shamus O'Brien*, a convivial piece of stage Irishry, was well received when produced at the Opéra Comique, in London.[1] In 1901 *Much ado about Nothing* had two performances at Covent Garden. Fifteen years later *The Critic*, in the course of a war-time Beecham season, came and went. Finally, in 1919 there was *The Travelling Companion*, a charming piece based on a story by Hans Christian Andersen, which was published under the terms of the Carnegie Trust but which had to wait for seven years for a performance—at the Theatre Royal, Bristol. By this time Stanford had been dead for two years.

With Wagner and Verdi, Strauss and Puccini, Dvořák and Tchaikovsky in spate, it was difficult for a lesser talent to make itself heard. In Germany, where provincial houses needed to maintain a constant repertory (including some 'novelties' that were not too taxing), there was

[1] The conductor was Henry Wood. In the orchestra, as trombonist, was Gustav Holst, then a student at the R.C.M.

room for opera composers of Stanford's calibre. In England there was not.[1]

When Stanford first went to Germany he maintained his office as organist at Cambridge. While in Germany he conceived the 'great plan of a conservatoire in connection with Cambridge University which will reform the Musical degree'.[2] The hope of initiating such a scheme was abandoned almost as soon as it was conceived. Vested academic interests are deterred by the thought of reform, let alone revolution, and Stanford's tenure of office at Cambridge was as distressing to him as it was distasteful to most of his senior colleagues. Nevertheless by 1887 his standing in the world of music was such that his claims to the Professorship at Cambridge in succession to Macfarren could hardly be ignored. He was Cambridge music; the driving force behind the University Musical Society, of which the reputation soared when coaxed to give such important new works as Brahms's First Symphony (1877)[3]; the inspiration of chamber music recitals; the brilliant organist whose registration, by the sober standards of the time, was sensational; the compelling teacher. If Cambridge had hitherto been provincial so far as music was concerned, it was so no longer. In the course of years Stanford brought a large number of European musicians to Cambridge under some pretext or other. He was wayward, irregular, prone to cancel lectures if he could not have professional instrumentalists to illustrate them, or to change their context if he felt so inclined. His professorial reign was marked increasingly by discord and discontent. Yet the stimulus he gave left a profound influence. Among his pupils were E. J. Dent and C. B. Rootham, who had the imagination, intellectual capacity, and practical skill between them to put into order the untidy but rich legacy that they inherited.

The pattern of professional life that Berlioz had deplored among musicians in London continued, so that Stanford, whose zest for hard work was as much in conflict as his temper was in harmony with the 'Irish' nature, practised plurality with the rest. While Professor at Cambridge he was also the principal composition teacher at the Royal College. He had been appointed to this office when the College was opened. His career was as at Cambridge tempestuous. He quarrelled periodically with Parry and, at the same time, taught his craft with an understanding that

[1] Cf. R. Vaughan Williams whose 'opinion was that a composer of Stanford's calibre, if he had been German or Italian would have been celebrated, in every opera house in his country. But in England, instead of *Much Ado* or *Shamus O'Brien*, we were content to resuscitate *Norma* and *Samson and Delilah*'. Discussion after Herbert Howells's Centenary address, 'Charles Villiers Stanford (1852–1924)', *P.R.M.A.*, 79, 1952–3, p. 31.

[2] Letter of 23 December 1875, quoted in Plunket Greene, op. cit., p. 57.

[3] Brahms, who was offered an honorary degree together with Joachim, should have been present, but refused to visit England when the Crystal Palace authorities announced that they hoped he would conduct a concert of his works.

few, if any, other composition teachers in England possessed. From his teaching, there emerged a whole generation of British composers, to whom reference will be made.

From 1855–1902 Stanford conducted the London Bach Choir and in 1901 took over the direction of the Leeds Festival. He retained this appointment until 1910—when inevitable disagreement brought his resignation. Stanford was unhappy about the Committee's readiness to intervene in matters which he regarded as outside its competence. From the beginning he was at cross-purposes with Frederick Spark, the Festival Secretary, whose tendency to interfere was also noted by Elgar. In 1910 the Festival Committee, realising that Stanford was a musician who conducted rather than a conductor who was a musician, proposed the engagement of Nikisch. That was enough. Stanford went, leaving behind a sheaf of fiery correspondence. But he had also left his mark. The Festival had been brought up-to-date. Brahms, Verdi, Wagner, Strauss, and Dvořák were made familiar to Yorkshire. Then off-beat works by Bach and Handel, such as *Singet dem Herrn*, and the sixth *Chandos Anthem*, were given. Modern Britain was represented by Parry,[1] Stanford,[2] Mackenzie,[3] Elgar,[4] Walford Davies,[5] Charles Wood,[6] Vaughan Williams,[7] Rutland Boughton,[8] and Granville Bantock[9]—and others. The range of the Leeds programmes under Stanford's direction is ample evidence of his catholic tastes and of his generosity to his adopted compatriots.

Stanford (like Sterndale Bennett) set out to be a composer. In the end, duly knighted in 1901, he was found to be an educationalist. At the same time he composed ceaselessly, and his list of works, covering virtually every field, is enormous. When in due course revivalism arrives at Stanford there will be ample opportunity for a second view of a corpus of music that in its day opened many windows. Stanford—to coin a term in line with a convenient expression from elsewhere—was above all a 'composerly' composer. There is virtually nothing that he wrote that does not sound musical. He was, of course, an excellent craftsman. He constructed his symphonies and chamber music after classical precedent, and with a frequent deference to Brahms that is exemplified by the opening theme of his first pianoforte trio (1889) [Ex. 8]. He had a sure ear for sonorities, both instrumental and vocal. He adjusted tonalities to moods

[1] *A Song of Darkness and Light*, 1901; *Voces Clamantium*, 1904; *Blest Pair of Sirens*, 1907.
[2] *Five Songs of the Sea*, 1904; *Stabat Mater*, 1907.
[3] *The Witch's Daughter*, 1904.
[4] *'Enigma' Variations*, 1901; *In the South*, 1904; *The Kingdom*, 1907.
[5] *Everyman*, 1904.
[6] *A Dirge for two Veterans*, 1901.
[7] *Toward the Unknown Region*, 1907.
[8] Folk-song arrangements, *The Berkshire Tragedy* and *King Arthur*, 1907.
[9] *Sea Wanderers*, 1907.

8.

Allegro grazioso

with an instinct for colour effect that was frequently stimulating and sometimes moving. He had the gift of melodic invention. And he had wit. Unfortunately he came to maturity some twenty years too late. There are two criteria here to be taken into account. Within the British context Stanford was phenomenal: the standard bearer of modernity. Within the European context (and Stanford kept his eyes on the wider scene) he said very little that had not been, or was not being, better said by indisputably greater composers. And these composers—Verdi, Brahms, Dvořák, Strauss, Glazunov, and even Grieg—were bearing down on the British market.

Stanford is left with the individuality of the Irishman. His folk-song arrangements were the most creative works of this kind that had so far appeared in Britain. His introduction of Irish folk-music into the general romantic-classical apparatus that he used was, however, seldom convincing. There are an *Irish Symphony* (no. 2), five *Irish Rhapsodies*, various dances and fantasies: charming, occasionally nostalgic, but superficial. In the 'Irish' Symphony Stanford goes to great pains to quote 'Remember the glories of Brian the Brave' and 'Let Erin remember', but damages the symphonic structure irreparably by holding everything up until their self-conscious arrival. The best bit of Irishry (of the *Shamus O'Brien* order) is the second movement theme—to be compared with that of the Scherzo of the Pianoforte Quintet—where there is at least a show of spontaneity [Ex. 9]. There is life in *Shamus O'Brien* and *Phaudrig Crohoore* (both to texts

9.

Allegro molto vivace

by Joseph le Fanu), but an artificial life. Once or twice the genius that was in Stanford stirred at the thought of landscape. His settings of poems in the cycles *Cushendall*, *A fire of Turf*, and *The Glens of Antrim*—though handicapped by the flaccid quality of the verses—are warm and evocative. Stanford mastered the combination of solo voice and pianoforte better than any of his British contemporaries. Once or twice he becomes memorable. The haunting play of harmonies in the 'Fairy lough' is familiar: less so, perhaps, the delicate, evanescent, sad magic of the Yeatsian feeling of Moira O'Neill's 'A Broken Song' (*An Irish Idyll*, no. 5.), which begins [Ex. 10*a*] and ends [Ex. 10*b*]. Evocative passages are also to be found in

10a.

10b.

the oratorios (especially *Eden*,[1] with a more or less Protestant angelical chorus to set against the Catholic ones of *Gerontius*) and his part-songs. Of these—the pride of the collection by common consent being the impressionistic *The Blue Bird*—the poetic sense inherent in them proved a congenial guide to choral societies all over the country. They, as much as any works, sensitivised British choral practice and helped to turn it away from the massive utterances bred out of Handelian orgies. The real weakness of Stanford as a composer was stated by himself. Addressing students in his treatise *Musical Composition* he wrote: 'It is not necessary, in order to depict an ugly character or a possible situation, to illustrate it with ugly music'. To read Stanford's views on 'modern music', in a paper read before the Musical Association in 1920, in which he fulminates against the cult of consecutive fifths and the exploitation of the whole-tone scale, makes a sad commentary on the standards then prevailing among the musical hierarchy. What, in fact, did the so-called Renaissance amount to? The predicament of the composer himself was more cruelly stated by Bernard Shaw: 'I do not say that Mr. Stanford could not set Tennyson's ballad (*The Revenge*) as well as he set Browning's Cavalier songs, if only he did not feel that, as a professional man with a certain social position to keep up, it would be bad form to make a public display of the savage emotions called up by the poem. But as it is, Mr. Stanford is far too much the gentleman to compose anything but drawing-room or class-room music.'[2]

Edward Elgar

It will be appreciated that Parry and Stanford, unwittingly, gave rise to a heresy that had been stirring in the womb of the national music: the heresy that an 'educated' musician was superior as musician to an 'uneducated' musician. The prestige enjoyed by the two ancient universities increased during their lifetime and the influence on the social pattern was immense. So far as the Philistines and Barbarians were concerned, if there were to be professional musicians then the acceptable pattern would be according to the Stanford-Parry precedent. Those who followed this precedent established a cosy circle and for an outsider to break into it was, for many years, difficult. Graduates of this fraternity filled the posts of influence—in 'public school' and cathedral. No one understood the position more clearly than Edward Elgar (1857–1934), whose observations

[1] *Eden* is otherwise to be noted for the inclusion of the plainsong melody *Sanctorum meritis*. Stanford developed a late interest in modal music through the researches of the theorist William Rockstro.

[2] 16 May 1890, quoted from *London Music in 1888–89*, London, 1937, p. 377.

on it during his lifetime caused concern and dismay. Elgar had a habit of saying what he meant: an unwelcome practice to those whose stability depended on mute acceptance of what had come to be regarded as the *status quo*.

Elgar pulled himself up into the first rank of English composers by his own exertions, supported by the faith of a few friends. In an era in which a composer embarked on oratorios at grave risk to his subsequent reputation, in which an English symphonist was thought to be a contradiction in terms, in which no foreign musician would have regarded it as remotely possible that an Englishman could score an orchestral work even respectably, Elgar composed *The Dream of Gerontius*, two symphonies and two concertos of which the merits have increased rather than decreased with the passage of time, the '*Enigma*' *Variations*, *Falstaff*, and the *Introduction and Allegro for Strings*. He also composed salon pieces—among which a *Salut d'Amour* (truly a labour of love) captured the innate sentimentality of the English—and the *Pomp and Circumstance Marches*, from the first of which came the melody made famous in the guise of a 'patriotic' song. Elgar's music swept across the British scene and left virtually no one unaffected. He composed for those whose taste was for 'serious' music, for those whose preference was for 'light' music, and also for those who had no inclination one way or the other. He was, in the full sense of the word, a national composer. It may not be too extravagant to suggest that he was the only English-born composer so regarded in his lifetime.

A great composer appears at a period which he finds to be propitious. During the later nineteenth century music in Britain was insecure, but whatever separatist tendencies there might have been there could be descried a certain community of interest and understanding. The basic vocabulary of the popular ballad was that of the oratorio. The cult of classical music, through the prestigious acquisition of domestic pianos, was widespread. Those of the working classes who aspired towards middle-class values took their culture as seriously as circumstances permitted. There was, in fact, no segregation of musical tastes. Rich and poor alike approved the worst songs and the best operettas of Sullivan. The part-songs of Parry and Stanford stimulated choral groups among university students, but also the more heterogeneous choral societies that were by then taking part in the provincial competitive musical festivals. Elgar understood that an effective composer is one whose principles are catholic and whose works represent a synthesis of his principles. He understood that a composer's methodology is of less general consequence than his music. Elgar wrote with spontaneity: his purpose, summarised by himself in respect of the Cello Concerto, was to express 'an attitude to life'. It is the apparent relevance of Elgar's music that brings the two symphonies and the Cello Concerto especially into the consortium of those major compositions that hold significance at the present time.

Elgar is the rare example of a completely professional composer in Britain. Apart from a brief occupancy of the Chair of Music in Birmingham University (a post created for him),[1] he held no official appointment other than the late sinecure of Master of the King's Music. Against all the odds he survived on the emoluments to be extracted from his works. With a rare persistence he fought against every set-back, determined only to fulfil ambitions he shaped as a boy in the Worcestershire countryside.

Elgar's father was a piano-tuner in Worcester, where he kept a music-shop, and where he also played the organ in St. George's Roman Catholic Church. Elgar's mother, a countrywoman with roots in Gloucestershire, read widely—especially in poetry and history—and exerted a strong influence on her children. Edward thus grew up to be a practising musician (the violin being his main instrumental interest), but with an enthusiasm for books, for local legend and history, and a love for and knowledge of the countryside. Acquaintance with the services of the Roman liturgy brought him in touch with music not accessible to his Anglican contemporaries, while the proximity of cathedral music and the triennial festival gave him opportunity to obtain adequate experience of the normal English repertoire. Having left school at the age of fifteen, Elgar spent a few months in a lawyer's office and then opted out, the conviction that music was the only possible career for him then having become irresistible. Until 1882 he lived a varied musical life—educating himself from the music and text-books in his father's shop, taking part in almost every local concert, superintending the music of St. George's Church, of the local orchestral society, and the nearby Asylum at Powick. Whenever possible he composed *pièces d'occasion*. Some of these remain and from certain of the sketches of the period 1879–82 material was to be drawn to be used in later years.[2]

Elgar's early sketches show the catholic tendency to which allusion has already been made. They included arrangements of Beethoven, Handel, Corelli, Wagner, Schumann, and a symphonic design after Mozart's fortieth, in G minor; variations (on an Irish air); rhapsodies—including one that was designated Hungarian, which reflected, no doubt, the influence of his London violin teacher, Pollitzer;[3] pieces for an amateur

[1] This post, however, gave him the opportunity to deliver eight lectures, now published as *A Future for English Music, and other lectures*, (ed. Percy M. Young), Dobson, 1967.

[2] Notably in the two *Wand of Youth* suites, the *Nursery Suite*, and the unfinished opera, *The Spanish Lady*.

[3] Adolphe Pollitzer (1832–1900), a Hungarian Jewish violinist, was one of the best teachers in London. In 1877 Elgar, having saved up for the purpose, took a few lessons from him. In due course Pollitzer gave Elgar an introduction to Manns.

wind-group ensemble to which he belonged; marches, dances, minstrel pieces and other trifles for Asylum Band and social gatherings; and some Catholic church music. Dating from 1882 there were even some arrangements of Yorkshire folk-songs, of which only one is extant.[1] In retrospect it can be seen how Elgar's isolation from the main stream of English academic teaching was to his ultimate advantage as a composer. His consistent purpose was to write music that was to be heard, and this encouraged the appreciation of values that lay outside the routine of formal instruction. He responded from the start to emotional stimuli—from family, friends, and transient love affairs; the character of his melodies, often conditioned by the customs and rhythms of effusive German Romantic style, and the expansiveness of his harmonies, show how readily he reacted to those stimuli. The characteristics evident in the sketches of his early years remained constant in Elgar's music. Thus the lucid scoring and inherent sadness of a tentative *Scene* [Ex. 11]; the Geron-

11.

tian shifts of a harmony exercise [Ex. 12], the rhythmic bravado of an unfinished March [Ex. 13]; and the feeling for mysticism of a *Salutaris Hostia*

12.

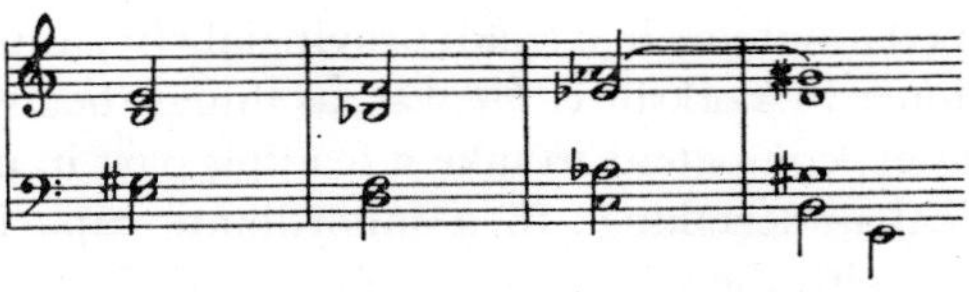

13.

[1] 'During my visit [to Dr. C. W. Buck, a Yorkshire doctor who was a friend of Elgar] he produced a folio containing some of his "finds" [in folk-music] which have been harmonised in a most sympathetic manner by no less a master than Sir Edward Elgar . . . I accompanied Dr. Buck while he sang in a very realistic and traditional way such songs as "Clapham Town End", and "Horse cropping". He told me he had heard old Betty Stockdale—a character of the dales—sing these songs; and he made a strong point of imitating her accent and style as nearly as possible.' J. Sutcliffe Smith, *A Musical Pilgrimage in Yorkshire*, Leeds, 1928, p. 241.

composed for St. George's Church on 17 April 1882 [Ex. 14].[1] In these examples there is a clear and original instinct for musical colour. Elgar did not write music (according to accepted method) and then determine

14.

its instrumentation: he thought from the outset in tone-colour[2]. Behind most of the fragments available for study is a strong programmatic sense, which, through personal relationships, tended to turn on appropriate occasions to subtle allusions to individuals. The characterisations within the '*Enigma*' *Variations* (possibly affected by the work of the same title by Cipriani Potter, and by Schumann's 'Abegg' Variations) were foreshadowed in a number of early pieces.

At the age of twenty-six (by which time a composer nearer the centre of affairs would have 'arrived') Elgar was admired by a group of reasonably well-informed amateurs in a small provincial city, and by a percipient medical practitioner in Yorkshire. He was, as things then went, an accomplished all-rounder, competent to take a leading part in any more or less ambitious musical undertaking. In a subordinate capacity, as violinist, he was in contact with the wider world of music through participation in the orchestra of the Three Choirs Festival and that established by W. C. Stockley in Birmingham. The value of playing the standard works (which as a boy he had studied in score) as well as such new music as was performed was immense. For this experience endowed Elgar with the superb professionalism that is one of the distinctive features of his music.

On 13 December 1883 Stockley included Elgar's *Intermezzo Moresque* in a Birmingham Concert. During the next year—through Pollitzer's advocacy—another timely example of Elgar's exotic fancy, *Sevillana*, was included in a Crystal Palace concert. One or two miniature pieces were published. But it seemed that escape from the limited provincial round

[1] This, completed from the sketches, is recorded on Alpha PHA 3016. The same record contains Elgar's arrangement of *Clapham Town End*.

[2] Cf. p. 534.

was impossible. In 1889 Elgar, by marrying Caroline Alice Roberts, daughter of a major-general in the Indian Army, took a step up the social ladder in that he was now qualified to mix on more nearly equal terms with the upper crust of Worcestershire society. It was a remarkable marriage. Mrs. Elgar, seven years her husband's senior, was determined that her action in marrying out of her class should be justified by the full florescence of the genius which she (and not only she) believed to lie behind the nervous diversity of Edward's outer personality. Mrs. Elgar, whose ambitions allowed her to tolerate some relationships that other women would have dealt with in ruthless manner, prepared her husband's scoring paper, assured him and everyone else with whom she was in contact that each work as it appeared was a masterpiece, and fought off enemies on all fronts. It was hard going at first. The Elgars lived briefly in London after their marriage, but discouragement followed discouragement. They moved back to Worcestershire, Edward's attempt to make his name resulting only in a performance by Manns of the orchestrated version of *Liebesgrüss* (*Salut d'Amour*). The overture *Froissart*, however, which had been composed in London, was performed at the 1890 Worcester Festival. What was more important was that it was published by Novello, whose editorial assistant, August Jaeger, now begins to play a decisive role in the emergence and recognition of Elgar.

Nonetheless, at the end of 1890 the Elgars had had enough of trying to make ends meet in the unfriendly atmosphere of London. They moved back to Worcestershire, Edward conceding defeat by returning to the chores of teaching in girls' schools. He pursued his main aim, however, with resolution. In 1892 the sensitive *Serenade for String Orchestra* was published. In the same year the symphonic cantata, *The Black Knight*, was written, and given its first performance at the 1893 Worcester Festival. Three years later an oratorio, *The Light of Life* (*Lux Christi*), was also given a first performance at Worcester. By now three things were clear: Elgar's music had begun to make some impression and a steady arrangement with Novello (through Jaeger's sponsorship) resulted in a little cluster of works that could not be overlooked in a diligent perusal of their catalogue; the path to fame was the familiar one, of music for choral societies—even if this meant laying aside for the time being the wider ambitions; the dedicated composer's life was one of poverty. Elgar was not averse from publicity, but he recognised that on the Novello list were composers who got more than he did even though he (and Jaeger) knew their talents to be inferior. He was suspicious of the well-placed, and in spite of acts of generosity in the next few years from Sullivan, Parry, and Stanford, he often found it difficult to adjust himself to their way of thinking. Confidence in his own powers gave him the assurance that he could write great works, of symphonic stature; but the improbability of reconciling the economic facts of life with the financially unproductive sacrifice of time required for large-scale composition made him put off from year to year the serious undertaking of symphonic composition.

As it happened, Elgar's concentration on large-scale choral works brought him to the forefront. In 1896 *King Olaf* was performed at the North Staffordshire Musical Festival, in 1897 *The Banner of St. George* was given a performance in Kensington; in 1898 *Caractacus* was conducted by Stanford at Leeds. It was dedicated to Queen Victoria. Elgar was firm in his loyalty to the Crown, and his faith in the virtues of British Imperialism was profound. His *Imperial March*, which was played at the Crystal Palace during the spring of 1897, symbolised this. But it symbolised more—his conviction that it was the special responsibility of the composer to inspire his fellow-countryman. This he did by harnessing the old tradition of native tunefulness to a certain, and irresistible, flamboyance of expression that showed itself in a wholly splendid and uninhibited style of instrumentation. There was, towards the end of the nineteenth century, only Sullivan, perhaps, who could so disarmingly display a similar lack of inhibition. Parry and Stanford were inclined to over-restraint, and this left them in more or less academic isolation. Cowen,[1] and Mackenzie,[2] both for a brief period front-runners in the race, had imaginative '*sinnig-schwärmerische*'[3] ideas but insufficient technique to establish consistency. But Elgar had the capacity to imbue music with a living spirit. Such was his dedication that he could not separate what he composed from what he was: and he was sufficiently gifted to be able to achieve musical credibility.

The lines of development were laid down in the works written before he was forty. That development up to that point was slow was entirely due to the way in which public performances of music were controlled. The handicap of being provincial was considerable. Nevertheless the disappointments of the early years intensified the emotions with which Elgar suffused his works. Thus it was that in 1899 and 1900 the two most remark-

[1] Sir Frederic Cowen (1852–1935) studied in Leipzig and Berlin, and among other compositions produced six symphonies, of which the Fourth ('Scandinavian', 1880) enjoyed success in England, Germany, and America. Cowen's principal contribution to British music, however, was through his conducting. He directed numerous festivals (including that in Melbourne, Australia, in 1888) and the Hallé Orchestra (1896–9), the Liverpool Philharmonic Orchestra (1896–1913) and the Philharmonic Orchestra (1900–07).

[2] Sir Alexander Mackenzie (1847–1935), Scottish violinist, composer, and conductor. A prolific writer (he lived abroad for many years in order to devote himself to composition), Mackenzie, like Cowen, was at his best with exotic or fantastic ideas, but his skill in orchestration was unmatched by any substantial sense of musical logic. In 1888 Mackenzie succeeded Macfarren as Principal of the Royal Academy of Music, an office which he held until 1924.

[3] *Neue Zeitschrift für Musik*, review of Mackenzie's op. 20, 1880, p. 200.

able English works of the nineteenth century, the '*Enigma*' *Variations* and *The Dream of Gerontius*, were first heard; the former at a Richter Concert at St. James's Hall, the second at the Birmingham Festival. In both cases the fullest appreciation of their genius came not from the English, but from immigrants—Richter, the conductor, and Jaeger, the publisher's assistant, and from Julius Buths, of Dusseldorf, the director of the Lower Rhine Festival. In the first ten years of the twentieth century Elgar's music was welcomed throughout Germany, and the mastery of the composer generously acknowledged by Richard Strauss.

There followed a period of rich and varied achievement. If Elgar, long anxious to compose an heroic symphony (on the subject of General Gordon),[1] balked at symphonic composition for some years, on account of the meagre returns that were then to be expected, he enriched the orchestral repertoire with the first four *Pomp and Circumstance Marches* (1901–7),[2] with the Overtures *In the South*,[3] and *Cockaigne* (1901), the tender sequence of children's pieces in the two *Wand of Youth Suites* (1907–8), and the *Introduction and Allegro for Strings* (1905). Two more oratorios, designed as part of a trilogy that was never completed, were given at Birmingham in 1903 and 1906. These were *The Apostles* and *The Kingdom*. During this period Elgar was given honorary doctorates, a knighthood (King Edward VII was devoted to Elgar's music), and made Professor at Birmingham—a post which he quickly found uncongenial and resigned, but not before speaking *ex cathedra* a number of unpalatable truths about music in England. Having for some years directed the Worcestershire Philharmonic Society,[4] Elgar was at least an experienced conductor and after its foundation in 1904 he was not infrequently invited to conduct the newly-formed London Symphony Orchestra,[5] for which he wrote the *Introduction and Allegro*, and with which he maintained a close connection until his death.

At the height of his reputation in the years preceding the First World War Elgar, despite frequent bouts of neurotic discomfiture, and the burden of relative poverty, at last produced his major orchestral works. The First Symphony in A Flat, dedicated to Richter, was given its first performance

[1] For reference to 'Gordon' Symphony, see *Mus. T.*, March 1889, p. 161.

[2] A fifth March was published in 1930.

[3] Written for the Leeds Festival of 1904 in place of a commissioned symphony, but first performed at the Elgar Festival at Covent Garden, 16 March 1904.

[4] 1898–1904. Elgar also wrote the programme notes for the concerts.

[5] The L.S.O. was founded as a protest against Henry Wood's attempt to eliminate the system of substitutes from the Queen's Hall Orchestra. But players, who chiefly relied on free-lance activity to make a living, were incensed that Wood should have first claim on their services for an annual fee of £100. The principal founders of the L.S.O. were the horn-players, A. Borsdorf, T. R. Busby, and H. van Meerschen, and the trumpeter, J. Solomon.

in Manchester at the end of 1908. Two years later the Violin Concerto had its première at Queen's Hall, while during the London Music Festival of May 1911, the Second Symphony,[1] in memory of King Edward VII, was produced. In 1913 the Symphonic Study, *Falstaff*, was performed for the first time at the Leeds Festival.

In the last years of the war Elgar, disillusioned and in retirement in Sussex, took up threads that he had let go at a much earlier period. There are traces of chamber music in his sketches of 1878, and also of 1907. It was not, however, until 1918 that the String Quartet in E Minor and the Pianoforte Quintet in A Minor were finalised. To this same period belongs the Cello Concerto.

Lady Elgar died in 1920. Thereafter Elgar composed little, although the old urge returned a decade later, when the opera *The Spanish Lady* and a Third Symphony were projected, and for which sketches remain. Appointed Master of the King's Music in 1924, a venerated figure at the annual Three Choirs Festival, enjoying a popularity throughout all sections of the community unparalleled by any preceding English composer, Elgar had achieved three things. He had lifted English music from the doldrums—not least of all by his capture of a place in the European and American repertoire; he had restored faith in the ability of the Englishman to be a composer rather than a musician who composed; and he had given a new dignity to the provincial impulses that lie behind English music. The last point needs little further consideration. Elgar did not pay a particular regard to folk-music,[2] in the manner of Vaughan Williams: not because he disapproved of it (which, as early adventures in Yorkshire show, he didn't) but because it seemed an irrelevance. He was well acquainted with rural England (and Wales[3]), but either didn't find or didn't seek out elderly folk-singers. What he did appreciate was the subtle pattern of English provincial life—the cathedral city with its dignities, dignitaries, and internecine bickering; the solid middle-class block of friendly people, some with taste, some without; the way in which the outer world of industry and commerce impinged on the traditional ways of life and behaviour; the thinning-out of town into country, and the vast stretches of fertile ground bounded by hills that were instinct with legend and marked by history. Elgar loved, and he hated. He loved the English *ethos* as he understood it from life and from literature. He hated the impedi-

[1] The Second Symphony was begun before the First and parts of it seem to date from 1904, when a symphonic project was in mind. See Percy M. Young, *Elgar O.M.*, London, 1955, p. 336.

[2] When his friend A. Troyte Griffith addressed him on the then fashionable cult of folk-music Elgar replied: 'I am folk-music.'

[3] The viola theme of the opening section of the *Introduction and Allegro* was modelled on an overheard Welsh melody and was at first specified as for a 'Welsh Overture'.

ments placed before the English commonalty by the Philistines. He was a Conservative, with powerful radical tendencies. He was a religious man, whose doubts were not all hidden.

The sum total of these qualities and defects is contained within his works, which, although all highly personal and therefore unmistakable, swing across the various fields of music in a manner formerly alarming to too nice critics but not out-of-line with the practice of the great masters. Elgar wrote salon music—not only because he had to, but because he wanted to; of its kind it is impeccable. He wrote patently vulgar music (this is inescapable) but full-blooded, vital, and compelling and not (as Sullivan's) either attenuated or unintended. But the popular music of Elgar's invention was a reflection of his social environment, while his major works were a refinement of his evaluation of social values. On this point Elgar as Professor tied himself in knots,[1] but as a composer not at all. Music was meaningful, but it also lived according to its own principles and established system of logic.

The great English composers were bold, and Elgar's refusal to countenance half-measures was in striking contrast to the relative timidity of the best-known of his contemporaries. He did not stand still to consider 'good taste' in abstraction.

Elgar's reputation as a composer rests on his foundations: his mastery of form, and his fluency in expression. It may be said that in the '*Enigma*' *Variations* he gave a new dimension to the variation convention as a vehicle for psychological insight, while in the symphonies he treated the classical pattern from an English point of view but in a manner generally acceptable. Self-taught, Elgar learned that formal concepts were only valid when apposite: thus when he refers to the rigours of counterpoint, as in the 'Demon's Chorus' in *Gerontius*, in the *Introduction and Allegro*, or in the Meercraft music of the unfinished opera, it is with the intention of defining a particular situation. A habit of jotting down germinal ideas when on country excursions[2] put him into a *Leitmotiv* way of thinking, and the application of the principle, especially to *Gerontius*, was not only due to an enthusiasm for Wagnerian method. In any case Wagnerian influence was crossed with the extrovert habits of Italian music, absorbed from Verdi, but also, earlier, from the stock of liturgical music available in the Catholic organ-loft. Elgar's melodies have range, and are contoured by evocative intervals of sixth and seventh, and frequent (sometimes too frequent) sequence. His harmony arrives intuitively; sudden flashes of colour, and areas of plain diatonic simplicity. In respect of orchestration, in which

[1] See 'Elgar and Programme Music', an Appendix to Ernest Newman's *Elgar*, London, 1904 (3rd edn., 1922), p. 177.

[2] A series of sketch books containing other ideas are preserved in the Elgar archives.

Elgar remains the supreme English master, he expressed the secret of his supremacy in a lecture:

'Accepting the fact that orchestration is not simply arranging for instruments but composing directly for those instruments, we feel that we are dealing with a real, living branch of creative art, not (as the erroneous definition would lead us enquirers to think) a mere labour: a transference of ideas from one medium to another, or painting, as it were, a picture in colour from a mezzotint. A musical idea, whether phrase, theme, melody, or harmonic progression, may have a certain value in itself apart from its presentation to the hearer. It may be pleasing, dignified, or possess one of a thousand other qualities; it may even be interesting because it is "scholarly"—but this is so unusual that we need not build upon it.

'A musical idea may be interesting to read without hearing, or it may hold the attention when played on a keyed instrument: or by a combination of instruments, but its inventor must have had some definite medium in his mind . . . I find it impossible to imagine a composer creating a musical idea without defining inwardly, and simultaneously, the exact means of its presentation.'[1]

Frederick Delius

This ability to think music integrally is the connecting link between Elgar and Delius. Elgar, as he acknowledged to Delius on the only occasion on which they met,[2] fitted into (or, rather, forced himself to fit into) the pattern of English musical life. Delius did not. He, the 'pure artist' of the late Romantic mould, escaped the trammels of English philistinism early and, living abroad, worked without reference to what was taking place at home. After a lifetime of voluntary exile, the fact that his reputation (largely due to the championship of Sir Thomas Beecham) stood high led to his being awarded the decoration of Companion of Honour, and the Freedom of his native city of Bradford.

As provincial cities went in the 1860's and 1870's, Bradford, like its neighbours Leeds and Sheffield, was tolerably well supplied with music. The festival movement gave impetus to choral societies, while regular series of orchestral concerts were given by the Hallé Orchestra. Julius Delius, the father of Frederick, like many other German businessmen settled in the north of England, carried into his home life in the West

[1] Birmingham Lecture, 8 November 1906.

[2] In 1933: Delius complained about Elgar's oratorio-writing propensities. 'That', said Elgar, 'is the penalty of my English environment.' Eric Fenby, *Delius as I knew him*, London, 1936, p. 124.

Riding the sociable musical habits of Germany.[1] Chamber music was cultivated, and among those who played and were guests at the Delius's were Joachim and Piatti.[2] Frederick Delius, taught the violin by Bauerkeller of the Hallé Orchestra and having other music lessons from a teacher from Leeds, was commended as a boy of twelve by Joachim when he deputised in a chamber ensemble for a professional player. To Delius music was a private pleasure, and his experiences were for the most part within the domestic circle. He passed through the local grammar school, developed an enthusiasm for cricket that remained as the one distinctly English characteristic to the end of his life, and reluctantly prepared himself to enter the wool trade.

Wool proved Delius's salvation. For, on the presumption that he was going to widen his business experience, he was sent to Chemnitz (now Karl-Marx-Stadt). Making this a convenient centre, he explored and revelled in the musical life of Saxony. After Germany Delius visited Scandinavia and France and then, his restlessness and lack of assiduity in his commercial duties disturbing his father's plans for his future, he was despatched to undertake a new venture in the hope of reformation. At the age of twenty-one Delius set out to become an orange-grower in Florida. Neglecting his responsibilities in this connection, he became more and more immersed in music, adding to his somewhat eclectic store of memorable items the folk-songs that were to be heard and later recollected in *Appalachia*. Some casual lessons from an organist in Jacksonville were sufficient to convince Delius that academic training on the one hand was unnecessary and, on the other, that he had acquired sufficient for his purposes. Nevertheless, the feeling that Florida was hardly the ideal place for commencing the career of a composer renewed a nostalgia for Germany. In 1886 he went to Leipzig, where he studied intermittently with Hans Sitt and Carl Reinecke and met Grieg. From his previous visit to the Scandinavian countries Delius had developed an enthusiasm for Norway and the Norwegian language, and acquaintance with Grieg, Sinding, and Halvorsen deepened this enthusiasm. Through the intervention of Grieg, whose reputation was known to Julius Delius, Frederick's future was redeemed from commerce. At the end of eighteen months in Leipzig

[1] 'The Bradford Liedertafel was formed in 1846 by a number of German residents in this town, including Messrs. Schlesinger, Delius, Philipp, Hoffmann, Hurter, Wiechers, Fiedler, and Speyer, the latter gentleman, who was a first-rate pianist, acting as conductor. For many years the practice of German part-songs for male voices was carried on, and every winter a concert was given in the room over the old Exchange . . . in conjunction with the members of the Manchester Liedertafel.' *Musical Reminiscences of Bradford* [William Cudworth], Bradford, 1885, p. 42. In the 1840's an attempt was made to revive the Philharmonic Society by 'Mr. Martin Hertz, Mr. M. Schlesinger, and one or two other of the German residents who had taken up their abode here . . .' ib. p. 21.

[2] See Clare Delius, *Frederick Delius, Memories of my Brother*, London, 1935, p. 47.

a small income was settled on him, and he was given a modified blessing by his father and permission to become a composer.

Delius settled in France. He lived in Paris until 1896. After 1899, now married to Jelka Rosen, a Norwegian artist, he moved to Grez-sur-Loing, which was his home for the rest of his life. Associating with artists and poets living in the Latin Quarter, Delius, whose acquaintance with composers and professional musicians in general was and remained slender, lived according to the self-sufficient convention that they established. Removed from the normal trade of the world, he composed. It was not until 1899 that he was heard of in England. He had, as a matter of fact, hardly been heard of elsewhere, for only on four occasions had performances of his music been given.[1] Inspired by the encouragement of the Elberfeld conductor, Alfred Hertz, Delius arranged (and paid for) a concert at the St. James's Hall, on 30 May 1899. Hertz came to conduct. The programme included a *Legend*, for violin and orchestra, two movements from the *Folkeraadet* suite, five Danish songs, a symphonic poem *The Dance goes on*,[2] *Mitternachtslied*, *Over the Hills and far away* and excerpts from the opera *Koanga*. The reaction to this concert[3] was that which has since become typical of the English towards 'modern music'. The (reasonably large) audience was polite; the critics, having nothing to work on, were generally perplexed by the alternating languors and asperities of a harmonic idiom that seemed to stem from no legitimate antecedents, and by the generally exotic flavour. They stood firm on the sole assumption that the composer had something to say, but were not sure that they understood his method of saying it. *The Yorkshire Post*, however, displayed an exceptional warmth: '[The] hearty force and intense life [of the music] are, however, such that it is with a feeling of patriotic pride that we are able to say that Mr. Delius was born and brought up in Yorkshire.'

It was eight years before the name of Delius again appeared before the English public. In the intervening period, able to live independently on his own and his wife's legacies, he composed a number of major works which won limited, but influential, support in Germany. *A Village Romeo and Juliet*, based on a novel by Gottfried Keller, was completed in 1901, and the one-act opera *Margot-la-Rouge*, during the next year. In 1902 the set of variations for chorus and orchestra thematically referring back to his folk-song excursions in Florida, *Appalachia*, was revised into its present shape from an earlier orchestral version. The impulse towards

[1] *Florida*, an orchestral suite, privately performed in Leipzig, 1888; *Sur les Cimes*, tone poem for orchestra, in Monte Carlo, 1893; *Folkeraadet*, incidental music to Gunnar Heiberg's play, *Christiana*, 1896; *Over the Hills and far away*, tone poem for orchestra, Elberfeld, 1897.

[2] Revised and published in 1911 as *Life's Dance*.

[3] See *Mus. T.*, July 1899, p. 472.

freedom (after Delius's way of thinking) resulted in the setting of Whitman's *Sea Drift* in 1903. While during the next two years the influence of Nietzsche's *Also sprach Zarathustra* led to the composition of *A Mass of Life*. In the two years following came the *Songs of Sunset*, *On Craig Dhu* (words by Arthur Symons), *Cynara* (words by Ernest Dowson), and the orchestral variations on the Lincolnshire folk-song *Brigg Fair*.[1]

In 1904 *Koanga* was performed in Elberfeld, the conductor being Fritz Cassirer. *Appalachia* was played in the same town in the same year. Towards the end of 1904 the revised versions of *The Dance goes on*, now re-entitled *Life's Dance*, was performed in Düsseldorf, where Julius Buths (to whom *Appalachia* was dedicated) became as enthusiastic in his support of Delius as he was already in respect of Elgar. In 1906 *Sea-Drift* was given a first performance at Essen.[2] In 1907 a programme by Delius took place at Queen's Hall, conducted by Cassirer, and the English were again reminded of the limits set on their musical appreciation by the academic and otherwise restrictive conventions that prevailed. *Appalachia*, not without praise for its effective atmospherics, was a bewildering experience. It served, however, to arouse the immediate enthusiasm of Thomas Beecham, to whose total commitment to the music of Delius for the rest of his life the English reputation of the composer is almost entirely due. In 1909 Beecham conducted *A Mass of Life*, for which the chorus was that from North Staffordshire; in 1910 a performance of *A Village Romeo and Juliet*, which had been given in Berlin three years previously, at Covent Garden; in 1911 a concert of Delius's orchestral works. Beecham's final apotheosis of Delius came in 1929 when, in the presence of the now paralysed composer, a Delius Festival took place in the Queen's and Aeolian Halls on 12, 16, 18, and 23 October. On 17 October Hubert Foss gave a lecture on 'The past neglect of Delius's music' at Trinity College of Music.

Delius's output, which included concertos for violin and cello, as well as a double concerto for these instruments, and two operas not previously named—*Irmelin* (1890–92) and *Fennimore and Gerda* (1908–10),[3] was large and his latest works—among which the most prominent were the *Songs of Farewell*—were composed under severe disability and dictated to his amanuensis, Eric Fenby. Apart from the trifles for a small orchestra—*On hearing the first Cuckoo in Spring* and *Summer Night on the River*—none of Delius's music has taken a firm place either in the national or the international repertoire. Nor, with the exception of Peter Warlock, has his highly individual style affected the general tenor of British music. The truth

[1] Cf. setting of *Brigg Fair* (together with other folk-songs collected from the singing of Joseph Taylor, of Saxby All Saints) by Percy Grainger.

[2] The first English performance was during the Sheffield Festival of 1908.

[3] Produced at Frankfurt in 1919.

is that he was essentially a *fin de siècle* figure, whose languorous melodic lines and emulsive harmonic clusters represented as much the decadence of Romantic idioms as the independence of the artist. Delius was strong in evocation of atmosphere. The darkness of *Paris* at the one extreme and the hard coldness of the 'Winter Landscape' of *North Country Sketches* at the other are splendid tone-poems, or rather tone-pictures; with each piece one is conscious of standing in one place looking at one vision; such is the measure of the composer: beguilement. Delius, whose rhythmic pulse often appears to stop altogether, is a master of immobility. In the variations a sense of development is factitiously engaged. In the operas, where the essence of the medium is movement, there is, virtually, none. Delius is a composer about whom facile generalisation is not possible. The usual criteria are inapt. Delius was original. Well, yes; but originality *per se* is neither here nor there. Delius is original in this manner.

15.

Within the context of British music this passage—from the Double Concerto (1915–16)—is strangely liquescent, but within the context of European music not notably adventurous. Delius is the apostle of 'the mysterious beauty of things half-seen'[1] on the one hand: on the other he strays 'into the harsh regions of sensual passion as the poem centred on the god Pan [in *Arabesk*] treats of the illusive sweetness of voluptuous love and in its briefness finds the symbol of the passing of life'.[2] His achievement lies in the fact that he blew down the theory that a composer must belong to a 'school'; he asserted the right to remain apart.

1 *The Yorkshire Post*, 24 October 1929.
2 ib., 19 October 1929.

Two Women Composers and a Scotsman

Of the same generation as Elgar and Delius were three composers whose place in musical history depends less on genuine musical achievement than on certain accidents of birth or career. Maude Valerie White (1855–1937) and Ethel Smyth (1858–1944), if not the first women composers, were the first in Britain seriously to adopt composition as a career. Maude Valerie White, sometime a pupil at the Academy under Macfarren and also in Vienna, was a fairly prolific writer of songs. She ranged widely in selecting lyrics—her poets including Goethe, Heine, Herder, Sturm, Bjørnson, and, more unexpected, Petőfi—but her limited technical accomplishment gave no more than adequately processed drawing-room songs.

Ethel Smyth, a robust character distinguished for her Suffragette activities, studied in Leipzig and developed a style that was both masculine and Teutonic. Her earlier works were performed in Germany and these included the operas *Fantasio* (Weimar, 1898), *Der Wald* (1902), *Standrecht*—translated as *The Wreckers* (Leipzig, 1906). The last, which was based on a Cornish story, was Smyth's best work, and characterised by a strong dramatic sense. Her capacity for treating themes of the sea is also shown in *The Boatswain's Mate*, which, after a story by W. W. Jacobs, was first performed in London in 1916. *The Boatswain's Mate* has a refreshing sense of realism, and the characterisation is skilfully done. So skilfully that more than once the composer puts us in mind of Britten. Thus Mrs. Waters, landlady of the 'Beehive', clears the bar: [Ex. 16]. Another work which

16.

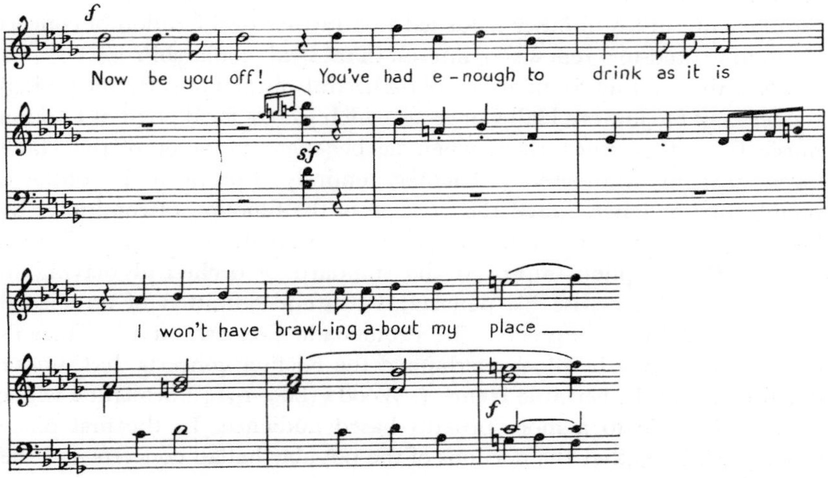

showed Ethel Smyth's capacity for handling large pieces in a compelling, if not strikingly original, manner was the *Mass in D*, which was included in a Royal Choral Society concert in 1893, and then put aside until revived by the Birmingham Festival Choral Society thirty-one years later. Despite the praise often accorded to it, the *Mass*, sometimes touching the vapid progressions of English Victorian oratorio and sometimes the religious idiom of Dvořák, is a pretentious piece of writing: an exercise rather than an invention.

William Wallace (1860–1940), born in Greenock in Scotland, was an ophthalmic surgeon of considerable promise before he abandoned this profession in 1889 to enter the Royal Academy of Music as a student. He composed numerous works, including a set of six symphonic poems (1892–1909). Of these the first—*The Passing of Beatrice*—was reputed to have been the first work in such form written by a British composer. Wallace also composed a few programmatic works on Scottish subjects and a number of successful songs. He was for some time honorary secretary of the Royal Philharmonic Society, and also the author of several books.

End of an Era

The period under review represents the last age of the individualist in British social philosophy. In the twentieth century (in spite of the often justifiable reluctance of the British composer to fit into a pattern designed by others) the story is of a movement towards group-activity of one sort or another. Parry, Stanford, Elgar, Delius, and Ethel Smyth struck out boldly as individuals, to establish themselves, or even to re-establish British music. Similar enterprises in other fields led to a further proliferation of concert promotion, and to a renewal of interest in musical scholarship.

On the existing foundations of orchestral music Hans Richter raised the series of St. James's Hall Concerts, which were a focal point of London music from 1879 until 1897, when he became conductor of the Hallé Orchestra, in Manchester. Richter, entirely European in outlook, popularised Wagner, raised the prestige of the function of conductor by his accepted authority, and brought Elgar into the forefront of British music. His discipline improved the standard of orchestral playing in England, but otherwise his paternalist attitude admitted of no special favours for British composers. The Promenade Concerts at the Queen's Hall, commencing in 1895, overlapped the Richter concerts, but, under the direction of the versatile Henry J. Wood (1869–1944), brought a wider variety of music to a more broadly-based audience. In the first place Wood joined together the portions of the popular ballad concerts and the middle-brow and occasional orchestral concerts. Through pursuing his own enthusiasm, especially for Russian and for modern music, and giving congenial if sometimes wayward interpretations of Classical and Baroque works as well as the Romantic masterpieces, he laid the foundation for twentieth-century concert-going and musical appreciation. In the provinces the dignities of orchestral music were most worthily upheld in Manchester, where the Hallé Orchestra, attracting a nucleus of instrumentalists of distinction, was supported both by the immigrant German business community and by local citizens whose civic pride at this time was considerable. The Liverpool Philharmonic Orchestra, though no more than semi-permanent, upheld the honour of Merseyside, while a fusion of interests north of the border in 1895 brought into being the Scottish Orchestra. Two years later Granville Bantock (1868–1946)[1] was engaged to conduct an orchestra at the newly built Tower Theatre in New Brighton and by dint of enormous perseverance built up a band of passable quality and presented programmes of considerable diversity. Considering that Bantock was working within the limits of commercial speculation, his achievement in matching Wood's Promenade programmes for interest was spectacular. Throughout this period, as has been seen, the propriety of devoting public funds to music was urged time and time again. One Corporation, and one alone, stepped boldly (or fairly boldly) into the field and implemented the intention to subsidise a musical undertaking. This was in Bournemouth, where the Municipal Orchestra was instituted in 1893. The first conductor of this organisation was Sir Dan Godfrey (1868–1939)[2] whose sterling work is symbolised by the perpetuation of the tradition which he established.

The perilous state of professional musical organisation in Britain at the close of the reign of Queen Victoria, and during the Edwardian era, left large areas of the population entirely uncatered for unless by amateur organisations. These flourished and it is symptomatic of the times that Edward Elgar held only the conductorship of an amateur society.

The amateur cultivation of music was not only desirable: it was essential. Because many of its results, especially in choral music, were

[1] Bantock, a friend of Elgar, was a prolific composer of large-scale choral, and orchestral, works of a programmatic nature in which legendary and mystical subjects from the Orient are often to be found. A skilful orchestrator (see *Fifine at the Fair*), Bantock is one of the now forgotten composers of his generation who might seem to merit occasional revival. He was busily occupied in music in many directions and was the first effective Principal of the School of Music in the Midland Institute, Birmingham.

[2] The musical tradition of Bournemouth was settled on the popularity of the 'Italian Band' that played in the town from 1876, and the succeeding group of miscellaneous instrumentalists, which Godfrey, son of a military band-master, took over in 1892. The papers of Godfrey, in 13 volumes, are in the possession of the Bournemouth Central Library.

entirely praiseworthy it was easy to use the fact as a means of denigration of the professional. Musical organisation, musical education, musical criticism, and frequently musical compositions, came to be regarded as of secondary importance because they were successfully dealt with on an amateur footing. It is hardly surprising that musicology—as a science distinct from the earlier zeal for antiquarian exploration—was established as a side-line.

Folk-song collection and edition became a thriving industry in the nineteenth century and was frequently a pursuit of otherwise under-employed clergymen. The main part of the present repertoire of popular Christmas carols was collected by Davies Gilbert[1] and William Sandys.[2] In the middle years of the century William Chappell covered many branches of popular traditional music. But fieldwork was not undertaken seriously until a later date. A start to more scientific study was given by John Broadwood's *Old English Songs*,[3] and songs taken down at first hand (although the words were bowdlerised to a greater or lesser extent in most cases) were issued in Miss M. H. Mason's[4] *Nursery Rhymes and Country Songs* (1877–8), J. Collingwood Bruce's *Northumbrian Minstrelry . . .* (1882), *Songs and Ballads of the West*, edited by Rev. Sabine Baring-Gould[5] and Rev. H. Fleetwood Sheppard (1889–92), Frank Kidson's *Traditional Tunes, a Collection of Ballad Airs, chiefly obtained in Yorkshire* (1891), and *English County Songs*, edited by Lucy Broadwood (niece of John) and J. A. Fuller-Maitland. In 1899 Cecil Sharp (1859–1924), the most notable of English folk-song scholars, began his life's work, with consequences of importance both to musical education in schools and also to composition. The (English) Folk-Song Society was founded in 1898; in 1904 an Irish Folk-Song Society and in 1908 a Welsh Folk-Song Society were established. In Scotland there already was a National Song Society.

John Stainer (1840–1901) was one of the most industrious of nineteenth-century musicians, with a finger in every pie. The successor to Goss as organist of St. Paul's Cathedral, and to Sullivan as Principal of the National Training School for Music, Professor of Music at Oxford, Examiner at other universities, Inspector of Music for the Board of

[1] *Some Ancient Christmas Carols*, 1822–3.

[2] *Christmas Carols, Ancient and Modern . . .*, 1833.

[3] '*. . . as now sung by the peasants of the Weald of Surrey and Sussex, and collected by one who has learnt them by hearing them sung every Christmas from early childhood, by The Country People, who go about to the Neighbouring Houses, singing, or "Wassailing" as it is called, at that season. The Airs are set to Music exactly as they are now sung, to rescue them from oblivion, and to afford a specimen of Genuine Old English Melody: and The Words are given in their original Rough State, with an occasional slight alteration to render the sense intelligible.*'

[4] Miss Mason was an Inspector of Boarded-out Poor Children.

[5] See his *An Historical Sketch of English National Song*, in *English Ministrelsie* (1895) and reprinted privately (1964).

Education,[1] composer,[2] and author of numerous text-books, he still found time for musical research. His *Dufay and his contemporaries* (1898) is one of the cornerstones of English musicology, and the first work in which palaeographic skills were exposed. Largely through Stainer the (Royal) Musical Association was established in 1874. H. E. Wooldridge (1845–1917), a painter and sometime Professor of Fine Arts at Oxford, was also a medieval scholar, whose principal work lies in the first two volumes of the *Oxford History of Music* (1901). William Barclay Squire (1855–1927), the librettist of Stanford's first opera, was the Keeper of Printed Music in the British Museum, a principal in the inauguration of Purcellian research, and the joint editor, with Fuller-Maitland, of the *Fitzwilliam Virginal Book*. This, together with a number of English madrigals edited by Barclay Squire, was published not in England, but in Germany, by Breitkopf and Härtel, of Leipzig. J. A. Fuller-Maitland, a friend and pupil of Stanford, as well as W. S. Rockstro (1823–95),[3] became music critic of *The Times* and, in addition to collaborating with Barclay Squire in the edition of the *Fitzwilliam Virginal Book*, edited the second edition of *Grove's Dictionary*[4] and contributed the fourth volume (*The Age of Bach and Handel*) to the *Oxford History of Music*.

It may very well be that the labours of this group of scholars, in relation to the music of Britain during the twentieth century, represented the most significant achievement of the Victorian era.

[1] See his report on Training Colleges, and Schools, for the Board of Education, *Mus. T.*, 1885, pp. 714–15. This is a gloomy account of the state of general musical education. In an age of payment by results, of 3,293,202 children a grant of 1s. per head was made in respect of 1,282,586 pupils for 'singing by note' and of 6d. in respect of 1,997,572 pupils for 'singing by ear'. Stainer attributed frequent bad singing to poor physique.

[2] *The Crucifixion* (1887) rivals *Messiah* and *Elijah* in popularity but not in quality. Study of this work should be compulsory for those who would understand the musical taste of the British people during the Victorian era.

[3] Rockstro, a pupil of Sterndale Bennett and of the Leipzig Conservatorium, and a friend of Mendelssohn, was an early authority on Gregorian music. See p. 524 fn. 1.

[4] 1st edn. 1879–89.
2nd edn. 1904–10.
3rd edn. 1927–8 (ed. H. C. Colles).
4th edn. 1940 (ed. H. C. Colles).
5th edn. 1954 (ed. Eric Blom).

13

First Principles

Folk Song in an Urban Society

REGARDING THE history of music there are two theories—both based on irrational premises—which are, at least popularly, commonly held. The first is pessimistic, maintaining that the best has been; and that so far as British music (in this theory narrowed to English) is concerned, Byrd, Purcell, Handel, and perhaps Elgar, stand unapproachable in their national pre-eminence. Of these, only one, and he German-born, ranks among the world masters. The position is improved somewhat if the 'Elizabethans' are lumped in as a body and a 'Golden Age' adduced—as by G. M. Trevelyan: 'The music in the Chapel Royal was perhaps the best in Europe. . . . The Tudor age was the great age of English music and lyrical poetry, two sisters at a birth . . . the whole country was filled with men and women singing songs, composing the music and writing verses.'[1] This is gratifying in a romantic way, but otherwise unencouraging. The second theory, largely promoted by enthusiastic educationists, is that since the 'Renaissance of English music' a steady rate of progress has been maintained, so that by the middle of the twentieth century conditions are such that England [*sic*] may be set among the leading musical nations of the world. A realist examining the situation quickly discovers that this conclusion is not to be proved, that in any case it is almost certainly founded on carefully selected evidence, and that overall there is a long way to go before music is, as it was in the seventeenth and eighteenth centuries, integrated within itself and relevant to the social pattern. For reasons which lie outside the province of music it seems improbable that this will ever take place. Musical experience, except for a

[1] *English Social History*, 1944, p. 134. The manner in which music is all but ignored by the general run of academic historians is an index to the attitude of a wider and influential section of the community.

minority, will continue to be a detachable recreation. The two theories outlined above come together at the point at which we observe the British as incurably sentimental-romantic. This condition took shape during the expansive years of the Victorian era and has intensified in the aftermath of abdication of Great Power and Imperial status.

The inessentiality of music in Britain has long been a cardinal principle. If we return to the beginning of the twentieth century we may discover its application in an acute form. Thus, in respect of a friendship between the fourth Earl of Leicester and the viola-player Lionel Tertis, we read: 'The [Earl] was a good amateur violinist and the two of them often played at his Norfolk seat, Holkham Hall. As a boy, however, he had to hide his violin under his bed, music not then being considered a fit occupation for one in his position.'[1]

The genius of Elgar enabled him both to satisfy the romantic disposition of his compatriots but also to imbue his music with a sense of purpose, an inner life of its own, and a comprehensiveness that is its greatest merit. Elgar, having no fixed views on the subject of permissiveness in relation to taste, was the one English composer of modern times who could write music in such a way as to convince the unmusical that they were, perhaps, not irredeemably so. If Elgar avoided discussion of aesthetics (or only engaged in such discussion with distaste and unease), he was not without a guiding thought. Expressed on various occasions, and in different words, it was: 'I would like to see that vast working population of this country able to have and enjoy the same music we possess and enjoy ourselves.'[2] The history of English music over the past half-century is, in some measure, a record of attempts to put this ideal into practice.

The first means of approach was by way of folk-song (and dance), the revival of which coincided with a realisation that other ancient traditions were either being forgotten or eroded, and that the 'people' presented a new set of problems. Those among the privileged classes who considered these problems were set on 'improvement'. In broad terms this implied the ultimate appreciation by the under-privileged of the established cultural conventions of their social superiors. Through the inauguration of People's Palaces and People's Concerts, and so on, a start had been made. But earnest do-gooders, who had background encouragement for their faith from Wordsworth, also believed in the creativity of the people—especially that creativity inherent in what was taken to be the truly popular music. If it was not popular then it should be. Folk-songs, being of the people, theoretically appeared as a convenient bridge to a higher musical appreciation, and indeed to a deeper sense of national awareness.

[1] The *Daily Telegraph*, 28 December 1965.
[2] Birmingham Lecture, 13 December 1905.

It was not long before the thesis that a truly national music must be based on national idiom, that is the idiom of folk-song, emerged. Cecil Sharp was innocent of such intention when he commenced his activities, but some of those around him, adding a mild taste for undoctrinaire Socialism to an existing faith in the preachings of William Morris, were inspired with a zeal for reclamation and reconstitution. Devoted work in the field uncovered a vast repository of folk-music (the work still continues), but the effect of this activity has been less than appears to have been hoped for. 'The test of whether the revival of folk-song has been a success or not is how many such songs the average Englishman carries about with him in his mind, to refresh himself with at odd moments. The work of the folk-song collectors has not been in vain if "Twanky dillo" or "Mowing the Barley" is sung, each morning, in a fair proportion of British bathrooms.'[1] When this was written, of course, the number of British bathrooms was limited; their multiplication has not, however, increased the popularity of *Twanky dillo* or *Mowing the Barley*.

In other countries in Europe folk-music, at an earlier period, had reinvigorated national music. In such cases as Czechoslovakia and Hungary (to take the most conspicuous) folk-music was a reality to large numbers of citizens. Further, it could be used as a means of political protest. In England—where ballads had long been more popular than folk-songs—the tradition was almost completely out of sight. Rural England was a delight to the romantic scholar, but in terms of population and cultural importance less significant. By 1914, for example, there was only eight per cent of the employed population working on the land[2]—the typical Englishman therefore being thoroughly urbanised—and, since the nation was at the zenith of its imperial career, the exploitation of folk-music for emancipatory purposes was hardly necessary.[3] The folk-song revival, however, was the means whereby two considerable composers came into prominence: Ralph Vaughan Williams and Gustav Holst. Through their influence British music was for a time withdrawn from Europe—and especially from Germany—and some other composers were encouraged to review again the bases of their craft and to take a more realistic attitude to their function. The greater masters of British music in the past had in common a pragmatism—sometimes thought of as a national characteristic—that dissuaded them from relentless pursuit of dogmas. The

[1] I. A. Williams, *English Folk-Song and Dance*, London, 1935, pp. 190–91.

[2] In contrast with 33 per cent in Germany, and 43 per cent in France.

[3] For these reasons the Welsh and Irish possess a more vivid sense of the essence of folk-music. In addition to running a successful war of Independence on the inspiration of traditional songs and a fine crop of new ones invented before and during the 'Troubles', the Irish have kept their internal dissensions alive on engaging songs in praise of, or in contempt of, such national symbols as William of Orange and the Pope.

same pragmatism distinguishes the careers of Vaughan Williams and Holst and effectively marks them off from the main body of their more or less distinguished nineteenth-century predecessors. Pragmatism, however, was not antithetical to idealism. Vaughan Williams and Holst were both idealists, and humanists. Of the two Holst was the more professional composer and—often an isolated figure in his lifetime—may now seem as the more influential and durable. Vaughan Williams, perhaps, was more of a nineteenth-century figure who carried the best qualities of the age in which he was born into the twentieth century; whereas Holst, detached from temporal considerations to a large extent, thought timelessly and, therefore, with a greater insight into the future. It is relevant that whereas Vaughan Williams's interests tended towards literature, Holst was a student of Eastern traditions and languages on the one hand, and astronomy on the other.

Vaughan Williams and Holst

Ralph Vaughan Williams (1872–1958) was born in Gloucestershire, but was taken to Surrey in early childhood, after the death of his father—a Church of England vicar of Welsh descent. His mother, a niece of Charles Darwin, was a member of the Wedgwood family. Family connections and avocations developed a sense of 'tradition', which was modified and expanded by the conventions of preparatory and public school, and university education. Before going to Cambridge, however, Vaughan Williams studied at the Royal College of Music, to which he returned after taking a degree in History. Parry and Stanford were among Vaughan Williams's teachers at the College; more important during his studentship was the beginning of his life-long friendship with Holst. In 1895 the Bicentenary of the death of Purcell was modestly celebrated, by performances of *Dido and Aeneas*, by students of the College, and of the *Ode on St. Cecilia's Day*, by the Philharmonic Society. Further stimulus to a reconsideration of the place of Purcell in the national tradition[1] came from the researches of Barclay Squire, while the re-issue of the three Masses of William Byrd further focussed attention on English masterpieces of a bygone age. Vaughan Williams settled down for a three-year period as a church organist (at St. Barnabas, Lambeth), but, after visiting Germany (where he had some lessons from Max Bruch), was able, through the enjoyment of a small inheritance, to relinquish regular employment and to devote himself to composition. But composition was combined with other musical activities. He played the viola and could sometimes be prevailed upon by Holst to

[1] Vaughan Williams published editions of the *Welcome Songs* for the Purcell Society in 1905 and 1910.

help out in the amateur music-making to which Holst was deeply committed. And there was folk-song—the study of which lay well within the philosophy and tradition of the more enlightened members of that section of society to which Vaughan Williams belonged. From 1903 he became a vigorous collector and his work in this connection was, on the musicological side, important, and recognised as such internationally. Collateral researches went into the compilation of the *English Hymnal* (1906) with which Vaughan Williams was associated. After publishing a number of part-songs and solo songs, in which the contours of English folk-melody and a matter-of-fact harmonic system began to show as distinctive features Vaughan Williams attracted wider attention by the performance of his *Norfolk Rhapsodies* and the choral work *Toward the Unknown Region* in 1907. Within the next two years appeared the song-cycle (with string quartet and piano accompaniment) *On Wenlock Edge*, and the incidental music for Aristophanes' *The Wasps*. The *Rhapsodies* were built on tunes collected in Norfolk and showed the intention of the composer not merely to frame his melodies (as Stanford had done) but to integrate them into the texture of the score. *Toward the Unknown Region*, an optimistic *Credo* for an agnostic, reflected a general appreciation among progressives in England at that time for Walt Whitman, while the *Wenlock Edge* cycle (still to be counted among Vaughan Williams's major achievements) was the expression of a contrasting pessimism but also of an awareness of the English landscape. Behind the settings of Whitman and Housman lay a sense of mysticism that Vaughan Williams was more fully to explore at a later point. In 1910 two major works put him in the forefront of English composers. On 6 September the *Fantasia on a Theme of Thomas Tallis* was played at the Three Choirs Festival at Gloucester, and on 12 October the *Sea Symphony* (to words by Whitman) was given at the Leeds Festival.[1] The first of these works showed that a renewal of techniques of former times and a juxtaposition of idioms could, when controlled by a strong and purposeful hand, lead into new reaches of musical experience. Written for solo string quartet and double string orchestra, the *Fantasia* has the merit of clarity of statement—or even understatement—and, apart from its reminiscences of the Tudor period, is an outstanding example of contemplativeness in music. The *Sea Symphony*, a virtuoso piece so far as the choir is concerned, is in the vigorous style of choral music enjoined by Parry and Stanford. 'The ideas', commented the *Yorkshire Post*, 'are never puny or finicking, and the music has breadth and grandeur.'[2] The assessment may stand as generally apt to Vaughan Williams, and as a reasonable statement of his

[1] The first London performance of the *Sea Symphony*, by the Bach Choir, conducted by Hugh Allen, took place on 4 February 1913.

[2] 13 October 1910.

intention to establish an independent English manner. The intention depended, of course, somewhat on his interpretation of the English character, and in recent years the heroic or 'manly' aspect has faded from view. Before the First World War the ideals of Vaughan Williams's kind of patriotism (no less deeply felt, but less intuitional than Elgar's) were further expanded through *A London Symphony*[1] and the ballad opera *Hugh the Drover*.

After service in the war Vaughan Williams became a professor at the Royal College and succeeded Hugh Allen[2] as Conductor of the Bach Choir. Although reckoned a slow worker when a student he now became prolific in output. Landmarks of the twenties were the *Pastoral Symphony* (1922), *Flos Campi* (1925)—for solo viola, wordless choir, and chamber orchestra, and the short but striking oratorio *Sancta Civitas* (1926). In the last of these works the mystical impulse that had been previously evident shone with a harder light, and the formerly cumbrous harmonic manner acquired an acrid flavour. Vaughan Williams no longer was the patient purveyor of rural fancies to an urban civilisation, but appeared to be as the voice of the times and the prophet of the near future. An apocalyptic note was sounded again, more powerfully, in the Fourth Symphony (1935). Other outstanding works of this decade were *Job* (1930), a '*Masque for Dancing*' but only generally known in its concert version, the *Serenade to Music* (1938), composed in honour of Sir Henry Wood's Jubilee as a conductor, and the one-act opera *Riders to the Sea* (John Millington Synge). In the years between the wars, and especially after the death of Elgar, Vaughan Williams took over the first place in English music. This was due not entirely to his music (as was the case with Elgar) but also to his forceful, kindly, modest personality, which was backed by a patrician authority much esteemed by the English. Never too self-absorbed to neglect other people's interests, Vaughan Williams took a keen and practical interest in the festival movement,[3] in educational

[1] Local colour is added to this work by the incorporation of the 'Westminster Chimes'. In this Vaughan Williams had been anticipated by Mackenzie whose *London Day by Day* (Norwich Festival, 1902) had exploited the same motiv. (See *Mus. T.*, 1902, p. 747.)

[2] 1869–1946; sometime organist of New College, Oxford, Parry's successor as Director of the R.C.M. and Parratt's as Professor of Music at Oxford, Allen (knighted in 1920), a powerful personality, exercised a strong influence in the filling of important musical positions.

[3] The Competitive Festival movement, which in its modern form began in 1885, in Kendal, sponsored by Miss Mary Wakefield, developed greatly after the First World War, and after the Incorporation of the British Federation of Musical Festivals in 1921 the standard of performance rose greatly. At the present time there are approximately 300 such competitions in the Federation.

Non-competitive festivals (with the aim of enabling amateurs to participate in the performance of major works) have also developed. Of these the Leith Hill Festival, for which Vaughan Williams edited the *St. Matthew Passion*, composed a number of works, and conducted, is a notable example.

developments, and amateur societies which sprang up during this period in some profusion. The long list of his compositions shows the extent of his involvement, and if many of the pieces for schools, for amateur orchestras, for social organisations such as Women's Institutes and Rural Music are of little intrinsic interest, they filled a need, were superior—because invariably practicable—to almost anything already existing, and set an example which has been widely followed by a younger generation of composers. As a folk-song specialist and as a consciously nationalist composer, Vaughan Williams worked parallel to Kodály[1]; as a provider of material for unconventional combinations of amateurs and as a practitioner in the province of *Gebrauchsmusik*, his work had affinities with that of Hindemith. With undiminished vigour Vaughan Williams composed symphonic, and chamber and choral works, operas, and incidental music for film[2] and radio, until the end of his long life. The culmination of this last creative phase was the Ninth Symphony, in E Minor, which was first performed in London on 2 April 1958. Vaughan Williams inspired affection and devotion and not least of all among his fellow musicians. Of a liberal-democratic persuasion and strongly independent, he refused all honours from the State other than the Order of Merit (1935).

Apart from occasional performances (more particularly of the *Tallis Fantasia*) Vaughan Williams's music is virtually unknown outside Britain. His place in musical history therefore depends on his place in British music. In the years that have elapsed since his death critical opinion and musical techniques have swung away from the enthusiasm that was generated during his lifetime. The provincial character of the music now often seems something of an embarrassment. Yet it is clear that without the purgative effect of Vaughan Williams's works British composers of later date (some of whom are beneficiaries of the Vaughan Williams Trust) would speak with less assurance.

As far as musical style was concerned Elgar pointed one way to independence, Vaughan Williams another. Elgar showed how European music could, through selection and reintegration and emotional readjustment, become English. Vaughan Williams demonstrated how a new mode of expression could be discovered by by-passing the Romantics, though by no means missing out on Romanticism. Insofar as we connect Vaughan Williams with Romantic idealism it is with that of the poets, especially of

[1] 'It is', said Kodaly, 'a special honour for me today to be able to fill the late Vaughan Williams's place as the Chairman of the International Folk Music Council' (interview in *New Hungary*, December 1962).

[2] Among Vaughan Williams's film scores the finest were *49th Parallel* (1940) and *Scott of the Antarctic* (1948), from the second of which material for the *Sinfonia Antartica* was drawn. Regarding the composer's introduction to and interest in the medium see John Huntley, *British Film Music*, London, 1948, *passim*.

Wordsworth and Coleridge. Using folk-music in the first place as a form of *cantus firmus* (in arrangements and rhapsodies), Vaughan Williams seized its distinctive intervals, contours, and rhythms, and incorporated them within a vocabulary already drawn away from the established quasi-Brahmsian norm by the influence of Parry's diatonicism. Folk-song taught Vaughan Williams not to err in treatment of the voice, and to be explicit. His explicitness (sometimes termed 'bluntness') was enhanced by the basically triadic, and unsophisticated character of his harmonic expression:

1.

Chor. (Sop. only)
ff
With 'Hey dog hey! Have there hop a-way! With 'Get me a staffé, The swine eat my daffé!
Orch.
ff marc.

and the urgency of his frequently dissonant contrapuntal method.

2.

Vl. I
Vl. II
Vla.
Vcl.
p
cresc.

If Vaughan Williams was the beneficiary of the English musical tradition he was also affected by the powerful subsidiary English tradition of Bach, who, by the beginning of the century, was almost by way of being accepted as an English composer (as Shakespeare was often adopted as an honorary German). The local character of Bach's music fascinated Vaughan Williams and he represented that master's unwilling period of long residence in Leipzig as evidence of the necessity for and the virtue of a parochial attitude. The Bachian manner shows through the *Concerto*

Accademico, the fugal unity of the Fourth Symphony, the linear concepts of the *Passacaglia* of the Fifth and of the *Epilogue* (to which the following bars belong) of the Sixth Symphonies.

3.

From the pastoral to the mystical is a short step. The ruminative *Pastoral Symphony* is an essay in one sort of mystical contemplation. The *Mass in G Minor* (an imposing essay in neo-Tudorism), *Flos Campi*, and the moving *Magnificat* represent other facets of a visionary perception that also invades some of the movements of *Job* and of the symphonies. It has been seen that by antecedent Vaughan Williams was something of an amateur, and the character of amateurism is sometimes detectable in his handling of musical material. He was no assured orchestrator, as were Elgar, Delius, and Holst, yet his manipulation of the string forces in the *Tallis Fantasia* is superb, while the selection and integration of colours in *Job* are no less impressive.

Frequently drawn by unusual literary works (by his selection he gave incentive to younger composers to look further afield than had previously been the case), Vaughan Williams was often able to illuminate striking texts by music which had the merit of leaving free rein to words but which could synchronise climax. This is to be recognised in the choral suite, based on John Skelton's poems, *Five Tudor Portraits*, as also in the contrasting *Riders to the Sea*. Vaughan Williams tried hard to become an opera composer, and if he was as persistent as Stanford he was even less successful. Apart from those works of this kind already mentioned he composed a Falstaffian *Sir John in Love* (1929); a comic opera to a poor libretto, *The Poisoned Kiss* (1936); and the 'Morality founded on Bunyan's Allegory', *The Pilgrim's Progress* (1951). The latter, being more in line with oratorio, did not commend itself to opera-goers. Few composers can hope to leave more than a handful of works that have survival value. Vaughan Williams's ultimate ranking probably depends on the middle symphonies (4–7), the *Tallis Fantasia*, *Job*, and a few songs (e.g. *Linden Lea*) and hymn-tunes (e.g. *Down Ampney* and *Sine Nomine*) that have passed into common usage.

Whatever sins he may be guilty of an English composer is normally forgiven if he can provide the nation with a tune: a broad, diatonic, swinging tune apt for occasions and for communal performance. Gustav Holst (1874–1934) composed one such tune: the great melody in 'Jupiter', of *The Planets*, subsequently pared down and attached to the words 'I vow to thee, my country.'[1] The list of similarly favoured melodies, at least from the time of Purcell, leaves one in no doubt as to the most effective kind of sublimation of those ideas which belong to the collective unconsciousness of the English. The music of the people is represented not by folk-music as such but by a handful of items that fortuitously have assumed a symbolic value on account of varying expressions of and appeals to patriotic conformity. The validity of the argument is enhanced by study of reactions and responses on a lower level. For instance, the school population—teachers and children alike—have given the same kind of warrant to such pieces as Quilter's *Non nobis, Domine* and Thiman's *Gloria in Excelsis Deo* (poor relations of the nobler works in the popular repertoire). Acceptance by the commonalty was fundamental to the general philosophy of Vaughan Williams and Holst, but their approach to this ideal was hardly direct.

Holst's ancestors came to England from the Baltic port of Riga. His father was a music teacher in Cheltenham. Before going to the Royal College of Music, Holst, whose health was always indifferent, edged into the profession of music through a village church organ assignment and the conductorship of a choral society at Bourton-on-the-Water. Having left the Royal College—a confirmed Wagnerian and an industrious but unsuccessful composer—he joined the Carl Rosa Opera Company as trombonist. In this capacity he joined the Scottish Orchestra and also played at Covent Garden for Richter, to that great man's satisfaction. The experience was invaluable—a composer working from inside knowledge of the orchestra (as Elgar proved) knows what is viable and what is not.

In his early days as a composer Holst was subject to two powerful influences. His respect for Wagner was deep and affected the texture of his harmonic thinking, notably in *The Mystic Trumpeter*, which was performed at a Patron's Fund[2] Concert at Queen's Hall in 1905. At the same

[1] Words by Sir Cecil Spring-Rice (1858–1918), sometime H.M. Ambassador to the U.S.A.

[2] The Patron's Fund was established in 1903 on the gift of £20,000 by Ernest Palmer with the intention of enabling young British composers to have performances of their works. The choice of composers was in general arbitrary and severely criticised in the early years. See William Wallace's long letter to *The Times*, 30 May 1904.

time, however, he was absorbed in the study of Sanskrit, from which he made translations for his *Rig Veda* hymns, and libretti for the operas *Sita* (1906) and *Savitri* (1908). *Sita*, which had taken seven years to compose, was submitted for the Ricordi Prize[1] in 1908 and placed second. Holst did not find that success came easily.

By now, however, other factors are to be taken account of in respect of his creative activity. Association with Vaughan Williams and Cecil Sharp induced a lively interest in folk-song, and Holst, like Vaughan Williams, began to see this as a prophylactic. The first results of this interest were the *Country Song* and *Marching Song* (1906), and *A Somerset Rhapsody*, for orchestra (1907). Since 1905 Holst had been Director of Music at St. Paul's School for Girls and this connection with musical education also affected his attitude to the techniques of composition. Folk-song reduced music to its essentials; so too did schoolgirls. In both cases, for different reasons, if one note was sufficient then two should not be used.

Holst was an unusual combination of qualities. In public affairs he took little interest and, except to a few intimates, appeared as withdrawn. The impression was deepened by his remote interests. On the other hand he was a born teacher. His work at St. Paul's—memorialised in the *St. Paul's Suite for strings*—was remarkable and continued so to the end of his life. His enthusiasm for adult amateur music-making led him first to the Passmore Edwards Settlement and then to Morley College, of which he was musical director from 1907 until his death. In 1915 he took his Morley College musicians to the Essex village of Thaxted (where he had a cottage) and, with the goodwill of the then vicar, Rev. Conrad Noel, inaugurated his Whitsuntide Festivals of Music. The girls at St. Paul's had their old song-books taken away and replaced by copies of works by Lassus and Palestrina. The 'Whitsuntide Singers', to whom Vaughan Williams dedicated the Mass in G Minor, took into the country music by Byrd (which had come out of Essex in the first place), Purcell, Lassus, Palestrina, Weelkes, Bach, and so on. Holst generated enthusiasm. So far as choral singing was concerned he set a standard of high excellence. He explored new ways, and, in the best sense of the word, he popularised great works from many sources that were hitherto virtually unknown.

The debt owed to Holst in respect of music in English education is enormous. In a quiet and undoctrinaire way he showed that what mattered was first-hand experience gained through a sound working technique. He

[1] The Italian publishing house of Ricordi offered a prize of £500 for a new English opera. The competition was won by E. W. Naylor (1867–1934), a Cambridge scholar and organist, with *The Angelus*. This opera was performed at Covent Garden in 1909, and subsequently revived by the Carl Rosa Company.

gave point to music in adult education, moving it away from the 'appreciation class' to which the earnest Victorian lecture had deteriorated, and the increasing tendency at the present time to accommodate music within adult and polytechnical education may justly be ascribed to Holst's pioneering. Finally his performances at Thaxted, in Chichester Cathedral,[1] and in the city churches in London, were largely responsible in persuading the dignitaries of the Church to allow non-oratorial and secular music into places of worship. In all of this Holst showed a profound understanding. He recognised that to engender a love of music he must encourage pride in achievement, and that the best way to realise his high ideals was to remain true to them. Integrity of purpose marked his career as a teacher. It also marked his career as a composer. The two aspects of his life were complementary. The link was his mysticism: 'a form of union . . . Art is likewise a matter of union . . . it is in Music that this feeling of unity shows itself most obviously and easily.'[2]

In the essay in which the fragments of a socio-musical philosophy appear, Holst demolished the mimetic principle in the teaching of composition: 'So one of the safe uses of your knowledge of the details of Mozart's Form is to remember that, as you are not Mozart and are not living in his age or in his circumstances, if you produce music which has Significant Form, its external details will probably be different from his. . . . Each Significant Form in Art occurs once and is unique.' As a composer Holst spent a lifetime in searching for Significant Form. Thus he detached himself from the full rigours of folk idiom and sought to express his ideas in whatever manner seemed most economical and appropriate.

The English had looked for 'warmth' in music—the quality that was perceived in the great mass of oratorio choral tone on the one hand, and in the harmonic idioms of the late nineteenth century on the other. Holst introduced a new element—of coldness. This is why he is more essentially a twentieth-century composer than Vaughan Williams, and why his reputation has waited for the passing of a generation more fully to be appreciated. So far as subject matter was concerned Holst was more often than not remote: *Savitri*, the *Rig Veda*, *The Hymn of Jesus* (the text taken from *The Apocryphal Acts of the Apostles*), *Egdon Heath*, and, for that matter, *The Planets*. His development from early Wagnerism, across the territories of folk-song and sixteenth-century polyphony, was towards austerity and asperity, and emancipation from the introversion of stereotyped musical formulae. Perhaps as it developed his music approximated more to the

[1] Holst was particularly attracted to Chichester, and his ashes were buried in the cathedral near to the memorial to Weelkes, who had been organist there.

[2] 'The Mystic, The Philistine and the Artist', in *The Quest*, 1920, reprinted in Imogen Holst, *Gustav Holst*, London, 1938, pp. 184 *et seq.*

shape of his own personality, and as it did it turned away from the popular forum. The finest of Holst's later works, *Egdon Heath*, is an essay in solitude: which is why it is the complement to and extension of Hardy's landscape.

Holst relaxed the rigours of the metrical system in English music; and this came through a recognition of the relationship between words and melody in folk-song, together with an appreciation of the genius of Purcell in his setting of language to music. Flexibility of vocal melody, exemplified by [Ex. 4] is accompanied by harmonic flexibility also, this

4.

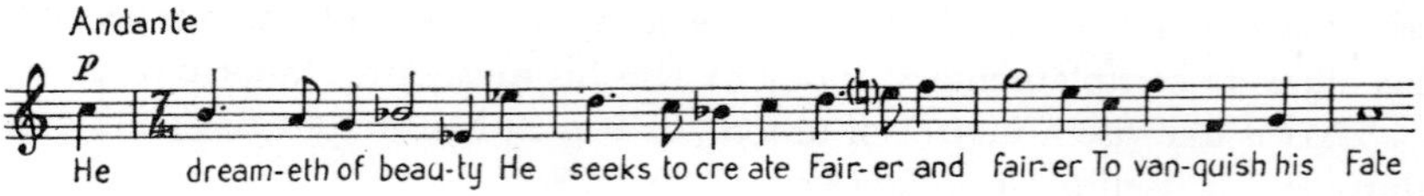
Andante
p
He dream-eth of beau-ty He seeks to cre ate Fair-er and fair-er To van-quish his Fate

deriving from a consistent linear attitude. Thus Holst's harmonies, solidified by parallelism of parts and sometimes anchored by powerful inner pedal notes, are aggressive or mystical according to dynamic and scoring [Ex. 5 and 6] and sometimes merely fortuitous. On the other hand, Holst,

5.

fff
meno f

6.

Str.
8va
Solo (or Semi-chorus)
Re-joice ye dead, where'er your spi-rits dwell,
8va

like Vaughan Williams, was debtor to the Baroque, and the relentlessness of *ostinato* or the convenience of formal figurations mark his purely instrumental works. Immensely gifted in his sense of musical colour, Holst was a first-rate orchestrator, and *The Planets* and *The Hymn of Jesus* stand up out of a ruck of contemporary works by reason of their brilliance and their inevitability. In both these works the skill of Holst is comparable to that of Stravinsky. While, for obvious reasons, Holst's place in the repertoire depends on his originality and skill in using large forces, it is his capacity for thinning-out that is more distinctive. Thus the songs for voice and violin are masterly in their completeness. This is true also of the score of *Savitri*, which, sixty years after its composition, may still sound contemporary.

So far as the stage was concerned Holst suffered the same handicaps as other English composers. *The Perfect Fool* and *At the Boar's Head* were produced by the British National Opera Company in 1923 and 1925 respectively, but neither succeeded in doing more than irritating the critics and perplexing the public. The first (of which the fine, pointed ballet music survives) because of the composer's libretto, the second because of its contrived folk-tunery. *The Tale of the Wandering Scholar*, however, produced at Liverpool shortly before the composer's death, is more effective, and (newly edited by Imogen Holst and Benjamin Britten) shows a happy understanding of the principles of chamber opera since a lively narrative (based on an episode in Helen Waddell's *The Wandering Scholars*) is allowed to run to a lightweight but active and apt score.

Dead Ends in Composition

Vaughan Williams and Holst were musicians of high originality, by British if not by European standards; they were idealists but also of a practical turn of mind. They were, to borrow a contemporary label, 'involved'. This was important—not necessarily because it enabled them to write better music (in fact much of their intentionally 'useful' music is pedestrian) but because it kept them more or less close to the general climate of thought. Of composers contemporary with them the great majority preferred to ignore this and to settle back on the principle of giving the least offence to the greatest number. Composers other than Vaughan Williams and Holst, with rare exceptions, did little to carry forward the ideals of Parry and Stanford. Stanford, the most vital influence in the 'Renaissance', was a fine teacher. Unfortunately many of his pupils were content to continue writing in fluent Stanfordian vein. Not that they could be blamed. The kind of professional posts available for the support of

German musicians who were also composers were not available in Britain; and certainly not in the undernourished provinces. There were, of course, cathedral and parish church appointments; but the atmosphere of Anglicanism proved no great spur to adventure, and the services and anthems of the first part of the twentieth century, despite an infection of mild modality, rarely show much more vitality than those of the nineteenth. The records of the Three Choirs Festival, a reasonable barometer of English average taste, show practically nothing new and endurable except works which have already been mentioned.

The principal composers born in the same decade as Vaughan Williams and Holst were Samuel Coleridge-Taylor (1875–1912), William Yeates Hurlstone (1876–1906), Havergal Brian (b. 1877), Roger Quilter (1877–1953), Rutland Boughton (1878–1960), Frank Bridge (1879–1941), John Ireland (1879–1962), Cyril Scott (b. 1879), and Martin Shaw (1879–1943). Of these Coleridge-Taylor, Hurlstone, Boughton, Bridge, Ireland, and Shaw were graduates of the Royal College of Music, to which Hurlstone, Bridge, and Ireland returned as teachers. Boughton, dissatisfied with the complacent attitudes at the R.C.M., left before they had had time to influence him. Havergal Brian, a native of the Potteries, was self-taught. Scott and Quilter (together with the Australian Balfour Gardiner) were pupils of Ivan Knorr in Frankfurt.

Coleridge-Taylor, befriended at the outset of his career by Elgar, sprang into prominence with a trilogy of settings of parts of Longfellow's *Hiawatha*. This work, with its easy melodic charm and vivid colouring, was enthusiastically welcomed into the choral society repertoire. But, compelled to devote himself to private teaching in order to eke out a living, Coleridge-Taylor's subsequent works showed a steady decline from the first flush of promise. Hurlstone was also one of those whose promise came more to be noted than actual achievement. With considerable fortitude he entered a field of music most unpropitious for a British composer—that of chamber music. Despite a considerable competence—exemplified in violin and piano, and clarinet and piano sonatas, and a number of works for wind ensemble—Hurlstone lacked a distinctive style. His Fantasy Quartet, for strings, however, was awarded the first of the prizes offered by W. W. Cobbett.[1] Havergal Brian, almost unknown and generally ignored by those in musical authority, has lacked neither ambition nor persistence. A thorough-going Romantic, of the order of Granville Bantock, Brian has exploited the exotic; sometimes with thrilling effect—as in the

[1] W. W. Cobbett (1847–1937), businessman, amateur violinist, and patron of music, who initiated a competition for chamber music composition and the Cobbett Medal for chamber music (first holder, Thomas Dunhill, 1924). In 1929 he published an invaluable *Cyclopedia of Chamber Music*.

vast, 'Gothic Symphony', the second of twenty-six symphonies.[1] Roger Quilter, an Etonian and able to enjoy his music as a recreation rather than as a vocation, was the most professional song-writer of his day, and the lyric ease of his style is gratefully accepted by thousands of entrants to vocal classes in competitive festivals. Quilter's songs, fragile but beautifully poised, are within their limits almost perfect. Frank Bridge also composed amiable songs, engaging piano pieces, and chamber music. A viola player, Bridge handled the medium of chamber music expertly and the refinement of his style (in the direction of economy) revealed him as a writer of integrity and independence. In later life he made a change of direction that was unusual for an English composer of the period and works written from the late 1920's showed affinities—possibly unconscious—with the idiom of Bartók. The Rhapsody Trio for the unusual combination of two violins and viola, in which his later manner is most evident, was unperformed in his lifetime and waited for nearly forty years for publication.[2] Bridge's posthumous fame largely depends on the fact that he was the teacher of Benjamin Britten. John Ireland, a miniaturist, wrote songs and chamber music of passing charm, but his talent lay especially in the province of piano music. Since very few English composers had much feeling for music for this instrument, his statically romantic, if considerable, contribution has been overrated. The Piano Concerto in E flat (1930) is a splendid piece of writing and may be reckoned as one of the more significant English works in this genre.

These composers (except for Brian) were, or came to be accepted as, Establishment Composers—safe bets for an approving tick for the schoolgirl asked in an examination paper to nominate modern composers of eminence. One has only to note that their European contemporaries included Debussy, Ravel, and Schoenberg, to see how becalmed the average English composer lay. He achieved a moderate reputation by tactfully keeping himself thirty years behind the times.

Cyril Scott, however, pushed out in unaccustomed directions. A student of theosophy and of oriental philosophies, he aspired to the composition of music that would enshrine his esoteric interests. He sought this by way of Scriabinesque harmonies and subtly colourful instrumentation that briefly engaged the interest of Debussy. Scott's music, too irrational for English promoters and lacking such sponsorship as Delius enjoyed from Beecham, was performed in Germany and Austria rather

[1] The 'Gothic Symphony' (for 500 singers and an orchestra including some 50 brass and 30 woodwind) was given its first performance forty-four years after its completion. This, conducted by Sir Adrian Boult, took place in the Royal Albert Hall on 30 October 1966. The composer was present.

[2] Faber and Faber, 1966.

more than at home. Scott, like Bridge in his later years, tried to alter the body politic of English music by reform from within—by attention to its structure and vocabulary. Rutland Boughton, on the other hand, preferred revolution to reformation, but found too few to share his views. The English musician in general has not been a political creature—or, if he has, he has in the past conformed to a deferential convention and followed the views of his patrons—and one who has marked tendencies towards the left may sometimes be found to be penalised. Boughton's highly personal and emotional brand of communism (or communalism), stirred by the discontents engendered by the smugness of metropolitan musical life, crossed with a pious faith in Wagner to produce a row of English music-dramas and a zest for providing for the many what was still the privilege of the relatively few. For some years Boughton taught in Birmingham, but in 1914 he began a brave venture in Glastonbury. Here, with a company assembled by himself, he staged his *The Immortal Hour*. Boughton lived in Glastonbury for thirteen years and, although his work was interrupted by the First World War, he gave performances of operas, or parts of operas, by Purcell, Wagner, and Gluck, as well as of his own projected Arthurian cycle. Boughton enjoyed a short *succes d'éstime* with *The Immortal Hour* and *Bethlehem* and almost brought to fruition the ambition to put the Glastonbury Players on a permanent footing. But lacking a sense of opportunism and a talent for making effective propaganda, Boughton failed to stimulate any cohesive attack on the ramparts of self-satisfaction that stood firm before him. Nor was he sufficiently competent as a composer to make worthwhile outflanking movements. His music, though somewhat simplified towards a preliminary type of socialist realism, is the romantic mixture more or less as before.

Less ostentatiously, and choosing a different route, Martin Shaw followed the same star. In the broadest sense he achieved much in the field of musical education, both adult and juvenile, sacred and secular. Also one of Stanford's pupils, Shaw declined to follow a conventional career. Friendly with Gordon Craig, he was drawn to the theatre and, after composing incidental music for plays by Ibsen and Shakespeare, undertook a pioneer production of *Dido and Aeneas* in 1900. Also acquainted with Vaughan Williams and Percy Dearmer, Shaw was drawn into the reforming movement in church music (symbolised by *The English Hymnal* and *Songs of Praise*, 1925), within which he established Summer Schools. He also helped in the foundation of the Royal School of Church Music in 1927. As composer, Shaw's voice sounded modestly; but his style—tuneful, diatonic, modal in inflection, out of Stanford by way of Vaughan Williams—represents a characteristic 'English' style as it was understood and applauded in the 1920's and 1930's.

Education and Musicology

As in the early part of the nineteenth century there were those who were conscious of the necessity not only to improve musical education but also to broaden it. This was partly a continuation of the devoted labours of the Victorian pioneers; partly the result of the implications of the idealistic philosophy of the folk-music enthusiasts; and partly the consequence of the stimulus afforded by the growing tendency to accommodate music more or less comfortably in the life of the 'public schools' and the more exclusive independent schools for girls. In respect of the two last categories the work done by music masters, especially at Rugby, Uppingham, Clifton, Eton, Oundle, and Christ's Hospital (where the ancient tradition of practical music never ceased) resulted in effective missionaries being sent out into the world, and in the profession of music-master becoming less risible than formerly. In the broader field of education a more enlightened policy towards state schools was conducted by Sir Arthur Somervell (1863–1937). Somervell, a pupil at Uppingham School, Cambridge University, the R.C.M. and the Hochschule in Berlin, composed a good deal of unpretentious but not unrewarding music in his early years. Of this a number of quietly but genuinely lyrical songs—particularly those of *The Shropshire Lad* cycle—still walk in the outer corridors of broadcast music. In 1901 Somervell became an Inspector to the Board of Education and his activity as composer decreased. He was zealous in his office and campaigned against indifferent standards both of selection and performance. Due to his insistence *The National Song Book*, edited by Stanford, was introduced into schools in 1906, and collections of folk-music were encouraged for class-room use. Somervell also made an attempt to reaffirm the importance of sight-reading. During his tenure of office instrumental music developed spasmodically, and 'Musical Appreciation' (developed as a cult by the pedagogic Stewart Macpherson) was welcomed by many for its relaxative virtues. While Somervell was Inspector some municipalities began to pick up the threads of their own musical traditions, and in the first cities in which the light of culture penetrated into the Council Chambers officers were appointed to superintend the music of the schools. Manchester, London, Bradford, Birmingham, Stoke-on-Trent, as well as the West Riding of Yorkshire, were early in the field, and enabled musicians of some standing to try out such ideas as might be practicable within the exiguous budgets allowed by municipal Treasurers. In recent times the Musical Advisor and his (usually peripatetic) specialist staff have taken the place in civic organisation of the waits of former times. Somervell's successor at the Board of Education was Geoffrey Shaw (brother to Martin), whose bonhomie made more friends for music than enemies. He was followed by another ex-chorister of St. Paul's Cathedral, the ebullient Cyril Winn. Between them Shaw and Winn saw to it that musical festivals, particularly non-competitive, developed under the aegis of Local Authorities, sometimes to become sources of local pride.

In a modern society the cause of music in education requires special pleading. This is not only true of Britain, where the record of achievement in musical education overall has been considerable. The finest evangelist of the century was probably the Anglo-Welsh Sir Walford Davies (1869–1941), who saw the possibilities and seized the opportunity offered by the medium of broadcasting. The first commentator on music for the layman—as a Royal Institution Lecturer Davies was amplifying an already long-established tradition—he gave talks that were an amalgam of sound musicianship, sympathy with the listener, and charm of manner, to children and adults alike. His broadcasts ran uninterruptedly from 1924 until the time of his death. Walford Davies was a man of parts, a general practitioner with special gifts. A choirboy under Walter Parratt at Windsor, he graduated from the R.C.M., where he studied with Parry and Stanford. He was a fine church musician—organist of the Temple Church and St. George's Chapel, Windsor, and a good, if somewhat academic, composer. His major success was his oratorio *Everyman* (by now the medieval Mystery was part of every English composer's luggage) produced at the Leeds Festival of 1904. In 1919 Davies was Professor of Music in the University College of Aberystwyth and he exerted wider influence on the music of the Principality as Chairman of the National Council of Music for Wales. On the death of Elgar, Davies succeeded him as Master of the King's Music.

During the Victorian era music gained a foothold in the universities—in large measure because of the devoted interest of amateurs. In Oxford and Cambridge, where musical societies took their place in the general pattern of university life, where the influence of the choral foundations and the organists of college chapels became considerable and beneficial, and where degrees offered professional respectability, the academic foothold was secure. The Universities of London (1879), Durham (1889), Edinburgh (1893), Manchester (1894), Wales (1894), Birmingham (1905), the National University of Ireland[1] (1908) made provision for (external) degrees in music but without any clear idea as to the place of music in a university. In a few cases, as at Newcastle (Armstrong

[1] Although a Chair at Trinity College, Dublin, was established in 1764, it lasted for only ten years. On its revival in 1861 (R. P. Stewart being Professor) the duties of the holder were solely to conduct examinations. As at Oxford and Cambridge, however, there was a University Choral Society and a College Chapel to maintain the broader traditions.

College), tuition was available to B.A. students. At Edinburgh the Reid Concerts remained a distinctive feature and afforded opportunity to Donald Tovey (1875–1940) to canalise his considerable learning into a series of programme notes which, when published in book form, exerted much influence on British musical thought. The first Professor of Music at Birmingham was Elgar, whose lectures—in continuation of the adult education tradition strongly developed in the city—were stimulating and provocative. On the whole musical degrees (often obtainable externally) were considered primarily as useful passports for organists and school-teachers. The syllabuses had a strong odour of Anglicanism and little thought was given either to serving the needs of scholarship or to establishing a connection with contemporary practices and requirements. Until the Second World War a university education in music (or external preparation for a degree) for the most part guaranteed a sober academicism. One outstanding figure, however, overturned many old shibboleths, and inaugurated a fresh outlook. This was Edward Dent (1876–1957), a member of a wealthy Yorkshire family, an Etonian, and a graduate of King's College, Cambridge. In 1902 Dent was elected a Fellow of his College. Twenty-four years later he succeeded Charles Wood (1866–1926) as Professor of Music in the University, which post he held for fifteen years. A non-organist, and a free-thinker, Dent escaped the more constricting conventions of English music, and his first love was opera. Through his *Alessandro Scarlatti* (1905) and *Mozart's Operas* (1913), in which precision of scholarship was matched by precision in the prose style, Dent did as much as anyone to re-vitalise opera in England. His translations (about thirty) of opera libretti were fundamental to the operations of the Sadler's Wells Opera which he helped to found in 1934; and his encouragement of amateur productions, especially of Purcell, Mozart, and of dramatised versions of Handel's oratorios at Cambridge, were epoch-making. On the other hand, Dent, who introduced original composition into the Cambridge syllabus, was greatly concerned for contemporary music and was one of the instigators of the International Society for Contemporary Music. A highly respected figure in the international field, especially of musicology, Dent not only gave greater purpose to musical studies in the university but also enabled his colleagues and pupils to enjoy the vision of wider horizons. During the Dent period at Cambridge practical musicianship was largely controlled by Cyril Rootham (1875–1938), an underrated composer, a zealous if often erratic conductor, and a fine teacher, while the choral music at King's College came to occupy a place of national importance under the direction first of A. H. Mann (1850–1929) and then of Bernhard (Boris) Ord (1897–1962).

The casual progress of musical life in Britain, by intermingling amateur enthusiasm and professional skill, has brought certain advantages, not least in the field of musicology. This has been related on the one hand to the general tradition of literature, and on the other to performance. If the indigenous literary tradition has cast belletristic qualities over musical scholarship (as for instance in *Grove*) a general appreciation of music and a perception of its place in civilised living have thereby become more widespread. Tovey and Dent were classical scholars and their distinction as writers was considerable. So too was that of Henry Hadow (1859–1937), a distinguished educationist and sometime Vice-Chancellor of the University of Sheffield[1], who contributed to the *Oxford History of Music*, wrote *Studies in Modern Music*, and a concise history of *English Music*. Charles Sanford Terry (1864–1936), whose early education was as a chorister at St. Paul's Cathedral, became lecturer in history at Newcastle and Professor at Aberdeen. In addition to important historical works of widely varied character Terry wrote a scrupulously documented and lucidly expressed biography of *Bach* (1928). This, turned away from hagiography, represented a key point in Bach scholarship, which was recognised when Terry was given an honorary Doctorate at Leipzig University in 1930. This work was the centre from which much else radiated—essays on various aspects of Bach research, useful handbooks on particular works, translations of texts, and new editions. A practical musician (with a handful of original compositions to his name), Terry saw his musical studies in the broad field of musical experience. His presence in the north-east of England gave a new incentive, and W. G. Whittaker (1876–1944), infected by Terry's enthusiasm, prepared and performed the whole series of Bach's Church Cantatas first in Glasgow and then in Newcastle upon Tyne. In 1930 Whittaker—largely a self-taught musician—moved to Glasgow as head of the new Scottish National Academy of Music and Professor of Music in the University.[2] Carrying on from Barclay Squire and Fuller-Maitland, E. H. Fellowes (1870–1951), Minor Canon of St. George's Chapel, Windsor, brought back into general use the major part of the output of the English madrigalists, while Anselm Hughes (b. 1889), a member of the Benedictine Order within the Church of England, continued the exploration of medieval music begun by Rockstro and Stainer. Fellowes and Hughes became musicologists by the light of nature and in the knowledge that there was work to be done. Each has contributed much to the general store of musical enjoyment, as well as furnishing a strong case for musical scholarship.

[1] On taking up his Sheffield appointment in 1920 Hadow instituted recitals of chamber music, and in 1927 a Chair of Music was founded in the University.

[2] The Professorship grew out of the Cramb Music Trust Lectures, established in 1923, and delivered by Walford Davies, Percy C. Buck, Holst, Tovey, Hugh Allen and H. C. Colles, music critic of *The Times*.

The British Conductor Arrives

Within the established processes of musical activity the emergence of British conductors of international stature and a general quickening of responses to orchestral music was an important feature of the early twentieth century. Henry Wood, becoming a virtuoso conductor by way of provincial choral societies and opera pits, turned the Jullien-type of popular concert into the Promenade Concert of modern times and this has proved an immensely powerful factor in stimulating a general interest in music. Not least of all because Wood's catholicity of taste ensured that much that was previously unfamiliar became familiar. Landon Ronald (1873–1938), who owed his technical competence to close study of Nikisch and Weingartner, was a guest-conductor of the Berlin Philharmonic Orchestra in 1908–9, and a fine interpreter of Elgar's works—which in themselves were a means of raising the standard of orchestral playing. The London situation, however, was improved most of all at the beginning of the century by the establishment—as a self-governing organisation—of the London Symphony Orchestra, which gave its first concert, under Richter, on 9 June 1904. 'The L.S.O's brilliance', wrote Sir Adrian Boult, who was present, 'staggered all those who knew the London orchestral world at that time'.[1] Eight concerts were given in the first season, with Cowen, Nikisch, Steinbach, Stanford, Colonne, and Elgar as guest conductors. The principle of inviting guest conductors to undertake occasional concerts, established by the L.S.O., was stimulating to audiences, challenging to players, and of benefit to other conductors and would-be conductors. In 1906 the L.S.O. visited Paris. In the following year it played in Antwerp, and in 1912 successfully undertook an American tour.

The career of Thomas Beecham (1879–1961) constitutes a small epic and supplies more anecdotes than are available for the whole of the rest of British music. Largely self-taught in music, and adequately supported by the funds of a wealthy Lancashire industrial family, Beecham combined autocracy and idiosyncrasy with a fine appreciation of musical patterns and sonorities in such a way that he became a national institution and a figure of international significance. Like Charles Hallé and Henry Wood, Beecham was cognizant of the fact that lack of security (with players piling up engagements and then having to substitute deputies in their places) was playing havoc with standards, even though the rigours of the game developed an unrivalled skill in sight-reading. As a young man he tried to establish a fresh outlook by his direction of the New Symphony Orchestra;

[1] Quoted in *London Symphony Orchestra, World Tour 1964.*

but it was not until 1932, when he founded the London Philharmonic Orchestra, that he was able to achieve his aim of a handpicked body of players owing their first loyalty to their orchestra. Beecham's taste and interpretations were as capricious as his attitude to music. He gave a particular image of a *galant* Mozart—and of other classical composers, inspiring versions of the as yet not fully appreciated Berlioz, of Strauss, and of a wide range of late romantic exotic works, and, of course, authoritative interpretations of Delius—the one English composer who, in his view, possessed genius. In Manchester a spur to critical appreciation came with the appointment of the Ulster-born Hamilton Harty (1879–1941) to the conductorship of the Hallé Orchestra. A lively composer (his *Irish Symphony* and the symphonic poem *With the Wild Geese* are vivid latecomers in the nationalist tradition) and a brilliant accompanist, Harty brought the Manchester orchestra into the forefront of British music, especially by his compelling championship of Berlioz. Like many conductors Harty had a flair for making arrangements: in so doing he displayed a greater musicianship than some of his colleagues, for he never made orchestration merely an end in itself. In 1930 a new chapter in the history of orchestral music opened by the foundation of the B.B.C. Orchestra, under the conductorship of Adrian Boult (b. 1889), a disciple of the Nikisch school, whose balanced judgement has brought authoritative interpretations of the classics as of the major modern British works.

Opera and the Amateurs

If the condition of orchestral music improved during the first part of the century that of opera remained distinctly unpromising. Beecham worked heroically to improve matters, but in the end, having sacrificed a large part of the family's fortunes, had to acknowledge defeat. In 1909 he made his operatic debut in introducing Ethel Smyth's *The Wreckers*. In the following year he undertook *Electra* (Strauss being one of his approved composers) and Delius's *Village Romeo and Juliet.* In succeeding years, undeterred even by wartime conditions, Beecham, with his own company, produced an astonishing wealth of operas—included among the composers were Mozart, Strauss, Stravinsky, Rimsky-Korsakov, and Ravel. He also persuaded the Russian Ballet to visit London in 1911. After the war Beecham made Manchester—where a spacious Opera House was built—his headquarters. Ahead of his time and picking up a trail laid by earlier optimistic British musicians, he tried to associate his Company with the Manchester Royal College of Music under a financial umbrella to be provided by the City Council. Disappointed in this ambition, embarrassed by personal financial complexities, he temporarily retired. Apart from an abortive attempt to launch an Imperial League of Opera in 1927 his work thereafter lay mostly in the concert hall. Out of the wreck of the Beecham Opera Company a British National Opera Company was formed in 1923. Sterling work was done in the provinces—unlike other touring companies an adequate orchestral standard was maintained—and London seasons were given. In addition to works already noted as having been given by this Company the repertoire included Mackenzie's *Eve of St. John*, Rutland Boughton's *Alkestis*, and Vaughan Williams's *Hugh the Drover*. The conductor of this enterprise at the outset was Percy Pitt, sometime Musical Adviser at Covent Garden and an associate of Beecham. He was succeeded in 1924 by Frederick Austin (editor of the unidiomatic but vastly popular version of *The Beggar's Opera* first put on at the Lyric Theatre, Hammersmith, in 1920). After five years and as an inevitable consequence of economic stringency the venture folded up: a melancholy addition to the long list of discarded operatic projects. A year later, however, a new star dimly glowed: Philip Snowden, Chancellor of the Exchequer in the Labour Government, allowed for a small grant to Covent Garden in the 1930 Budget. This was not renewed.

The fact that twenty years later opera slowly began to find a warmer welcome in Britain was due nonetheless to the energies and enterprises thus recorded. A great deal was also due to peripheral experiments (of which Glastonbury was one), in which amateur enthusiasm again played a large part. In 1925 Monteverdi's *Orfeo*, edited by J. A. Westrup (then an undergraduate), was performed in Oxford and proved to be the first of many distinguished productions by the University Opera Club. In 1926 Gluck's *Alceste* was performed, and in the next year Monteverdi's *L'Incoronazione di Poppea*. R. L. Stuart, translator of *Orfeo*, directed a season of professional opera at the New Scala Theatre, in London, during which *Cupid and Death* was revived and the first performance since the eighteenth century of Handel's *Giulio Cesare* took place. The programme also included *Dido and Aeneas* (conducted and produced by Dennis Arundell), Mozart's *La Finta Giardiniera* (conducted by Leslie Heward), and Weber's *Freischütz* (conducted by Beecham, produced by Humphrey Procter-Gregg)[1]. In 1923 an even less probable venture was launched. The Falmouth Opera Singers in Cornwall, nursed into being by two music-loving sisters, Maisie and Evelyn Radford, began their lively career. The opening production was of Gluck's *Orpheus*, after which they gave the first English performances of Mozart's *La Clemenza di Tito* and *Idomeneo*, as well as going into the business of turning Handelian oratorios into

[1] See Father Robert Stuart, 'Operatic Pioneering in England 36 Years Ago', *The Times*, 31 December 1965.

operas.[1] These scattered organisations and events sowed seeds which have since ripened.

Romanticism Still Prevalent

Of the composers born within the last two decades of the nineteenth century some showed pronounced signs of benefiting from the heterogeneous influences indicated above, as well as from others. Arnold Bax (1883–1953), as a young man captivated by the poetry of Yeats, sought inspiration in Irish landscape and culture and, like many Englishmen, became more Irish than the Irish. The effectiveness of the idiom thus acquired may be judged by the relative ineffectiveness of the gentle but narrowed Scottish inflections of Sir John McEwen (1868–1948).[2]

George Butterworth (1885–1916), a fellow-worker in the field of folk-song, approached composition from the same vantage point as Vaughan Williams. The work of the two composers overlapped in that both were attracted by Housman's *Shropshire Lad.* Butterworth's two sets of Housman songs (1911, 1912), delicate and lying midway between Vaughan Williams and Gurney, and the collateral orchestral Rhapsody *A Shropshire Lad*, tinted like a water-colour, achieved modest fame as tokens of a high talent that was cut off before it had time fully to develop. Butterworth was killed during the Battle of the Somme. Although his father was Irish, and Irish culture affected him, E. J. Moeran (1894–1951) was born in London and lived most of his life in Norfolk. The landscape of East Anglia and the folk-music of that region were prominent influences. Thus it is that the disparate elements in Moeran's style, warmed by harmonic characteristics derived from Delius by way of Warlock, tend to neutralise each other. Percy Grainger, an Australian whose generosity to fellow-musicians was considerable, was also a zealous collector of folk-music. His treatment of it came from a zest for engaging and provocative sonorities and unconventional instrumental combinations rather than for any purist regard for ethnomusicology. In 1915 Grainger, who effectively disguised a deep scholarship shown in researches into medieval music, settled in America and became a naturalised citizen of the United States. Grainger's high spirits were welcomed by the less sophisticated part of the public, but his vigorous and untrammelled attitude to music, discountenanced by the academics, was premature. It has made a timely reappearance in recent years in the works of another Australian, Malcolm

[1] See Maisie and Evelyn Radford, *Musical Adventures in Cornwall*, London, 1966.

[2] From 1898 McEwen taught at the R.A.M. and in 1924 he succeeded Mackenzie as Principal. He retained this post until 1936. Having previously experimented with 'recitations' to instrumental accompaniment, McEwen essayed the first British *Sprechgesang* in his fourteen songs (words by Margaret Forbes) 'for inflected voice and pfte.' of 1943.

Williamson. Ivor Gurney (1890–1937), a Gloucestershire man whose career came to an end as a result of the war and his subsequent confinement in a mental hospital, absorbed the new lyricism engendered by the song techniques of Parry and the quietism of Vaughan Williams, and, within rather narrow limits, composed beautiful and temperate, yet distinctive, songs. In apposition to Gurney may be placed the relatively unknown Scottish composer Francis George Scott (1880–1958)[1] whose rough edges of rhythm and strenuous accompaniments caught the north wind, and the voice and moods of the best of Scottish poets both ancient and modern [Ex. 7]. The first song-writers of this generation, however,

7.

Adagio assai
The auld man's mear's dead; The
poco accell.
puir bo-dy's mear's dead;

was Peter Warlock (1894–1930). Warlock was not only a composer but a scholar and, if his own debt to the Jacobean composers of ayres was considerable, ours to him is the greater for his bringing to light many examples of the best music in the native heritage. More or less in the main stream, and a steady Three Choirs Festival composer, Herbert Howells (b. 1892) refined familiar conventions, sounded a personal note—frequently of pessimism—and achieved a style apt to many departments of music, without, however, ever quite fulfilling the promise of earlier years. The mark of all these composers was assurance in technical application,

[1] See M. Lindsay, 'Francis George Scott, Scottish Songs', *M. & L.*, 26, no. 1, 1945, pp. 1–11.

and this element of professional competence was a vital factor in the refurbishing of creative talent. No composer has proved more practical in outlook than Arthur Bliss (b. 1891), who, like Bax, has shown himself the master of many mediums, not least of all the orchestra. Part of the composer's duty, both to himself and his prospective audience, is to find out opportunity. The diversity of this group is a testimonial to this ability to make or to command opportunity. Diversity of outlook was also an aid to a healthier artistic climate. When supported by certainty of method the British composer's indifference to fashion can even be an incentive to originality of musical expression.

Bax once described himself as 'a brazen romantic, by which I mean that my music is the expression of emotional states. I have', he added, 'no interest whatever in sound for its own sake or in any modernist 'isms or factions'.[1] It may be observed that as between classical and romantic principles in music the British generally prefer to be guided by the latter. Apart from any inherited tendencies this may be ascribed to an overwhelming literary tradition, to the peripheral place which music occupies in the social pattern, and, latterly, to a heightened respect for the past. Coming to terms with the present has frequently been seen to have been an uncongenial occupation, and sometimes one that appears irrelevant. Bax, Warlock, and Bliss—the most substantial composers of the group outlined above—are all romantic composers; but each within the national context is an important figure—not least of all because of unassailable techniques. There is no doubt of the professionalism of all three. Bax and Bliss have worked in most fields, Warlock's territory is more limited, but his exploration deep. The three composers have in common a perceptive appreciation of literature and a talent for the selection of texts that are not only worthwhile for their own sakes but also viable for musical treatment.

Bax's early life is entertainingly and stylishly set out in his autobiographical *Farewell, my Youth*.[2] Belonging to a family whose literary talent emerged in the writings of his brother, Clifford, Arnold became a student at the R.A.M., where his 'senses were drunk with Wagner, [his] nerves a-twitch to the titillating perversities that Richard Strauss was obtruding for the first time into a fundamentally diatonic style, whilst [his] brain staggered at that man's complex audacities of counterpoint and infernal orchestral cleverness.'[3] Acquaintance with Parry, Stanford, and Mackenzie assured him that 'they were all three solid reputable citizens and ratepayers of the United Kingdom, model husbands and fathers without a

[1] Quoted in Alan Frank, *Modern British Composers*, London, 1953, p. 27.
[2] London, 1943.
[3] *Farewell, my Youth*, p. 22.

doubt, respected members of the most irreproachably Conservative clubs, and in Yeats's phrase had "no strange friend".'[1] It was Elgar who convinced him—as the outside world—'that even the despised Englishman could be a musical genius.'

Bax travelled in Germany and Russia as a young man, but the chief catalyst to his musical invention was the literary group he encountered in Dublin—George Russell (AE), Padraic Colum, Seamus O'Sullivan, and Yeats. Under the pseudonym of Dermot O'Byrne, Bax published some short stories on Irish subjects. His allegiance, about 1910, was, he said, divided between literature and music. Urged on by Balfour Gardiner (a generous support to young English composers at that time), Bax translated his Celtic enthusiasm into terms of music and four pieces for orchestra were performed in 1914 at a concert organised and subsidised by F. Bevis Ellis.[2]

In these, as in the earlier *In the Faêry Hills* (1909), Bax's felicity in handling rich orchestral colours was apparent. A succession of symphonic poems—*The Garden of Fand* (1916), *Tintagel* (1917), and *November Woods* (1917)—showed this capacity to a higher degree. If Wagner, Strauss, and Elgar had contributed to the manner of blending sonorities, Bax had developed his own atmospheric idiom. On the one hand he dispensed

8a.

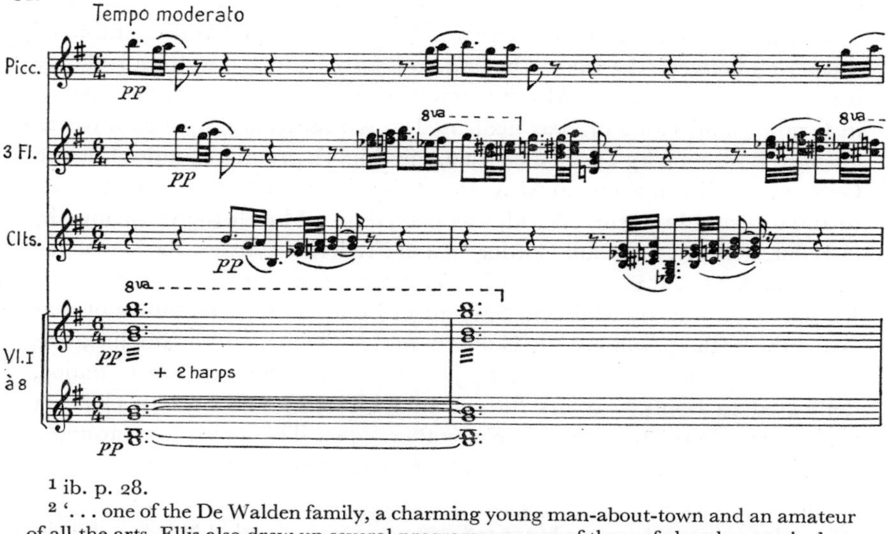

[1] ib. p. 28.

[2] '... one of the De Walden family, a charming young man-about-town and an amateur of all the arts. Ellis also drew up several programmes, one of them of chamber music, but, since experience had proved that public and critics alike were apt to look upon an all-British concert as a kind of raree-show outside the main trend of the art, he deemed it wiser to leaven native music with little-known works by established foreign masters.' Bax, op. cit., p. 93.

8b.

a generous rhapsodic idiom, on the other a contrasting terseness. Picturesqueness—and few English pieces are more picturesque than *Tintagel*—is thus not permitted to run into musical incoherence; for rhythmic drive intervenes to prevent it. *The Garden of Fand* begins in this characteristic and evocative manner [Ex. 8*a*] but chooses for second subject [Ex. 8*b*]. In 1922 Bax was accepted as an established composer by reason of the programme of his major works given at Queen's Hall on 13 November.

In the years following, Bax—fortunate in being able to devote himself wholeheartedly to composition—was prolific, especially as symphonist. The symphonies are in themselves a miniature history of British music of the period between the wars. The first, in E flat, dedicated to John Ireland, was first performed under Albert Coates[1] on 2 December 1922; the second, in E minor and C major, was dedicated to Koussevitzky, by whom it was given in Boston on 13 December 1929, the English première, under Eugene Goossens,[2] following on 20 May 1930; the third, in C major, dedicated to and directed by Henry Wood, was played on 3 March 1930; the fourth, in E flat, dedicated to Paul Corder (son of Frederick Corder, Bax's teacher at the R.A.M.), was conducted by Basil Cameron[3] in San Francisco, in March 1932, and by Malcolm Sargent in London on 5 December of that year; the fifth symphony, in C sharp minor, dedicated to Sibelius, was performed under Beecham on 14 January 1934; the sixth, in C major, dedicated to Boult, was first heard at a Philharmonic Society Concert under Hamilton Harty on 21 November 1935. The seventh symphony, in A flat, was completed in 1939 and has remained unpublished.

[1] 1882–1953; Anglo-Russian conductor and composer.

[2] b. 1893; Anglo-Belgian conductor and composer who has worked in U.S.A., Britain, and Australia.

[3] b. 1884, he came into prominence during the inter-war years when he conducted the San Francisco and Seattle Symphony Orchestras. Of late years Cameron has been a familiar and popular figure at Promenade Concerts.

The whole of this body of symphonic music is marked by the same melodic invention as the symphonic poems, while the harmonic idiom remains constant, and constantly evocative. From the formal point of view Bax, though using cyclical principles, retained the classical outline more or less intact; except that a three-movement pattern was preferred. Tonally he ranged far afield, but always within familiar terms of reference. The formal structure, however, in each symphonic work, appears to be imbued with a programmatic intention that is only avowed in the fourth. This symphony, characteristically, is part sea-scape and largely Celtic.

Bax, who was Master of the King's (Queen's) Music from 1941 until his death, was prolific in every direction. Rather less addicted to choral music than his contemporaries, he nevertheless contrived to produce two of the most striking works of this order written during this period—*Mater ora filium* (1921) and *This Worlde's Joie* (1922); both, to medieval texts and for *a cappella* singing, are compelling by reason of the unwonted but apposite sternness let into the style and a brilliant appreciation of medium. These more or less gaunt pieces stand away from the greater part of Bax's output which—the essential manner hardly varying—increasingly carried the stigma of anachronism. Bax belonged to an age that died, but he lived on into an era for which his voice lost significance. Thus the music of this vivid composer at present largely lies dormant.

In the case of Bliss the process of development makes a curious inversion, for in the latest works we are taken back to a point behind that from which he started. By the early 1920's Bliss, like Lord Berners,[1] was a cosmopolitan and somewhat cavalier figure disturbing the cosiness of the English tradition with a sequence of experimental works that showed characteristics acquired from Ravel, from 'Les Six', and from Stravinsky. In 1918 *Madam Noy*, a Stravinskyan 'witchery' song for soprano and six instruments, showed an independent assessment of sonorities that owed little to English antecedents. When this was followed by a wordless *Rhapsody* for two voices and seven instruments (the whole forming a nonet, since the voices were treated as instrumental values in the ensemble), and *Rout*, for soprano (singing disconnected syllables) and ten instruments, Bliss was well on the way to being regarded as *avant garde*.

Educated at Rugby School and Cambridge, Bliss had just finished additional studies at the R.C.M. when war broke out. After active service he returned to a different world from the one he had left, and a mood of critical interrogation characteristic of the immediate post-war period is summarised in his early compositions. In the *Colour Symphony* of 1922 (the

[1] 1883–1950; Berners was littérateur, diplomat, painter, and self-taught composer with Stravinskyan inclinations. He composed much parodistic music and a ballet, *The Triumph of Neptune*, for Diaghilev (1926).

programme was removed in the revision of 1932) Bliss emerged as a composer of high competence, if uncertain accent, on a large scale. But six years later he retreated to a refined romanticism, well within English terms of reference, in *Pastoral*, a choral work based on poems by Ben Jonson John Fletcher, Poliziano, Theocritus, and Robert Nichols. Elegant as this work is, it suggested reaction. A lack of genuine musical invention is covered up by expert placing of solo mezzo-soprano, flute, strings, and chorus. The work was dedicated to Elgar. Elegance in composition, however, was unfamiliar in British music and Bliss, in turning away from his early experiments, settled on this as a basis for further operations. A fine precision in writing distinguishes his chamber music, of which the best examples are the Clarinet Quintet (1931), the Sonata for Viola and Piano (1932), and the two string Quartets (1941, 1950). In the chamber music the unexceptionable romantic idiom is relieved by an astringency in the harmonic texture that brought the music into line with that of William Walton.

Bliss's abilities are as varied as his interests. He is a purposeful conductor and his capacity for achieving clarity in performance without excessive 'interpretation' complements the character of his orchestral works. A long association with the United States (from 1923 he lived for a time in California) produced the Oboe Quintet (commissioned by Mrs. Sprague Coolidge in 1926–7) and the fine Piano Concerto in E flat (commissioned for the New York World Fair of 1939). The latter work is a splendid and often rhetorical piece, ranging from the pointed rhythms and ebullient melodic shapes which are the mark of Bliss's public manner [Ex. 9] to the whimsical fancy that underlies his innate lyricism [Ex. 10]. From the former manner Bliss developed an outstanding technique for film and ballet. The music for the film *Things to Come* (1935), and for the ballets *Checkmate* (1937) and *Miracle in the Gorbals* (1944) recognises that music

9.

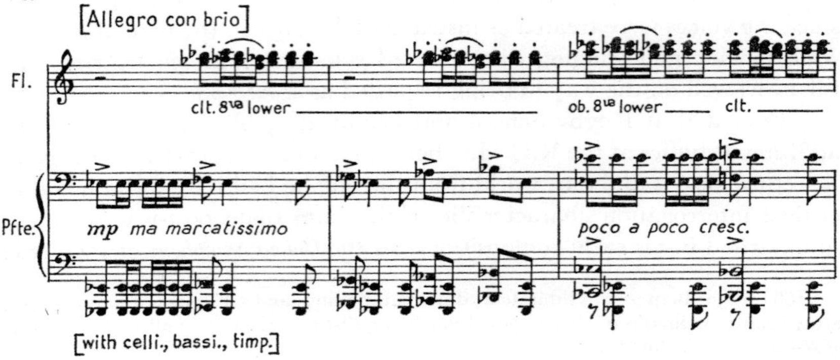

10.

for these media depends on rhythmic vitality and explicitness. *Miracle in the Gorbals*, the setting in the slums of Glasgow, is an expert example of realism, without, however, any loss of musical integrity or concession to doctrinaire theory. This brings us to the 'Englishness' of Bliss, which lies more in his pragmatism and adaptability than in any overt gestures towards a national idiom. In keeping with the national tradition, Bliss, whose dramatic talent is so strongly marked in the works just mentioned, has ventured into opera without success. His one work of this order, *The Olympians* (libretto by J. B. Priestley), was performed at Covent Garden in 1949, but never revived. There are two major choral works: *Morning Heroes* (1930), a war memorial symphony-cantata to texts from Homer, Walt Whitman, Li-Po, Wilfred Owen, and Robert Nichols; and *The Beatitudes*. The latter work, a biblical text fashionably crossed with English poems (Henry Vaughan, George Herbert, Dylan Thomas), was composed for the Coventry Festival of 1962.

Warlock and English Song

In theory there should be a large body of distinguished and distinctive English solo song. In fact there is not. Until well into the twentieth century the popularity with singers, the technical methods, and the allusive vocabulary of the German *Lied* was inhibiting—in spite of the merits of Parry and Stanford as song composers. Vaughan Williams and Holst were handicapped in this medium by incompatibility with the piano. For the rest John Ireland, Roger Quilter, Frank Bridge, although reasonably active, broke no noticeably new ground. Peter Warlock did. By recapturing the spirit of the Jacobean ayre and incorporating it within a modern terminology he stood out as a highly individual figure. If, as happens, Warlock is listed beside Hugo Wolf and Gabriel Fauré that ranking does rather less than justice to him. More than either he reformed an attitude, and by so doing helped to liberate English song by demonstrating its origins.

A man of acute sensibility, Warlock (who changed his name from Philip Heseltine) pursued unconventional ways. He discovered the music of Delius when young and this became a powerful, but not overpowering, influence on his own style. He also became friendly with Delius, whose encouragement was a main support to his intention to become a composer. On the whole Warlock, who found education at Eton and Oxford uncongenial in the extreme, was self-taught in music. He relied on his acute impressionableness and a sharp-edged critical acumen. While readily absorbing the essence of Delian harmony he also acquired something of the intellectual manner of his friend Bernard van Dieren (1884–1936).[1] Warlock's interests were wide. His literary inclinations (which brought him into contact with D. H. Lawrence[2]) led him to the byways of English literature and he became authoritative on the poetry of the Jacobean era. At the same time he appreciated the values of that of his own time. Like Bax he became aware of the modern Celtic movement and discovered an affinity with the verse of Yeats. As a prose-writer, Warlock, seeking means whereby he might express his enthusiasms, founded the journal *The Sackbut* (1920). He also wrote books on Delius (1923), Gesualdo (1926), and *The English Ayre* (1926). On the side of scholarship, however, his main contribution lay in his valuable editions of the works of the lutenist school, of the chamber music of Locke and Purcell, and in his discovery of the merits and importance of Thomas Whythorne. In the light of present-day tendencies it will be seen that Warlock's work in this connection was significant; the more so, because his objective was not musicology but music.

In character Warlock was unpredictable, in no way conforming to the gentlemanliness attributed to more successful composers by Bax. Intensely sensitive, ranging in mood from an excessive rumbustiousness to a profound melancholy, ill-equipped for dealing with the normal problems of life, and spasmodic in application, he was an unusual and uncomfortable phenomenon in the English musical world. He seemed to carry into the twentieth century something that had disappeared from the national character since the seventeenth century. In his art, however, he

[1] Born in Holland, van Dieren settled in England and pursued an intensely personal course as a composer. Although held in regard by a small group of supporters, among whom the critic Cecil Gray and Warlock were prominent, he made little general impression on English music.

[2] Whose Halliday of *Women in Love* was a caricature of Warlock.

discovered the secret of co-ordination and of orderliness that otherwise eluded him.

Warlock's reputation rests on a corpus of about 100 songs, each one of which is marked by a recognisably personal quality. The limits are marked by the vigour of *Captain Stratton's Fancy* (John Masefield) and *Good Ale* (16th cent.) on the one hand, and the lithe, nostalgic, disillusionment of *The Curlew* cycle (W. B. Yeats, set for tenor, flute, cor anglais, string quartet) on the other. In between there are many varieties of mood and atmosphere. Warlock's feeling for melody was unerring, his contours and subtly changing rhythms catching both the shape and the meaning of his texts. Thus, in Nicholas Breton's *Fair and True*, he is content with a simple Campionesque line, whereas in *Robin Good-fellow* he mutates chromatic notes with a picturesque abandon. Bound by no dogmas, Warlock used modal, classical, Romantic and post-Romantic tonal practices, sometimes arriving at startling conclusions [Ex. 11]. The lyrical

11.

dim.
molto ritenuto
A - las, thy cru-el - ty! And will thou leave me thus? Say nay, say nay.

character of Warlock's songs may be approached by that of some songs by Delius and Bax, but neither of these composers had a similar instinctive feeling for the relationship of voice and piano accompaniment. Delius used too few notes, Bax too many. Warlock had a Schubertian talent for discovering the figurative impulses proper to a particular song. In general, these impulses were more musical than literary by nature. That is to say, accompanimental patterns are rarely obviously or obtrusively programmatic, though equally they are seen to carry awareness of textual meaning. From the sixteenth- and seventeenth-century traditions and van Dieren Warlock acquired an aptitude for unselfconscious contrapuntal development. So he may dispose of an artless descant [Ex. 12], or leave incipits in

12.

tranquillo
Sweet-ly dear, and dear-ly sweet, Bles-sèd

mid-air [Ex. 13], or darken the colouring by the interplay of inner parts

13.

[Ex. 14]. Apart from his solo songs Warlock left a number of small but

14.

exquisite choral pieces, a string *Serenade* composed in honour of Delius's sixtieth birthday, and the *Capriol* Suite, based on dance-tunes from Thoinot Arbeau's *Orchésographie*.

14

Modern Times

New Thinking About Music

AS IN OTHER aspects of life the great divide between the past and the future in British music was the Second World War. During the war, music, propagated through countless concerts sponsored by the Council for the Encouragement of Music and the Arts (1940), almost arrived at the point of being regarded as a necessity rather than a luxury. If since then the development of the principle has run an unsteady course, the principle itself has persistently nagged the political and social conscience. The former thesis that music ought to be commercially viable has been replaced by one that accepts the need for subsidy but, for want of precedents, the most satisfactory method of application still remains to be found. This initiation of public spending on music will be explored at a later point.

In Western Europe the concept of nationalism as a foundation for creative music collapsed; partly under the strain of maintaining a belief in nationalism as such, and partly under the influence of new techniques. It takes a keen perception to determine the nationality of serial, electronic, or even atonal music. Thus the modern British composer—of the newest school—practises an idiom that is indifferent to frontiers. With the growth of a belief in larger communities it is possible that the British, or the French, or the German composer as such will disappear. Paradoxically this may be the salvation of the British composer who for too long has been hampered by an irresolute sense of nationalism.

If nationalism as a shibboleth has disappeared, so too have other notions. The demarcation line between 'serious' and 'light' is harder to discover, and 'popular' music (of different kinds) has arrived at the point of critical scrutiny as a valid form of artistic expression. If 'popular' music is upgraded, then church music—for reasons which are obvious in a predominantly secular, if not pagan, society—continues to decline in significance, even though standards of performance are high. It is no longer obligatory to qualify as a composer by writing an oratorio—even though a surprising number of composers still do so. Old habits may be seen to die hard.

Political concern for the mass society has led to a general belief in statistical expansion. Thus more people listen to music, more people take part in musical performance (not always of tolerable standard), more children may appear to have music-lessons, and more students are encouraged to pursue music as a career. In respect of the latter too many, with too little competence, appear merely to sublimate frustrated and romantic ambition; with the result that there are in the schools too many unimaginative teachers of music not at all sure as to which direction they should take, and too few of genuine creative talent who are encouraged to use that talent.

In the present situation there is, nevertheless, a good deal of vigour and vitality, qualities that had for too long been missing from British music. The summary of the achievement of the middle years of the century lies in the works of Benjamin Britten, whose emergence on to the international stage since the Second World War has been one of the more remarkable phenomena of English music. His career has depended on a rare musicianship, but also a capacity to relate the particular to the general. In one sense he is an intensely local composer, but his talent for communication and his perception of the human values that may be discussed through music has compelled the attention of a world audience. At the very least Britten has diminished foreign faith in the dogma that the English are unmusical. It may be that recognition of the fact that there is in fact a great musical potential is the most important facet of the music of Britain of the present time.

Support for Opera and Orchestra

The chequered story of British opera shows a number of composers who had the talent to compose operas, but not in any real sense the opportunity: not even Purcell. Britten's remarkable success in this field is due not only to his sensitive feeling for the theatrically expressive qualities of music but also to a change of general attitude towards opera. In that opera is seldom available outside London—except for tours by the metropolitan companies—the persistence of the Welsh National Opera Company[1], and the initiative of amateurs, it is still widely regarded as

[1] Founded in 1946, this company, noteworthy on account of its chorus, although without adequate headquarters, and dependent on an English orchestra, has achieved much

irrational and exotic, and devoid of the apparent purposefulness of the 'Musical', which, to be truthful, is basically an indigenous form of entertainment in spite of its now inevitable American connections. But by the increased prominence of native (or Commonwealth) opera singers and the mediation of television, more people at large are ready to accept the idea that opera should have its place and even to campaign for its implantation in other parts of the country than London. The real foundations of modern English Opera were laid by Lilian Baylis whose achievement it was to popularise standard operas in English for audiences of a more local character than those attracted to Covent Garden—which remains an international Opera House. Not only was a varied repertoire of opera firmly established at Sadler's Wells, but also of ballet. Enthusiasm for ballet is widespread and a remarkable feature of present-day popular artistic appreciation. The Vic-Wells Ballet Company was created by Ninette de Valois, an Irish dancer formerly in Diaghilev's Company, and on the musical side it gained early distinction through the inventive brilliance and interpretative authority of Constant Lambert (1905–51), whose many-sided abilities tended to obscure the quality of his compositions. During the war, although deprived of their own premises, both opera and ballet companies toured extensively—often under conditions of great difficulty—and built up the framework for future development and expansion. The Sadler's Wells Theatre was re-opened on 7 June 1945, the work chosen for the occasion being Britten's *Peter Grimes*, the company being that which had been valiantly recruited and kept together by Joan Cross.

At this time the future of Covent Garden (not for the first time) was in doubt. At the end of 1945 a short lease of the building was taken by Messrs. Boosey and Hawkes, who sub-let it to the Covent Garden Opera Trust (of which the Chairman was Lord Keynes, also Chairman of the Arts Council of Great Britain[1]). Through the Arts Council a certain measure of State support was obtained. The Sadler's Wells Ballet, by now a national institution, was at this juncture transferred to the Royal Opera House, which was re-opened with a gala performance of Tchaikovsky's *The Sleeping Beauty* on 20 February 1946. By the end of the year a new opera company had been assembled and, under the direction of Constant Lambert, made its first appearance—together with the Ballet Company—in a version of Purcell's *The Fairy Queen*. The permanent Musical Director of Covent Garden was then Karl Rankl, under whom the Company made

in giving a new purpose to Welsh music. Among operas by Welsh composers commissioned by the company are Arwel Hughes's *Menna*, and *Love's the Doctor*, and Grace Williams's *The Parlour*.

[1] The Arts Council was incorporated by Royal Charter on 9 August 1946.

its first independent appearance in a performance of *Carmen* on 14 January 1947.

The treasury grant to Covent Garden at this time was £55,000.[1] Ten years later this had risen to £270,000, but the increase, through rising costs, was largely illusory and comparatively speaking the House was still managing on a shoe-string.[2] Rankl resigned in 1951 and there was no permanent Musical Director until 1955, when Rafael Kubelik was appointed. During the interregnum a notable performance of Berg's *Wozzeck* was given under Erich Kleiber; but during the 1950's fresh encouragement was given to English opera. Bliss's *Olympians* (1949), Vaughan Williams's *Pilgrim's Progress* (1951), Britten's *Billy Budd* (1951) and *Gloriana* (1953), Walton's *Troilus and Cressida* (1954), Tippett's *Midsummer Marriage* (1954) and *King Priam* (1962) were all produced for the first time at Covent Garden. At the same time the company began to show names of singers that were of international significance: among those who have reached the front of the profession through Covent Garden are Joan Sutherland, Geraint Evans, Richard Lewis, Michael Langdon, Amy Shuard and Marie Collier. After three years, during which he did much to raise the standard of singing, Kubelik left. In 1961 Georg Solti, already attached to Covent Garden, took over the musical directorship. A mark of the distance travelled in respect of opera in Britain since the war was the production, by an all-British cast, of Schoenberg's *Moses and Aaron* in 1965.

An effective part in the development of opera in Britain has been played by the Glyndebourne Opera House,[3] created in 1934 in the grounds of his Sussex home by John Christie, whose wife was Audrey Mildmay, an operatic soprano. In the first place this undertaking was under the direction of Fritz Busch (musical director) and Carl Ebert (producer), and the main stress was on Mozart. The aim of the founder was to promote the highest possible standards. Insofar as English opera is concerned Glyndebourne has given performances of Delius's *Koanga*, Albert Coates's *Pickwick*, and Eugene Goossens's *Don Juan de Manara*. A Glyndebourne English Opera Group was formed soon after the war, and gave the première of Britten's chamber opera, *The Rape of Lucretia*, conducted by Ansermet, on 12 July, 1947. This group became independent, but gave the first performance of *Albert Herring* at Glyndebourne in that year. The English Opera Group, inspired in the first

[1] Sadler's Wells received £15,000, and the English Opera Group £3,000.

[2] In 1964–5 the Treasury grant of £769,132 was inadequate: see 'The Finances of the Royal Opera House', in *Annual Report (1964–5), Royal Opera House, Covent Garden*, pp. 28–42.

[3] A full account is available in Spike Hughes, *Glyndebourne: A History of the Festival Opera*, London 1966.

place by Britten and dedicated to the principle of chamber opera, has subsequently taken a major part in the Aldeburgh Festival.[1] In 1961, however, the Group—like all those bodies already mentioned in receipt of funds from the Government—came under the administrative jurisdiction of Covent Garden. While the English Opera Group sustained one side of the Aldeburgh Festival, the Glyndebourne Company has for many years been an integral part of the Edinburgh International Festival.[2]

The destruction of the Queen's Hall in 1941 left London—a city never over-endowed with such buildings—with no other concert-hall than the Albert Hall. This took the place of Queen's Hall so far as Promenade Concerts were concerned, but for general use its acoustics, its size, and its lack of general amenities rendered it unsuitable. The need for a modern building was met by the erection of the Royal Festival Hall in 1951 as a focal point in the Festival of Britain organised in that year. The Royal Festival Hall, with ancillary chamber music facilities (since extended[3]) and spacious and pleasant ante-rooms, and with the attraction of its riverside setting, rapidly established itself as a centre for musical activity and enthusiasm, and the opportunity to hear not only the major British but also the great orchestras and artistes of the world under ideal conditions has done much to stimulate a general appreciation of music. It should also be said that the organ, built by Harrison and Harrison to the design of Ralph Downes and including Baroque features, has had a marked effect on a renewal of interest in the organ recital as such.

As has been shown, the state of orchestral music in Britain became more and more unbalanced as the large orchestra became firmly established. The imbalance between London and the provinces has intensified, with the result that the former is better furnished with symphony orchestras than any other capital city in the world, whereas large parts of industrial Britain are inadequately provided for. The more important provincial orchestras, however, across the last thirty years or so have striven first to establish high standards and then to maintain them, against the impoverishment of their playing resources by the lure of greater metropolitan opportunity. In consequence of this there is a tendency for London to have too many orchestral players (the number of competent free-lances is enormous) and everywhere else too few. The old practice of rushing from engagement to engagement to supplement a modest income (rife a hundred years ago) has continued, while major orchestras, under-

[1] Founded in 1948.

[2] Instituted in 1947, the idea having been worked out in the first place by Audrey Mildmay and the impresario Rudolf Bing, who for the first ten years acted as General Manager at Glyndebourne.

[3] The Queen Elizabeth Hall (seating 1,100) and the Purcell Room (seating 387) were opened 1 March 1967.

endowed, have ridden crisis after crisis on the financial front. The adequate remuneration of talented players—on whose undivided loyalty the welfare of an orchestra depends—still remains a problem.

In 1963 one might have concluded that Haydn's musicians at Eisenstadt were better off than the orchestral players of London. 'Apart from the B.B.C., no London concert orchestra can to-day offer its players a contract. As a result there are no salaries, no pension schemes, no organised sick relief, no holidays with pay. What an orchestra does is in effect to offer a steady flow of free-lance work, paid at rates rather above the modest union[1] minimums. What this will produce naturally varies from orchestra to orchestra. The London Philharmonic Orchestra reckons that their rank and file earn about £1,300 a year, and that this involves something very near a six-day week, generally with a rehearsal in the morning and a concert in the evening. And even this figure is attained only by accepting the sort of engagements that, musically speaking, are mere charring.'[2] Since that was written steps have been taken to ameliorate the situation of the player, but reasonable security only becomes possible when orchestras themselves enjoy security.

Just as a symphony orchestra, musically speaking, is a kind of status symbol, so frequently, on another plane, is attendance at a symphony concert. Music of this order is immensely popular, but audiences—mainly of what may still be described as of bourgeois habits and aspirations—hold fast to what is familiar. Thus the orchestral director, with his slender budget before him, is generally bound to focus attention on a relatively small number of box-office certainties. Too many orchestras, therefore, have been compelled to play too few works too often.[3] Modern, or otherwise unfamiliar, music is under-represented; partly on account of unfavourable audience reaction, partly on account of the expense and time incurred in adequate preparation.[4] The problem of keeping orchestral music on the highest level is acute and not to be solved by musicians alone.

Municipalities have their part to play. Most have been laggardly and few have acted with alacrity or enthusiasm on an Act of Parliament of 1948 which allowed for anything up to the proceeds of a 6d. rate to be devoted to cultural ends. The City of Liverpool, one of the leading

[1] Formed in 1921 by combining the Amalgamated Musicians' Union and the National Orchestral Union of Professional Musicians. There is a membership (1965) of 28,000 (of whom 7,000 are in London). The Musicians' Union is affiliated to the Trades Union Congress.

[2] Peter Heyworth, 'The Concert Crisis', *The Observer*, 10 November 1963.

[3] See 'London Concert Life Reconsidered', *The Times*, 15 November, 1963.

[4] At the Royal Festival Hall between September 1962 and July 1963 636 works were performed at 199 concerts. Of these works 58 were by contemporary foreign composers, 20 by British (Britten 12, Walton 5, Tippett 2, R. Simpson 1); *The Times*, 23 May 1964.

provincial cities, invests approximately ½d. rate in music: thus the Royal Liverpool Philharmonic Orchestra is allowed about £50,000 annually. In Amsterdam the comparable sum of subsidy is £172,000. To make order out of chaos is a gigantic task in a country where the principle of *laisser-faire* has nowhere been more tolerated than in respect of music. At the time of writing, however, the whole matter is at least under sympathetic review. The Minister responsible for culture (Miss Jennie Lee) is aware of the problem. The position of the major orchestras has been reviewed by the Arts Council under the guidance of Lord Goodman, the present Chairman.[1] Thus, in 1966 each of the four independent London symphony orchestras was to receive from the Government and the Greater London Council an annual grant of about £30,000, with an allowance of £1,200 for each approved London concert, while the Corporation of the City of London plans a new concert hall, to become the home of the London Symphony Orchestra. In addition to central and local government aid the major orchestras have also benefited from sometimes substantial grants from industry and commerce.

The principal London orchestras, in order of seniority, are the Royal Philharmonic, the London Symphony, the London Philharmonic and the (New) Philharmonia. That of the B.B.C. will be detailed under its parent body. The Royal Philharmonic Orchestra was re-formed in 1946 by Beecham who retained the conductorship until his death, when he was succeeded by Rudolf Kempe. The London Symphony Orchestra, a self-governing and co-operative institution, has developed a remarkable virtuosity in recent years and, in addition to its normal domestic routine, has played in many parts of the world. Threatened with disbandment in 1939, the London Philharmonic Orchestra also became a self-governing organisation. A long sequence of foreign guest-conductors enabled this orchestra to make a considerable contribution to the international character of London musical life, which was greatly enriched by the influx of refugee musicians of distinction both before and after the war. In 1949 Eduard van Beinum was principal conductor. A year later Sir Adrian Boult took over, and in 1958 he was followed by William Steinberg, who divided his time between the L.P.O. and the Pittsburgh Symphony Orchestra. In 1962 John Pritchard, formerly of the Liverpool Philharmonic Orchestra, became conductor, relinquishing the post in 1966. The Philharmonia Orchestra, dating from 1945, but subsequently reconstituted, was founded by Walter Legge. An offshoot of this orchestra is the

[1] See Nicholas Tomalin, 'How Jennie Lee fixed the arts pay-out', *The Sunday Times*, 20 February 1966. For a more or less detailed survey of the attitudes, activities, and expenditure of municipal bodies, see *The Sponsorship of Music; the Role of the Local Authorities* (V. Schur) P.E.P. pamphlet, 1967.

(New) Philharmonia Chorus, a highly efficient professional body that has given lustrous performances, particularly under Otto Klemperer and Carlo Maria Giulini.

There are major orchestras outside London. The Royal Liverpool Philharmonic Orchestra (the orchestra of the Philharmonic Society established in 1840) became fully permanent in 1942. Under John Pritchard's direction the orchestra boldly launched a series of contemporary programmes under the heading of 'Musica Viva', while further enterprise led to the inauguration of 'Industrial Concerts', for the benefit of office, shop, and factory workers. Although not able to re-enter its rebuilt home—the Free Trade Hall—until 1951 the Hallé Orchestra followed the example of Liverpool in 1943 and placed its members on a full-time basis. Since that time the conductor has been Sir John Barbirolli. The City of Birmingham Orchestra was reformed in 1944 under the direction of George Weldon. In 1951 Rudolf Schwarz became conductor, and after him came Panufnik, Boult, and Hugo Rignold. Through the Feeney Trust the C.B.S.O. has been able to commission works and among the beneficiaries are Bliss, Tippett, Rubbra, and Lennox Berkeley. Each of these orchestras, supported to a greater or lesser extent by guarantees or subsidies from neighbouring authorities, has served a regional function. None more so than the Bournemouth Symphony Orchestra, which, under the aegis of the Western Authorities Orchestral Association, has strengthened its foundations and been able to provide music for an otherwise undernourished part of the country. Since 1954, when the size of the orchestra was effectively increased, the direction has been in the hands of Charles Groves and then Constantin Silvestri. A Scottish Orchestra in one form or another has existed since 1874, but permanency was not established until 1950 when the Scottish National Orchestra was instituted, with Walter Susskind as conductor. In 1959 the conductorship passed into the hands of a Scotsman—Alexander Gibson, who also directs Scottish Opera.

The maintenance of these symphony orchestras (although a glance at the map will reveal too many considerable cities without such orchestras) represents a brave achievement, and their quality ensures for them at least respectful, and sometimes more, attention when they appear in London.

In Belfast, where ambitions for a new cultural centre are nursed, a small professional orchestra was recruited in 1966 to serve Northern Ireland, but the only well established permanent orchestra in Ireland is that of Radio Eireann in Dublin. The orchestra was formed in 1948, from a group of interned German musicians, since when it has included French, Italian, Jugoslav, Hungarian, Polish, and English players. Until 1967 the conductor was Tibor Paul, Hungarian by birth. 'With an enlightened and firm musical director . . . the prospect is one that Londoners may envy—a regular and balanced musical diet, co-ordinated on television, radio, and in the concert hall.'[1]

The activities of the symphony orchestra are in continuation of an established pattern. On the other hand, the chamber orchestra reflects new influences: reaction against mere size, and response to musicological research —especially in the field of the Baroque and Rococo.[2] One of the most interesting developments has been the inauguration (in 1958) of the Northern Sinfonia Orchestra, in Newcastle upon Tyne, which city thus renews something of the independence and vitality it possessed in the eighteenth century. The Northern Sinfonia, started on a modest scale by its first conductor, Michael Hall, and subsequently effectively protected by a Sinfonia Concert Society, was formed initially to fill the gap caused by the demise of the Yorkshire Symphony Orchestra (1947–55). The formation of a small ensemble was thus a matter of prudence, but across the years the virtues of modest proportions—in stimulating more variety in programme-making and in proving convenient for small halls in the region —have become apparent. The orchestra, doing for the towns of the north-east what the Bournemouth Orchestra does for the south-west, but similarly travelling further afield, has made a niche for itself. It has also been able to commission works (with aid from the Gulbenkian Foundation), some from local composers. In this manner one or more vigorous regions of England challenges metropolitan domination.[3]

In London numerous chamber orchestras were formed in the 1950's, mostly with the laudable intention of promoting the authentic interests of Bach, Handel, and Mozart, whose works were becoming increasingly available in more accurate editions. At one time there were no fewer than twenty-five chamber orchestras, mostly using the same group of players and performing after inadequate rehearsal. The most celebrated of the smaller ensembles was the Boyd Neel Orchestra[4] which in 1955 was renamed the Philomusica of London and directed by Thurston Dart, one of the more brilliant and active musicologists of the period. In 1948 Arnold Goldsborough established an ensemble which has been transformed into the English Chamber Orchestra. A third chamber orchestra

[1] 'The Spread of Symphonic Music in Ireland', *The Times*, 16 November 1962. The first performance by the Radio Eireann Symphony Orchestra outside Ireland was given in the Festival Hall, London, on 30 November 1966.

[2] In this context there should also be mentioned the Handel Opera Society (1955), which has given a new impetus to a fuller appreciation of Handel.

[3] For the year 1964–5 the Northern Sinfonia was allotted £29,000 by the North Eastern Association of the Arts.

[4] Boyd Neel (b. 1905) qualified as a doctor of medicine, but devoted himself to music after the formation of his orchestra in 1932.

that has survived is the London Mozart Players, founded by the violinist Harry Blech in 1949.

The case for the chamber orchestra is strong, but the fallacy that size and excellence are correlative is difficult to dislodge. Thus the larger organisations receive more generous treatment (although, as has been stated, not over-generous) than those that are smaller. In 1966, for example, the English Chamber Orchestra approached the Arts Council for a grant of £10,000. It was allowed £2,500 for a season of London concerts. Thus, behind the fine façade of British orchestral music there remain both unease and uncertainty.

Broadcasting and Festivals

Standing apart from the other orchestras is the B.B.C. Symphony Orchestra which, resting securely on the resources of the B.B.C., not only is free of financial concern but also in a position to offer superior conditions of service and in so doing to draw first-class players from other orchestras. The B.B.C. is, no doubt, the major force in British music today, and its powers of patronage are enormous. These powers and the authority they convey have greatly increased during the past decade. Apart from the normal run of symphony concerts given by the Symphony Orchestra and the regional orchestras maintained by the Corporation, almost the whole range of music (including that of the most recondite order) is exhibited, formerly through the 'Third Programme', now the 'Music Programme.' Both in performance and by the spoken word there is a firm liaison with musicology; thus it is that the 'ordinary listener' to whom Sir Walford Davies once appealed has no need to feel himself excluded from the more remote areas of music The benefit to the student at least is clear. Since 1959 the Controller of Music has been William Glock (b. 1908), whose influence has left no excuse for the British to feel out of touch with the contemporary situation in world music. Schoenberg, Webern, Berg, Bartók, and Stravinsky appear to be the established classics of the age; if Stockhausen, Boulez, Messiaen, and Nono do not become so it will not be due to any sins of omission on the part of the B.B.C. Though how long it will take to persuade musicians at large of their stature is not easy to estimate. To the British composer the blessings of the Corporation may not always seem apparent. Works have been and are commissioned with some frequency, but the selection of new indigenous music sometimes may seem to be arbitrary. From a study of all modern works played in 'serious' programmes it is difficult to notice any real consistency of critical standard. If the patron scores as many 'misses' as 'hits', it is, of course, an integral part of the general history of patronage. It is well to remember that no body, however august, is infallible; but monopoly tends to lead to an assumption of infallibility.

The complex network of public musical life is greatly affected by broadcasting. The Promenade Concerts are sponsored by the B.B.C. The major orchestras (though some have been spasmodically assisted by the Independent Television Companies) benefit in various ways. The principal festivals could not exist without the subventions drawn from transmissions. In addition to those festivals long established and those already named in this chapter attention should be drawn to the Cheltenham, Bath, Swansea, Oxford, York, and Durham Festivals, all enterprises of distinctive character which are of recent institution.

Musical Education

As much growth as has been recorded in the foregoing pages has resulted from a renovated attitude towards the arts in their social setting, a wider appreciation of native musical ability and receptivity, and a recognition of the value to the musical community both of immigrant talent and of newer European traditions. These latter, however, have been regarded on their intrinsic merits and not under the impression, that formerly bedevilled British musical life, that what was foreign was therefore necessarily superior. Such development as has taken place has furnished wider opportunity for musical careers and stimulated more young people to chase ambition and seriously to consider music as a career. In the past the profession in its higher reaches was approached by way of the cathedral choir school, and university, or school of music. For the most part the musical training given in choir schools was fundamental and thorough, and was begun at an early age. The church tradition of singing carried over into general education and, if it was more strongly felt in the 'public schools' (many of them with strong religious connections), it had its effect also in schools in general. 'Cathedral tone' may still be experienced in the sometimes over-refined quality of vocal colour produced at a state school assembly. When this is experienced it will normally be found to be the result of extra-curricular effort. This brings us to the particular problem of music in modern British education—of which the whole pattern is in any case in a state of almost continual change. Being in a state of change the demand on the public purse is insatiable—and music falls well behind in any order of priorities.

It is axiomatic that, for executant careers in music, early and specialised training is essential. The ideal has been achieved perhaps in Hungary where the inauguration of specially geared primary and secondary schools under the inspiration of Zoltán Kodály (whose interest in musical education was much stimulated by the singing of English children) gives adequate opportunity for the gifted children to make full use of their talents.[1] In Britain it is still a matter of chance, of dependence on external assistance, of willingness often to persist against the demands of the regular educational system.[2] In spite of much lip-service to its virtues, music in the school has either been regarded as a recreational side-issue, which has led to a broad expansion of instrumental music-making out of school hours where the teacher (specialist or, more probably, non-specialist) has enthusiasm and willingness to sacrifice private time, or as an area for narrowly academic exploitation. In the first case the prior claims of 'essential' subjects have made the teaching of music irregular and unco-ordinated, and it would be over-sanguine to suppose that more than a very small minority leave school musically literate. In the second, conveniences of staffing and time-table, and the tendency to justify effort by acceptable results have put young people in their lively teens into the straight-jacket of syllabuses that are often remote both from practice and from current musical affairs.

Since the Second World War most local Education Authorities have appointed Music Organisers, and a number have provided groups of peripatetic instrumental teachers. There is also frequent provision of children's concerts, and of vacation courses. In a number of towns and counties the existence of a schools and/or a youth orchestra indicates the manner in which instrumental music has made up lost ground in the broad field of educational and amateur musical endeavour. The crowning achievement in this province was the National Youth Orchestra, founded in 1947 by Ruth Railton, which, drawing candidates from all parts of the country, rapidly became an outstandingly exciting prospect and a fine advertisement for the national musical tradition, and the capacity of young British instrumentalists. Lacking official support (the orchestra was assisted by the *Daily Mirror* group of newspapers and private subscribers), the National Youth Orchestra folded up after a European tour in the autumn of 1965. Dr. Railton, who retired at that point, observed that an annual grant of £20,000 would be necessary for administration of the

[1] The Yehudi Menuhin School (founded 1963) at Stoke D'Abernon, Surrey, is the only institution of similar character in Britain; and this is a private enterprise. In a very few cases pupils at this school (where the fees are necessarily high) are assisted by Local Authorities.

[2] In London, however, there are 300 places available for pupils between the ages of eleven and sixteen at the principal schools of music. Such pupils attend for free tuition on Saturday mornings; while some ten other Authorities in the country have comparable schemes.

orchestra and the allied National Junior Music School. In July 1966, however, it was announced that the National Youth Orchestra would recommence activities, under the joint direction of Miss Ivey Dickson and Mr. Maurice Jacobson. The National Youth Orchestra of Wales, founded in 1945, has been fortunate in that it has proceeded across the years under the protection first of the Monmouthshire Education Committee and, since 1952, of the Welsh Joint Education Committee. Until 1966, when he was succeeded by Arthur Davison, the orchestra was conducted by Clarence Raybould.

The utilitarian concept that prevails on the official level (and this, expressed through controlling committees, fairly reflects a general national attitude) means that those young musicians who intend making music their career are strongly influenced towards teaching. In most cases, students, who depend on grants from their authorities, are required to qualify not only in music but in a reasonably broad range of other disciplines (General Certificate of Education, 'Ordinary' and 'Advanced'). This again militates against the full development of a special talent, say, in instrumental music, or in composition. The schools of music, therefore, spend much time on pedagogy which may or may not be relevant to the particular student's needs and real aptitudes. In the year 1963–4 out of 753 students at the Royal Academy of Music 379 followed the normal curriculum, while 271 were engaged on teaching courses; at the Royal College of Music the corresponding figures were 673, 400, and 198. At two important regional schools the stress on teaching was even stronger: at the Royal Manchester College of Music, out of 401 students 315 were following the teaching courses, and at the Royal Scottish Academy 144 out of 195 were similarly involved.[1] So far as the schools of music are concerned the relative financial situation is not greatly improved since the time when Lord Burghersh supplicated for Government subvention. 'In 1964–5 the Royal Academy of Music received a Treasury grant of £23,250, the Royal College of Music £17,500, and the Royal Manchester College of Music £17,000. The Department of Education and Science gave the Royal College of Art more than six times as much as the *total* for those three Colleges, £368,000.'[2] It is remarkable then that the Royal Scottish Academy receives £74,000 from the Scottish Board of Education.

By the side of the schools of music[3] are Colleges of Education (specifically for the training of teachers), some of which have special courses in music of a more or less advanced nature, and the Universities. Some

[1] *Gulbenkian Report, Making Musicians,* quoted in *Where,* March 1966, p. 12.

[2] ib. p. 12, cf. p. 495 fn. 1.

[3] Additional to those named are the Guildhall School, Trinity College (see p. 495), London College, Northern School (Manchester), Birmingham School, and Cardiff College of Music. The last, like the Guildhall School, is also a College of Drama.

universities (Keele, Sussex, East Anglia, for example) maintain Directors of Music for the laudable purpose of providing a cultural amenity. The majority, however, now have departments under the direction of a Professor, and there has been a general overhaul of curricula. The new discipline is musicology, and rigorous development of the principles laid down in the first place by Edward Dent at Cambridge has produced a small, but formidable and well-equipped, army of musicologists. It is the distinctive feature of the music studies of a British University, however, that theory and practice—the latter often cultivated according to tradition less formally—are conjoined. In many cases executant musicians of high calibre have been attached to university departments, and the programmes of contemporary university musical societies are of increasing significance. Especially, as at the Barber Institute in the University of Birmingham, in respect of the revival of Handel operas, in the resurrection of forgotten masterpieces. 'The aim of a University music department', writes Wilfrid Mellers, Professor at York,[1] 'should surely be to achieve a sensitive equilibrium between the objective historical study which is an inevitable consequence of the museum culture we live in, and that creative exploration which alone can preserve, and renew, our musicianship.' Since university departments enjoy a considerable freedom in academic matters, there is room for experiment. So it is that at York a refreshing realism prevails—'Awareness of the present in relationship to the past also implies, in the polyglot culture in which we live, a breaking down of barriers between the *genres*. Music, in the modern world, has sundry connotations; so our course for teachers already includes, in synthesis with the normal historical studies, consideration of the world of folk music, jazz and pop. This we explore not as a *pis aller* that might be exploited in schools that couldn't take serious music, but as a valid manifestation of our time, existing—no less than art music—at many levels of value and authenticity.'[2]

Trends in Musical Thought and Behaviour

According to temperament it is either exhilarating or depressing to live through any sort of revolution. It is clear that the changes which have affected British music in all its aspects during the past two decades, and those which continue to affect it, constitute the most drastic process through which it has ever passed. If the revolution thus engendered can

[1] 'Music at a University', *Where*, March 1966, p. 13.

[2] loc. cit. Some part of this philosophy carries on ideas enunciated by Matyas Seiber, thirty years earlier. Seiber, a perceptive student of jazz techniques, essayed to establish classes in them at Frankfurt, wherefore he fell foul of the authorities.

hardly be said to be imperceptible, it has taken place without bloodshed, and, this being the case, it is sometimes ignored. Some factors, however, cannot be ignored.

For the first time in history it is possible for a composer to have a nation-wide audience. Not, in fact, through the concert programme nor the regular medium of broadcasting, but through the sound-track of feature, documentary, fictional, or commercial film. In the eighteenth century the 'serious' composer wrote without self-consciousness for the Gardens. The wheel has come back almost to the same point: background music has significance. How much significance depends on circumstance and the individual composer's insight. Certainly he must rub out the frontier between the genres. For part of the revolution is the at least partially successful attack on hitherto accepted standards by a wide variety of popular music. After walking behind the American masters of jazz (and allied music) for many years the British (more particularly the English) have developed their own idioms in timbre, rhythm, and, latterly, melody. Such names as those of Humphrey Lyttleton, Chris Barber, John Dankworth, Cleo Laine, Acker Bilk, the Beatles, even now seem assured of some claim on immortality. Such musicians—and they cover a fairly wide field—having responded to a wind of change in social mores, have taken advantage of what the age has to offer to creative minds and have enjoyed an unprecedented mass approbation and acclaim. What is more, they have caught the attention of the serious critic—it is well-known that *The Times* discovered Mahlerian antecedents in the art of the Beatles. Popular music—whether it is liked or not is immaterial—is a vital part of contemporary musical experience. It was so in former times—but the estrangement that took place in the nineteenth century has taken some time to get over. Thus the right and left wings of music-lovers and musicians have their suspicions of each other. Those below the age of, say, twenty-five happily carry few animosities—living experience matters more than a prestigious 'culture'.

Conservative music-teaching, which prevailed in Britain and still is not a negligible factor, was conservative in more ways than one. It resulted in maintenance of the reputation of the classics (in the broad sense) to the disadvantage of non-classics—whether ancient or modern. It resisted technical innovation. It bred a too great reverence for the written symbol, and for formalism. Altogether it insisted that music was a mystery, to be 'understood' by the initiate or the elect. Thus one easily saw a deep cleavage of interest that was not without its social connotations and caused much travail in the minds of school-teachers. The ideal of one people, one music, which was the first reaction against separatism, is no longer acceptable dogma. The vigour of present musical life in Britain derives from a respect for group interests. Thus on the fringes are enthusiasts for medieval music on the one hand, and for intellectualised 'pop' on the other. The composer aware of specialised interests takes advantage of them. Thus, in a highly profitable area for development, music for children and for schools is at the beginning of a new deal. Creativity belongs to the composer; but also to the performer. We therefore find an increasing amount of music of various kinds which depends for its completion on the creative talent of the intended performer or performers. Extemporisation is back in fashion, and for this a line of popular musicians is to be thanked. Folk-music is also in fashion—not on account of any abstract virtues that it might contain, nor of its historicity, but because it is instinct with a sense of freedom, of rebellion, and because it has a sort of realism that consorts with contemporary permissiveness. Whether in America or Britain, the folk-tune, or the ballad, has returned to the armament of political protest.

The quality of the music of any period is at least superficially marked by the relevance of the music to the general situation, or some part of it. This is recognised by the necessarily imprecise categorisation of works into Renaissance, Baroque, Rococo, Romantic, and so on. The failure of many creative musicians in Britain—their culpability is lessened by the cultural pressures put on them by a clientèle in search of escape routes—for a long period lay in selling the pass. Coming to terms with modern times has been (and is) a painful operation. But the very disparateness of composers born in the twentieth century is an indication of new and independent attitudes. Since reputations fluctuate it is not proposed here to attempt appraisal of composers below the age of fifty: partly because any kind of objectivity becomes impossible; partly because any omission (according to the scale of this book a degree of selectivity has necessarily prevailed throughout) would appear invidious; and partly because it takes time for a composer to be accepted or rejected by the society—excluding both colleagues or critics—to which he belongs. Those composers who have reached the age of fifty in any case represent a wide cross-section of thought, and of influence, and illustrate the consequences of the moods and movements shown and inaugurated by such older masters as Elgar, Vaughan Williams, and Holst, as well as of other trends.

Composers

Part of the process of modernisation of British music has been in coming to terms with Europe—for once it may here be observed that musical practice has been in advance of social and political acceptance of the inevitable, for there are few contemporary composers who have not drawn on continental experience. The opportunity to discover at first hand what was happening in central Europe came with the influx of refugee musicians during the 1930's. Egon Wellesz (b. 1885) left Austria in 1938 and was given a research fellowship by the University of Oxford of which he was already an honorary Doctor. He has remained in Britain since that time. Roberto Gerhard (b. 1896) came to England after the fall of the Spanish Republic and in 1939 was awarded a research fellowship at Cambridge. Matyas Seiber (1904–60), Hungarian by birth but mainly active in Germany in the inter-war period, also found it expedient to emigrate; having arrived in London he taught at Morley College and later at the Guildhall School of Music. All these composers have done much to widen the horizon of the British-born composer, and not only through varied demonstration of Schoenbergian concepts. Wellesz is both composer and musicologist. As the latter, his work has been principally in the fields of Byzantine music and of seventeenth-century opera. The study of the former made it inevitable that as a composer he should see European music against a wider background, and this capacity, communicated to pupils and subsequently meeting with a similar extension of interest on the part of other European musicians, has helped to add new areas for exploration to the composer's enterprise. Wellesz brought to England the classical tradition of Vienna and his own early works were imbued with the feeling of Mahler—who has lately become a strong influence in English musical affairs. As a fellow pupil of Schoenberg, together with Webern and Berg, Wellesz was able to communicate the principles of the fundamental theory of 'modern music'. He did not, however, remain a dodecaphonist and in his later phases of composition renewed the romanticism of former times though without loss of intellectual virtue. Although Wellesz's compositions belong to the German and Austrian repertoire, his eightieth birthday sent a rush of blood to the English musical head and a performance of his Fifth Symphony by the City of Birmingham Orchestra on 21 October 1965 demonstrated both the individuality and the power of this musician and scholar.

Originally a pupil both of Granados and Pedrell, Gerhard also went to study with Schoenberg, with whom he remained for five years. A Spanish brilliance and vivacity proved ineradicable and Gerhard, although finding the disciplines of dodecaphony helpful not only to an organisation but also to expression, made himself the master rather than the slave of the techniques acquired. He was also a scholar and made a substantial contribution to knowledge of eighteenth-century Spanish—especially Catalan—music. After long years of residence in the country Gerhard considers himself an Englishman and as a composer has added to the diversity of the contemporary repertoire by works ranging from symphony and concerto to ballet and opera. Of particular interest and distinction in the *Concerto for Orchestra* (1966), a work, fascinating in its sonorities, in which team-work is extolled by treating the whole, virtuoso, orchestra as solo instrument. Seiber, teacher and conductor as well as composer, displayed an enviable versatility. A pupil of Kodály in Budapest, he founded his style on the idioms of the new Hungarian school, but added to it other elements, from Asiatic folk-music, from the twelve-note technique, from jazz. Seiber's major English work was his cantata *Ulysses* (1946–7), based on passages from the book by James Joyce. In this work his eclecticism is readily apparent; for traditional vocal formulae and such Baroque patterns as passacaglia are fused into dodecaphonic structures.

While at the present time Schoenbergian method stands in the background and not the foreground of musical techniques, it was adopted in Britain with reluctance and against a characteristic scepticism. In fact the three composers above-mentioned demonstrated that, as it was not an end in itself, dodecaphony called for no total surrender on the part of the composer. Most composers now of middle age (Britten not excluded) have noted the principles but few have driven it to a logical conclusion. Among those who have is Elisabeth Lutyens (b. 1906), whose strong sense of definition and economy has led her to the composition of small-scale chamber music, often intriguing by reason of unusual effects of colour, that is sometimes of Webernesque quality. Lutyens, like Lennox Berkeley, spent some part of her formative years in Paris; and the influence of Debussy is not entirely covered up by serial processes.[1] In a setting of aphorisms by the philosopher Wittgenstein (1954), Lutyens runs up a Schoenbergian banner at the masthead and, by 'unvocal' writing, challenges the most sacred tenets of classical English music: that it should have an intrinsically vocal character. For stronger draughts of dodecaphony one turns to Humphrey Searle (b. 1915), a pupil of Webern, who, however, derives a certain robustness from his special study of the music of Liszt. Inevitably, for reasons already made apparent, a composer with Searle's outlook does not readily find a regular place in the normal repertoire so that his influence is restricted. Even so, he crossed one bridge successfully; by showing that by consistently embracing a twentieth-century style an English composer was not of necessity obliged to lose his soul. Among the more clearly accessible works of Searle are the three pieces for speakers, men's chorus (in the first and third), and orchestra: *Gold Coast Customs* (E. Sitwell), *The Riverrun* (J. Joyce), and *The Shadow of Cain* (E. Sitwell). Evocative, colourful, and alive to textural subtleties, these works effectively extend the local tradition of words and music.

[1] See Robert Henderson, 'Elisabeth Lutyens', *Mus. T.*, August 1963, pp. 551–5.

If Lutyens and Searle represent a deviation from the English norm in one direction, then so does Alan Bush (b. 1900) in another. A committed Marxist, Bush, who like Searle was once a pupil of John Ireland, succeeded Rutland Boughton in 1929 as conductor of the London Labour Choral Union and in 1936 founded the Workers' Music Association. Through this body—by means of week-end and summer courses—he has directed the idealism of Holst and Vaughan Williams towards the working classes with a measured determination that has been proof against a fair amount of censorious observation. Between the wars Bush's music became strongly influenced by European styles and his *Dialectic* for string quartet (1929),[1] a lucid musical argument following the principle of his own 'thematic' method, which, in turn, had affinities with dodecaphony insofar as each individual note carried its own structural significance, was regarded as a landmark in English chamber music. In later years Bush's attempt to simplify his style in line with the *Realismus* practised by composers such as Eisler, Dessau, and Meyer, has resulted in the triteness that is apparent, for instance, in his programmatic *Byron Symphony*, or, on the other hand, the austerity that distinguishes the fine *Passacaglia and Fugue* for orchestra. If political opinions have dictated Bush's choice of subjects for opera, they have also led to a refreshing purposefulness and drive in this field. *Wat Tyler* was a prizewinning entry for the competition organised by the Arts Council for the Festival of Britain. Both this and *Men of Blackmoor* have been successfully produced in eastern Germany.[2]

Bush's melodic fluency unmistakably stems from his Englishness: some antecedents are inescapable unless (as in the case of the dodecaphonic neophyte) rejection is absolute. With Gerald Finzi and Edmund Rubbra, both born in 1901, there is no attempt to move far from the central, conservative tradition. Consequently both limit themselves in substance, in form, and—in an age that demands change—in accessibility. Neither composer remains quite free of the urbane academicism that marks much twentieth-century British music by composers of competence rather than distinction. Finzi (who died in 1956) was primarily a vocal composer, sensitive to the shape and the outer patterning of words but lacking a profound sense of conviction. A cultured style, related to both Elgar and Vaughan Williams in harmonic grouping and melodic contour, is admirable for the middle reaches of lyrical verse. Of Finzi's songs the best are contained in his two cycles of settings of Thomas Hardy, while the cantata *Dies Natalis*—the words by Thomas Traherne—which is laid out for high voice and strings, shows his skill in carrying ideas from the voice

[1] Played at the I.S.C.M. Festival, Prague, in 1935.

[2] See Hugh Ottaway, 'Alan Bush's "Wat Tyler",' *Mus. T.*, December 1956, pp. 633–4; also Anthony Payne, 'Alan Bush', *Mus. T.*, April 1964, pp. 263–5.

is to a well integrated accompanying instrumental texture. A measure of the full talent that never entirely emerged is to be found in the posthumously published Cello Concerto, where Finzi eloquently came to terms with instrumental music, but without loss of the lyrical impulse that dominated his life. At best Finzi ranks among the minor composers. In the long run no doubt so too will Rubbra, but at one point it seemed that he was likely to be set higher. Having left school at the age of fourteen, he worked for some years as a railway clerk. Encouraged by Cyril Scott and enabled by a scholarship to become a student at Reading University, he came under the influence of Holst, of R. O. Morris,[1] and of Vaughan Williams. A strong feeling for expression through contrapuntal means developed. Rubbra's major works, whether vocal or instrumental, emerge as well-wrought essays in what appears as a neo-Romantic vein, but, as is the case with Finzi, on the whole lacking in tension. Neither rhythmically nor harmonically does Rubbra venture far enough afield, either convincingly to establish his own identity or to compel an inattentive ear.[2] An extensive output includes seven symphonies (of which the fifth is best known), concertos, chamber music (in which some of Rubbra's best work is to be found), and vocal works. The latter include a number of settings of the Mass for liturgical use, and a sense of Catholic mysticism tends to pervade other works, including the symphonies. With Finzi and Rubbra one is aware of a certain self-conscious dedication to style. In the case of Lennox Berkeley (b. 1902) there is, on the other hand, a complete sense of assurance in this respect. Partly French by origin, Berkeley lived for a time as a young man in Paris. He was helped by Ravel and was a pupil of Nadia Boulanger—a teacher with a world-wide influence—and his music has consistently demonstrated qualities that might be considered as French rather than English. It is conceivable that Berkeley has never written a piece of music that is infelicitous: his sense of balance and design is keen, his competence in conditioning idea to medium is never in doubt, and his argument is polished and logical. The classical poise of Berkeley's music gives, on the one hand, an aristocratic quality, appreciable particularly in such works as the *Diversions for Eight Instruments* and other chamber music of beguiling refinement, and, on the other, an incisiveness of utterance that in certain works reveals a rare poignancy. This shows in the *Four Poems of St. Teresa of Avila*, for contralto (Kathleen Ferrier, in the first

[1] 1886–1948; Morris, a professor of counterpoint and composition at the Royal College of Music, was one of the best teachers of his generation. An authority on sixteenth-century techniques, his responsibility for certain aspects of modern English style was considerable. See Edmund Rubbra, 'R. O. Morris: An Appreciation', *M. & L.*, 30, no. 2, 1949, p. 107.

[2] As corrective to this generalisation see Elsie Payne, 'Edmund Rubbra', *M. & L.*, 36, no. 4, 1955, pp. 341–56.

instance) and strings, and in a terse *Stabat Mater* composed for the English Opera Group in 1946. The professionalism of Berkeley's music, his aptitude for handling small ensembles without any apparent sense of restriction, and an innately musicianly quality show an affinity with Britten.[1]

William Walton, born in the same year as Berkeley, has genius where many others have talent; and three or four of his works must be placed among the classics of English music. One qualification for this selection must be originality: a classical work says something quite independent from other works in the same genre. A further qualification is durability. Among oratorios *Belshazzar's Feast* (Leeds Festival, 1931) is an undisputed masterpiece, containing an appreciation of the barbaric and mystical elements in the text (written by Sir Osbert Sitwell) within an unmistakably contemporary and sharply dissonantal idiom. At the same time the chorus is accommodated with scoring that is not only evocative but also practicable. The vividness of Walton's style and the uninhibited directness of his utterance distinguish his major orchestral works, among which the Viola Concerto (1929) and the first Symphony (1934) still hold their place. These works are landmarks not only on account of their intrinsic excellence and vitality but also because they reveal a musical personality for whom no kind of stylistic interpretation is necessary. *Façade* (1922), 'an entertainment for speaking-voice and six instruments', witty and satirical, was also a landmark, for it was a major factor in releasing English music from the burden of respectability.

Born at Oldham, in Lancashire, Walton became a choir-boy at Christ Church, Oxford, where his formative years were spent as schoolboy and as undergraduate. For practical purposes, Walton, although nurtured in a musical climate, was self-taught. This enabled him to develop in independence, but independence was kept from irresponsibility by a determined and acute gift of self-criticism. Being self-critical, Walton has written with deliberation and for a major composer his list of works is relatively modest. His reputation was established early, and from the happy accident of quick recognition less happy consequences have flowed. Because Walton, preferring to explore the rich possibilities of his early established but highly distinctive style rather than to 'move on' across the gamut of other styles since fashionable, has been obstinate in adhering to his own musical principles he has of recent years been tucked away as a reactionary. This attitude ignores the quality of his music, which, never lacking interest in texture, design, and vocabulary, is rarely other than self-evident. Thus Walton, to whom also an Elgarian panache is attributable, is always audience-worthy. To have reached this point without

1 See Peter Dickinson, 'The Music of Lennox Berkeley', *Mus. T.*, May 1963, pp. 327–30.

sacrificing musical and intellectual integrity is a considerable achievement; especially, for reasons stated at various times, for an English composer. Distinguishable in the first place by the nervous energy of sharp-edged rhythmic and melodic contours, Walton yet has a strong lyrical instinct, which has increased rather than decreased with the passage of time (as shown by the Violin and Cello Concertos and the opera *Troilus and Cressida*). His occasional music, whether for film or public occasion, synthesises the extremes with a resultant warmth and enthusiasm. In no sense consciously borrowing from the antique glories Walton nonetheless sounds a kind of Purcellian aptness in his Coronation pieces, his film music (in particular, *Henry V*), and the splendid *Gloria* with which he celebrated the 125th anniversary of the Huddersfield Choral Society. Apart from its intrinsic merits, Walton's music, being instrumental for the most part, has encouraged the English composer to feel less obliged than formerly to do the conventional stint of music for voices, and, while Walton can hardly be adduced as an 'influence' (for which text-book writers are always seeking), his example has been an incentive. A composer whose development is in some ways similar to Walton's is Alan Rawsthorne (b. 1905).

Rawsthorne, a native of Haslingden, in Lancashire, was trained to be a dental surgeon and only took up serious musical study—at the Manchester Royal College of Music—at the age of twenty-one. After a course in Manchester he became a pianoforte pupil of Egon Petri, and the value of this teaching is reflected in the masterly way in which he handles the piano in his compositions, among which a few miniatures for piano are as distinguished as any British pieces for the instrument. It was in 1939 that Rawsthorne appeared as a figure of some national significance, for in that year his *Symphonic Studies* for orchestra were highly praised when performed at the I.S.C.M. Festival at Warsaw. This work—a set of five variations, a form which Rawsthorne like other English composers uses expertly, written round a central theme—sounds to have been conceived directly for orchestra. Like Walton, Rawsthorne has this gift, formerly rather exceptional among English composers, of using instrumental sonorities with conviction and versatility. There are other affinities with Walton (to whom Rawsthorne dedicated his first Violin Concerto)—a freely tonal vocabulary that looks more atonal than it sounds, with an abundance of well-calculated dissonance; a certainty in handling large designs in musical architecture that shows in a line of finely structured 'abstract' works; a talent for meeting an audience more than halfway (Rawsthorne's spontaneity in the 'Street Corner' overture and the second Piano Concerto is infectious); and a passionate feeling that is, for example, allowed full expression in the choral suite, *Carmen Vitale* (1963). In this work, the composer comes to terms with the inherited tradition, but broadens it by pushing back, through the text and by means of melismatic vocal passages, to the Middle Ages, and by employing also those Baroque formulae which are frequent in his instrumental works (for example, the Chaconne of the first Piano Concerto, the Sarabande of the third Symphony,[1] and a general frequency of contrapuntal development). Rawsthorne has, so to speak, developed into English music, supplying it with a sense of security, a feeling of purposeful energy, a judicious but not unrelieved seriousness, and an accumulation of original statements that are both thought-provoking and comprehensible. In attitude and invention, but not by any direct references, Rawsthorne is characteristically English if not indeed Lancastrian—but his music stands up well and unapologetically in a more cosmopolitan setting. His whole achievement is brilliantly summarised by a young Welsh composer, Alun Hoddinott (b. 1929), who after justly praising Rawsthorne's mastery of material observes: 'Many composers today are so preoccupied with the search for new and startling textures, that they forget to put the music in.'[2]

If Hindemith (for whom Walton's Viola Concerto was written) may be felt to have left ideas which were occasionally scrutinised and remembered by Rawsthorne, this is hardly surprising. For his music and his teaching were welcomed by many British musicians during the period between the wars. An acknowledgment of his standing in England is given by Walton in his *Variations on a Theme by Hindemith.* Of Hindemith's pupils Arnold Cooke (b. 1906), who was fortified by the teaching of the Music School at Cambridge before going to Berlin for three years in 1929, is the most familiar. Cooke's undoubted capacity for intelligent musical disquisition is, however, somewhat hampered by tendencies towards introversion, with the result that his works gain respect rather than affection. His ideas have effectively found expression in chamber works, of which the Clarinet Quintet commissioned for the 1962 Festival of the City of London deserves notice, first because of its display of characteristic qualities in lighter mood, second because it supplements a none too well-stocked repertoire for this particular combination.

It is probably an overstatement to say that more chamber music has been composed in Britain within the last twenty years than in the whole intervening period since the seventeenth century. But the fact of a new-found enthusiasm on the part of composers for the medium is indisputable. Partly it stems from reaction against inflation, partly from a rejection

[1] Cheltenham Festival, 1964: of recent years Rawsthorne's works have been conspicuous at this festival.

[2] 'Rawsthorne at Sixty', *Mus. T.*, May 1965, pp. 346–7. For an earlier perceptive and generous note by a fellow-composer see Herbert Howells, 'Note on Alan Rawsthorne', *M. & L.*, 32, no. 1, 1951, pp. 19–28.

of programmatic concepts in favour of abstraction, and partly from the fact that on a high professional level there are more performers available than formerly. Opportunities for performance, however, are largely confined to broadcast and festival recitals—the chamber music recital as such is a rarity, and amateur performance is for the most part sensibly restricted to what is viable. Two composers of the generation of Rawsthorne and Cooke with a special stake in chamber music are Benjamin Frankel (b. 1906) and Elizabeth Maconchy (b. 1907). The former is a characteristic and highly professional representative composer, and one of the most versatile and engaging. His chamber works include four string quartets, two string trios, a trio for clarinet, cello and piano, a clarinet quintet, and an unaccompanied sonata for violin. This music, lyrical in character and often marked by a nostalgia that is akin to a frequent mood of Bloch, harmonically motivated by responses to vertical organisation often similar to those of Rawsthorne, but latterly moving to the ambit of dodecaphony, is accomplished and precise in execution. An admirable example of Frankel's refinement is the set of *Bagatelles* (op. 35) for eleven instruments. Insistence on precision is itself a reflection of a more sophisticated, more professional attitude within British music. Frankel's excellence of craftsmanship is rooted in a wealth of practical experience. As a young man he earned his living in the field of light music; in nigh-clubs and cafés, and as arranger of scores for musical comedies and revues. From this came commissions to compose film music. For more than thirty years Frankel has written scores for films, among which are such classics as *The Seventh Veil*, *The Importance of being Earnest*, and *The Deep Blue Sea*. It is doubtful whether any other composer in England has made more effective use of this medium to enlarge the general experience. The captive audience listens to (or hears) the music of Frankel not ungratefully, and then discovers that what it has taken in is 'modern music'. Elizabeth Maconchy, whose style carries echoes of Vaughan Williams and Bartók, is a relentless composer, dedicated to the matter in hand and impatient of irrelevance. A hardness of line and astringently diatonic counterpoint shows a toughness of fibre that demands close attention, which may be rewarded by glimpses of determined musical excavation. Maconchy is modern to this extent; that she can make an unpromising handful of generating notes go a long way. Her output includes seven string quartets, and a good deal of other chamber music. Her single-mindedness is given in her own words: 'The great thing is for the composer to keep his head and allow nothing to distract him. The temptations to stop by the way and to be side-tracked by felicities of sound and colour are ever present, but in my view everything extraneous to the pursuit of [the] central idea must be rigorously excluded—scrapped'.[1]

[1] Quoted in Anne MacNaghten, 'Elizabeth Maconchy', *Mus. T.*, June 1955, pp. 298–302.

Single-mindedness of a somewhat different kind distinguishes Michael Tippett (b. 1905), who has become a central figure in contemporary English music. Tippett's music, not to be linked to this school or that, has a comprehensiveness that takes in a large part of the extended English tradition that has lately become accessible and also reaches out to the European tradition. With strongly marked philosophical, psychological, and social preoccupations, Tippett precipitates into the music of the age a powerful, moving humanism. This was first revealed to the public by his most famous work, the oratorio *A Child of our Time*. Together with humanism is also to be found a marked mystical urge, to be appreciated in the subjects, the sonorities, and the designs of *The Midsummer Marriage*, *King Priam*, and *The Vision of St. Augustine* (1966). Across the years Tippett has sought for a reconciliation between idealism and pragmatism, and for a style which is capable of conveying his ideas to a public that at first, at least, was largely indifferent. One of the fascinating aspects of Tippett, the composer, is the manner in which he has drawn more and more on the wider field of musical experience as his works have become established apparently as a vital part of the tradition. As his references have multiplied, however, the personality of the music has remained constant, and recognisable; thus development has been organic. There is about Tippett something of the vatic quality of Beethoven, the result of intellectual and emotional effort, of deep probing into human motivation, and a continual search for a valid and conclusive means of expression.[1]

Of Cornish stock, Tippett was born in London and educated at Stamford, in Lincolnshire, and at the Royal College of Music. Here he was taught by R. O. Morris. The influence of the sixteenth century is strong in Tippett, not only because the techniques were communicated to him by an expert tutor but because the kind of the music overlapped his own concepts. As a teacher, whether in the classroom, through radio or television, or by means of the written word, Tippett is inspiring. It is the conviction that inspires, and so it was at Morley College where he inherited the mantle of Holst, whose work he continued in the spirit in which it was started. Rather slow to develop his own creative talents, it was not until the late 1930's that he began to be appreciated as a composer. Among the early works were a choral and orchestral setting of William

[1] Cf.: 'Tippett [String Quartet, no. 3] seems to have been influenced by Beethoven's C major Quartet, Op. 59, No. 3', Colin Mason, *Cobbett's Cyclopedic Survey of Chamber Music*, 2nd edn., 1963, vol. III, p. 101; 'Perhaps Tippett's intentions [in first part of the cantata] are here similar to those of Beethoven in the finale of the Choral Symphony', and 'The climax of Alleluias in this second part . . . recalls not only the March Section in Beethoven's *Ode to Joy* but a passage in *The Midsummer Marriage* which might almost be a conscious allusion to Beethoven', Tim Souster, 'Michael Tippett's "Vision" ', *Mus. T.*, January 1966, pp. 20–22.

Blake's *A Song of Liberty* (1937), the first of three string quartets (1935, rev. 1943), and a Concerto for Double String Orchestra (1939). Before the war, the fundamental nature of Tippett's style was clear. There were strong diatonic elements; melodic gestures that were connected with but not derived from folk-song; a striking subtlety in rhythmic invention and development, originating somewhat in the polyrhythmic freedom of the English sixteenth- and seventeenth-century schools;[1] a spacious expansion of idea through polyphony. The expressive power of Tippett's counterpoint is especially to be appreciated in the fugues of the second and third string quartets (1942, 1946), while the finale of the sonata for four horns (composed for Dennis Brain in 1955) is also fugal. It will be discovered that polyphony—derived as in the case of Tippett from English antecedents—provides common ground for a number of contemporary British composers, and the manner in which it is handled tends to show something that is inherent in the national tradition. In the case of Tippett's earlier works the proximity of vocal to instrumental music enhances this indigenous quality, but rhythmic freedom and frequent employment of melismata in melodic outline added spontaneity and freshness.

As with Vaughan Williams, and less obtrusively with Holst, there is a strong moral undertone to Tippett's music. Most clearly this appears in *A Child of our Time*, of which the focus of musical and spiritual interest is a sequence of negro spirituals. A compassionate work, a kind of ethical cantata, *A Child of our Time* is as direct as *The Midsummer Marriage* is complex and difficult to penetrate.[2] This opera suffers from a libretto, full of mythological and symbolic allusions, that is hardly likely to prove congenial to the British public; yet the music, of which the *Ritual Dances* are familiar as concert items, shows Tippett at the height of his powers. Here, as in the Symphony of 1945, he shows how polyphonic method is extended to orchestration.

The mystical element in Tippett has released a visionary and distinctive style of instrumentation that has grown increasingly 'magical' and exotic through *The Midsummer Marriage*, the Second Symphony (1956–7), *King Priam*, and the Concerto for Orchestra (1963) to *The Vision of St. Augustine*. In this work Tippett adds to the apparatus of melody wordless vocal elaborations taken over from medieval practice, while his orchestration carries still further the principle of dramatic contrast of sonorities.

[1] See composer's note in score of String Quartet No. 2 where he refers to a rhythmic derivation 'from Madrigal technique where each part may have its own rhythm and the music is propelled by the differing accents, which tend to thrust each other forward. The bar-lines are thus sometimes only an arbitrary division of time, and the proper rhythms are shown in the notation by the groupings of the notes and by the bowing'.

[2] See A. E. F. Dickinson, 'Round about "The Midsummer Marriage" ', *M. & L.*, 37, no. 1, 1956, pp. 50–60.

In the end he exemplifies modern man's search for some truth other than that revealed by theology on the one hand, or by scientific processes on the other. He 'reveals the nature of a mystic's striving for a "beyond" in music which distils a generalised emotion from a particular set of ideas'.[1]

The progress of Tippett, by way of often indifferent first performances of major works and across the impediments of opaque operatic libretti, has been slow and deliberate.[2] This is in contrast to the brilliant career of Benjamin Britten (b. 1913).

For practical purposes Benjamin Britten, so far as the world is concerned, is English music. It is certain that no other English composer at any time has so effectively conquered prejudice and gained universal acclaim during his lifetime. The achievement is immense; whether it is completely understood or appreciated at home is another matter. If it is, then it should also be recollected that it is only twenty-five or so years ago that Britten, as a disconsolate and considerably disillusioned young composer of acknowledged promise, went away from England with the intention of staying away. If now the prospects for a composer are better, Britten has had something to do with making them so.

The English (but not the Welsh, who are more intuitive) accept a composer on account of an attitude which he may, or may not, protest. This may be a matter for regret; but substantially it is the case. At different times Purcell, Arne, Elgar, Vaughan Williams were found to mirror various shades of collective emotion within a consciousness of nationalism or patriotism. Handel and Bach and Beethoven all appeared to offer specific information on moral, theological, ethical, and/or social questions. The cults of Sibelius and Mahler were similarly bolstered up with geographical, philosophical, psychological argument. What is music about? This is a fair question to the non-musician, if an impossible one for many creative musicians effectively to answer. Yet, in Britain, it is on some sort of satisfactory answer to this question that the future of music depends. Again, no doubt, this is regrettable—but inescapable. What Britten has done is to give an answer—in the only effective way, through music.

Britten's music on one level is utilitarian; on another it represents a sublimation of the utilitarian. It is localised, often by subject but more consistently by unconscious rather than conscious references to what is indigenous: for instance, to love of melody, aptitude for choral singing, and to the lyrical quality of English poetry. It is underlined by moral

[1] Souster, ib. p. 22.

[2] An analysis of the composer's situation in Britain with special reference to Tippett is given by Alexander Goehr, who at the same time pays tribute to Tippett's significance to a younger school of composers in 'Tippett at Sixty', *Mus. T.*, January 1965, pp. 22–4. See also *Michael Tippett, A Symposium on his Sixtieth birthday*, ed. Ian Kemp, London, 1965.

concern. Britten considers the problems of the time; of persecution, of corruption of good by evil, of personal alienation and rejection, of mental and spiritual isolation. The impulses that lie behind this moral attitude find expression elsewhere, as in the music of Tippett. But no other composer has the same special talent for limiting the terms of reference and for clear and comprehensible definition of issues. Contemporary life is dominated by the communicator. Britten in music is the complete master of communication. In this lies both his contemporaneity and his adherence to the distinguishing element of English music, at any rate during the last five hundred years. What this has to do with greatness is a matter not to be determined here, nor for some time to come. But, in those periods and places in which music was nearest to the centre of cultural experience, effectiveness was an important criterion. The idea of the composer as craftsman has been renewed in modern times; not least of all in this case.

Britten was superbly equipped to master the arts of communication. His musical skills *per se* were of an uncommon order, and it was early established that there were few purely musical problems that he could not solve. With the whole apparatus of musical expression at his finger-tips he did not need to travel far from the essential musical idea to discover its appropriate physical form. In the shaping of his music Britten has also been aware of the relationship of its form and pattern to conditions of performance. Thus he has covered a wide field, having composed for film, radio, theatre, opera-house, church, school, amateur choral society, chamber ensemble, symphony orchestra (rather rarely), and for many occasions of both national and international significance. 'I want my music', said Britten, 'to be of use to people, to please them, to "enhance their lives".'[1] Since no composer has been more ready to accept commissions and to execute them with punctuality, the matter of 'use' is explained by the catalogue of his works. That of 'pleasure' and 'enhancement' can be referred to the nature of occasion and place. It will be found that Britten's purposefulness (stimulated also by friendships with other artists, and by his own great talent as an executant) is a powerful spur to the imagination.

Born in Lowestoft, Britten has spent the greater part of his life in East Anglia. His early teachers included Frank Bridge, Harold Samuel, John Ireland, and Arthur Benjamin. After a course at the Royal College of Music Britten produced a *Sinfonietta* for chamber orchestra, a set of choral variations—*A Boy was born*, a Phantasy Quartet for oboe (Leon Goossens), violin, viola, and cello, and some children's songs. The *Sinfonietta* showed the astonishing deftness with which Britten can transform commonplace sounds through impeccable scoring; *A Boy was born*, a powerful and

[1] On receiving the Aspen Award, 1964.

imaginative handling of the choral medium as well as a perception of the living qualities of medieval poetry and the picturesque associations of religious imagery; while the children's songs were already imbued with a Blake-like innocence. After spending some time in Vienna, Britten came back and, in conjunction with W. H. Auden, worked on scores for documentary films. In *Night Mail* and *Coal Face* he demonstrated the immediacy of his vision by adapting rhythm and sonority to subject and medium in compelling manner. It was in 1937 that his reputation soared, on the strength of a work commissioned by Boyd Neel for performance in Salzburg: *Variations on a theme of Frank Bridge*. Variation form has tended to bring out the best in British composers: Britten is no exception. Within these and other variations he used the patterns of aria, bourrée, waltz, and fugue, in each case suggesting, not that he was pouring music into conventional moulds, but that the moulds were of his own devising. The political and social turmoil of the 1930's affected Britten greatly, and in the *Ballad of Heroes* and *Advance Democracy* he became a 'committed' composer. The sense of commitment has persisted, but has led neither to narrowed ideals nor sterile dogmas.

A period in America in the early part of the war ended with production of *Les Illuminations*, *Seven Songs of Michelangelo*, the *Hymn to St. Cecilia*, and *A Ceremony of Carols*, and the idea of *Peter Grimes* was beginning to take shape. The *Sinfonia da Requiem* had been given a first performance by the New York Philharmonic Orchestra in 1941. Britten's feeling for words and his ability to transfer verbal into musical symbols, by rhythmic subtlety, melodic appositeness, figurations in accompaniment—either singly or in combination—are almost unrivalled in contemporary music. But out of a Schubertian romanticism there also arises a Schubertian perception of the dramatic conflict inherent in poetic observation. From the *Serenade*, through *The Holy Sonnets of John Donne* and an increasing devotion to Purcellian habits (as shown in the Chacony of the Second String Quartet of 1945), Britten arrived at *Peter Grimes*. Here he had the advantage of a libretto that was clear and meaningful within the accepted field of opera; he also had opportunity to launch this work at the right point in time. What he achieved was the realisation of the story on two levels, of narrative and of psychological insight. The narrative is carried by the inevitability of melody in relation to words and by the implications of virtuoso instrumentation; the psychological implications by the veracity of individual characterisation and the manner in which (as in the Interlude of Act III) the musical vocabulary is removed to some extent from accessibility. By the placing of discord, of distorted melodic figures, of tonal contrarieties, Britten can quickly substitute interrogation for affirmation and set up a reaction of fear or of pity.

Pity runs through *The Rape of Lucretia* and through *Albert Herring*—a comedy, but a tragi-comedy—two chamber operas which are so much nearer the ideals of *opera seria* than most previous essays by English composers in the field of 'grand opera'. Fear and pity are stirred by *Billy Budd* and *The Turn of the Screw*. Most of all by the *War Requiem* in which time and eternity—with all that therein is implied—are featured through the bitter beauty of Wilfred Owen's poetry, the grave impersonality of the Latin liturgy, and the catholic style of a composer whose eclecticism here stirs no incongruity. The *War Requiem* was composed for the Coventry Festival of 1962.

Britten is not afraid of the commonplace; but he is restless in pursuit of the uncommon. He has often reached back to the Middle Ages to refresh the present, and a masterly example of adaptation of the material of one period to the requirements of another is *Noye's Fludde*—a children's pageant out of a Mystery. Reaching out in other directions he has brought the spirit of the Japanese *Noh* play into *Curlew River*. With its relaxation of earlier disciplines—especially of time—Britten here moves into a new area of technical development. But (as in the case of the dodecaphonic experiments in *The Turn of the Screw* and the *Cantata Academica*) he takes the appropriate subject with him. Technique is a means and not an end.

In that lies the basic principle of British music. Hence, unless in the Middle Ages, British musicians have started no revolutions, enunciated no significant dogmas, nor made outstanding contributions to the science of musical design. They have, as a matter of fact, not been ungenerous in appreciation of the work of others, and if there is a national musical tradition it is one that rarely feeds on arrogance. The British have been willing to recognise the Great Masters. Once or twice a British composer has reached this rank. For the most part, however, society having been capricious in respect of its obligations, the line of achievement is uneven. But not perhaps as uneven as was once supposed. To show that this is so is one of the aims of this book, from which it may be discovered that the past still has a good many unfamiliar treasures to yield. And the future is to come.

Appendix

List of Music Examples

Chapter 5

Chapter 6

Chapter 8 – contd.

Chapter 9

Chapter 10

Chapter 10 – contd.

Chapter 11

Chapter 12

Chapter 12 – contd.

Chapter 13

Indexes

I People

II Places

Type set by Gloucester Typesetting Co. Ltd.
Printed in Great Britain by
Western Printing Services Limited
Bristol

The Package

Ref: MIX PARCELS

5-8
EC1R 4RG

EC1R

Contact ID 372

SEBASTIAN
FITZEK

The Package

Ref: MIX PARCELS

5-8
EC1R 4RG

EC1R

Contact ID: 372aaa

translated from the German by
Jamie Bulloch

HEAD of ZEUS

First published in German in 2016 by Droemer Knaur
First published in the UK in 2020 by Head of Zeus Ltd

9 7 5 3 1 2 4 6 8

A catalogue record for this book is available from the British Library.

ISBN (HB): 9781838934477
ISBN (XTPB): 9781838934484
ISBN (E): 9781838934507

Typeset by Siliconchips Services Ltd UK

Printed and bound in Great Britain by
CPI Group (UK) Ltd, Croydon CRO 4YY

FSC www.fsc.org
MIX
Paper from responsible sources
FSC® C020471

Head of Zeus Ltd
5–8 Hardwick Street
London EC1R 4RG

WWW.HEADOFZEUS.COM

For my dream team: Manu, Roman, Sabrina, Christian, Karl, Barbara and Petra

For the indispensable Carolin and Regine

And of course for those who I miss even when I'm hugging them: Sandra, Charlotte, David and Felix

In grateful and loving memory of my father,
Freimut Fitzek

… all stories, if continued far enough, end in death,
and he is no true-story teller
who would keep that from you.

—*Ernest Hemingway*

It's impossible to observe something
without changing it.

—*Heisenberg's uncertainty principle*

Prologue

When Emma opened her parents' bedroom door she didn't know that it would be for the last time. Never again would she clamber into their bed, toy elephant in hand, to snuggle up to her mother at half past midnight, trying her best to avoid waking her father who'd be kicking about, mumbling random words or grinding his teeth in his dreams.

Tonight he wasn't kicking, mumbling or grinding his teeth. Tonight he was just whimpering.

'Papa?'

Emma toddled into the bedroom from the darkness of the corridor. The light of the full moon, which towered over Berlin like a midnight sun on this spring night, shimmered into the room like mercury through the drawn curtains.

Screwing up her eyes, over which her fringe hung like a chestnut-brown curtain, Emma could make out her surroundings: the rattan chest at the foot of the bed, the glass tables that flanked the wide bed, the wardrobe with sliding doors where she used to hide.

Until Arthur entered her life and spoiled the game of hide and seek.

'Papa?' Emma whispered, feeling for her father's bare foot that was sticking out from under the duvet.

Emma herself was only wearing one sock, and even that was barely attached to her foot. She'd lost the other while asleep, somewhere along the way from the sparkling unicorn palace to the valley of the silver-grey flying spider, who sometimes frightened Emma in her dreams.

But not as much as Arthur frightens me.

Even though he kept assuring her he wasn't wicked. Could she trust him?

Emma pressed the elephant more tightly to her chest. Her tongue felt like a dry lump of chewing gum stuck to the roof of her mouth. She'd barely heard her thin voice, so she tried again:

'Papa, wake up.' Emma tugged at his toe.

As her father retracted his foot he turned to the side with a whine, briefly lifting the duvet and filling Emma's nostrils with his sleepy odour. She was certain that if she were blindfolded she could pick her father out of a dozen men by his smell alone. The earthy mixture of tobacco and eau de cologne, which was so familiar. A smell she loved.

Emma briefly wondered whether she'd be better off trying her mother. Mama was always there for her. Papa often grumbled. Mostly Emma had no idea what she'd

Items on Loan

Library name: Enniskillen Library
User name: Mrs Joanne Kenny

Author: Fitzek, Sebastian, 1971-
Title: The package
Item ID: C904012769
Date due: 26/6/2021,23:59
Date charged: 29/5/2021, 15:31

LibrariesNi
****
Make your life easier
****
Email notifications are sent two days before item due dates
Ask staff to sign up for email

done when doors were slammed with such force that the entire house shook. Later Mama would say that her father didn't really know himself. She explained that he was 'earasable', or something like that, and that he felt sorry afterwards. Just sometimes, albeit rarely, he even apologised. He'd come to her room, caress her tear-stained cheek, stroke her hair and say that being a grown-up wasn't so easy, because of the responsibility, because of the problems you had to deal with, and so on. For Emma these select moments were the happiest of her life, and just what she was in need of right now.

Today, especially, it would mean so much to her.

Seeing as how frightened I am.

'Papa, please, I...'

She was moving to the other end of the bed to touch his head when she tripped over a glass bottle.

Oh no...

In her excitement she'd forgotten that Mama and Papa always had a bottle of water by the bed in case one of them got thirsty in the night. When it toppled over and rolled across the parquet floor, to Emma's ears it sounded as if a freight train were ploughing through the bedroom. The noise was deafening, as if the darkness amplified sound.

The light went on.

On her mother's side.

Emma let out a high-pitched cry when she suddenly found herself in brightness.

'Sweetheart?' said her mother, who looked like a saint in the beam of her reading light. Like a saint with dishevelled hair and pillow creases on her face.

Startled, now Emma's father opened his eyes too.

'What the hell…?' His voice was loud, his eyes were scanning the room, trying to get their bearings. He'd obviously woken from a bad dream, maybe it was still in his head. He sat up.

'What's wrong, sweetie?' her mother said. Before Emma could reply, her father shouted again, this time even louder.

'Fucking hell!'

'Thomas,' her mother chided him.

Maintaining his strident tone, he waved his hand towards Emma.

'For Christ's sake, how often have I told you…'

'Thomas!'

'… to leave us alone at night!'

'But my… my… my… cupboard…' Emma stuttered, her eyes welling with tears.

'Not again,' her father scowled. Her mother's attempts to calm him only seemed to make him angrier.

'Arthur,' Emma said nonetheless. 'The ghost. He's back. In the cupboard. You've got to come, please! He might hurt me otherwise.'

Her father was breathing heavily, his face darkened, his lips quivered and for a split second he looked how she imagined Arthur to be: a small, sweating devil with a big tummy and bald head.

'Like hell we have to. Get out, Emma, right now, or *I* might hurt you. No, I *will* hurt you!'

'Thomas!' she heard her mother cry again as she staggered backwards.

Those words had struck Emma hard. Harder than the table-tennis bat she accidentally got in the face last month in games. Tears flooded her face. It was as if her father had slapped her. Emma's cheeks were burning even though he hadn't even raised a finger.

'You can't talk to your daughter like that,' she heard her mother say. Anxiously, with a soft voice. Almost imploring him.

'I'll talk to her as I like. She's finally got to learn that she can't come bursting in here every night...'

'She's a six-year-old girl.'

'And I'm a forty-four-year-old man, but it seems as if my needs count for nothing in this house.'

Emma dropped her elephant without realising it. She turned to the door and left the room as if she were being pulled along like a puppet on a string.

'Thomas...'

'Will you shut up with your *Thomas*,' her father said, imitating his wife. 'I've only been asleep for half an hour. If I'm not on form in court tomorrow and lose this case then that's my practice up the spout and you can wave goodbye to all this: the house, your car, the baby.'

'I know...'

'You know *fuck all*. Emma's already eating us out of

house and home, but you were adamant about having a second kid, who'll stop me from sleeping altogether. For Christ's sake. It might not have escaped you that I'm the only one earning money in this family. And I NEED MY SLEEP!'

Although Emma was already halfway down the corridor, her father's voice wasn't any quieter. Only her mother's. 'Shhh, Thomas. Darling. Relax.'

'HOW THE FUCK CAN I RELAX HERE?'

'Come on, let me, please. I'll look after you now, okay?'

'LOOK AFTER? Ever since you got pregnant again, you've only looked after…'

'I know, I know. That's my fault. Come on, let me…'

Emma closed her bedroom door, shutting out her parents' voices.

Or at least those from the bedroom. Not those in her head.

Get out, Emma, right now, or…

She wiped the tears from her eyes and waited for the roaring in her ears to disappear, but it wouldn't. Just as the moonlight, which shone more brightly here than in her parents' room, wouldn't vanish back out the windows. Her blinds were made of thin linen, while the luminous stars stuck to the ceiling also glowed above her bed.

My bed.

Emma wanted to crawl into it and cry beneath the duvet, but she couldn't do that until she was certain that the ghost wasn't in his hiding place. Certain that he wouldn't pounce on her while she was asleep, certain that he had gone, like he had every time when Mama went to take a look with her.

The old farmer's cupboard was a monstrosity with crude carvings in the oak doors, which mimicked the cackle of an old witch when they were opened.

Like now.

Please let him not be there.

'Hello?' Emma said into the black hole before her eyes. The cupboard was so big that her things only took up the left-hand side. On the other side there was space for her mother's towels and tablecloths.

And for Arthur.

'Hello,' the ghost with the deep voice answered. As always it sounded as if he were putting a hand in front of his mouth. Or a cloth.

Emma let out a short scream. Oddly, however, she didn't feel that profound, all-embracing fear she'd experienced earlier, when she'd heard a clattering inside the cupboard and she'd gone to take a look.

Maybe fear is like a bag of gummy bears, she thought. *I've finished it all in my parents' bedroom.*

'Are you still there?'

'Of course. Did you think I'd leave you alone?'

I hoped you would.

'What if my papa had come to look?'

Arthur laughed softly. 'I knew he wouldn't come.'

'How?'

'Has he ever looked after you?'

Emma hesitated. 'Yes.'

No. I don't know.

'But Mama...'

'Your mother is weak. That's why I'm here.'

'You?' Emma sniffled.

'Tell me...' Arthur paused briefly and his voice went deeper. 'Have you been crying?'

Emma nodded. She didn't know if the ghost could see her, but his eyes probably didn't need any light. Maybe he didn't have any eyes at all. She couldn't be sure as she'd never seen Arthur.

'What happened?' he asked.

'Papa got angry.'

'What did he say?'

'He said...' Emma swallowed. Hearing the words in her head was one thing. Saying them out loud was a different thing altogether. It was painful. But Arthur insisted and, worried that he might become just as irate as her father, she repeated them.

'Get out or I'll hurt you.'

'He said *that*?'

Emma nodded again. And Arthur did seem to be able to see her in the dark, because he reacted to her nodding. He grunted his disapproval and then something quite extraordinary happened. Arthur left his hiding place. For the first time ever.

The ghost, who was much bigger than she'd imagined, pushed a number of hangers aside and as he climbed out he stroked her hair with his gloved fingers.

'Come on, Emma, go to bed now and settle down.'

She looked up at him and froze. Instead of a face she saw a distorted image of herself. As if she were in a chamber of horrors, gazing at a mirror mounted on a long black column.

It took a while before she realised that Arthur was wearing a motorbike helmet and she was staring at her grotesque likeness in his visor.

'I'll be right back,' he promised, making for the door.

There was something about the way he moved that Emma found familiar, but she was far too distracted by the sharp object in Arthur's right hand.

It would be years before she realised that this was a syringe.

With a long needle that glinted silver in the moonlight.

A liar will not be believed
even when he speaks the truth

—*Proverb*

1

Twenty-eight years later

'Don't do it. I was lying. Please don't...'

The audience, consisting almost entirely of men, tried not to show any emotion as they watched the half-naked, black-haired woman being tortured.

'For God's sake, it's a mistake. I just made it all up. A terrible mistake... Help!'

Her cries echoed around the whitewashed, sterile room; her words were clearly intelligible. Nobody present would be able to claim later that they'd misunderstood her.

The woman didn't want this.

Despite her protests, the slightly overweight, bearded man with wonky teeth stuck the syringe into the crook of her strapped arm.

Despite her protests, they didn't remove the electrodes attached to her forehead and temples, nor even the ring around her head, which reminded her of those unfortunate tortured monkeys in animal testing laboratories, their skulls opened and probes inserted into their brains.

Which basically wasn't so different from what was about to be done to her now.

When the sedative and muscle relaxant began to take effect, they began manual ventilation. Then the men started administering the electrical impulses: 475 volts, 17 times in succession, until they triggered an epileptic fit.

From the angle of the closed-circuit camera it was impossible to tell whether the black-haired woman was offering resistance or whether her limbs were twitching spastically. The backs of the figures sporting aprons and face masks blocked the audience's view. But the screaming had stopped. Eventually the film stopped too and it became a little brighter in the hall.

'What you have just witnessed is a horrific case…' Dr Emma Stein began her observations, breaking off briefly to pull the microphone a bit closer so the conference guests could hear her more clearly. Now she was annoyed she'd spurned the footstool the technician had offered her during the soundcheck. Usually she would have asked for one herself, but the guy in overalls had given her such a condescending grin that she'd rejected the sensible option of making herself taller. As a result she was having to stand on tiptoe behind the lectern.

'… a horrific case of coercive psychiatry which had long been thought consigned to history.'

Like Emma, most of those present were psychiatrists. Which meant she didn't have to explain to her colleagues that her criticism wasn't levelled at electroconvulsive therapy. Conducting electricity through a human brain might sound terribly mediaeval, but it produced promising results in combating psychoses and depression. Performed under general anaesthetic, the treatment had virtually no side effects.

'We managed to smuggle this footage captured by a surgery-monitoring camera from the Orphelio Clinic in Hamburg. The patient whose fate you've just witnessed was committed on 3 May last year, diagnosed with schizoid psychosis, based solely on what the forty-three-year-old herself said upon admission. But there was nothing wrong with her at all. The supposed patient faked her symptoms.'

'Why?' a faceless individual from somewhere in the left middle of the hall asked. The man practically had to shout for her to understand him in the theatre-like space. The German Association of Psychiatry had hired for its annual conference the main hall of the International Congress Centre in Berlin. From the outside, the ICC resembled a silver space station, which from the infinite expanses of the universe had spun to a halt directly beneath the television tower. And yet when you entered this seventies building – which was possibly contaminated with asbestos (experts disagreed about this) – you were reminded less of science fiction and more of a retro film. Chrome, glass and black leather dominated the interior.

Emma allowed her gaze to roam across the packed rows of chairs but, unable to locate the questioner, talked in the vague direction she imagined him to be.

'Here's a question of my own: What does the Rosenhan Experiment mean to you?'

An older colleague, sitting in a wheelchair at the edge of the front row, nodded knowingly.

'It was first performed at the end of the sixties, with the aim of testing the reliability of psychiatric prognoses.' As ever when she was nervous, Emma twisted a strand of her thick, teak-brown hair around her left index finger. She hadn't eaten anything before her lecture, for fear of feeling tired or needing to burp. Now her stomach was rumbling so loudly that she was worried the microphone might pick up the noise, lending further succour to the jokes she was convinced were going around about her fat bum. In her eyes, the fact that she was otherwise quite slim only highlighted this bodily imperfection.

Broom up top, wrecking ball below, she'd thought again only this morning when examining herself in the bathroom mirror.

A second later Philipp had hugged her from behind and insisted she had the most beautiful body he'd ever laid his hands on. And when they kissed goodbye at the front door he'd pulled her towards him and whispered into her ear that as soon as she was back he urgently needed relationship therapy with the sexiest psychiatrist in Charlottenburg. She sensed he was being serious, but she also knew that her husband was well versed in dishing out compliments. Quite simply, flirting was hardwired into Philipp's DNA – something Emma had been forced to get used to – and he seldom wasted an opportunity to practise it.

'For the Rosenhan Experiment, named after the American psychologist David Rosenhan, eight subjects had themselves admitted to psychiatric clinics on false pretences. Students, housewives, artists, psychologists and doctors. All of them told the same story on admission: they'd been hearing voices, weird, uncanny voices saying words like "empty", "hollow" or "thud".

'It will not surprise you to hear that all of the fake patients were admitted, most of them diagnosed with schizophrenia or manic-depressive psychosis.

'Although the subjects were demonstrably healthy and behaved perfectly normally after admission, they were treated in the institutions for weeks on end, supposedly taking a total of more than two thousand pills.'

Emma moistened her lips with a sip of water from the glass provided. She'd put on some lipstick, even though Philipp preferred the 'natural look'. She did in fact have unusually smooth skin, although she thought it far too pale, especially given the intense colour of her hair. She couldn't see the 'adorable contrast' that Philipp kept going on about.

'If you think the 1970s were a long time ago, that this took place in a different century, i.e. in the Middle Ages of psychiatric science, then let this video shatter your illusions. It was filmed last year. This young woman was a test subject too; we repeated the Rosenhan Experiment.'

A murmur rippled through the hall. Those present were less worried about the scandalous findings than they were about perhaps having been subjects of an experiment themselves.

'We sent fake patients to psychiatric institutions and once again investigated what happens when totally sane people are admitted into a closed establishment. With shocking results.'

Emma took another sip of water, then continued. 'The woman in the video was diagnosed with schizoid paranoia on the basis of a single sentence when she arrived at the clinic. After that she was treated for more than a month. Not just with medicine and conversational therapy, but with brute force too. As you've seen and heard for yourselves, she was unequivocal about not wanting electroconvulsive therapy. And no wonder, because she is perfectly sound of mind. But she was forcibly treated nonetheless.

'Even though she manifestly rejected it. Even though after admission no one noticed anything else unusual about her and she assured the doctors several times that her condition had returned to normal. But they refused to listen to her, the nurses or fellow patients. For unlike the doctors who passed by only sporadically, the people she spent all her time with at the clinic were convinced that this locked-up woman had no business being there.'

Emma noticed someone in the front third of the hall stand up. She gave the technician the agreed sign to turn up the lights slightly. Her eyes made out a tall, slim man with thinning hair, and she waited until a long-legged conference assistant had battled his way through the rows to the man and passed him a microphone.

The man blew into the microphone before saying, 'Stauder-Mertens, University Hospital, Cologne. With all due respect, Dr Stein, you show us a blurry horror video, the origin and supplier of which we'd rather not know, and then make wild assertions that, were they ever to become public knowledge, would cause great damage to our profession.'

'Do you have a question as well?' Emma said.

The doctor with the double-barrelled name nodded. 'Do you have more evidence than this fake patient's statement?'

'I selected her personally for the experiment.'

'That's all well and good, but can you vouch for her unquestioningly? I mean, how do you know that this person really is sound of mind?'

Even from a distance Emma could see the same haughty smile that had annoyed her on the technician's face.

'What are you getting at, Herr Stauder-Martens?'

'That somebody who volunteers to be admitted to a secure unit for several weeks on false pretences – now, how can I put it carefully? – must be equipped with an extraordinary psychological make-up. Who can tell you that this remarkable lady didn't actually suffer from the symptoms for which she was ultimately treated, and which perhaps she didn't exhibit until her stay at the institution?'

'Me,' Emma said.

'Oh, so you were with her the whole time, were you?' the man asked rather smugly.

'I was.'

His self-assured grin vanished. 'You?'

When Emma nodded, the mood in the hall became palpably tenser.

'Correct,' Emma said. Her voice was quivering with excitement, but also with fury at the outrage that had greeted her revelations. 'Dear colleagues, on the video you only saw the test subject from behind and with dyed hair, but the woman who first was sedated and then forcibly treated with electric shocks against her expressed will, that woman was… me.'

2

Two hours later

Taking hold of her wheelie case, Emma hesitated before entering room 1904, for the simple reason that she could barely see a thing. The little illumination that did penetrate the darkness came from the countless lights of the city, nineteen floors beneath her. The Le Zen on Tauentzienstrasse was Berlin's newest five-star chrome-and-glass palace, with over three hundred rooms. Taller and more luxurious than any other hotel in the capital. And – in Emma's eyes, at least – decorated with relatively little taste.

That, at any rate, was her first impression once she'd found the main switch by the door and the overhead light clicked on.

The interior design looked as if a trainee had been instructed to exploit every possible Far Eastern cliché when selecting the furnishings.

In the hallway, which was separated from the neighbouring bedroom by a thin, sliding door covered in tissue paper, stood a Chinese wedding chest. A bamboo rug extended from the door to a low futon bed. The lamps beside the floor sofa looked like the colourful lanterns that the toddlers carried on St Martin's Day in the parade organised by the Heerstrasse Estate kindergarten. Surprisingly stylish, on the other hand, was a huge black-and-white photograph of Ai Weiwei that stretched from floor to ceiling between the sofa and fitted wardrobe. Emma had recently visited an exhibition by this exceptional Chinese artist.

She looked away from the man with the tousled beard, hung her coat in the wardrobe and took her phone from her handbag.

Voicemail.

She'd already tried calling him once, but Philipp hadn't answered. He never did when on duty.

With a sigh she moved over to the floor-to-ceiling windows, slipped off her peep toes, without which she shrunk to the average height of a fourteen-year-old, and gazed down at the Kurfürstendamm. She stroked her belly, which still showed nothing, although it was a bit too early for that yet. But she was comforted by the idea that something was growing inside her, which was far more important than any seminar or professional recognition.

It had taken a while before the second line on the pregnancy test finally showed up, five weeks ago.

And this was also the reason why Emma wasn't sleeping in her own bed tonight, but for the first time in her life staying the night at a hotel in her home city. Her little house in Teufelssee-Allee was currently like a building site because they'd started extending the loft to make a children's room. Even though Philipp thought it might be a little overzealous to begin nest-building before the end of the first trimester of her pregnancy.

As he was working in another town again, Emma had accepted the overnight package that the German Association of Psychiatry offered all the guest speakers at the two-day conference – even those who lived in Berlin – as it allowed them to have a few drinks at the evening function in the hotel's ballroom (which Emma was bunking off).

'The lecture ended just as you predicted,' she said in the message she left for Philipp. 'They didn't stone me, but that was only because they didn't have any stones to hand.'

She smiled.

'They didn't take my hotel room away, though. The key card I got with my conference documents still worked.'

Emma concluded her message with a kiss, then hung up. She missed him terribly.

Better to be alone here in the hotel than alone at home amongst paint pots and torn-down walls, she thought, trying to put the best possible gloss on the situation.

Emma went into the bathroom and, as she took of her suit, looked for the volume control for the speaker in the false ceiling, which transmitted the TV sound.

Without success.

Which meant she had to go back into the living room and switch off the television. Here too it took a while for her to find the remote control in a bedside table drawer, which was why she was now fully up to speed about a plane crash in Ghana and a volcano explosion in Chile.

Emma heard the nasal voice of the newsreader begin a new item – '*... the police have issued a warning about a serial killer, who...*' – and cut him off at the press of a button.

Back in the bathroom it was some time before she found the temperature setting.

As someone who felt the cold Emma loved hot water, even now in high summer, and it had been an unusually fresh and particularly windy June day at below twenty degrees. So she set the water to forty degrees – her pain threshold – and waited for the tingling sensation she always felt when the hot jet hit her skin.

Emma normally felt alive the moment she was enveloped by steam and the hot water massaged her body. Today the effect was weaker, partly because the dirt that had been hurled at her after the lecture couldn't be washed away with water and hotel soap.

There had been furious reactions to her revelation that,

even in the twenty-first century, people risked becoming the playthings of demigods in white abusing their power just because of sloppy misdiagnoses. The validity of her research findings had been questioned more than once. The publisher of the renowned specialist journal had even announced he would undertake meticulous review before he 'might consider' publishing an article about her work.

Sure, some colleagues had ventured their support after the event, but in the eyes of these few she'd still been able to read the unspoken reproach: *'Why on earth did you put yourself in danger with this stupid experiment? And why are you risking your career and picking a fight with the bigwigs who run the clinics?'*

Something Philipp would never ask. He understood why Emma had for years been fighting to improve the legal status of patients undergoing psychiatric treatment. Because of their mental illness they were usually viewed with more suspicion than patients who, for example, complained of faulty dental care.

And Philipp understood why she also took unusual, sometimes dangerous routes to get there. No doubt because they were so similar in this respect.

In his work, too, Philipp overstepped boundaries that no normal person would cross freely. In truth, the psychopaths and serial killers he hunted as chief investigator in the offender profiling department often left him with no other choice.

Some couples share a sense of humour, others have

similar hobbies or the same political outlook. Emma and Philipp, on the other hand, laughed at completely different jokes, she couldn't stand football and he didn't share her love of musicals, and whereas in her youth she had demonstrated against nuclear power and the fur industry, he had been a member of the conservative youth association. What formed the bedrock of their relationship was empathy.

Intuition and experience allowed them to put themselves in other people's souls and bring the secrets of their psyches to the light of day. While Emma did this to liberate the patients who visited her private practice on Savignyplatz from their psychological problems, Philipp used his extraordinary abilities to draw up behaviour and personality profiles. Thanks to his analyses, some of the most dangerous criminals Germany had ever known had been put behind bars.

Recently, however, Emma had been wishing that both of them would take a step backwards. She was continually nagged by the feeling that in their time off, which was fairly meagre anyway, Philipp was also finding it increasingly difficult to achieve the necessary distance from his work. And she was worried that they were well on the way to proving Nietzsche's dictum about the abyss: if you gazed into it deeply and for long enough, it would start gazing into you.

Some time out, or a holiday at least. That would be enough.

The last trip they'd taken together was so long ago that the memories of it had already faded.

Emma lathered her hair with the hotel's shampoo and could only hope that she wouldn't look like a poodle the following morning. Her brown hair might be strong, but it reacted sensitively to the wrong products. It had taken numerous experiments and tears till she found out what made her hair shine and what turned her head into a ripped sofa cushion.

Emma rinsed her hair, pushed the shower curtain aside and was just wondering why such an expensive hotel hadn't installed glass sliding doors when she was suddenly incapable of another lucid thought.

What she felt was *fear*.

The first thing that came into her mind when she saw the letters was *run!*

The letters on the bathroom mirror.

In neatly written letters, across the steam-covered glass, it read:

GET OUT.

BEFORE IT'S TOO LATE!

3

'Yes?'

'Sorry for disturb. Everything okay?'

The tall, slim Russian woman in the doorway appeared genuinely concerned. And yet the woman who spoke broken German didn't look to Emma like the sort of person who worried unnecessarily about her fellow human beings. More like a model aware of how beautiful she was and who regarded herself as the centre of the universe. Dressed in a close-fitting designer suit, drenched in Chanel and perched on sinfully expensive-looking high heels that would have allowed even Emma to gaze down at others.

'Who are you?' Emma said, annoyed that she'd opened the door. Now she was standing face to face with a Slav beauty, bare-footed, with soaking wet hair and dressed only in a hastily thrown-on hotel kimono. The material was so fine that every curve of her naked body, which was far less perfect than the Russian woman's, must be showing beneath it.

'Sorry. Very thin walls.'

The woman swept one of her blonde extensions from her forehead. 'Hear scream. Come to look.'

'You heard a scream?' Emma said impassively.

In truth, all that she could recall was having felt faint, partly a result of the eerie message on the mirror, but doubtlessly also because the shower had been too hot.

Both these things had well and truly pulled the rug from under her feet.

To begin with, Emma had managed to hold onto the edge of the basin, but then she'd collapsed onto the tiled floor, from where she'd stared at the writing:

GET OUT.

BEFORE IT'S TOO LATE!

'Hear crying too,' the Russian woman said.

'You must have been mistaken,' Emma replied, even though it was perfectly possible that her fall had been accompanied by tears. Her eyes were still burning. The message on the mirror had awoken the darkest memories from her childhood.

The cupboard.

The creaking doors, behind which a man lurked in a motorbike helmet.

Arthur.

The ghost who had spent countless nights with her. Again and again. As a monster at first, then as a friend. Until at the age of ten she was finally 'cured', even though this concept didn't actually exist in psychotherapy. After many sessions the child psychiatrist that Emma visited had succeeded in banishing the demon. From both her cupboard and her head. And he'd made her aware who was really responsible for this phantasm.

Papa!

Ever since that course of therapy, which had first stimulated an interest in her current profession, Emma had known that no ghost had ever existed. And no Arthur. Only her father, who she'd spurned and feared throughout her life, but who she'd have dearly loved as a close ally. For her alone. Always there. To call on at any time, even at night in the cupboard.

But Emma's father had never been a friend. Not in her childhood, not during her studies and certainly not now that she was a married psychiatrist. His work had always been more important. His files, witnesses and cases. Leaving the house too early in the morning, and back too late for supper in the evening. Or not at all.

Although he'd retired a while ago, he only just about managed to send her a card for her birthday. And even that – she would bet – had been dictated by Mama, with whom he now lived in Mallorca. Phrases such as 'I'm missing you' or 'I hope we'll get to spend more time together this year' were simply absent from the lexicon of someone as irascible as him. He'd be more likely to write:

'Get out, right now, or I'll hurt you.'

And now a similar threat was scrawled across the mirror in her hotel bathroom.

Could this be a coincidence?

Of course!

Before the knock at her door Emma had already found a logical explanation for the incident.

A trick!

The guest who'd occupied the room before her must have scribbled with their greasy fingers on the dry mirror to give the next person a fright. And they'd succeeded.

So well that she'd practically screamed the hotel down. The joker would no doubt have been shocked by the violence of Emma's reaction, but they couldn't have imagined that the words on the mirror would have awakened an old trauma.

Back then it wasn't what her father said that had unnerved her most, but the fact that Arthur had come out of the cupboard for the first time that night. The motorcycle helmet, the needle, his voice… everything had seemed so real.

And sometimes it still did in her memory.

'You okay?' the woman asked her, continuing to stare at Emma with a mixture of concern and patience. Then she said something that sounded as kind as it did ghastly, and Emma didn't know whether to laugh or cry.

'Client make trouble?'

Oh God.

Of course.

She's a prostitute.

Which explained why she was dressed up to the nines. Half of the conference were staying at Le Zen; the hotel was full of men on their own in single rooms. How many of them had booked an escort for tonight? Scumbags like Stauder-Mertens, for sure, who would definitely use every opportunity they got when away from their wives and families.

'Need help? I can…'

'No, no. It's very kind of you, but…'

Emma shook her head.

… but I'm not a prostitute. Just a jumpy psychiatrist.

How sweet that the woman wanted to help her. How awful that she seemed to have experience of violent punters. *And of beaten-up whores who howl on the floor of hotel bathrooms.*

Emma smiled, but she didn't think it looked sincere. In the woman's dark eyes she could see that her doubts had not been dispelled, which is why Emma decided to tell her the truth.

'Don't worry. I'm alone in my room. But I thought somebody had crept in here and secretly watched me take a shower.'

'Peeper?'

'Yes, but it was just a stupid joke by the previous guest.'

'Okay.'

Although the escort girl still didn't look convinced, she shrugged and glanced at the Rolex on her wrist. Then she left with her first grammatically correct sentence: 'Take care nothing happens to you.' She must have heard this often from colleagues.

Emma thanked her and closed the door. Through the spyhole she saw the woman make her way down the corridor to the right.

The lifts were in the opposite direction, which meant her 'appointment' must be almost at hand.

Her heart pounding, Emma secured the door with all the available locks and levers. Only then did she realise how exhausted she was. First the lecture, then the mirror and now the conversation with the Russian prostitute. She longed to relax. To be able to sleep.

Especially in Philipp's arms.

Why couldn't he be here with her now, so they could joke together about this absurd situation?

Emma briefly toyed with the idea of calling her best friends – Sylvie or Konrad – as a bit of distraction, but she knew that both of them were on a date. Not with each other, of course, as Konrad was gay.

And even if she could get through to either of them,

what would she say? *'Sorry, but I'm slightly anxious because my mirror's steamed up'*?

Was steamed up, she discovered when she went back into the bathroom to clean her teeth.

The steam had vanished, likewise the joke message.

As if it had never existed.

4

Emma froze.

Streaks were all that remained of the condensation that had dissipated, leaving ugly edges on the silvered glass. Without thinking she wiped the patches away with a cloth, but immediately felt annoyed for not having breathed against the mirror to bring the message to life again.

Then she felt annoyed that she wasn't sure of herself any longer.

'What on earth is wrong with you, Emma?' she whispered, her head pressed into a towel.

She hadn't imagined the message. It was just a silly prank. No reason to feel so nervous.

Emma switched off the light in the bathroom without another glance at the mirror. She hung the kimono in the wardrobe and swapped it for some pyjamas. But she couldn't resist the paranoid impulse to check the wardrobe for secret hiding places (there weren't any). And as she was up, she could also take a peek behind the bed, inspect the curtains and try the locks again. All the while watched by Ai Weiwei, whose eyes had been photographed in such a way that they held Emma in his gaze wherever she moved to in the room.

She knew that all of this was displacement activity, but she felt better for having given in to her irrational stress symptoms.

When she finally crawled under the freshly starched bedclothes after her 'patrol', Emma felt tired and heavy. She tried one last time to contact Philipp and left a message on his voicemail that said, 'Dream of me when you've listened to this.' Emma set the alarm and closed her eyes.

As so often when she was overtired yet completely overwrought, flittering lights and shadows filled the darkness she wanted to sink into.

As she drifted off to sleep Emma asked herself, *Why did you say that?* in a woolly memory of her lecture. *Why did you say that you were the patient being tortured in the video?* That had never been her intention, she just acted out of impulse because Stauder-Martens, the narcissistic old goat from Cologne, had pestered her.

Do you have more evidence than this fake patient's statement?

Yes she did. Now it was out. Unnecessary shock tactics.

Emma rolled onto her side and tried to banish the images of the horde of men listening in the conference centre. She felt a pricking in her ear because she'd forgotten to remove her pearl studs.

Why do you always do things like that? she asked herself and, as so often in the transition between being awake and dreaming, she wondered why she was asking this question and what she actually meant by 'always', and while she was stuck in this analytical loop it suddenly happened.

She fell asleep.

Briefly.

Not even for two minutes.

Until the noise woke her up.

The buzzing.

In the darkness.

Very close, right beside her bed.

Emma turned over to the other side, opened her eyes and saw the light on her mobile. She'd placed it on the floor because the charging lead didn't reach from the plug up to the bedside table. Grabbing the phone from the carpet was quite tricky.

Caller unknown.

'Darling?' she said, in the hope that Philipp was calling back from some office phone.

'Frau Dr Stein?'

She'd never heard this man's voice before. Irritation mingled with the disappointment at the fact she wasn't speaking to Philipp. Who the hell was calling her this late at night?

'I hope it's important,' she yawned.

'I'm very sorry to disturb you. This is Herr Eigenhardt from reception at Le Zen hotel.'

On my mobile?

'Yes?'

'We just wanted to see if you'd still be checking in this evening.'

'What?'

Emma groped in vain for the switch to turn on the bedside light.

'What do you mean check in? I'm already asleep.'

Or at least trying to.

'So it's fine if we give the room away?'

Can't he hear me properly?

'No, listen. I already checked in. Room 1904.'

'Oh, please accept my sincere apologies, but...'

The receptionist sounded bemused.

'But what?' Emma asked.

'But we don't have a room with that number.'

What?

Emma sat up in bed and stared at the tiny blinking light on the smoke alarm attached to the ceiling.

'Are you having me on?'

'We don't have a single *four* in the hotel. It's an unlucky number in the Far East and so...'

Emma didn't hear the rest of the sentence as her mobile was no longer in her hand.

Instead she heard something that wasn't possible. Right by her ear.

A man clearing his throat.

And while her own throat constricted with fear, she felt the pressure on her mouth.

She tasted fabric.

Emma was stabbed by something, then she felt a cooling liquid flow into the crook of her arm through the puncture.

The man cleared his throat again and when she was certain she was freezing internally she sensed the blades.

Invisible in the darkness, but unmistakeably close to her face because they were vibrating.

Bzzzzzz.

An electric carving knife, a saw or an electric corkscrew.

Ready to stab, slash or puncture her.

She heard the sound of a zip being unfastened.

'I'm pregnant!' she wanted to cry, but Emma's tongue and lips failed her.

Immobilised, she was unable to scream, kick or thrash about.

Only wait and find out where she'd first feel pain.

And pray that this horror would soon be over.

Which it wasn't.

5

Six months later

Emma opened her eyes and wondered how long the person opposite had been watching her sleep.

Professor Konrad Luft sat in his usual chair, his hands folded in front of his stomach, and his thoughtful gaze lay on her face with a melancholic heaviness.

'Are you okay?' he asked. To begin with she didn't know what her best friend was getting at, but then she noticed the side table by her bed. On it were the pills she'd been given in the psychiatric clinic, where the judge had committed her to the secure unit.

Just in case.

In case she felt pain as soon as she woke up.

She stretched her limbs beneath the covers and with her elbows tried to shift herself up in the hospital bed. Too weak, she sank back down onto the pillow and rubbed her eyes.

She'd slept throughout the journey there, which was no surprise considering all the pills she'd been given. The side effects alone would knock out the strongest elephant, and on top of that she'd been administered a sedative.

After waking up it took her a while to recognise her surroundings. The room where she'd spent so many hours in the past felt unfamiliar, albeit not as unfamiliar as the secure unit she hadn't left over the past few weeks.

Maybe the strange feeling was down to the fact that Konrad had recently renovated his office, but Emma doubted it.

It wasn't the room that had changed so fundamentally, but her.

The smell of paint and freshly oiled walnut parquet still hung in the air, some pieces of furniture had been moved around during the redecoration, but basically everything was as it had been on her first visit almost ten years ago. Then she'd slouched on the sofa in trainers and jeans. Today she was in a nightie on a height-adjustable hospital bed, almost in the middle of the room. At a slight angle, with a view of Konrad's desk and the window behind.

'I bet I'm the first client of yours to have been wheeled in here on a hospital bed,' she said.

Konrad smiled softly. 'I've had some who couldn't be moved so I went to see them. But in the clinic you refused all contact, Emma. You wouldn't even speak to the doctors. So I obtained exceptional judicial authorisation.'

'Thank you,' she said, although there was no longer anything she could be grateful for in life. Not even the fact that she'd been allowed to leave her cell.

She'd refused to receive Konrad in the institution. Nobody was going to see her like that. So ill and broken. Locked up like an animal. The humiliation would have been too much to bear.

'You've lost nothing of your pride, my dear Emma.' Konrad shook his head, but there was no disapproval in his eyes. 'You'd rather go freely to prison than allow me to pay you a visit. And yet now you need my help more than ever.'

Emma nodded.

'Everything depends on how the conversation with your lawyer goes,' they'd told her. The psychiatrists and the police officers, who would surely be waiting outside to take her back.

Did Konrad really have the power to alter her fate? Her old confidant, although 'old' had to be the wrong description for a sporty, almost athletic man of fifty-eight. Emma had met him in the first semester of her medical studies; his name had sounded strangely familiar. Only later did she recall why. Her father and Konrad Luft were colleagues and had joined forces to work together on cases that Emma had read about in the newspaper.

The case that brought her and Konrad together didn't make it into the papers, however.

Emma's ex-boyfriend, Benedict Tannhaus, had drunk one too many and harassed her in a bar near the university. Konrad, who regularly took his evening meal there, saw the guy groping her and actively intervened. Afterwards he'd given Emma his card in case she needed legal assistance, which was indeed the case as her ex turned out to be a persistent stalker.

Emma could have asked her father for help too, of course, but that would have meant swapping one abusive man for another. Although Emma's father had never got physical with her like Benedict, his temper and uncontrolled fits of rage had become worse over the years and she was glad to have avoided contact with him since having moved into her student house. It was a complete mystery to her how her mother managed to stick it out living with her father.

They became friends during the lengthy process by which Konrad obtained a court order against Benedict. To begin with Emma thought that Konrad's interest in her was motivated by other things, and in truth she felt considerably attracted by his paternal charm, despite the big difference in age. As he had in the past, Konrad still kept his prominent chin hidden beneath a meticulously trimmed beard and wore a dark-blue, bespoke double-breasted suit with hand-stitched Budapest shoes. His curly hair was a little shorter now, but still hung over his high forehead, and Emma understood perfectly well why this defence lawyer was contacted so often by well-to-do elderly ladies. They could not suspect that although he loved women, they had no place in his erotic fantasies. Konrad's homosexuality was a secret he'd shared with Emma ever since they became friends.

She hadn't even told Philipp about Konrad's sexual preferences, albeit for selfish reasons, as she had to secretly admit. Because of his appearance and his charms Philipp was frequently the subject of female advances that he wasn't even aware of any more, such as when a sweet waitress would offer him the best table in a restaurant or when he got the friendliest smile in the queue at the supermarket.

This is why it was sometimes good for Emma have her husband react jealously, when Konrad rang yet again to invite her out for brunch. Let Philipp believe that she had admirers too.

Konrad kept his secret to avoid damaging his reputation as a hardcore macho lawyer. He would regularly appear at official functions with pretty law students. *'Better the eternal bachelor unable to commit than the faggot in the courtroom,'* he'd said to Emma as an explanation for his secrecy.

And thus the adventurous, well-coiffed widows showed their disappointment when Konrad told them that he only took on criminal cases rather than divorces, and within his area of expertise only selected the most spectacular, often hopeless-looking cases.

Like hers.

'Thanks for helping me out,' Emma said. A cliché, but she was doing her duty and breaking the silence.

'Again.'

She was now his client for a second time, following the stalking case. Ever since that night in the hotel, when she became the victim of a madman. A serial killer, who'd lain in wait for three women in hotel rooms, then shaven their heads with an electric razor.

... after having brutally raped them...

The hours Emma spent afterwards in hospital were scarcely better than the rape itself. Barely had she regained full consciousness than her orifices were again being manipulated by a stranger. Once again she felt latex fingers in her vagina and objects for taking swabs as evidence. Worst of all, however, were the questions put to her by a grey-haired policewoman with a poker face.

'Where were you raped?'

'In Le Zen. Room 1904.'

'There is no room with that number at the hotel, Frau Stein.'

'They told me that there, too, but it's impossible.'

'Who checked you in?'

'Nobody. I was given the key card along with my conference documents.'

'Did anybody see you in the hotel? Any witnesses?'

'No, I mean yes. A Russian woman.'

'Do you know her name?'

'No.'

'What's her room number?'

'No, she's a…'

'What?'

'Forget it.'

'Okay. Could you describe your attacker?'

'No, it was dark.'

'We couldn't find any defensive wounds.'

'I was drugged. I expect the blood test will reveal what with. I felt a pricking.'

'Did the attacker shave your head before or after penetration?'

'Do you mean before he rammed his dick into my cunt?'

'Look, I understand how upset you must feel.'

'No, you don't.'

'Okay, but I'm afraid I have to ask you these questions all the same. Did the attacker use a condom?'

'Probably, if you say you didn't find any sperm.'

'Nor any major vaginal injuries. Do you frequently change sexual partners?'

'I'm pregnant! Can we please change the subject?'

'Fine. How did you get to the bus stop?'

'I'm sorry?'

'The bus stop at Wittenbergplatz. Where you were found.'

'No idea. I must have lost consciousness at some point.'

'So you don't know for sure that you were raped?'

'The madman shaved off my hair. My vagina's burning as if it had been poked with a cattle prod. WHAT DO YOU THINK HAPPENED TO ME?'

The question of all questions.

Emma recalled how Philipp had brought her home by taxi and laid her on the sofa.

'Everything's going to be okay,' he'd said.

She'd nodded and asked him to fetch a tampon. A large one for heavy flow, right at the back of the bathroom cabinet. Emma had started bleeding in the taxi.

It was the first time they'd cried together.

And the last time they'd spoken about children.

The following day Emma lit a candle for the unborn child. It had long burned out.

Emma coughed into her cupped hand and tried to distract herself from these gloomy memories by letting her gaze wander across Konrad's office.

The floor-to-ceiling shelves, which housed not only the leather-bound rulings of the Federal Supreme Court, but also Konrad's favourite works of Schopenhauer, looked slightly lower, probably due to the new coats of paint which made the room appear smaller. And of course the massive desk was in the same place, in front of the almost square windows through which on a clear day you had a view across the Wannsee all the way to Spandau. Today she could see only as far as the promenade on the shore of the lake, along which a handful of pedestrians were struggling through the ankle-deep December snow.

All of a sudden Konrad was beside her bed and Emma felt him gently caress her arm.

'Let me make you a little more comfortable,' he said, stroking her head.

She smelled his spicy aftershave and closed her eyes. Even the idea of being touched by a man had triggered a feeling of revulsion in these last few months. But she allowed Konrad to put his arms around her body and carry her to from the bed to the sofa by the fireplace.

'That's better,' he said, as she sank into the soft cushions, half sitting, half lying, and he covered her carefully with a cream cashmere blanket.

And he was right. It *was* better. She felt secure; everything here was familiar. The seating area opposite with the wingback chair to which Konrad returned. The glass coffee table between them. And of course the circular rug at her feet. Fluffy white threads in a black border that looked like a brushstroke thinning out in a clockwise direction. Seen from above the rug appeared to be a hurriedly drawn 'O'. How Emma had loved lying on top of this 'O' in the past and staring into the gas fire as she daydreamed. How happy she'd felt when they ate sushi together. How safe and secure when they discussed relationship troubles, failures and self-doubt and he gave her the advice she wished all her life she'd had from her father.

Over the years the black threads of the rug had faded slightly and assumed a brownish hue.

Time destroys everything, Emma thought, feeling the warmth of the fire on her face, although the cosy feeling she'd always got when visiting Konrad remained absent.

No wonder – this wasn't a visit, after all.

More of a meeting essential to her survival.

'How's Samson?'

'Very well,' Konrad said, and Emma believed him. He'd always had a way with animals. The dog was in the very best hands with him – while she was locked up.

Philipp had given her the snow-white husky with its black-grey mop of frizzy hair soon after that night in the hotel.

'A sledge dog?' she'd said in astonishment when he handed her the lead for the first time.

'He'll get you out of there,' Philipp insisted, by which he meant the *'miserable place'* she was stuck in.

Well, he'd been wrong, and as things looked Samson would have to do without his mistress for quite a while longer.

Maybe for ever.

'Shall we begin?' Emma asked, hoping that Konrad would say no, stand up and leave her alone.

Which of course he didn't.

'Yes, let's,' said the best listener in the world, as a reporter had once described the star lawyer in a newspaper portrait. It was, perhaps, his greatest strength.

There were people who could read between the lines. Konrad could hear between the sentences.

This ability had made him one of the few people Emma could open up to. He knew her past, her secrets and all about her exuberant imagination. She'd told him about Arthur and her psychotherapy, which she believed had liberated her from imaginary friends and other visions. Now she was anything but sure of this.

'I don't think I can, Konrad.'

'You have to.'

Out of a decades-old habit, Emma felt for a strand of hair to twist around her fingers – but her hair was far too short for that.

It had been almost six months ago, but she still couldn't get used to the idea that her long hair, once so splendid, had disappeared. Even though it had already grown back six centimetres.

Konrad gave her such a penetrating look that she had to avert her eyes.

'I can't help you otherwise, Emma. Not after everything that's happened.'

Not after all the deaths. I know.

Emma sighed and closed her eyes. 'Where should I begin?'

'With the worst!' she heard him say. 'Take your mind back to where the memories cause the greatest pain.'

A tear fell from her eyes and she opened them again.

She stared out of the window and watched a man taking a mastiff for a walk along the promenade. From a distance it looked as if the large dog was opening its mouth to catch snowflakes on its tongue, but Emma couldn't be sure. All she knew was that she'd rather be out there, with the man holding the mastiff and the snow at their feet, which couldn't be as cold as the core of her soul.

'Okay,' she said, even though there was nothing about what was to follow that would be okay. Nor would it probably ever be, even if she survived the day, which right now she was not counting on.

'I just don't know what good it will do. I mean you were there during the interrogation.'

At least during the second session. She'd made her first statement alone, but as the officer's questions became more sceptical and Emma started to feel more like a suspect than a witness, she'd demanded her lawyer. Unlike Philipp, who'd had to drive through the night to get to her from where he was working in Bavaria, her best friend had been with her at the hospital at half past one.

'You took me through my statement and you were there when I signed the policewoman's protocol. You know what the Hairdresser did to me that night.'

The Hairdresser.

How the press had made him sound so harmless. Like calling a man who flayed women a scoundrel.

Konrad shook his head. 'I'm not talking about the night in the hotel, Emma.'

She blinked nervously. She knew what he would say next and she prayed she was mistaken.

'You know exactly why you're here.'

'No,' Emma lied.

He wanted to talk about the package, obviously. What else?

'No,' she repeated, less vigorously than before.

'Emma, please. If I'm going to defend you, you have to tell me everything that happened on that day three weeks ago. At your house. Don't leave anything out.'

Emma closed her eyes, hoping that the sofa cushions would swallow her up forever, as the leaves of a carnivorous plant devour a fly, but unfortunately it didn't happen.

And because she probably had no other choice, she started to recount her story in a brittle voice.

The story of the package.

And how, with this package, the horror which had begun that night in the hotel knocked at the door of the little house with its wooden fence at the end of the cul-de-sac and found its way inside.

6

Three weeks earlier

The screw pierced Emma's eardrum and threaded straight into her brain. She didn't know who had switched on the acoustic drill that was puncturing her fear centre. Who it was ringing at her door so early in the morning and throwing her into a panic.

Emma had never regarded her house in Teufelssee-Allee as anything special, even if it was the only detached house in the neighbourhood, the rest of the Heerstrasse Estate consisting of charming 1920s semi-detached properties. And until Philipp turned it into a fortress over the past few weeks, for almost an entire century their small house had been unremarkable, save the fact that you could walk around it without setting a foot on somebody else's land. Very much to the delight of the local children, who on warm summer days used to hold races across their garden. Through the open wooden gate, anticlockwise along the narrow gravel path past the vegetable patch, a sharp left around the veranda, left again beneath the study window and through the overgrown front garden back into the street, where the winner had to tap the old gas lantern and shout, 'First'.

Used to.

In the time before.

Before the Hairdresser.

Now the wooden fence had been replaced by massive grey-green metal struts anchored into the ground and supposedly secure against wild boar, although wild boar were the last things Emma was afraid of.

Her good friend Sylvia thought she was utterly terrified of the man who'd done those dreadful things to her that night in the hotel. But she was wrong. Sure, Emma was afraid that the guy might come back and pick up where he'd left off.

But she was even more afraid of herself than of him.

As a psychiatrist Emma was well aware of the symptoms of severe paranoia. Ironically she'd done her PhD on this subject and it was one of her specialist areas, besides pseudology: pathological lying. She'd treated many patients who got lost in their delusions. She knew how their story ended.

And even worse: she knew how their story began.

Like mine.

The shrill ringing still in her ears, Emma crept to the front door together with Samson, who'd been wrenched from his sleep by the doorbell. It felt as if she'd never get there.

Emma's heart was running a marathon. Her legs were virtually marking time.

A visitor? At this hour? Right now, when Philipp has left?

Samson pushed his nose into the back of her knees, as if encouraging her to go on and saying, '*Come on, it's not that hard.*'

He wasn't growling or baring his teeth, as he usually did when a stranger was at the door.

Which meant she probably wasn't in danger.

Or was she?

Emma just wanted to burst into tears right here in the hallway. Crying – her favourite pastime at the moment. For the last 158 days, 12 hours and 14 minutes.

Since my new haircut.

She felt the hair above her forehead. Felt how much the strands had grown back. She'd already done that twenty times today. In the past hour.

Emma stepped up to the heavy oak door and opened the tiny curtain across the palm-sized pane of glass set into the wood at head height.

According to the land registry, Teufelssee-Allee was in the Westend district, but compared to the villas this posh areas was famous for, her little house looked more like a dog kennel with steps.

It was at the apex of the turning circle of a cobbled

cul-de-sac, which was difficult for large cars to navigate and practically impossible for small lorries. From a distance the house blended in well with the neighbourhood, with its light, coarse render, the old-fashioned wooden windows, a clay-coloured tiled roof and the obligatory reddish-brown clinker steps leading up to the front door, through which she was spying.

Apart from the fence, the most recent modifications were not visible from outside: the glass-break sensors, the radio-controlled locking system, the motion detectors in the ceilings or the panic button in the wall connected to the emergency services, which Emma had her hand on right now.

Better safe than sorry.

It was eleven o'clock in the morning, and a miserable day – the grey, impenetrable cloud seemed almost close enough to touch – but it wasn't raining (it was probably too cold), nor was it snowing as it had done almost uninterruptedly for the past few days, so Emma could clearly make out the man at the gate.

From afar he looked like a Turkish rocker: dark skin, clean-shaven head, ZZ Top beard and silver, coin-sized metal rings that filled the earlobes of his 120-kilo hulk like alloy wheels would a tyre. The man wore blue-and-yellow gloves, but Emma knew that each finger inside them was tattooed with a different letter.

It's not him! Thank God! she thought, a massive weight falling from her soul. Samson stood beside her, his ears pricked in anticipation. She gave him the sign to make room.

Emma pressed the button to open the gate and waited.

Sandwiched between Teufelsberg in the north, several sports grounds and schools in the west, the AVUS Circuit in the south and the S-Bahn and federal railway tracks in the east, the Heerstrasse Estate was home to around 150 mainly middle-class families. A rural community in the middle of the metropolis, with all the advantages and disadvantages of living in a village, such as the fact that everybody knew everybody else by name and what they were up to.

Even the delivery man.

7

'Hello, Salim.'

'Good morning, Frau Doktor.'

Emma had waited for the delivery man to climb the few steps before opening the door a crack, as far as the metal bolt inside would allow.

Sitting beside her, Samson started wagging his tail, as he always did when he heard the delivery man's voice.

'Sorry to keep you waiting so long, I was upstairs,' Emma apologised with a frog in her throat.

She wasn't used to speaking any more.

'No problem, no problem.'

Salim Yüzgec put the delivery on the top step under the porch, kicked some snow from his heels and smiled as he fished the obligatory treat from his trouser pocket. As he did every time, he checked that Emma didn't mind and, as every time, she gave Samson the sign to grab the dog biscuit.

'How are you today, Frau Doktor?' he asked.

Fine. I've just swallowed ten milligrams of Cipralex

and spent from nine o'clock till half past ten breathing into a bag. Thanks for asking.

'Getting a little better by the day,' she lied and felt that her attempt to return his smile was a desperate strain.

Salim was a sympathetic chap, who occasionally brought over a pot of vegetable soup his wife had made. *'So you don't lose any more weight.'* But his concern for the psychiatrist was based on false assumptions.

To stop the neighbourhood from gossiping wildly about why the Frau Doktor no longer stepped outside the house, spent the whole day in her dressing gown and was neglecting her practice, Philipp had told the woman who owned the kiosk that Emma had suffered severe food poisoning, which had attacked her vital organs and almost killed her.

Frau Kolowski was the biggest gossip on the estate and by the time the message had reached Salim's ears, the poisoning had escalated into cancer. But it was better for people to think that Emma had lost her hair through chemotherapy than for them to chinwag about the truth. About her and the Hairdresser.

Why should strangers believe her if her husband didn't? Of course, Philipp tried as hard as he could to hide his doubts. But he'd done his own investigation and found practically nothing that supported her version of the events.

In everyday Chinese, Japanese and Korean the number four has a similarity to the word 'death', which is why it's considered unlucky in some circles. In the areas where Cantonese is spoken, the number fourteen even means 'certain death', which is why the Le Zen owners, who were from Guangdong, not only did away with the corresponding room numbers, but the fourth and fourteenth floors too.

Not even the suspicion that Emma had mistaken her room number was of much help. From her description of the view the only possibilities were rooms 1903 and 1905. Both had been booked for the entire week by a single mother from Australia with three children, who were having a holiday in Berlin. In neither room was there any sign of forceful entry or a physical assault. And neither room had a portrait of Ai Weiwei, which wasn't a surprise as there wasn't a picture of the Chinese artist anywhere in the hotel. This was another reason why the investigating team didn't accord Emma's 'case' a particularly high priority.

And why she increasingly doubted her sanity.

How could she blame Philipp for being sceptical, given such an unbelievable story? A rape in a hotel room that didn't officially exist and which she'd searched thoroughly just before the alleged attack had taken place?

Emma also claimed she'd been abused by a serial killer notorious for shaving the heads of his victims. But all of these so far had been prostitutes and none had lived to tell the tale. For that was another of the Hairdresser's trademarks: he killed female escorts who he'd ambushed in their rooms.

I'm the only one he let live. Why?

It was no surprise that the police were reluctant to attribute her case to the Hairdresser. Amongst Philipp's colleagues she was seen as a self-mutilating madwoman who invented horror stories. But at least she wasn't being hassled by the press.

Only by the delivery man.

'I didn't expect you so early,' Emma said, opening the door to Salim.

'I just fell out of bed this morning,' the delivery man laughed.

Since she'd stopped leaving the house (even walking the dog was Philipp's job), she had many things she needed delivered to her door. Today Salim stood there with relatively few packages. She signed for the receipt of her contact lenses; the online pharmacy had finally sent the painkillers; and the larger, lighter box probably contained the warm slippers you could put in the microwave. Finally there was her daily crate of food for which she'd set up a standing order with the online supermarket.

Philipp was responsible for drinks and all non-perishable items such as preserves, detergents or loo paper. But it was better that vegetables, milk, fish, butter and bread didn't hang around in his car when, as so often, he was suddenly called away and came home hours later than expected.

Recently he hadn't spent several days away at a time, as he did that fateful weekend. Not since the madman had rendered Emma immobile with an injection, stripped off her pyjamas and lain on top of her with all his weight.

In the last few months Philipp had insisted on spending the nights with her. He was even prepared to cancel the Europa Meeting this weekend, even though it was the most important workshop of the year. The leading profilers throughout Europe met only once every twelve months to pool their knowledge. Two days, and a different city every year. This time it was in Germany, in a hotel in Bad Saarow beside the Scharmützelsee. A must-attend event for this sworn band of extraordinary personalities who had to spend every day engaging with the worst things that mankind was capable of – and on this occasion Philipp even had the honour of giving a lecture about his work.

'I insist! If anything happens I'll call you right away. I mean you're practically round the corner, only an hour away,' Emma had said this morning as she gave him a goodbye kiss, while actually wanting to scream, *'An hour? It didn't take that madman much longer to turn me into a psychological wreck.'*

'Step by step I've got to drag myself out of this hole,' she'd said, hoping he'd realise that she was merely parroting hollow phrases from the psychiatry manual that she no longer believed in. Nor did she believe the final lie she sent Philipp off with: 'I'll cope on my own.'

Yes, for five whole seconds as she waved to him from the kitchen window. Then she'd lost her composure and started headbutting the wall until Samson jumped up at her and stopped her from doing herself further injury.

'Thanks very much,' Emma said once she'd taken everything off the delivery man and trudged back into the hallway.

Salim offered to carry the boxes into the kitchen (*I'm not that bad yet*) then slapped his forehead.

'I almost forgot. Could you take this for your neighbour?'

Salim picked up a shoebox-sized package from the floor. Emma had thought it couldn't be for her, and she'd been right.

'For my neighbour?' Her knees began trembling as she evaluated the potential consequences of this dreadful request if she were to be so crazy as to agree to it.

Just like the last time, when she'd kindly accepted the book delivery for the dentist, she'd sit for hours in the darkness, unable to do anything but think constantly about *when* it would happen. *When* the bell would shred the silence and announce the unwanted visitor.

As her hands became clammier and her mouth drier, she would keep counting the minutes and later the seconds until the strange object had vanished from her house.

But that was not the worst thought running amok in

her mind when she read the name of the addressee on the sticker.

Herr A. Palandt
Teufelssee-Allee 16a
14055 Berlin

Having the strange object in her house was one thing – she might be able to cope with that. It would change her routine and throw her emotional balance into disarray, but in itself the package wasn't a problem.

It was the name.

Her pulse racing and hands getting wetter by the second, she stared at the address printed on the package and just wanted to weep.

8

Palandt?

Who… *the hell*… is Herr A. Palandt?

In the past she wouldn't have given the matter a thought, but now her ignorance gave free rein to her darkest fantasies, which frightened her so much that Emma was on the verge of tears.

Teufelssee-Allee 16a?

Wasn't that the left-hand side of the street, three or four houses along, just around the corner? Hadn't old Frau Tornow lived there alone for years? Not…

A. Palandt…?

She knew everybody in the area, but she'd never heard *his* name before, and this unleashed a general feeling of helplessness inside her.

She'd been living in this small cul-de-sac for four years now. Four years since they'd bought the far-too-expensive property, which they'd only been able to afford because Philipp had inherited some money.

'You want me to take it?' Emma asked, without touching the package.

It was wrapped in normal brown paper and the edges reinforced with sticky tape. Two lengths of fibrous string were tied around the package, forming a cross on the front. Nothing unusual.

Apart from the name...

Herr A. Palandt?

'Please,' Salim said, inching his hand with the package closer to her. 'I'll pop a note through his door to say he can pick it up from you.'

No, please don't!

'Why not?' Salim asked in astonishment. She must have spoken her thoughts out loud.

'Those are the regulations, you see. I have to do it. Otherwise the package isn't insured.'

'I understand, but today I'm afraid I can't...'

'Please, Frau Stein. You'd be doing me a huge favour. My shift is almost over. For a very long time, I fear.'

For a very long time.

'What do you mean?'

Emma unconsciously took a step backwards. Sensing her anxiety, Samson sat up beside her and pricked up his ears.

'Don't worry, I'm not getting the sack or anything like that. It's good news for me Naya and Engin.'

'Naya's your wife, isn't she?' Emma said, confused.

'That's right, I showed you a picture of her once. For

the moment there's only an ultrasound thing of Engin.'

A cold draught blew through the door, fluttering Emma's dressing gown. She froze internally.

'Your wife's... *pregnant?*'

The word weighed so heavily inside her that she could barely get it out of her mouth.

Pregnant.

A combination of eight letters that had a completely different meaning today from half a year ago.

Back then, in the time before, the word represented a dream, the future, it was a symbol of joy and the very meaning of life. Today it merely described an open wound, lost happiness, and spoken softly sounded similar to 'never' or 'dead'.

Salim, who'd clearly interpreted her visible bewilderment as stunned delight, was grinning from ear to ear.

'Yes, she's in her sixth month,' Salim laughed. 'She's already got a belly like this,' he added, making the corresponding gesture with his hand. 'It works brilliantly with the admin job. You know, office work? The pay's better, but I'll be sorry not to see you any more, Frau Stein. You've always been really nice to me.'

All Emma could say was, 'What wonderful news' in a rather monotone voice, which made her feel ashamed. In the past she'd responded with enthusiasm to every baby announcement amongst her acquaintances. Even when some of her friends started asking why it was taking her so long, and whether there was a problem. She hadn't once felt envious, let alone bitter, just because it hadn't worked immediately for her and Philipp.

Unlike her mother, who became really irate when others revelled in their delight at being pregnant. The unexpected miscarriage when Emma was six had changed her. And her mother never fell pregnant again.

What about now?

Now was the time afterwards; now she could understand her mother's bitterness.

Fecund? Feck off!

Emma had turned into a different person. A woman with a sore vagina who knew the taste of latex as well as the feeling of vibrating steel on her shaven head. A woman well aware that a single, fateful event could change or even kill off all emotions.

Nice.

She thought of the last thing Salim had said and something occurred to her.

'Just wait a sec, please.'

'No, please don't. It's not necessary, really,' Salim called out after her. He knew what she had in mind when she instructed Samson to sit by the door.

To guard the delivery man too.

In the living room she noticed she was carrying the small package by her chest; she must have taken it from Salim after all – *Christ!*

Now it's in the house.

Emma placed it next to her laptop on the desk, which stood in front of the window that looked onto the garden, and opened the top drawer. She rummaged around for her purse that hopefully had enough for a tip she could give Salim as a parting gift.

The purse had slid into the corner at the very back of the drawer, which meant she had to take out some papers obstinately stuck in front of it.

A letter from the insurance company, bills, unread get-well-soon cards, brochures for washing machines and…

Emma froze as she saw the flyer in her hand.

She was desperate to turn her gaze from the glossy photo.

Bzzzzzz.

A buzzing started up in her head. A loud buzzing. She felt the vibrations on her scalp. It immediately started itching. She wanted to scratch herself but there was as little chance of doing that as there was of freeing herself from the vice that was keeping her head in position and forcing her to stare at the flyer.

Philipp had taken down all the mirrors in the house so that Emma didn't have to be continually reminded of that night by looking at her 'haircut'. All scissors and razors had been banned from the bathroom.

But he hadn't thought about a simple flyer that came with the paper.

Hand-held appliance with stainless-steel blades.

Only €49.90. With hair-cutting function! Save on your hairdressing bills!

Emma heard a soft click, which always preceded the avalanche of her nightmares, right before they fell from the precipice of her soul.

She closed her eyes. And as Emma collapsed to the floor she fell into the rats' nest of her memories.

9

Most people think that sleep is death's little brother, whereas in fact it is his arch enemy. Not *sleep*, but *tiredness,* is the vanguard of eternal darkness. It is the arrow the man in the black hood shoots unerringly at us every evening, and which sleep endeavours with all its might to pull out of us every night. Unfortunately, however, it is poisoned, and however much the flow of our dreams tries to wash the poison away, a residue always remains. The older we get, the more difficult it becomes to climb out of bed feeling recovered and rested. Like a once-clean sponge, the capillaries of our existence soak up a black ink, and the sponge becomes ever more saturated. The dream images that were once happy and colourful turn into nightmarish distortions until sleep finally loses its battle against tiredness and one day, exhausted, we pass over into a dreamless oblivion.

Emma loved sleep.

Only she didn't like the dreams that the poison of exhaustion had transformed into horrific visions.

Horrific because they were so real, and this reflected what had actually happened to her.

As every time when she was unconscious, it began with a sound.

Bzzzzzz.

Not with the violent penetration, the heavy breathing in her ear or the fitful coughing that thrust waves of peppermint-smelling breath into her face while the Hairdresser pinched her nipples as he came inside his condom. She couldn't be certain if these visions were real memories or the excruciating attempt by her brain to fill with nightmares the lost hours between the attack in the hotel and waking up at the bus stop.

It always began with the buzzing of the razor, which grew shriller and sharper when the vibrating blades touched hair.

Hair.

Symbol of sexuality and fertility since the dawn of time. The reason why women in many cultures cover their heads to avoid arousing the devil inside men. The devil, who otherwise…

… would overwhelm, rape and then scalp me…

The Scalper, an awkward but far more accurate term for the attacker than *the Hairdresser*, because he didn't style his victims' hair, he tore their lives from their heads.

As ever, Emma was unable to distinguish between dream and reality when she felt the cool blade on her head, paralysed as she was either by exhaustion or an anaesthetic in her bloodstream. She felt the electric blade vibrating on her forehead, and it didn't hurt when it moved upwards and to the back of her head. It didn't hurt and yet it felt like dying.

Why does he do it?

A question to which Emma thought she'd found the answer.

The attacker had raped her and he felt ashamed. An intelligent man, well aware of what he'd done, he wasn't trying to undo the crime, but to shift the responsibility to the victim.

Emma hadn't covered herself; her plainly visible, abundant locks of hair had enticed the male animal from his lair. For this she didn't have to be punished, but made to look respectable so that no man gazing at her could possibly get wrong idea.

That's why he shaved my head.

Not to humiliate me.

But to drive out the devil that led him into temptation.

Emma heard a crackling whenever the blades hit a crown, felt her head being turned to the side so he could get at her temples, felt a burning when the foil went in too deep and caught a bit of skin, felt a latex glove on her mouth, smelled the rubber covering her lips which would have probably opened to scream, and it dawned on her…

… that he waited for me…

He'd sought her out. He knew her!

He'd been watching her beforehand. Her hair when she twisted a strand around her finger. Her locks that danced on her shoulder blade when she turned around.

He knows me. Do I know him too?

At the very moment she asked herself this question, Emma felt the tongue. Long, rough, full of spittle. It was licking her face. Slobbering over her nose, closed eyes and forehead. This was new.

This had never happened before.

Emma felt a damp pressure on her cheek, opened her eyes and saw Samson above her head.

It took a while for her to realise that she was lying on the living-room floor beside her desk.

She was awake. But the arrow of tiredness had buried itself deeper than before. Her body felt as if it were full of lead, and she wouldn't have been surprised if her own weight had dragged her down into the basement, if she'd crashed straight through the parquet floor into the laundry room or into the study that Philipp had set up down there so he didn't have to keep on going to the office at weekends.

But of course she didn't crash through the robust parquet; she stayed where she was, lying on the ground floor, a couple of metres away from the sizzling fireplace, its flames flickering with unusual vigour.

They were being stirred, as if by the wind. Immediately Emma felt a breath of cold on her face, then on the whole of her body.

A draught.

The fire dancing in the cold draught could only mean one thing.

The front door!

It was open.

10

sorry, had to go.

take care!

A tiny Post-it note with little space, which was why Salim had written his farewell note in small letters.

With clammy fingers Emma removed the yellow sticker from the wooden frame of her front door and screwed up her eyes. It had started snowing again. At the other end of the street, just before the junction, children were playing 'It' between the parked cars, but there was no sign of the delivery man or his yellow van.

How long was I out of it?

Emma checked her watch: 11.13.

So she'd been unconscious for almost a quarter of an hour.

During which the front door had been open.

Not wide open, just a few centimetres, but still.

She shuddered.

What now? What should I do?

Samson was rubbing up against her legs like a cat. It was probably his way of saying it was bloody cold, so she finally went to shut the door.

Emma had to brace herself against it, for all of a sudden a violent gust of wind blew straight at the house, howling and hurling a few snowflakes into the hallway before the lock clicked and the room fell silent.

She looked to her left, where the mirror that had been left in the wall unit would have shown her red cheeks had it not been covered in packing paper.

It would have probably been fogged up by her breath too.

With writing on it?

Emma was briefly tempted to rip the paper from the mirror to check for hidden messages. But she'd done this so often and never found any writing on the glass. No *'I'm back'* or *'Your end is nigh'*. And Philipp had never complained about having to repaper the mirror.

'I'm sorry,' Emma told herself, unsure what she was referring to. The conversations she had with herself, which ran into the dozens per day, were making less and less sense.

Was she sorry that she'd abandoned Salim without giving him a tip? That she was causing Philipp all this trouble? Ignoring his suggestions, avoiding being intimate with him and having refused him her body for months now? Or was she sorry that she was letting herself go? As a psychiatrist she knew, of course, that paranoia wasn't an illness but a weakness, for which you needed therapy. *If you've got the strength for it.* And that the overreactions were a symptom of this suffering, which wouldn't go away of its own accord, just because she 'got a grip on herself'. Those who weren't afflicted were often suspicious of the mentally ill. They would wonder, for example, how a world-famous actor or artist who 'had it all' could possibly commit suicide, in spite of their fame, wealth and endless 'friends'. But these people knew nothing of the demons that would embed themselves, particularly into sensitive souls, then at the moment of that person's greatest happiness whisper into their ear and reel off their shortcomings. Psychologically healthy people would tell depressives to stop being so miserable all the time, and urge paranoid individuals like her to stop making such a fuss and checking the front door every time the beams creaked. But that was a bit like asking a man with a broken shin bone to run the marathon.

What now?

Unsure, she looked at the post by her feet, which Salim had delivered. The narrow, white packet of contact lenses could stay in the hallway for the time being, as could her medicines and the slightly larger box with the gloves. The food had to be put into the fridge, but at the moment Emma felt too weak to drag the crate into the kitchen.

I can't be afraid and carry stuff at the same time.

At her ankles, Samson shook himself and Emma wished she could do the same, simply shake her entire body and cast off everything that was currently bearing down on her.

'You would have barked, wouldn't you?' she asked him. Samson pricked up his ears and put his head to one side.

Of course he would have.

Samson was so attached to his mistress that he growled whenever a stranger approached the house. Never in his life would he allow an intruder to enter.

Or would he?

Although she was paralysed by the thought that she couldn't be one hundred per cent sure she was alone in the house, she could hardly call Philipp and ask him to come back for no reason at all.

Or was there a reason?

She had an idea.

'Don't move!' she ordered Samson, and opened the fitted cupboard by the front door, which housed the small white box that controlled the alarm system. The digits on the control panel lit up as soon as her hand moved close.

1 – 3 – 0 – 1

The date they met. At Sylvia's birthday party.

The alarm was programmed to call Emma's mobile at the sign of a break-in. If she wasn't available or didn't give the correct code word (*Rosenhan*), a police patrol would be dispatched immediately.

Emma pressed a pictogram showing an empty house, thereby activating all motion detectors. With a second button (*G*) she switched the ground-floor sensors back off.

'Now we can move around,' she said. 'But we're staying downstairs, do you hear me?' If anyone entered unauthorised, she'd hear as soon as they moved upstairs or in the basement.

It was highly unlikely that anyone was hiding on the ground floor. There were no curtains in the living room, no large cupboards, chests or other hiding places. The sofa was right up against the wall, which itself had no nooks and crannies.

But better to be safe than sorry.

Emma took her mobile from the pocket of her dressing gown, opened her list of favourites and pressed her thumb on Philipp's name, so she could contact him in an emergency. She was about to go back into the living room with Samson, but had to turn around again because she was no longer certain if she'd turned the key twice.

Once she'd had another check and again resisted the impulse to look in the mirror, she followed Samson who'd already pattered noisily back to his sleeping blanket beside the fire.

I really ought to get his claws cut, she thought, but

not out of concern for the parquet, which was tatty anyway and urgently needed a good polish as soon as she could cope with people in the house again.

In another life, perhaps.

She was ashamed that he got so little exercise. This morning a mere quarter of an hour, when Philipp had taken him once around the block before leaving for the conference. Emma herself always let him out on his own in the garden, where he did his business like a good dog at the rhododendron beside the tool shed, while she waited behind the locked door for him to come back.

The fact that the dog was behaving so peacefully was a sure sign that they were alone, at least here downstairs. A mere fly would get Samson worked up and he'd start wagging his tail excitedly. He was so fixated on Emma that even in Philipp's presence he never relaxed completely. She was never far from Samson, which meant that her husband automatically assumed the role of a guest who was watched affectionately, but without a break.

Emma sat at the desk, its drawer still open. She managed to stuff back in the flyer that had triggered her memory, without looking at the razor advertisement again. Then she decided to break from her usual routine and take a closer look at the package before embarking on her 'work'.

Taking it in both hands she turned it around. It couldn't weigh more than three bars of chocolate, perhaps less, which probably made it a parcel, although

Emma wasn't an expert in these matters. As far as she was concerned, anything in a solid container and larger than a shoebox was a package.

She shook it beside her head as a barman might a cocktail mixer, but she couldn't hear anything. No ticking, no humming, nothing that suggested an electrical item or (God forbid) a creature. All she could feel was that something light was moving inside. Sliding back and forth. It didn't seem particularly fragile, although she couldn't say this with any certainty.

Emma even gave the package a sniff, but couldn't detect anything out of the ordinary. No pungent, acrid smell of some caustic chemical or maybe a poison. Nothing that pointed to anything dangerous inside.

Apart from the fact that Emma found its mere existence threatening, it appeared to be a perfectly normal package, of the sort that is delivered in Germany every day by the tens of thousands.

You could get that packing paper in any stationer's or at the post office, if you could still find one open. In *the time before*, Emma remembered, they were closing at an alarming rate.

The string tied around the package looked exactly like the stuff she used to make things out of as a child: grey, coarse strands.

Emma studied the sticker on the front, which gave A. Palandt as the addressee, but oddly the box for the sender's details was empty. No company or private address.

It must have been dispatched via an automated Packstation, the only way of sending packages anonymously, something Emma had discovered this last Christmas when wanting to send her mother a package without her immediately realising who it was from. All the same Emma had entered an invented name *(Father Christmas, 24 Santa Street, North Pole)*. On this package, however, the address box was completely empty, which nearly unnerved her more than the fact that she didn't know of a neighbour by the name of Palandt.

She put the package aside again, almost in disgust, pushing it well away from her to the far end of the desk.

'Do you really not want to keep me company?' Emma said, turning back to Samson. In all her hours of loneliness she'd become used to talking to him as if he were a small child carefully watching whatever she did during the day. Today, however, he seemed peculiarly sleepy, having snuggled up so peacefully next to the fire rather than at her feet beneath the desk.

'Oh well,' Emma sighed when he continued to make no reaction. 'The main thing is you don't snitch on me. You know I promised Philipp I wouldn't.'

But today of all days she couldn't help herself. No matter how angry he'd get if he found out.

She simply had to do it.

Feeling as if she were betraying her husband, she flipped open her laptop and began her 'work'.

11

There was only one photo of her with Philipp that Emma didn't hate, and that had been taken by a two-year-old thief.

Around five years ago, on the way to an exhibition of a photographer friend of theirs, they'd taken refuge from a downpour in a tourist trap on Hackescher Markt – a 'potato restaurant' with long benches lined up along a sort of trestle table, which they had to share with a good dozen other fugitives from the weather.

Obliged by the waiting staff to order more than just drinks, they opted for potato cakes with apple sauce. It is unlikely that this unspectacular late-April afternoon would have branded itself on her memory if Emma hadn't found these strange photos on her mobile the next day.

The first four were completely dark. The fifth showed the edge of a table, as did the six that followed, plus the individual responsible for these blurred pictures, starting with just the thumb and ending with the entire person:

a blonde girl with sticking-up hair, a semolina-smeared mouth and the sort of diabolic smile that only small children are capable of. She must have stolen the phone without them noticing.

Seven photographs taken without a flash showed bits of Philipp and Emma. On one of them they were even smiling, but the nicest picture was the one in which time seemed to have fled into another room: Emma and Philipp standing side by side, gazing into each other's eyes while both their forks had spiked the same piece of potato cake. It was as if the image were from a film in which the sound – restaurant guests yelling over one another, children bawling and the noisy clatter of cutlery – breaks off abruptly and the freeze frame is accompanied by a romantic piano melody.

Emma had no idea that she and her husband still exchanged such loving glances, and the fact that this photo had been taken unawares, free from any suspicion that it might have been staged, made it all the more prized in her eyes. For Philipp too, who loved the picture, he thought there was something 'James Dean' about his gangly poise, whatever he meant by that.

Earlier, in the time before, Emma looked at the photograph every day at five o'clock, when Philipp called her to say if he'd be back for dinner or not, because she'd selected the image as the contact photo for his number. She kept a copy of the picture in the inner pocket of her favourite handbag, and for a while it had even been the screensaver on her notebook, until a system update inexplicably wiped it from the computer.

Just like my self-confidence, my zest for life. My life.

Sometimes Emma wondered whether the Hairdresser had also given her a system reboot that night in the hotel and restored her emotional hard drive to its factory settings. And clearly she was a dud: defective goods that unfortunately couldn't be exchanged.

Emma clicked the Outlook icon on the taskbar, the standard screensaver vanished and now she could focus on her unpleasant, but necessary daily task.

Her daily 'work' consisted of trawling the internet for the latest reports about the Hairdresser. Philipp had expressly forbidden her to do this after the papers had got hold of the criminal profile he'd drawn up thanks to an indiscretion by the public prosecution department. They'd slugged it out for days. Philipp was worried that the sensational tabloid reports would unsettle Emma even more, and so she had to proceed with caution.

Secretly, like an adulteress.

She surfed in private mode via a search engine that didn't save browser history. And the folder where she chronologically stored all the reports and information about the case was labelled 'Diet' and password protected.

Currently the internet was awash with another flood of speculation because the Hairdresser had struck again the previous week. Again in a five-star Berlin hotel, this time on Potsdamer Platz, and once more a prostitute had been poisoned with an overdose of gamma-hydroxybutyric acid. Residues of it had been identified in Emma's blood test too, but the investigating officers didn't see this as conclusive proof. She was a psychiatrist, which meant that it was easy for her to get hold of this product, which in small doses was a stimulant and often used as a party drug. Even easier than shaving her hair off.

The tabloid articles gave more details about the sexual preferences of Natascha W. (22) than the person who'd lost her life in agonising pain. A study of readers' comments in internet forums gave the impression that the majority pinned at least some of the blame on the women, for who offered themselves to total strangers for money?

It didn't occur to most of the commentators that the victims were sentient beings. The Russian woman who'd knocked at Emma's hotel door that night had more empathy than all of them put together.

It was just bad luck that the investigation team hadn't been able to find her. But hardly a surprise. What female escort would give their real name to reception or say which room they were booked in? In luxury hotels such 'girls' were unavoidable but invisible guests.

Crack.

A log fell from its burning pile in the fireplace, and whereas Samson's nose didn't even twitch, Emma jumped in fright.

She glanced out of the window, staring at the fir she decorated as a Christmas tree every year. Its branches were weighed down by the snow.

The sight of nature was one of the few things that calmed her. Emma loved her garden. To be able to get back outside and tend to it was a major impetus to ridding herself of this ridiculous nuisance in her head. At some point she was certain she'd find the strength to go into therapy and let an expert check her self-medication.

At some point, just not today.

In her inbox Emma found what was obviously a spam email threatening to block her bank cards, as well as several news alerts for the keyword 'hairdresser', including an article in *Bild* and one in the *Berliner Zeitung*, which she opened first. When she established that it didn't say anything new, she copied it as a PDF in the 'Hairdresser_THREE_Investigations_NATASCHA' folder.

In truth she'd taken the place the Hairdresser had earmarked for Emma. Natascha was already number four.

I'm just the woman who doesn't count.

For each victim Emma had subfolders for 'Private life', 'Professional life' and 'Own theories', but those dedicated to the official investigations were obviously the most important.

Here there was also the *Spiegel* article about Philipp's initial profile, which characterised the killer as a psychopathic narcissist. Affluent, cultured and with a high level of education. So in love with himself that he was incapable of forming a firm relationship. Because he believed himself to be perfect, he blamed women for his loneliness. Women who gave men the come-on, but who only wanted one thing from them: money. It was their fault that such a handsome chap like himself couldn't control his urges. He regarded the act of shaving as a service he was performing for the world of men by making the women ugly.

It was possible that there were other victims, like Emma, who'd 'only' had their hair shorn off after the rape. Maybe he didn't necessarily want to kill his victims, only if he still found them attractive when they were bald.

This idea had led Philipp to the suggestion that the Hairdresser might have worn a night-vision device during his attacks to assess the end results. A supposition that Emma had put in the 'Theories' folder, along with the one that the attacker could be repulsed by the sight of blood. But he'd cut Emma while shaving her head. In hospital they'd treated the wound on her forehead and washed away the encrusted blood. This had possibly been the reason for her survival, for the wound and the blood might have disfigured her in such a way that the Hairdresser considered his deed complete.

Philipp was not officially on the case because of his personal involvement, although 'involvement' was a polite euphemism for 'crazed wife with madcap violent fantasies'.

Unofficially, of course, Philipp was tapping all his sources to keep abreast of the investigations. Emma was convinced he wasn't telling her everything he knew, otherwise she wouldn't have gasped when she opened the *Bild* home page.

Jesus Christ!

Emma slapped a hand over her mouth and blinked.

The headline above the photograph consisted of only three words, but these filled two thirds of her monitor:

IS THIS HIM?

The green-tinged colour photo had been taken by a camera in the ceiling of a lift.

From the back right-hand corner a man in a grey hoodie was visible. His face was three quarters covered and the rest could have belonged to pretty much any white adult male wearing jeans and sneakers.

What unnerved Emma wasn't the sight of the slim, average-height man about to step into the lobby of the hotel where victim number two had lost her life.

But what the man was holding as he left the lift.

'Here you can see a man who wasn't registered as a guest leaving the hotel on the night that Lariana F. died,' the article said. As it was not certain that this man was the killer, they had refrained earlier from publishing the photograph for reasons of data protection. Now, however, they were doing it given the lack of alternatives.

The usual telephone numbers were listed for information relevant to the case, as well as a direct link to the police.

God almighty! Are my eyes playing tricks on me, or is that…?

Emma looked on the desk for a paper bag she could breathe into. When she couldn't find a bag she considered going into the kitchen to fetch one, but then decided to enlarge the photo first.

Zoom into the hands that were still wearing latex gloves.

Into the fingers.

Into the object they were gripping.

'*The authorities are working on the assumption that this is the Hairdresser making off with his trophies*,' the lurid text continued.

Her hair? In a package.

Emma looked up. Her eyes wandered across the desk, then back to the picture.

A small package wrapped in plain brown paper.

Roughly like the one in front of her. The anonymous package that Salim had given Emma for her neighbour.

A. Palandt.

Whose name she'd never heard before.

Emma felt a small bead of sweat drip from the back of her neck and trickle down her spine, then she heard Samson growl before the alarm sounded in the attic.

12

What was that?

Once the fear had coursed into her limbs, Emma forced herself not to panic but to find out what was going on.

The noise was too quiet and too distant for the shrill din that the motion detector would have set off. Captured by the infra-red sensors, a single movement would trigger a deafening interval alarm throughout the entire house. Not just on one of the upper floors.

Besides, the sound was too rich, almost melodic.

Like a…

Emma had an inkling, but couldn't put a finger on it. Her thoughts dissipated almost simultaneously with the beeping that stopped as abruptly as it had started.

'What was that?' she asked out loud, but Samson remained horizontal, not even raising his head from his fat paws, which was very unlike him and caused Emma to worry that she might have imagined the sound.

Am I suffering from aural hallucinations now too?

Emma shut her laptop, pushed her chair from the desk and stood up.

The parquet creaked beneath her feet, which is why she tiptoed her way to the stairs in her ballerina slippers. Leaning against the wooden banisters in the hallway she listened, but could hear nothing save for a soft whooshing in her ear, the tinnitus that everyone experiences when they focus too hard on their own hearing.

Emma switched off the motion detectors using the control panel by the front door.

Then she crept upstairs to the first floor, where there was the bedroom, a dressing room and a large bathroom.

She'd forgotten to turn on the light by the stairs, and up here (she was just two steps from the first-floor landing) the roller blinds were still down (sometimes when the migraine side effects of her psychotropic drugs set in she blocked out the light all day long), so it felt as if Emma were climbing into the darkness.

Bugger this, she'd go into the basement. At least there she could defend herself with the fire extinguisher that was hanging on the wall by the stairs.

'Samson, come here, boy!' she called out without turning around because she was suddenly afraid that someone might slip out of the black hole and come at her on the stairs. And then, as if Philipp had also installed a voice detector for her security, these words set the alarm off again.

Oh God!

Emma bit her bottom lip to stop herself from screaming.

It could, of course, be pure coincidence that she was hearing it again now. But there it was: the mysterious sound. And she wasn't imagining it.

A high-pitched beeping, somewhat louder now because she had moved towards the source, which evidently wasn't on the first floor, but higher up, below the roof. And the alarm reminded Emma of her incomplete thought from a few minutes ago, with a number of associations.

An alarm clock was the most harmless, but also the most unlikely, explanation, because up in the attic there was nothing but paint pots, pulled-up floorboards, a torn-down drywall and all manner of tools dotted about the place. But no clock! And even if there had been, why should it start ringing today, half a year after they'd abandoned their renovation?

No, there wasn't an alarm clock in the nursery building site, which Emma secretly called BER after the capital's airport which probably would never be finished either. That night her desire for children had been shorn along with her hair.

'For the time being,' Philipp had told her. *'For good,'* her soul said.

But if it wasn't an alarm clock, then it could only be a…

… mobile phone.

'Samson, come on!' Emma called out again, louder and more energetically. She was unsettled by the thought of a mobile ringing in the attic above her head. The inevitable conclusion that it must belong to somebody pushed Emma to the edge of panic.

Which she toppled over when the bathroom door slammed shut only a few metres ahead of her.

13

She ran. Without thinking, without making any rational decisions or even weighing up her options, because then she would have certainly hurried downstairs, back to Samson. To the exit.

Instead she leaped up the last couple of steps, crossed the narrow landing virtually blind, losing a slipper, yanked open her bedroom door and shut it again behind her. Emma locked the door with the simple key which – thank God – was on the inside. She grabbed a chair and wedged the backrest under the handle, as she'd seen in films…

… but does that make any sense?

No, nothing made sense here, it hadn't for a long while. Ever since she'd been picked up off the ground by the bus stop outside Le Zen.

Without hair.

Without dignity.

Without reason.

Emma's eyes slowly became accustomed to the darkness.

In the scant daylight that seeped through the slats of the roller blind she could only make out shapes. Shadows. Vague surfaces. The bed, the wardrobe, the heavy door.

Squatting down beside a chest of drawers, an heirloom from her grandmother where she kept her underwear, Emma fixed her gaze on the door handle, the only reflective object in the room.

What her eyes had forfeited in vision, her ears had evidently made up in hearing. Besides the fitful noises of her own breathing, which was going far too fast, and the rustling of her dressing gown rising and falling over her pumping torso, dull thuds were sounding in the background.

Footsteps.

Heavy footsteps.

Coming up the stairs.

Emma did the worst thing she possibly could.

She screamed.

A high-pitched, piercing scream. She heard her own mortal fear wresting from her throat. Despite the fact that she was only drawing attention to herself, she couldn't stop.

Sinking to her knees, Emma pressed her hand to her mouth, bit her knuckles, whimpered and despised herself for such weakness.

How proud she used to be of her ability to keep

her feelings under control, even in the most emotional situations. For example when the jealous borderliner who she was referring to a colleague punched her goodbye in the face. Or when an eleven-year-old patient died of a brain tumour and she'd held her mother's hand in the clinic until it was over. She'd always managed to put off her collapse till she was home alone, where, at a time and manner of her own choosing, she could bawl her anger or grief into a pillow pressed onto her face. But this form of self-control was history now and she hated herself for it.

I'm a wreck.

A screaming, howling misery guts who starts crying every time she sees an advertisement with a baby in it. Who thinks of the Hairdresser every time she meets a man.

And who anticipates certain death when the handle is being shaken on the other side of the door.

The last thing she saw was the door trembling from the hammering it was getting. Then Emma closed her eyes, tried pulling herself up on the chest of drawers, but slipped feebly like a drunkard unable to keep her balance.

Howling, she sank to the floorboards again, tasted her tears, smelled the sweat dripping from her eyebrows *(why didn't he shave those off too?)* and couldn't help thinking of the roller blind, *which I didn't open this morning, stupid cow.* Now there wasn't enough time to pull the heavy thing up. And jump.

It wasn't so far from the first floor, especially with all that snow on the ground in the garden.

Maybe I could have done it…

Her screams and thoughts broke off when the door splintered and at once a cold draught cooled her tear-stained face.

Emma could hear panting. Footsteps. Shouting. Not coming from herself. But from the intruder.

Male shouting.

Two hands yanked away her arms which she'd wrapped over her head in protection, crouched like a little child waiting to be punished.

No, more like a woman waiting for death.

Finally she heard her name.

Emma.

Being yelled again and again by a voice, the last voice she'd been expecting in what were likely to be her last few seconds without pain.

Then the blow came. Straight to the face.

Her cheek burned as if it had been stung by a jellyfish and her tears bit open her eyelids from the inside. Through the blur she could see that she had two intruders to deal with.

The two men were standing close beside one another. Despite the meagre light and veil before her eyes she recognised both faces.

Which was hardly surprising.

She was married to one of them.

14

Philipp was no dream husband, or at least not by the apparent standard of the average woman's dreams. He wasn't a shining prince who called three times a day just to say 'I love you' before stopping on the way home at a florist's, jeweller's or lingerie boutique to pick up a small token to surprise his beloved, every day till their golden wedding anniversary and beyond. He wasn't a husband who never argued, never glanced at other women, was always kind to his mother and loved nothing better than to cook for her friends.

He was, however, a reliable partner by her side.

Someone who voiced his opinions, a man with a mind of his own, which she found more important than being helped into her coat.

He gave her security and trust. In spite of all the difficulties that had marked the start of their relationship.

It had taken him months to disentangle himself from his ex, and he ended up two-timing Emma with 'Kilian' for weeks.

That wasn't his ex-girlfriend's real name, of course, but at the time Philipp had stored Franziska's number on his mobile under the name of a football chum, so that Emma wouldn't get suspicious if there was another call or text message. When she by chance discovered the truth, they had their first major row, which almost brought an end to their relationship. Finally, however, she believed Philipp that the ploy hadn't been an attempt to keep something going with his ex. Because it wasn't possible just to change his work number, Philipp couldn't prevent Franziska's wine-fuelled, sometimes hysterical calls. What he'd been trying to do was at least to protect Emma from unnecessary hurt, and himself from unnecessary arguments. In vain.

In the end the problem solved itself: Franziska found a new boyfriend and moved with him to Leipzig. There were no more calls from 'Kilian'.

Otherwise he possessed the usual male quirks. Philipp enjoyed staying out late with friends without sending her a text to tell her they were moving on to yet another pub. He snored, flooded the bathroom and put his elbows on the table when they were eating. Once he forgot their wedding anniversary and, in a fit of rage, hurled a full cup of coffee at the wall (the stain was still visible), but he'd never, ever hit her.

But Emma had never given him such a compelling reason to do so before.

'I'm sorry,' he said, a few minutes later. He'd helped

her downstairs into the kitchen, where she'd sat at their square wooden table. In the past they loved having breakfast there at the weekends because it offered such a pretty view of the garden. The neighbouring one was totally overgrown, giving the impression that you were gazing into a forest.

Emma nodded and tried to say, 'It's okay,' but her voice sank back down into her throat. She was clutching a bulbous cup of coffee, but wouldn't take a sip. Philipp was leaning against the work surface by the sink. Keeping his distance.

Not because he wanted to, but because he knew this was what she needed right at the moment. For a few minutes at least, until the voice of terror in her head was screaming not quite so loudly.

'Jesus, I'm really sorry,' Philipp said, grinding his teeth and staring at his hands as if unable to comprehend what he'd done.

'No.' Emma shook her head, pleased to have found her voice again, even if it emerged from her mouth as little more than a croak. 'What you did was absolutely right.' The slap that was still burning her cheek had smothered the flames of panic. It was only afterwards that she'd stopped screaming and calmed down again.

'I was completely off my rocker,' she admitted, while thinking: *So that's how my patients feel when they confide in me.*

Do they also realise how absurd their behaviour is in hindsight?

Emma had thought a stranger had slammed the bathroom door, but Philipp's sudden return explained everything.

Having forgotten the papers for his lecture in the study, he'd turned off the motorway and headed back immediately. He'd even called Emma to let her know, but the call had gone straight to voicemail when she was lying unconscious in the living room.

'I came straight upstairs when I heard you screaming.'

Her husband looked as if he'd aged several years, and Emma was worried that this wasn't just an effect of the pendant light. His temples appeared grey, his hair slightly thinner and his brow furrowed. All this, she suspected, was less a result of his forty years than what had completely changed half a year ago: their life.

Emma wanted to stand up, put her hand out to Philipp, stroke his chin – hastily shaven early this morning – and say, *'Don't worry, everything's fine now. Let's go to Tegel and take the first plane to somewhere we've never been before. It's just got to be far away. Let's leave fate behind us.'*

But she couldn't. Emma wouldn't make it to the front door. Christ, she couldn't even move the kitchen stool. So all she said was, 'I thought somebody had broken in.'

'Who?'

'No idea. Somebody.'

Philipp gave a sad sigh, like a young boy who's been hoping that the toy he's carefully mended will finally work again, only to discover when he tries it out that it's still broken.

'There's nobody here, Emma. The bathroom door slammed when I opened up downstairs. You know how draughty it gets here.'

She nodded, but with a grimace. 'That doesn't explain the ringing.'

'What sort of ringing?'

Emma turned to the voice behind her. Jorgo Kapsalos, Philipp's best friend and partner at the Federal Criminal Police Office, was standing in the kitchen doorway. He was the second man she'd seen in the bedroom.

This morning when he'd come to pick Philipp up, Jorgo had stayed in the car. Now he'd come in and was gazing at her as he always did when they met: wistfully and with subliminal hope.

Philipp overlooked his partner's secret looks, or misinterpreted them, but Emma guessed what was going on in Jorgo's mind when he eyed her so melancholically. If Emma sometimes used Konrad to stir Philipp's jealousy, she'd never abuse Jorgo's feelings for such a purpose. For unlike the defence lawyer, her husband's partner was anything but gay. The poor guy was hopelessly in love with her, something Emma had known even before her wedding day when a totally drunk Jorgo slurred into her ear as they danced that she'd married the wrong man, *for heaven's sake!*

'What sort of a ringing?' he repeated.

'No idea. An alarm clock or a mobile phone. I think it was coming from the attic.'

She hadn't heard anything since the two men had broken down the bedroom door and rushed in to her.

'Would you mind checking the rooms?' Philipp asked his partner.

'No, please don't!' In vain Emma racked her brain for words to explain that she'd been through all this once before.

Once before she'd searched a room and convinced herself that she was alone, only to be raped afterwards. Of course it was totally irrational and illogical, but Emma was worried that another search would summon the evil back and the horror would repeat itself. As if there were a times table of evil. An equation with an unknown by the name of 'danger' and a foregone conclusion: 'pain'.

Emma knew better than anyone else that this reasoning was pathological. Which is also why she didn't verbalise it to the two psychologically stable men, but just said, 'You've got to go. I've detained you long enough.'

'Don't be silly,' Jorgo said with a dismissive wave of the hand. 'It's not a problem.' He was incredibly well built, a compact, muscular man you'd be very glad to have at your side on a dark underground platform when a horde of drunks were coming your way. 'We can miss the first seminar. It's not that important anyway.'

Philipp nodded. 'My lecture's not indispensable either. Maybe it would be best if you went without me, Jorgo.'

'If you say so.' Jorgo shrugged, looking not particularly pleased. Emma guessed why. *He* would rather stay alone with her. Her husband's best friend had sent her several emails offering her his help in the wake of her great misfortune. She'd deleted them all, the last few without even reading them.

'Yes, I think it's better if I stay here.' Philipp nodded once more. 'You can see how distraught she is.'

He pointed to Emma and spoke as if she weren't in the room. Another of his non-dream-husband habits. 'I can't leave her here alone.'

'Of course you can. It's not a problem,' Emma protested, even though *'It's not a problem'* expressed roughly the opposite of what she thought.

Philipp went over to her and took her hand. 'Emma, Emma, what was it that upset you so much today?'

Good question.

The advertisement for the electric razor? Her fainting?

Salim's farewell? The photo of the Hairdresser in the lift?

Or… wait, no…

'What sort of a package?' she heard Philipp say,

realising that she'd thought out loud for the second time this morning.

'The food crate in the hall?' he asked.

'No, I'm sorry, I haven't unpacked it yet.'

The fact that she'd almost forgotten to tell her husband about the strange package on her desk made her aware of just how all over the place she was. Deep inside she sensed that she was overlooking something different, something crucial, but she couldn't work out what for the moment. And the package was probably far more important.

'Salim asked me to look after something for our neighbour.'

'And?' Jorgo and Philipp chorused in unison.

'But I've never heard the name before,' Emma added.

Bloody hell, what's he called again? In her distress, Emma had actually forgotten, but then recalled the name. 'Do you know an A. Palandt?'

Philipp shook his head.

'There you go. Nor do I.'

'Maybe he's new to the area?' Jorgo suggested.

'We would know,' Emma said, almost truculently.

'And this is what worked you up?' Philipp squeezed her hand more tightly. 'A package for a neighbour?'

'An *unknown* neighbour. Darling, I know I overreact...'

She ignored Philipp's slight sigh.

'... but we really do know everyone here, and—'

'And maybe he's subletting, perhaps he's a son-in-law living with his fiancée's parents for a while and having his post sent here,' Philipp said. 'There are hundreds of potentially innocent explanations.'

'Yes, you're probably right. But still I'd like you to take a look at the package. You must know that photograph from the security camera in the lift at—'

Philipp's face darkened and he let go of her hand. 'Have you been on the internet again?'

As if he'd given the magic word it happened again.

Two floors above them.

There was a beeping.

The sad look with which Jorgo, leaning against the doorframe, had listened to their conversation, vanished and was replaced by expression of hard concentration.

Philipp, too, had put on what Emma called his 'policeman's face': narrowed eyes, knitted brow, head to one side, lips slightly open, tongue pressed against the upper incisors.

After a brief exchange of glances in the interval between two rings, the two men nodded to each other and Jorgo said, 'I'll take a look.'

Before Emma could object, Philipp's partner disappeared into the hallway. He climbed the stairs with confident steps, his hand on the belt holding the holster of his service weapon.

15

'It can't go on like this, Emma,' Philipp whispered, as if he were worried that Jorgo might hear him two floors up. 'You've got to make a decision.'

'What do you mean?'

The distant beeping was gnawing at Emma's nerves and she couldn't concentrate on her husband's voice. Nor could she deal with the horrific images in her head. Images of what might happen to Jorgo up there – a slit throat, for example, opening and closing, and each time the policeman unsuccessfully tried to scream a torrent of blood spurting onto the floor of the children's room that would forever remain unfinished.

'What are you talking about, Philipp?' she asked again.

Her husband came up close and bent down so that his cheek touched her slapped one. 'Therapy, Emma. I know you want to get over this alone, but you've crossed a line.'

Emma shuddered when she felt his breath on her earlobe. For a moment she thought she was remembering the tongue that, in the darkness of the hotel room, had buried itself in her ear, while she, paralysed, had only been capable of muffled cries. But then Philipp said softly, 'You've really got to look for a therapist, Emma. I've spoken to Dr Wielandt about this.'

'The police psychologist?' Emma asked in horror.

'She knows your case, Emma. Lots of people are familiar with it. We have to check the…' He faltered, obviously because he realised he couldn't finish the sentence without hurting his wife.

'… check the facts of my statement. Say no more. So what does Dr Wielandt think? That I'm a pathological liar who invents rape stories for fun?'

Philipp took a deep breath. 'She's concerned that you were deeply traumatised as a child…'

'Oh, shut up!'

'Emma, you have a lively, exuberant imagination. In the past you saw things that weren't there.'

'I was six years old!' she yelled.

'A child neglected by her father, making up an imaginary substitute to compensate for his lack of affection.'

Emma laughed. 'Did Dr Wielandt have to write that out for you or did you learn it by heart first time?'

'Emma, please…'

'You don't believe me then?'

'I didn't say that—'

'So now you also think I suffer from hallucinations,

don't you?' she hissed, interrupting him. 'I imagined the whole thing? The man in my hotel room, the injection, the pain? The blood? Oh, what am I saying, perhaps I wasn't even really pregnant. Maybe I made that up too? And the alarm in the attic, that's just in my head too…'

She fell silent abruptly.

Oh God.

The beeping wasn't even in her head any more.

It had stopped.

Emma held her breath. Looked up at the ceiling that was urgently in need of a coat of paint. 'Please tell me you heard it too,' she said to Philipp and pressed her hand to her mouth. After her outburst the sudden silence felt like a harbinger of dreadful news.

'You heard it, didn't you?'

Philipp didn't answer her, but Emma heard footsteps coming down the stairs. She turned to the door, where Jorgo appeared with a red face.

'Have you got any batteries?' he asked.

'Batteries?' she repeated, confused.

'For the smoke alarm,' Jorgo said, presenting her with a small nine-volt battery in the palm of his hand. 'You need to change these every five years at the latest, otherwise they start to beep like the one in your attic.'

Emma closed her eyes. Happy that there was a harmless explanation for the beeping, but also disappointed in an irrational way. Basically, she'd had a nervous breakdown because of the signal from a smoke alarm, and this overreaction can only have reinforced her husband's doubts about her mental faculties.

'Strange,' Philipp said, scratching the back of his head. 'That can't be right. I only checked the things last week.'

'Not thoroughly enough, so it seems. So, Emma?' she heard Jorgo ask, and for a moment she had no idea what he was getting at.

'Batteries?' he repeated.

'Wait, I'll have a look.' She pushed past Jorgo and Philipp and was on her way into the living room when she suddenly remembered what she'd forgotten earlier.

Samson!

In all the kerfuffle she'd completely forgotten about him, and only now that she was looking at his sleeping blanket by the fireplace did she realise what her subconscious had been nagging her for.

Why didn't he come when I called him?

Samson just raised his head wearily and seemed to smile when he saw his mistress. Emma was horrified by his sad expression. His breathing was shallow and his nose dry.

'Are you in pain, little one?' she asked, wandering over to the shelves where the electric thermometer was in the bottom drawer. She glanced at the desk and all of a sudden was unable to think about Samson's condition any more.

Not when she saw the desk.

Where the package was that Salim had given her earlier.

Wrong.

Where it ought to have been.

Because in the place where she'd put it before opening up her notebook, to take yet another look at the lift photo of the Hairdresser, there was nothing to be seen now.

The package for A. Palandt had vanished.

16

Three weeks later

'And then they left you alone?'

Konrad had barely moved while listening; he hadn't even uncrossed his legs or unclasped his hands in his lap. Emma knew why: he'd told her when she'd once remarked on his bodily control.

With difficult clients – those who had something to hide – the merest distraction would disturb their flow.

I'm one of those for him now.

Emma was no longer a daughter-like friend, she was a difficult client whose statements had to be meticulously scrutinised.

'So in spite of the fact that the package had disappeared without trace Philipp and his colleague left?' Konrad clicked his fingers. 'Just like that?'

'No, of course not just like that.'

Emma turned to look at the window. The lake was

buried beneath a thin layer of snow. From this distance it looked inviting for ice-skating, but Emma knew how deceptive the appearance could be. Every year people fell through the ice on the Wannsee, having overestimated its strength. Luckily she didn't see anyone bold or reckless enough to tempt fate today, the miserable weather playing a part. There wasn't a soul to be seen on or around the lake. Only a few ducks and swans had flocked by the shore, defying the prevailing sleet that bathed the entire scene in a sad grey.

'I lied to Philipp,' Emma said by way of explanation. 'I told him that my nerves must have been playing a trick on me and probably I hadn't drunk enough. Hence I blacked out and hallucinated about a package that never existed.'

'And he believed *that*?' Konrad asked doubtfully.

'No, but when I took a diazepam in front of him he knew I'd sleep half the day.'

'You take that for anxiety disorder?' Konrad asked. Emma remembered he was a lawyer rather than a doctor. In her head she could already see him working on a theory of diminished responsibility due to excessive tablet consumption. And yet he had far more in his hand than paltry substance abuse to plead mental incapacity on her behalf. But they'd come to that in good time.

'Yes. Lorazepam would have actually been my drug of choice. It's newer, takes effect more rapidly and doesn't sedate you as much as diazepam, which makes you incredibly tired. But unfortunately it was all I had in the house.'

'So you took your pill and then the two of them went to the conference in Bad Saarow?'

'After they'd checked the smoke alarms in every room and thus done a search of the entire house including the basement, yes.'

Emma couldn't say whether it was his tightly pressed lips or the growl in his voice, but she clearly sensed that Konrad seriously frowned on her husband's behaviour. The two men had never got on, which wasn't helped, of course, by the fact that Emma had ignored Philipp's 'sugar daddy' comments and had even cultivated his jealousy. For his part, Konrad had often raised an eyebrow about the vulgar 'peasant' who would pass over the phone without saying hello or barely shake his hand on the rare occasions they met.

In this specific instance, however, Konrad's criticism of Philipp as an oaf was unjustified. If he'd been in Philipp's shoes and she'd implored him in the same way, he'd have found it difficult to refuse her request too.

'I need my peace and quiet, Philipp. I'd be even more stressed if I knew you were missing your lecture just because of me. I've taken my medicine now. You've searched the entire house and, anyway, Sylvia's popping by this afternoon to check on me, so please do me and yourselves a favour and leave me alone. Okay?'

None of that was a lie, and yet none of it was honest.

'Did the medicine work?'

Konrad poured her some tea. He'd soon have to replace the tealight in the warmer as the wick was virtually swimming in wax.

'Oh boy, did it work.'

'You felt tired.'

Emma took the cup offered to her and sipped some tea. The Assam blend tasted bittersweet and furry, as if it had been left to brew for too long.

'The diazepam almost floored me. I felt sleepy like before an operation.'

'And free of anxiety?'

'Not to begin with. But that was also because…'

'What?'

'Something… something happened. As they were leaving.'

Konrad raised his eyebrows and waited for her to continue talking.

'Jorgo. He gave me his hand…'

'And?'

'And he put something in mine.'

'What?'

'A note.'

'What did it say?'

'The nicest thing that any man had said to me in ages.'

'I love you?' Konrad asked.

Emma shook her head.

'I *believe* you,' she said, pausing to allow the words to take effect.

Konrad didn't appear surprised, but with his well-trained poker face that didn't mean much.

'I believe you,' he repeated softly.

'Jorgo had scribbled that on a tiny piece of paper. And that I should ring him. I was speechless when I read the message as soon as they were out of the door.'

'What happened then?'

Emma winced before answering Konrad. 'You know what happened.'

'I want to hear it from your mouth.'

'I, I...'

She closed her eyes. Pictured her front door. From the inside. Saw her hand stretching out for the handle, turning the key twice.

'I did the unthinkable,' she said, completing her sentence.

Konrad nodded slowly. 'For the first time in six months?'

'Yes.'

Konrad bent forwards. 'Why?'

She raised her head and looked him straight in the eye. She could see herself as a tiny reflection in his pupils.

'Because of the blood,' she whispered. 'All of a sudden there was blood everywhere.'

17

Three weeks earlier

Emma was kneeling in a pool of red in the middle of the living room, halfway between the fireplace and her desk. She felt strangely calm. The blood had gushed out, completely unexpectedly in spite of the wheezing and panting that had preceded it.

A deep breath, a spastic convulsion of the upper chest muscles. A sound as if a living creature were being breathed out of the body, then Samson vomited at her feet.

'My poor darling, what's wrong?'

As she stroked his head she could feel him shivering, as if he were just as cold as her. Philipp and Jorgo had been gone barely half an hour, in which time she'd turned the house upside down again looking for the package that had actually disappeared.

But that's impossible!

Unbelievably tired, her back soaked with sweat, Emma had returned to the living room from the hallway, having searched it yet again. In a moment of desperation, she was going to check beneath Samson's blanket to see whether the dog might have thought to take the package to his sleeping place. Instead she'd found him in this pitiful state.

'Hey, Samson. Can you hear me?'

The husky started retching again.

In normal circumstances Emma would have been scared witless and slapped her hands over her mouth, terrified that this desperate situation was too much for her. But now the first diazepam tablet was smoothing the largest waves of anxiety without eliminating them altogether. It was like being anaesthetised at the dentist's. You no longer felt the shooting pain, but there was a general, dull ache just waiting to flare up again the moment the injection wore off.

What now?

She looked outside. A jackdaw came to rest on a bare magnolia and seemed to wave at her, but of course Emma was imagining it. Heavy snow was still falling and Emma couldn't make out the bird's eyes.

It was more her subconscious telling her what she had to do.

'You've got to leave the house!'

'No!' she said, but she could barely hear herself because Samson was being sick again. This time it was accompanied by less blood, but that didn't make it any better.

'Yes, and you know it. You've got to get out, Samson needs help!'

'No way.' Emma shook her head and went over to the desk where her mobile was.

'Who are you going to call then?'

'Who do you think? The emergency vet.'

'Are you sure?'

'Of course, just look at him.'

She looked at Samson.

'I hear what you're saying,' said the voice in her head, which sounded like a precocious version of her own. *'He probably doesn't have much time left. But is that what you really want to do?'*

'Save him?'

'Put yourself in danger,' the voice said.

As if thunderstruck, it took Emma a while to digest these words. Then she put her mobile back on the desk.

'You're right.'

I can't call anyone.

Because it wouldn't just be that one call. At some point there would be a stranger at her front door. A vet she didn't know, but who she'd have to let in, because she could hardly send Samson out into the cold to be examined. And in the end she'd have to go with him to the veterinary clinic after all when it turned out that they wouldn't be able to treat him at home.

'Fuck,' she cursed.

Samson was now lying on his side, almost in a foetal position, and panting. His tongue was hanging wanly out of his mouth and his nose was completely dry. A string of blood ran from his black muzzle to the parquet floor.

'What on earth is wrong with you?'

And what should I do?

She couldn't let a stranger into the house, not in her condition. But the only logical alternative – to leave the house – was at least as terrifying.

For a moment Emma wondered whether she ought to ring Philipp, but that would put paid to his conference for good, and Emma didn't want that.

Maybe it's just a virus?

As Emma stroked Samson's white coat she was hardly able to feel his ribs when he breathed. It could be a lung inflammation, but the symptoms were too drastic and had come on too suddenly.

At least she now knew why Samson had been so limp the whole time.

My poor bear, it looks more likely that someone…

She jumped to her feet, flabbergasted by this shocking thought.

… that someone poisoned you!

Emma couldn't get out of her head the image of Salim asking her if it was okay and giving Samson a treat.

No, no, no. That's nonsense.

Emma's thoughts were flowing into her consciousness at half speed, a typical effect of the sedative. She was still capable of reasoning, but everything took twice as long.

But not Salim. He gives Samson something every time, and nothing ever happened before.

Outside, the jackdaw had left its perch. Emma could see just its tail feathers as it flew exactly in the direction she had to move in now too.

Dr Plank's veterinary practice was just one block towards Heerstrasse.

But she'd have to wear something warm, put Samson on a lead, even carry him perhaps, although this was not what made her so worried.

The biggest problem was that she'd have to open the front door and leave the protection of her own four walls for the first time in almost six months.

'No, I can't. It's inconceivable,' she said, which of course was a paradox because she'd just been mulling it over in her mind. She was also thinking that she'd never manage to tear down the wall that had built up between her and life outside, and take not just one but several steps into a world she wanted nothing more to do with.

No, I won't manage it.

Even though Dr Plank was the closest vet, only five minutes' walk away, and his practice stayed open till six o'clock, whereas most others in Berlin were closed on Saturdays.

I still can't.

It's inconceivable.

Emma stood motionless for a quarter of an hour beside the suffering animal at her feet, until she made the decision to try and cope without outside help for the time being.

Then Samson had his first respiratory arrest.

18

Anxiety eats into the soul and hollows people out from the inside. It also feeds on human time: it took Emma half an hour to put on something warm, and she needed several attempts just to lace up her boots before her clammy fingers pulled up the zip of her puffer jacket and, dripping with sweat, she opened the door, which required another eternity, or so it seemed to her.

At the moment the diazepam that she'd washed down with a gulp of tap water was having more side effects than direct ones. Emma was incredibly tired, but the iron ring around her chest would not loosen its grip.

Luckily Samson had started breathing again, although he couldn't stay on his feet for long. So to make matters worse Emma had to make a detour to the shed, a small, grey, metal shack that stood at the back of the garden. If she wasn't mistaken, the sledge was still hanging on the wall in there. Philipp had bought it when they moved, on the erroneous assumption that they'd use it regularly, given that they were now living so close to the Teufelsberg.

Well, maybe it was paying for itself today as transport for Samson.

Emma was breathing heavily and focusing on her path across the snowy lawn. Shuffling tentatively, like a patient attempting her first step after a major operation, she teetered forwards.

Each step was a test of courage.

The walk was so arduous, as if she were having to make it with diving cylinders on her back and wearing flippers. Her feet sank to her ankles and more than once she had to stop to regain her breath.

At least she wasn't shivering, which may have been because her soul was already so frozen that there was no room left to feel the cold physically.

Or I'm already suffering from 'hypothermic madness', the name given to a psychological phenomenon whereby some people on the point of freezing to death believe they're terribly hot. Which was why sometimes you found frozen corpses naked outside. As they died, the poor souls ripped the clothes from their bodies.

Well, if fear were a shirt, I'd be happy to take it off, Emma thought, surprised that she couldn't smell anything out here in the garden. No snow, no earth, not even her own sweat. The wind was blowing in the wrong direction, bringing the rattling of the S-Bahn from nearby Heerstrasse station into the gardens. Although her hearing was a little better than usual, her sight was worse.

The garden seemed to get narrower with every step. It took her a while to realise that the panic was constricting her field of vision.

First of all the bushes disappeared, then the cherry and rhododendron, and in the end there was just a long, black tunnel leading straight to the shed.

Visual disorders.

Emma knew the symptoms of an oncoming panic attack: dry mouth, racing heart and a change in the perception of colour and form.

Worried that she'd never get any further if she stopped again now, Emma staggered onwards until she finally reached the shed.

She jerked open the door and grabbed blindly for the sledge which Philipp had hung neatly on the wall beside the door.

A bright-red plastic object that was light, wide and shaped like a shovel. Thank goodness it wasn't one of those old-fashioned, heavy wooden things with runners, which Samson could very easily have fallen off.

On the way back Emma felt a little better. Her success in having found the sledge immediately imbued her with some confidence.

Her field of vision had widened again too. The bushes were in their place, although they were moving about in a most unnatural fashion. Not sideways, as if being blown by the wind, but up and down like an accordion.

Disconcerting, but nowhere near as terrifying as the footprints that Emma hadn't noticed on the way there.

She looked at the heavy boot prints in the snow in front of her. They couldn't be her own as they were at least three sizes too big. They were only going in one direction.

To the shed.

Emma turned back to the grey shack. She'd left its door open.

Was it moving?

Was anyone in there?

Had she maybe grabbed the sledge in the darkness and just missed a man crouching behind the lawnmower?

Emma couldn't see anything or anyone, but the feeling lingered that she was being watched.

GET OUT!

'Samson,' she called, speeding up. 'Samson, come here! My poor thing, please come!'

The suffering creature did her bidding, struggling up from the doormat where he'd been waiting for her. It sounded as if he had whooping cough.

'Thank you, my darling. Good dog.'

She tapped on the seat of the plastic sledge and he dragged himself onto it, then slumped, sniffling.

'Don't worry,' Emma said comfortingly to the dog and herself. 'I'll help you.'

She patted his head, gritted her teeth and pulled Samson with a rope towards the road. Unwisely, she turned back and thought she saw a shadow behind the small window in the door.

Did the curtain just move?

No, it was hanging serenely and there was no light behind it that could have cast a shadow.

And yet. Emma felt as if she were being followed by invisible eyes.

GET OUT

BEFORE IT'S TOO LATE.

And these eyes opened wounds, out of which all her courage seeped.

If my will to live were fluid, I'd leave a red trail behind me, she thought. *Which would be practical; I'd only need to follow it to find my way back.*

She took hold of the sledge rope, which had briefly slipped from her hand, and forced herself onwards again. To the vet.

Away from the dark house behind her, from which she believed she was being watched by dead eyes at the window. Waiting for her to come back.

Assuming she ever did.

19

'How long has he been in this condition?' Dr Plank asked as he listened to Samson's chest.

The poor creature was on a drip providing him with electrolytes and a substance that should induce him to vomit in a few minutes' time. Ever since the vet had heaved the husky onto the treatment table with Emma's help, Samson had barely been conscious. Now and again he shuddered as he exhaled, but that was the only sign of life.

'How long? Well, I, I think…' Emma's voice was trembling as badly as her knees.

She felt as if she'd run for her life, rather than merely having gone three hundred metres around the corner. In her mind, three hundred metres equated to a marathon.

My first time outside alone, and with a dog as close to death as I am to insanity.

Contemplating her feat in the harsh light of the halogen lamp that hovered above Samson, she could scarcely believe that she'd made it. Made it here, to the broad, end-of-terrace house with its cream façade and green shutters. The garage had been converted into a waiting room years ago. Fortunately Emma didn't have to spend too much time there. With the exception of a small girl, who'd sat crying with a cat basket on her lap, she was the only patient. And because of the severity of Samson's symptoms she'd been shown in immediately.

'I'm not sure. He's been droopy since this morning,' Emma finally managed to complete her sentence. 'I think it started around eleven.'

The vet grunted and Emma couldn't tell if it was a grunt of satisfaction or concern.

He'd put on a bit of weight since she'd last seen him, but that was a while ago now, in the time before, at the neighbourhood party organised every year by the residents' association. The freshly starched apron was a little tight around the tummy of the 1.90-metre man. He'd developed a slight double chin and fuller cheeks, which made him appear more affable than before. Now Plank resembled a large teddy bear with light-brown, unkempt hair, a broad nose and melancholic button eyes.

'Did he eat anything unusual?'

Emma felt nervously for the headscarf covering her short hair. If Plank was wondering why she hadn't taken it off he wasn't letting it show.

'Yes, I mean, no. You know Salim, don't you?'

'Our delivery man?'

'He gave Samson a dog biscuit, he always gives him one.'

'Hmm.'

Plank was wearing latex medical gloves, similar to those that had stroked her head. Back in the darkness of the hotel room.

'What's going to happen now?' she asked the vet, one hand on Samson's chest, gazing at a white, glass-front cabinet, her eyes fixed on packets of gauze bandages and surgical collars as if they were as captivating as a work of art.

'We're going to have to wait to begin with,' Plank replied, checking the drip with a critical eye. He pointed to the drain of the table. 'We're treating him on spec; there are lots of signs that he's been poisoned. As soon as he's been sick we'll give him some charcoal to bind any toxins. My assistant is just calling the laboratory courier. Once that's done we'll hook Samson up to a urinary catheter to prevent the toxin from being reabsorbed by the bladder wall. Then, of course, there's the usual cocktail of medicines.'

Emma nodded. The same procedure as for humans.

'Everything on spec until we have the haemogram.'

'Could it be anything else apart from poisoning?'

Plank managed to nod and shrug at the same time. 'Unlikely. We'll know in more detail when the lab results are back.'

He patted the plaster covering the injection site on Samson's hind leg, from where he'd taken the blood.

'I've got good contacts at the veterinary clinic in Düppel, I'll have the results tomorrow morning at the latest.'

Emma noticed that her eyes were filling with tears. She couldn't say whether this was due to exhaustion or fear that it might be too late and the poison had already worked its way irreparably through Samson's body.

'The best would be if you left him here under observation for the next twenty-four hours, Frau Stein.'

Plank paused and accidentally brushed her hand briefly as the two of them stroked Samson's head together. 'He's better off here than at home.' He followed this up with a baffling question.

'Talking of home. Is your basement dry again?'

'I'm sorry?'

'The water that got in last month. The same thing happened here once. It was ages before we could get rid of the fan heaters. *Dearie, dearie me,* I thought, *poor old Frau Stein*. I mean, first your illness and then something like that. Nobody needs that. Your husband told me all about the palaver with the burst pipes.'

'Philipp?'

The door to the treatment room opened and a plump elderly woman in a nurse's coat entered. She gave Emma a cheery smile as she walked over to the medicine cabinet in her squeaky Birkenstock sandals, presumably to get everything ready for Samson's treatment.

Plank kept talking regardless.

'I met him in town by chance. It must have been four weeks ago pretty much to the day. A freaky coincidence. I was on call and that evening I had to go to a hotel, the chihuahua, do you remember?' he said to the nurse, who nodded wearily.

Plank grinned, shaking his head. 'An American woman's plaything had stepped on a piece of glass. As I left I saw your husband sitting in the lobby.' As Emma listened to the vet's words a wave of heat surged against her ribcage from the inside.

'My husband? In the lobby?' she repeated as if in a trance.

'Yes. *Well, well,* I thought, *I wonder what Herr Stein's doing here*. Then I saw the two drinks on the table and when I said hello he told me that the two of you were having to spend the night here until the worst was over.'

There was a ring at the door and Plank's assistant returned to the reception.

'Not that I was being nosy, mind, or thinking he was up to something, but afterwards I thought one could easily have drawn the wrong conclusions. I mean, who sleeps in a hotel in their own town, if…'

'… they haven't got the builders in?' Emma completed his sentence flatly.

Converting the nursery.

Which will never be used.

Or repairing water damage.

Which never happened.

'Well, I hope the pumps are out and your floor is dry again. Frau Stein?'

Emma removed her clenched fist from Samson's coat, realising that she must have been gaping at Plank for quite a while with an expressionless face. Without the sedative she would have probably screamed the place down, but the diazepam had deadened her emotions.

'Is everything okay with you?'

She forced a smile. 'Yes, everything's fine. I'm just a bit out of sorts because of Samson.'

'I understand,' Plank said, softly stroking her hand. 'Don't worry about him. He's in the best hands. And take a card with my mobile number from reception. If you have any questions you can call me at any time.'

Emma nodded. 'I've got one question already,' she said, on her way out.

'Go ahead.'

'The hotel.'

'Yes?'

'Where you bumped into my husband. Do you remember the name?'

20

Emma opened her mouth and waited to taste her childhood as soon as the snowflakes landed on her tongue.

But this sensuous experience failed to occur.

The fragrance of winter, the smell of the wind, the taste of the snow and all other sensations that could only be experienced rather than described, and which would bring back memories of her first sledge ride, difficult walks with wet socks and falling off her bike, but also a comforting hot bath in the evening, dunking lebkuchen into warm milk on the bench by the window while watching the tits pecking at the feed scattered from the birdhouse – Emma couldn't recall any of this.

She just felt cold. The way back was long and arduous, even without the sledge that she'd left behind at the practice. She felt her way forwards circumspectly, step by step on the pavement, which was icy in parts, listening to the crunching of her boots.

In her first December here in Teufelssee-Allee, Emma thought the estate could have been made for Christmas.

Small, cosy houses with fat candles in the windows, evergreen firs in the front gardens that needed merely a chain of lights to look Christmassy. Hardly any cars to spoil the atmosphere with their noise and which the foxes would have to watch out for as they scurried into the road from the Grunewald early in the afternoon.

Even the local residents, most of them slightly older, fitted the picture perfectly. Old Mother Frost type women in their pinafores returning with their shopping trolleys from the weekly market in Preussenallee, white-haired men in billowy cords, puffing on pipes as they cleared the snow from the pavement, and who you wouldn't be surprised to hear say 'Ho, ho, ho' as a greeting.

At the moment, however, there wasn't a soul about, except for a teenage boy who'd obviously been forced by his parents to grit the driveway.

This is something at least.

Emma couldn't have coped with being stopped by a neighbour for some small talk.

'Well, Frau Stein, what a nice surprise this is. We haven't seen you in ages! You must have missed at least four community breakfasts.'

'Yes, I'm sorry. A rapist stuck his penis in my far too dry vagina and then cut my hair off afterwards. I've been a bit all over the place since then, but if you don't mind me suddenly getting up and screaming during the meal, smashing my head against the edge of the table or pulling out clumps of hair, just because for a

second it occurs to me that the man opposite could be the instigator of my paranoid panic attacks, then I'll happily turn up to the next breakfast and I'll bring some croissants with me. How does that sound?'

Emma smiled briefly at this absurd inner dialogue, before starting to cry. Tears ran down her face, already damp from the snow. She went around the corner, turned into her street, then, after a few short steps, had to cling onto a fence and regain her breath.

She couldn't, no, she didn't *want* to comprehend just how far she'd fallen. Only a few months ago she'd been running an excellent practice. Today she couldn't complete even the most basic of everyday tasks and was being defeated by a pavement of no more than a few hundred pathetic metres.

And all because I didn't go back home that night.

Pitying oneself. Reproaching oneself. Killing oneself.

Emma knew the tragic trinity, and she'd be lying if she claimed never to have considered the last option.

'How absurd,' said her reason.

'How inevitable,' said that part of the human system that essentially makes all the decisions and which cannot be monitored nor cured, but only ever damaged: the soul.

The problem with psychological illnesses was that self-diagnosis was impossible. Trying to understand your brain using your brain held out about as much hope as a one-armed surgeon trying to sew back their own hand. It didn't work.

Emma knew that she was overreacting. That there must be a harmless explanation for why the vet had met Philipp in the hotel.

'Le Zen. A palace of Oriental kitsch, don't you think?'

And in all likelihood the mystery of the package would have a ridiculously simple explanation too.

It was pointless to spend hours poring over whether Salim really had given her a delivery for the neighbour, because her brain would never accept the alternative conclusion – that she'd lost her mind. Perhaps she hadn't seen Salim at all today; perhaps it wasn't the delivery man who rang at her door, but a stranger who'd given Samson poison rather than a biscuit?

Maybe she hadn't been to the vet either today, and instead she was strapped to a bed in the secure unit of the Bonhoeffer psychiatric hospital?

Emma didn't think this very likely. Such serious, audiovisual schizophrenic episodes were extremely rare and weren't triggered by a single traumatic incident. They were preceded by years and years of the most horrific damage. But maybe she *couldn't help* thinking this and it was a lie to protect herself.

Deep down she was convinced that although her self-control and communication skills had gone, she hadn't lost all relation to reality. But there was never a one hundred per cent certainty, especially when one's soul had suffered as severe damage as hers.

'The package was there!' she exclaimed, to tear

herself from the vicious circle of her thoughts. She repeated the words, as if to give herself courage. 'The package was there. I had it in my hand.'

Emma said it three more times and with each repetition she felt a little better. With rediscovered determination she took her mobile from her pocket and called her husband's number.

It beeped and went to his voicemail.

There was poor reception on sections of the A10 motorway; maybe they were going through a tunnel. At any rate Emma was grateful that she could deliver her message without being interrupted by critical questions.

'Darling, I know this is going to sound strange, but do you think it's possible that our delivery man isn't completely kosher? Salim Yüzgec. Is there any way you could run a background check on him?'

She explained the reason for her suspicion and finished with the words, 'There was one more thing. The vet says he saw you in Le Zen. You mentioned something to him about water damage. Could you tell me what that's all about?'

She put the phone back into her trouser pocket and wiped the snow from her eyes.

It was only when she took a step backwards that she realised which fence she'd been gripping onto all this time.

The garden gate, which had seen better days, was hanging crookedly from a rusty post. It was lined with chicken wire, the holes far larger than normal. For a name plate someone had simply stuck some tape to the edge of the door and written on it in permanent marker.

The letters were somewhat faded and, just to make sure, Emma looked up again at the ancient enamel sign which, as was customary in this area, was affixed between the kitchen window and the guest lavatory: Teufelssee-Allee 16a.

No doubt about it.

Her gaze returned to the fence. For a split second she was afraid that the letters on the sticky tape might have vanished into thin air just like the package on her desk, but they were still there, unchanged:

A. P.

Like 'A. Palandt'.

In the twinkling of an eye Emma made a momentous decision.

21

The logic was straightforward: *if the card exists, so does the package.*

Simple proof.

If, as he claimed, Salim had posted a delivery note through A. Palandt's door, then he must have given Emma the package beforehand.

So simple. So logical.

To be certain, the most obvious thing Emma could do was ring the doorbell and ask for Palandt, assuming he was back home now. But after everything Emma had seen on the internet this morning, that was out of the question. She felt sick with fear at the idea that the door might open to reveal a man only vaguely resembling the guy in the lift.

No, the only possible option was to take a quick glance in the post box which – and here Emma was confronted with another problem – appeared to be non-existent. Like much about this house, it seemed to have gone missing.

Emma recalled that the delicate widow who lived here alone had always kept the house in good nick. Now there were bulbs missing from the outside lights and the small, clay garden ornaments had disappeared. As far as Emma could see, there were no longer curtains inside the windows either, which was why the plain, grey house with its coarse, pockmarked render didn't just look uninviting, but abandoned.

I don't think there's anyone here.

The garden gate she'd been leaning against was stuck, but the entrance to the carport was wide open. She should abort her plan and go back home. But Emma felt magically drawn to the open gates. And if she were being honest with herself she'd know the reason why. It wasn't just about proving the existence of the package; she was being driven by the paranoid compulsion to gain some certainty about the identity of A. Palandt.

As improbable as it was that this individual had anything to do with the Hairdresser and what Emma had suffered, she was sure that she'd be driven mad by the thought of the stranger and the contents of that package if she didn't investigate further.

And so Emma sank into the ankle-deep snow on the way up to the house. She didn't mind the wet that crept into her boots through the eyelets, nor the fact that the snow was making her headscarf damp, flattening her hair beneath.

More uncomfortable were the penetrating looks she

thought she could feel in her back. Neighbours standing at the window, watching Emma make her way to the entrance, which unusually was at the side of the house, rather than the front. It was covered with corrugated iron and stood in the shade of a fir tree whose branches drooped like a curtain over the steps leading up to the house.

Emma climbed the four stairs and looked back at the street, but couldn't see anyone. Nobody watching her from a car or a neighbouring garden, not even any passers-by wondering why the woman who hadn't shown her face in public for half a year was suddenly crouching beside a stranger's front door.

As she'd feared, the post was delivered directly through an aperture in the door at A. P.'s house.

Shit.

If he'd had an external post box, she might have been able to feel the card with her slim fingers, *but like this?*

Emma lifted the metal flap, peered through the hole and of course she saw nothing. Inside the house it was darker than outside.

She took out her mobile and with her clammy fingers switched on the torch function.

In the distance a dog barked, and the sound mingled with the ever-present drone of Heerstrasse, which she only ever noticed when friends visiting for the first time brought the subject up while they were sitting in the garden.

Or when fear sharpened her senses.

Not just the fear of being discovered (for what was she supposed to say if the door suddenly opened?), but also the fear of being totally overwhelmed psychologically. Until this morning the world outside her front door had seemed like a raging ocean, with her as a non-swimmer on the beach, and now she was about to venture way too far out into the wide-open sea.

But I don't have a choice.

The light from her smartphone torch didn't get her any further. Given the narrow aperture and the oblique angle available to her, all she could make out were some floorboards and something that did actually look like paper or letters scattered on the floor. But was the card for the missed delivery amongst them? It was impossible to tell.

Okay, that's that then.

Emma felt relieved when she stood back up. Her brain had identified an acceptable reason for her not being able to conclude her plan. It was a good sign, a healthy sign that she wasn't so driven by impulse as to look for spare keys hidden beneath the mat, shake the side window of the guest room, or simply try the doorknob, which...

... turned without any resistance!

Emma withdrew her hand. There was a loud creaking as the door ground across the dark floorboards, pushing the post inwards.

She glanced over her shoulder, but nobody was

behind her, or at least nobody she could see. When she turned back she realised that it wasn't as dark inside the house as she'd first thought. A wan, yellowish light fell into the hallway from one of the rooms, and in the glow Emma could see that the front door was wedged by a pile of bulk mail.

There was something else too.

Something that made her take two steps into the unfamiliar house, even though she found the slim, metre-tall object she was heading towards more repellent than attractive.

But Emma couldn't believe what she was staring at here in the hallway, right beside the coat stand. And as she was worried that it might be her imagination, a vision dreamed up by her deranged brain as further fuel for her paranoia, she *had* to inspect it close up to be sure.

Emma stretched out her hand.

Noticed her own breath, as here inside it was barely warmer than outside.

Touched the cold polystyrene.

And felt a strip of adhesive tape on the replica of the human head, to which a few hairs were stuck.

No doubt about it.

That's a wig stand.

As she came to this realisation, which induced a numbness in Emma's hands, her mobile phone started to buzz.

Luckily she'd switched it to vibrate, otherwise

the sound would have echoed through the hallway like church bells.

'Hello,' she said, when she saw it was the veterinary practice on the line. Besides the wig stand, her concern for Samson was another reason to leave this house as quickly as possible.

'Frau Stein? It's Dr Plank's practice here. I'm very sorry to disturb you, but we've got a problem with the payment for the laboratory analysis. The animal clinic at Düppel says your credit card has been blocked.'

'That must be a mistake,' Emma whispered on the way back out, which was now obstructed. Not by a person, nor an object, but by light.

Bright, white xenon light, flooding the driveway and pouring into the house she had just entered illegally.

Broad headlight beams swept across the hedge as the vehicle, its engine gurgling, slowly turned into the entrance to the carport.

22

Back entrance.

This was the only thing she could think of as soon as she'd cut off the call.

Emma's body had switched into flight mode, and now her head felt clear. The fear of being discovered tore through the fog she'd been drifting in thanks to the diazepam.

For the time being at least.

There must be a back entrance here somewhere, she thought.

No way was she going to leave via the front door. Back past the mail, down the steps and straight into the arms of the owner of the wig stand as he was getting out of his car.

Out the back then.

And fast.

If, like most of the houses on the estate, this one was from the 1920s, it would have a similar floor plan with a living room that led onto a terrace.

Emma hurried down the hallway and opened the first door on the right into a large room that was even darker.

Initially she was worried that the external blinds might be down, but she only had to yank the heavy curtains stinking of dust and cold smoke to the side of the French doors.

These did indeed lead into the garden, which stretched out before her like a long, narrow towel.

The doors were old and their wavy glass panes made it seem as if you were looking at the world through a fisheye lens. But Emma wasn't in the slightest bit interested in the distorted view of a massive weeping willow, several gnarled fruit trees and a scattering of snow-covered boulders.

Hearing footsteps in the doorway, she breathed in the particle-heavy air, suppressed a cough and tried to make as little noise as possible as she slowly turned the handle of the French doors anticlockwise. The piercing sound when she pulled the jammed door tore painfully at her eardrums. Louder than a school bell signalling break time, the noise resonated throughout the entire house.

An alarm system?

Surely Palandt hadn't left the front door open, but secured the exit to the garden electronically?

It didn't make any sense, particularly as there was nothing to protect here, going by the squalor of the living room.

The sofa to Emma's left was half covered in old

newspapers. On the other side a spring had worn through the fabric cover. An upturned beer crate served as a coffee table. Unsophisticated drawings of horses' heads gaped from the walls, there was no dining table, no bookshelves, no rugs or chairs. An ugly statue of a dog stood on a mat right beside the door, a porcelain Labrador that could be used as an umbrella stand. She was reminded of Samson.

What I'd do to have him beside me now!

Otherwise there was just an empty chipboard display case, sitting diagonally in the room, as if it had been hurriedly dumped there by packers.

Certainly nothing that might interest a burglar, and yet an ear-splitting ringing had just shredded the silence.

Emma was sweating and her mouth felt parched, but the diazepam and adrenaline were performing great teamwork. Fear was spurring her on, her tiredness taking a break. It now dawned on her that it had only rung once, which was also unusual for a burglar alarm.

Emma let go of the handle and was just about to shove the door, clearly stuck, with her shoulder when she heard voices.

Foreign voices.

Albanians, Slovenes, Croats?

She couldn't tell; all she could say was than none of them could be A. Palandt because the two men who must have first rung at the front door and were now coming down the hall, were shouting the house owner's surname loudly and aggressively over and over again. 'PAAALANDT? PAAAAALANDT!'

One of them had a hoarse rattle, as if he'd just had surgery on his larynx. The other man's barking could have been coming straight from the stomach of a bull terrier.

Between the shouting, the two men hissed at each other in their native language, which sounded anything but friendly.

'AAANTON?'

So now she knew his first name, but not the way out of here.

In vain Emma pushed and pulled at the door to the terrace. It was stuck fast, as if it had been glued or nailed to the floor, unlike the living-room door through which she'd just entered. This was kicked open with a fury that almost threw it off its hinges.

If the first of the two men hadn't turned back to his accomplice because he couldn't understand what he was saying, Emma would have been discovered immediately. But now she had a second or two to dart past the empty cabinet, where she'd intended to hide until she suddenly realised that it had been blocking her view of something which was, temporarily at least, her salvation: a connecting door.

It was open and Emma slunk through it while behind her the men seemed to be cursing in their mother tongue.

Did they see me?

She didn't waste time thinking, nor did she look back,

only forwards, where she saw a staircase. It led upstairs along the internal wall of the house.

Up is good…

… Better, at least than down… *into the cellar*. People in danger only went into the cellar in horror films. *But not in a strange house, escaping from strange men looking for a strange neighbour, to do something to him they'd probably rather have no secret witnesses to.*

So Emma held onto a narrow banister and tried to climb the old, well-worn wooden stairs as quietly as possible.

Behind her came a crash – had the men pushed over the cabinet? Glass shattered but the loudest sound was her breathing.

On the first floor, equally sombre, Emma felt her way along the ingrain wallpaper on the landing to a door.

Locked. Just like the second one, directly opposite.

That's not possible.

She kept walking, towards a bright slit at the end of the landing. Another door, from beneath which the light slanted into the otherwise dark corridor that seemed like a tunnel to Emma. But this one wouldn't open either.

Emma wanted to scream with fury, fear and despair, but the men downstairs were already doing just that.

'PAAALAAANDT!'

Not just their bellowing, but their footsteps were approaching too. Hard, heavy boots climbing the stairs quicker than she had just done.

She turned to the left, having completely lost her bearings – she didn't know whether she was facing the street or the garden – and shook another door handle.

Nothing.

With the strength of desperation she finally threw herself against it in one last attempt, and almost flew into the room.

Emma tripped, slipped from the handle, her knees crashed on the floor that was covered with a rug, and she used her elbows to prevent her from hitting her head.

Shit.

She immediately got up again and closed the door from the inside.

Did they hear me?

Overcome by faintness, Emma looked for something to hold onto and came across a small chest of drawers. She kneeled beside it, unaware that she'd hidden in exactly the same position only hours ago.

Her back to the wall, her eyes fixed on a large bed.

It was warmer than in the rest of the house; she could smell sweat and another slightly rotten odour.

Either the curtains here weren't as thick as in the living room, or the tension had sharpened her senses. At any rate, Emma could see more than just shadows and shapes now.

She was obviously in Palandt's bedroom, which was dominated by an antique four-poster bed.

It had been freshly made; a patchwork quilt bulged over a thick duvet that peeked out at the foot of the bed.

At the other end, cushions of various sizes were neatly arranged in three rows that took up a third of the bed.

Like in a hotel, Emma thought, detesting the comparison.

'PAAALAAANDT?'

The men, now upstairs, rattled the same door handles she had only moments ago, except less gingerly.

Wood splintered, hinges creaked.

And Emma didn't know where to go.

Under the bed?

No, that would be the first place they'd look.

There weren't any large cupboards, just a clothes rail on wheels, a valet stand and a bedside table, right next to her, holding half a pharmacy's worth of pillboxes, sprays, tablets in foil packaging and other medicines.

All of a sudden she couldn't hear anything apart from the constant humming of fear inside her ears, then the proverbial calm before the storm was past. The bedroom door crashed open, knocking into the side of the chest of drawers she was hiding beside, and Emma was blinded.

Bright, glowing. Light.

From the ceiling it shone far too brightly and mercilessly onto the bed and everything else.

Including me.

Emma closed her eyes, not in that sort of childish reflex hoping nobody could see her just because she couldn't see anything herself, but because she'd been mistaken.

The thing next to the window wasn't a valet stand, but another wig stand. And it wasn't as bare as the one in the hall downstairs; this polystyrene head wore a long, blonde, lustreless woman's wig.

What the hell have I done? What sort of place have I entered?

Caught between two attackers and a pervert?

Hearing a pair of boots enter the room she still didn't dare open her eyes… and then her mobile rang.

Shit.

A loud, piercing ring. Like the alarm.

Shit, shit, shit!

Sweat was oozing from her pores as if the room had been turned up to sauna temperature.

She knew the game was up. That she wouldn't have time to grab the phone from her pocket, take the call and scream for help. She tried anyway.

Too late.

She held the telephone and stared at a dark display, cursing the caller who'd only let it ring twice to give her away. Then she heard the man with the bull terrier bass give a filthy laugh.

She opened her eyes, in the certainty that she'd be staring at her own death, but nobody was there.

The laughing grew quieter, moved away from the bedroom and down the landing, along with the sounds that the second man's boots made on the floorboards.

It was only when the two of them were back downstairs that Emma realised it wasn't her phone that had rung, but the bull terrier's.

It had the same standard ringtone as her own. The man had been called by someone who'd made him laugh and had evidently said something to make them abandon their search.

'Get outta there, we've found Palandt.'

or

'Forget the neighbour, there's something else for you to do.'

or

'Hi, it's me, Anton Palandt. They also call me the Hairdresser. I know we'd arranged for you to come here, but could we meet somewhere else? Right at this moment I've got problems with a dying tart.'

Whatever the message, Emma felt as if the caller had saved her life.

For now.

She got to her feet, gripped onto the chest of drawers, and wondered whether to grab one of the pillboxes that, as she could see now in the harsh light of the overhead lamp, all had Cyrillic writing on them. But there was no time to translate her decision into action.

Right in front of her the cushions jerked.

The quilt arched, bulging in some places like a pregnant woman's belly where the unborn baby kicks.

Then an arm emerged from beneath the exposed duvet and a bald, skinny man sat up.

23

His torso was bare and bony; he looked like a prisoner on the verge of starvation.

His eyes were wide open, swimming in a pool of tears. He didn't blink once.

Not when he turned his head to Emma.

Nor when he fixed his stare on her.

Not even when she let out a high-pitched scream and tore from the room. Along the landing, down the stairs to the front door where initially she thought she'd run slap into the two men. But it was just the wig stand, which she knocked to the ground, falling over herself in the process. She got up again at once and rushed into the street, without a thought for the neighbours or anyone else who might be watching. Emma slipped several times on the icy cobbles, but not so badly as to fall a second time.

Emma ran and ran and ran... Startled by the crunching gravel her feet was spraying up. By the panting of her own lungs.

She pressed her hand to where the stitch hurt most and kept running until she finally came to her house. The only detached building in the area, which Philipp had made as secure as a bank, with electronic locks she needed a transponder to open. This was a round, coin-like chip you had to hold beneath the lock before it beeped twice and now Emma pulled it from her pocket as she went up the steps.

She almost dropped it when she noticed that the LED light on the lock was green. And then Emma saw a dim glow coming through the curtain behind the small pane of glass in the door.

No. That's impossible, Emma screamed silently.

That *has* to be impossible!

Someone had switched off the alarm system, opened the door and turned the light on inside.

And it wasn't Philipp, because his car wasn't there.

24

'Where are you going?'

Emma, who'd made a sharp about-turn and was searching in vain for her mobile to call the police, was infinitely relieved to hear her best friend's voice behind her.

She turned back to the door, which was now open. 'Christ, Sylvia. You gave me a fright.'

Instead of an apology or at least a normal greeting, Sylvia just left her standing on the step and went back into the house without a word.

Emma followed her, now overcome with sheer exhaustion. Samson, stealing into Palandt's house, the intruders, the way back when she'd overexerted herself – all this had taken Emma to her limits. She could happily do without another problem, which her friend's strange behaviour suggested was on the cards.

Emma closed the door.

Her fingers trembling, she hung her coat on the rack, took off her snow-drenched boots and went into the living room. With the sudden change in temperature blood shot to her cheeks.

'Are you alright?'

Sylvia shook her head angrily. Her dark hair, which was usually pinned up, hung limply on her shoulders.

Normally when she came to visit Sylvia would make herself comfortable with her legs up on the sofa. She'd ask Emma for a macchiato before chatting about the most trivial things that had happened over the past week. Today she was wearing a mouse-grey tracksuit instead of the habitual designer clothes, and she sat as stiff as a statue on the edge of the sofa, her gaze fixed on the glowing embers in the fire.

'No, I'm not. Nothing's alright,' Sylvia said, as if to explain her unusual outfit and strange behaviour.

Sylvia Bergmann was not only her best friend, but the tallest too. Even amongst her widest circle of acquaintances, there was no woman on a par with her, and not just metaphorically speaking. The fact that she wore size forty-two shoes said a lot, as did the fact that she might have become a professional basketball player if her conservative parents hadn't insisted on a proper career, although as far as study was concerned they'd been thinking more on the lines of medicine rather than physiotherapy. The patients in Sylvia's practice on the Weinberg loved her because of her huge, magical hands that, as if equipped with a sonar, first felt for tension and blockages, then made them vanish by pressing energy and reflex points known to her alone.

Today, however, Sylvia looked as if she could do with one of her own treatments. Everything about her appeared cramped and tense.

'Sit down,' she demanded gruffly, as if this were her house and Emma a summoned guest.

Emma was fighting a wave of tiredness that was causing her to sway now that she was back within her own four walls. The house didn't feel as safe as it had this morning, partly because Sylvia had opened the door to her.

'Sylvie, I hate to say it, but you know that I gave you the key only for emergencies?'

'Sit down!' Sylvia repeated in a cold voice. 'This *is* an emergency.'

'What's wrong with you?' Emma asked, deciding to stay standing. Despite her wobbly knees she thought it was important to keep her distance. If necessary she could hold onto the mantelpiece above the fire.

'What's wrong, you ask?' Sylvia achieved the impossible and managed to sound even less friendly. 'Why are you doing this to me?' she blurted out.

'What are you talking about?'

'This!'

Her friend took a white pillbox with a red cap from the pocket of her tracksuit top.

'You know what this is?' she asked.

Emma nodded. 'Looks like the progesterone I gave you.'

A drug that increases the chances of pregnancy. The medicine stimulates circulation in the uterus. Women who've been unable to have children are encouraged to take this before conception and also afterwards to prevent them from miscarrying. Emma had it prescribed by her gynaecologist after the first ultrasound scan and gave the opened packet to her friend.

After the bleeding, *after the night in the hotel*, she'd had no further use for it.

'Why are you doing this to me?' Sylvia said again, putting the pillbox onto the coffee table.

'What the hell are you talking about?'

'Do you not want me to have any children?'

'I'm sorry?'

'Do you want me to suffer the same fate as you?'

'What on earth has got into you?' Emma raised both hands, opened and closed her fingers and kneaded the air like invisible dough, feeling helpless, with no idea how to respond to this unbelievably hurtful accusation. 'Why should I think that?' she asked, tears welling in her eyes. 'I love you, Sylvia. I wouldn't wish a night with the Hairdresser on my worst enemy.'

Sylvia looked at her in silence for a while, then nodded scornfully, as if she'd been expecting a lie like that. 'Over the last few weeks I've been suffering permanent sickness, headaches and tiredness,' she said flatly.

Welcome to the club.

'I was delighted to begin with, because I thought it

had finally worked. But the tests remained negative and I got my period. So I went to the doctor and he asked me if I was taking any medicines. Only Utrogestan, I said, which he approved of. *Yes, that can help.*'

As Sylvia's eyes wandered across Emma's face they felt like acupuncture needles. Her best friend opened her mouth and Emma took an involuntary step backwards, as if Sylvia were a growling dog baring its teeth.

'That's assuming that the packet your dear friend gives you *is* progesterone. And not Levenor-something,' Sylvia said in a voice that was too quiet for such an outrageous accusation.

'Levonorgestrel?' Emma became hot. She started sweating for the first time that day. 'That's impossible,' she spluttered. She wobbled over to the mantelpiece and felt even hotter.

'What were you thinking?' Sylvia asked. 'When the bleeding got heavier, Peter took a look at the pills. His ex-wife had taken them too, you see, and he said hers looked very different.'

Peter!

Sylvia's boyfriend with no surname. Or at least Emma didn't know his surname, which might have been because she barely listened to her best friend when she talked about him. Sylvia had only met him in the time afterwards, when Emma didn't mind listening to anything apart from relationship stories. She hadn't even wanted to see a photo of him. All she knew about

Peter was that he was supposedly 'the one', the dream man she wanted to have children with.

'So I took the pills to a pharmacist and he analysed them.'

Her best friend started to weep. In tears, she grabbed the packet from the table and flung it in Emma's direction, missing her head by miles and crashing into shelves behind her. As it hit the ground the box opened and the pills rolled across the parquet floor like tiny marbles. 'You swapped them,' Sylvia screamed. 'You gave me the morning-after pill, you crazed bitch!'

25

From a slight distance Emma stared at the packet that looked exactly like the one she'd given Sylvia a good three months ago.

The morning-after pill?

'There's got to be a logical explanation,' Emma said, without having the slightest clue what it might be.

'Why doesn't it surprise me that you're going to try to come up with one of your stories?'

'Sylvia, you know me.'

'Do I?'

I don't know. I don't even know if I know myself.

Emma scratched her forearm nervously. Suddenly she felt her whole body itching. 'If what you're saying is right, then someone else must have swapped the pills.'

'Oh yes, an ominous somebody. Like the somebody who supposedly raped you.'

Ouch!

Now it was out in the open. *Supposedly.*

A single word. That was all it needed to toss their friendship into the bin and put the lid on.

'I didn't mean it,' Sylvia croaked. She looked as if she'd just awoken from a bad dream. With a different, slightly softer expression, she put her hand to her mouth in regret.

'But you said it,' Emma said impassively.

'I know. But just put yourself in my situation. What am I to think?'

'The truth.'

'But what is the truth, Emma?'

The brief pause for breath was over. Sylvia now talked herself into a rage again, and every word brought her closer to the fury of a few moments before.

'A hotel room that doesn't exist? A witness who can't be found? For Christ's sake, Emma, you don't even fit the profile. The Hairdresser kills whores. You're the most faithful wife I know. And you're alive.'

'I was shaved and raped. There was a man in my room…'

'Yeah, like Arthur in your cupboard…'

Ouch again!

The dustbin where their friendship was festering was ready to go to the tip.

'What are… you… you…?' Emma felt so hurt she couldn't speak. She closed her eyes and was in danger of getting lost in a maelstrom of memories.

Letters on a mirror flashed in her mind.

GET OUT.

She heard her father's voice.

GET OUT RIGHT NOW. OR I'LL HURT YOU.

Heard the vibrating blades.

BZZZZ.

Heard a door slamming. So hard that the whole living room shook.

'That night I didn't just lose consciousness and my hair, but my baby too,' Emma screamed with her eyes closed, striking her stomach in anger. Once, twice. Until the pain was so intense that she sank to her knees.

She retched, gasped and was on the verge of throwing up.

'Help me,' she said, the words coming from her lips as if spontaneously. 'Help me. I don't know what's happening to me.'

She opened her eyes, put her arms out and groped for her friend.

But there was nobody there to help her any more.

Sylvia had already gone.

26

Emma dragged herself coughing to the sofa.

Her throat burned from the retching and her stomach felt inflamed as a result of the blows. She thought of Samson, who was in a far worse state, but who was hopefully in good hands and being treated.

With pills.

You swapped them! You crazed bitch…

Sylvia had gone, but her voice lingered in Emma's head where it continued to level accusations that Emma couldn't make head nor tail of.

She'd never even taken the morning-after pill, let alone built up a supply she could have passed on. As a doctor she felt she had a duty to life. She'd never intentionally give her best friend the wrong medicine. Not Emma, who'd revived the Rosenhan Experiment as a protest against the abuse of patients.

And yet, although Sylvia's accusations were terrible and her suspicion had hurt Emma deeply, their argument was nothing compared to what she'd experienced in Palandt's house.

Emma hauled herself to her feet again.

She had to call Philipp.

He would of course take her to task as soon as he heard about her solo effort. But in the end he'd have to admit she was right: Anton Palandt was a very strange neighbour, who they ought to keep an eye on.

She shuffled to the coat rack.

'Hello, Philipp? Can you please tell the investigators they should check out the resident of Teufelssee-Allee 16a? A bald man who swallows mountains of pills, lives in a gloomy house, is obviously being threatened by someone and – just listen to this – stuffs his house with wig stands. There's even a woman's hair in the bedroom – don't ask how I discovered that.'

This, or something along those lines, was what she wanted to tell him on the phone, but she couldn't, as she realised to her horror when she felt her coat pocket. Because her mobile had disappeared.

No! No, no, no…

In distress, Emma let her hands fall to her sides.

'Disappeared' was the wrong word for what had happened to her mobile.

I've lost it, she thought, then cursed out loud when it dawned on her that there was only one likely place where it could have fallen out of her pocket.

At A. Palandt's house.

When I tripped over the wig stand on my way out.

27

Emma felt as if she were being buffeted by a cold draught, a psychosomatic stress reaction. One part of her brain told her she had to go back to fetch her mobile; the other asked if she was seriously so insane as to want to return to the lion's den.

She froze and took her thick, sky-blue towelling dressing gown from the cupboard in the hall. It smelled of the perfume that she'd fished out again only yesterday, in the hope that the scent Philipp had bought her on the first day of their honeymoon in Barcelona would remind her of the happiest days of the time before. At that moment, however, all the mixture of cassis, amber and lotus did was to confirm Emma in her belief that she'd irretrievably lost the happiness of the past.

With sluggish steps she dragged herself to the kitchen, where she took the cordless house telephone from its charging station beside the coffee machine.

Her back leaning against the vibrating fridge, she looked out into the garden and keyed in Philipp's number.

Please pick up. Please pick up…

A crow landed in the middle of the garden on the splintered trunk of a headless birch tree, which had been hit by lightning years before, and which they ought to have removed ages ago. Outside it was already getting dark and the lights of the neighbouring houses were shimmering cosily between the trees like small sulphur lamps.

In the time before, she would have poured herself a cup of tea at this hour, lit a candle and put on some classical music, but now the only soundtrack accompanying her depressive mood was the endlessly ringing telephone.

She was expecting to hear it go to voicemail when there was a click on the line and she heard a cough.

'Yes? Hello?'

Emma moved away from the fridge, but the vibrations in her back remained. They got stronger when she realised who had answered her husband's mobile.

'Jorgo?'

'Everything alright?' the policeman whispered.

'Yes. Where's Philipp?'

'He's… hold on a sec.' She heard a rustling, then footsteps and finally something like a door closing. Jorgo spoke louder now; his voice sounded strangely distorted, as if he were standing in an empty room.

'He can't talk right now.'

'I see.'

'He's just giving his lecture. I've had his mobile all this time.'

Was that an excuse?

Emma pressed the receiver closer to her ear, but couldn't detect any background noises that might either confirm or refute Jorgo's claims.

'And you don't want to listen to your best friend talk?'

'I left the room especially because of you. Is there a problem?'

Yes. My life.

'How much longer will it go on?' she asked.

'A while yet. Listen, if it's about his visit to Le Zen again…'

An icebox opened in Emma's stomach.

'How do you know about that?' she gasped.

The explanation was as simple as it was embarrassing. 'Philipp had his phone on speaker in the car when he listened to his messages earlier.'

She blinked nervously.

Shit.

She'd completely forgotten her first call. And Jorgo had heard everything.

'Four weeks ago Philipp was at the hotel in a professional capacity. I know, because I accompanied him. We got them to show us all the rooms on the nineteenth floor again. What else could he have said when he suddenly found himself face to face with that vet? *Hello, I'm waiting for the hotel manager? We want to find the room where my wife was raped.*'

Emma gave an involuntary nod.

The icebox in her stomach closed again.

'Haven't you listened to your voicemail?' Jorgo asked after a slight pause.

'Sorry?'

'Philipp called you back a number of times. But you didn't answer your mobile or landline.'

Because I broke into Palandt's house, where I lost my phone, Emma almost said.

What a fuck-up.

As soon as her neighbour found it in his hallway it was just a matter of time until he discovered who'd made their way into his house.

He also saw me in his bedroom!

Emma froze at the memory of those wide, unblinking eyes.

'Could you please tell Philipp that I'm contactable again. He should call me on the landline. And thanks for your note.'

It grew louder in the background, as if Jorgo had put the phone on speaker.

'Which note?' he asked.

'You know, the one you put in my hand earlier. Thanks for believing me.'

'I'm sorry, but I don't know what you're talking about.'

'What?'

Emma felt woozy, as if she'd been running too quickly. She sat at the desk and stared out into the garden, looking for a fixed point that at least her eyes could latch onto, even if her mind had become derailed.

She saw the splintered birch again.

The crow had gone.

'But you… you gave…'

The note!

Emma hastily felt in her trouser pockets, but couldn't find it. She tried to concentrate, but couldn't remember where she'd put Jorgo's note. Far too much had happened in the meantime; maybe she'd lost it at the vet's, on the way to Palandt's or even in his house with her mobile.

'I didn't give you any note,' she heard Jorgo say, his voice suddenly sounding strangely irritable.

'YOU'RE LYING!' she was about to yell, but then noticed an object on the desk, so large that it would have been impossible to miss. Like the proverbial wood you fail to see for the trees. Emma shuddered.

'Is there anything else?' she heard Jorgo ask as if from a great distance.

Emma couldn't prevent her shudder from intensifying into a shake.

'No,' she croaked and hung up, even though what she really wanted to scream was, *'YES. THERE IS SOMETHING ELSE. SOMETHING DREADFUL!'*

She was shaking so badly now that she dropped the cordless phone. This extreme reaction had nothing to do with Palandt's eyes or her escape from his house.

But with the package.

The item that Salim had given her this morning for her mysterious neighbour.

It was there again.

On the desk.

In the very place she'd put it earlier.

As if it had never been anywhere else.

28

Just as an alcoholic knows what they're doing when they lift the glass for their first sip, so Emma knew what she was doing when she untied the string around the package. She was embarking on the most dangerous leg of her self-destructive journey, deep into the slums of her pointless existence.

One of the first things she had learned in her psychiatry lectures was the meaning of the word 'paranoia', which comes from the Greek and is best translated as 'contrary to all reason'. Which was exactly how she was behaving at the moment: contrary to all reason. She was even committing a crime, although violating the law on the privacy of correspondence was the least of her worries. She was far more afraid of herself. What if everyone else was right? The police psychologist who'd claimed Emma had invented the rape to get attention. Jorgo who'd sworn he'd never given her a note.

But the package had turned up again.

Emma was sure that it contained the key to solving all

the puzzling events of the last few hours, if not weeks.

But how many people had she met with a completely distorted sense of reality? How many patients had she treated, lost souls who did nothing all day long apart from mentally twisting their observations and experiences until eventually they could serve as proof for the most malicious conspiracy and persecution theories? Had she changed sides? Was she now doing the same?

Emma knew that you could see things differently. That although she'd discovered a number of 'discrepancies' in the past few hours, she hadn't found an ounce of proof to suggest that this package was connected with what had been done to her. Even so, she cut her thumb on the edge of the paper as she tore it open.

She yanked the flaps apart, virtually breaking the package open, and with her right hand burrowed amongst the polystyrene balls that protected the contents during transit. Emma excavated boxes about the size of tablet packets with foreign writing on the top:

МОРФЕЙ N60 ТАБЛ.

There were at least ten packets, white cardboard with a sky-blue stripe, and Emma opened one of them.

Medicines after all.

Tear-sized, ochre pills in a transparent strip.

But what sort?

Emma had learned English and Latin at school, but no Russian. She picked up the open box again.

МОРФИЙ N60 ТАБЛ.

Some of the writing was a reference to the dosage of the pills, she could work that out, but not the brand name or what it contained.

Emma found an instruction leaflet, squashed rather unprofessionally into the box. She unfolded it and the Cyrillic characters reminded her of the medicines on Palandt's bedside table. She rummaged further in the polystyrene balls and came across something that curiously didn't cause her to scream, even though she found herself holding a deadly weapon.

A plastic-handled scalpel.

Emma only gasped when she undid the already torn cellophane wrapping to expose a coloured blade.

Is that blood?

Struck by the surreal feeling that someone behind Emma was stretching out their hand towards her, she turned around, but nobody was there. Not even Samson, who she wished was here right now.

She pushed the knife aside in disgust and kept searching through the package.

Emma found a brown bottle, its label without a logo or anything printed on it, just some handwriting:

ГАММА-ГИДРОКСИМАСЛАЯНЯ КИСЛОТА

Emma rubbed her eyes and had to force herself not to close them for more than a moment. She felt like a car driver trying to avoid a microsleep.

I ought to pull over and take a break. Good idea.

She longed for her sofa *(oh yes, just a little lie down, wouldn't that be lovely?)*, but that was out of the question. *What if Palandt comes to pick up his package?*

Emma picked up the scalpel with the smeared blade and put it in her dressing gown pocket.

Despite the weapon she felt totally defenceless, for quite apart from the fact that she was hardly in a fit state to handle a blade should it come to that, the scalpel would be useless against the most terrifying of all enemies.

The demons corroding my mind.

What if she had a rest and the package had disappeared again once she'd slept off the diazepam?

Emma toyed with the idea of taking photographic proof of the medicine packets scattered across her table, *but with what?*

Her mobile was at A. Palandt's house, where the brutal foreign visitors sounded as if they'd be able to read these hieroglyphics that Emma couldn't decipher… *Hang on…*

She looked at her laptop.

… the computer can!

She opened her notebook, went to the country settings and put a tick next to 'Russia'.

That was quick.

It took her considerably longer to find the right characters on her keyboard. She could only proceed using trial and error, so it was some time before she'd managed to type МОРФИЙ N60 ТАБЛ and ГАММА-ГИДРОКСИМАСЛАЯНЯ КИСЛОТА into Google Translate.

When she saw the results in the right-hand box she wished she'd never done it:

Morphine & gamma-hydroxybutyric acid.

Every child knew the first of these, every doctor the second.

GHB. A liquid anaesthetic that in higher doses made patients not only limp and defenceless, but also impaired their memory. Sadly the drug had gained notoriety in the press as the 'date-rape drug' after numerous rapists had secretly mixed it into their victims' drinks.

Emma panted, gasping for air.

The package contained the drug that the Hairdresser had used on all his victims.

There was a shimmer before her eyes, as if she were staring at the hot tarmac of a road in high summer.

She'd reached the point where this solo effort at research had to stop. Strictly speaking, she'd crossed that point some time ago. Terribly lonely, utterly shattered and with an almost painful feebleness, Emma stood up from the desk, dragged herself over to the sofa and sank exhausted into the cushions.

She thought about the package and its contents, which she'd hoped would dispel her morbid suspicions, only to achieve the opposite.

She thought about A. Palandt who, threatened by

thugs, wept silently in the darkness of his bedroom, and about Philipp, who'd left her on her own with her inner emptiness and who she couldn't get in touch with now.

Not because her mobile phone was lying next to Palandt's wig stand in the hallway, because she had her landline. Nor because she was afraid of his anger when he found out that she'd already committed three crimes today: trespass, violation of correspondence privacy and wilful damage to a package.

No, there was a very simple reason why Emma couldn't phone her husband – her eyes were closing.

The last thing she saw of her surroundings was a shadow moving a few metres to her right at the door to the living room. A shadow that seemed to be in the form of a dark, male figure. Although Emma was deeply troubled by the apparition, it couldn't keep her awake. With every step he came closer, Emma slid further from consciousness. Even the shuffling sound of his boots couldn't stop her from drifting into a dreamless sleep.

29

Three weeks later

When Emma opened her eyes she had difficulty getting her bearings. She knew where she was (in Konrad's office), who she was (a paranoid patient in the dock) and why she was here (to make an important statement – much was at stake). But she didn't have a clue where the last few minutes had disappeared. The hand of the clock on the shelf had advanced a quarter of an hour and the Assam tea in her cup, which Konrad had just poured, was no longer steaming in spite of the fact that she'd only blinked.

'What happened?' she asked Konrad with a yawn.

'You fell asleep,' he said. His legs were no longer crossed, but that was the only change in his otherwise flawless poise. He sat as straight as a die in his seat, without looking the least bit tense. Emma knew that he'd been a passionate advocate of autogenic training for years and he'd perfected the mindset for keeping calm.

'I fell asleep? During our conversation?' she asked in disbelief, massaging her tensed neck.

'In the middle of a sentence,' he asserted. 'The medication is making you tired and it's also very hot here. I've turned down the fire.'

What a pity.

Emma looked at the glass panel in the wall, behind which the gas flames were lapping with less vigour, and couldn't help yawning again.

Raising his eyebrows, Konrad asked gently, 'Maybe we should stop there today, Emma.'

'Do I have to go back?'

She swallowed. The very thought of her 'cell' produced a lump in her throat.

'I'm afraid so, but I guarantee that they won't sedate you tonight.'

Wow, what progress!

'I think I'd like to stay for bit longer.'

'Okay, but…'

'No, it's fine. Tiredness isn't an illness, is it? I've still got some strength left, so we should make use of the time. It does me good to tell you everything.'

'Everything?' Konrad pressed her.

'What are you getting at?'

He took a deep breath and paused. 'Well, I note that there are some things you merely touched upon before quickly changing the subject.'

'Like what?'

'The money, for example.'

'What money?'

Konrad gave a mischievous smile, as if this question were the proof of his assertion.

'Didn't you say that the vet was complaining your credit card was blocked?'

'Oh, that.' Emma folded her hands in her lap.

'What was that all about? Was it a bank error?'

'No,' she admitted softly.

'So it really was blocked?'

'Yes,' she said with a nod.

'And the email you casually mentioned before. The one referring to the blocking of your account, which you thought was spam…'

'It was real, yes.'

Konrad narrowed his eyes. 'Did you and Philipp have financial problems?'

'No.'

'What, then?'

Emma cleared her throat in embarrassment, then pulled herself together. 'You asked if *we* had financial problems. I said no, because it was just me in trouble.'

It was barely conceivable that Philipp would ever get into financial difficulties. His parents had left him a fortune they'd accumulated from building motorway service stations, before the two of them were swept away by cancer.

'I'd ordered too much, all manner of rubbish teleshopping and on the internet, from expensive cosmetics to microwavable slippers. Useless stuff I was buying to try and take my mind off things. Meanwhile my practice wasn't earning a cent.'

'But surely Philipp didn't leave you in the lurch?' Konrad asked.

'No, you know how generous he is. We didn't sign a pre-nuptial agreement, even though he brought all the money into our marriage. But he was already paying the loan on my practice. I used my own account for my shopping addiction.'

'And when it was empty you were too ashamed to tell him?'

Emma lowered her gaze. 'Yes.'

'Okay,' Konrad said as if ticking off an item from the list, and indeed he did change the subject.

'Let's discuss what you told me about Sylvia. What got you more worked up? When she alleged you swapped the pills, or when she talked of the "supposed" rape?'

Emma swallowed. 'I don't know. I think they're one and the same. She called me a mad liar who was out to hurt her.'

'Did she?' Konrad put his head to one side. 'Didn't she in fact doubt your sense of perception?'

Emma frowned. 'I don't see the difference.'

'Oh, it's huge. You know very well how three witnesses to a car crash can sometimes come up with four different accounts of the accident. None of them is lying, but in stressful situations the brain often plays tricks.'

'Maybe, but I'd definitely know if I'd deliberately swapped her pills and whether or not I was raped.'

Konrad nodded and something uncanny occurred. He changed, and so rapidly, as if a switch had been pressed. His paternal smile vanished as quickly as the laughter lines around his eyes. His expression became tight, almost rigid, as sharp as the drawing pins on his desk. His jawbones stuck out and his breathing grew very calm.

That's what a fox looks like just before it pounces on the rabbit, Emma thought, and indeed her kind mentor had become the notorious star lawyer whose cross-examinations were feared by witnesses and public prosecutors throughout Germany.

'So you're sure?' he asked.

'Yes.'

Beneath the cashmere blanket Emma clenched her fists.

'As sure as you were that you were forcibly treated during the Rosenhan Experiment?'

'Konrad, I...'

'At least that's what you told the audience at your lecture. You showed them a video. Although the woman had different-coloured hair, you explained that it was you being given electric shocks.'

'Yes, but...'

And with that the cat was out of the bag. The 'but'

that changed everything. Emma rubbed her eyes in the vain attempt to hold back the tears.

'But even I don't know why I fibbed about that,' she said, then corrected herself straight away. 'Well, yes, I do. I wanted to take the wind out of the sails of a colleague by the name of Stauder-Mertens. He's an arrogant arsehole who was trying to make me look ridiculous with his questions. It was really stupid of me, but…'

She left the second 'but' hanging in the air, because there was nothing that could undo her deception.

'Those critical questions from a colleague may have been the trigger for your lie. But not the cause,' Konrad said.

'I know that.'

She turned to the window and gazed at the snow on the lake. Wished she could be out there. Floating lifelessly, beneath the ice.

'Of course you do,' Konrad said, still pressing her. 'Pseudology is your specialist subject. You know the circumstances that can give rise to pathological lying.'

'Konrad, please…'

Emma turned back and looked at him imploringly, but the criminal defence lawyer knew no mercy and enumerated the symptoms: 'Neglect in childhood. Rejection by one's parents, one's father, for example. A highly fertile imagination that allows one to escape into a world of make-believe where one invents a substitute attachment figure, who might be called Arthur.'

'STOP!'

Emma threw the blanket from her knees. 'Why are we bothering to talk if you don't believe a word I say?' she cried and was about to leap up from the sofa. But, overestimating her strength, she teetered back, knocking over her teacup.

Fat drops fell from the coffee table onto the white part of the rug. A stain wouldn't have been so obvious on the once-dark black threads that had faded to brown over the years.

'I'm really sorry, Konrad. Christ, I didn't mean it.' More tears filled her eyes, and this time she didn't bother fighting against them.

'It's not a problem,' she heard Konrad say, who'd jumped up instinctively, and basically he was right. It was a minor stain, which would easily come out in cleaning, yet she felt as if she'd defiled the thing most sacred to him.

Why did it have to be the O rug?

She knew what the old, round thing meant to Konrad. He'd brought it back decades ago from a trip to Tibet when he was a student. It had been his first major acquisition, his lucky charm – and she'd soiled it.

'Where are you going?' Konrad asked, when she tried to get up from the sofa again.

She pointed at the door beside the exit that led to Konrad's private loo.

'To get some water and soap.'

He shook his head gently, her old friend and mentor

once more. Again the change had occurred in a split second, and even if he wasn't smiling he sounded as warm and friendly as before: 'The rug isn't important, Emma. What is important is that you tell me the truth.'

'I *am* trying, but you're scaring me.'

Konrad shrugged as if meaning to say, *'I know, but what can I do?'*

'Don't feel intimidated by me,' he said gently and sat down again. 'I'm just playing the *advocatus diaboli* here. During the trial the public prosecutor will try to faze you with quite different tricks.'

Emma swallowed, wishing he'd hug her, or at least hold her hand, but he just watched her sit back down. Only then did he stand up again, take a large handkerchief from his trouser pocket and wipe the glass table. He ignored the dark stain on the floor. 'The prosecutor will reveal all your dark secrets, which is what he must do. After all, he wants to see you locked up in prison for life.'

'I know.'

Emma scratched the top of her forehead, resisting the urge to check the length of her hair. She wiped her nose with a tissue, then said, 'I didn't intend any of it to happen, do you believe me?'

Konrad tapped his lips, then pursed them and replied after a brief deliberation, 'Normally at this point I always say that it's not important. That it doesn't matter to me whether my client's lying or telling the truth. But in this case it's different.'

'Because we're friends?'

'Because I don't yet know the whole story, Emma. Tell it to me! And not just what I already know from the files. You need to go deeper and talk about things that you find painful.'

Emma's eyes glazed over.

Looking right through Konrad, of course she understood what he meant. He wanted to hear about the bodies.

Alright then...

Her eyes focused again, wandered across the fire and the huge desk to the window, beyond which lay a lake she'd probably never walk on again in her life.

On the other hand she had pictures in her head that would accompany her everywhere, no matter how fast she ran away from herself.

For example, the barrel with the severed limbs.

Yes, that's a good idea.

Why don't I tell him about the barrel?

But before that she had to explain how she'd come to be in the shed in the first place and why she'd had to leave the house for a second time, without noticing that she was being watched by the delivery man... Everything in good time.

And so Emma lay back on the sofa and obliged Konrad by going where she found it most painful.

Back to the house in Teufelssee-Allee, where soon she'd lose everything that had once been important to her.

30

Three weeks earlier

She stayed quite calm.

Emma had fallen asleep sitting up, her head had slipped to the side and was now resting on the edge of the sofa cushion, tipping the room about forty-five degrees anticlockwise.

The cup on the coffee table, the photo frame on the mantelpiece, the vase with dried flowers in the window – everything appeared to be defying gravity.

Including the man three paces away from her.

For a moment Emma thought she was trapped in a dream and to begin with she was surprised that she *could* dream with the sleeping pill. Then she was surprised that she was surprised, because normally she tended not to reflect on her state of consciousness while asleep. Eventually she realised that she'd opened her eyes and everything around her was real: the dust on the coffee table, the burned embers in the fire, the dressing gown that she'd soaked through with sweat in her short, but intense sleep. And the man with the chunky winter boots, dripping melting snow onto the floorboards.

The man!

Emma sat up so quickly that she momentarily felt giddy and the world started to spin.

She reached for the switch on the standing lamp and clicked it on. Warm, soft light flooded the living room, which had been in a dusky gloom.

'Hello,' the man said, raising his hand.

'What do you want?' Emma said, feeling for the scalpel in her pocket. Strangely she was far less frightened than she ought to feel looking at a man who'd entered her house while she was sleeping.

She was agitated, nervous, felt as she might before an exam she hadn't revised for, but she was far from becoming paralysed with shock or even screaming. Not because she was resigned to her fate, but because the man looked less scary than the first time she'd seen him.

Not an hour ago.

Weeping in his bedroom.

'Herr Palandt?' she said, and the intruder nodded silently.

He'd been bald before, but now he was wearing a short, dark-brown wig that had turned black in the sleet.

He was tall, almost Sylvia's height, and slim, even

gaunt. His black raincoat hung over his sunken shoulders like a tarpaulin. It had yellow buttons, which looked curiously fashionable for someone who otherwise didn't seem to care about his appearance. His cords, which were also far too thin for this weather, were several sizes too big, as if Palandt was having to wear an elder brother's clothes. Yet he must be at least sixty.

The most striking thing about him were his glasses. Beige, plastic monstrosities with lenses so thick you could hardly make out his eyes behind them. Could he see anything at all without them?

'What do you want?' Emma asked again in the hope that Palandt hadn't recognised her in his bedroom. 'How did you get in here?'

Emma pushed herself up from the sofa cushions and felt as if she had to apologise, even though it was her neighbour who had intruded into *her* house, *and trespass is a more serious offence than criminal damage, isn't it?*

'I'm sorry. I hope I haven't frightened you, but your front door was open.'

The front door?

Emma recalled lying howling on the floor and hearing Sylvia angrily slam the front door. So hard that she'd felt it in the living room.

Maybe it had jumped out of the latch again.

I didn't check – stupid cow!

Palandt turned away from her and looked over at the desk.

At the package!

Ripped open as if by an impatient child at Christmas, its contents lay scattered amongst polystyrene balls on the desk.

'I'm sorry,' she said guiltily, pointing at the package. 'I'm... well... I'm not in a good way. It was a stupid idea to look through the post after taking a sleeping tablet. I thought the package was for me. Sorry.'

'No problem,' Palandt said. His words sounded friendly and warm, but his voice was weak. 'As I said, it's me who should apologise.'

Emma unconsciously shook her head, and so Palandt went on: 'Yes, yes. I should never have just burst in here to pick up my package.' He put his hand in the back pocket of his cords and pulled out Salim's card. 'I knocked, but couldn't find a bell...'

'It's out by the garden gate.'

'Oh, yes, right. I didn't go back to the gate once I'd climbed the steps. I'm a bit unsteady on my legs, you see.' He looked down as if checking that his scrawny legs were still attached to his emaciated body.

'Anyway, when nobody answered I was worried that this house had been burgled too.'

'Too?' Emma asked, and all of a sudden it was there, the fear. Because of course she knew what Palandt was talking about.

'Oh, I've been robbed several times, including today,' her neighbour said, scratching the back of his head.

'Today they even came into my bedroom and watched me.'

Emma turned cold. She opened her mouth, intent on posing the questions that an innocent person would ask immediately: 'Who are you talking about? What did they want from you? Have you called the police?' But no sound would issue from her lips.

Not when she saw the wig moving on Palandt's head while he kept on scratching.

He muttered something that sounded like 'this damned itching…' and at the same time his monstrous glasses turned into an aquarium of tears.

Palandt had started to cry.

31

'Would you mind...?' Palandt sniffled and looked around as if he were searching for something specific in the living room, then he appeared to have found it, for he turned away from Emma and took a step to the right. 'Would you mind if I sat down?'

Without waiting for an answer, he slumped into the armchair that stood at an angle to the sofa and where Philipp liked to read the paper on a Sunday. It was made of dark-green leather with concrete-coloured armrests, an ugly industrial look, Emma thought, that was totally out of place in this otherwise rustically furnished house. But it was an heirloom from Philipp's mother and he was attached to it. Palandt appeared to be comfortable in it too; at any rate he gave a sigh of relief, wiped the tears from his cheeks with the back of his hand and closed his eyes.

Emma, who was standing indecisively beside the coffee table, was worrying that her neighbour would fall asleep when Palandt opened his eyes again. 'I find it very embarrassing, Frau Stein, but I'm not especially well, as you can perhaps see.'

Frau Stein.

Emma wondered momentarily where the neighbour could know her name from, because it wasn't on the door. Then it occurred to her that Salim must have written it on the delivery note.

'What's wrong with you?' she asked, although she was actually seeking other answers. Whether he'd found her mobile phone, for starters. What was wrong with his hair. Whether he was playing a game of cat and mouse with her and they'd just entered a quiet phase in which Emma was supposed to think that the weak, suffering Palandt represented no danger, whereas in truth he was just waiting for the right moment to go for her throat.

'I've got cancer,' he said tersely. 'A tumour in my liver. Metastases in the lungs.'

'That's the reason for the medicines?' They both looked over at the desk.

'Morphine and GHB,' Palandt said outright. 'One takes away the pain, the other either stimulates me or helps me get to sleep depending on the dose. Today I probably took too much and missed the delivery man.' He laughed sadly. 'I'd never have thought I'd become a junkie one day. All my life I've played sport, eaten healthily, never drunk – well, I wasn't allowed to in my profession.'

Palandt spoke quickly with that mixture of excitement and shame so typical of lonely people who after a long time finally find the opportunity to talk to someone, even if it's a total stranger.

'I was in the circus,' he explained. 'Daddy Longlegs they called me. Perhaps you've heard of me. No? Oh well, it was a while ago. Anyway, Daddy Longlegs like the spider, because I've got long legs too, but I can make myself very small. My God, I was really flexible. I used to get the loudest applause for my suitcase routine.'

'Suitcase routine?' Emma asked.

'Yes, I could bend my body to fit into a small suitcase.' Palandt gave a sad smile. 'I had rubber bones back then. These days it hurts when I tie my shoelaces.'

Emma swallowed. She couldn't shake off the thought of a man squashing himself into the farthest corner of a room to avoid being discovered before its occupant went to bed.

But in Le Zen there wasn't a single corner to hide in. Not even for a contortionist.

Emma looked at the window. Snowflakes spun beneath the head of the streetlamp like a swarm of moths around the light in summer. She felt a dull ache pressing against her forehead from the inside. Emma couldn't help thinking that even half of one of those pills on her desk would be enough to kill the pain, however severe the migraine became that was now brewing.

Noticing that Palandt had followed her pensive gaze over to the package, she said, 'It's none of my business, but, well, I'm a doctor.'

Palandt gave a squeaky laugh. 'And you want to know why I order these cheap copycat drugs on the black market?'

Emma nodded.

'It was a stupid idea,' Palandt explained. 'I never had any health insurance, you see. What was the point? All my life I was healthy and if things took a bad turn, I thought, I could live off my savings in my mother's house.'

'Frau Tornow?'

'That was her maiden name. She took it again after the divorce. Did you know her?' Palandt appeared to be delighted and he smiled softly.

'We bumped into each other on the street from time to time,' Emma said. 'I haven't seen her in ages.'

'She's in Thailand,' he said. 'In a nursing home right on the beach.'

Emma nodded. That made sense. More and more German pensioners were spending their retirement years in Asia, where you could get better healthcare for far less money. And where it didn't get as cold in winter as at home. 'I'm supposed to be looking after the house in her absence.' Palandt was about to add something, but put his hands to his mouth abruptly. A sudden coughing fit shook his entire body.

'Sorry…' He tried to say something, but had to keep interrupting himself and didn't seem to be getting enough air.

Emma fetched him a glass of water from the kitchen. When she came back his face was bright red and he was scarcely intelligible as he wheezed, 'Would you mind giving me a pill?'

She handed him the morphine from the desk.

Eagerly he swallowed two pills at once, then coughed for a further thirty seconds until eventually settling down and relaxing.

'Excuse me,' he said with jittery eyelids. He'd briefly removed his glasses to dry his tears with the back of his hands. 'Sometimes I wake up with such bad pain that I can't help crying.'

Palandt put his glasses back on the bridge of his nose and smiled apologetically. 'I know I look like a scarecrow with these on, but if I didn't wear them you could get up and leave the room and I'd continue chatting to the sofa cushions.'

Emma spontaneously wrinkled her nose and sat back down on the sofa.

Is that true?

It was probably the reason why he was behaving so naturally towards her. Particularly as when he woke up earlier he may have been suffering the pain he was talking about. Without his glasses and with tears in his eyes he wouldn't have been able to see her standing beside his bed.

Maybe he hasn't found my mobile yet?

Emma's paranoid self wanted to see things in a

different light, of course, with Anton Palandt as a gifted actor merely feigning his illness to lull her into a false sense of security, *after all, he is wearing a wig!* But she was longing for a harmless, logical explanation for all the mysterious occurrences she'd experienced and witnessed today, and so Emma asked her neighbour bluntly, 'Did you lose your hair because of the chemotherapy?'

Palandt nodded. 'Yes, it looks ghastly, doesn't it?' He lifted the toupee briefly and Emma could see age spots dotted all over his head. 'It's a cheap thing off the internet and itches like hell. But I don't dare go out into the street without it. With a bald head I look like a rapist.'

He gave a throaty laugh and Emma tried to put on a brave face by raising the corners of her mouth too.

A coincidence, her hopeful self said. *'He's playing with you,'* her paranoid identity countered.

Emma bent forwards on the sofa, as she used to do in her therapy sessions when she wanted patients to believe they had her undivided attention. 'You said the foreign medicines were a bad idea? Do they not work?'

Palandt nodded. 'They're cheap copies. I should never have got involved with the people who supply me with them.'

'Russians?'

'No. Albanians. They get them on the black market and send them by post, anonymously of course, because they haven't obtained them strictly legally.'

'So what's the problem?'

'Those bastards are scammers. When you order the medicines, they cost less than a third of the normal products, which is why I opted for them. I can't afford anything else, you see. All my money has gone on alternative therapies. Shamans, gene therapy, miracle healers – I wasted all my savings and hopes on these. But after the first delivery the bastards suddenly demanded more than a thousand euros from me. I don't have that sort of money.'

'And so they burgle your house?'

With this question Emma had flicked a switch. Palandt's good-natured, grandfatherly facial features hardened. His lips turned to lines, then vanished, while his eyes assumed an other-worldly expression. 'Yes, to collect the cash.'

He raised his right hand and pointed in Emma's direction. His fingers were shaking like someone with Parkinson's.

'The threats were more subtle to begin with,' he said, upset. His fury at the people who were blackmailing him made him forget his polite choice of words from earlier. 'Those fucking arseholes continue to send me drugs. The quality keeps on deteriorating. They barely work any more, they just do enough to stop me from kicking the bucket before they get their money.'

Palandt wiped some spittle from his lower lip, then he appeared to notice how tense Emma was. Bewildered and shocked by his sudden mood swing, she was holding her breath.

'I'm sorry, I got carried away,' Palandt said, and the anger in him died down as quickly as it had flared up.

Emma wondered whether his illness might have set off a bipolar manic-depressive disorder. Deciding not to underestimate him, she invited Palandt to continue.

'Well, Frau Stein, what should I say? They are doing all they can to intimidate me. For example they'll put newspaper cuttings about gruesome murders in a package.'

Or a bloody scalpel.

'As a warning that my name might appear in print too, do you see? But they're not sticking to hints any longer. They're rummaging through my house, threatening to beat me up. I can't close my door any more, they broke it last time. And they were back there today.'

'Why don't you go to the police?'

Palandt sighed feebly. 'There wouldn't have been any point up till now. I mean, I don't know who they are or where they live. Don't know any names. What could the police do? Keep a round-the-clock watch on the house of a cancer patient? I fear they've got better things to do.'

'How did they get onto you?'

'I ordered via a Russian website.'

'And what do you mean by *till now*?'

'Pardon?'

'You said you couldn't report them till now. What's changed?'

'Oh, I see. Yes, the blackmailers made a mistake. They lost a mobile phone.'

Palandt gave a smile of triumph, while Emma's body temperature rose by several degrees.

'A mobile phone?' she echoed.

'Yes. I found it in the hall. You can get the owner's number from it, can't you?'

Emma shrugged. Her right eyelid started to twitch.

Yes, you can. Like a good girl I put in my contact number in case it ever got lost.

She felt sick.

'Have you informed anyone about the break-in yet?'

To Emma's relief he shook his head.

'No. When I found the delivery card I decided to come to you first to pick up my medicines. I've got morphine at home, but I'm running out of drops.'

Palandt stood up. 'Thanks so much for listening to me. And, of course, for the water. And please excuse me again if I gave you a fright by just coming in like that. Oh, would you have a bag by any chance?'

'A bag?'

Palandt pointed at the torn package.

'For my medicines. Then I can go back home and examine the phone.'

'Why?' Emma asked uneasily.

'No idea. I'm not really sure yet. In truth I'm not a great fan of the police. But perhaps they can do something if I give them the name of the person whose mobile it is.'

32

Emma had rarely felt so unable to deal with a situation as this one. She wasn't really tired any more, even though the sleep her neighbour had torn her from had been far too short to be at all restorative. But, just as in Palandt's house earlier, the fear of being caught had a revitalising effect.

Emma had to prevent her 'break-in' from becoming public knowledge. Palandt must under no circumstances call the police. What would it look like if it got out that because of a mental aberration on her part she'd intruded into the house of an old, terminally ill man? Most people already doubted her sanity. Even Philipp had suggested quite openly today that she get some therapy, and her best friend was accusing Emma of having poisoned her.

If her intrusion became known, her reputation would be destroyed for good. And everybody would say that the doctors unwittingly involved in the Rosenhan Experiment would have been better off giving her forced therapy after all. Because she really was a basket case.

'Are you alright?' Palandt asked, when she came out of the kitchen with a plastic bag. 'You look so pale.'

'What, oh, yes, no, I'm fine. I was just thinking.'

She handed him the bag and he went to the desk while she stayed by the fire.

'What about?' her neighbour asked, as the bag rustled each time it swallowed a box of pills.

I didn't ask him whether he wanted to take his coat off, Emma thought as she stared at his bony back. Suddenly she had an idea.

'Have you touched it yet?' she asked.

'I'm sorry?'

Palandt turned to her.

'The mobile,' she said. 'Have you already held it?'

'I'll be honest with you, yes. Why?'

'Well, my husband's a policeman.'

He didn't seem fazed by this rather strange answer.

'Oh, really?'

'Yes, Philipp often deals with these sorts of blackmail cases,' she lied. 'Usually they're linked to organised crime.'

Palandt coughed, them said, 'I can imagine. I bet that those brutes persecuting me are part of an organised gang.' He put away the last packet and turned to go.

Emma stood in his way. 'I work as a psychiatrist and sometimes help my husband out when he's compiling reports, so I know a bit about his work. I'm afraid you've just caused a problem for the investigation.'

'Because of my fingerprints?' Palandt took off his glasses and rubbed his tired eyes.

'Yes. They've got top lawyers, these Mafiosi. They were probably wearing gloves, which is why your prints might be the only ones on the phone.'

'But that doesn't matter, because if they trace the number they'll see it's not my phone, won't they?' Palandt said, but he sounded slightly unsure.

'If the burglars were so stupid as to use a mobile with a contract. But I'd lay money on it being a prepaid phone.'

'Oh.'

The floorboards beneath his feet creaked as Palandt put his weight on one leg, then the other. His eyes still looked friendly, but his expression was tense. Standing was clearly uncomfortable for him. 'Oh well, doesn't matter. It's worth a try, isn't it?' he said, putting his glasses back on and making to leave finally, but she made herself touch his arm.

'I'd be careful, if I were you.'

He stopped again. 'Why? What can happen?'

'Okay. You ring the police, they come by, examine the phone, run a check on the numbers dialled, but can't prove anything in the end. But because the officers have checked those numbers, you've flushed out the rats, Herr Palandt, and ultimately you've achieved nothing except for making your medicine dealers even more angry at you.'

'Hmm.'

Her words had hit their target. His head was processing them.

'Maybe you're right. I should let it rest; I don't want any more trouble. Having said that...' He looked Emma uncertainly in the eye. 'Dammit! I want it all to stop. They're bound to come back to fetch the phone, aren't they? I can't just carry on, hoping that everything will work out fine on its own.'

'I understand,' Emma said, without being able to offer Palandt a solution to his quandary that would get her out of trouble too.

'Give it to me,' she suggested, devising a plan even as she was talking.

'You?'

'Thanks to my husband I know a little police trick that can tell you if the phone is registered or not. Every manufacturer has a hidden system function.'

That was of course nonsense, a complete pack of lies, but it had the desired effect.

'You'd do that for me?'

'Sure.'

I'll do a few things before you find out who the mobile really belongs to.

She turned to the window, snowflakes were spattering the glass as if it were the windscreen of a moving car. She briefly wondered whether she could ask Palandt to bring the phone to her. But before he could change his mind it would be better if they lost no time.

'Right then...' Emma picked at her sweaty and now damp dressing gown. 'I've just got to put on something warm before we go.'

33

Arthur once told her about a weather switch her parents had hidden in the cellar. That was some time after Emma had stopped being afraid of her imaginary companion, not least because he hadn't appeared to her again in his terrifying helmet. Emma chatted to the voice in the cupboard, in secret so her parents wouldn't find out.

Ever since that night when she'd seen Arthur for the first time, she'd never entered her parents' bedroom again. Not even during the day.

Nor did Mama come into her room any more to read her a goodnight story. That stopped the day she lost the baby – for a while Emma blamed herself for this, even though she didn't know exactly why. Arthur comforted her and said it wasn't her fault that she wasn't going to have a baby brother. And he took over the job of reading the goodnight stories. Or at least until one night her father noticed that Emma was talking to the cupboard, and the very next morning arranged an appointment with the child psychiatrist.

After more than twenty sessions her father was pleased that his daughter had abandoned her flights of fancy. In truth, however, Emma felt as if she'd lost a friend. She missed the voice that told her all those funny stories, such as the one about the weather switch that allowed you to change seasons, so that fathers who didn't want to go the playground with their daughters could switch from sun to sleet.

And because this theory sounded no less plausible than the story of the man with the white beard who managed to deliver millions of presents to all the children in the world in a single night, one day Emma went down into the cellar to look for the legendary switch.

All she found, sadly, was the isolation valve in the boiler room, which is why it turned much colder in the house for a while once she'd successfully turned off the heating.

The weather switch remained undiscovered. Unfortunately. Because even today Emma would love to have something to turn off the early onset of darkness, the frost and especially the biting wind that sunk its sharp teeth into her face the moment she closed the front door and left the protection of the porch.

'That's what I call weather,' Palandt complained ahead of her. She pulled up the collar of her puffer jacket and had trouble keeping pace. Emma couldn't help feeling respect for her neighbour's straight back and controlled movement. Cancer or no cancer, Palandt's former life as an artiste still seemed to be paying off today. Unlike her, he wasn't shuffling forwards shakily and tentatively, nor did he adopt the cowering posture of a beaten dog against the gusts of snow. He swapped the bag with his medicines from one hand to the other and glanced back over his shoulder. 'It's very kind of you. But you don't have to do this for me.'

Get my mobile back before you identify it? Oh yes, if only you knew just how much I have to do it.

There was no 'wanting' to do it, however. It was bad enough that Emma had already exposed herself to the horror of the outside world once today, and she wasn't thinking of the weather, but the streets, lamps, *strangers!*

The effect of the diazepam continued to wear off, which meant she was no longer yawning every few seconds, but fear was once more perched on her shoulders.

In every parked car a shadow was lurking on the back seat. The light from the streetlamps illuminated the wrong sections of her route, leaving an entire world full of dangers in the dark. And the only reason the wind driving the snow was blowing so loudly was to swallow all those sounds that could warn her of impending disaster. In fact it was blustering so violently about her unprotected ears (in her hurry Emma hadn't put on a headscarf this time) that the wind even drowned out the ever-present drone of traffic on Heerstrasse.

They were passing the open drive of a corner house whose owners had wisely scattered grit, when Palandt gave Emma a shock. He turned to her and shouted, 'Have you been to my place before?'

Emma made the mistake of looking up at him, and so failed to see the snowed-over pothole and tripped. She felt a sharp pain shoot up to her knee, threw her hands up and lost her balance. Then a ring closed around her wrist like a handcuff and brute force pulled her forwards, where she hit something hard that also wrapped itself around her like a collar.

Palandt!

He'd grabbed her arm, yanked her towards him and prevented her from falling.

'Thanks,' Emma said, far too quietly for the wind, and far too uncertain about being in the arms of her bony neighbour, whose strength she must have completely underestimated. She felt for the scalpel in her pocket and groaned when she realised that of course she wouldn't find it in her winter jacket. Now the scalpel was in the washing basket on the steps down to the basement, where she'd thoughtlessly stuffed it in her clammy dressing gown before putting on the puffer jacket.

I'm unarmed, she thought.

And this thought heightened her fear.

'I think, perhaps, that this wasn't such a good idea. I'd better go home now,' was what she wanted to say before turning around and running back.

'I think… that was close,' was all she manged to utter.

Emma had tears in her eyes, from pain, fear and of

course the weather. She blinked because she was terrified that the water could freeze on her contact lenses.

'I mean, to my mother's,' Palandt said when she'd regained her balance and he let her go, his hands still stretched out protectively, like a father standing beside his child the first time they ride without stabilisers.

'Did you ever visit my mother when she lived here?'

Emma shook her head.

'That figures,' Palandt said, and if Emma wasn't mistaken he seemed to chuckle quietly, but that too was swallowed by the wind. 'She's always been a bit of a loner.'

They walked the rest of the short way side by side in silence, until Emma was standing outside 16a for the second time that day. She went up the covered steps for the second time, and a few moments later saw the inside of the house for the first time in the light. 'Do excuse me, my place isn't as cosy as yours,' Palandt apologised, making to take Emma's puffer jacket, but she was far too cold.

According to an old mercury thermometer on the wall it was a scant sixteen degrees in the hall. Nor was it better in the other rooms, as Palandt acknowledged.

'I'm afraid my finances don't allow me to heat all the rooms day and night. But how about I make us some tea and we sit by the stove in the living room?'

She declined politely but firmly. 'Have you got the mobile?'

'Yes, of course. Please wait a minute.'

Palandt put his medicines on a chest of drawers and went through a door to the left, leading to what she imagined must be the bathroom.

That's where he's keeping my mobile?

Emma used his temporary absence to have another look around the hallway.

The post was no longer on the floor by the front door and the coat stand was still empty. As was the stand with the mouthless, eyeless polystyrene head that was presumably for Palandt's chemotherapy wig.

In the flickering light of the old incandescent bulb hanging bare from the ceiling, the wig stand cast what looked like a living shadow. Emma stepped closer and saw something flash briefly, a shimmer on the otherwise dull surface.

She put out her hand, stroked the rough polystyrene and then looked at her fingers.

No! she cried silently to herself. She hit her chest, rubbed her hand on her thigh, tried again on her coat, but the hair, *the long, blonde* WOMAN'S HAIR that she'd picked up from the wig stand wouldn't come off her finger.

'Everything okay?' said Palandt behind her, who'd come back out of the bathroom. Emma turned to him, to his bespectacled eyes, his strained smile – and his slim surgeon's fingers in skin-tight latex gloves, holding a freezer bag.

34

'I found them in the cupboard under the sink,' Palandt said, smiling one second, then with watery eyes behind his glasses the next. 'I'm sorry,' he said, sniffling. 'I always get sentimental when I think of my mother. She's so far away now.'

He raised his hands and wiggled his fingers in the surgical gloves. 'Mother always used them to dye her wigs.'

Emma felt like screaming, but fear has its own fingers, which at that moment were slithering around her neck and cutting off her air.

'Unlike me she likes wearing these hairy things.'

Palandt strode down the hallway to the chipboard chest of drawers, on top of which was the bag. His raincoat crumpled with every step.

Emma recoiled, her hands pressed defensively to her chest, beneath which her heart was galloping with wild hoofbeats. As Palandt was now blocking her way out the front door, she scanned her surroundings for other escape possibilities. Or for weapons to defend against the attack she was anticipating. *The coatrack?* Too heavy and anyway it was screwed to the wall. *The polystyrene head?* Useless – too light.

The door ahead on the left? With a bit of luck and legs that weren't so paralysed by fear she might make it to the kitchen, but what guarantee did she have that she'd find a knife block she could reach before Palandt grabbed her by the hair? It was now long enough for a man's fist to grasp hold of it.

'Would you hold this for a sec?'

Emma flinched.

In her hand she felt a piece of flexible plastic, a small bag. Palandt had given her the freezer bag and turned back to the chest of drawers. He opened the top drawer.

A few seconds later he turned around with a smile of satisfaction on his dry lips. And Emma's mobile in his hand.

'Here it is.'

He gave her a nod of encouragement. Clearly he misconstrued Emma's expression, for he said, 'Yes, I know. The gloves are probably unnecessary, but at least there won't be any new fingerprints on it. May I?'

He pointed to her hand.

Emma looked at her fingers that were holding the freezer bag.

Palandt asked her to hold the bag so he could put the phone inside it.

'That's how you handle evidence, isn't it?' he said, then paused. 'When will he be able to examine it?'

Emma blinked nervously and bit her lower lip, which had started to tremble uncontrollably.

Panic was like an invisible night-time monster. Even if you'd checked that it wasn't hiding in the cupboard or under the bed, you would still lie there for a while in the darkness, your heart pounding, unable to trust the tranquillity.

'Examine?' asked Emma, who'd momentarily forgotten the lie she'd served up. Her face was bathed in sweat, but even with his thick glasses Palandt seemed not to notice, or he thought it was the rest of the snow melting on Emma's forehead.

'The special function,' he reminded her. 'That lets you find out who the phone belongs to…'

He fell silent and flinched, as if he'd received an electric shock. This involuntary reaction matched the electric buzzing and the flash in his right hand.

The mobile.

Illuminated all of a sudden, the device vibrated in Palandt's latex fingers and it took him a while to realise what he was seeing on the display: an image of two people. A man. A woman. Sitting snug side by side. Secretly photographed in a restaurant as the two of them, in an affectionate pose, are forking a potato cake. The potato cake photo signalling a call from Philipp!

35

The full significance of what he was looking at trickled into Palandt's consciousness between the fourth and fifth ring.

'What the devil…?' he said quietly. Emma put out both her hands, but this time it was Palandt who recoiled.

'I can explain,' she said, trying to get hold of the mobile, but he withdrew his hand.

'You?' Palandt exclaimed, pointing to the display.

The switch had been flipped again. From one moment to the next Palandt had lost his temper. Unlike back in Emma's living room, however, his blind rage wasn't directed at the blackmailers. But at her.

'That's you!'

Emma nodded. 'Yes, but it's not what you think!'

'You were here?'

'Yes…'

'You broke into my house?'

'No…'

'So it was your voice I heard in the bedroom!'

'Yes, but…'

'Your shrill scream…'

'Yes.'

'You were trying to scare me to death!'

'No.'

Emma's vocabulary had shrunk to that of a small child.

Was she in danger?

The expression in Palandt's eyes had drastically changed. Nothing about him now was reminiscent of a loveable, elderly uncle suffering from a serious illness. He looked as if he were in another world.

'Why can't you lot just leave me alone?' he bellowed.

You lot?

Emma tried to salvage what was salvageable and adopted a calm, friendly tone, almost like when her patients used to flare up in their consultations.

'Please give me a moment to explain.'

Palandt wasn't listening. 'Where were you?' he shouted. 'Were you outside too?'

'Outside?'

'In the garden. Did you find it?'

'Find what?'

'Don't lie to me!' he screamed, striking Emma the first blow. A slap, right in the face. For a second he seemed to be shocked by what had got into him and Emma hoped this meant he'd calmed down. But the opposite was the case; he became more aggressive, like a fighting dog losing all inhibitions about biting. He yelled at her even more loudly and his clenched fists hovered above her head.

'Of course you did. That's why you opened the package too, isn't it? To get me sent down? But you won't succeed. It won't work!'

Emma wanted to retreat further, but she already had her back against the wall. Palandt grabbed her shoulders.

'I'm not going to prison. Never!'

He shook her so violently that if Emma had been a baby she'd have likely suffered lifelong brain damage. Then, in a further sudden onset of fury, he pushed her away from the wall. She stumbled and grabbed onto the coatrack. Although it was screwed to the wall, it wasn't secured tightly, and so she ripped out the fixings and toppled to the floor with it.

Palandt had now completely lost it. 'You fucking bitch,' he cried. He kicked Emma, bent down and grabbed her hair, but slipped because it was too wet *(or was it too short after all?)*. Emma jabbed her elbow backwards, painfully hitting another bone, maybe his chin or the side of his head. She didn't know because she wasn't looking behind, only forwards. But ahead of her the hall was leading in the wrong direction – deeper into the house.

Into the house of the man who was holding onto her ankles (he must have tripped over the coatrack too) and yelling crazy sentences: 'I had to do it. I had no other choice. I haven't got any money! Why can't anybody understand that? Why can't you all just leave me in peace?'

Emma kicked out, ramming her foot into his face. This time she did turn around and saw the blood streaming from his nose as he stayed on his knees.

But Palandt didn't leave her alone; he made Emma tumble again. As she fell she kicked out one of his incisors, which finally had the desired effect: he let her go and, howling, put his hands up to his bloodied face. Emma crawled on all fours to the door that she knew because she'd already stood outside it some hours before.

As she pulled herself up on the doorknob she heard herself scream, a mixture of fear and hatred. She briefly contemplated going to the kitchen to look for a weapon, no longer to defend herself with, *but to bring it to a conclusion.*

Then she thought she saw a shadow behind Palandt, by the front door. She felt a breath of wind on her tear-stained face and watched Palandt regain his balance and wipe the bloody saliva from his mouth. With the expression of a rabid fox he screamed at her, 'You're not going to destroy my life, you whore!'

Emma jerked the door open, shut it behind her straight away and ran past the sofa beneath the goggling horses' eyes on the wall to the garden door. Emma wasn't going to lose any time finding out whether it was still stuck and now she didn't have to worry about making any noise. So she picked up the ugly umbrella stand by the door, ignoring the twinge in her lower back as she lifted it high, and slung the kitsch Labrador statue through the pane of glass.

The shatter sounded like a scream, but maybe that was her imagination, a faulty signal from her completely distorted senses. Turning her back to the garden and shielding her face with her arms, Emma pressed herself backwards, ripping her puffer jacket on the shards that remained in the doorframe.

She ran across the terrace, into the garden and sank into ankle-deep snow. She wanted to head right around the house, but heard a man's voice coming from that direction. *Not Palandt, but maybe an accomplice?*

So Emma kept running straight, intending to climb over the fence at the end of the garden and turn into the service road that ran between the properties here. A useless path that most neighbours used as a loo for their dogs, but now it might be her chance of escape.

Although it didn't look like that.

Turning around she saw Palandt only a few metres away.

Whereas her path was marked by footprints and feathers, Palandt left a trail of blood behind him.

For a moment she wondered how she was able to see him so well, see his bald head – he must have thrown off his wig.

Then she noticed the light source. Garden lamps that were probably motion sensitive, a relic of his mother who'd kept house and garden in such good nick before handing it over to her son (*the Hairdresser?*).

Emma could hear Palandt behind her, could feel his anger on her neck. She followed the lights in the snowy ground, which led to a grey tool shed. The door was ajar.

Should I?

There was only yes or no, right or wrong. But no time to weigh up the pros and cons. Perhaps it was the fear of slipping on the fence, losing her strength and being pulled down again by Palandt that made her opt for the shed. But maybe rather than make a conscious decision she just followed an innate survival instinct which, in case of any doubt, preferred a lockable door to open ground. That's assuming the shed *was* lockable.

Emma's nose was hit by a pungent cocktail of engine oil, wet cardboard and disinfectant. And there was something else. A mixture of air freshener and rancid liver sausage.

She slammed shut the thin aluminium door of the shed and hunted for a key. It wasn't in the lock nor on the doorframe, although she could hardly see her own hand in the gloom because only a fraction of the light from the outdoor lamps made it in through the small, grimy window.

But even if there had been an 80,000-watt bulb to assist her, Emma wouldn't have been able to search the shed. She didn't have time to catch her breath.

The door that opened inwards was shaking from the

thundering of Palandt's fists. She could have locked it with a thin bolt, but this was only supposed to prevent the door from flying open and shut in gusts of winds. It wouldn't survive a physical attack for long. 'Get out of there!' Palandt yelled. 'Get out of there right now!'

It could only be a matter of seconds before he launched the weight of his entire body against the door and broke it open. Emma would never be able to defend it with her own body.

I've got to push something in front of it.

Her eyes darted around the shed, passing a rubbish-strewn workbench, metal shelving, a military-green box for garden cushions, and alighting on an organic waste bin. A 240-litre container with the city refuse and recycling collection logo. A toolbox sat on the lid.

Emma swept the toolbox to the floor and grabbed the bin, which to her relief was sufficiently full. Even with wheels it was incredibly difficult to pull, but it wasn't very far, *and maybe I'll be lucky and the thing will be the right height so I can wedge it right under the...* 'Haaaaaaandle!' Her thoughts turned straight into a scream when she realised that it was too late. That she hadn't heaved the bin forwards quickly enough and had thus given Palandt a crucial few extra seconds.

He'd thrown himself against the door with all his might, hitting it so hard that the lock broke and he fell into the shed, knocking Emma to the side.

When she caught his elbow in her midriff, she

couldn't breathe and felt faint. To try and prevent her inevitable collapse, she grabbed onto a handle, unaware where it had come from. But as soon as she felt the cold plastic she realised she was clutching the organic waste bin, which tipped over with her.

As Emma fell her head hit the toolbox, but she wasn't granted unconsciousness. Staring upwards she wanted to scream when she saw the sea of air fresheners dangling from the ceiling of the shed. Then Emma really did scream when Palandt was standing beside her holding something that looked like a utility knife.

Now she was bathing in a stench that made her lose her mind, if not yet her consciousness. And in this case, 'bathing' was almost literally correct.

'Nooooo!' she heard Palandt cry. Clearly his mind was already in the no man's land of the soul where Emma was heading too.

Help me, please God, let this be over!

She was lying in a viscous, foetid liquid, which had slopped out of the bin over the floor. A sweetish, rancid, organic and vomit-inducing infusion.

Emma wanted to throw up on the spot, but couldn't. Not even when she saw the lower leg.

With foot but without knee, and very little skin over the calf and shin. It was, however, populated with endless maggots. The slimy worms had nested in the severed limbs that had tipped out of the organic bin along with the decomposed bodily waste and other body parts.

36

With every breath the taste of death made its way into Emma's lungs, clawing itself into the most remote bronchial tubes as if it had talons. Not even the loudest scream or worst coughing could shake it off. Emma knew that even if she survived this encounter (which didn't look likely), deep inside her something would survive forever, a germ of horror, fertile ground for the most appalling nightmares.

'Leave her in peace!' Palandt yelled in a scream-cum-sob. Staring death in the face had afforded Emma some moments of lucidity, and now Palandt's words confirmed her suspicion that the bony foot and decomposing lower leg belonged to a woman. She was also in no doubt that Palandt, brandishing the utility knife above her, must be the Hairdresser.

Emma was lost. She was still sitting on the damp floor beside the toolbox. She was armed now too, having hectically fished from the tool box the first thing she could find that was long, fitted comfortably in her hand and even had sharp jagged edge. But what was she going to do with a jigsaw?

She slammed it against Palandt's leg, but he hardly felt a thing through his thick trousers.

'You'll pay for that,' he cried, punching her square in the face with the fist gripping the knife. As her head jerked back Emma finally lost consciousness, dropped the jigsaw and, paradoxically, was revived again by the pain when her head hit the edge of the tool box for a second time.

Emma could taste blood and felt as if the skin on her head had torn. Palandt's hand was grabbing her hair. She heard a click. Opened her eyes. Saw the utility knife hovering right before her pupils. The edge of the blade was only a tear-width from her eye.

He's going to scalp me, she thought, her mind instinctively turning to Le Zen... *Get out. Before it's too late...* In the same breath she could have screamed because she didn't want this dreadful image of the hotel mirror to be the final memory with which she exited this world.

There were so many nicer, life-affirming moments. Such as Philipp's crumpled skin in the morning, when the pillow had left a wavy impression on his cheeks overnight.

The tiny pair of lamb's fleece boots, size four, that had stood on her dressing table for a while in preparation for having children – light brown, because they didn't know if it would be a boy or a girl. Even the dent in Philipp's company car, which she'd deliberately made with her foot getting out, after a silly argument about *I'm a Celebrity* (which he found funny and she thought was inhuman). Yes, even this ridiculous attestation that she couldn't control her temper sometimes would have been a better final image than the mirror in Le Zen.

Fuck, I don't want to die. Not like this.

Palandt drew his hand back then lunged.

How strange it was, Emma thought, that now should be the moment – for the first time in weeks – when she felt free of anxiety and perfectly calm. It was probably, she concluded, because finally she had proof that she wasn't as paranoid as she'd secretly feared. But maybe she had just given up. Her next thought was her surprise at how utterly painless death was.

'So this is how it is,' she thought as the blade sliced open her forehead and the blood created a waterfall before her eyes. A red veil, behind which Palandt vanished.

Emma closed her eyes, heard her own breath, but this sound strayed from her, mingling with a deep, guttural scream.

Palandt's voice had changed since he'd readied for the second thrust. It was deeper, as if he'd gained weight.

'Emma!' he cried from what seemed like further away, while an unbearable weight fell onto her body.

Her head rolled feebly from the toolbox and for a surreal moment she feared it had been severed, but then, in a near-death experience, she saw Palandt floating away from her.

Her neighbour, who had just (for whatever reason) lain on her, thus expelling the air from her chest, was moving away from her.

Or me from him?

Emma's eyes saw a light, not in the distance as people always claimed, but close and blazing, edged with red. It was shining straight into her eyes.

Then the light moved to the side. Presumably now came that part of the afterlife when you saw the people who'd been most important to you in life, although Emma wondered why this particular man should be the first to appear.

'Salim?' she said to the delivery man.

Who was kneeling beside her.

Who asked if she could hear him.

Who wasn't her final vision.

But her first responder.

And who was shining the torch in her eyes, the torch he'd knocked Palandt out with from behind. Now her neighbour lay beside the waste bin with the female corpse and looked as dead as Emma had thought herself to be only moments before.

'Everything's going to be okay,' she heard Salim say, and with this lie she passed out.

37

Emma felt the snow coming through the seat of her trousers and her underwear getting soaked, but the air out here was so clear and restorative that wild horses wouldn't have got her to leave the plastic garden bench Salim had taken her to.

From here she had a view of everything: the shed, its door secured by Salim's belt; the small window beneath the cheap door lamp, where she expected Palandt's face to appear at any second. But Salim had reassured Emma that her neighbour wouldn't be getting up again in a hurry.

'I knocked that bastard's lights out!'

She couldn't see Salim for the moment. He was wandering around the shed for the second time, his boots crunching loudly in the snow.

'There's no other way out,' he said in satisfaction when he came back around the corner. 'That lunatic is not going to escape.'

Unless he digs himself a tunnel, Emma thought, but

the base of the shed was as hard as concrete and the ground beneath it must be frozen solid. All the same, she didn't feel safe. And this wasn't just because of the acute pain that she now felt from the cut.

To check the bleeding she was pressing to her forehead the blue microfibre cloth which Salim probably used to clean the inside of his windscreen, because it smelled of glass cleaner, but right now an infection was the least of her worries.

'Why?' she asked Salim. In the distance she could hear the rattling of the S-Bahn, which at this time of day would mostly be carrying pleasure-seekers. Young people on their way to Mitte, starting with a few drinks in a bar or going straight to a party.

'I've no idea what got into him. I saw you enter his house with him, Frau Stein, and it looked a bit odd somehow. When you tripped it didn't look as if you were following him willingly.'

'I didn't mean that,' Emma said, shaking her head and wondering how long it would take for the police to arrive. Salim had called them on his mobile.

'Why did you come back? Your shift was over ages ago.'

Your very last shift.

'What? Oh yes.' Salim assumed a guilty expression.

'Because of Samson,' he said contritely, and it struck her that the vet hadn't yet got back to her with the laboratory results.

Or had he?

Perhaps there was a message from Dr Plank on her mobile, which was still in Palandt's hallway, having dropped from her hands a second time during their struggle.

'I'm not sure, but I think I made a terrible mistake,' Salim said, breathing out large clouds of condensation.

'You poisoned Samson!'

To Emma's astonishment he didn't object, but asked with concern, 'So he's in a bad way?'

Salim scratched his beard and pulled a face suggesting he wanted to slap himself. 'Listen, Frau Stein, I'm terribly sorry. I think I accidentally gave the poor thing the chocolate bar from my right-hand pocket and not the dog biscuit I always keep on the left.'

Chocolate.

Of course!

Cocoa powder could be fatal for dogs, even in the minutest quantities.

Now that she knew, Emma recognised the typical symptoms of theobromine poisoning: cramps, vomiting, apathy, diarrhoea.

Samson clearly reacted particularly badly to chocolate.

'I only realised when I was getting changed back home.'

Salim pointed to himself. In place of his postal uniform he was wearing a tight-fitting motorbike outfit – the obligatory Harley jacket, leather trousers and matching steel-capped boots.

'I didn't have your phone number and you aren't in the phone book, so I thought it best to come back in person.'

He pointed to the shed with his tattooed hand.

'I wasn't expecting to find something like that.'

Salim essayed a sad smile. 'I suppose that's what people mean when they say a blessing in disguise, isn't it?' he asked, returning to the shed to check his belt was still securing the door.

At that moment blue lights flickered in the evening sky and danced on the snow in the garden like disco lights.

The police were arriving.

In large numbers but with no sirens.

Three patrol cars and a police van, out of which four officers poured in black combat uniform. They ran up the drive into the garden, towards her, led by an unarmed policeman in civilian clothes, who wasn't dressed warmly enough – a suit, leather shoes and no trench coat over his jacket.

'What happened here?' he asked when he'd got to Emma, and for a moment she couldn't believe that it was him.

'Thank you,' she said, bursting into tears as she got up from the bench and threw her arms around Philipp.

38

In Emma's mind the men in black skiing masks positioned themselves one behind the other in front of the door to the shed.

Four men, all with their weapons drawn.

The shortest, a compact body-builder type (so far as one could make out beneath his uniform), probably stood at the front and had already cut through the belt with his combat knife. His hand was on the doorknob, ready to open it for the three others.

Philipp must be standing somewhere away from the shed, out of her angle of vision through the window. What luck that he'd come back to Berlin early. He'd been worried when Jorgo had told him that she'd simply hung up during her last call. After that she hadn't been reachable again. When Philipp called her on the mobile that was in Palandt's hands, he was going to tell her that he'd be back in ten minutes.

Now he was here for when the officer in charge gave the order to storm the shed.

As she knew from films, the men behind would enter shouting loudly and their guns cocked. And the torches screwed to the barrels would light up every corner of the shed.

'Good God,' Emma heard Philipp exclaim in her head as he saw the tipped-over container with the corpse. Or Palandt lying in a pool of blood because Salim might have smashed his head in. All this, however, was nothing but conjecture.

Emma saw, heard and felt it in her mind only. She sat forty metres away from the action on an ambulance stretcher that had parked outside Palandt's carport.

'That's going to need stitching up,' said a young paramedic or doctor (Emma hadn't been listening when he introduced himself), who resembled a younger Boris Becker: tall, well built and with a mop of strawberry-blonde hair. He'd wiped the blood from her face and treated the wound with a disinfectant spray and a flesh-coloured head bandage. When he was finished she heard an aggressive struggle coming from the garden. No words, only screams.

'What's going on?' Emma asked loudly enough that Salim, who'd been waiting by the ambulance steps could hear her.

'It's happening,' he told her, although surely that could only be a guess.

A uniformed officer ensured that no unauthorised persons could gain entry to the property. But as far as Emma could make out from the open doors of the ambulance no onlookers had dared come outside anyway, perhaps because neighbours were intimidated by the host of flashing police vehicles blocking Teufelssee-Allee. Also, perhaps, because it was snowing more heavily than before and you could barely see a thing.

Emma sat alone with Salim in the ambulance because the Becker paramedic had gone into the driver's cab to write his report, then Philipp turned up.

'Nothing!' he said, his head poking through the door.

'Nothing?' She got up from the stretcher.

'Body parts, yes. But no neighbour.'

'What are you saying?'

That was impossible.

Turning to Salim, Philipp said, 'So you knocked Herr Palandt to the floor and tied him up?'

The delivery man shook his head. 'I didn't tie him up. But he was unconscious.'

'Herr Stein?'

A policewoman appeared behind Philipp and said that the officer in charge urgently needed a word with him.

'Stay where you are,' he said, but of course Emma wasn't going to sit in the ambulance any more.

She followed him for a few steps of the way before the policewoman blocked her path and Emma shouted, 'Please let me through!'

I've got to see it. The empty shed.

Only the fact that Salim had seen him too prevented her from thinking that she'd lost her mind altogether.

'I want to go to my husband. I'm a witness!'

Philipp turned back to her. He was about to call out 'Emma' in that tone with which parents reprimand their naughty children, but then just shrugged and in response to an invisible signal the policewoman let Emma through.

'Maybe you really can help us,' he said, although half his words were swallowed by the strong wind that was making the snow fly around in places.

Philipp stepped into the open shed, where someone had found the light switch.

Besides him there was only one other officer in there, presumably the commander of the operation. His ski mask was over his nose and he waited for the newcomers with an expression that appeared to say, *'Look here, you wimps. I'm standing with my boots in the middle of this corpse liquid, but I can cope with the stink.'*

'You should take a look at this,' he told Philipp.

'There are more body parts here.'

Philipp turned around to Emma. 'You'd better stay outside,' he advised.

As if she hadn't already left enough traces in the shed, *but what the hell? I'll stand in the doorway.*

Outside the stench of putrefaction was easier to bear.

From the door Emma watched her husband step over

the severed lower leg, trying his best to avoid stepping in the rotting puddle beside the overturned organic waste bin, where the rest of the naked female corpse lay.

Squashed like offal.

Despite her disgust, Emma couldn't help studying the body of the woman who'd gone through what she'd been spared.

That could have been me lying there instead of you, she thought, mourning this unknown creature whose name would doubtlessly be on the front page of every newspaper very soon. Together with her own, which the press would no doubt be interested in too.

'Oh, Jesus Christ!' Philipp cursed in the back right-hand corner of the shed.

He'd taken a glance inside the cushion box, its lid positioned in such a way that Emma was unable to glimpse its contents. If her husband's face was turning green, what he was looking at must be even more repulsive than the female corpse on the floor.

'Are there any more crates here?' Philipp said breathily to the officer in charge. 'Storage for more corpses?'

The officer shook his head. 'And no place where the lunatic could hide either. We've searched everything.' Emma's legs were shaking. The sense of déjà vu was unavoidable.

A room with a secret.

'There's nobody here.'

That's impossible.

'He was with the circus,' Emma heard herself say. In a monotone, almost a whisper.

'What was that?'

The two men turned to her.

'His speciality was the suitcase routine.'

Philipp looked at her as if she'd started speaking a foreign language.

'What are you trying to say?'

That he can make himself so small that he can fit in hand luggage.

'Is it dressed?' she asked uneasily, but Emma already knew the answer. Of course. There was no other explanation.

'What do you mean?'

'The corpse, for God's sake. In the cushion box.' She was almost screaming now. 'IS IT DRESSED?'

Because that was the only thing which made sense.

They haven't found any new body parts.

But Daddy Longlegs.

Palandt, who's made himself small and will leap out of the box at any moment…

'No, it's not,' Philipp said very calmly, his words like a needle pricking the bubble of her worst fears.

'There are severed body parts. A torso. A head, a whole leg. Naked. Full of maggots!'

And then he said something that changed everything. 'But there are clothes here, *beside* the crate.'

The commanding officer bent down and lifted a coat with the barrel of his rifle.

A black raincoat with yellow buttons.

So Palandt had got undressed! Why?

At that moment Emma hadn't yet solved the puzzle.

Not even when her gaze fell for at least the tenth time on the waste bin with the sticker, the carrot that served as the 'I' in ORGANIC.

Only when she kneeled by the overturned container and blocked out the stench did the cogs of realisation all click into place, because Emma did the only logical thing and focused solely on the breathing.

Not her own.

But the corpse's.

First its chest moved. Then the entire naked body.

As quickly as only a man could who'd once been known as Daddy Longlegs and who now, despite his illness, shot from his hiding place in the waste bin like a bullet.

'He's alive!' Emma was just able to say before all hell was let loose.

39

Three weeks later

'Seventeen stab wounds.'

Konrad opened the murder squad's investigation report and put it on his lap. To get a better understanding of her testimony he'd fetched the file from his desk after giving Emma a glass of water.

'Three in the eye. Most in the neck and larynx, only two on the forehead and one – the last one – in the left ear.'

Emma shrugged. 'Self-defence.'

'Hmm.'

Konrad looked at the file as if it were a restaurant menu on which he couldn't find anything he fancied.

'Self-defence?'

'Yes.'

'Emma, he was incapacitated after the first cut, when you severed his carotid artery.'

'But still…'

'But still it escalated into a bloodthirsty attack. With the utility knife…'

Looking up from the documents he frowned. 'How did you get hold of that again?'

Till now Emma had been staring impassively out of the window to study the dark, low-hanging bank of cloud above the Wannsee, its grey-black seemingly reflective of her emotional state, although at least it wasn't snowing – for the time being. They had now been talking for three hours, but unlike her Konrad didn't display the slightest signs of tiredness. And he seemed to have a concrete bladder. She really wanted to go to the loo, but couldn't summon the energy even for that.

Over the last few weeks she'd learned bitterly how depressives have to suffer when their illness is misconstrued by those who don't know such intensive sadness. In truth, you were in such a deep psychological hole that you weren't even able to pull the proverbial blanket over your head. This was a reason for the high suicide rate when depressives took medication for the first time to relieve their symptoms. Rather than a new lease of life, all it gave them was the strength to finally end it.

'The knife was still on the floor,' she said in response to Konrad's question. 'Not long before, he'd tried to kill me with it, remember?'

'Yes. But excuse me for pointing out that, as the law

sees it, this attack was definitively over. It had occurred a quarter of an hour before. Your wound had already been treated.'

'And what about when he leaped out of the waste bin smeared in blood. How does "the law see that"?' Emma said, making quotation marks with her fingers.

'As an escape.' Konrad moved the tips of his manicured fingers towards his mouth and tapped his lips with both index fingers.

'Escape?'

'He was naked and unarmed. He didn't pose any danger. That's how the public prosecutor will see it at any rate, especially as there was an armed policeman close by.'

'Who didn't shoot!'

'Because he couldn't. You and Palandt were like a ball on the ground. The risk of hitting you was far too great. Anyway the danger at that moment wasn't from him, but you...'

'Huh!' Emma snorted. 'That's absurd. A sick man dismembers a woman and stuffs her into a bin, gets undressed, stores the body parts in a cushion box so he can disguise himself as a naked corpse. Finally this guy, who'd kicked, punched and practically scalped me, leaps out from his hiding place – and now *I'm* the one in the dock?'

Konrad's answer was laconic and thus doubly painful. 'Seventeen stab wounds,' was all he said. 'You were crazed. Both men together, your husband and the commanding officer, had great difficulty peeling you away from Palandt. You were stabbing with such fury that you even cut them.'

'Because I was beside myself with fear.'

'Excessive self-defence. Not particularly rare, but unfortunately no justification. At best an excuse, which' – now it was Konrad's turn to make quotation marks with his fingers – '"as the law sees it" is unfortunately a weaker argument for the defence than a real emergency.'

The pressure increased behind Emma's eyes, which felt like the harbinger of a flood of tears.

'I'm in real trouble, aren't I?'

Konrad did not oblige her by shaking his head.

'But how could I have known what it all really meant?'

Her eyes were aching more painfully. Emma wiped invisible tears from her cheeks; she hadn't started crying yet.

Not yet.

'You were mistaken. That's human too, Emma. Many of us in that situation would have drawn the wrong conclusions and regarded Palandt as a criminal.'

Konrad closed the file and leaned forwards. 'In truth he didn't mean you any harm. Not to start with at least. And that's why, I'm afraid, it makes my job of defending you so tricky.'

She couldn't withstand his penetrating look. Nor could she gaze into the flames of the fire, which were higher again now and felt like they were burning her face. But perhaps it was just the shame of realisation.

'What happened next?' Konrad asked calmly. The best listener in the world had put on his poker face again.

'You mean how did I find out that I'd been wrong about Palandt?' Sighing, Emma picked up the water glass and moistened her lips. 'If only that had been my worst mistake that evening.' She glanced briefly again at the lake, then closed her eyes.

Emma found it easier to talk about her darkest moments if she shut out the light and the world within it.

40

Three weeks earlier

Emma knew that she was at home, in her own bed. She also knew that she'd sunk into a feverish sleep, physically and mentally exhausted by the consciousness of having killed a man after the skirmishes in Palandt's shed.

So she knew she was dreaming, but that didn't make it any better.

Emma was crouching in the hotel bathroom, looking up from the tiled floor to the message on the mirror.

GET OUT.

OR I'LL HURT YOU.

There was a knock, but it was Emma herself at the door rather than the Russian woman. She looked like a victim of radiation sickness: a bald head, encrusted in places, interspersed with the odd strands and tufts of hair that remained like forgotten weeds, ready to be plucked out.

But worse than what she could see (the dried blood on her forehead and cheek, the blouse buttoned up wrong, the snot in her nostrils) was what she could not see: an expression on her face, life in her eyes.

That life had been switched off in the darkness of the hotel room. All that remained was the buzzing of the electric shaver in her ears and the pressure in her upper arm at the puncture site, now throbbing like a tooth after drilling.

She slammed the door to number 1904. Ran barefoot to the lifts. But when the lift opened she couldn't get in. The cabin was almost entirely taken up by an organic waste bin. A monstrosity with a brown lid and a sticker on the front that said 'EMMA', the second 'M' formed by a bunch of carrots.

Emma heard, *no, she felt*, a noise emanating from the very bottom of the bin, as if it were several hundred metres deep. Something was carving its way from the depths of this well of horror, something which, once released, would never be able to be caught again.

'You fucking bitch,' Anton Palandt howled. 'I had to do it. I had no other choice. I haven't got any money! Why can't anybody understand that? Why can't you all just leave me in peace?'

Emma stepped closer. Looked into the bin, which

was actually a shaft that Palandt was squatting inside. Maggots were crawling from his unmoving eyes. Only his lips were moving. 'I had to do it. I had no other choice. I haven't got any money! Why can't anybody understand that? Why can't you all just leave me in peace?'

'But I haven't got any money!' he yelled from the shaft, and when the naked, blood-smeared corpse, stinking of decay, leaped into Emma's face she woke up.

Her heart was ready to burst out of her chest. Everything about her was pulsing: her right eyelid, the artery on her neck, the cut on her forehead.

She felt for the bandage, happy to find it there. It covered a large section of her head, including her hair – she'd retch if she touched that now.

Emma had been given some medication for this too.

Ibuprofen for the pain, Vomex for the nausea and pantoprazole to stop the cocktail from making her stomach churn.

They had been able to patch the cut. Now the only thing that urgently needed stitching back together was her life, which was ripped into several parts when she killed the Hairdresser. Maybe it had been shredded earlier.

The Hairdresser. The Hairdresser. The Hairdresser.

It didn't matter how many times she repeated this name, he remained a person. A person. A person.

I killed a person.

Emma looked at herself and wouldn't have been

surprised to see her hand chained to the bedframe with a metal clamp.

Philipp had managed to arrange things so that she was allowed to go to bed after giving a short preliminary statement in the living room. Tomorrow morning the interrogation wouldn't finish so quickly.

Nor, in all likelihood, would it turn out to be so friendly when the coroner's report was ready.

She had no idea how many times she'd stabbed Palandt, but she knew that it had been too many to count. And that it hadn't merely been a case of self-defence, but a desire to bring it to an end.

Back in the shed it wasn't only Palandt she would have killed, but anybody trying to stop her from ridding the world of this danger for good.

Revenge.

There was no other response that felt more important when you were done an injustice. And none that left you feeling guiltier once you'd exacted it.

Emma felt for the light switch and knocked a teacup that Philipp had considerately put beside her bed, its contents now cold. It was just after half past ten. She'd slept for more than an hour.

'I haven't got any money,' Emma whispered with a shake of the head as she put a cushion behind her back so she could sit upright in bed.

Why were these the words she'd taken from her dream?

Emma didn't believe in dream analysis as a means of psychotherapeutic treatment. Not every vision that appeared at night had a meaning in the cold light of day. It was just that, even out of a dream, these words made little sense.

Why had Palandt said them?

Even if in some points Philipp's profile analysis didn't match the reality, for example over the question of wealth, there were still universal, almost indisputable, characteristics that defined a sex offender. They were driven less by lust than power, their motor was impulsivity, and money rarely or never played a role with a serial rapist.

And yet Palandt had uttered these words in a state of great distress and agitation. At a point when he could no longer think, only act instinctively like a trapped animal fighting desperately for its life.

And he chooses this moment to articulate his financial problems?

In her own terror, Emma hadn't spent a second thinking about her blocked credit card and the fact that she urgently needed to ask Philipp to top up her account again.

Then there was something else, something really bizarre: Palandt was terminally ill and being harassed by strangers. Even if he'd shown himself to be surprisingly strong on occasion, the whole thing really didn't fit. If the Hairdresser was in such bad physical condition that he couldn't keep blackmailers at bay, how on earth was he able to rape and kill women?

Emma threw back the duvet.

Someone – Philipp, probably – had changed her into silk pyjama bottoms before putting her to bed. She was wearing sports socks, which was useful because she didn't now have to hunt for her slippers before going downstairs to talk to Philipp about what was unnerving her – she was worried that the danger posed by the Hairdresser still hadn't disappeared.

She checked again to see if her bandage was in place and, as she breathed into her hand to see if the smell was as bad as the taste in her mouth, Emma saw the red light.

A small diode on the display of her house phone beside the charging unit.

It showed that the device would soon have to be recharged.

'I don't have any money. I'm not going to prison. Never!' she heard Palandt shouting in her mind, and she couldn't help thinking of the corpse in the bin, another inconsistency.

The Hairdresser's other victims had been left at the crime scene.

This gave her an idea.

Emma picked up the phone on the bedside table, deactivated the caller ID function and hoped that Philipp hadn't reassigned the saved numbers recently.

41

'Lechtenbrinck?'

Hans-Ulrich's voice was unmistakeable. Nasal, almost as if he had a cold, and far too high-pitched for a sixty-year-old professor.

From a single word Emma had recognised the head of the forensic medicine department at the Charité clinic.

She, by contrast, tried to disguise her voice so Professor Lechtenbrinck didn't guess who he was really talking to, even though it was unlikely he would remember her. They'd rarely spoken in the past.

'My name is Detective Superintendent Tanja Schmidt,' Emma introduced herself, using the name of the police officer who'd questioned her earlier in the living room. She gave the name of the department responsible for the Stein/Palandt investigation. 'The body of Anton Palandt, victim of an attack in Westend, was brought in to you this evening.'

'Where did you get this number from?' Lechtenbrinck asked angrily.

'It's in the computer,' Emma lied. In fact it was stored in the speed dial memory of their phone: button 9. Philipp and Lechtenbrinck had cooperated for some time on the puzzle murderer case. Over the course of several months a Berlin serial killer had put a victim's body parts in plastic bags and left them in public places. In the final week, shortly before the killer was apprehended, they'd telephoned each other almost daily and their professional connection became a casual friendship, which was why Lechtenbrinck's private number was still stored in the phone.

'This is outrageous!' the forensic scientist objected. 'This number is only for emergencies and a select few individuals. I demand you delete it at once.'

'I will,' Emma promised. 'But now I've got you on the line…'

'I'm in the middle of a post-mortem.'

Excellent!

'Listen, I really don't want to interrupt you. It's just that we're about to question the suspect, Emma Stein, a second time and it would be of great help to us if we knew the cause of death of the female victim in the organic waste bin.'

'Puh…'

Just from this exhalation Emma knew that she'd cracked him. Forensic scientists couldn't stand the fact that in books and films they were generally portrayed as oddballs who were only ever deployed when it was all too late. They tended to feel that their work was undervalued. After all, they didn't just cut up corpses, but often played a key role especially in the questioning of witnesses and suspects. On one occasion Lechtenbrinck had been able to nail a suspect thanks to a telephone connection between the autopsy room and the interrogation room at the police station. Whenever the murderer tried to depict the death of his victim as a tragic accident, by analysing the wounds Lechtenbrinck was able to advance proof to the contrary, in parallel to the interrogation.

And now the renowned expert didn't seem to want to pass up the opportunity to have a decisive influence on another investigation.

'Well, the cause of death is fairly unspectacular. The report isn't yet cut and dried, but I'd lay money on multiple organ failure as a result of age-related ischaemia.'

'Are you... *having me on?*' Emma almost cried, her panic making her forget to disguise her voice when she next spoke. 'A natural cause of death? The woman was chopped up.'

'Post-mortem. Looks like a classic case of benefits fraud.'

Emma wondered whether Lechtenbrinck had suffered a stroke. Or if she had, because his words made no sense unless he was trying to pull her leg.

'A classic case of fraud whereby the cheat climbs into a bin without legs?'

'Not the cheat. That's Anton Palandt, of course.'

'I don't understand.'

Lechtenbrinck was breathing heavily again, but he seemed to be relishing his role as the experienced scholar able to teach a thing or two to a naïve policewoman.

'Look, Frau Schmidt. I haven't seen the crime scene, but I bet you ten to one that our perpetrator lives in poverty. One day he comes back home and finds his mother dead in bed—'

'His mother?' Emma interrupted Lechtenbrinck, who added with palpable irritation, 'Didn't I mention that? The corpse in the waste bin is almost certainly Palandt's mother. We're still waiting for the final dental analysis, but she's over eighty at any rate.' Then he elaborated on his theory, which Emma listened to as if in a diving bell: muffled, with numbed ears.

'Anyway, after a moment of sorrow, the son says, "Bloody hell, I've got access to Mama's account. Who says I have to ring the police just because she's dead?" He decides to keep his mother alive, as far as the authorities are concerned, so he can cash in on her pension.'

'I haven't got any money!'

'He tells the neighbours about a lengthy stay abroad, spending time at a health resort or something like that, but to tell you the truth in Berlin nobody wonders if an old person stops showing their face. At some point the smell becomes noticeable, which is why the perpetrator organises a burial in a waste bin. He just stuffs the remains into the container, which is a bit of a mess as corpses usually don't fit in without amputations. Then he leaves the waste bin in the cellar or shed, and chucks in cat litter or sprays litres of air freshener. The classic case.'

So my dream put me on the right track, Emma thought.

Palandt wasn't the Hairdresser and she hadn't killed a ripper, but at most a hot-tempered benefits cheat who'd done nothing worse than to prevent his mother from resting in peace just because he needed the money.

Which meant the danger is still very much present!

Emma wasn't sure how she'd managed to avoid bellowing this last thought down the line. She thought she thanked the doctor and said a rapid goodbye, but she couldn't recall another word that was said. Exhausted, she fell back into the cushions and pillows.

I killed a person!

Not the Hairdresser!

Palandt didn't have the slightest thing to do with him.

His wig, the medication, the package… In her paranoia she'd bent the facts, which had cost an innocent man his life.

Emma closed her eyes and couldn't help thinking of the blood that had spurted from Palandt's body. After she'd stabbed him again and again.

Which in turn reminded her of the pool of blood she'd had to wipe up in the living room this morning.

Samson!

She hadn't thought about him once since she'd

woken up. In the uneasy hope that he, at least, was better, she dialled the number to access her voicemail from the landline. Her mobile had been confiscated as evidence by the police.

'You have three new messages,' the robotic voice announced. And indeed the first was from Dr Plank, reassuring Emma that Samson was over the worst. *Thank God.* But they'd have to wait for the definitive results on Monday before she could pick him up, and what was happening now about payment?

The next was from Philipp, sounding concerned and informing her that he'd be back home in a few minutes.

And finally she heard another voice that sounded so agitated that Emma didn't recognise it at first. It didn't help that Jorgo was practically whispering either.

'Emma? I'm sorry about earlier. I mean that I lied to you. Of course I gave you that note.'

The note!

Something else that Emma, in her distress, had temporarily forgotten. The telephone beeped because the battery was low. It needed to be put back on the dock, but then she wouldn't be able to make any more calls, which is why Emma decided to go downstairs where she hoped the second handset would be waiting fully charged.

'Your husband has a spy program on his mobile,' she heard Jorgo say. 'It automatically records every incoming call.'

A spy program? What the bloody hell is that about?

It beeped again three times before she got to the bedroom door.

But there was just enough juice left in the battery for a few more words from Jorgo.

'I didn't want your husband to find out about the note when he listened to our conversation later on. So please call me on my mobile. Please. It's important. We found out something. Philipp doesn't want to tell you, but I think you ought to know. In the hotel, in Le Zen—'

Beep.

The line was dead and the display as dark as the hallway on the ground floor.

Emma felt her way to the light switch as Jorgo's final words echoed slowly in her head.

'We found out something...'

She went into the kitchen first, but the second handset wasn't in the dock.

'Philipp doesn't want to tell you...'

On the way into the living room Jorgo's voice went quiet, but now she thought she could hear the buzzing of the shaver in her head, only that this time it wasn't a long, penetrating drone, but an intermittent stutter.

'In the hotel, in Le Zen...'

Like a drill.

An insect.

Emma went over to the desk where that afternoon she'd ripped open Palandt's package. She couldn't find the second house phone here either, although she did locate the source of the buzzing: Philipp's mobile.

With every ring it rotated to the rhythm of the vibrations. The caller's name flashed ominously.

Emma turned around, but the vague inkling that her husband would suddenly be standing there was unfounded.

She hesitantly picked up the mobile and pressed the green symbol to take the call.

'What did you find out in the hotel, Jorgo?' she asked anxiously.

'Help me!' screamed the voice on the other end.

42

She recognised it straight away, even though Emma had never heard this voice sound so unfamiliar before.

Muffled, choking with gurgling in the background.

'Sylvia?' she said, and her friend started to sob by way of an answer. 'What's wrong?' Emma asked. 'Are you hurt? How can I help you?'

And why are you calling from Jorgo's phone?

'I... I'm dying,' Sylvia slurred. The panic and terror were still in her voice, but the force of her initial scream had dissipated.

'No, you're not. Do you hear me? You're not dying. I'll fetch help and everything will be alright.'

'No. Never... alright... again!'

Emma could virtually hear Sylvia drifting away. The more tightly she pressed the phone against her ear, the quieter it sounded.

In her mind she saw her friend with a utility knife in her neck, sitting in a pool of blood she'd coughed up in a torrent. Sylvia was no longer speaking now, just coughing and gasping, no matter how loudly Emma implored her to say what on earth had happened.

'Where are you?'

Now Emma screamed, because this question could apply to both Sylvia and Philipp, whose help she desperately needed.

Emma hurried through the living room, the mobile still at her ear. She saw Philipp's keys on the chest of drawers, his jacket hanging on the rack, so he couldn't be out. Anyway he'd never leave the house without his mobile, but he had left it in the living room, *which he only does when...*

'Sylvia, are you still there?' Emma said into the phone, and a cold silence washed back.

... he goes down to his laboratory...

Emma looked at the old cellar door. The light from the cellar stairs seeped into the hallway through a large gap between the floor and the bottom of the door.

... where his mobile doesn't get any reception!

'Sylvia, stay on the line. I can't take you down into the cellar, do you understand? The connection will go, but I'll be right back. Don't hang up!'

No reaction.

Emma briefly wondered whether it would be smarter to cut Sylvia off and call the police, but what if her friend wasn't at home? The telephone connection might be the only way of pinpointing her location.

She put the mobile on the chest of drawers, yanked

open the cellar door and yelled as she went down the concrete steps, 'Philipp? Quick. You've got to help me. Philipp?'

The ceiling in the cellar was so low that the seller had agreed to knock some money off the price when he saw that even Emma had to duck as they looked around.

After moving in they cladded the ceiling on the stairs with wood, which meant there was even less room now. Stooped, Emma hurried downstairs, taking the sharp turn to the right and then straight on to the 'laboratory'.

They'd originally earmarked the area as storage for the vacuum cleaner, broom and mop, but then Philipp replaced the old linen curtain with a folding door and made himself a little office behind it. Inside were a tiny desk with a laptop connected to the internet, two metal shelves on the wall, completely cluttered with specialist literature and all manner of stackable hard plastic boxes containing magnifying glasses, tweezers, microscopes and other utensils. These he used for examining photographs and analysing signatures or other evidence essential to his work as a profiler.

Down here in his 'cave', cut off from the rest of the world, Philipp was best able to concentrate. While he worked he usually listened through headphones to music that calmed him, but would have given Emma hearing loss in a few seconds: Rammstein, Oomph and Eisbrecher.

It was no surprise, therefore, that he hadn't responded to her calling. Nor that he got the fright of his life when

Emma opened the folding door and pulled off the headphones.

'What the hell…'

'Philipp… I—'

Emma stared at his hands, which were wearing mouse-grey latex gloves.

Dull bass drumbeats pounded out from the headphones into the tiny room, providing an accompaniment to her fitful breathing.

Emma was gasping for air, which wasn't a result of the few steps and quick dash down here, nor of her concern for Sylvia. The reason was that she couldn't find an innocent explanation for what lay in front of Philipp.

The utility knife.

The gloves.

THE PACKAGE!

She'd wondered where her slippers had got to. The shoebox-sized package with her internet order that you could put in the microwave. Philipp had put away the food delivery in the fridge and her contact lenses were in the bathroom.

But the light package wrapped in normal brown paper? It was down here. Right beneath Philipp's reading lamp, beside his laptop on the mini desk.

The paper cut open.

The flaps opened.

Some of its contents spread beneath the desk magnifier, the rest still inside the box padded with cotton wool.

Not microwavable slippers.

Emma had obviously been mistaken and she'd neglected to check who the package was addressed to.

For the long, thick, lifelike tufts of brunette hair that had been sent in this box were not for her.

But for Philipp.

43

'What's that?' Emma asked.

Her mind was seeking a logical, but most of all an innocent, explanation.

'Were you sent those by the Hairdresser?'

Definitely. The killer has contacted him. He's just doing his work here and examining the trophies.

'What do you mean?' asked Philipp, who'd stood up from his chair.

'You know, the hair,' Emma said. An icy ring closed around her heart when she watched Philipp open a desk drawer and shut the bunch of dark hair inside.

'What hair?' he asked. 'I don't know what you're talking about, darling.'

Then he turned his notebook so that she could see the screen.

'What... how... where...?' she heard herself stammer. Her monosyllabic questions changed in time to the pictures that appeared on the screen as a sort of slideshow.

Photos of women.

Of *beautiful* women.

Escort girls. Secretly photographed outside various doors. *Hotel-room doors*, opened by a man who was always the same, while the prostitutes changed.

'You?' Emma said, still desperately trying to deny the obvious.

'You met these girls?'

The escort girls. The victims?

'So *you* killed them?'

'Emma, are you feeling okay?' Philipp asked with an expression that made her think he was feigning surprise as he pressed the spacebar on his keyboard. And called up a different picture that showed another victim.

Emma screamed when she recognised herself.

With a wheelie suitcase in one hand, right by a dark door she was just opening. Like all the other clips, this was badly lit, but the room number on the walnut veneer was easy to make out: 1904.

'It was you!' Emma screamed into Philipp's face. 'You're the Hairdresser!'

How could have I been so mistaken?

So deceived?

Perturbed by the package for her unknown neighbour, Emma hadn't paid any attention to the second one.

And thus nor to the enemy in her own house.

Having become lost in the labyrinth of her own paranoid thoughts, Emma had destroyed innocent lives.

'You bastard!'

Her husband smiled and spoke with a tone of great concern, which didn't go with his diabolical grin. 'Emma, calm down, please. You're out of your mind,' he said, at the same time pressing his keyboard again, which turned the screen black.

'What are you going to do?' Emma cried, with no idea what *she* should do. She felt paralysed by bewilderment and horror. 'Are you trying to drive me mad?'

'What do you mean? I'm worried you're seeing things again that aren't there, darling.'

Yes. That's it. I don't know why, but he's feeding my paranoia.

Emma looked around, searching instinctively for an object to defend herself with if Philipp attacked her. Then she saw a small camera on the ceiling, which was fixed so that Emma was in the picture the whole time, whereas her husband would not be visible on the film.

'You're filming me?' she said, devastated.

'But darling, you asked me to make the cellar secure,' he replied piously. 'For fear of burglars.'

'I never said anything about cameras,' she yelled at him. And whereas she was still far from clear as to what Philipp's motives could be, she was struck by another, horrendous realisation:

Sylvia.

She didn't call from Jorgo's phone.

But from her own.

On this point, at least, she was sure about the game Philipp had been playing with her the whole time.

It's just like he did with his ex.

He'd saved Sylvia's number under a different name.

What sort of a man would do that?

One who had something to hide.

An affair.

So it wouldn't attract any attention if his lover called several times a day, sent texts or missed calls.

Emma's stomach tightened.

Of course, how clever.

Jorgo was Philipp's partner, so it was only natural that he'd make lots of calls. At least there was an explanation when the naïve wifey at home saw the display and asked.

How clever and deceitful.

For him Sylvia was Jorgo, while Sylvia called him Peter.

And she's got such wonderful long hair. Just like me.

Just like all the Hairdresser's other victims.

'But why did you have to kill them all?' Emma croaked. The revelations seemed to have blocked her airways. 'The whores, your affairs. Even Sylvia? Why did she have to die?'

As if the name of the woman she'd once regarded as her best friend was the cue, the devilish smile vanished from Philipp's face and for the first time he looked seriously worried. 'What's wrong with Sylvie?' he asked, as if really unaware that she'd just tried to call him in the throes of death.

Maybe it was the brief moment of weakness she thought she could detect in his eyes, or the fact that he'd called his latest affair by her nickname that unleashed an aggressive, unrestrained fury in Emma.

But possibly it was just the courage of despair that tore her from her paralysis.

44

'Emma, stop!' Philipp cried, but she had no intention of surrendering with no way out.

She knocked away the arm he was trying to grab her with, turned around and ran up the stairs as fast as she could, but it wasn't fast enough.

Philipp easily seized her foot and held her where she was. He was bigger, stronger and faster than her. And he didn't have a wound to the head that throbbed like a living insect below its bandage, sending out new waves of pain with every movement.

Emma stumbled and the heels of her hands slapped hard against the edge of the concrete steps.

She flipped onto her back and started kicking as she'd done with Palandt just a few hours before. Now, however, she was only wearing socks; without her heavy boots she couldn't even hurt Philipp, let alone shake him off.

'Emma!' her husband cried, now with a grip on both ankles. The edges of the steps dug into her back and yet she kept thrashing about as if possessed.

Until Philipp yelled 'Stop that!', rushed forwards and hit her.

Hard. Harder than this morning when he'd slapped some sense back into her.

Emma's head dashed backwards against the stairs and she saw bright lights. When she opened her eyes again it was as if she were looking at Philipp through a cracked kaleidoscope.

She saw that his lip was bleeding, which meant she'd probably caught him with her foot.

Not good.

The minor injury had only made him furious like a wounded animal, thus giving him more strength than it had sapped.

Emma, on the other hand, had no more resistance to offer. She could hardly bear the pressure of his fingers around her wrists.

She wanted it to stop.

For it to finally come to an end.

The pain. The violence.

The lies!

Her sudden passivity gave Philipp new impetus. He climbed and lay on top of her with all his weight, like a lusty husband desperate to shag his willing wife on the cellar stairs, the only difference being that he didn't want to make love, *but quite the opposite.*

'Help!' Emma cried, although to whom she didn't

know. In her head she was shouting more loudly than in the dimly lit reality of the cellar steps.

She closed her eyes and the simple wooden panelling on the walls vanished, as did the plastic planter below the banisters, the fuse box by the entrance, which she could only see if she tilted her head back, and the door to Philipp's 'laboratory'.

And Philipp vanished of course, although only the sight of him. His words wouldn't go away.

'Everything's going to be fine,' she heard him say. In a gruesomely friendly tone. She heard his breathing, sensed a hand (probably the right one) push beneath her head, felt him stroking her brow (probably with the back of his left) – he ought not to have done that.

The feeling of latex on her face, the typical smell of rubber and talcum powder, was like a dagger to her heart, twisting, twisting and twisting with every movement.

When Emma opened her eyes she saw Philipp smile, presumably the same grin he'd worn in the darkness of the hotel room. His head came closer and she thought about butting her own into his face. But again she was too feeble to do any serious damage; she'd only make him even angrier.

Emma started crying and heard him make shhhing noises, no doubt aimed at pacifying her. But they made Emma think of snakes and the very next moment she rammed her knee between his legs.

Philipp groaned and loosened his grip, which gave

her the opportunity to chop the side of her hand against his jaw.

He screamed, turned to the side, pressed a hand to his mouth and spat out blood. She'd hit him so hard that she must have knocked a tooth out. Or he'd bit his tongue, so heavy was the bleeding.

He'd now let go of her entirely; Emma could no longer feel any pressure on her body or around her wrists and ankles.

Finally she got to her feet, ran upstairs, but once again she was too slow. Once again Philipp caught hold of her, this time her foot, and started to drag her back. To him.

Into the abyss.

Emma felt for the banisters, tried to hold on, but her hand slipped and knocked against a hard edge, which she instinctively clasped.

Even though it felt like a handle, it wasn't fastened to the wall, but why would there be a handle on the cellar stairs, *unless…*

… it belonged to the fire extinguisher.

As she faltered Emma saw her chance. While her body was still busy trying to regain its balance she yanked the fire extinguisher upwards, swivelled on the balls of her feet, swayed and tried to fall forwards, towards Philipp. But gravity had other ideas, and so once more she toppled onto the stairs on her back.

As she fell there was no way she could launch the heavy

fire extinguisher at Philipp, who was over her again.

All she saw was him raising his hand, then everything went white. The cellar, the walls, the stairs, Philipp, herself. Like in a sandstorm, everything was surrounded by a veil of dust from one moment to the next.

Emma heard a hissing, then pressed down harder with her right hand, which evidently had control over the dust and the hissing noise, and for a split second there was a hole in the fog.

In the hole stood Philipp.

Covered with the contents of the fire extinguisher she was spraying right at him. With the foam he was trying to wipe from his eyes Philipp looked like a ghost with a blood-smeared mouth.

'EMMAAA,' she heard him scream as he managed to grab the banister while stumbling. Now he started moving again. Slowly and carefully. Step by step he came closer.

And agonisingly slowly, step by step, Emma crept up the stairs on her belly.

She'd almost got to the top when he seized her foot from behind and tugged her back.

Emma felt for something to hold onto, but only succeeded in pulling over the washing basket, the contents of which poured out onto her.

She was reminded of the corpse liquor in Palandt's shed, could smell the decay clinging to the dirty washing. Jeans, blouse, underwear. Everything that Philipp had taken off her and must have stuffed into the basket.

Nothing that could assist her now, *because how can I defend myself with a dressing gown?*

DRESSING GOWN!

The thought shot through her mind together with the pain she felt as she was dragged down another step and her jaw hit the hard surface.

Philipp was beside himself; he continued to yell something that could have been her name, but also sounded like pain, torture and death.

Emma would not let go, however. Lying on her tummy, she clutched the dressing gown.

Rummaged through the right-hand pocket.

Fuck.

The left pocket.

And finally had it in her hand.

Just as Philipp grabbed her waist to turn her around, her fingers clasped the plastic handle.

Emma yielded to her husband's strength, used it for her own backswing, raising her hand up high.

Holding the bloody blade.

From Palandt's package.

And in one sweeping movement sliced the scalpel across Philipp's throat.

45

Three weeks later

It was strange she wasn't crying.

In the lonely hours in the psychiatric unit the mere thought of Philipp had been enough to bring tears to her eyes, but now that she'd confessed her dreadful deeds to Konrad, recounting for the first time everything in all its detail, it seemed her reservoir of tears had dried up. Although she could feel the dull, headache-inducing pressure behind her eyes, her cheeks remained dry.

'I'm finished,' she said, and both of them knew that she wasn't referring to her testimony.

Two men, both killed by her own hand on the same day.

Just because of a package for the neighbour.

If she hadn't accepted it, she wouldn't have lost her mobile in Palandt's house. And if she hadn't opened the package she wouldn't have had a scalpel.

'Didn't you notice?'

Konrad was looking at her, standing by the bookshelf with the works of Schopenhauer. He was holding a thin cardboard folder and Emma couldn't have said how it got there. She hadn't even been aware that Konrad had stood up and wandered across the room. Two minutes must have passed since she'd uttered her last word, two minutes during which she'd stared fixedly at the tea stain on the round carpet, comparing its contours with the map of New Zealand.

Her hand tingled, her tongue felt numb – typical symptoms of withdrawal. She'd have to take her tablets again soon, but didn't dare ask Konrad for another glass of water, also because the pressure on her bladder was now almost intolerable.

'What didn't I notice?' she asked after some delay. She was tired and she was reacting with the speed of a drunk.

'That it was your own husband who raped you, Emma. Do you really believe you wouldn't have noticed?'

Apart from the fact that he was using her first name, there was no longer any intimacy in his words. In just a single phrase he'd managed once more to change her whereabouts. She wasn't on the sofa any more, but in the dock.

Where I belong, after all.

'I had paralysing drugs in my body that distorted my senses,' Emma said, trying to answer the question she'd asked herself over and over again. Konrad wasn't satisfied.

'Your own husband materialises in your hotel room from out of nowhere like David Copperfield, just to do what he could have got from you far more easily a day later within the own four walls of his house? Voluntarily too!'

'You know full well that for a rapist it's about power rather than sex.'

'Are you telling me that you've caressed and felt him thousands of times, yet on this occasion you didn't even get a whiff of suspicion?'

'I know what you're thinking, Konrad. You said it straight to my face earlier. Once a liar, always a liar, am I right?'

Konrad gave her a sad look, but didn't disagree.

'But you're wrong,' Emma said. 'Yes, I did lie when I foolishly claimed to have been the woman in the Rosenhan video. But in this case things are very different.'

'How?'

'Well, they found hair belonging to all the victims in Philipp's laboratory. All of them!'

'Apart from yours.'

Konrad opened the folder and took from it four large black-and-white photographs.

'What do you know about these photos?' He spread them out on the glass table.

Emma averted her eyes from the women. She didn't

need to see their large eyes, high cheekbones and certainly not their thick hair to recognise them. In the pictures they were laughing, pursing their lips for a kiss or looking brazenly and wickedly into the camera. They had no opportunity to do this in life any more.

'The victims,' Emma said.

'Correct, these are the escort girls that the Hairdresser murdered.' Konrad fixed her with an inscrutable look. 'These women have a lot in common with you, Emma. Dreadful things were done to them. They've got wonderful hair, they even vaguely look like you. But assuming you've told me the truth about the important things, then there's one key difference between you and these sorry creatures, and by that I don't mean that all of them are dead.'

... assuming you've told me the truth about the important things...

Emma felt even more exhausted than when she'd taken the diazepam earlier on.

'What are you talking about?'

'These women had their heads shaved and they were killed, but...' Konrad tapped each photograph in turn and put an exclamation mark behind each of his words: 'But! These! Women! Were! Not! Raped!'

Silence. Not completely, for the office was filled with the constant roaring of the gas fire, but all the same the stillness that followed Konrad's outburst was oppressive.

Emma wanted to say something. She felt that deep

inside her, words were buried, which now had to come together into a meaningful, logical sentence, but she could manage nothing other than: 'You're lying.'

'*I'm* lying?' Konrad said. 'There was no forensic evidence of forced penetration. With none of the victims.'

'But in the news…'

'Forget the news,' Konrad interrupted her. 'The first newspaper that printed the false information, in twenty-centimetre-high letters on a double-page spread lied to increase its circulation. And all the other hastily put-together news tickers, tweets, posts and internet reports, which more people believed and nobody bothered to verify, *these* spread the lie. Later, the serious magazines, weeklies and television features followed. They lied too, but this time at the request of the investigating officers.'

'But… but why?'

'Why was information withheld from the public?' He answered his own question: 'I hardly need to tell you about the problems police have with psychologically deranged nutcases who crow about having committed other people's spectacular crimes.'

Pathological liars.

'Which is why detailed knowledge about killers isn't disseminated in the media. So that confessions can be checked for truth.'

Konrad paused to lend his words more weight. 'Normally this is a way of filtering out people just trying to jump on the bandwagon. It's not as often used for victims, though.'

He got up and strode across his office as if through a courtroom, his hands crossed behind his back.

'Do you have any idea how many women rang the police hotline having cut their own hair off? Women who said they'd been raped but were able to escape?'

'I'm not one of those,' Emma said, making the error of running her hand through her hair as she'd done all her life whenever she was nervous.

'I've spoken to the public prosecutor. Do you know what he thinks? That you were trying to make Philipp stick with you because of your financial worries. He wanted to leave you so you pretended to be pregnant. But because this isn't a lie you can keep up forever, you invented a rape to explain the miscarriage. At the same time you were aiming for sympathy with your psychological trauma. But when you realised that none of this was enough to keep Philipp, you killed him, making you his sole heiress.'

'Konrad... how... how... can you even entertain the... I know what happened. I mean, I'm not mad.'

'No?'

No?

Did he really just ask that?

Konrad took a few steps towards her and now stood so close again that she'd only have to raise her hand to stroke his well-trimmed beard.

'Leave me alone,' she said when she sensed he was going to touch her. 'Go away!' she protested, but more for the sake of it rather than with any force. Nor did she shake his hand off when he put it on hers.

'You were mentally abused,' he whispered softly. 'But not physically!'

'Yes, I was. I was…' She closed her eyes. 'I *was* raped and now I want you to stop your *advocatus diaboli* routine, or…'

'EMMA!'

Konrad shouted so loudly that she trembled.

'Open your eyes and listen to me. This is not a negotiating tactic. I'm not speaking to you as a lawyer, but as a friend.' He took a deep breath. 'Your husband abused you. But only psychologically. He didn't abuse your body. Nor those of the other victims.'

No, no that's impossible.

'Philipp wasn't the Hairdresser?'

'No.'

All she could see in Konrad's eyes was a sad certainty. Emma turned away. She couldn't stand the gaze which seemed to be telling her that in Palandt and her husband she'd killed two innocent men in one day.

46

'So who was it then?'

Emma's entire body was itching. She was desperate to scratch her arms, legs and tummy. Or even better, cast off this skin she no longer wanted to be in.

'Who murdered those women if it wasn't Philipp?' she repeated her question.

'Think about it, Emma,' Konrad said, getting to his feet and picking up the photos of the dead women from the coffee table. He held them in his hands like a fan. 'All these victims – look closely and then you'll see the connection between them.'

Reluctantly her eyes wandered to the photos.

Yes, they look like me. They've got hair like I used to have.

'They're all Philipp's type.'

'Precisely, Emma,' Konrad agreed. 'But unlike you they're prostitutes. High-end escorts. Your husband cheated on you. With every one of them.'

He shook the fan of photos in his hand.

'And this infidelity is the motive. It points the way to the murderer.'

Emma couldn't breathe until a tortured cough freed her passages.

'What did you just say?'

'Think about it, Emma. Who was so close to Philipp that he could discover his amorous escapades? Who was so hurt yet intelligent enough to forge a plan to remove from those women the very thing that had triggered Philipp's desire?'

Their hair.

'You're crazy,' Emma protested. 'You must have totally lost your mind. Do you seriously believe that all these women...'

'... your rivals in love!'

... were murdered by me? She wasn't able to say this out loud.

'Put yourself in his position, Emma. Philipp knows that the Hairdresser is after women who he's had sex with. The killer taunts him by sending packages to your home with his trophies, as if trying to say, '*Look what I've done to those women you sleep with.*' If your husband discloses this information and passes the evidence to the investigation team, it gets out that he's been cheating on you. Which is the last thing he wants. So he has to take the matter in hand himself. In his laboratory he examines the pieces of evidence and undertakes research without knowing that the Hairdresser is someone close to him. Even though Philipp knows the women haven't been raped he makes the mistake of looking for a man. And yet any child knows who uses poison, the weapon that that killed the escorts.'

The weaker sex. Women.

Emma crossed her arms behind her head. The scar for which she had Palandt to thank was throbbing and itching, but she resisted the urge to scratch her forehead.

'So why did he show me the photos in the cellar? And behave as if there weren't any hair? Was he trying to drive me mad?'

Konrad nodded. 'I have to say that this is what most bothered me in preparation for our conversation. And it won't be easy to convince the court that Philipp exploited your vulnerable mental state for his own purposes.'

'Which purposes?'

'I think he wanted to obtain a reservation of consent.'

'Have me declared incapacitated?'

'That's another way of putting it.'

'But that makes no sense,' Emma protested. 'Philipp was the one with the money, not me.'

'For that very reason,' Konrad said. 'Your husband had the fortune and because there was no pre-nuptial contract he would have lost half of it if you got divorced. Unless as your guardian he had regained full access to it while you were legally committed to a psychiatric hospital.'

The motive. His cheating had brought it to light.

And yet…

'Okay, you say that Philipp wasn't the one who killed the women. He didn't even rape them, but just slept with them. And someone else, the Hairdresser, shaved their hair and sent the trophies to Philipp to show him that they knew about him cheating on me. And you claim that Philipp then resorted to emotional blackmail to destroy me.'

Konrad nodded. 'That's about right.'

'And you think that the Hairdresser…'

Emma let her words hang in the air and Konrad made a grab for them.

'I think that only an extremely jealous person is capable of such acts. Someone who wants Philipp for herself and can't stand the thought of having to share him.'

'I didn't know anything about Philipp's infidelity,' she told Konrad. 'I didn't know those prostitutes. So I didn't kill them.'

'You?' Konrad asked, perplexed. In a gentle, conscience-stricken voice he said, 'Oh my, Emma, I'm really sorry. You thought I was talking about you the whole time?'

47

Emma's head started spinning.

Konrad doesn't think I'm the killer? He wasn't talking about me? But... but who then?

She mulled over the questions her old friend had just asked her.

Who was close to Philipp? Who was intelligent enough to forge a female's plan of revenge? And who would suffer most from his sleeping with the escort girls if not his wife?

'His mistress!' Emma blurted out, putting her head in her hands at the moment of realisation.

'Correct,' said Konrad, who'd regained his confidence. 'Not a whore, but the woman who was important to him. Who was close to him because he saw her regularly.'

All the hairs on Emma's forearms stood up.

'Sylvia?' she whispered.

Konrad nodded.

Emma laughed hysterically, tapped the side of her head, then put her head in her hands again.

'Noooo,' she screamed. 'That's absurd. Impossible. She died while…'

'… while you were in the cellar with Philipp. That's correct. She loved him, Emma. She loved him so much that she wouldn't forgive his flings and dalliances. You found it out yourself: there was no Peter. The man she wanted children with was called Philipp.'

A sound entrenched itself in her ear, preparing to drown out all others, especially Konrad's voice.

'She loved Philipp and she hated the women he consorted with. Unworthy whores who deserved to die.'

'But what about me? She let me live.'

That made no sense.

'She didn't have to murder you, darling. He could separate from you. In all likelihood he'd promised Sylvia to leave you for her. To have children with her. Since that night you hadn't even touched Philipp, had you? I'm sorry to have to say it, but in her eyes you were no longer any competition. Unlike the prostitutes. Sylvia wanted to prevent all sexual contact between Philipp and other women. Which was one of the reasons for sending him her trophies. To show him: *I know who you're fooling around with. Every one of those whores you sleep with will die.*'

Without sinking to the floor, Emma felt as if she were falling.

That's why Philipp reacted so strangely when she mentioned Sylvia's name in the cellar. Emma had asked him why he'd had to kill her, but he'd had no idea that Sylvia was dying.

Konrad gave her cheek a soft caress. 'A moralist would say that your husband had all these women on his conscience. But he didn't murder them. Nor did he lay a finger on Sylvia. When she tried to call Philipp on his mobile and you answered she'd already taken an overdose of sleeping pills.'

'The call was a cry for help?' Emma asked.

She withdrew the hand that Konrad had tried to hold and gazed at the fire. The gas flames were shimmering violet and blue, reminding her of bruises from wounds that would never heal.

'But why did she come to visit me that day? Why did she scream that I'd slipped her the morning-after pills to stop her from getting pregnant?'

Konrad sighed. 'She was mad, Emma. You can't measure the behaviour of a serial murderer by normal standards. But your question contains the answer you're looking for.'

Bang.

It struck her with the momentum of a guillotine.

'Because *he* didn't want her getting pregnant,' Emma whispered in horror.

'And Sylvia must have realised that at some point after having visited you, darling. Now she knew that Philipp didn't want to have children with her. She feared that he'd go back on his promise and never leave you, and her suspicion can only have been reinforced when he abandoned his conference because of you.'

The world before Emma's eyes blurred behind a wall of tears.

'All of that may be true,' she sobbed. 'But your story has one massive flaw. I may well be paranoid and have overreacted to Philipp. But the reason for that goes back to what the Hairdresser did to me in my hotel room. And that wasn't Sylvia.'

'How come?'

Now it was her turn to yell each word with an exclamation mark.

'BECAUSE! I! WAS! RAPED!' She was quaking. 'I felt it. A woman does feel something like that.'

Konrad looked again as if he were rooted to the floor of his office. Very calmly, without making a face, he asked, 'Are you quite sure, Emma?'

'Yes, one hundred per cent sure.' She turned to the window and gave a fake laugh. 'I know I have a fertile imagination. And sometimes I tell stories, yes. But on this point I'm absolutely sure! It was a man. Inside me. That's why I lost my baby. I can still feel…'

She couldn't breathe. Images flickered before her eyes and veils drifted past her field of vision as if she'd spent too long looking at the sun, rather than the Zehlendorf winter landscape behind Konrad's desk.

'What's wrong?' Konrad asked, sounding more intrigued than concerned.

'The light,' Emma said, pointing out at the Wannsee.

Ought it not to be much darker?

'How long have I been here in your… in your…' Once more she was unable to complete a sentence, and this time it was because of the man on the promenade. And the large mastiff on its lead. Which opened its mouth as if intent on catching snowflakes on its tongue. '… in your practice?' Emma mumbled, seized by a surreal, completely irrational feeling of having got caught up in a time loop.

She wasn't just looking at a similar backdrop, but exactly the same one she'd seen at the start of her session. She stood up. It took some effort, but this time she found the strength to stay on her feet.

'What's going on here?' she asked, wandering over to the window.

Behind her Konrad started talking to someone, even though he was alone in the room.

'That's enough now,' he said sternly. 'I repeat, that's enough.'

She heard footsteps approaching from the corridor outside. At the same time her nose again picked up a smell of fresh paint and other renovation work as she got closer to the window. Just as the doors were opened behind her and she was about to touch the glass with her fingertips, the lake vanished before her very eyes, and with it the walker, the snow, the mastiff, the promenade, everything. Even the window wasn't there any more.

Just a black hole in the wall.

'Frau Dr Stein?' she heard a man's voice say. It wasn't Konrad's and she ignored it.

'But I know who I am,' she insisted, starting to cry as she heard the electrostatic clicking of the high-resolution television her head was leaning against.

'Please don't be afraid, Frau Stein,' the man said, but when she turned to him and saw her psychiatrist in a white coat with two nurses standing beside Konrad, that's exactly what she felt: a fear that took hold of every cell inside her body and seemed to have settled there for good.

Emma felt faint and, when her knees gave way and she was losing consciousness, she tried to hold onto something for support, but failed.

48

Behind the scenes, Park Clinic

'Splendid. That was splendidly done.'

Dr Martin Roth pointed to the screen on the table on front of them, having just turned down the volume. On it they could see the mock-up office where Emma was being attended to by two nurses. After passing out, she'd come around again soon afterwards and now was lying on the sofa with her legs bent. If Konrad hadn't known better he would have actually believed he was watching his office by the Wannsee on the security camera. It was incredible how perfectly the carpenters and builders had reproduced it.

And as for the technicians!

Up till the very last minute he'd been sceptical, but in the end they'd been proved right: in truth the picture on an ultra-HD television was no longer distinguishable from reality.

Time and again during the experiment he'd caught himself gazing pensively out of the window until he remembered that the 'view' from his office was just an ultra-HD film processed with a new playback technology that allowed the perspective to change according to the position of the viewer.

'We can't be certain, of course, but there's a very good chance that Emma Stein's treatment has been a success.'

Dr Roth appeared to be trying to encourage Konrad with a broad smile as well as his words. The exhausted lawyer let the psychiatrist's praise bounce off him. He'd listened to Emma for almost four hours, trying all the while to follow the doctor's instructions. It might not be obvious from looking at him – he couldn't afford to show any weakness in public – but in truth Konrad's head was droning in the wake of this marathon session, and the last thing he fancied now was an analytical conversation with the senior doctor who looked far too young, but whose reputation was legendary in professional circles. Ten years ago Dr Martin Roth had apparently succeeded in treating a schizophrenic patient by using his own hallucinations, thereby laying the foundation for his reputation. He sometimes attempted unusual therapies to help out his patients.

Such as the one today.

To make the hoped-for breakthrough with Emma Stein, Dr Roth had ordered a full-scale replica of Konrad's office to be built in the clinic's small gym, where the physiotherapists did their rehabilitation exercises.

Such an effort was necessary because they hadn't been able to get legal authorisation for an interview outside the clinic, while Emma had refused any contact within the institution.

'I need a beer first,' Konrad said, pulling over a folding chair. Here, right behind the scenery walls, which from Emma's side created the perfect illusion of his office in Zehlendorf, it looked like a building site.

Large posts prevented chipboard panels from toppling over. The wires for the hidden microphones and miniature cameras (almost all of which were on the bookshelves) ran across the lino of the gym floor like threads of yarn.

In fact the whole place looked very much like a film set. On a camping table were juices, pretzels and pre-packaged sandwiches: the catering for the Konrad & Emma Show. Dr Roth had no doubt made himself comfortable while observing his patient from here.

'A cold beer and a cigar,' Konrad extended his request.

'You've earned both,' Roth said, pulling a radio from the belt pocket of his white jeans. 'Now, there's a strict smoking and alcohol ban here in the Park Clinic, but as its head I'm sure I can make an exception today.'

He pressed a button and relayed the order, presumably to his bow-legged assistant who Konrad had spoken to regularly on the phone over the past few days to finalise the details. The woman was tediousness and slowness personified. If she organised the beer and cigar with the same speed she'd arranged for the furniture to be moved here from his practice, he'd be taking his first puff tomorrow morning and first sip next week.

'They'll be here in five minutes.'

Hmm. Who'd have thought?

After Roth had scribbled a few notes on a clipboard, he also fetched himself a folding chair and sat opposite Konrad, his back to the monitor.

'I thought it was all over when Emma knocked over the cup and wanted to clean up the mess,' he said, smiling.

Konrad agreed. 'Yes, she was this close to visiting the non-existent loo.'

For plumbing reasons this detail of the mock-up office hadn't been possible. A replica loo would have been okay, but a functioning WC with flush and running water? The premises hadn't permitted such an installation. If Emma had shaken the fake door that led to a non-existent lavatory, the entire illusion would have been dispelled. In actual fact this had been part of the plan, to open Emma's eyes to the situation, just not so early, but as a dramatic climax and as close to the end of the session as possible.

'So how do you feel now?' Dr Roth asked, with emphasis on the *now*, for to begin with Konrad had been very much opposed to the psychiatrist's treatment methods.

'I still don't feel comfortable that I had to lie to Emma and make her believe in a pretend world. But

I have to admit that your unusual idea did have the desired outcome.'

The fact that Emma had refused any visit on her ward had presented her helpers with an almost insoluble problem. She hadn't made a statement, nothing that a decent defence team could work with. The public prosecutor, on the other hand, was in possession of a video that showed Emma slitting her husband's throat in the cellar of her house after she'd hurled totally crazed, partly babbled accusations at him.

Roth hadn't made any progress with his therapy either until it dawned on him how they could kill two birds with one stone – have Emma give a testimony and engage in conversation therapy at the same time. He figured that Emma was a person who opened up to very few people, and to nobody more than her paternal friend.

But this on its own wasn't enough. To ensure a truthful statement she also needed familiar surroundings.

If the patient won't come to the mountain, the mountain must be moved, he'd said to Konrad ten days ago on a damp, cold Friday afternoon, by which time Emma hadn't been under his supervision for even two weeks. Konrad recalled wanting to take a closer examination of Dr Roth's mental state too, when the latter laid out his plan in detail:

'Let's assume that Frau Stein trusts you. She's going to find it extremely difficult to dish up lies to her closest confidant, especially in an environment where she's

always felt secure. There are still many things we can't explain. Whether Frau Stein was really attacked in a hotel room or whether she gave herself those injuries somewhere else. Or how exactly she came to kill the two men. Was it intentional or carelessness? If you, Professor Luft, were to undertake a lawyer's consultation that we might be able to observe, it would give us the priceless opportunity to analyse Emma Stein's testimony from a psychiatric perspective.'

Konrad had laughed and looked around for one of those cameras he and Emma had been filmed with for the last few hours.

'You want to completely replicate my office? You're having me on!'

'Not at all, and if you care to do some research into me you'll discover that I sometimes go down unconventional paths to—'

'*Wait a second, stop!'* Konrad had interrupted him, propping himself up on his desk with his elbows and looking down at Roth. *'Are you seriously suggesting that I deceive my client? Breach my lawyer's confidentiality?'*

Roth had vigorously shaken his head.

'We're in this together. Your client is my patient. That means your client confidentiality overlaps with my patient confidentiality. Emma Stein is accused of the manslaughter of Anton Palandt and her husband. At the same time she appears to suffer from severe paranoia, perhaps even pathological lying.'

'And with my help…'

'We can kill two birds with one stone. We discover what really happened, and maybe we'll come up with not just a defence strategy, but also a therapy plan. But this will only work with your help. It's a "condition without which it wouldn't be possible". That's a specialist legal term, isn't it?'

'A "*condition* sine qua non",' Konrad had confirmed.

'Your lawyer–client interview would also be a psychotherapeutic analysis. It's a means of both discovering the truth and making her better. And no third party would get wind of any of it. The two of us would be the only ones with access to the recordings. There are no cameramen, just fixed lenses.'

This was the chat that had finally persuaded Konrad, even though he asked for a weekend to think it over. But in fact he knew he'd give his consent when, just before leaving, he'd asked Dr Roth, *'You want to move my entire office?'*

'Just the furniture,' the psychiatrist had said calmly, as if it were a perfectly normal procedure paid for by statutory health insurance. *'We'll build the rest of the office.'*

And so Emma had been sedated in her room with the promise of seeing her old friend again, who might be able to save her from a prison sentence. When she awoke, having apparently been transported, she imagined herself to be in Konrad's practice.

But was all the effort really worth it? Konrad wondered.

He heard a muffled knocking, which surprised him because the door to the gym they were sitting closest to was made out of glass. And nobody was behind it.

'What was that?' Konrad asked when the noise sounded again, only this time it sounded more like stamping. He turned to the monitor.

Emma.

She wasn't on the hospital bed nor the sofa, but standing in the middle of the room, stamping her right foot. A rather clumsy nurse was trying to hold her arm, but Emma easily shook her off.

'Sound!' Konrad ordered with his authoritative, courtroom-trained voice, and the senior doctor picked up the remote control on the table. Emma's voice grew louder.

'Hello? Konrad?' she said, several times over, turning in a circle. She'd realised, of course, that she was being filmed and listened to, but till now she'd had no idea where the microphones and cameras were.

'Konrad, can you hear me?'

'Yes,' he replied, even though Roth had explained this morning that the mock-up office was so well soundproofed that you could have thrown a plate on the floor out here without anyone inside hearing anything of the smash.

'Konrad?' Emma asked, thick tears running down her cheeks. Her voice strained in the small speakers. 'Please come back, Konrad. There's something I've got to confess.'

49

Emma had a beautiful view from her room in the clinic. Not quite as glamorous as that from his office, but at least it wasn't taped, Konrad thought.

If Emma were standing beside him at the window she'd be able to see a small family of hares hopping across the snowy lawn of the park and leaping two metres out of the beam of the spherical garden lanterns into the darkness, shortly afterwards to leave visible prints in the powdery whiteness once more.

She'd also be able to see his old Saab in which he sometimes used to drive her to university. But to see all of this Emma would have to get out of bed, and at the moment she was too weak. The convertible was covered in a thick layer of snow and stood in the small car park that was actually reserved for senior doctors. Roth had offered him his space.

'Have you searched everything?' he heard Emma ask from her bed. It was wider and more comfortable than the one on which she'd been pushed into the fake office a few hours earlier.

'Yes,' Konrad said.

At her request he'd combed the entire room for hidden cameras and microphones, searching very thoroughly even though Roth had assured him that up here on the ward nothing and nobody was wired up. He wouldn't dare undertake such an intrusion into his patients' privacy.

'I'm sorry,' Konrad said contritely, and that was the truth. In the text books of the future it would look good when people wrote of Dr Roth that he'd treated a supposed liar with a lie. But this didn't alter the fact that Konrad had hoodwinked his best friend and ward.

'No, *I'm* the one who's sorry,' Emma countered wearily. She sounded oblivious to everything around her; the skin around her eyes was sunken and crumpled, as if she hadn't drunk anything in a long time.

'Maybe it would be better if we spoke tomorrow. You look exhausted, darling.'

'No.'

She patted the duvet beside her. 'Please come and sit close to me.'

He moved away from the window bench and was beside her in a couple of steps. He loved being close to her. Now that he no longer had to affect a professional distance, Emma wasn't his client, but his little darling protégée once more.

She whispered as he pushed the bedside table slightly aside so he could sit on the mattress.

'I wanted to speak to you up here. In my cell.'

'In your clinic room, you mean.'

She smiled as if he'd cracked a joke.

Roth had immediately agreed to let Emma return to her room. The mock-up lawyer's practice had done its job. When Emma discovered the HD television was a fake window she realised that humans can lose the capacity to distinguish between fiction and reality. Konrad couldn't judge the psychiatric benefit of this awareness, but he agreed with the head of the clinic that Emma was better off in her hospital bed than down in the gymnasium.

'I didn't want to tell you down there. Not in front of all those cameras. And microphones.'

Konrad nodded.

He took her hand. It was dry and as light as a piece of paper.

'Nobody should hear us,' she said and it sounded as if she had a hot potato in her mouth. Her tongue was heavy. Roth had given her another tranquiliser, which seemed to work slowly, and then left them, saying that he'd wait in the corridor.

'Relax,' Konrad said, squeezing her hand affectionately.

'What I've got to say is for your ears only,' she said.

Konrad felt a pang in his heart, as he always did

when someone close to him was in a bad way and he didn't know how to help. On the battlefield of articles and clauses he always had the right weapons to hand. But when it came to personal problems he was often clueless. Especially with Emma.

'What's troubling you?' he asked.

'Do you know what? As time goes by I'm less and less sure that I was in that hotel.'

He gave her his gentlest smile. 'Well done, Emma. Well done for saying it. And believe me, nobody's going to blame you. We're going to do all we can now to cure you.'

'There's no cure in psychotherapy,' she objected.

'But there is help.'

'I don't want help.'

'No? What do you want then?'

'To die!'

50

Konrad's emotional reaction was forceful.

His hand tensed painfully around Emma's and from his quivering lip she could see how he was struggling to retain his composure.

'You're joking.'

'No, I'm being serious.'

'But why?'

'Lots of reasons. Because of my paranoia I killed Philipp and Palandt. And prevented Sylvia's life from being saved.'

'None of it intentional,' Konrad countered vigorously. 'None of it your fault.'

Emma shook her head, her eyes were red, but clear. She wasn't crying any more.

'Philipp…' she said. 'Without Philipp there's no point to my life. I loved him. I don't care what a shit he was. I'm nothing without him.'

'You're so much more without that cheat,' Konrad said in a surprisingly loud voice. 'If there's anybody who's to blame for your misery, then it's your adulterous, self-absorbed husband. It's bad enough that he was unfaithful and neglected you while he was alive. But even after his death he's plunging you into deep despair.' Konrad then tempered his grip and tone, which was a visible effort for him. 'You're not to blame, Emma. It was self-defence.'

She sighed. 'Even if you were to convince the judges, I still don't want to go on living. Not like this. You have to understand that, Konrad. I'm a psychiatrist. I know the darkest psychological abysses. I could barely cope with looking into them. And now I'm at the very nadir myself.'

'Emma…'

'Shh… Listen to me, please, Konrad. I don't know what to think any more. I was so convinced that I'd been raped. And now? What sort of life is it if you can't distinguish between madness and reality? Not a life for me. I have to end it. But I can't do this without your help. I'm sure you know somebody who can get me the medication I'm going to write down for you.'

'But you're…'

'Mad. Precisely.'

'No, that's not what I meant.'

Konrad shook his head. She'd never seen him look so sad and helpless before.

'Yes, it's true. I'm off my trolley…'

'Just a vivid imagination, darling. And stress. Lots of stress.'

'Others have that too, but they don't hallucinate about being raped in imaginary hotel rooms.'

'But they don't have your power of imagination, Emma. Look. That evening you had a difficult lecture, colleagues were openly hostile and you had to defend yourself. It's only understandable that you lost control in an extreme psychological situation. I suspect you saw a television report about the Hairdresser and your febrile imagination turned you into one of his victims. It's going to take a long time, but together with Dr Roth I'm sure we'll find out the truth.'

'I don't want that.'

Konrad squeezed her hand again as if it were a pump to force new vitality into Emma.

'Emma, just think. You were helped once before. Back when you were a girl, when your imagination was also turning somersaults.'

Arthur.

Gripped by an unexpected melancholy, Emma couldn't help thinking of the imaginary childhood friend, of whom she'd been so frightened to begin with. Much of her memory was a blur. Only the motorbike helmet and the syringe in Arthur's hand had stayed with her, even years after her therapy which – it now seemed – can't have been that successful after all.

Emma's eyes closed and she no longer fought against the tiredness that brought forth more scraps of memory as harbingers of her dreams.

Her father's words: *'Get out right now. Or I'll hurt you.'*

The voice in the cupboard: *'He said that?'*

Her mother's screams when she lost the child at four months.

The morning-after pill.

Her own voice yelling at Sylvia: *'I was shaved and raped. There was a man in my room…'*

'Yeah, like Arthur in your cupboard…'

Emma tore her eyes open. Fought her way back to the surface through the fog of torpidity.

'What's wrong?' Konrad said, still holding her hand.

'How did she know his name?' Her tongue weighed several kilos; she could barely move it any more.

'What?'

'Arthur. How did Sylvia know his name?'

'Are you talking about the ghost now?'

She looked at Konrad's puzzled face.

'Look, I didn't even tell you his name. You heard it for the first time today when I told you about my row with Sylvia. When she came to my house and accused me of stopping her from having a child, she said something about me lying even as a child. When I made up *Arthur*. But I only met Sylvia after I'd been through therapy. I never told her about Arthur.'

Konrad shrugged. 'She had an affair with Philipp,' he muttered. 'She probably heard it from him.'

Emma was blinking frenziedly. 'Listen. Even Philipp

knew nothing about it. I kept Arthur's name to myself. After the therapy sessions in my younger days I never wanted to say it out loud again; it was a superstition. I thought that if I didn't say it then Arthur would never come back, do you understand?'

I only told my parents and psychiatrist about him. So how did Sylvia know the name?

Emma was shaking. For a split second she knew the answer. And this answer pointed the way to such a terrible, blood-curdling truth that she just wanted to run screaming out of her room.

But then the answer had vanished, together with her capacity to struggle any longer against a loss of consciousness.

And all that accompanied Emma on her deep descent into sleep was a feeling of fear, far worse than the one when she'd accepted the package.

51

Dr Roth was delighted. The experiment he'd mostly funded out of his own pocket was a complete success.

He was almost regretting not being able to continue, but the rehabilitation hall he was blocking was urgently needed and, in any case, no more success could be expected from this set-up.

'We're done then?' Konrad asked beside him, watching two removal men like a hawk as they took away his sofa. After his chat with Emma the defence lawyer had gone for a walk in the park to get some fresh air. Now he looked refreshed.

'The charade is over?'

Konrad had to raise his voice because in front of and behind him cordless screwdrivers buzzed as they took apart the wall panels. The air was heavy with the aroma of wood shavings, a smell Roth had loved since childhood. He'd attended a school with a strong artistic focus. Carpentry was part of the core curriculum, which maybe explained his penchant for creative methods.

'Yes, I think we're done,' Roth replied. 'Unless Frau Stein disclosed something else to you that could be important for my work.'

'Client confidentiality,' Konrad grinned, but then waved his hand dismissively. 'No, to tell you the truth she was all over the place. She expressed suicidal thoughts, so you've really got to keep an eye on her.'

'Don't worry, we're geared up for that possibility.' Roth scratched his receding hairline. 'I'm afraid that reaction was only to be expected.'

'Why?'

'We've seriously rocked Frau Stein's world.'

Roth pointed to the bookshelf with the complete works of Schopenhauer. One of the cameras was still in the spine of *The World as Will and Representation.*

'And at the moment she can't see any way of putting it back in order,' Roth said.

'Hey, hey. Please be careful!' Konrad excused himself for a moment and went up to one of the removal men who was trying to yank the round O rug from under the coffee table.

'That's for the dry cleaner's, not the dustbin.'

'Is that an *enso*?' asked Roth, who'd followed him.

Konrad gave him an admiring look. 'Do you know about Zen symbolism?'

'A little,' Roth smiled, pointing to the black edging of the white rug. 'In Zen art an *enso*, or circle, is painted with a single flowing brushstroke. Only those who are mentally composed and balanced can paint a uniform *enso*. For that reason, the way the circle is executed gives us a particularly good idea of the painter's state of mind.'

'I take my hat off to you,' Konrad laughed. The worker had now exited with the coffee table under his arm. The other packers too were taking items outside, leaving Konrad and Roth alone for the moment. 'I didn't know you were a philosopher manqué.'

Roth nodded, seemingly lost in thought. His fingers grasped the threads of the *enso* rug again, then he stood up. For one last time he allowed his gaze to roam the replica office, then he asked Konrad, almost incidentally, 'You were practically inseparable from her, weren't you?'

'I'm sorry?'

'You always had to have her there. Be near her.'

'What on earth are you talking about?' Konrad said, slightly put out.

Instead of giving an answer Roth looked at the fluff in his hand, which he'd just plucked from the rug. The fibres were dark brown and unusually thin for a rug. Almost like hair.

'In Philipp's laboratory they found the trophies from all the victims, apart from Emma,' the psychiatrist said, looking Konrad straight in the eye.

The defence lawyer turned pale and seemed to age from one moment to the next. The firm ground of Konrad's self-assurance had suddenly become a trapdoor.

'What the hell are you getting at?'

Roth replied with a question of his own: 'Are you not surprised by all the time and money that's gone into this, Professor Luft?' The psychiatrist opened up his arms as if seeing the set-up for the first time. 'A completely furnished replica lawyer's office, HD television, hidden cameras and microphones. And all just to free a paranoid patient from her hallucinations?'

'What's going on?' Konrad asked flatly. His gaze wandered helplessly across the set, looking for a way out.

But before he'd found one, Roth let the guillotine of truth come swishing down. 'We were observing you, not Emma!'

52

Emma was swimming on the bottom of an oil-black lake, feeling seasick. And yet the waves upsetting her balance were borne by a strange melody.

A voice, half whispering, half smiling.

A madman's voice.

Konrad's voice.

'I love you, Emma.'

Seized by an immense swell of nausea, Emma wrenched open her eyes and threw up right beside her bed.

She was still woozy, seeing the world as if through frosted glass, but she knew who she was (a raped woman), where she was (in the Park Clinic) and what Konrad had confided to her.

'Don't worry, I'll look after you,' he'd said, holding her hand and believing her to be in a state of total unconsciousness, whereas in fact she was just hovering below the surface of sleep.

'I'll protect you like I've always done.'

She kept drifting off, but each time his voice brought her back.

Now that she'd vomited up her medication before it could make its way throughout her body, Konrad was no longer in the room.

But his voice was still in her head. This eerie, whispering sing-song of memory.

'I'm your guardian angel, Emma. I've been watching over you these last few months, just as I have for years and years. Do you understand? I killed the whores for your sake. To restore your honour.'

Only now did the madness in his words make complete sense to Emma. She was still incredibly tired. But the pull of the psychotropic drugs was no longer trying to drag her so forcefully into the quagmire of her consciousness.

'I wanted you from the first second I laid eyes on you. You were far too young, three years old, when you came to my practice with your father. It was furnished almost exactly as it is now. Even the rug was there. You loved playing on the O, but I bet you can't remember as you were too small.'

That's why I felt so at home there from the start.

Right then Emma had tried opening her eyes again, but couldn't manage it.

'I noticed at once that your father was no good for you. You tried to get close to him, but he was always gruff and cold. I, on the other hand, couldn't show my feelings. I had to hide to be able to see you.'

In my cupboard!

'I watched you, cared for you, guarded you and protected you. I was the father you never had.'

Konrad wasn't just the Hairdresser.

He was Arthur too!

That's how Sylvia knew his name. She didn't get it from Philipp, but from the man pretending to be Arthur, Emma remembered her own, very sluggish thoughts, interrupted again and again by Konrad's whispers.

They'd had contact, *of course*. Konrad must have visited Sylvia when Emma was in a bad way, to discuss how they could help her. From one best friend to another.

'Throughout your life I looked out for you, my darling. Like when your ex-boyfriend Benedict was hassling you, do you remember? I so often held my protective hand over you, but you weren't aware of it. Then, when you were old enough, I showed myself to you. But I was worried you'd realise my true feelings and break off contact with a man who was so much older.'

But aren't you gay?

'I only pretended to be gay. I lied so I could always be close to you, but unfortunately it kept us apart too. Oh, the desire I felt for you. All these years.'

Until the night in the hotel!

'I wanted you to leave Le Zen and go home, darling. Back to your husband who was in bed with a whore. So you'd catch him in flagrante. But you stayed. Even though I frightened you with the writing on the mirror, you wouldn't go. So I cut your hair to stop Philipp from wanting you. To stop him from sleeping with you as he always did when you came home.'

At this point Emma thought she recalled Konrad clearing his throat, just as he'd done that night in the hotel.

'I didn't rape you. It's just that when you were lying in front of me, so peacefully…'

Emma had to retch again. She threw the covers back and fell beside the bed when she tried to stand up.

'No!' she screamed at the voice of truth, which had taken hold inside her head.

'I know, it was a mistake,' she heard Konrad say. 'But I couldn't wait any longer, Emma. After all those years of abstinence it was perfectly natural, you see. And it was beautiful, all very gentle. An act of love.'

Emma felt a powerful tugging in her abdomen. She sank to her knees and threw up again.

When nothing more would come from her stomach the voice in her head had vanished too, as if she'd expelled Konrad from her body with the last of the bile.

Gasping, she pulled herself up on the window sill and looked outside.

She almost expected to see Konrad in the park, waving at her, but there was just a snowy landscape. Hare prints in the snow. A lantern giving off a gentle light.

And the car.

The old Saab stood covered in snow in the clinic car park where only the senior doctors were allowed to park.

Emma looked at the door, wiped some spittle from her mouth with the sleeve of her nightshirt and made a decision.

53

The defence lawyer, once so energetic, staggered through the mock-up of his office like a boxer out for the count. He hadn't said anything to Dr Roth yet. And he wasn't able to look the psychiatrist in the eye.

Konrad stood there, trembling. With his face to the false window, from which the television had already been removed and where only a chipboard recess was left as a reminder of the installation.

Turning around, Konrad tried to support himself on the edge of his desk, but slipped and just struggled to fall into his chair.

'You wove Emma's hair into the *enso* rug,' Roth said. Without reproach. Without the slightest hint of sensationalism in his voice. As a psychiatrist he'd come across far more disconcerting abnormalities in human behaviour.

'That… that's…' Konrad stuttered, finding his voice again 'There's an explanation for that.'

'I'm sure there is,' Roth replied. 'Everything will be

explained. Including the issue of the room number. Was it 1903 or 1905?'

'What?'

'Which of the two connecting rooms was it where you replaced the number on the door with 1904?'

Roth could see beads of sweat on Konrad's brow. He'd turned ashen and his skin had a waxy shimmer.

'Yes, I know. Nobody likes it when people see through their tricks,' Roth said. 'Even though it was an excellent ploy to book both rooms via a foreign hotel portal for a family of four. At Le Zen, as in most Berlin hotels, you only have to present your credit card at check-in, so you just needed someone to pick up the key for you.' Roth knitted his brow. 'This is where we don't know for sure how you did it. We're assuming that this mother and her three children actually exist – a former client of yours, perhaps, who you invited to come to Germany. But who left a little earlier, which meant that on the day Emma was checking in you had free rein for your plans. You had all the time to put up the Ai Weiwei portrait, right over the frameless connecting door so that Emma wouldn't notice there was access to the neighbouring room. You waited in there till she went to bed. Unlike in the past you didn't have to hide in the cupboard.' Roth gave a wan smile. 'By the way, I like the name Arthur. I'm a fan of Arthur Schopenhauer too.'

Konrad winced when the provisional office door opened with a loud crunch. A black-haired police officer with Greek features strode confidently in.

'Professor Konrad Luft, I am arresting you,' the policeman said. Jorgo Kapsalos stood two metres from the desk, his hand on the service revolver at his hip. 'I don't suppose I have to inform you of your right to remain silent.'

Konrad looked up and gazed at the tall, broad-shouldered policeman as if he were an alien.

'Why?' he croaked.

Roth, who'd stayed beside the sofa, fancied he could make out a smile on Jorgo's lips, but perhaps it was just the diffuse light of the desk lamp that gave him this impression.

There was nothing sadistic about Emma's husband's former partner. Although Jorgo had been deeply affected by Philipp Stein's death, because he blamed himself for not having made the connections earlier, Roth didn't think that Jorgo was driven by revenge. It was understandable, however, that he was feeling great satisfaction now at being able to arrest the Hairdresser.

'How did you get onto me?'

Jorgo shook his head and he felt for the handcuffs on his belt. 'We'll have plenty of time to discuss all that at the station when we take your confession.'

Konrad nodded, acknowledging defeat.

'Unbelievable,' he said, letting his eyes marvel at the fake office where he'd thought he was helping Emma, whereas the whole time he himself had been under observation. 'You pulled the wool over my eyes,' the lawyer muttered. He looked towards the exit. None of the removal men had come back into the gym; they were obeying the orders Jorgo had given them.

'It wasn't about making Emma feel secure here, but me, here, in my familiar environment.'

Even in the moment of his greatest defeat, Konrad's intellect was working impeccably. 'You would never have obtained a warrant to search my real office. You orchestrated that perfectly. I give you respect.'

Konrad was supporting himself feebly on the desk, and already then Roth ought to have realised. But even more so when the lawyer breathed out heavily and let both arms fall beneath the desktop.

Konrad was crestfallen, so severely affected by having been unmasked that perhaps he'd never recover. But his transformation had occurred too quickly, especially for someone who'd practised all his life being in control of his body and mind.

We made a mistake, Roth thought, then heard these words echo, but with a slight time delay and in a different voice: they were coming from Konrad's mouth.

'But you made a mistake,' he said.

Within the twinkling of an eye the pistol that the defence lawyer had pulled from a secret compartment beneath the desktop was already in position. Konrad was aiming right between Dr Roth's eyes.

54

'My desk. My secret compartment. My life insurance,' Konrad said. 'Actually intended for furious clients whose cases I lost. And when you look at it that way, this is about right.'

The lawyer gave a sad laugh and gripped the pistol more tightly. 'I will shoot,' he said, and Roth knew he was being deadly serious.

'I'll pull the trigger and then rather than removal men you'll need forensic cleaners specialising in spatters of brain.'

'Okay, okay,' Roth said, coming closer with his hands up. This was his area of expertise. Psychologically damaged individuals in extreme emotional situations.

'What do you want?' he asked.

'Answers,' Konrad said with astonishing calmness, now aiming the weapon at Jorgo's chest. Only a throbbing artery in his neck betrayed how worked up he was. 'How did you come to suspect me?'

With a quick glance at Roth, Jorgo checked that he

could answer truthfully, then said, 'We had no DNA, no evidence, nothing. We were poking around in the dark in the Hairdresser case. From the profile that Philipp had compiled we knew that it must be an "older, conservative-leaning man with a high level of education and a pronounced sense of order".'

Konrad nodded and with his free hand motioned to Jorgo to continue.

'I've known Emma for years. I couldn't see her as a deranged copycat just trying to get her husband's attention. Even less that she'd turn violent for no reason.'

'Hardly likely,' Konrad agreed. 'More like Philipp.'

Jorgo nodded. 'But nor did I think my partner capable of physical violence against women.'

'Psychological violence, on the other hand...' Konrad said and Jorgo hesitated briefly, checking again that he could continue to talk. Either he interpreted Roth's look correctly, or as a policeman he was trained to tell the truth to people who were just about to commit an act of violence.

'Philipp started behaving suspiciously, telling me again and again how he doubted his wife's mental state. And when we searched Le Zen together, it seemed as if he was looking for proof of her paranoia rather than the opposite. And he was adamant that Emma shouldn't find out about the connecting door, even though that would have been a balm for her tortured soul. Nor did he tell her that we found residues of glue on the wall, presumably from the picture you'd covered the door with.'

Jorgo shrugged. 'From there the logical step was to investigate Emma's private life. And see: the profile matches, as if Philipp had been looking right at you when he drew it up.'

Konrad grasped his neck. Once again he aimed his eyes and the barrel of his gun at Roth.

'What about you? You're the mastermind behind all of this, aren't you?'

'Well, I'd prefer to say that I was helped on my way by chance. I also attended the conference where Frau Stein talked about the Rosenhan Experiment. I don't suppose you remember, but we happened to bump into each other in the cloakroom. Later, when the police brought me on board I recalled our meeting. I assume you weren't there out of any medical interest, but to change the key cards in Emma's documents?'

Konrad nodded and said, 'That wasn't my question. I wanted to know if the strategy with this trap here was your idea?'

Roth hesitated. Although Konrad would be bound to notice if he lied to him, the senior doctor could hardly be honest without insulting the lawyer.

After he'd been asked by the police for help as a renowned expert, he'd spent the last few weeks looking into the defence lawyer's psyche. He'd studied all of Konrad's seminar videos and films of his public appearances on the internet. Analysed his almost pedantic outward appearance, his deportment which was minutely managed and geared towards maximum success. Soon he guessed that Konrad's biggest weakness would also represent the investigators' best opportunity: his narcissism.

'To nail you we had to put you in a position where you felt powerful,' he said. 'You had to believe that you were pulling all the strings and were the lead actor in a performance, just like in court. I was convinced that you'd agree to my idea of replicating your office, seeing how you'd gone to all that effort with the hotel room so that the police wouldn't take Frau Stein seriously.'

'So none of this was ever about Emma?' Konrad blinked. His eyes were damp, but it didn't look as if he was feeling sorry for himself. Even in this extreme situation he actually seemed to be far more concerned for Emma's welfare.

'Yes, of course I was interested in Frau Dr Stein too,' Roth explained. 'By building your office in here we could kill the proverbial two birds with one stone. After those terrible events Emma was refusing all communication. The fake setting finally made her open up. And condemned you as a murderer.'

Konrad's expression turned hard. For a moment he looked like a lawyer again, cross-examining the other side's witness. 'How did you know? How did you know that I'd take the rug with me?'

Roth gently shook his head. 'I didn't. To be honest, until the moment you tried to stop Emma from cleaning the stain it didn't even occur to me that this might be a piece of evidence. But then on the close-up I saw your pupils dilate. A second later you'd already leaped up, almost on instinct. You didn't want Emma to touch the rug under any circumstances. Herr Kapsalos and I asked ourselves *why?* We took a closer look and discovered the hair that Emma must have pulled out when she cleaned it.'

Konrad rapped his knuckles on the table in admiration, as students do to applaud a professor.

Jorgo slid his hand down to his holster, which didn't escape Konrad's notice.

'That's not a good idea,' he said laconically, and his knuckles turned white as his grip tightened further on the pistol, which was now pointing at the policeman's heart.

At that moment there was a creaking behind Roth. Like Jorgo, he turned around towards the door of the 'office', which here only led to the changing rooms rather than the corridor in the law firm. It opened.

Very slowly, as if the person pushing from the other side was having to battle a powerful wind blowing in the other direction.

Or as if they had no strength.

'Emma!' Konrad screamed so loudly, like a warning, but it was too late.

She was already in the doorway with her short hair, in white slippers, the clinic nightshirt tied at the back.

'What… *are you doing here?*' he was presumably going to ask, but this was lost in the tumult that ensued once the shot had been fired.

Konrad looked, baffled, at the gun in his hand, then wondered what had happened. He let his arm drop and at that moment was knocked to the ground by Jorgo. The policeman had dived across the table with his pistol drawn.

Roth wasn't watching the unequal struggle in which the lawyer, offering no resistance, allowed himself to be pushed to the floor and have his arms twisted behind his back.

All he saw was Emma.

Teetering towards him.

Blood dropped onto the freshly laid parquet floor. A whole torrent, pouring onto the floor like a sticky, red waterfall. Over the leather armchair to where the coffee table must have been and where now just the enso rug lay, onto which she finally collapsed.

55

Four weeks later

'Number three,' said the hollow-cheeked woman with the man's haircut, who was responsible for welcoming visitors at the security checkpoint. She was tall, plump, with nicotine-stained teeth, and hands that she could have grasped a basketball with. But she was friendly, something verging on a miracle when you had to work in the high-security wing of a psychiatric prison.

'You've got five minutes.' The prison officer pointed to the seat with the specified number above the glass separating the free world from the inmates.

Konrad was already sitting there.

Chalky white, gaunt. They'd shaved off his beard, but this made him look even older. Seeing him, many people would have thought of death and how it already scarred some people in life.

The visitors room was awash with the faint smell

of decay, but this was just in the mind of course, an olfactory error, because Konrad's chest was rising and falling, and his nostrils were quivering almost as badly as the age-spotted hand holding the receiver. But nowhere near as firmly as the pistol back in the clinic. It was no surprise that the inmates here were sometimes called zombies by the care workers.

The living dead. Pacified by medication, locked away forever.

Even here in the visitors' area, where relatives sat opposite the particularly severe cases separated by a glass wall, any normal person would feel an unease similar to that when imagining a tarantula crawling across their tongue.

Emma picked up the receiver and sat down.

'Thank you,' said the man who'd shaven four women, killed three of them and given her the most horrific night of her life. 'Your coming to visit means a lot to me.'

'This is an exception,' Emma said impassively. 'I'm coming just this once then never again.'

Konrad nodded, as if he'd been expecting this. 'Let me guess, Dr Roth sent you. He thinks that closure would help your therapy, doesn't he?'

Emma couldn't help feeling admiration for her once-closest friend. In a short period of time incarceration had eroded his health, his commanding presence and his youthful charm, but not his intelligence.

'He's waiting outside,' she said truthfully. With

Samson, who was following her every step again. And Jorgo, who somehow she'd probably never be rid of.

Emma changed the receiver to the other ear and rubbed her left elbow. The bandage had been taken off recently; the edges of the wound from the operation scars were still visible.

Because the single rooms in the security wing of the Park Clinic were only locked at night she'd been able to leave her room that day. But in her state it had taken more than ten minutes to labour the few metres to get to the gym.

Because of the bullet that had been fired accidentally from Konrad's pistol when Emma appeared so unexpectedly in the fake office, she'd be reminded of him all her life whenever she bent her arm. But even if he hadn't shattered her wrist, it was unlikely she'd ever be able to forget him.

'I'm so sorry. I never wanted to hurt you,' he said in the voice she'd last heard while half asleep. In the Park Clinic. The memory his tone evoked was so powerful that Emma had that same taste of gastric acid and vomit in her mouth as back in her hospital room when she'd thrown up. Dr Roth said the medication had given her an upset stomach, but she knew better. It was Konrad's voice that had stopped her from losing consciousness altogether. And it was his confession that had turned her stomach upside down and eventually made her wide awake again.

'What is it really?' she heard Konrad ask. Emma frowned.

'Pardon?'

'What has really brought you here? You're a wilful girl, Emma, that's something I've always admired about you. Your strength, even as a child. You wouldn't allow him to order you here unless you had something on your mind.'

Emma took a deep breath and felt respect for Konrad once more. He hadn't lost his talent for reading her like an open book.

'After everything that's happened, it's really quite unimportant. But the question… it haunts me.'

Konrad raised his eyebrows. 'What question?'

'Philipp. Why did you let him live?'

She picked nervously at her thumb. Her fingernails were neatly trimmed and painted with transparent polish again. Emma had sprayed on some perfume and shaved her legs. External signs of psychological healing. Inside, however, a heavy cold seemed to be looming. She felt as if her facial muscles were contracting and her ears aching, perhaps because she didn't want to hear Konrad's answer.

'I mean, you killed all those women, but not the guy you hated most. He was the adulterer after all. Wouldn't it have just been simpler to get him out of the way?'

Konrad shook his head sadly. 'Darling, don't you understand? I wanted to protect you from any pain, never inflict it on you. Emma, you must believe me when I say I always loved you. And whatever I did, it was never done out of selfishness. Even when I made sure that you remained an only child.'

Now Konrad's head was in a motorbike helmet and rather than a phone in his hand there was a syringe with a long needle, glistening silver in the moonlight.

'Come on Emma, go to bed now and settle down,' she heard Arthur say. *'I'll be right back.'*

Emma blinked and the vision from her memory dissipated.

'What was in the syringe?' she asked Konrad behind the glass.

'Something to induce an abortion,' he admitted candidly. 'I injected it into the water glass your mother had put beside her bed. Please don't hate me for it. I mean, how could I allow her to bring another child into the world which might go on to suffer the same psychological abuse your father inflicted upon you? A man who wants to hurt his daughter just because she's afraid?'

'You're sick,' Emma said, then it struck her: 'It was you! You swapped Sylvia's pills too!'

'To stop Philipp from hurting you again by giving her a child.'

Emma's fingers tensed around the receiver. 'You told her about Arthur to further undermine my credibility. And later you told her it was Philipp to make her kill herself.'

'I just wanted Sylvia to keep away from him. I really couldn't anticipate her suicide.'

'But you've got her on your conscience just the same. You're completely insane, do you know that?'

'Yes,' Konrad said. 'But I was never selfish, do you hear? The only thing important to me was that you were alright. Even if that meant your having to be with Philipp, that worthless pleb.'

For a second it looked as if he were going to spit on the glass separating them.

'The bastard left you alone when you were in distress. I had to slip into your house and watch out for you. I even took the package from your desk and hid it in the garden shed for a few hours so that Philipp would see what a state you were in. That he couldn't leave you on your own all weekend! Not in your condition! But the bastard went anyway. Cold-hearted, no scruples.'

'You hid?'

How often did you secretly watch me all these years?

Emma knew that this was another creepy thought, just like her hair being woven into Konrad's *enso* carpet. A thought which, if she was lucky, might fade over the years, but would never totally lose its horror.

'In the shed. In the cellar. When the two of you were in conversation I was in the kitchen, separated from you by just a thin door.'

'Like behind the connecting door in Le Zen,' Emma snorted.

Konrad's eyes turned watery. 'Oh, sweetie, you must really despise me now.' His lower lip was trembling and he started to dribble, but made no attempt to wipe the spit away.

'I wanted him to stop hurting you. I only sent him the hair so he knew what the consequences were of his cheating on you. But instead the bastard just used it to torture you even more. I'm so sorry.'

'What for?' Emma asked. She'd resolved to be furious with him. On the way here she'd run through the course of the conversation and its conclusion in her head. She'd pictured herself leaping up and slamming the receiver against the glass panel again and again until it shattered and she could slit Konrad's throat with one of the shards.

But now that he was sitting there like a little boy whose favourite toy has been taken away, she felt nothing but a great emptiness tinged with pity.

'You're not sorry for having killed all those women?' she asked, and watched as a tear rolled down his cheek. 'Not even for having hounded me all my life?'

He shook his head, weeping.

'And you're not sorry for having sedated and raped me, before dragging my body out of the hotel? So turning me into a paranoid wreck who stabbed innocent men to death?'

'No,' he sobbed. 'I'm only sorry that I didn't confess my love for you earlier. Maybe the two of us would have had a chance.'

Emma closed her eyes, wiped her eyelids with back of her hand and hung the receiver back up.

Of course, she thought. *He's sick. I should understand that better than anyone.*

She opened her eyes and gave Konrad one final look.

And although she'd never learned how to lipread, nor even ever tried, she was able to read from Konrad's lips what he was saying to her from behind the pane of glass:

'Out of love, Emma. I did it all only out of love.'

Ten Years of Sebastian Fitzek

When I was ten years old I was in class 5b at the Wald primary school and as popular as you can only be if you wear the clothes of your brother who's seven years older, while your haircut (a Mum special) is about a decade out of fashion.

Picture, if you can, a sullen young boy with a big nose, bowl haircut, leather trousers and an aluminium briefcase, who likes to spend all his breaktime in the library. Yes, precisely: I was that classic book nerd who nobody wanted on their dodgeball team apart from as cannon fodder.

And then Ender came.

Ender, a German of Turkish origin, was the biggest thug in the school and had to repeat a year twice. When he first entered the classroom I thought he'd come to pick up his child early from school. But then the coolest of the cool boys was seated right next to me.

Our class teacher probably thought that the swot (me) might have a positive influence on the problem child (Ender). But of course the reverse happened. Ender changed my life, first and foremost by liking me, which might have been because I helped him out with homework. Believe me, no coercion was involved, nor did I have to surrender my trainers to Ender. On the contrary, from his dad's sports shop he brought me my first Adidas customisable sneakers and so liberated me from my ugly clodhoppers.

And because he, Mr Popular, became my friend, this rubbed off on the mob that were my classmates, who till then hadn't even wanted to ignore me.

Ender taught me lots of useful things essential to the daily life of a primary school pupil, such as how to smoke a cigar (although it was a bad idea to try it behind the gym as the sports teacher was jogging past). Later he smuggled his father's 18-rated videos out of their apartment (*Rollerball*, *Class of 1984*, *The Evil Dead*, *Dawn of the Dead* and – of course – *Escape from New York* with Kurt Russell). This might give you an inkling of where my passion for thrillers comes from. To cut a long story short, I have much to thank Ender for and – mate – it's great to still be friends with you after all these years. Of course I'll come to visit you next Sunday in prison (just joking).

This is the second time I'm celebrating a ten-year anniversary. And I can rightly say that the last few years have been some of the most intense but also happiest of my life.

I'm often asked what has changed in my life since I became an author. My standard response is: not much. I still drive a Ferrari and sleep in my twenty-room villa in Grunewald. (Here I ought to add a smiley to make it clear that this is a joke too. Preferably one with tears of joy. I'd love to know the last time I laughed quite so much as this overused tears-of-joy smiley, but I'm digressing.)

In truth my life has changed drastically over the past decade, chiefly because I've had the privilege of getting to know so many great people I'd never have met had I not become a writer. And first and foremost this means you, dear readers.

I admit that when I published my email address in my debut novel, *Therapy*, I was utterly naïve. I reckoned on getting a handful of messages. A dozen emails, perhaps, in which readers would point out typos, voice their criticism, or maybe offer some fleeting praise. But how wrong I was! So far I've received over 40,000 emails and have been chuffed about each one.

Now to the acknowledgements. I should like to point out that the thanks I'm offering here are also an apology. So let me say thank you and sorry to (in no particular order of importance): Hans-Peter

Übleis, Theresa Schenkel, Josef Röckl, Bernhard Fetsch, Steffen Haselbach, Katharina Ilgen, Monika Neudeck, Patricia Kessler, Sibylle Dietzel, Iris Haas, Hanna Pfaffenwimmer, Carolin Graehl, Regina Weisbrod, Helmut Henkensiefken, Manuela Raschke and the rest of the family (including Karl and Sally), Barbara Herrmann, Achim Behrend, Ela and Micha, Petra Rode, Sabrina Rabow, Roman Hocke, Claudia von Hornstein, Gudrun Strutzenberger, Cornelia Petersen-Laux and Markus Michalek, Christian Meyer, Peter Prange, Gerlinde Jänicke, Arno Müller, Thomas Koschwitz, Jochen Trus, Stephan Schmitter, Michael Treutler and Simon Jäger, Clemens and Sabine Fitzek, Franz Xaver Riedel, Thomas Zorbach, Marcus Meier, the Krings brothers, Jörn Stollmann and all the booksellers and librarians out there. On this occasion all of you find yourselves just plonked onto a list, even though this book and my ten-year anniversary would have been impossible without all your efforts, love and friendship. But, as you can't have failed to notice, I've needed the space for something more important: my readers.

And you on the sofa at home, in the car, on the beach or on the tram – if you've made it this far then all that remains for me to say to you finally (as I've been doing for ten years at this point) is 'thank you'. Thanks for all your words, the time and the experiences we've shared. Either in real life or in the virtual world.

I hope you will continue to write to me at fitzek@sebastianfitzek.de, because I'd still love to hear from you.

And I promise that I'll strive to ensure that the reverse remains true.

Best regards
Sebastian Fitzek

On 8 May 2016, forty-four years old, 1.8 metres tall (so long as I don't slouch) and weighing seventy-eight kilos, that's two kilos heavier than when I started *The Package*. (Bloody chocolate bars between chapters.)

About the author

Sebastian Fitzek is Germany's most successful author. His books have sold 12 million copies, been translated into more than twenty-four languages and are the basis for international cinema and theatre adaptations. Sebastian Fitzek was the first German author to be awarded the European Prize for Criminal Literature. He lives in Berlin.

About the translator

Jamie Bulloch is the translator of almost forty works from German, including novels by Timur Vermes, Martin Suter and Robert Menasse. His translation of Birgit Vanderbecke's *The Mussel Feast* won the 2014 Schlegel-Tieck Prize. He is also the author of *Karl Renner: Austria*.

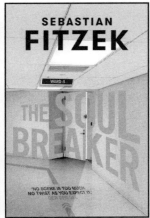